PHYSICS

Custom Edition for the University at Buffalo
Dr. Surajit Sen
Department of Physics

Senior Vice President, Editorial: Patrick F. Boles
Executive Marketing Manager: Nathan Wilbur
Senior Acquisitions Editor: Debbie Coniglio
Development Editor: Christina Martin
Editorial Assistant: Jeanne Martin
Operations Manager: Eric M. Kenney
Production Manager: Jennifer Berry
Art Director: Renée Sartell
Cover Designer: Chrissy Kurpeski

Cover Art: "Glass Building," courtesy of iStockphoto.

Please visit our website at *www.pearsonlearningsolutions.com*.

Attention bookstores: For permission to return any unsold stock, contact us at *pe-uscustomreturns@pearson.com*.

Pearson Learning Solutions, 501 Boylston Street, Suite 900, Boston, MA 02116
A Pearson Education Company
www.pearsoned.com

PEARSON ISBN 10: 1-256-23836-8
ISBN 13: 978-1-256-23836-2

Contents

1 Models, Measurements, and Vectors
Hugh D. Young 1

Problem Set (9/e): Models, Measurements, and Vectors
Hugh D. Young 23

2 Motion along a Straight Line
Hugh D. Young 31

Problem Set (9/e): Motion along a Straight Line
Hugh D. Young 61

3 Motion in a Plane
Hugh D. Young 71

Problem Set (9/e): Motion in a Plane
Hugh D. Young 97

4 Newton's Laws of Motion
Hugh D. Young 105

Problem Set (9/e): Newton's Laws of Motion
Hugh D. Young 129

5 Applications of Newton's Laws
Hugh D. Young 137

Problem Set (9/e): Applications of Newton's Laws
Hugh D. Young 161

6 Circular Motion and Gravitation
Hugh D. Young 173

Problem Set (9/e): Circular Motion and Gravitation
Hugh D. Young 195

7 Work and Energy
Hugh D. Young 203

Problem Set (9/e): Work and Energy
Hugh D. Young 237

8 Momentum
Hugh D. Young 249

Problem Set (9/e): Momentum
Hugh D. Young 277

9 Rotational Motion
Hugh D. Young 287

Problem Set (9/e): Rotational Motion
Hugh D. Young 307

10 Dynamics of Rotational Motion
Hugh D. Young 317

Problem Set (9/e): Dynamics of Rotational Motion
Hugh D. Young 347

11 Elasticity and Periodic Motion
Hugh D. Young 361

Problem Set (9/e): Elasticity and Periodic Motion
Hugh D. Young 387

12 Mechanical Waves and Sound
Hugh D. Young 395

Problem Set (9/e): Mechanical Waves and Sound
Hugh D. Young 431

13 Fluid Mechanics
Hugh D. Young 439

Problem Set (9/e): Fluid Mechanics
Hugh D. Young 467

14 Temperature and Heat
Hugh D. Young 475

Problem Set (9/e): Temperature and Heat
Hugh D. Young 505

15 Thermal Properties of Matter
Hugh D. Young 515

Problem Set (9/e): Thermal Properties of Matter
Hugh D. Young 547

16 The Second Law of Thermodynamics
Hugh D. Young 557

Problem Set (9/e): The Second Law of Thermodynamics
Hugh D. Young 583

Appendix: Unit Conversion Factors
Hugh D. Young 591

Appendix: The International System of Units
Hugh D. Young 593

Appendix: Numerical Constants and Astronomical Data
Hugh D. Young 595

Appendix: The Greek Alphabet
Hugh D. Young 597

Appendix: Periodic Table of the Elements
Hugh D. Young

. . . . 599

Index 601

Models, Measurements, and Vectors

Scott Cunningham/Getty Images

The study of physics is an adventure. You'll find it challenging, sometimes frustrating, and often richly rewarding and satisfying. It will appeal to your sense of beauty as well as to your rational intelligence. Our present understanding of the physical world has been built on foundations laid by scientific giants such as Galileo, Newton, and Einstein. You can share some of the excitement of their discoveries when you learn to use physics to solve practical problems and to gain insight into everyday phenomena. Above all, you'll come to see physics as a towering achievement of the human intellect in its quest to understand the world we all live in.

In this chapter we go over some important preliminaries that we'll need throughout our study. We need to think about the philosophical framework in which we operate—the nature of physical theory and the role of idealized *models* in representing physical systems. We discuss systems of *units* that are used to describe physical quantities, such as length and time, and we examine the *precision* of a number, often described by means of *significant figures*. We look at examples of problems in which we can't or don't want to make precise calculations, but in which rough estimates can be interesting and useful. Finally, we study several aspects of *vector algebra*. We use vectors to describe and analyze many physical quantities, such as velocity and force, that have direction as well as magnitude.

Like these players, you already know a lot of physics. Your brain easily computes forces and motions in complex situations. In this course, your goal is simply to build a conscious model of the physical world you live in.

1 Introduction

Physics is an *experimental* science. Physicists observe the phenomena of nature and try to discover patterns and principles that relate these phenomena. These patterns are called *physical theories* or, when they are very broad and well established, *physical laws.* The development of physical theory requires creativ-

(a) Shutterstock **(b)** Space Telescope Science Institute

▶ **FIGURE 1** Two research laboratories. (a) The Leaning Tower of Pisa (Italy). According to legend, Galileo studied the motion of freely falling objects by dropping them from the tower. He is also said to have gained insights into pendulum motion by observing the swinging of the chandelier in the cathedral to the left of the tower. (b) The Hubble Space Telescope, the first major telescope to operate in space, free from the effects of earth's atmosphere.

ity at every stage. The physicist has to learn to ask appropriate questions, design experiments to try to answer the questions, and draw appropriate conclusions from the results. Figure 1 shows two famous experimental facilities.

According to legend, Galileo Galilei (1564–1642) dropped light and heavy objects from the top of the Leaning Tower of Pisa to find out whether they would fall at the same rate or at different rates. Galileo recognized that only an *experimental* investigation could answer this question. From the results of his experiments, he had to make the inductive leap to the principle, or theory, that the rate at which an object falls is independent of its weight.

The development of physical theory is always a two-way process that starts and ends with observations or experiments. Physics is not a collection of facts and principles; it is the *process* by which we arrive at general principles that describe the behavior of the physical universe. And there is always the possibility that new observations will require revision of a theory. We can *disprove* a theory by finding a phenomenon that is inconsistent with it, but we can never *prove* that a theory is *always* correct.

Getting back to Galileo, suppose we drop a feather and a cannonball. They certainly *do not* fall at the same rate. This doesn't mean that our statement of Galileo's theory is wrong, but that it is incomplete. One complicating feature is air resistance. If we drop the feather and the cannonball in vacuum, they *do* fall at the same rate. Our statement of Galileo's theory is valid for bodies that are heavy enough that air resistance has almost no effect on them. A feather or a parachute clearly does not have this property.

Every physical theory has a range of validity and a boundary outside of which it is not applicable. The range of Galileo's work with falling bodies was greatly extended half a century later by Newton's laws of motion and his law of gravitation. Nearly all the principles in this text are so solidly established by experimental evidence that they have earned the title **physical law.** Yet there are some areas of physics in which present-day research is continuing to broaden our understanding of the physical world.

An essential part of the interplay of theory and experiment is learning how to apply physical principles to a variety of practical problems. At various points in our study, we'll discuss systematic problem-solving procedures that will help you set up problems and solve them efficiently and accurately. Learning to solve problems is absolutely essential; you don't *know* physics unless you can *do* physics. This means not only learning the general principles, but also learning how to apply them in a variety of specific situations.

Bruce Ayres/Getty Images

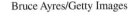

▲ **Application Where are the tunes coming from?** These dancers may not realize it, but they are enjoying the application of fundamental principles of physics that makes their music possible. We will learn about electric charge and current and about how batteries are used to store electrical potential energy. We will see how this energy can be harnessed to perform the mechanical work of rotating the CD within the CD player. We will learn about lasers and optics, which provide the means to "read" a CD. And we will learn about harmonic motion, sound waves, and how these waves travel through space to bring us these "good vibes."

2 Idealized Models

In everyday conversation, we often use the word **model** to mean either a small-scale replica, such as a model train or airplane, or a human figure that displays articles of clothing. **In physics, a** *model* **is a simplified version of a physical system that would be too complicated to analyze in full without the simplifications.**

Here's an example: We want to analyze the motion of a baseball thrown through the air. How complicated is this problem? The ball is neither perfectly spherical nor perfectly rigid; it flexes a little and spins as it moves through the air. Wind and air resistance influence its motion, the earth rotates beneath it, the ball's weight varies a little as its distance from the center of the earth changes, and so on. If we try to include all these things, the analysis gets pretty hopeless. Instead, we invent a simplified version of the problem. We neglect the size and shape of the ball and represent it as a *particle*—that is, as an object that has no size but is completely localized at a single point in space. We neglect air resistance, treating the ball as though it moves in vacuum; we forget about the earth's rotation, and we make the weight of the ball exactly constant. *Now* we have a problem that is simple enough to deal with: The ball is a particle moving along a simple parabolic path.

The point is that we have to overlook quite a few minor effects in order to concentrate on the most important features of the motion. That's what we mean by making an idealized model of the system. Of course, we have to be careful not to neglect *too much*. If we ignore the effect of gravity completely, then when we throw the ball, it will travel in a straight line and disappear into space, never to be seen again! We need to use some judgment and creativity to construct a model that simplifies a system without throwing out its essential features.

When we analyze a system or predict its behavior on the basis of a model, we always need to remember that the validity of our predictions is limited by the validity of the model. If the model represents the real system quite precisely, then we expect predictions made from it to agree quite closely with the actual behavior of the system. Going back to Pisa with Galileo once more, we see that our statement of his theory of falling objects corresponds to an idealized model that does not include the effects of air resistance, the rotation of the earth, or the variation of weight with height. This model works well for a bullet and a cannonball, not so well for a feather.

The concept of an idealized model is of the utmost importance in all of physical science and technology. In applying physical principles to complex systems, we always make extensive use of idealized models, and it is important to be aware of the assumptions we are making. Indeed, the *principles* of physics themselves are stated in terms of idealized models; we speak about point masses, rigid bodies, ideal insulators, and so on. Idealized models will play a crucial role in our discussion of physical theories and their applications to specific problems throughout this text.

3 Standards and Units

Any number that is used to describe an observation of a physical phenomenon quantitatively is called a **physical quantity.** Some physical quantities are so fundamental that we can define them only by describing a procedure for measuring them. Such a definition is called an **operational definition.** In other cases, we define a physical quantity by describing a way to *calculate* the quantity from other quantities that we can measure. As an example of an operational definition, we might use a ruler to measure a length or a stopwatch to measure a time interval. As

Gerard Lacz/Peter Arnold/Photolibrary

▲ **BIO Application How can I find lunch in the dark?** Insect-eating bats utilize the laws of physics in their quest for prey in a process known as echolocation. To locate and capture an insect, these flying mammals first emit an extremely rapid series of 20 to 200 bursts of high-frequency sound. Without using a stopwatch or calculator, they are able to determine the insect's position by sensing the direction of the reflected sound waves and the time it takes for these waves to reach their ears. Luckily for us, the sounds they emit are above the range of human hearing, as they can be over 100 decibels, or about as loud as a typical smoke alarm.

The meter was originally defined as 1/10,000,000 of this distance.

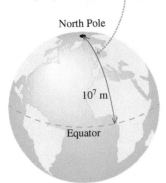

▲ FIGURE 2 The original definition of the meter, from 1791.

(a)

National Institute of Standards and Technology

(b)

Bureau International des Poids et Mesures

▲ FIGURE 3 (a) NIST-F1, the atomic clock that serves as the primary time standard for the United States. This clock is accurate to one part in 10^{15}, meaning that it will neither gain nor lose more than 1 second in 30 million years. (b) This platinum–iridium cylinder, kept in a vault in Sèvres, France, is the standard for the unit of the kilogram. Duplicates are kept at various locations around the world.

an example of a quantity we calculate, we might define the average speed of a moving object as the distance traveled (measured with a ruler) divided by the time of travel (measured with a stopwatch).

When we measure a quantity, we always compare it with some reference standard. When we say that a rope is 30 meters long, we mean that it is 30 times as long as a meterstick, which we *define* to be 1 meter long. We call such a standard a **unit** of the quantity. The meter is a unit of length, and the second is a unit of time.

> **NOTE** ▶ When we use a number to describe a physical quantity, we *must* specify the unit we are using; to describe a distance simply as "30" wouldn't mean anything. ◀

To make precise measurements, we need definitions of units of measurement that do not change and that can be duplicated by observers in various locations. When the metric system was established in 1791 by the Paris Academy of Sciences, the **meter** was originally defined as one ten-millionth of the distance from the equator to the North Pole (Figure 2), and the **second** was defined as the time taken for a pendulum 1 meter long to swing from one side to the other.

These definitions were cumbersome and hard to duplicate precisely, and in more recent years they have been replaced by more refined definitions. Since 1889, the definitions of the basic units have been established by an international organization, the General Conference on Weights and Measures. The system of units defined by this organization is based on the metric system, and since 1960 it has been known officially as the **International System,** or **SI** (the abbreviation for the French equivalent, Système International).

Time

From 1889 until 1967, the unit of time was defined in terms of the length of the day, directly related to the time of the earth's rotation. The present standard, adopted in 1967, is much more precise. It is based on an atomic clock (Figure 3a) that uses the energy difference between the two lowest energy states of the cesium atom. Electromagnetic radiation (microwaves) of precisely the proper frequency causes transitions from one of these states to the other. One second is defined as the time required for 9,192,631,770 cycles of this radiation.

Length

In 1960 an atomic standard for the meter was established, using the orange-red light emitted by atoms of krypton in a glow discharge tube. In November 1983 the standard of length was changed again, in a more radical way. The new definition of the meter is the distance light travels (in vacuum) in $1/299,792,458$ second. The adoption of this definition has the effect, in turn, of *defining* the speed of light to be precisely 299,792,458 m/s; we then define the meter to be consistent with this number and with the atomic-clock definition of the second. This approach provides a much more precise standard of length than the one based on a wavelength of light.

Mass

The standard of *mass* is the mass of a particular cylinder of platinum-iridium alloy. Its mass is defined to be 1 **kilogram,** and it is kept at the International Bureau of Weights and Measures at Sèvres, near Paris (Figure 3b). An atomic standard of mass has not yet been adopted, because, at present, we cannot measure masses on an atomic scale with as great precision as on a macroscopic scale.

TABLE 1 Prefixes for powers of ten

Power of ten	Prefix	Abbreviation
10^{-18}	atto-	a
10^{-15}	femto-	f
10^{-12}	pico-	p
10^{-9}	nano-	n
10^{-6}	micro-	μ
10^{-3}	milli-	m
10^{-2}	centi-	c
10^{3}	kilo-	k
10^{6}	mega-	M
10^{9}	giga-	G
10^{12}	tera-	T
10^{15}	peta-	P
10^{18}	exa-	E

Prefixes

Once the fundamental units have been defined, it is easy to introduce larger and smaller units for the same physical quantities. One of the great strengths of the metric system is that these other units are always related to the fundamental units by multiples of 10 or 1/10. (By comparison, the English system bristles with inconvenient factors such as 12, 16, and 36.) Thus, 1 kilometer (1 km) is 1000 meters, 1 centimeter (1 cm) is 1/100 meter, and so on.

We usually express these multiplicative factors in exponential notation, sometimes called *powers-of-ten* notation or *scientific* notation. For example; $1000 = 10^3$ and $1/100 = 10^{-2}$. With this notation,

$$1 \text{ km} = 10^3 \text{ m}, \qquad 1 \text{ cm} = 10^{-2} \text{ m}.$$

The names of the additional units are always derived by adding a **prefix** to the name of the fundamental unit. For example, the prefix "kilo-," abbreviated k, always means a unit larger by a factor of 1000; thus,

$$1 \text{ kilometer} = 1 \text{ km} = 10^3 \text{ meters} = 10^3 \text{ m},$$
$$1 \text{ kilogram} = 1 \text{ kg} = 10^3 \text{ grams} = 10^3 \text{ g},$$
$$1 \text{ kilowatt} = 1 \text{ kW} = 10^3 \text{ watts} = 10^3 \text{ W}.$$

Table 1 lists the standard SI prefixes with their meanings and abbreviations. Note that most of these are multiples of 10^3.

When pronouncing unit names with prefixes, always accent the *first* syllable: KIL-o-gram, KIL-o-meter, CEN-ti-meter, and MIC-ro-meter. (Kilometer is sometimes pronounced kil-OM-eter.)

Here are a few examples of the use of multiples of 10 and their prefixes with the units of length, mass, and time. Some additional time units are also included. Figure 4 gives a partial idea of the range of length scales studied in physics.

Length

$$1 \text{ nanometer} = 1 \text{ nm} = 10^{-9} \text{ m} \quad \text{(a few times the size of an atom)}$$
$$1 \text{ micrometer} = 1 \text{ } \mu\text{m} = 10^{-6} \text{ m} \quad \text{(size of some bacteria and cells)}$$
$$1 \text{ millimeter} = 1 \text{ mm} = 10^{-3} \text{ m} \quad \text{(point of a ballpoint pen)}$$
$$1 \text{ centimeter} = 1 \text{ cm} = 10^{-2} \text{ m} \quad \text{(diameter of your little finger)}$$
$$1 \text{ kilometer} = 1 \text{ km} = 10^{3} \text{ m} \quad \text{(distance traveled in a 10 minute walk)}$$

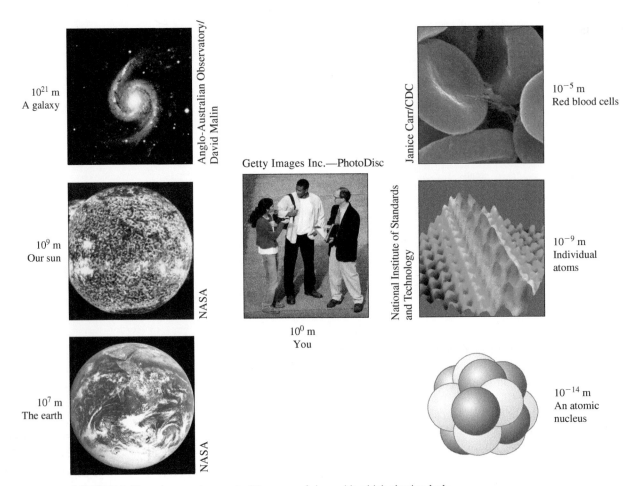

▲ FIGURE 4 These images show part of the range of sizes with which physics deals.

Mass

$$1 \text{ microgram} = 1 \ \mu\text{g} = 10^{-9} \text{ kg} \quad \text{(mass of a 1 mm length of hair)}$$
$$1 \text{ milligram} = 1 \text{ mg} = 10^{-6} \text{ kg} \quad \text{(mass of a grain of salt)}$$
$$1 \text{ gram} = 1 \text{ g} = 10^{-3} \text{ kg} \quad \text{(mass of a paper clip)}$$
$$1 \text{ kilogram} = 1 \text{ kg} = 10^{3} \text{ g} \quad \text{(mass of a 1 liter bottle of water)}$$

Time

$$1 \text{ nanosecond} = 1 \text{ ns} = 10^{-9} \text{ s} \quad \text{(time required for a personal computer to add two numbers)}$$
$$1 \text{ microsecond} = 1 \ \mu\text{s} = 10^{-6} \text{ s} \quad \text{(time required for a 10-year-old personal computer to add two numbers)}$$
$$1 \text{ millisecond} = 1 \text{ ms} = 10^{-3} \text{ s} \quad \text{(time required for sound to travel 0.35 m)}$$
$$1 \text{ minute} = 1 \text{ min} = 60 \text{ s}$$
$$1 \text{ hour} = 1 \text{ h} = 3600 \text{ s}$$
$$1 \text{ day} = 1 \text{ day} = 86{,}400 \text{ s}$$

Finally, we mention the British system of units. These units are used only in the United States and a few other countries, and in most of those countries they are being replaced by SI units. British units are now officially *defined* in terms of SI units, as follows:

Length: 1 inch = 2.54 cm (exactly).

Force: 1 pound = 4.448221615260 newtons (exactly).

The fundamental British unit of time is the second, defined the same way as in SI. British units are used only in mechanics and thermodynamics; there is no British system of electrical units.

In this text we use SI units for almost all examples and problems, but in the early chapters we occasionally give approximate equivalents in British units. As you solve problems using SI units, try to think of the approximate equivalents in British units, but also try to think in SI as much as you can. Even in the United States, we now use metric units in many contexts; we speak about 4 liter engines, 50 mm lenses, 10 km races, 2 L soda bottles, and so on. The use of SI in everyday life is not far off.

Quantitative Analysis 1

SI measurement of hand

With your hand flat and your fingers and thumb close together, the width of your hand is about

A. 50 cm

B. 10 cm

C. 10 mm

SOLUTION If you're not familiar with metric units of length, you can use your body to develop intuition for them. One meter (100 cm) is slightly more than a yard, so the distance from elbow to fingertips is about 50 cm; this eliminates answer A. Ten millimeters (1 cm) is about the width of your little finger. Ten centimeters is about 4 inches and is about the width of your hand.

4 Unit Consistency and Conversions

We use equations to express relations among physical quantities that are represented by algebraic symbols. Most algebraic symbols for physical quantities denote both a number and a unit. For example, d might represent a distance of 10 m, t a time of 5 s, and v (for velocity) a speed of 2 m/s.

An equation must always be **dimensionally consistent.** You can't add apples and pomegranates; two terms may be added or equated only if they have the same units. For example, if a body moving with constant speed v travels a distance d in a time t, these quantities are related by the equation

$$d = vt. \quad (\text{distance} = \text{speed} \times \text{time})$$

If d is measured in meters, then the product vt must also be expressed in meters. Using the above numbers as an example, we may write

$$10 \text{ m} = (2 \text{ m/s})(5 \text{ s}).$$

Because the unit 1/s cancels the unit s in the last factor, the product vt does have units of meters, as it must. In calculations, with respect to multiplication and division, units are treated just like algebraic symbols.

NOTE ▶ When a problem requires calculations using numbers with units, *always* write the numbers with the correct units and carry the units through the calculation, as in the preceding example. This provides a very useful check for calculations. If at some stage in a calculation you find that an equation or an expression has inconsistent units, you know you have made an error somewhere. In this text we will always carry units through all calculations; we strongly urge you to follow this practice when you solve problems. ◀

NASA

▲ **Application A \$125 million unit consistency error.** In 1998, the Mars Climate Orbiter was sent by NASA to orbit Mars at an altitude above the Martian atmosphere; instead, it entered the atmosphere in 1999 and burned up! The key error that led to this disaster was a miscommunication between the Jet Propulsion Laboratory (JPL) and the spacecraft engineers who built it. The engineers specified the amount of thrust required to steer the craft's trajectory in units of British pounds, while the JPL assumed the numbers were in SI units of newtons. Thus, each correction of the trajectory applied a force 4.45 times larger than needed. While there were other compounding errors, this unit inconsistency was a major factor in the failure of the mission and the loss of the Orbiter.

PROBLEM-SOLVING STRATEGY 1 Unit conversions

Units are multiplied and divided just like ordinary algebraic symbols.

This fact gives us an easy way to convert a quantity from one set of units to another. The key idea is that we can express the same physical quantity in two different units and form an equality. For example, when we say that 1 min = 60 s, we don't mean that the number 1 is equal to the number 60, but rather that 1 min represents the same physical time interval as 60 s. In a physical sense, multiplying by the quantity 1 min/60 s is really multiplying by unity, which doesn't change the physical meaning of the quantity. To find the number of seconds in 3 min, we write

$$3 \text{ min} = (3 \text{ min})\left(\frac{60 \text{ s}}{1 \text{ min}}\right) = 180 \text{ s}.$$

This expression makes sense. The second is a smaller unit than the minute, so there are more seconds than minutes in the same time interval.

A ratio of units, such as 1 min/60 s (or 1 min = 60 s), is called a **conversion factor.** A table of conversion factors is given in Appendix D and on the inside front cover. If you are used to English units, it may be useful to realize that 1 m is about 3 ft and that 1 gallon is about 4 liters ($1 \text{ gal} \approx 4 \text{ L}$).

 Inches vs. centimeters

If you express your height both in inches and in centimeters, which unit will give the larger number for your height?

A. The result in centimeters is larger, since you are comparing your height to a unit of length smaller than the inch.
B. Your height in inches is larger, since an inch is larger than a centimeter.
C. Either approach will give the same number, since your height does not depend on the unit used to express it.

SOLUTION Suppose you had a ruler just 1 cm long. To measure the height of a 5 ft person, you would have to move the ruler end-to-end up the person's body about 150 times. However, if your ruler were 1 inch long, you would have to move it just 60 times (5 ft = 60 in). Thus, the smaller your unit of measure, the larger the number you will get when you measure something with it. The correct answer is A.

EXAMPLE 1 Driving the autobahn

Although there is no maximum speed limit on the German autobahn, signs in many areas recommend a top speed of 130 km/h. Express this speed in meters per second and miles per hour.

SOLUTION

SET UP We know that 1 km = 1000 m. From Appendix D or the inside front cover, 1 mi = 1.609 km. We also know that 1 h = 60 min = 60 × (60 s) = 3600 s.

SOLVE We use these conversion factors with the problem-solving strategy we've outlined above:

$$130 \text{ km/h} = \left(\frac{130 \text{ km}}{1 \text{ h}}\right)\left(\frac{1000 \text{ m}}{1 \text{ km}}\right)\left(\frac{1 \text{ h}}{3600 \text{ s}}\right) = 36.1 \text{ m/s},$$

$$130 \text{ km/h} = \left(\frac{130 \text{ km}}{1 \text{ h}}\right)\left(\frac{1 \text{ mi}}{1.609 \text{ km}}\right) = 80.8 \text{ mi/h}.$$

REFLECT In physics, speeds are often expressed in meters per second, but if you're American, you're probably used to thinking in miles per hour. These calculations show that the number of miles per hour is roughly twice the number of meters per second; that is, a speed of 36.1 m/s isn't very different from 80.8 mi/h.

Practice Problem: Suppose you leave the autobahn and reduce your speed to 55 km/h. What is this speed in m/s and mi/h? *Answer:* 55 km/h = 15 m/s = 34 mi/h.

EXAMPLE 2   **The age of the universe**

The universe is thought to be about 13.7 billion years old. **(a)** What is the age of the universe in seconds? **(b)** Our species evolved about 4.7×10^{12} seconds ago. How many years is that?

SOLUTION

SET UP AND SOLVE We calculate the answer by using the appropriate conversion factors, starting with $1\ y = 3.156 \times 10^7\ s$.

Part (a): $13.7 \times 10^9\ y = (13.7 \times 10^9\ y)\left(\dfrac{3.156 \times 10^7\ s}{1\ y}\right)$

$= 4.32 \times 10^{17}\ s.$

Part (b): $4.7 \times 10^{12}\ s = (4.7 \times 10^{12}\ s)\left(\dfrac{1\ y}{3.156 \times 10^7\ s}\right)$

$= 1.5 \times 10^5\ y.$

REFLECT These numbers tell us that the universe is about 10^5 times older than the human species. That is, the universe has existed about 100,000 times as long as we have. A handy approximate conversion factor is $1\ y \approx \pi \times 10^7\ s$; this is within 0.5% of the correct value.

Practice Problem: The average human life span in the United States is about 76.1 years. Calculate this time in seconds. *Answer:* $2.40 \times 10^9\ s.$

Quantitative Analysis 3   **Consistency of units**

When an object moves through air, the air exerts a force on it. (You notice this force when you put your hand out of the window of a moving car.) The strength of the force, which we denote by F, is related to the speed v of the object by the equation $F = bv^2$, where b is a constant. In SI units (kg, m, s), the units of force are $kg \cdot m/s^2$ and the units of speed are m/s. For the preceding equation to have consistent units (the same units on both sides of the equation), the units of b must be

A. kg/m
B. $kg \cdot m/s$
C. kg/m^2

SOLUTION   To solve this problem, we start with the equation $F = bv^2$. For each symbol whose units we know (in this case, F and v), we replace the symbol with those units. For example, we replace v with (m/s). We obtain

$$\left(\frac{kg \cdot m}{s \cdot s}\right) = b\left(\frac{m}{s}\right)\left(\frac{m}{s}\right).$$ (Algebraically, units are treated like numbers.)

We now solve this equation for b. When we multiply the equation on both sides by s^2, the seconds (s) cancel, and one of the meter units (m) cancels. We obtain $b = kg/m$, so the correct answer is A.

5 Precision and Significant Figures

Measurements always have uncertainties. When we measure a distance with an ordinary ruler, it is usually reliable only to the nearest millimeter, but with a precision micrometer caliper, we can measure distances with an uncertainty of less than 0.01 mm. We often indicate the precision of a number by writing the number, the symbol $\pm$, and a second number indicating the likely uncertainty. If the diameter of a steel rod is given as 56.47 ± 0.02 mm, this expression means that the true value is unlikely to be less than 56.45 mm or greater than 56.49 mm.

When we use numbers having uncertainties or errors to compute other numbers, the computed numbers are also uncertain. It is especially important to understand this when comparing a number obtained from measurements with a value obtained from a theoretical prediction. Suppose you want to determine the value of π (pi), as in Figure 5, using the relation of the circumference C of a circle to its diameter D: $C = \pi D$. Then

$$\pi = \frac{C}{D} = \frac{\text{circumference}}{\text{diameter}}.$$

The true value of this ratio, to 10 digits, is 3.141592654. To make your own calculation, you cut a circular piece out of a sheet of plywood and measure its diameter and circumference to the nearest millimeter, using a flexible measuring tape. Suppose you obtain the values 135 mm and 424 mm, respectively. You

135 mm

424 mm

▲ **FIGURE 5** Finding π with a plywood disk and a tape measure.

Roger Viollet/Getty Images

▲ Application **What went wrong?** While a 0.01% error may sound insignificant, in this case it resulted in a spectacular mishap. In a journey of 500 kilometers, a 0.01% error represents only 50 meters. Yet going 0.01% too far had tragic results in this instance. In physics, measurements can be considerably more precise than ±0.01%. For example, according to the National Institute of Standards and Technology, the mass of the electron has been determined to be 9.1093826 ±0.0000016 × 10^{-31} kg. This represents a relative uncertainty of 1.7×10^{-7}, or only ±0.000017%, in measuring the mass of the electron.

punch these numbers into your calculator and obtain the quotient 3.140740741. Does this quantity agree with the true value or not?

First, the last seven digits in this answer are meaningless, because they imply greater precision than is possible with your measurements. The number of meaningful digits in a number is called the number of **significant figures** or **significant digits.** ("Figure" in this context means "digit.") **When numbers are multiplied or divided, the number of significant figures in the result is no greater than in the factor with the fewest significant figures.** For example, $3.1416 \times 2.34 \times 0.58 = 4.3$. Thus your measured value of π using the plywood circle has only three significant figures and should be stated simply as 3.14. Your value *does* agree with the true value, although only to three significant figures.

NOTE ▶ Zero can be a significant figure. The number 0.580 has three significant figures. The initial zero doesn't matter, but the final zero implies that the number is probably between 0.579 and 0.581. Writing 0.58 implies only that the number is probably between 0.57 and 0.59. Leading zeroes aren't significant, but trailing zeroes are. ◀

When you add or subtract, the rule for handling significant figures is slightly different than when you multiply or divide: **When you add or subtract, the answer can have no more decimal places than the term with the fewest decimal places.** For example, $5.232 + 0.31 = 5.54$, not 5.542.

Here's one additional point: In symbolic relationships, when unitless numerical constants appear, usually they should be taken to have infinitely great accuracy, with no uncertainty at all. For example, in the relation $C = 2\pi R$ between the radius R and circumference C of a circle, the factor 2 is taken to be exact, with no uncertainty. It could appropriately be written as 2.000000000000000.

Most examples and problems in this text give data to two or three significant figures (occasionally more). In each problem, your answer should have no more significant figures than the preceding rules allow. You may do the arithmetic with a calculator having a display with 5 to 10 digits. But you should *not* give a 10 digit answer for a calculation using numbers with three significant figures. To do so is not only unnecessary; it is genuinely wrong, because it misrepresents the precision of the results. Always round your answer to keep only the correct number of significant figures.

When we calculate with very large or very small numbers, we can show significant figures much more easily by using powers-of-ten notation, sometimes called *scientific notation,* as we discussed in Section 3. For example, the distance from the earth to the sun is about 149,000,000,000 m, but writing the number in this form gives no indication of the number of significant figures. Certainly, not all 12 are significant! Instead, we move the decimal point 11 places to the left (corresponding to dividing by 10^{11}) and multiply by 10^{11}. That is,

$$149{,}000{,}000{,}000 \text{ m} = 1.49 \times 10^{11} \text{ m.} \quad \text{(three significant figures)}$$

In this form, it is clear that we have three significant figures. In scientific notation, a common practice is to express a quantity as a number between 1 and 10, multiplied by the appropriate power of 10.

EXAMPLE 3 **Mass is energy**

The energy E corresponding to the mass m of an electron is given by Einstein's famous equation

$$E = mc^2, \quad \text{(equivalence of mass and energy)}$$

where c is the speed of light. Calculate the value of E for an electron, using powers of ten and three significant figures.

Continued

SOLUTION

SET UP We find the needed numbers inside the front cover or in Appendix D: $m = 9.11 \times 10^{-31}$ kg and $c = 3.00 \times 10^8$ m/s.

SOLVE We use these numbers to calculate the value of E:

$$
\begin{aligned}
E &= (9.11 \times 10^{-31}\ \text{kg})(3.00 \times 10^8\ \text{m/s})^2 \\
&= (9.11)(3.00)^2(10^{-31})(10^8)^2(\text{kg} \cdot \text{m}^2)/\text{s}^2 \\
&= (82.0)(10^{[-31 + (2 \times 8)]})(\text{kg} \cdot \text{m}^2)/\text{s}^2 \\
&= 8.20 \times 10^{-14}\ \text{kg} \cdot \text{m}^2/\text{s}^2.
\end{aligned}
$$

REFLECT Most pocket calculators can use scientific notation and do this addition of exponents automatically for you; but you should be able to do such calculations by hand when necessary. Incidentally, the value used for c in Example 3 has three significant figures, even though two of them are zeros. To greater precision, $c = 2.997925 \times 10^8$ m/s.

Conceptual Analysis 4

Significant figures

To seven significant figures, the speed of light is $c = 2.997925 \times 10^8$ m/s. Which of the following choices is or are correct?

A. $c = 3.0 \times 10^8$ m/s
B. $c = 3.00 \times 10^8$ m/s
C. $c = 3.000 \times 10^8$ m/s

SOLUTION Answer C is incorrect, because when we round to four significant figures, we get 2.998, not 3.000. But A and B are both correct; they represent different levels of precision, even though the numerical value is the same.

6 Estimates and Orders of Magnitude

PhET: Estimation

We've talked about the importance of knowing the precision of numbers that represent physical quantities. But there are also situations in which even a very crude estimate of a quantity may give us useful information. Often we know how to calculate a certain quantity but have to guess at the data we need for the calculation. Or the calculation may be too complicated to carry out exactly, so we make some crude approximations. In either case our result is also a guess, but many times such a guess is useful, even if it is uncertain by a factor of 2, or 10, or more. Such calculations are often called **order-of-magnitude estimates.** The great nuclear physicist Enrico Fermi (1901–1954) called them "back-of-the-envelope calculations."

EXAMPLE 4   **Espionage**

You are writing an international espionage novel in which the hero escapes across the border with a billion dollars worth of gold in his suitcase. Is this possible? Would that amount of gold fit in a suitcase? Would it be too heavy to carry?

SOLUTION

SET UP AND SOLVE We can guess at both the mass of gold needed and its density. From these numbers we can then find the volume of gold needed.

Gold sells for around $400 an ounce. On a particular day, the price might be $200 or $600, but never mind. An ounce is about 30 grams. Actually, an ordinary (avoirdupois) ounce is 28.35 g; an ounce of gold is a troy ounce, which is 9.45% more. Again, never mind. Ten dollars worth of gold has a mass somewhere around 1 gram, so a billion (10^9) dollars worth of gold is a hundred million (10^8) grams, or a hundred thousand (10^5) kilograms. This corresponds to a weight in British units of around 200,000 lb, or a hundred tons.

We can also estimate the *volume* of this gold. If its density were the same as that of water (1 g/cm^3), the volume would be

10^8 cm^3, or 100 m^3. But gold is a heavy metal; we might guess its density to be 10 times that of water. In fact, it is over 20 times as dense as water. But guessing 10, we find a volume of 10 m^3. Visualize 10 cubical stacks of gold bricks, each 1 meter on a side, and ask whether they would fit in a suitcase!

REFLECT Whether the precise weight is 50 tons or 200 doesn't matter. Either way, the hero is not about to carry it across the border in a suitcase. And 10 cubic meters certainly won't fit in the suitcase!

Practice Problem: Suppose our hero needs only a million dollars, not a billion. Are the answers the same or different? Would he do better if he used cut diamonds instead of gold? *Answer:* Weight is a few hundred pounds; volume is comparable to a small carry-on suitcase. Diamonds would be better.

Handwritten notation: $\vec{A}$

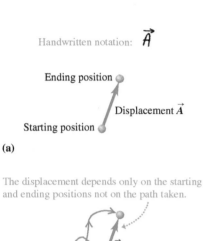

Ending position

Displacement $\vec{A}$

Starting position

(a)

The displacement depends only on the starting and ending positions not on the path taken.

Path taken

$\vec{A}$

(b)

If the object makes a round-trip, the total displacement is 0, regardless of the distance traveled.

(c)

▲ **FIGURE 6** Displacement is a vector quantity. A displacement vector represents a change in position (distance and direction) of an object from one point in space to another.

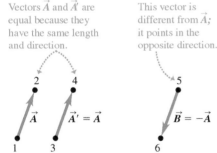

Vectors $\vec{A}$ and $\vec{A}'$ are equal because they have the same length and direction.

This vector is different from $\vec{A}$; it points in the opposite direction.

$\vec{A}$ $\vec{A}' = \vec{A}$ $\vec{B} = -\vec{A}$

2 4 5

1 3 6

▲ **FIGURE 7** Two displacement vectors are equal if they have the same length (magnitude) and the same (not opposite) direction.

7 Vectors and Vector Addition

Some physical quantities, such as time, temperature, mass, density, and electric charge, can be described completely by a single number with a unit. Many other quantities, however, have a *directional* quality and cannot be described by a single number. A familiar example is velocity. To describe the motion of an airplane, we have to say not only *how fast* it is moving, but also *in what direction.* To fly from Chicago to New York, the plane has to head east, not south. Force is another example. When we push or pull on a body, we exert a force on it. To describe a force, we need to describe the direction in which it acts, as well as its magnitude, or "how hard" the force pushes or pulls. A tow truck usually pulls a stalled car forward, not sideways.

When a physical quantity is described by a single number, we call it a **scalar quantity.** In contrast, a **vector quantity** has both a **magnitude** (the "how much" or "how big" part) and a **direction** in space. Calculations with scalar quantities use the operations of ordinary arithmetic. For example, 6 kg + 3 kg = 9 kg, or $(12\text{ m})/(3\text{ s}) = 4$ m/s. However, combining vector quantities requires a different set of operations. Vector quantities play an essential role in all areas of physics, so let's talk next about what vectors are and how they combine.

We start with the simplest of all vector quantities: **displacement.** Displacement is simply a change in position of an object, which we will assume can be treated as a pointlike particle. In Figure 6a, we represent the object's change in position by an arrow that points from the starting position to the ending position. Displacement is a *vector quantity* because we must state not only *how far* the particle moves, but also *in what direction.* Walking 3 km north from your front door doesn't get you to the same place as walking 3 km southeast.

We usually represent a vector quantity, such as a displacement, by a single letter, such as $\vec{A}$ in Figure 6. In this text, we always print vector symbols **in bold-face type with an arrow above them,** to remind you that vector quantities have properties different from those of scalar quantities. In handwriting, vector symbols are usually written with an arrow above, as shown in Figure 6a, to indicate that they represent vector quantities.

NOTE ▶ When you write a symbol for a vector quantity, *always* put an arrow over it. If you don't distinguish between scalar and vector quantities in your notation, you probably won't make the distinction in your thinking either, and hopeless confusion will result. ◀

A displacement is always a straight-line segment, directed from the starting point to the endpoint, even though the actual path of the object may be curved. In Figure 6b, the displacement is still $\vec{A}$, even though the object takes a roundabout path. Also, note that displacement is not related directly to the total *distance* traveled. If the particle makes a round trip, returning to its starting point as shown in Figure 6c, the displacement for the entire trip is *zero.*

The vector $\vec{A}'$ from point 3 to point 4 in Figure 7 has the same length and direction as the vector $\vec{A}$ from point 1 to point 2. These two displacements are equal, even though they start at different points. Thus we may write $\vec{A}' = \vec{A}$. By definition, two vector quantities are equal if they have the same magnitude (length) and direction, no matter where they are located in space. The vector $\vec{B}$, however, is *not* equal to $\vec{A}$, because its direction is *opposite* to that of $\vec{A}$. We define the *negative* of a vector as a vector having the same magnitude as the original vector, but opposite direction. The negative of the vector quantity $\vec{A}$ is denoted $-\vec{A}$. If $\vec{A}$ is 87 m south, then $-\vec{A}$ is 87 m north.

Thus, the relation between $\vec{A}$ and $\vec{B}$ may be written as $\vec{A} = -\vec{B}$ or $\vec{B} = -\vec{A}$. When two vectors $\vec{A}$ and $\vec{B}$ have opposite directions, we say that they are *antiparallel*.

NOTE ▶ Remember that two vector quantities are equal only when they have the same magnitude *and* the same (not opposite) direction. ◀

We usually represent the magnitude of a vector quantity (its length, in the case of a displacement vector) by the same letter used for the vector, but in light italic type rather than boldface italic. An alternative notation is the vector symbol with vertical bars on both sides. Thus,

Magnitude of $\vec{A} = A = |\vec{A}|$.   (notation for magnitude of a vector quantity)

By definition, the magnitude of a vector quantity is a scalar quantity (a single number) and is always positive. We also note that a vector can never be equal to a scalar, because they are different kinds of quantities. The expression $\vec{A} = 6$ m is just as wrong as "2 oranges = 3 apples" or "6 lb = 7 km"!

Now suppose a particle undergoes a displacement $\vec{A}$, followed by a second displacement $\vec{B}$ (Figure 8a). The final result is the same as though the particle had started at the same initial point and undergone a single displacement $\vec{C}$, as shown. We call displacement $\vec{C}$ the **vector sum,** or **resultant,** of displacements $\vec{A}$ and $\vec{B}$; we express this relationship symbolically as

$$\vec{C} = \vec{A} + \vec{B}. \quad \text{(vector sum of two vectors)}$$

The plus sign in this equation denotes the geometrical operation of **vector addition** that we've described; it is *not* the same operation as adding two scalar quantities such as $2 + 3 = 5$.

If we make the displacements $\vec{A}$ and $\vec{B}$ in the reverse order, as in Figure 8b, with $\vec{B}$ first and $\vec{A}$ second, the result is the same, as the figure shows. Thus,

$$\vec{C} = \vec{B} + \vec{A} \quad \text{and} \quad \vec{A} + \vec{B} = \vec{B} + \vec{A}. \quad \text{(Vector sum is commutative.)}$$

The last equation shows that the order of the terms in a vector sum doesn't matter; addition of vectors is **commutative.** We draw the tail of the second vector at the point of the first, and the results are the same with either order.

Figure 8b also suggests an alternative graphical representation of the vector sum. When vectors $\vec{A}$ and $\vec{B}$ are both drawn with their tails at the same point, vector $\vec{C}$ is the diagonal of a parallelogram constructed with $\vec{A}$ and $\vec{B}$ as two adjacent sides.

Figure 9 shows the special cases in which two vectors $\vec{A}$ and $\vec{B}$ are parallel (Figure 9a) or antiparallel (Figure 9b). When the vectors are parallel, the magnitude of the vector sum equals the *sum* of the magnitudes of $\vec{A}$ and $\vec{B}$; when they are antiparallel, it equals the *difference* of their magnitudes.

(a)

(b)

(c)

▲ **FIGURE 8** Vector $\vec{C}$ is the vector sum of vectors $\vec{A}$ and $\vec{B}$. The order in vector addition doesn't matter. (Vector addition is commutative.)

(a) The sum of two parallel vectors

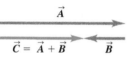

(b) The sum of two antiparallel vectors

▲ **FIGURE 9** The vector sum of (a) two parallel vectors and (b) two antiparallel vectors. Note that the vectors $\vec{A}$, $\vec{B}$, and $\vec{C}$ in (a) are not the same as the vectors $\vec{A}$, $\vec{B}$, and $\vec{C}$ in (b).

Conceptual Analysis 5

Resultant vector

Two vectors, one with magnitude 3 m and the other with magnitude 4 m, are added together. The resultant vector could have a magnitude as small as

A. 1 m;
B. 3 m;
C. 4 m.

SOLUTION The resultant has the largest magnitude when the two vectors are parallel and the smallest when they are antiparallel—that is, pointing in opposite directions. In the latter case, the resultant will be the difference between their lengths, which is 1 m. Thus, answer A is correct.

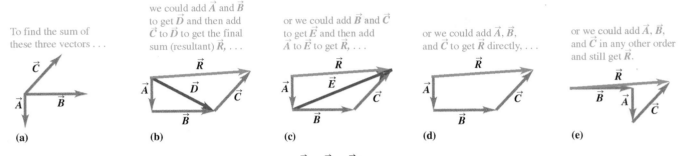

we could add $\vec{A}$ and $\vec{B}$ to get $\vec{D}$ and then add $\vec{C}$ to $\vec{D}$ to get the final sum (resultant) $\vec{R}$, . . .

or we could add $\vec{B}$ and $\vec{C}$ to get $\vec{E}$ and then add $\vec{A}$ to $\vec{E}$ to get $\vec{R}$, . . .

or we could add $\vec{A}$, $\vec{B}$, and $\vec{C}$ to get $\vec{R}$ directly, . . .

or we could add $\vec{A}$, $\vec{B}$, and $\vec{C}$ in any other order and still get $\vec{R}$.

To find the sum of these three vectors . . .

(a) (b) (c) (d) (e)

▲ **FIGURE 10** Several constructions for finding the vector sum $\vec{A} + \vec{B} + \vec{C}$.

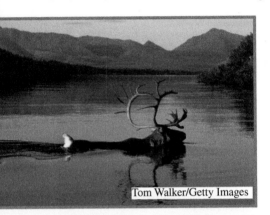

Tom Walker/Getty Images

▲ **Application** **Where will it end up?**
Although this caribou is trying to swim straight across the river, it will not end up directly across from its starting point. Its final position on the opposite bank can be determined by the addition of two vectors. One represents its movement directly across the river, and a second represents the downstream movement of the water. If it paddles across at the same speed as the river flows, summing these two vectors shows us that it will actually cross the river at a 45° angle. At the other side, it will end up a distance downstream equal to the width of the river, having traveled a distance of $\sqrt{2}$ times the river's width.

When we need to add more than two vectors, we may first find the vector sum of any two, add it vectorially to the third, and so on. Figure 10a shows three vectors $\vec{A}$, $\vec{B}$, and $\vec{C}$. In Figure 10b, vectors $\vec{A}$ and $\vec{B}$ are first added, giving a vector sum $\vec{D}$; vectors $\vec{D}$ and $\vec{C}$ are then added by the same process to obtain the vector sum $\vec{R}$:

$$\vec{R} = (\vec{A} + \vec{B}) + \vec{C} = \vec{D} + \vec{C}.$$

Alternatively, we can first add $\vec{B}$ and $\vec{C}$ (Figure 10c) to obtain vector $\vec{E}$ and then add $\vec{A}$ and $\vec{E}$ to obtain $\vec{R}$:

$$\vec{R} = \vec{A} + (\vec{B} + \vec{C}) = \vec{A} + \vec{E}.$$

We don't even need to draw vectors $\vec{D}$ and $\vec{E}$; all we need to do is draw the given vectors in succession, with the tail of each at the head of the one preceding it, and complete the polygon by a vector $\vec{R}$ from the *tail* of the first to the *head* of the last, as shown in Figure 10d. The order makes no difference; Figure 10e shows a different order, and we invite you to try others.

NOTE ▶ When adding vectors graphically, always arrange them tip to tail, so that the tip of one points to the tail of the next. The vectors can be in any order. The resultant always points from the tail of the first vector to the tip of the final one. ◀

Quantitative Analysis 6 **Pythagorean vectors**

If you walk 40 m east, then 30 m north, how far from the starting point are you?

A. 10 m
B. 50 m
C. 70 m

SOLUTION The two legs of your trip form the sides of a right triangle; your final displacement is the hypotenuse. Draw a diagram showing the two successive displacements and the vector sum. You can use the Pythagorean theorem to calculate the length of the vector sum, 50 m.

You can confirm the length of this resultant vector by using what you know about parallel and antiparallel vectors. If the two legs of your trip were antiparallel (rather than at right angles), the resultant would have a magnitude of 10 m. So A can't be right; the correct answer must be larger. If the two legs were parallel (i.e., if you walked 40 m and then continued 30 m in the same direction), the resultant would have a magnitude of 70 m, so C can't be right either; the correct answer must be smaller. That leaves B as the correct answer.

Diagrams for the addition of displacement vectors don't have to be drawn actual size. Often, we'll use a scale similar to those used for maps, in which the distance on the diagram is *proportional* to the actual distance, such as 1 cm for 5 km. When we work with other vector quantities with different units, such as force or velocity, we *must* use a scale. In a diagram for velocity vectors, we might use a scale in which a vector 1 cm long represents a velocity with magnitude 5 m/s. A velocity with magnitude 20 m/s would then be represented by a vector 4 cm long in the appropriate direction.

A vector quantity such as a displacement can be multiplied by a scalar quantity (an ordinary number). As shown in Figure 11, the displacement $2\vec{A}$ is a displacement (vector quantity) in the same direction as the vector $\vec{A}$, but twice as long. The scalar quantity used to multiply a vector may also be a physical quantity having units. For example, when an object moves in a straight line with constant velocity $\vec{v}$ for a time t, its total displacement $\vec{d}$ is equal to $\vec{v}t$. The magnitude d of the displacement is equal to the magnitude v of the velocity multiplied by the time t. The directions of $\vec{d}$ and $\vec{v}$ are the same (assuming that t is positive). The units of d are the product of the units of v and t.

We've already mentioned that $-\vec{A}$ is, by definition, a vector having the same magnitude as $\vec{A}$ but opposite direction. This definition provides the basis for defining vector *subtraction*. (See Figure 12.) We define the *difference* $\vec{A} - \vec{B}$ of two vectors $\vec{A}$ and $\vec{B}$ to be the vector sum of $\vec{A}$ and $-\vec{B}$:

$$\vec{A} - \vec{B} = \vec{A} + (-\vec{B}). \qquad \text{(vector difference)}$$

Multiplying a vector by a positive scalar changes the magnitude (length) of the vector, but not its direction.

$2\vec{A}$ is twice as long as $\vec{A}$.

Multiplying a vector by a negative scalar changes its magnitude and reverses its direction.

$-3\vec{A}$ is three times as long as $\vec{A}$ and points in the opposite direction.

▲ **FIGURE 11** The effect of multiplying a vector by a scalar.

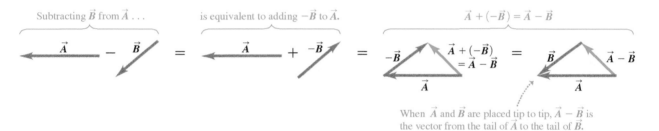

When $\vec{A}$ and $\vec{B}$ are placed tip to tip, $\vec{A} - \vec{B}$ is the vector from the tail of $\vec{A}$ to the tail of $\vec{B}$.

▲ **FIGURE 12** The definition of vector subtraction.

EXAMPLE 5   Displacement of a cross-country skier

On a cross-country ski trip, you travel 1.00 km north and then 2.00 km east. **(a)** How far and in what direction are you from your starting point? **(b)** What are the magnitude and direction of your resultant displacement?

SOLUTION

SET UP Figure 13 is a scale diagram. By careful measurement on the diagram, we find that the distance d from the starting point is about 2.2 km and the angle ϕ is about 63°. But it's much more accurate to *calculate* the result. The vectors in the diagram form a right triangle, and we can find the length of the hypotenuse by using the Pythagorean theorem. The angle can be found by simple trigonometry, from the definition of the tangent function.

SOLVE Part (a): Use the Pythagorean theorem to find the length d of the resultant displacement vector (the distance from the starting point):

$$d = \sqrt{(1.00\ \text{km})^2 + (2.00\ \text{km})^2}$$
$$= 2.24\ \text{km}. \qquad \text{(Magnitude of displacement vector)}$$

From the definition of the tangent function,

$$\tan\phi = \frac{\text{opposite side}}{\text{adjacent side}} = \frac{2.00\ \text{km}}{1.00\ \text{km}},$$
$$\phi = 63.4°. \qquad \text{(direction of displacement vector)}$$

▲ **FIGURE 13** A vector diagram, drawn to scale, for a cross-country ski trip.

Part (b): The magnitude of the resultant displacement is just the distance d we found in part (a), 2.24 km. We can describe the direction as 63.4° east of north, or 26.6° north of east. Take your choice!

Continued

REFLECT The method we've used here works only for vectors that form a right triangle. In the next section, we'll present a more general method.

Practice Problem: Your friend skis 3.00 km east and then 1.50 km north. **(a)** How far and in what direction is he from the starting point? **(b)** What are the magnitude and direction of his resultant displacement? *Answers:* (a) 3.35 km, 26.6°; (b) 3.35 km, 26.6° north of east.

8 Components of Vectors

We need to develop efficient and general methods for adding vectors. In Example 5 in the preceding section, we added two vectors by drawing and measuring a scale diagram or by making use of the properties of right triangles. Measuring a diagram offers only very limited precision, and our example was a special case in which the two vectors were perpendicular. With an angle other than 90° or with more than two vectors, we would get into repeated trigonometric solutions of oblique triangles, which can get horribly complicated.

So we need a simple, but more general, method for adding vectors. The usual method makes use of *components* of vectors. As a prelude to explaining this method, let's review the definitions of the basic trigonometric functions.

For a right triangle, the functions $\sin\theta$, $\cos\theta$ and $\tan\theta$ are defined as follows:

Definitions of trigonometric functions
For the right triangle shown,

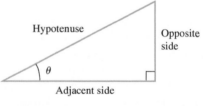

$$\sin\theta = \frac{\text{opposite side}}{\text{hypotenuse}}, \qquad \cos\theta = \frac{\text{adjacent side}}{\text{hypotenuse}},$$

$$\tan\theta = \frac{\text{opposite side}}{\text{adjacent side}}. \tag{1}$$

From these definitions, we can prove that, for any angle θ,

$$\tan\theta = \frac{\sin\theta}{\cos\theta} \qquad \text{and} \qquad \sin^2\theta + \cos^2\theta = 1.$$

Now, what are components, and how are they used to add and subtract vectors? To define what we mean by components, let's start with a rectangular (Cartesian) coordinate axis system as in Figure 14. We can represent any vector lying in the *x*-*y* plane as the vector sum of a vector parallel to the *x* axis and a vector parallel to the *y* axis. These two vectors are labeled $\vec{A}_x$ and $\vec{A}_y$ in Figure 14a; they are called the **component vectors** of vector $\vec{A}$, and their vector sum is equal to $\vec{A}$. In symbols,

$$\vec{A} = \vec{A}_x + \vec{A}_y. \quad \text{(vector } \vec{A} \text{ as a sum of component vectors)}$$

By definition, each component vector lies along one of the two coordinate-axis directions. Thus, we need only a single number to describe each component. When the vector points in the positive axis direction, we define the number A_x to

(a)

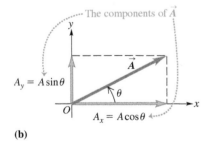

(b)

▲ **FIGURE 14** (a) The component vectors of $\vec{A}$ in the direction of the *x* and *y* axes. (b) The *x* and *y* components of $\vec{A}$.

be the magnitude of $\vec{A}_x$. When $\vec{A}_x$ points in the $-x$ direction, we define the number A_x to be the *negative* of that magnitude, keeping in mind that the magnitude of a vector quantity is always positive. We define the number A_y the same way. The two numbers A_x and A_y are called the **components** of the vector $\vec{A}$. We haven't yet described what they're good for; we'll get to that soon!

NOTE ▶ Be sure that you understand the relationship between $\vec{A}$ (a vector), A or $|\vec{A}|$ (the vector's magnitude), $\vec{A}_x$ (a component vector) and A_x (a component). The following tips are useful:

- A subscript x or y indicates that the quantity is a component vector or component along the x or y axis. Watch for these subscripts!
- A *magnitude* is always positive.
- A *component* is positive if the corresponding component vector points in the positive direction of the axis, negative if the component vector points in the negative direction of the axis. ◀

If, for the vector $\vec{A}$ in Figure 14, we know both the magnitude A and the direction, given by the angle θ, we can calculate the components, as shown in Figure 14b. From the definitions of the trigonometric cosine and sine functions,

$$\frac{A_x}{A} = \cos\theta \qquad \text{and} \qquad \frac{A_y}{A} = \sin\theta;$$

$$A_x = A\cos\theta \qquad \text{and} \qquad A_y = A\sin\theta. \tag{2}$$

NOTE ▶ These equations are correct for *any* angle θ, from 0 to 360°, provided that the angle is measured counterclockwise from the positive x axis. This is the usual convention, but sometimes you'll find it more convenient to measure θ from a different axis; then you'll have to identify the appropriate right triangle and use the definitions of the trigonometric functions for that triangle. Be careful! ◀

In Figure 15, the component B_x is negative because its direction is opposite that of the positive x axis. This is consistent with Equations 2; the cosine of an angle in the second quadrant is negative. B_y is positive, but both C_x and C_y are negative.

We can describe a vector completely by giving either its magnitude and direction or its x and y components. Equations 2 show how to find the components if we know the magnitude and direction. Applying the Pythagorean theorem to Figure 14, we find

$$A = \sqrt{A_x^2 + A_y^2}. \quad \text{(magnitude of vector } \vec{A}) \tag{3}$$

Also, from the definition of the tangent of an angle,

$$\tan\theta = \frac{A_y}{A_x} \qquad \text{and} \qquad \theta = \tan^{-1}\frac{A_y}{A_x}. \quad \text{(direction of vector } \vec{A}) \tag{4}$$

NOTE ▶ There's a slight complication in using Equations 4 to find θ. Suppose $A_x = 2$ m and $A_y = -2$ m; then $\tan\theta = -1$. But, as shown in Figure 16, there are two angles having tangents of -1, namely, 135° and 315° (or $-45°$). To decide which is correct, we have to look at the individual components. Because A_x is positive and A_y is negative, the angle must be in the fourth quadrant; thus, $\theta = 315°$ (or $-45°$) is the correct value. Most pocket calculators give $\tan^{-1}(-1) = -45°$. In this case, that is correct;

(a)

(b)

▲ **FIGURE 15** The components of a vector are numbers; they may be positive or negative.

In this case, $\tan\theta = \dfrac{A_y}{A_x} = -1$.

Two angles have tangents of -1: 135° and 315°. Inspection of the diagram shows that θ must be 315°.

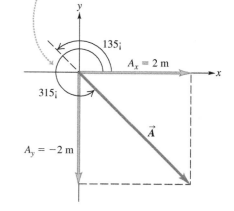

▲ **FIGURE 16** Two angles may have the same tangent; sketching the vector shows which angle is correct.

but if, instead, we have $A_x = -2$ m and $A_y = 2$ m, then the correct angle is 135°. You should always draw a sketch to check which of the two possibilities is the correct one. Similarly, when A_x and A_y are both negative, the tangent is positive, but the angle is in the third quadrant. ◄

The next example will give us some practice in finding components of individual vectors; then we'll talk about how the components are used to find vector sums and differences.

EXAMPLE 6   Finding components of vectors

Raoul and Maria set out walking from their aunt's house. Raoul walks a certain distance straight east and then a certain distance straight north. A crow passing overhead starts from the same point as Raoul, but flies in a straight line. Raoul observes that the crow flies a total distance of 500 m in a direction 35° north of east to reach the same final point as Raoul. Maria starts from the same point as Raoul, but she walks first straight west and then straight south. Her final point is 700 m from the starting point in a direction that is 55° south of west. How far did Raoul walk on the east leg of his trip? How far on the north leg? Similarly, how far did Maria walk on the west leg and how far on the south leg? Express these quantities in terms of displacement vectors and their components, using a coordinate system with the $+x$ axis pointing east and the $+y$ axis pointing north.

SOLUTION

SET UP First we sketch a diagram showing each displacement, as in Figure 17. We draw a rectangular coordinate system and label the axes, with the $+x$ axis east and the $+y$ axis north. Be sure to make your sketch large enough so that you will be able to draw and label the components of each vector. Note that the vector representing Maria's displacement lies in the third quadrant, so both the x and y components of this vector will be negative.

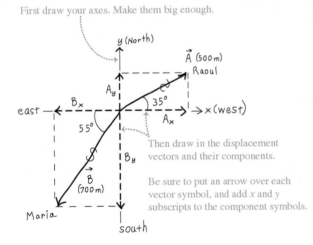

FIGURE 17 The diagram we draw for this problem.

SOLVE We'll label Raoul's displacement vector $\vec{A}$ and Maria's $\vec{B}$. Then to find the components we use Equations 2:

$$A_x = A\cos\theta \quad \text{and} \quad B_x = B\cos\theta$$
$$A_y = A\sin\theta \quad \quad \quad B_y = B\sin\theta$$

We measure the angles counterclockwise from the $+x$ axis. So the direction of Maria's displacement is $180° + 55° = 235°$. The components of the two displacement vectors are as follows:

Raoul	Maria
$A_x = 500 \text{ m} \,(\cos 35°)$	$B_x = 700 \text{ m} \,(\cos 235°)$
$\quad = 410 \text{ m (east)}$	$\quad = -402 \text{ m (west)}$
$A_y = 500 \text{ m} \,(\sin 35°)$	$B_y = 700 \text{ m} \,(\sin 235°)$
$\quad = 287 \text{ m (north)}$	$\quad = -573 \text{ m (south)}$

REFLECT Because Maria walked west and south, the x and y components of her displacement are both negative. To get the correct signs, we must measure the angles counterclockwise from the $+x$ axis.

Practice Problem: Raoul's friend Johnny sets out from his house in the city. His displacement is 600 m 40° north of west. What are the x and y components of his displacement vector? *Answers:* $A_x = -460$ m; $A_y = 386$ m.

Using components to add vectors

Now, at last, we're ready to talk about using components to calculate the vector sum of several vectors. The component method requires only right triangles and simple computations, and it can be carried out with great precision. Here's the basic idea: Figure 18a shows two vectors $\vec{A}$ and $\vec{B}$ and their vector sum (resultant) $\vec{R}$, along with the x and y components of all three vectors. You can see from the diagram that the x component R_x of the vector sum is simply the sum

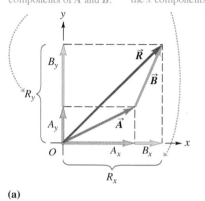

$\vec{R}$ is the sum (resultant) of $\vec{A}$ and $\vec{B}$.

The y component of $\vec{R}$ equals the sum of the y components of $\vec{A}$ and $\vec{B}$.

The same goes for the x components.

(a)

When we replace a vector with its components, we cross out the original vector with a squiggle for clarity.

(b)

◀ **FIGURE 18** (a) When two vectors $\vec{A}$ and $\vec{B}$ are added to give a vector sum (resultant) $\vec{R}$, the sum of their x components is the x component of $\vec{R}$, and the sum of their y components is the y component of $\vec{R}$. (b) When we replace a vector with its components, we cross out the original vector to avoid confusion.

$(A_x + B_x)$ of the x components of the vectors being added. The same is true for the y components. In symbols,

$$R_x = A_x + B_x,$$
$$R_y = A_y + B_y. \quad \text{(components of vector sum)} \quad (5)$$

Once we know the components of $\vec{A}$ and $\vec{B}$, perhaps by using Equation 2, we can compute the components of the vector sum $\vec{R}$. Then if the magnitude and direction of $\vec{R}$ are needed, we can obtain them from Equations 3 and 4, with the A's replaced by R's.

Mastering PHYSICS

PhET: Vector Addition

NOTE ▶ As Figure 18b shows, when you represent a vector in terms of its components, it's always a good idea to use a squiggly line to cross out the original vector in your diagram. Otherwise there's danger that you'll count the same vector twice when you have to perform a vector addition or some other vector operation. ◀

This procedure can easily be extended to find the vector sum of any number of vectors. Let $\vec{R}$ be the vector sum of $\vec{A}, \vec{B}, \vec{C}, \vec{D},$ and $\vec{E}$. Then

$$R_x = A_x + B_x + C_x + D_x + E_x,$$
$$R_y = A_y + B_y + C_y + D_y + E_y.$$

NOTE ▶ In sums such as this, usually some of the components are positive and some are negative, so be very careful about signs when you evaluate such sums. And remember that x and y components are *never* added together in the same equation! ◀

EXAMPLE 7 **Adding two vectors**

Vector $\vec{A}$ has a magnitude of 50 cm and a direction of 30°, and vector $\vec{B}$ has a magnitude of 35 cm and a direction of 110°. Both angles are measured counterclockwise from the positive x axis. Use components to calculate the magnitude and direction of the vector sum (i.e., the resultant) $\vec{R} = \vec{A} + \vec{B}$.

SOLUTION

SET UP We set up a rectangular (Cartesian) coordinate system and place the tail of each vector at the origin, as shown in Figure 19a. We label the known magnitudes and angles on our diagram.

SOLVE We find the x and y components of each vector, using Equations 2, and record the results in the table shown next. We add the x components to obtain the x component of the vector sum $\vec{R}$, and we add the y components to obtain the y component

Continued

of $\vec{R}$. (But be very careful *not* to add the x and y components together!) The resulting table is as follows:

Magnitude	Angle	x component	y component
A = 50 cm	30°	43.3 cm	25.0 cm
B = 35 cm	110°	−12.0 cm	32.9 cm
		R_x = 31.3 cm	R_y = 57.9 cm

Now we use Equations 3 and 4 to find the magnitude and direction of the vector sum $\vec{R}$. From the Pythagorean theorem,

$$R = \sqrt{R_x^2 + R_y^2} = \sqrt{(31.3 \text{ cm})^2 + (57.9 \text{ cm})^2} = 66 \text{ cm}.$$

From the definition of the inverse tangent,

$$\theta = \tan^{-1}\frac{R_y}{R_x} = \tan^{-1}\frac{57.9 \text{ cm}}{31.3 \text{ cm}} = 62°.$$

Figure 19b shows this resultant vector and its components.

REFLECT We used the components of the vector sum $\vec{R}$ to find its magnitude and direction. Note how important it was to recognize that the x component of $\vec{B}$ is negative.

Practice Problem: Find the vector sum of the following two vectors by using components: 45 m, 55°, and 70 m, 135°. *Answers:* magnitude = 90 m; direction = 105°.

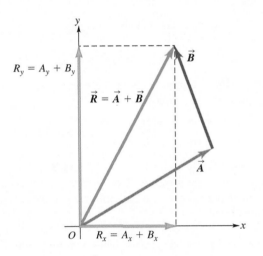

(a) Our diagram for this problem

(b) The resultant $\vec{R}$ and its components

▲ **FIGURE 19**

EXAMPLE 8   **Vector addition helps win a Porsche**

The four finalists in a hog-calling contest are brought to the center of a large, flat field. Each is given a meterstick, a compass, a calculator, a shovel, and (in a different order for each contestant) the following three displacements:

72.4 m, 32.0° east of north;
57.3 m, 36.0° south of west;
17.8 m straight south.

The three displacements lead to the point where the keys to a new Porsche are buried. The finder gets the Porsche. Three of the four contestants start measuring immediately, but the winner first *calculates* where to go. What does he calculate?

SOLUTION

SET UP The situation is shown in Figure 20. We have chosen the x axis as east and the y axis as north. This is the usual choice for maps. Let $\vec{A}$ be the first displacement, $\vec{B}$ the second, and $\vec{C}$ the third. We can estimate from the diagram that the vector sum $\vec{R}$ is about 10 m, 40° west of north. The angles of the vectors, measured counterclockwise from the $+x$ axis, are 58°, 216°, and 270°. We have to find the components of each.

SOLVE The components of $\vec{A}$ are

$$A_x = A\cos\theta = (72.4 \text{ m})(\cos 58°) = 38.37 \text{ m},$$
$$A_y = A\sin\theta = (72.4 \text{ m})(\sin 58°) = 61.40 \text{ m}.$$

The table below shows the components of all the displacements, the addition of components, and the other calculations. To find the magnitude R and direction θ, use the Pythagorean theorem $R = \sqrt{R_x^2 + R_y^2}$ and the definition of the inverse tangent,

Continued

$\theta = \tan^{-1}\dfrac{R_y}{R_x}$. Always arrange your component calculations systematically as in the table. Note that we have kept one too many significant figures in the components; we'll wait until the end to round to the correct number of significant figures. Here's the table:

Distance	Angle	*x* component	*y* component
$A = 72.4$ m	58°	38.37 m	61.40 m
$B = 57.3$ m	216°	-46.36 m	-33.68 m
$C = 17.8$ m	270°	0.00 m	-17.80 m
		$R_x = -7.99$ m	$R_y = 9.92$ m

$$R = \sqrt{(-7.99\ \text{m})^2 + (9.92\ \text{m})^2} = 12.7\ \text{m}$$

$$\theta = \tan^{-1}\frac{9.92\ \text{m}}{-7.99\ \text{m}} = 129° = 39° \text{ west of north.}$$

REFLECT The losers try to measure three angles and three distances totaling 147.5 m, 1 meter at a time. The winner measures only one angle and one much shorter distance.

Practice Problem: In a second contest, the three displacements given are 63.5 m, 52° west of north; 12.6 m straight north; and

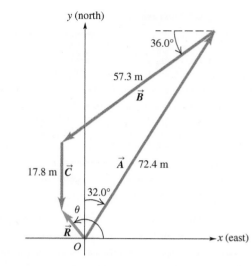

▲ **FIGURE 20** Three successive displacements $\vec{A}$, $\vec{B}$, and $\vec{C}$ and the resultant (vector sum) displacement $\vec{R} = \vec{A} + \vec{B} + \vec{C}$.

81.9 m, 41° south of east. What magnitude and direction does the winner calculate for the displacement to find the keys to the Porsche? *Answers:* $R = 11.9$ m and $\theta = 9.8°$ south of east.

Our discussion of vector addition has centered mostly on combining *displacement* vectors, but the method is applicable to all other vector quantities as well, including force, velocity, acceleration, and many other vector quantities.

CHAPTER SUMMARY

Standards, Units, and Unit Conversions

(Sections 3 and 4) The fundamental physical quantities of mechanics are mass, length, and time; the corresponding SI units are the kilogram (kg), the meter (m), and the second (s), respectively. Other units, related by powers of 10, are identified by adding prefixes: for example, 1 kilometer (km) = 10^3 meters (m). Derived units for other physical quantities are products or quotients of the basic units. For example, the units of speed are meters/second (m/s). Equations must be dimensionally consistent; two terms can be added, subtracted, or equated only when they have the same units.

Significant Figures

(Section 5) The uncertainty of a measurement can be indicated by the number of significant figures or by a stated uncertainty. For example, 1.40×10^6 has three significant figures. A typical metric ruler has an uncertainty of 1 mm. When numbers are multiplied or divided in a calculation, the number of significant figures in the result is no greater than in the factor with the least number of significant figures. Thus, the product $3.1416 \times 2.34 \times 0.58 = 4.3$ has only two significant figures, because 0.58 has only two significant figures.

Calculating pi from measured values of radius r and circumference C:

Three significant figures (the leading zero doesn't count)⋯⋯

We are dividing, so the result can have only three significant figures.

$$\pi = \frac{C}{2r} = \frac{0.424 \text{ m}}{2(0.06750 \text{ m})} = 3.14 \leftarrow$$

This exact number has no uncertainty and thus doesn't affect the significant figures in the result.

⋯⋯Four significant figures (the trailing zero counts)

Vector Addition

(Section 7) Vector quantities have direction as well as magnitude and are combined according to the rules of vector addition. To add vectors graphically, we place the tail of the second vector at the tip, or point, of the first vector. To subtract vectors, as in $\vec{A} - \vec{B}$, we first obtain the vector $(-\vec{B})$ by reversing the direction of $\vec{B}$. Then we write $\vec{A} - \vec{B} = \vec{A} + (-\vec{B})$ and apply the usual rule for vector addition.

$$\vec{A} + \vec{B} = \vec{A} + \vec{B}$$

To add vectors graphically, arrange them tip to tail in any order.

$$\left(\vec{A} - \vec{B} \right) = \left(\vec{A} + -\vec{B} \right) = \left(\begin{array}{c} \vec{A} - \vec{B} \\ = \vec{A} + (-\vec{B}) \end{array} \right)$$

Subtracting $\vec{B}$ from $\vec{A}$ is equivalent to adding $-\vec{B}$ to $\vec{A}$.

Components of Vectors

(Section 8) We can represent any vector $\vec{A}$ lying in the x-y plane as the sum of a vector $\vec{A}_x$ parallel to the x axis and a vector $\vec{A}_y$ parallel to the y axis; these are called x and y **component vectors** of $\vec{A}$. If $\vec{A}_x$ points in the positive x direction, we define the number A_x to be its magnitude. If $\vec{A}_x$ points in the $-x$ direction, we define A_x to be the negative of its magnitude. (Remember that a magnitude is always positive.) We define the number A_y the same way. The two numbers A_x and A_y are called the **components** of the vector $\vec{A}$.

Vector addition can be carried out using components of vectors. If A_x and A_y are the components of vector $\vec{A}$, and B_x and B_y are the components of vector $\vec{B}$, the components R_x and R_y of the vector sum $\vec{R} = \vec{A} + \vec{B}$ are given by

$$R_x = A_x + B_x \quad \text{and} \quad R_y = A_y + B_y. \quad (5)$$

$$A_x = A \cos\theta; \quad A_y = A \sin\theta; \quad A = \sqrt{A_x^2 + A_y^2}; \quad \theta = \tan^{-1}\frac{A_y}{A_x}$$

Models, Measurements, and Vectors: Problem Set

For instructor-assigned homework, go to www.masteringphysics.com

Conceptual Questions

1. A guidebook describes the rate of climb of a mountain trail as 120 m per kilometer. How can you express this as a number with no units?

2. Suppose you are asked to compute the cosine of 3 meters. Is this possible?

3. A highway contractor stated that in building a bridge deck he poured 250 yards of concrete. What do you think he meant?

4. (a) Would 200 cm be a reasonable height for an adult male? (b) Is it unusual for a human to have an age of 6×10^8 s? (c) Would 10^6 g be a reasonable mass for an adult person?

5. What physical phenomena (other than those discussed in the text) could be used to define a time standard?

6. Atomic quantities are now used to define the second and the meter. Could some atomic quantity be used for a definition of the kilogram? What advantages (or disadvantages) might this definition have compared with that based on the 1 kg platinum cylinder kept at Sèvres?

7. Suppose your lab partner tells you to calculate the volume of a cone of radius r and height h using the formula $V = \pi r^3 h$. Could this formula be correct?

8. Why is an angle a dimensionless number when measured in radians?

9. How could you determine the average thickness of a page of this textbook with an ordinary ruler?

10. (a) The mass m of an object is proportional to its volume V: $m = kV$. What are the SI units of k? (b) If the distance d an object moves in time t is given by the equation $d = At^2$, find the SI units of A. (c) If the speed v of an object depends on time t according to the equation $v = A + Bt + Ct^4$, what are the SI units of A, B, and C?

11. Based *only* on consistency of units, which of the following formulas could *not* be correct? In each case, A is area, V is volume, C is circumference, and R is radius. (a) $A = 2\pi R$, (b) $V = \frac{4}{3}\pi R^2$, (c) $A = 2\pi R^2$, (d) $V = 6\pi R^3$, (e) $C = \pi R^2$, (f) $V = CA$.

12. Based *only* on consistency of units, which of the following formulas could *not* be correct? In each case, x is distance, v is speed, and t is time. (a) $v = x/t$, (b) $x = vt$, (c) $t = v/x$, (d) $vx = t$, (e) $xt = v$, (f) $v_2^2 = v_1^2 + 2x^2$.

13. (a) In adding scalars, is 1 m + 1 m necessarily equal to 2 m? (b) In adding two vectors, each of magnitude 1 m, does the resultant *necessarily* have a magnitude of 2 m? Explain your reasoning in each case.

14. Is it possible for the magnitude of a vector (a) to be smaller than the magnitude of any of its components or (b) to be equal to the magnitude of one of its components? How?

15. (a) Does it make sense to say that a vector is *negative*? Why? (b) Does it make sense to say that one vector is the negative of another? Why? Does your answer here contradict what you said in part (a)?

Multiple-Choice Problems

1. Andy Roddick can sometimes serve a tennis ball at 150 mi/h (about 75 m/s). The length of a tennis court is 78 ft. Approximately how long does his opponent have to react, from the instant he sees Roddick hit the ball until the ball reaches the opponent?
   A. 1/10 s   B. 1/3 s   C. 3/4 s   D. 1 s

2. Suppose that bacon is sold for $2 per pound. If you were to buy 1 kilogram of bacon, what would you expect to pay for it?
   A. More than $2
   B. Less than $2
   C. $2

3. The distance from an adult's elbow to her fingertips is closest to
   A. 5 cm   B. 10 cm   C. 50 cm   D. 1 m

4. A vector is directed at an angle θ above the $+x$ axis, pointing into the first quadrant. If the x component of this vector is 10 m, the magnitude of the vector is
   A. greater than 10 m
   B. equal to 10 m
   C. less than 10 m
   D. the same as the y component of the vector

5. A mass of 1.0×10^{-3} μkg is the same as
   A. 10^{-12} g   B. 10^{-6} g   C. 1 kg   D. 1 mg

6. If the vector $\vec{B}$ has a magnitude of 25 m and makes an angle of 30° with the $+x$ axis, the vector $-\vec{B}$
   A. has a magnitude of 25 m.
   B. has the same direction as $\vec{B}$, but a magnitude of -25 m.
   C. makes an angle of $-30°$ with the $+x$ axis.
   D. has the opposite direction of $\vec{B}$ and a magnitude of -25 m.

7. The mass of a dime is closest to
   A. 1 mg   B. 1 g   C. 100 g   D. 1 kg

8. The number of kilometers in 1 mile is closest to
   A. 0.001   B. 1   C. 100   D. 1000

From Chapter 1 of *College Physics*, Ninth Edition, Hugh D. Young. Copyright © 2012 by Pearson Education, Inc. Published by Pearson Addison-Wesley. All rights reserved.

9. If vector $\vec{A}$ has components A_x and A_y and makes an angle θ with the $+x$ axis, then
   A. $A = A_x + A_y$ (where A is the magnitude of $\vec{A}$).
   B. $\theta = A_y/A_x$.
   C. $\cos\theta = \dfrac{A_x}{\sqrt{A_x^2 + A_y^2}}$.
   D. $\tan\theta = A_x/A_y$.

10. If the distance d (in meters) traveled by an object in time t (in seconds) is given by the formula $d = A + Bt^2$, the SI units of A and B must be
    A. meters for both A and B.
    B. m/s for A and m/s^2 for B.
    C. meters for A and m/s^2 for B.
    D. m/s^2 for both A and B.

11. The surface area of a typical classroom floor is closest to
    A. 1 cm^2
    B. 1 m^2
    C. 10 m^2
    D. 100 m^2

12. If vector $\vec{A}$ has unity magnitude and makes an angle of 45° with the $+x$ axis, then the x and y components of $\vec{A}$ are
    A. $A_x = A_y = 1$.
    B. $A_x = A_y = \dfrac{1}{\sqrt{2}}$.
    C. $A_x = A_y = \frac{1}{2}$.
    D. $A_x = A_y = \sqrt{2}$.

13. If vector $\vec{A}$ has components $A_x = -3$ and $A_y = -4$, then the magnitude of $\vec{A}$ is
    A. 7
    B. -7
    C. $\sqrt{7}$
    D. 5
    E. -5

Problems

3 Standards and Units

4 Unit Consistency and Conversions

1. • (a) The maximum sodium intake for a person on a 2000 calorie diet should be 2400 mg/day. How many grams of sodium is this per day? (b) The recommended daily allowance (RDA) of the trace element chromium is 120 μg/day. Express this dose in grams per day. (c) An intake of vitamin C up to 500 mg/day is considered safe (although the safety of higher doses has not yet been established). Express this intake in grams per day. (d) The electrical resistance of the human body is approximately 1500 ohms when it is dry. Express this resistance in kilohms. (e) An electrical current of about 0.020 amp can cause muscular spasms so that a person cannot, for example, let go of a wire with that amount of current. Express this current in milliamps.

2. • (a) How many ohms are there in a 7.85-megohm resistor? (b) Typical laboratory capacitors are around 5 picofarads. How many farads are they? (c) The speed of light in vacuum is 3.00×10^8 m/s. Express this speed in gigameters per second. (d) The wavelength of visible light is between 400 nm and 700 nm. Express this wavelength in meters. (e) The diameter of a typical atomic nucleus is about 2 femtometers. Express this diameter in meters.

3. • (a) The recommended daily allowance (RDA) of the trace metal magnesium is 410 mg/day for males. Express this quantity in μg/day. (b) For adults, the RDA of the amino acid lysine is 12 mg per kg of body weight. How many grams per day should a 75 kg adult receive? (c) A typical multivitamin tablet can contain 2.0 mg of vitamin B$_2$ (riboflavin), and the RDA is 0.0030 g/day. How many such tablets should a person take each day to get the proper amount of this vitamin, assuming that he gets none from any other sources? (d) The RDA for the trace element selenium is 0.000070 g/day. Express this dose in mg/day.

4. • (a) Starting with the definition 1.00 in. = 2.54 cm, find the number of kilometers in 1.00 mile. (b) In medicine, volumes are often expressed in milliliters (ml or mL). Show that a milliliter is the same as a cubic centimeter. (c) How many cubic centimeters of water are there in a 1.00 L bottle of drinking water?

5. •• (a) The density (mass divided by volume) of water is 1.00 g/cm^3. What is this value in kilograms per cubic meter? (b) The density of blood is 1050 kg/m^3. What is this density in g/cm^3? (c) How many kilograms are there in a 1.00 L bottle of drinking water? How many pounds?

6. • Calculate the earth's speed in its orbit around the sun, in m/s, km/h and mi/h.

7. • How many nanoseconds does it take light to travel 1.00 ft in vacuum? (This result is a useful quantity to remember.)

8. • **Metric wrenches.** (a) You have a new set of metric wrenches, but need to loosen a $\frac{3}{8}$ inch bolt. To find out which size metric wrench to use, convert the $\frac{3}{8}$ in. to millimeters, accurate to the nearest tenth of a millimeter. (b) If you want to tighten a 12 mm bolt, what size wrench should you use in inches, accurate to the nearest hundredth of an inch? (c) English-unit wrenches often come in $\frac{1}{8}$ inch intervals, not in decimal units. What size wrench should you use in part (b)?

9. • **Gasoline mileage.** You are considering buying a European car and want to see if its advertised fuel efficiency (expressed in km/L) is better than that of your present car. If your car gets 37.5 miles per gallon, how many km/L is this?

10. •• While driving in an exotic foreign land, you see a speed-limit sign on a highway that reads 180,000 furlongs per fortnight. How many miles per hour is this? (One furlong is $\frac{1}{8}$ mile, and a fortnight is 14 days. A furlong originally referred to the length of a plowed furrow.)

11. •• **Fill 'er up!** You fill up your gas tank in Europe when the euro is worth $1.25 and gasoline costs 1.35 euros per liter. What is the cost of gasoline in dollars per gallon? How does your answer compare with the cost of gasoline in the United States? (Use conversion factors.)

12. •• **Bacteria.** Bacteria vary somewhat in size, but a diameter of 2.0 μm is not unusual. What would be the volume (in cubic centimeters) and surface area (in square millimeters) of such a bacterium, assuming that it is spherical?

13. • Compute the number of seconds in (a) an hour, (b) a 24 hour day, and (c) a 365 day year.

14. • **Some commonly occurring quantities.** All of the quantities that follow will occur frequently in your study of physics. (a) Express the speed of light (3.00×10^8 m/s) in mi/s and mph. (b) Find the speed of sound in air at 0°C (1100 ft/s) in m/s and mph. (c) Show that 60 mph is the same as 88 ft/s. (d) Convert the acceleration of a freely falling body (9.8 m/s^2) to ft/s^2.

The BIO labels appear beside problems 1, 3, and 12.

5 Precision and Significant Figures

15. • Express each of the following numbers to three, five, and eight significant figures: (a) $\pi = 3.141592654\ldots$, (b) $e = 2.718281828\ldots$, (c) $\sqrt{13} = 3.605551275.\ldots$

16. • Express each of the following approximations of π to six significant figures: (a) $22/7$, (b) $355/113$. (c) Are these approximations accurate to that precision?

17. • An angle is given, to one significant figure, as $4°$, meaning that its value is between $3.5°$ and $4.5°$. Find the corresponding range of possible values of (a) the cosine of the angle, (b) the sine of the angle, and (c) the tangent of the angle.

18. • **Blood is thicker than water.** The density (mass divided by BIO volume) of pure water is 1.00 g/cm^3, that of whole blood is 1.05 g/cm^3, and the density of seawater is 1.03 g/cm^3. What is the mass (in grams) of 1.00 L of each of these substances?

19. •• **White dwarfs and neutron stars.** Recall that density is mass divided by volume. (a) Calculate the average density of the earth in g/cm^3, assuming our planet to be a perfect sphere. (b) In about 5 billion years, at the end of its lifetime, our sun will end up as a white dwarf, having about the same mass as it does now, but reduced to about 15,000 km in diameter. What will be its density at that stage? (c) A neutron star is the remnant left after certain supernovae (explosions of giant stars). Typically, neutron stars are about 20 km in diameter and have around the same mass as our sun. What is a typical neutron star density in g/cm^3?

20. •• **Atoms and nuclei.** The atom helium (He) consists of two protons, two neutrons, and two electrons. (Recall that density is mass divided by volume, and consult Table 1 as needed.) (a) The diameter of the He atom is approximately 0.10 nm. Calculate the density of the He atom in g/cm^3 (assuming that it is a sphere), and compare it with that of pure water, which is 1.0 g/cm^3. (b) The diameter of the He nucleus is about 2.0 fm. Assuming the nucleus to be a sphere, calculate its density in g/cm^3 and compare it with that of a neutron star in the previous exercise.

21. •• **Critical mass of neptunium.** In the fall of 2002, a group of scientists at Los Alamos National Laboratory determined that the critical mass of neptunium-237 is about 60.0 kg. (The critical mass of a fissionable material is the minimum amount that must be brought together to start a nuclear chain reaction.) Neptunium has a density of 19.5 g/cm^3. What would be the radius of a sphere made of this material that has a critical mass? (Recall that density is mass divided by volume.)

22. •• **Cell walls.** Although these quantities vary from one type of BIO cell to another, a cell can be $2.0 \mu\text{m}$ in diameter with a cell wall 50.0 nm thick. If the density (mass divided by volume) of the wall material is the same as that of pure water, what is the mass (in mg) of the cell wall, assuming the cell to be spherical and the wall to be a very thin spherical shell?

23. •• A brass washer has an outside diameter of 4.50 cm with a hole of diameter 1.25 cm and is 1.50 mm thick. (See Figure 21.) The density of brass is 8600 kg/m^3. If you put this washer on a laboratory balance, what will it "weigh" in grams? (Recall that density is mass divided by volume.)

▲ FIGURE 21
Problem 23.

6 Estimates and Orders of Magnitude

24. • Estimate the total mass of all the humans presently living on earth.

25. •• How many words are there in this book?

26. •• **How many cells in the body?** Although their sizes vary, BIO cells can be modeled as spheres $2.0 \mu\text{m}$ in diameter, on the average. About how many cells does a typical human contain, and approximately what is the mass of an average cell?

27. • How many times does a typical person blink her eyes in a BIO lifetime?

28. • You are using water to dilute small amounts of chemicals in the laboratory, drop by drop. How many drops of water are in a 1.0 L bottle? (Hint: Start by estimating the diameter of a drop of water.)

29. • How many dollar bills would you have to stack to reach the moon? Would that be a cheaper way to get there than building and launching a spacecraft (which costs a few billion dollars)?

30. •• **Space station.** You are designing a space station and want BIO to get some idea how large it should be to provide adequate air for the astronauts. Normally, the air is replenished, but for security, you decide that there should be enough to last for two weeks in case of a malfunction. (a) Estimate how many cubic meters of air an average person breathes in two weeks. A typical human breathes about $1/2$ L per breath. (b) If the space station is to be spherical, what should be its diameter to contain all the air you calculated in part (a)?

31. •• **A beating heart.** How many times does a human heart BIO beat during a lifetime? How many gallons of blood does it pump in that time if, on the average, it pumps 50 cm^3 of blood with each beat?

32. •• How long would it take you to walk to the moon, and how many steps would you have to take, assuming that you could somehow walk normally in space?

33. •• How much would it cost to paper the entire United States (including Alaska and Hawaii) with dollar bills? What would be the cost to each person in the nation?

7 Vectors and Vector Addition

34. • On a single diagram, carefully sketch each force vector to scale and identify its magnitude and direction on your drawing: (a) 60 lb at $25°$ east of north. (b) 40 lb at $\pi/3$ south of west. (c) 100 lb at $40°$ north of west. (d) 50 lb at $\pi/6$ east of south.

35. • Hearing rattles from a snake, you make two rapid displacements of magnitude 1.8 m and 2.4 m. In sketches (roughly to scale), show how your two displacements might add up to give a resultant of magnitude (a) 4.2 m; (b) 0.6 m; (c) 3.0 m.

36. • A ladybug starts at the center of a 12-in.-diameter turntable and crawls in a straight radial line to the edge. While this is happening, the turntable turns through a $45°$ angle. (a) Draw a sketch showing the bug's path and the displacement vector for the bug's progress. (b) Find the magnitude and direction of the ladybug's displacement vector.

37. • For the vectors $\vec{A}$ and $\vec{B}$ shown in Figure 22, carefully sketch (a) the vector sum

▲ FIGURE 22 Problem 37.

25

$\vec{A} + \vec{B}$; (b) the vector difference $\vec{A} - \vec{B}$; (c) the vector $-\vec{A} - \vec{B}$; (d) the vector difference $\vec{B} - \vec{A}$.

38. • **Chin brace.** A person with an injured jaw has a brace below
BIO his chin. The brace is held in place by two cables directed at 65° above the horizontal. (See Figure 23.) The cables produce forces of equal magnitude having a vertical resultant of 2.25 N upward. (a) Make a scale drawing showing both the forces produced by the cables and the resultant force. Estimate the angle carefully or measure it with a protractor. (b) Use your scale drawing to estimate the magnitude of the force due to each cable.

▲ **FIGURE 23** Problem 38.

8 Components of Vectors

39. • A rocket fires two engines simultaneously. One produces a thrust of 725 N directly forward, while the other gives a 513-N thrust at 32.4° above the forward direction. Find the magnitude and direction (relative to the forward direction) of the resultant force that these engines exert on the rocket.

40. • In each of the cases that follow, the magnitude of a vector is given along with the counterclockwise angle it makes with the $+x$ axis. Use trigonometry to find the x and y components of the vector. Also, sketch each vector approximately to scale to see if your calculated answers seem reasonable. (a) 50.0 N at 60.0°, (b) 75 m/s at $5\pi/6$ rad, (c) 254 lb at 325°, (d) 69 km at 1.1π rad.

41. • In each of the cases that follow, the components of a vector $\vec{A}$ are given. Use trigonometry to find the magnitude of that vector and the counterclockwise angle it makes with the $+x$ axis. Also, sketch each vector approximately to scale to see if your calculated answers seem reasonable. (a) $A_x = 4.0$ m, $A_y = 5.0$ m, (b) $A_x = -3.0$ km, $A_y = -6.0$ km, (c) $A_x = 9.0$ m/s, $A_y = -17$ m/s, (d) $A_x = -8.0$ N, $A_y = 12$ N.

42. • A woman takes her dog Rover for a walk on a leash. To get the little pooch moving forward, she pulls on the leash with a force of 20.0 N at an angle of 37° above the horizontal. (a) How much force is tending to pull Rover forward? (b) How much force is tending to lift Rover off the ground?

43. • If a vector $\vec{A}$ has the following components, use trigonometry to find its magnitude and the counterclockwise angle it makes with the $+x$ axis: (a) $A_x = 8.0$ lb, $A_y = 6.0$ lb, (b) $A_x = -24$ m/s, $A_y = -31$ m/s, (c) $A_x = -1500$ km, $A_y = 2000$ km, (d) $A_x = 71.3$ N, $A_y = -54.7$ N.

44. • Compute the x and y components of the vectors $\vec{A}$, $\vec{B}$, and $\vec{C}$ shown in Figure 24.

45. • Vector $\vec{A}$ has components $A_x = 1.30$ cm, $A_y = 2.25$ cm; vector $\vec{B}$ has components $B_x = 4.10$ cm, $B_y = -3.75$ cm. Find

(a) the components of the vector sum $\vec{A} + \vec{B}$; (b) the magnitude and direction of $\vec{A} + \vec{B}$; (c) the components of the vector difference $\vec{B} - \vec{A}$; (d) the magnitude and direction of $\vec{B} - \vec{A}$.

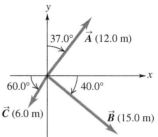

▲ **FIGURE 24** Problem 44.

46. •• A plane leaves Seattle, flies 85 mi at 22° north of east, and then changes direction to 48° south of east. After flying at 115 mi in this new direction, the pilot must make an emergency landing on a field. The Seattle airport facility dispatches a rescue crew. (a) In what direction and how far should the crew fly to go directly to the field? Use components to solve this problem. (b) Check the reasonableness of your answer with a careful graphical sum.

47. •• You're hanging from a chinning bar, with your arms at right angles to each other. The magnitudes of the forces exerted by both your arms are the same, and together they exert just enough upward force to support your weight, 620 N. (a) Sketch the two force vectors for your arms, along with their resultant, and (b) use components to find the magnitude of each of the two "arm" force vectors.

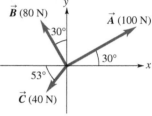

▲ **FIGURE 25** Problem 48.

48. • Three horizontal ropes are attached to a boulder and produce the pulls shown in Figure 25. (a) Find the x and y components of each pull. (b) Find the components of the resultant of the three pulls. (c) Find the magnitude and direction (the counterclockwise angle with the $+x$ axis) of the resultant pull. (d) Sketch a clear *graphical* sum to check your answer in part (c).

49. • A disoriented physics professor drives 3.25 km north, then 4.75 km west, and then 1.50 km south. (a) Use components to find the magnitude and direction of the resultant displacement of this professor. (b) Check the reasonableness of your answer with a graphical sum.

50. • A postal employee drives a delivery truck along the route shown in Figure 26. Use components to determine the magnitude and direction of the truck's resultant displacement. Then check the reasonableness of your answer by sketching a graphical sum.

▲ **FIGURE 26** Problem 50.

General Problems

51. • **Baseball mass.** Baseball rules specify that a regulation ball shall weigh no less than 5.00 ounces nor more than $5\frac{1}{4}$ ounces. What are the acceptable limits, in grams, for a regulation ball? (Use the fact that 16 oz = 1 lb.)

52. • As you eat your way through a bag of chocolate chip cookies, you observe that each cookie is a circular disk with a diameter of 8.50 cm and a thickness of 0.050 cm. Find (a) the volume of a single cookie and (b) the ratio of the diameter to the thickness, and express both in the proper number of significant figures.

53. •• **Breathing oxygen.** The density of air under standard laboratory conditions is 1.29 kg/m³, and about 20% of that air consists of oxygen. Typically, people breathe about $\frac{1}{2}$ L of air per breath. (a) How many grams of oxygen does a person breathe in a day? (b) If this air is stored uncompressed in a cubical tank, how long is each side of the tank?

BIO

54. •• The total mass of Earth's atmosphere is about 5×10^{15} metric tonnes (1 metric tonne = 1000 kg). Suppose you breathe in about 1/3 L of air with each breath, and the density of air at room temperature is about 1.2 kg/m³. About how many breaths of air does the entire atmosphere contain? How does this compare to the number of atoms in one breath of air (about 1.2×10^{22})? It's sometimes said that every breath you take contains atoms that were also breathed by Albert Einstein, Confucius, and in fact anyone else who ever lived. Based on your calculation, could this be true?

BIO

55. •• **How much blood in a heartbeat?** A typical human contains 5.0 L of blood, and it takes 1.0 min for all of it to pass through the heart when the person is resting with a pulse rate of 75 heartbeats per minute. On the average, what volume of blood, in liters and cubic centimeters, does the heart pump during each beat?

BIO

56. •• **Muscle attachment.** When muscles attach to bones, they usually do so by a series of tendons, as shown in Figure 27. In the figure, five tendons attach to the bone. The uppermost tendon pulls at 20.0° from the axis of the bone, and each tendon is directed 10.0° from the one next to it. (a) If each tendon exerts a 2.75 N pull on the bone, use vector components to find the magnitude and direction of the resultant force on this bone due to all five tendons. Let the axis of the bone be the $+x$ axis. (b) Draw a graphical sum to check your results from part (a).

BIO

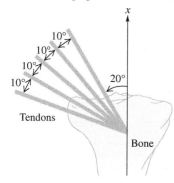

▲ **FIGURE 27** Problem 56.

57. •• **Hiking the Appalachian Trail.** The Appalachian Trail runs from Mt. Katahdin in Maine to Springer Mountain in Georgia, a total distance of 2160 mi. If you hiked for 8 h per day, estimate (a) how many steps it would take to hike this trail and b) how many days it would take to hike it.

58. •• Estimate the number of atoms in your body. (*Hint:* Based on what you know about biology and chemistry, what are the most common types of atom in your body? What is the mass of each type of atom?)

BIO

59. •• Biological tissues are typically made up of 98% water. Given that the density of water is 1.0×10^3 kg/m³, estimate the mass of (a) the heart of an adult human; (b) a cell with a diameter of 0.5 μm; (c) a honeybee.

BIO

60. •• **Density of the human body.** (a) Make simple measurements on your own body, and use them to calculate your body's average density (mass divided by volume) in kg/m³. (b) How does this result compare with the density of water, which is 1000 kg/m³? Is your result surprising?

BIO

61. •• While surveying a cave, a spelunker follows a passage 180 m straight west, then 210 m in a direction 45° east of south, and then 280 m at 30.0° east of north. After a fourth unmeasured displacement, she finds herself back where she started. Use vector components to find the magnitude and direction of the fourth displacement. Then check the reasonableness of your answer with a graphical sum.

62. •• A sailor in a small sailboat encounters shifting winds. She sails 2.00 km east, then 3.50 km southeast, and then an additional distance in an unknown direction. Her final position is 5.80 km directly east of her starting point. (See Figure 28.) Find the magnitude and direction of the third leg of the journey. Draw the vector addition diagram, and show that it is in qualitative agreement with your numerical solution.

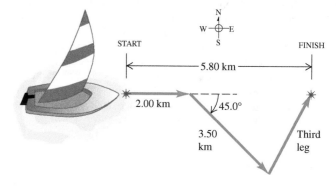

▲ **FIGURE 28** Problem 62.

63. •• **Dislocated shoulder.** A patient with a dislocated shoulder is put into a traction apparatus as shown in Figure 29. The pulls $\vec{A}$ and $\vec{B}$ have equal magnitudes and must combine to produce an outward traction force of 5.60 N on the patient's arm. How large should these pulls be?

BIO

▲ **FIGURE 29** Problem 63.

64. •• On a training flight, a student pilot flies from Lincoln, Nebraska to Clarinda, Iowa, then to St. Joseph, Missouri, and then to Manhattan, Kansas (Fig. 30). The directions are shown relative to north: 0° is north, 90° is east, 180° is south, and 270° is west. Use the method of components to find (a) the distance she has to fly from Manhattan to get back to Lincoln, and (b) the direction (relative to north) she must fly to get there. Illustrate your solutions with a vector diagram.

▲ **FIGURE 30** Problem 64.

65. •• **Bones and muscles.** A patient in therapy has a forearm
BIO that weighs 20.5 N and lifts a 112.0 N weight. The only other significant forces on his forearm come from the biceps muscle (which acts perpendicularly to the forearm) and the force at the elbow. If the biceps produce a pull of 232 N when the forearm is raised 43° above the horizontal, find the magnitude and direction of the force that the elbow exerts on the forearm. (*Hint:* The elbow force and the biceps force together must balance the weight of the arm and the weight it is carrying, so their vector sum must be 132.5 N upward.)

66. •• **Googols and googolplexes!** When the mathematician Edward Kasner asked his young nephew to coin a name for the huge number 10^{100}, the boy said *googol*. (a) Express the googol in standard notation as a 1 followed by the appropriate number of zeroes. (b) Approximately how many googols of atoms does our sun contain? For simplicity, assume that the sun consists of only protons and electrons, in equal numbers, which is approximately true. (c) The *googolplex* is an even larger number, 10 to the googol power: 10^{googol}. Express the googolplex in scientific notation. If you wrote it in standard notation with a 1 followed by the appropriate number of zeroes, how many zeroes would you need?

Passage Problems

BIO Calculating lung volume in humans. The portion of the human lung that is engaged in exchanging oxygen and carbon dioxide with the blood comprises many small sacs called alveoli. These alveoli are formed during embryonic development by repeated branching of the tubes of the airways and function to provide a large surface area for gas exchange. Recent careful measurements show that the total number of alveoli in a typical human lung pair is about 480×10^6 and that the average volume of a single alveolus is $4.2 \times 10^6 \ \mu m^3$. It may be useful to recall the equation for the volume of a sphere, $V = 4/3 \ \pi r^3$, and the equation for the area of a sphere, $A = 4\pi r^2$.

67. What is total volume of the gas-exchanging region of the lungs?
    A. 2000 μm^3
    B. 2 m^3
    C. 2.0 L
    D. 120 L

68. Assuming the alveoli are spherical, what is the diameter of a typical alveolus?
    A. 0.20 mm
    B. 2 mm
    C. 20 mm
    D. 200 mm

69. Individuals vary considerably in total lung volume. Figure 31 shows the results of measurement of total lung volume (horizontal axis) and average alveolar volume (vertical axis) for six individuals. What can you infer about the relationship between alveolar size, total lung volume and number of alveoli per individual from these data?
    A. As the total volume of the lungs increases, the number and volume of individual alveoli increase.
    B. As the total volume of the lungs increases, the number of alveoli increases and the volume of individual alveoli decreases.
    C. As the total volume of the lungs increases, the volume of the individual alveoli remains constant and the number of alveoli increases.
    D. As the total volume of the lungs increases, the number of alveoli and the volume of individual alveoli both remain constant.

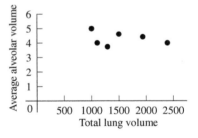

▲ **FIGURE 31** Problem 69.

ANSWERS TO SELECTED PROBLEMS

Conceptual Questions

5. Numerous possibilities exist, such as the time of swing of a pendulum of a certain length; the time required for an object to fall from a specific height; the pulse rate of a healthy adult; the flow rate of a specific volume of sand (e.g., an hourglass); and the constant-frequency electric signal generated by the vibrations of a quartz crystal. Each of these potential standards, however, has deficiencies and is thus less accurate than the atomic standard.

7. No, the formula cannot be correct. V has units of length cubed (e.g., m^3), r and h each have the units of length and π is dimensionless; therefore, $\pi r^3 h$ has units of length raised to the fourth power (e.g., m^4), which is dimensionally incorrect.

9. Measure the height of a stack of 100 pages, and divide that distance by 100 to obtain the thickness of a single page.

11. Consider the SI System of units: A has units of m^2; V has units of m^3; C has units

of m; R has units of m. If we compare the equivalency of only the units for each formula, we obtain (a) $\{m^2\} \neq \{m\}$; (b) $\{m^3\} \neq \{m^2\}$; (c) $\{m^2\} = \{m^2\}$; (d) $\{m^3\} = \{m^3\}$; (e) $\{m\} \neq \{m^2\}$; (f) $\{m^3\} = \{m^3\}$. Therefore, formulas (a), (b), and (e) cannot be correct.

13. (a) Yes, since scalar addition only involves adding numbers. (b) No, because vector addition is not done simply by adding magnitudes. The magnitude of the vector sum depends on the direction, as well as the magnitude, of each vector being added. For example, if two vectors have equal magnitude, but lie in opposite directions, their vector sum is zero.

Multiple-Choice Problems

1. B
3. C
5. B
7. B
9. C
11. B
13. D

Problems

1. (a) 2.40 grams/day
   (b) 1.20×10^{-4} grams/day
   (c) 0.500 grams/day (d) 1.50 kilohms
   (e) 20 milliamps
3. (a) $4.10 \times 10^5\ \mu g$/day (b) 0.900 g/day
   (c) 2 tablets/day (d) 0.070 mg/day
5. (a) 1.00×10^3 kg/m^3
   (b) 1.05 g/cm^3 (c) 1.00 kg, 2.20 lb
7. 1.02 ns
9. 15.9 km/L
11. $6.39 per gallon
13. (a) 3600 s
    (b) 8.64×10^4 s (c) 3.15×10^7 s
15. (a) 3.14; 3.1416; 3.1415927
    (b) 2.72; 2.7183; 2.7182818
    (c) 3.61; 3.6056; 3.6055513
17. (a) 0.9969 to 0.9981 (b) 0.061 to 0.078
    (c) 0.061 to 0.079
19. (a) 5.50 g/cm^3
    (b) 1.1×10^6 g/cm^3
    (c) 4.7×10^{14} g/cm^3
21. 9.0 cm
23. 18.9 g
25. 10^6
27. 4×10^8

29. 10^{12}; no
31. 3×10^9 beats; 4×10^7 gallons
33. 9×10^{14}; 3×10^6 per person
39. 1190 N; 13.4° above forward direction
41. (a) 6.4 m; 51° (b) 6.7 km; 243°
    (c) 19 m/s; 298° (d) 14 N; 124°
43. (a) 10.0 lb; 37° (b) 39 m/s; 232°
    (c) 2500 km; 127° (d) 89.9 N; 323°
45. (a) 5.40 cm, -1.50 cm (b) 5.60 cm, 344° counterclockwise from $+x$ axis
    (c) 2.80 cm, -6.00 cm (d) 6.62 cm, 295° counterclockwise from $+x$ axis
47. (b) 44° N
49. (a) 5.06 km; 20.2° north of west
51. 142 g to 149 g
53. (a) 2200 g (b) 2.1 m
55. 6.7×10^{-2} L $= 67$ cm^3
57. (a) 5.7×10^6 steps (b) 120 days
59. (a) 0.5 kg (b) 6×10^{-14} g (c) 0.3 g
61. 143 m; 41° south of west
63. 3.30 N
65. 160 N, 13° below the horizontal

Passage Problems

67. C
69. C

xcity

Motion Along a Straight Line

iStockphoto

How do you describe the motion of a racehorse coming down the homestretch, galloping toward the finish line? When you throw a baseball straight up in the air, how high does it go? How fast do you have to throw it to reach that height? When a glass slips from your hand, how much time do you have to catch it before it hits the floor? These are the kinds of questions you'll learn to answer in this chapter.

We're beginning our study of physics with **mechanics,** the study of the relationships among force, matter, and motion. Our first goal is to develop mathematical methods for *describing* motion; this discipline is called **kinematics.** Later we'll study the more general subject of **dynamics,** the relation of motion to its causes.

Motion is a continuous change of position with time. In this chapter we'll limit our discussion to the simplest possible situation, a single object moving along a straight line. We'll assume that the object can be treated as a particle. We'll always take the line to be one of the axes of a coordinate system. Then we can describe the position of the particle by its displacement from the origin of coordinates along this line. Displacement is a *vector* quantity. But when a particle moves along a line that is a coordinate axis, only one component of displacement is different from zero, and the particle's position is described by a single **coordinate.**

A fall is a classic example of straight-line motion. If air resistance could be neglected, these skydivers would be accelerating toward the earth at a constant 9.8 m/s². Luckily for them, air resistance exists—and later, when they deploy their parachutes, it will give them an *upward* acceleration.

From Chapter 2 of *College Physics*, Ninth Edition, Hugh D. Young. Copyright © 2012 by Pearson Education, Inc. Published by Pearson Addison-Wesley. All rights reserved.

▲ FIGURE 1 Positions of a AA-fuel dragster at two times during its run.

1 Displacement and Average Velocity

Suppose a drag racer drives his AA-fuel dragster in a straight line down the track. We'll use this line as the x axis of our coordinate system, as shown in Figure 1. We'll place the origin O at the starting line. The distance of the front of the dragster from the origin is given by the coordinate x, which varies with time. Note that x is positive when the car is to the right of O, negative when it is to the left. Suppose that, at a time 1 second (1.0 s) after the start of the race, the car is at x_1, 19 m to the right of the origin, and that, at 4.0 s after the start, it is at x_2, 277 m from the origin. Then it has traveled a distance of $(277\text{ m} - 19\text{ m}) = 258\text{ m}$ in the direction of increasing x in a time interval of $(4.0\text{ s} - 1.0\text{ s}) = 3.0\text{ s}$. We define the car's **average velocity** during this interval to be a vector quantity whose x component is the change in x (258 m), divided by the time interval (3.0 s); that is, $(258\text{ m})/(3.0\text{ s}) = 86\text{ m/s}$.

Now let's generalize this discussion. At time t_1 a point at the front of the car is at position x_1, and at time t_2 it is at position x_2. The displacement during the time interval from t_1 to t_2 is the vector from x_1 to x_2. The x component of this vector is $(x_2 - x_1)$; all other components are zero, because there is no motion in any direction other than along the x axis. For motion in the x direction, we define the average velocity as a vector in the direction from x_1 to x_2, with an x component of average velocity $v_{\text{av},x}$ given by

$$v_{\text{av},x} = \frac{x_2 - x_1}{t_2 - t_1}. \tag{1}$$

All other components of the average velocity vector are zero.

Changes in quantities, such as $(x_2 - x_1)$ and $(t_2 - t_1)$, occur so often throughout physics that it's worthwhile to use a special notation. From now on, we'll use the Greek letter Δ (capital delta) to represent a *change* in any quantity. Thus, we write

$$\Delta x = x_2 - x_1. \tag{2}$$

Be sure you understand that Δx is *not the product* of Δ and x. It is a *single symbol,* and it means "the change in the quantity x." Here, Δx is the x-component of the displacement of the particle. With this same notation, we denote the time interval from t_1 to t_2 as $\Delta t = t_2 - t_1$.

NOTE ▶ Values such as Δx or Δt always denote the final value minus the initial value, never the reverse. ◀

We can now define the x component of the average velocity.

Definition of average velocity

The x component of an object's average velocity is defined as the x component of displacement Δx, divided by the time interval Δt in which the displacement occurs. We represent this quantity by the letter v, with a subscript "av" to signify "average value" and a subscript "x" to signify "x component." Thus,

$$v_{av,x} = \frac{x_2 - x_1}{t_2 - t_1} = \frac{\Delta x}{\Delta t}. \tag{3}$$

Unit: m/s

When we express distance in meters and time in seconds, a component of velocity is expressed in meters per second (m/s). Other common units of velocity are kilometers per hour (km/h), miles per hour (mi/h), and knots $(6080 \, ft/h)$.

In the preceding example, we have $x_1 = 19$ m, $x_2 = 277$ m, $t_1 = 1.0$ s, and $t_2 = 4.0$ s, and Equation 3 gives

$$v_{av,x} = \frac{277 \text{ m} - 19 \text{ m}}{4.0 \text{ s} - 1.0 \text{ s}} = 86 \text{ m/s.}$$

In some cases, $v_{av,x}$ is negative, as shown in Figure 2. Suppose an official's truck is moving *toward* the origin, with $x_1 = 277$ m and $x_2 = 19$ m. If $t_1 = 6.0$ s and $t_2 = 16.0$ s, then $\Delta x = -258$ m, $\Delta t = 10.0$ s, and the x component of average velocity is -26 m/s. Whenever x is positive and decreasing, or negative and becoming more negative, the object is moving in the negative x direction and $v_{av,x}$ is negative.

We stress again that average velocity is a *vector* quantity, and Equation 3 defines the x component of this vector. In this chapter, all vectors have *only one* nonzero component, frequently only an x component. We'll often call x the displacement and $v_{av,x}$ the average velocity, remembering that these are really the x components of vector quantities that, in straight-line motion, have *only* x components.

When we deal with motion along a vertical line, we'll usually use a vertical y axis instead of an x axis, so our components will be called y components. Then Equation 3, with the x's replaced by y's, gives the y component of average velocity, $v_{av,y}$.

In Figures 1 and 2, it doesn't matter whether the car's velocity is or isn't constant during the time interval Δt. Another dragster may have started from rest,

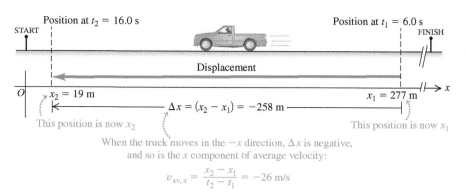

▲ **FIGURE 2** Positions of an official's truck at two times during its drive up the racetrack.

reached a maximum velocity, blown its engine, and then slowed down. To calculate the average velocity, we need only the total displacement $\Delta x = x_2 - x_1$ and the total time interval $\Delta t = t_2 - t_1$.

EXAMPLE 1   Swim competition

During a freestyle competition, a swimmer performs the crawl stroke in a pool 50.0 m long, as shown in Figure 3. She swims a length at racing speed, taking 24.0 s to cover the length of the pool. She then takes twice that time to swim casually back to her starting point. Find **(a)** her average velocity for each length and **(b)** her average velocity for the entire swim.

▲ **FIGURE 3**

SOLUTION

SET UP As shown in Figure 4, we choose a coordinate system with the origin at the starting point (often a convenient choice) and x increasing to the right. We add the information given to the diagram we sketch for the problem.

SOLVE Part (a): For the first length, we have $x_1 = 0$, $x_2 = 50.0$ m, $t_1 = 0$, and $t_2 = 24.0$ s. Using the definition of average velocity given by Equation 3, we find that

$$v_{av,x} = \frac{x_2 - x_1}{t_2 - t_1} = \frac{50.0 \text{ m} - 0 \text{ m}}{24.0 \text{ s} - 0 \text{ s}} = 2.08 \text{ m/s}.$$

For the return trip, we have $x_1 = 50.0$ m, $x_2 = 0$, $t_1 = 24.0$ s, and $t_2 = 24.0$ s + 48.0 s = 72.0 s. Using the definition of average velocity again, we obtain

$$v_{av,x} = \frac{x_2 - x_1}{t_2 - t_1} = \frac{0 \text{ m} - 50.0 \text{ m}}{72.0 \text{ s} - 24.0 \text{ s}} = -1.04 \text{ m/s}.$$

Part (b): The starting and finishing points are the same: $x_1 = x_2 = 0$. The average velocity for a round-trip is zero!

▲ **FIGURE 4** Our sketch for this problem.

REFLECT The average x component of velocity in part (b) is negative because x_2 lies to the left of x_1 on the axis and x is decreasing during this part of the trip. Thus, the average velocity *vector* points to the right for part (a) and to the left for part (b). The average velocity for the total out-and-back trip is zero because the total displacement is zero.

Practice Problem: If the swimmer could cross the English Channel (32 km), how many hours would she need if she could maintain the same average velocity as for the first 50 m in the pool? (Actual times are around 15 hours.) *Answer:* 4.3 hr.

You may have noticed that we haven't used the term *speed* in our discussion of particle motion. The terms *speed* and *velocity* are often used interchangeably (and erroneously), but there is a very important distinction between them. The average **speed** of a point during any motion is a *scalar* quantity equal to the total *distance* traveled (disregarding the direction of motion) during a specified time interval, divided by the time interval. Average *velocity* is a *vector* quantity, equal to the vector *displacement* of the particle, divided by the time interval. In Example 1, the average velocity during the two laps is zero because the total

Shutterstock

◀ **Application Will I ever get there?** Lombard Street in San Francisco is sometimes called "the crookedest street in the world." In descending the hill, a car travels a much greater distance than does a pedestrian walking down the adjacent stairs directly from top to bottom. However, both have moved the same overall distance through space; thus, the driver of the car and the pedestrian have experienced the same displacement. Therefore, if a car and a pedestrian left the top at the same time and arrived simultaneously at the bottom, they would have had the same average velocity (displacement divided by time), even though the car had a greater speed (overall distance traveled, divided by time).

displacement is zero. But the average speed is the total *distance* traveled (100.0 m), divided by the total time (72.0 s): $100.0 \text{ m}/72.0 \text{ s} = 1.39 \text{ m/s}$. The speedometer of a car is correctly named; it measures speed, irrespective of the direction of motion. To make a velocity meter, you would need a speedometer and a compass.

In Example 1, we could just as well have chosen the origin to be the other end of the pool and the positive direction for x to be to the left instead of to the right. Then the first x component of velocity would be negative and the second positive.

Conceptual Analysis 1

Signs and coordinate choices

You and a friend stand 10 m apart. Your dog, initially midway between you, runs in a straight line toward your friend. Each of you independently defines a coordinate system (position of origin and positive direction for the coordinate x) and calculates the dog's average x component of velocity. (Remember in this context, when we say "velocity," we really mean "x component of velocity.") What can you say with *certainty* about the average velocity?

A. The average velocity you calculate is positive.
B. The average velocity your friend calculates is negative.
C. Neither of you can obtain a negative velocity.
D. Both of you can obtain a negative velocity.

SOLUTION The question makes sense only if the coordinate axis is along the line joining you and your friend. But as Figure 5 shows, the axis can point to the left or to the right. If it points to the right, the dog moves in the positive x direction, so Δx is positive; if it points to the left, the dog moves in the negative x direction, so Δx is negative. Either person can choose either axis, so either person can obtain either sign for velocity. Thus, the correct

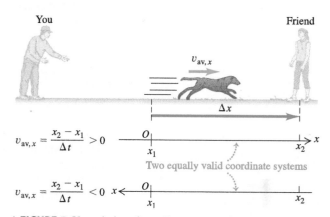

▲ **FIGURE 5** Your choice of coordinate system determines the sign of velocity.

answer is D. Notice that the sign of the average velocity does *not* depend on where you place the origin, but only on the direction you define as positive.

We've described motion of a particle along a straight line by stating the values of the coordinate x at various times t. In mathematical language, we say that x is a *function* of t. It's often useful to represent the relationship of x and t by means of a graph. We choose an axis system in which the coordinate x of the particle is plotted along the vertical axis and time t along the horizontal axis.

Figure 6 is a graph of the position of the dragster as a function of time. The curve in the figure *does not* represent the car's path in space; as Figure 1 shows,

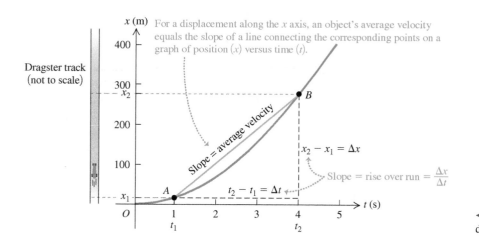

◀ **FIGURE 6** Graph of the position of the dragster as a function of time.

the path is a straight line. Rather, the graph is a pictorial way to represent the car's position at various times. Points A and B on the graph correspond to positions x_1 and x_2, respectively. The graph shows that, at time $t = 1.0$ s, the dragster's x coordinate (its displacement from the origin) is $x = 19$ m and that, at time $t = 4.0$ s, it is $x = 277$ m. During the 3.0-s interval from $t = 1.0$ s to $t = 4.0$ s, the x coordinate changes from 19 m to 277 m. The horizontal interval is $\Delta t = 3.0$ s, the vertical interval is $\Delta x = 258$ m. The average velocity $v_{\mathrm{av},x} = \Delta x / \Delta t$ is the vertical side of the triangle (Δx) divided by the horizontal side (Δt). This quotient is the **slope** of the line joining A and B (often described as the "rise" divided by the "run"). Thus, we obtain the following general principle:

> **The average velocity between two positions is the slope of a line connecting the two corresponding points on a graph of position as a function of time.**

We'll use this fact in the next section when we define instantaneous velocity.

2 Instantaneous Velocity

When a particle speeds up or slows down, we can still define its velocity at any one specific instant of time or at one specific point in the path. Such a velocity is called the particle's **instantaneous velocity,** and it needs to be defined carefully.

Suppose we want to find the instantaneous velocity (i.e., the x component) of the dragster in Figure 1 at the point x_1. We can take the second point x_2 to be closer and closer to the first point x_1, and we can compute the average velocity over these shorter and shorter displacements and time intervals. Although both Δx and Δt become very small, their quotient does not necessarily become small. We then define the instantaneous velocity at x_1 as the value that this series of average velocities *approaches* as the time interval becomes very small and x_2 comes closer and closer to x_1.

In mathematical language, the instantaneous velocity is called the **limit** of $\Delta x / \Delta t$ as Δt approaches zero or (in the language of calculus) the **derivative** of x with respect to t. Using the symbol v_x with no subscript for instantaneous velocity, we obtain the following definition:

Definition of instantaneous velocity
The x component of instantaneous velocity is the limit of $\Delta x / \Delta t$ as Δt approaches zero:

$$v_x = \lim_{\Delta t \to 0} \frac{\Delta x}{\Delta t}. \tag{4}$$

Like average velocity, instantaneous velocity is a vector quantity. Equation 4 defines its x component, which can be positive or negative. In straight-line motion, all other components are zero, and in this case we'll often call v the instantaneous velocity. From now on, when we use the term *velocity,* we'll always mean instantaneous rather than average velocity, unless we state otherwise.

The *sign* of a velocity component always depends on the choice of coordinate system, including the location of the origin and the choice of positive axis directions. We always assume that t_2 is a *later* time than t_1. (We always grow older, not younger.) Thus, Δt is always positive, and v_x has the same algebraic sign as Δx. If the positive x axis points to the right, as in Figure 1, a positive value of v_x means

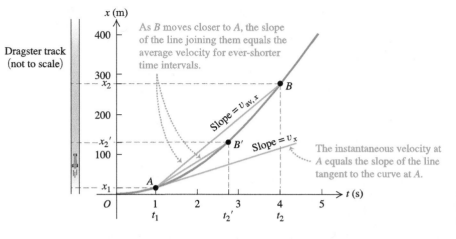

◀ **FIGURE 7** The relationship of average and instantaneous velocity for a graph of position as a function of time.

motion toward the right, and a negative value means motion toward the left. But an object can have a positive x and a negative v_x, or the reverse; x tells us where the particle *is,* and v_x tells us how it is *moving.* In Figure 2 the object is to the right of O but is moving toward the left, so it has a positive x and a negative v_x. An object to the left of O moving toward the right has a negative x and a positive v_x. Can you see what the situation is when *both* x and v_x are negative?

Figure 7 shows the relation of the graph of x vs t to the average and instantaneous velocities. As we saw in Figure 6, the average velocity between any two points A and B on a graph of x versus t is the slope of the line connecting the points. To approach the instantaneous velocity, as we just learned, we move x_2 closer and closer to x_1 (and t_2 closer and closer to t_1). Graphically, that means finding the slope for ever smaller intervals as point B approaches point A. As this interval becomes very small, the slope equals that of a line tangent to the curve at point A. Thus,

> **On a graph of a coordinate x as a function of time t, the instantaneous velocity at any point is equal to the slope of the tangent line to the curve at that point.**

As shown in Figure 8, if the tangent line slopes upward to the right, its slope is positive, v_x is positive, and the motion of the particle is in the positive x direction. If the tangent slopes downward to the right, the velocity is negative, and the motion of the particle is in the negative x direction. Where the tangent is horizontal, the slope is zero and the velocity is zero.

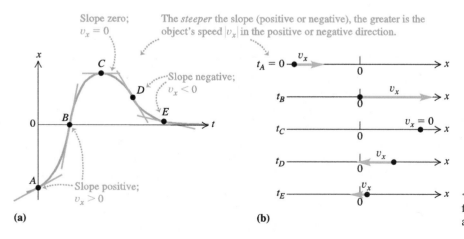

(a)　　　　　**(b)**

◀ **FIGURE 8** On a graph of position as a function of time, the slope of the tangent line at any point is the velocity at that point.

Conceptual Analysis 2

Velocity from graphs of position versus time

Figure 9 shows graphs of an object's position along the x axis versus time for four separate trials. Which of the following statements is or are correct?

A. The velocity is greater in trial 2 than in trial 3.

B. The velocity is not constant during trial 1.

C. During trial 4, the object changes direction as it passes through the point $x = 0$.

D. The velocity is constant during trials 2, 3, and 4.

(Remember that "velocity" means "x component of velocity.")

SOLUTION The graph of the motion during trial 1 has a changing slope and therefore v_x isn't constant. Trials 2, 3, and 4 all have graphs with constant slope and thus correspond to motion with constant velocity. (The velocity is zero during trial 2, as indicated by the slope of zero, but this value is still constant.) Trial 3 has a positive velocity, while the velocity in trial 4 is negative. Thus, choices B and D are correct.

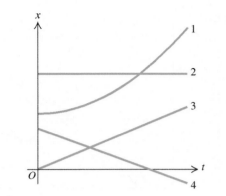

▲ **FIGURE 9**

EXAMPLE 2 ### Average and instantaneous velocities

A cheetah is crouched in ambush 20.0 m to the east of an observer's vehicle, as shown in Figure 10a. At time $t = 0$, the cheetah charges an antelope in a clearing 50.0 m east of the observer. The cheetah runs along a straight line; the observer estimates that, during the first 2.00 s of the attack, the cheetah's coordinate x varies with time t according to the equation

$$x = 20.0 \text{ m} + (5.00 \text{ m/s}^2)t^2.$$

(a) Find the displacement of the cheetah during the interval between $t_1 = 1.00$ s and $t_2 = 2.00$ s. **(b)** Find the average velocity during this time interval. **(c)** Estimate the instantaneous velocity at time $t_1 = 1.00$ s by taking $\Delta t = 0.10$ s.

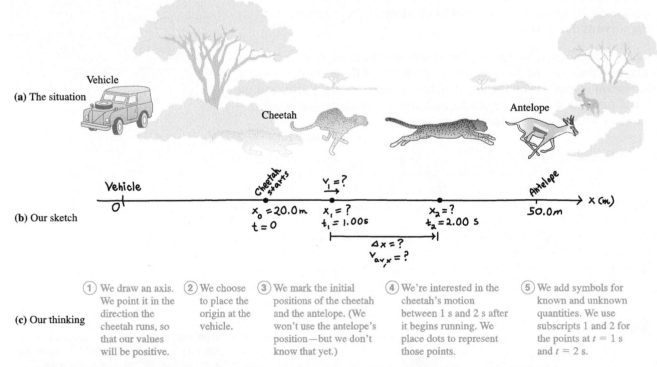

(a) The situation

(b) Our sketch

(c) Our thinking

① We draw an axis. We point it in the direction the cheetah runs, so that our values will be positive.

② We choose to place the origin at the vehicle.

③ We mark the initial positions of the cheetah and the antelope. (We won't use the antelope's position—but we don't know that yet.)

④ We're interested in the cheetah's motion between 1 s and 2 s after it begins running. We place dots to represent those points.

⑤ We add symbols for known and unknown quantities. We use subscripts 1 and 2 for the points at $t = 1$ s and $t = 2$ s.

▲ **FIGURE 10** (a) The situation for this problem, (b) the sketch we draw, and (c) the thinking that goes into the sketch.

Continued

SOLUTION

SET UP Figure 10b shows the diagram we sketch. First we define a coordinate system, orienting it so that the cheetah runs in the $+x$ direction. We add the points we are interested in, the values we know, and the values we will need to find for parts (a) and (b).

SOLVE Part (a): To find the displacement Δx, we first find the cheetah's positions (the values of x) at time $t_1 = 1.00$ s and at time $t_2 = 2.00$ s by substituting the values of t into the given equation. At time $t_1 = 1.00$ s, the cheetah's position x_1 is

$$x_1 = 20.0 \text{ m} + (5.00 \text{ m/s}^2)(1.00 \text{ s})^2 = 25.0 \text{ m}.$$

At time $t_2 = 2.00$ s, the cheetah's position x_2 is

$$x_2 = 20.0 \text{ m} + (5.00 \text{ m/s}^2)(2.00 \text{ s})^2 = 40.0 \text{ m}.$$

The displacement during this interval is

$$\Delta x = x_2 - x_1 = 40.0 \text{ m} - 25.0 \text{ m} = 15.0 \text{ m}.$$

Part (b): Having the displacement from 1.00 s to 2.00 s, we can now find the average velocity for that interval:

$$v_{av,x} = \frac{\Delta x}{\Delta t} = \frac{40.0 \text{ m} - 25.0 \text{ m}}{2.00 \text{ s} - 1.00 \text{ s}} = \frac{15.0 \text{ m}}{1.00 \text{ s}} = 15.0 \text{ m/s}.$$

Part (c): The instantaneous velocity at 1.00 s is approximately (but not exactly) equal to the average velocity in the interval from $t_1 = 1.00$ s to $t_2 = 1.10$ s (i.e., $\Delta t = 0.10$ s). At $t_2 = 1.10$ s,

$$x_2 = 20.0 \text{ m} + (5.00 \text{ m/s})(1.10 \text{ s})^2 = 26.05 \text{ m},$$

so that

$$v_{av,x} = \frac{\Delta x}{\Delta t} = \frac{26.05 \text{ m} - 25.0 \text{ m}}{1.10 \text{ s} - 1.00 \text{ s}} = 10.5 \text{ m/s}.$$

If you use the same procedure to find the average velocities for time intervals of 0.01 s and 0.001 s, you will get 10.05 m/s and 10.005 m/s, respectively. As Δt gets smaller and smaller, the average velocity gets closer and closer to 10.0 m/s. We conclude that the instantaneous velocity at time $t = 1.0$ s is 10.0 m/s.

REFLECT As the time interval Δt approaches zero, the average velocity in the interval is closer and closer to the limiting value 10.0 m/s, which we call the instantaneous velocity at time $t = 1.00$ s. Note that when we calculate an average velocity, we need to specify two times—the beginning and end times of the interval—but for instantaneous velocity at a particular time, we specify only that one time.

NOTE ▶ Here's a reminder about the term *speed*. It is distance traveled, divided by time taken, on either an average or an instantaneous basis. Speed is a scalar quantity, not a vector; it has no direction. If a race car makes one lap around the Indianapolis race track (2.5 mi in circumference) in 1.00 min ($=1/60$ h), its average speed is $(2.5 \text{ mi})/(1/60 \text{ h}) = 150 \text{ mi/h}$. Its instantaneous speed may or may not be constant, but its velocity is certainly not constant because the car changes direction at the turns. At the end of one lap, the race car is back where it started, so its average *velocity* for one lap is zero. ◀

3 Average and Instantaneous Acceleration

When the velocity of a moving object changes with time, we say that the object has *acceleration*. Just as velocity is a quantitative description of the rate of change of *position* with time, acceleration is a quantitative description of the rate of change of *velocity* with time. Like velocity, acceleration is a vector quantity. In straight-line motion its only nonzero component is along the coordinate axis.

To introduce the concept of acceleration, let's consider again the motion of an object (such as the dragster of Section 1) along the x axis. As usual, we assume that the object can be treated as a particle. Suppose that at time t_1 the particle is at point x_1 and has an x component of instantaneous velocity v_{1x} and that at a later time t_2 it is at point x_2 and has an x component of velocity v_{2x}.

Definition of average acceleration

The **average acceleration** a_{av} of an object as it moves from x_1 (at time t_1) to x_2 (at time t_2) is a vector quantity whose x component is the ratio of the change in the x component of velocity, $\Delta v_x = v_{2x} - v_{1x}$, to the time interval $\Delta t = t_2 - t_1$:

$$a_{av,x} = \frac{v_{2x} - v_{1x}}{t_2 - t_1} = \frac{\Delta v_x}{\Delta t}. \tag{5}$$

Unit: If we express velocity in meters per second and time in seconds, then acceleration is in meters per second per second $(\text{m/s})/\text{s}$. This unit is usually written as m/s^2 and is read "meters per second squared."

▲ **Application Haven't I been here before?** Gil de Ferran has just won the 2003 Indianapolis 500 auto race by completing 200 laps of the 2.5-mile oval course more rapidly than anyone else. He did this in under three hours, for an average speed of close to 200 miles per hour for the 500-mile race. However, since he finished the race right where he started, his total displacement during the race was zero. So don't tell him now, but despite his high average speed, his average velocity for the trip was 0 miles per hour!

In straight-line motion, we'll usually call $a_{av,x}$ the average acceleration, although we recognize that it is actually the x component of the average acceleration.

Acceleration in a space walk

An astronaut has left the space shuttle on a tether to test a new personal maneuvering device. She moves along a straight line directly away from the shuttle. Her onboard partner measures her velocity before and after certain maneuvers, and obtains the following results:

(a) $v_{1x} = 0.8$ m/s, $\quad v_{2x} = 1.2$ m/s; (speeding up)
(b) $v_{1x} = 1.6$ m/s, $\quad v_{2x} = 1.2$ m/s; (slowing down)
(c) $v_{1x} = -0.4$ m/s, $v_{2x} = -1.0$ m/s; (speeding up)
(d) $v_{1x} = -1.6$ m/s, $v_{2x} = -0.8$ m/s. (slowing down)

If $t_1 = 2$ s and $t_2 = 4$ s in each case, find the average acceleration for each set of data.

SOLUTION

SET UP We use the diagram in Figure 11 to organize our data.

SOLVE To find the astronaut's average acceleration in each case, we will use the definition of average acceleration (Equation 5): $a_{av,x} = \Delta v_x / \Delta t$. The time interval is $\Delta t = 2.0$ s in all cases; the change in velocity in each case is $\Delta v_x = v_{2x} - v_{1x}$.

Part (a): $a_{av,x} = \dfrac{1.2 \text{ m/s} - 0.8 \text{ m/s}}{4 \text{ s} - 2 \text{ s}} = +0.2 \text{ m/s}^2;$

Part (b): $a_{av,x} = \dfrac{1.2 \text{ m/s} - 1.6 \text{ m/s}}{4 \text{ s} - 2 \text{ s}} = -0.2 \text{ m/s}^2;$

Part (c): $a_{av,x} = \dfrac{-1.0 \text{ m/s} - (-0.4 \text{ m/s})}{4 \text{ s} - 2 \text{ s}} = -0.3 \text{ m/s}^2;$

Part (d): $a_{av,x} = \dfrac{-0.8 \text{ m/s} - (-1.6 \text{ m/s})}{4 \text{ s} - 2 \text{ s}} = +0.4 \text{ m/s}^2.$

REFLECT The astronaut speeds up in cases (a) and (c) and slows down in (b) and (d), but the average acceleration is positive in (a) and (d) and negative in (b) and (c). In other words, negative acceleration *does not* necessarily indicate a slowing down.

	BEFORE	AFTER
Part (a)	$v_{1x} = 0.8$ m/s	$v_{2x} = 1.2$ m/s
Part (b)	$v_{1x} = 1.6$ m/s	$v_{2x} = 1.2$ m/s
Part (c)	$v_{1x} = -0.4$ m/s	$v_{2x} = -1.0$ m/s
Part (d)	$v_{1x} = -1.6$ m/s	$v_{2x} = -0.8$ m/s

▲ **FIGURE 11** We can use a sketch and table to organize the information given in the problem.

The preceding example raises the question of what the sign of acceleration means and how it relates to the signs of displacement and velocity. Because average acceleration (i.e., the x component) is defined as $a_{av,x} = \Delta v_x / \Delta t$, and Δt is always positive, the sign of acceleration is the same as the sign of Δv_x. Figure 12 shows the four possible cases; make sure you understand why the acceleration is positive or negative in each case.

NOTE ► As Figure 12 shows, the velocity and acceleration of an object do not necessarily have the same sign. For instance, an object that is moving in the positive direction, but slowing down, has positive velocity and negative acceleration. Velocity describes the motion of an object at a given instant of time; acceleration describes how the object's motion is *changing* with time. ◄

The term *deceleration* is sometimes used for a decrease in speed; such a decrease can correspond to either positive or negative acceleration. Because of

The *direction of the axis* determines the signs of velocity and acceleration.

▲ **FIGURE 12** The relationship between the sign of acceleration, the sign of Δv, and the direction chosen as positive.

this ambiguity, we won't use the term in what follows. Instead, we recommend careful attention to the interpretation of the algebraic sign of a_x in relation to that of v_x.

We can now define **instantaneous acceleration,** following the same procedure that we used for instantaneous velocity. Consider the situation shown in Figure 13: A sports car has just entered the final straightaway at the Grand Prix. It reaches point x_1 at time t_1, moving with velocity v_{1x}. It passes point x_2, closer to the finish line, at time t_2 with velocity v_{2x}.

To define instantaneous acceleration at point x_1, we take the second point x_2 in Figure 13 to be closer and closer to the first point x_1, so the average acceleration is computed over shorter and shorter time intervals. The instantaneous acceleration at point x_1 is defined as the limit approached by the average acceleration when point x_2 is taken closer and closer to point x_1 and t_2 is taken closer and closer to t_1.

Definition of instantaneous acceleration

The x component of instantaneous acceleration is defined as the limit of $\Delta v_x / \Delta t$ as Δt approaches zero:

$$a_x = \lim_{\Delta t \to 0} \frac{\Delta v_x}{\Delta t}. \tag{6}$$

Instantaneous acceleration plays an essential role in the laws of mechanics. From now on, when we use the term *acceleration,* we will always mean instantaneous acceleration, not average acceleration.

▲ **Application** **Is this car accelerating?** Shortly after this jet-propelled car reached its top speed, the parachute was deployed to help bring it to a stop. As you know from your study of physics, the car is indeed accelerating while it is slowing down. Because acceleration is defined as a change in velocity per unit time, in this case the car has a negative acceleration component in the forward direction.

◀ **FIGURE 13** A race car at two points on the straightaway.

EXAMPLE 4 Average and instantaneous accelerations

Suppose that, at any time t, the velocity v of the car in Figure 13 is given by the equation $v_x = 60.0$ m/s $+ (0.500$ m/s$^3)t^2$. In this equation, v_x has units of m/s and t has units of s. Note that the numbers 60 and 0.50 *must* have the units shown for this equation to be dimensionally consistent.
(a) Find the change in velocity of the car in the time interval between $t_1 = 1.00$ s and $t_2 = 3.00$ s. **(b)** Find the average acceleration in this time interval. **(c)** Estimate the instantaneous acceleration at time $t_1 = 1.00$ s by taking $\Delta t = 0.10$ s.

SOLUTION

SET UP Figure 14 shows the diagram we use to establish a coordinate system and organize our known and unknown information.

SOLVE Part (a): We first find the velocity at each time by substituting each value of t into the equation. From these values, we can find the change in velocity in the interval. Thus, at time $t_1 = 1.00$ s,

$$v_{1x} = 60.0 \text{ m/s} + (0.500 \text{ m/s}^3)(1.00 \text{ s})^2 = 60.5 \text{ m/s}.$$

At time $t_2 = 3.00$ s,

$$v_{2x} = 60.0 \text{ m/s} + (0.500 \text{ m/s}^3)(3.00 \text{ s})^2 = 64.5 \text{ m/s}.$$

The change in velocity Δv_x is then

$$\Delta v_x = v_{2x} - v_{1x} = 64.5 \text{ m/s} - 60.5 \text{ m/s} = 4.00 \text{ m/s}.$$

Part (b): The change in velocity, divided by the time interval, gives the average acceleration in each interval.
The time interval is $\Delta t = 3.00$ s $- 1.00$ s $= 2.00$ s, so

$$a_{av,x} = \frac{v_{2x} - v_{1x}}{t_2 - t_1} = \frac{4.0 \text{ m/s}}{2.00 \text{ s}} = 2.00 \text{ m/s}^2.$$

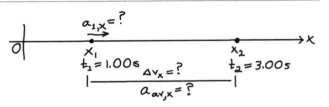

▲ **FIGURE 14** Our sketch for this problem.

Part (c): We use the same procedure to approximate the instantaneous acceleration at x_1 by calculating the average acceleration over 0.100 s. When $\Delta t = 0.100$ s, $t_2 = 1.10$ s, and it follows that

$$v_{2x} = 60.0 \text{ m/s} + (0.500 \text{ m/s}^3)(1.10 \text{ s})^2 = 60.605 \text{ m/s},$$
$$\Delta v_x = 0.105 \text{ m/s},$$
$$a_{av,x} = \frac{\Delta v_x}{\Delta t} = \frac{0.105 \text{ m/s}}{0.100 \text{ s}} = 1.05 \text{ m/s}^2.$$

REFLECT If we repeat the calculation in part (c) for $\Delta t = 0.01$ s and $\Delta t = 0.001$ s, we get $a_{av,x} = 1.005$ m/s^2 and $a_{av,x} = 1.0005$ m/s^2, respectively (although we aren't entitled to this many significant figures). As Δt gets smaller and smaller, the average acceleration gets closer and closer to 1.00 m/s^2. We conclude that the instantaneous acceleration at $t = 1.00$ s is 1.00 m/s^2.

As with average and instantaneous velocity, we can gain added insight into the concepts of average and instantaneous acceleration by plotting a graph with velocity v_x on the vertical axis and time t on the horizontal axis. Figure 15 shows such a graph for the race car from Figure 13. Notice that now we are plotting *velocity* against time, not position against time as before. If we draw a line between any two points on the graph, such as A and B (corresponding to a displacement from x_1 to x_2 and to the time interval $\Delta t = t_2 - t_1$), the slope of that line equals the average acceleration over that interval. If we then take point B and move it closer and closer to point A, the slope of the line AB approaches the slope

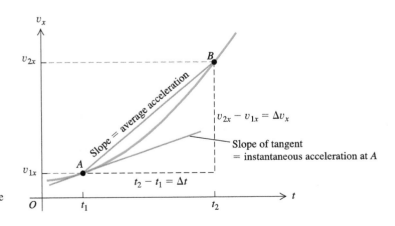

► **FIGURE 15** A graph of velocity versus time for the motion of the race car in Figure 13.

of the line that is tangent to the curve at point A. Accordingly, we can interpret a graph of velocity versus time as follows:

The average acceleration between any two points on a graph of velocity versus time equals the slope of a line connecting those points.

The instantaneous acceleration at any point on the graph equals the slope of the line tangent to the curve at that point.

Let's emphasize once again the significance of the *sign* of acceleration. First, the velocity v_x and acceleration a_x of an object don't necessarily have the same sign; they are independent quantities. When v_x and a_x *do* have the same sign, the object is speeding up. If both are positive, the object is moving in the positive direction with increasing speed. If both are negative, the object is moving in the negative direction with a velocity that becomes more and more negative with time, and again the object's speed increases. If v_x is positive and a_x is negative, the object is moving in the positive direction with decreasing speed. If v_x is negative and a_x is positive, the object is moving in the negative direction with a velocity that is becoming less negative, and again the object slows down.

Conceptual Analysis 3 | **Translating a graphical description to a verbal description**

Figure 16 shows a graph of velocity versus time for a moving object. (Notice that the vertical axis is velocity in this case, not position.) The object moves on an east-west axis, with west chosen as the positive direction. Which of the following verbal descriptions matches the graph?

A. The object speeds up continuously while moving westward.
B. The object moves toward the origin while slowing, then moves away from the origin while speeding up.
C. The object moves in the positive direction while slowing to a stop, then moves east while speeding up.
D. The object moves east while slowing to a stop, then moves west while speeding up.

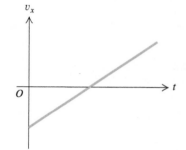

▲ **FIGURE 16**

SOLUTION The direction of motion and the sign of the velocity tell us the same thing; in this case, a positive velocity means that the object is going west and a negative velocity means that it is going east. A large negative velocity means that the object is going east at high speed, while a small negative velocity means that it is going east slowly. Since the vertical axis of this graph represents velocity, the velocity coordinate of any point on the plot tells you the object's direction and speed. The plot starts with a large, negative value of velocity, indicating that the object is moving east fast. When the plot reaches $v_x = 0$ (the point at which it crosses the horizontal axis), the object has slowed to a halt. From there, the object has progressively higher positive values of v_x; it is moving to the west with increasing speed. Thus, A cannot be true, because the object starts with negative v_x. Nor can B be true, since knowing your speed and direction of motion says nothing about where you are. The answer D matches the reasoning given here.

Acceleration and the Human Body

Accelerations require forces object subjected to sufficiently large accelerations and the associated forces may suffer damage. The earth's gravitational attraction causes objects to fall with a downward acceleration with a magnitude of about 9.8 m/s^2 (assuming that effects such as air resistance can be neglected). This acceleration is often denoted by g; we'll study its effects in greater detail in Section 5. For now, we simply note that $g = 9.8 \text{ m/s}^2$.

Because earth's land life evolved in an environment characterized by this magnitude of acceleration, it isn't surprising that the human body can withstand accelerations on the order of g without damage. Sport cars can accelerate at about $0.5g$, or 4.9 m/s^2. Accelerations on the order of $3g$ in a jet fighter cause serious impairment of the pilot's blood circulation, and above about $5g$ the pilot loses

▲ **BIO Application Are we there yet?**
Fortunately for this test pilot, the extreme *g* force he is experiencing will last only a second or two. He is strapped into a human centrifuge, an instrument designed to test the limits of human endurance when exposed to extreme *g* forces. The device consists of a simulated cockpit at the end of an 8-meter-long mechanical arm that can be rotated so rapidly that it can produce temporary accelerations of up to 15*g* in a period of 3 seconds. The centrifuge is able to simulate the types of extreme *g* forces a fighter jet pilot or astronaut might experience during takeoff or a rapid turn.

MasteringPHYSICS

PhET: Forces in 1 Dimension
ActivPhysics 1.1: Analyzing Motion Using Diagrams
ActivPhysics 1.3: Predicting Motion from Graphs
ActivPhysics 1.4: Predicting Motion from Equations
ActivPhysics 1.5: Problem-Solving Strategies for Kinematics
ActivPhysics 1.6: Skier Races Downhill

consciousness. The primary function of air bags in cars is to reduce the maximum acceleration during a collision to a value that can be sustained by the body without catastrophic damage. The human body can withstand accelerations on the order of 50*g* for very short time intervals (about 0.05 s).

4 Motion with Constant Acceleration

The simplest accelerated motion is straight-line motion with *constant* acceleration. In this case, the velocity changes at the same rate throughout the motion. Figure 17 shows four ways to represent the motion of a race car undergoing constant acceleration. Notice that the plot of velocity versus time (Figure 17c) is a straight line; that is, its slope is constant. That tells you that the car's velocity changes by equal amounts Δv_x in equal time intervals Δt. This characteristic of motion with constant acceleration makes it easy for us to derive equations for the position x and velocity v_x as functions of time. Let's start with velocity. In the definition of average acceleration (Equation 5), we can replace the average acceleration $a_{av,x}$ by the constant (instantaneous) acceleration a_x. We then have

$$a_x = \frac{v_{2x} - v_{1x}}{t_2 - t_1} \quad \text{(for an object moving with constant acceleration).} \quad (7)$$

Now we let $t_1 = 0$ and t_2 be any arbitrary later time t. We use the symbol v_{0x} for the velocity (again, the x component) at the initial time $t = 0$; the velocity at the later time t is v_x. Then Equation 7 becomes the following:

Velocity as a function of time for an object moving with constant acceleration

For an object that has x component of velocity v_{0x} at time $t = 0$ and moves with constant acceleration a_x, we find the velocity v_x at any later time t:

$$a_x = \frac{v_x - v_{0x}}{t - 0}, \quad \text{or}$$

$$v_x = v_{0x} + a_x t. \quad (8)$$

Unit: m/s

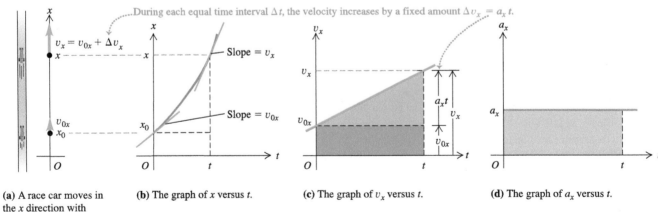

During each equal time interval Δt, the velocity increases by a fixed amount $\Delta v_x = a_x t$.

(a) A race car moves in the x direction with constant acceleration.

(b) The graph of x versus t.

(c) The graph of v_x versus t.

(d) The graph of a_x versus t.

▲ **FIGURE 17** Four ways to represent the motion of a race car moving with constant acceleration.

We can interpret this equation as follows: The acceleration a_x is the constant rate of change of velocity, that is, the change in velocity per unit time. The term $a_x t$ is the product of the change in velocity per unit time, a_x, and the time interval t. Therefore, it equals the *total* change in velocity from the initial time $t = 0$ to the later time t. The velocity v_x at any time t is the sum of the initial velocity v_{0x} (at $t = 0$) and the *change* in velocity $a_x t$. Figure 17c shows this analysis in graphical terms. The height v_x of the graph at any time t is the sum of two segments: one with length v_{0x} equal to the initial velocity, the other with length $a_x t$ equal to the change in velocity during time t.

MasteringPHYSICS

PhET: The Moving Man
ActivPhysics 1.8: Seat Belts Save Lives
ActivPhysics 1.9: Screeching to a Halt
ActivPhysics 1.11: Car Starts, Then Stops
ActivPhysics 1.12: Solving Two-Vehicle Problem
ActivPhysics 1.13: Car Catches Truck
ActivPhysics 1.14: Avoiding a Rear-End Collision

EXAMPLE 5 **Passing speed**

A car initially traveling along a straight stretch of highway at 15 m/s accelerates with a constant acceleration of 2.0 m/s² in order to pass a truck. What is the velocity of the car after 5.0 s?

SOLUTION

SET UP Figure 18 shows what we draw. We take the origin of coordinates to be at the initial position of the car, where $v_x = v_{0x}$ and $t = 0$, and we let the $+x$ direction be the direction of the car's initial velocity. With this coordinate system, $v_{0x} = +15$ m/s and $a_x = +2.0$ m/s².

SOLVE The acceleration is constant during the 5.0 s time interval, so we can use Equation 8 to find v_x:

$$v_x = v_{0x} + a_x t = 15 \text{ m/s} + (2.0 \text{ m/s}^2)(5.0 \text{ s})$$
$$= 15 \text{ m/s} + 10 \text{ m/s} = 25 \text{ m/s}.$$

REFLECT The velocity and acceleration are in the same direction, so the speed increases. An acceleration of 2.0 m/s² means

▲ **FIGURE 18** The diagram we draw for this problem.

that the velocity increases by 2.0 m/s every second, so in 5.0 s the velocity increases by 10 m/s.

Practice Problem: If the car maintains its constant acceleration, how much additional time does it take the car to reach a velocity of 35 m/s? *Answer:* 5.0 s.

Next we want to derive an equation for the *position* x of a particle moving with constant acceleration. To do this, we make use of two different expressions for the average velocity $v_{\text{av},x}$ during the interval from $t = 0$ to any later time t. First, when the acceleration is constant and the graph of velocity vs. time is a straight line, as in Figure 17, the velocity changes at a uniform rate. In this particular case, the average velocity throughout any time interval is simply the average of the velocities at the beginning and the end of the interval. Thus, for the time interval from 0 to t,

$$v_{\text{av},x} = \frac{v_{0x} + v_x}{2} \quad \text{(for constant acceleration).} \quad (9)$$

(This equation does *not* hold if the acceleration varies with time; in that case, the graph of velocity vs. time is a curve, as in Figure 15.)

We also know that v_x, the velocity at any time t, is given by Equation 8. Substituting that expression for v_x into Equation 9, we find that

$$v_{\text{av},x} = \tfrac{1}{2}(v_{0x} + v_{0x} + a_x t)$$
$$= v_{0x} + \tfrac{1}{2}a_x t. \quad (10)$$

We can also get an expression for $v_{\text{av},x}$ from the general definition, Equation 1:

$$v_{\text{av},x} = \frac{x_2 - x_1}{t_2 - t_1}.$$

We call the position at time $t = 0$ the *initial position*, denoted by x_0. The position at the later time t is simply x. Thus, for the time interval $\Delta t = t - 0$ and the corresponding displacement $x - x_0$, Equation 1 gives

$$v_{av,x} = \frac{x - x_0}{t}. \tag{11}$$

Finally, we equate Equations 10 and 11 and simplify the result to obtain the following equation:

Position as a function of time for an object moving with constant acceleration

For constant acceleration a_x, we solve

$$v_{0x} + \tfrac{1}{2}a_x t = \frac{x - x_0}{t} \quad \text{to find}$$

$$x = x_0 + v_{0x}t + \tfrac{1}{2}a_x t^2. \tag{12}$$

This equation states that if, at the initial time $t = 0$, a particle is at position x_0 and has velocity v_{0x}, its new position x at any later time t is the sum of three terms: its initial position x_0, plus the distance $v_{0x}t$ that it would have moved if its velocity had been constant, plus an additional distance $\tfrac{1}{2}a_x t^2$ caused by the changing velocity.

EXAMPLE 6 **Passing distance**

What distance does the car in Example 5 travel during its 5.0 seconds of acceleration?

SOLUTION

SET UP We use the same coordinates as in Example 5. As before, $v_{0x} = +15 \text{ m/s}$ and $a_x = +2.0 \text{ m/s}^2$.

SOLVE We want to solve for $x - x_0$, the distance traveled by the car during the 5.0 s time interval. The acceleration is constant, so we can use Equation 12 to find

$$\begin{aligned}
x - x_0 &= v_{0x}t + \tfrac{1}{2}a_x t^2 \\
&= (15 \text{ m/s})(5.0 \text{ s}) + \tfrac{1}{2}(2.0 \text{ m/s}^2)(5.0 \text{ s})^2 \\
&= 75 \text{ m} + 25 \text{ m} = 100 \text{ m}.
\end{aligned}$$

REFLECT If the speed were constant and equal to the initial value $v_0 = 15 \text{ m/s}$, the car would travel 75 m in 5.0 s. It actually travels *farther*, because the speed is increasing. From Example 5, we know that the final velocity is $v_x = 25 \text{ m/s}$, so the *average* velocity for the 5.0 s segment of motion is

$$v_{av,x} = \frac{v_{0x} + v_x}{2} = \frac{15 \text{ m/s} + 25 \text{ m/s}}{2} = 20 \text{ m/s}.$$

An alternative way to obtain the distance traveled is to multiply the average velocity by the time interval. When we do this, we get $x - x_0 = v_{av,x}t = (20 \text{ m/s})(5.0 \text{ s}) = 100 \text{ m}$, the same result we obtained using Equation 12.

Practice Problem: If the car in Example 5 maintains its constant acceleration for a total time of 10 s, what total distance does it travel? *Answer:* 250 m.

For some problems, we aren't given the time interval for the motion, and we need to obtain a relation for x, v_x, and a_x that doesn't contain t. To obtain such a relation, we can combine Equations 8 and 12 to eliminate t. This involves a little algebra, but the result is worth the effort!

We first solve Equation 8 for t and then substitute the resulting expression into Equation 12 and simplify:

$$t = \frac{v_x - v_{0x}}{a_x},$$

$$x = x_0 + v_{0x}\left(\frac{v_x - v_{0x}}{a_x}\right) + \frac{1}{2}a_x\left(\frac{v_x - v_{0x}}{a_x}\right)^2.$$

We transfer the term x_0 to the left side and multiply through by $2a_x$:

$$2a_x(x - x_0) = 2v_{0x}v_x - 2v_{0x}^2 + v_x^2 - 2v_{0x}v_x + v_{0x}^2.$$

Finally, we combine terms and simplify to obtain the following equation:

Velocity as a function of position for an object moving with constant acceleration

For an object moving in a straight line with constant acceleration a_x,

$$v_x^2 = v_{0x}^2 + 2a_x(x - x_0). \tag{13}$$

This equation gives us the particle's velocity v_x at any position x without needing to know the *time* when it is at that position.

EXAMPLE 7   Entering the freeway

A sports car is sitting at rest in a freeway entrance ramp. The driver sees a break in the traffic and floors the car's accelerator, so that the car accelerates at a constant 4.9 m/s² as it moves in a straight line onto the freeway. What distance does the car travel in reaching a freeway speed of 30 m/s?

SOLUTION

SET UP As shown in Figure 19, we place the origin at the initial position of the car and assume that the car travels in a straight line in the $+x$ direction. Then $v_{0x} = 0$, $v_x = 30$ m/s, and $a_x = 4.9$ m/s².

SOLVE The acceleration is constant; the problem makes no mention of time, so we can't use Equation 8 or Equation 12 by themselves. We need a relation between x and v_x, and this is provided by Equation 13:

$$v_x^2 = v_{0x}^2 + 2a_x(x - x_0).$$

Rearranging and substituting numerical values, we obtain

$$x - x_0 = \frac{v_x^2 - v_{0x}^2}{2a_x} = \frac{(30 \text{ m/s})^2 - 0}{2(4.9 \text{ m/s}^2)} = 92 \text{ m}.$$

Alternative Solution: We could have used Equation 8 to solve for the time t first:

$$t = \frac{v_x - v_{0x}}{a_x} = \frac{30 \text{ m/s} - 0}{4.9 \text{ m/s}^2} = 6.12 \text{ s}.$$

Then Equation 12 gives the distance traveled:

$$x - x_0 = v_{0x}t + \tfrac{1}{2}a_xt^2 = 0 + \tfrac{1}{2}(4.9 \text{ m/s}^2)(6.12 \text{ s})^2 = 92 \text{ m}.$$

▲ **FIGURE 19** A car accelerating on a ramp merging onto a freeway.

REFLECT We obtained the same result in one step when we used Equation 13 and in two steps when we used Equations 8 and 12. When we use them correctly, Equations 8, 12, and 13 *always* give consistent results.

The final speed of 30 m/s is about 67 mph, and 92 m is about 100 yd. Does this distance correspond to your own driving experience?

Practice Problem: What distance has the car traveled when it has reached a speed of 20 m/s? *Answer:* 41 m.

Equations 8, 12, and 13, are the *equations of motion with constant acceleration*. Any kinematic problem involving motion of an object in a straight line with constant acceleration can be solved by applying these equations.

Here's a summary of the equations:

Equations of motion for constant acceleration

$v_x = v_{0x} + a_xt$	(Gives v_x if t is known.)	(8)
$x = x_0 + v_{0x}t + \tfrac{1}{2}a_xt^2$	(Gives x if t is known.)	(12)
$v_x^2 = v_{0x}^2 + 2a_x(x - x_0)$	(Gives v_x if x is known.)	(13)

We can get one more useful relationship by equating the two expressions for $v_{\mathrm{av},x}$ given by Equations 9 and 11, and multiplying through by t. Doing this, we obtain the following equation:

Position, velocity, and time for an object moving with constant acceleration

$$x - x_0 = \frac{v_{0x} + v_x}{2}t. \qquad (14)$$

This equation says that the total displacement $x - x_0$ from time $t = 0$ to a later time t is equal to the average velocity $(v_{0x} + v_x)/2$ during the interval, multiplied by the time t. Equation 14 doesn't contain the acceleration a_x, so it is sometimes useful when a_x is not given in the problem.

Figure 20 is a graphical representation of Equations 12 and 8, respectively, for the case of positive velocity and positive acceleration. In Figure 20a, the blue curve represents Equation 12. The straight dashed line shows the plot we would get if the acceleration is zero: If $a_x = 0$, then $x = x_0 + v_{0x}t$. For this line, the slope (velocity) is constant. The vertical separation between the two curves represents the term $\frac{1}{2}a_x t^2$, which is the effect of acceleration. In Figure 20b, the green curve represents Equation 8. Make sure you understand how this graph represents the individual terms of the equation.

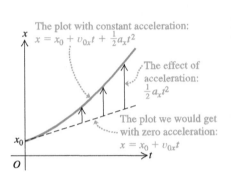

The plot with constant acceleration:
$x = x_0 + v_{0x}t + \frac{1}{2}a_x t^2$

The effect of acceleration: $\frac{1}{2}a_x t^2$

The plot we would get with zero acceleration: $x = x_0 + v_{0x}t$

(a) Plot of x versus t for an object moving with positive constant acceleration

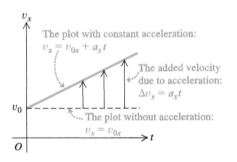

The plot with constant acceleration: $v_x = v_{0x} + a_x t$

The added velocity due to acceleration: $\Delta v_x = a_x t$

The plot without acceleration: $v_x = v_{0x}$

(b) Plot of v_x versus t for the same object

▲ **FIGURE 20** The graphical meaning of Equations 8 and 12 for an object moving with positive velocity and positive constant acceleration.

PROBLEM-SOLVING STRATEGY 1 **Motion with constant acceleration**

SET UP

1. You *must* decide at the beginning of a problem where the origin of coordinates is and which axis direction is positive. The choices are usually a matter of convenience; it is often easiest to place the origin at the object's location at time $t = 0$; then $x_0 = 0$. Draw a diagram showing your choices. Then sketch any relevant later positions of the object in the same diagram.
2. Once you have chosen the positive axis direction, the positive directions for velocity and acceleration are also determined. It would be wrong to define x as positive to the right of the origin and velocities as positive toward the left.
3. It often helps to restate the problem in prose first and then translate the prose description into symbols and equations. *When* (i.e, at what value of t) does the particle arrive at a certain point? *Where* is the particle when its velocity has a certain value? (That is, what is the value of x when v_x has the specified value?) The next example asks, "Where is the motorcyclist when his velocity is 25 m/s?" Translated into symbols, this becomes "What is the value of x when $v_x = 25$ m/s?"
4. Either on your diagram or in a list, write known and unknown quantities such as x, x_0, v_x, v_{0x}, and a_x. Write in the values for those that are known. Be on the lookout for implicit information; for example, "A car sits at a stoplight" usually means that $v_{0x} = 0$, and so on.

SOLVE

5. Once you've identified the unknowns, you may be able to choose an equation from among Equations 8, 12, 13, and 14 that contains only one of the unknowns. Solve for that unknown; then substitute the known values and compute the value of the unknown. Carry the units of the quantities along with your calculations as an added consistency check.

REFLECT

6. Take a hard look at your results to see whether they make sense. Are they within the general range of magnitudes you expected? If you change one of the given quantities, do the results change in a way you can predict?

EXAMPLE 8   Constant acceleration on a motorcycle

A motorcyclist heading east through a small Iowa town accelerates after he passes a signpost at $x = 0$ marking the city limits. His acceleration is constant: $a_x = 4.0 \text{ m/s}^2$. At time $t = 0$ he is 5.0 m east of the signpost and has a velocity of $v_x = 15 \text{ m/s}$. (a) Find his position and velocity at time $t = 2.0 \text{ s}$. (b) Where is the motorcyclist when his velocity is 25 m/s?

SOLUTION

SET UP Figure 21 shows our diagram. The problem tells us that $x = 0$ at the signpost, so that is the origin of coordinates. We point the x axis east, in the direction of motion. The (constant) acceleration is $a_x = 4.0 \text{ m/s}^2$. At the initial time $t = 0$ the position is $x_0 = 5.0 \text{ m}$, and the initial velocity is $v_{0x} = 15 \text{ m/s}$.

SOLVE Part (a): We want to know the position and velocity (the values of x and v_x, respectively) at the later time $t = 2.0 \text{ s}$. Equation 12 gives the position x as a function of time t:

$$x = x_0 + v_{0x}t + \tfrac{1}{2}a_xt^2$$
$$= 5.0 \text{ m} + (15 \text{ m/s})(2.0 \text{ s}) + \tfrac{1}{2}(4.0 \text{ m/s}^2)(2.0 \text{ s})^2 = 43 \text{ m}.$$

Equation 8 gives the velocity v_x as a function of time t:

$$v_x = v_{0x} + a_xt$$
$$= 15 \text{ m/s} + (4.0 \text{ m/s}^2)(2.0 \text{ s}) = 23 \text{ m/s}.$$

Part (b): We want to know the value of x when $v_x = 25 \text{ m/s}$. Note that this occurs at a time later than 2.0 s and at a point farther than 43 m from the signpost. From Equation 13, we have

$$v_x^2 = v_{0x}^2 + 2a_x(x - x_0),$$
$$(25 \text{ m/s})^2 = (15 \text{ m/s})^2 + 2(4.0 \text{ m/s}^2)(x - 5.0 \text{ m}),$$
$$x = 55 \text{ m}.$$

Alternatively, we may use Equation 8 to find first the time when $v_x = 25 \text{ m/s}$:

$$v_x = v_{0x} + a_xt,$$
$$25 \text{ m/s} = 15 \text{ m/s} + (4.0 \text{ m/s}^2)(t),$$
$$t = 2.5 \text{ s}.$$

A FIGURE 21

Then, from Equation 12,

$$x = x_0 + v_{0x}t + \tfrac{1}{2}a_xt^2$$
$$= 5.0 \text{ m} + (15 \text{ m/s})(2.5 \text{ s}) + \tfrac{1}{2}(4.0 \text{ m/s}^2)(2.5 \text{ s})^2$$
$$= 55 \text{ m}.$$

REFLECT Do the results make sense? The cyclist accelerates from 15 m/s (about 34 mi/h) to 23 m/s (about 51 mi/h) in 2.0 s while traveling a distance of 38 m (about 125 ft). This is fairly brisk acceleration, but well within the realm of possibility for a high-performance bike.

Practice Problem: If the acceleration is 2.0 m/s^2 instead of 4.0 m/s^2, where is the cyclist, and how fast is he moving, 5.0 s after he passes the signpost if $x_0 = 5.0 \text{ m}$ and $v_{0x} = 15 \text{ m/s}$? *Answers:* 105 m, 25 m/s.

EXAMPLE 9   Pursuit!

A motorist traveling at a constant velocity of 15 m/s passes a school-crossing corner where the speed limit is 10 m/s (about 22 mi/h). A police officer on a motorcycle stopped at the corner starts off in pursuit with constant acceleration of 3.0 m/s^2 (Figure 22a). (a) How much time elapses before the officer catches up with the car? (b) What is the officer's speed at that point? (c) What is the total distance the officer has traveled at that point?

A FIGURE 22 (a) A diagram of the problem. (b) Graphs of position as a function of time for the police officer and the car.

Continued

SOLUTION

SET UP Both objects move in a straight line, which we'll designate as the x axis. Then all positions, velocities, and accelerations have only x components. We'll omit the subscripts x in our solution; but always keep in mind that when we say "velocity," we really mean "x component of velocity," and so on.

The motorcycle and the car both move with constant acceleration, so we can use the formulas we have developed. We have two different objects in motion; Figure 22a shows our choice of coordinate system. The origin of coordinates is at the corner where the policeman is stationed; both objects are at this point at time $t = 0$, so $x_0 = 0$ for both. Let x_P be the police officer's position and x_C the car's position, at any time t. At the instant when the officer catches the car, the two objects are at the same position. We need to apply the constant-acceleration equations to each, and find the time when x_P and x_C are equal. We denote the initial x components of velocities (i.e., x components) as v_{P0} and v_{C0} and the accelerations (x components) as a_P and a_C. From the data given, we have $v_{P0} = 0$, $v_{C0} = 15$ m/s, $a_P = 3.0$ m/s^2, and $a_C = 0$.

SOLVE Applying Equation 12 to each object, we find that

$$x_P = x_0 + v_{P0}t + \tfrac{1}{2}a_Pt^2 = 0 + 0 + \tfrac{1}{2}(3.0 \text{ m/s}^2)t^2$$
$$= \tfrac{1}{2}(3.0 \text{ m/s}^2)t^2,$$
$$x_C = x_0 + v_{C0}t + \tfrac{1}{2}a_Ct^2 = 0 + (15 \text{ m/s})t + 0 = (15 \text{ m/s})t.$$

Part (a): At the time the officer catches the car, they must be at the same position, so at this time, $x_C = x_P$. Equating the preceding two expressions, we have

$$\tfrac{1}{2}(3.0 \text{ m/s}^2)t^2 = (15 \text{ m/s})t,$$

or

$$t = 0, 10 \text{ s}.$$

There are *two* times when the two vehicles have the same x coordinate; the first is the time ($t = 0$) when the car passes the parked motorcycle at the corner, and the second is the time when the officer catches up.

Part (b): From Equation 8, we know that the officer's velocity v_P at any time t is given by

$$v_P = v_{P0} + a_Pt = 0 + (3.0 \text{ m/s}^2)t,$$

so when $t = 10$ s, $v_P = 30$ m/s. When the officer overtakes the car, she is traveling twice as fast as the motorist is.

Part (c): When $t = 10$ s, the car's position is

$$x_C = (15 \text{ m/s})(10 \text{ s}) = 150 \text{ m},$$

and the officer's position is

$$x_P = \tfrac{1}{2}(3.0 \text{ m/s}^2)(10 \text{ s})^2 = 150 \text{ m}.$$

This result verifies that, at the time the officer catches the car, they have gone equal distances and are at the same position.

REFLECT A graphical description of the motion is helpful. Figure 22b shows graphs of x_P and x_C as functions of time. At first x_C is greater, because the car is ahead of the officer. But the car travels with constant velocity, while the officer accelerates, closing the gap between the two. At the point where the curves cross, the officer has caught up to the car. We see again that there are two times when the two positions are the same. Note that the two vehicles don't have the same speed at either of these times.

Practice Problem: If the officer's acceleration is 5.0 m/s^2, what distance does she travel before catching up with the car? What is her velocity when she has caught up? During what time interval is she moving more slowly than the car? *Answer:* 90 m, 30 m/s, 0 to 3 s.

5 Proportional Reasoning

The relationships for straight-line motion that we've developed in this chapter offer an ideal background for introducing an analytical technique that is useful in many areas of physics. We'll call this technique **proportional reasoning.** It's particularly useful when we want to describe general relationships between variables, without reference to specific details of numerical values.

Following are some examples of the sort of problems for which proportional reasoning is useful. Some are trivial, but they illustrate the methods we'll describe.

1. Two cars start from rest and have the same acceleration, but car A accelerates over a time interval twice as great as car B. How are the distances traveled related? Does A go twice as far as B? Four times as far? Half as far?
2. You have two circles. One has a radius three times the other. Is the area of the larger circle three times as great as the area of the smaller one? Or nine times as great? Or one-third as great?
3. Water flows through a pipe with a certain radius. The pipe is joined to another pipe having a radius twice as large. The volume flow rate (i.e., the number of liters per second) in each pipe is equal to its cross-sectional area times the

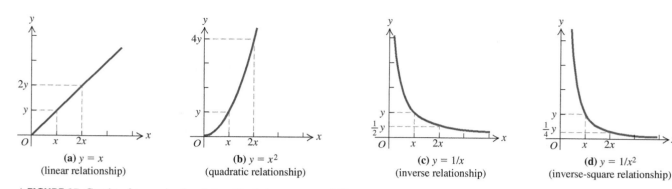

(a) $y = x$
(linear relationship)

(b) $y = x^2$
(quadratic relationship)

(c) $y = 1/x$
(inverse relationship)

(d) $y = 1/x^2$
(inverse-square relationship)

▲ **FIGURE 23** Graphs of some simple relationships between two variables.

speed of the water's motion. If the volume flow rate is the same in both pipes, does the water move twice as fast in the larger pipe? Half as fast?

In all of these situations, we have two variables, such as distance and time or the radius and area of a circle, that are related in a simple way. If we call the two variables x and y, the relationship between them often takes one of the following simple forms:

$$y = kx \ (\text{linear relation});$$
$$y = kx^2 \ (\text{quadratic relation});$$
$$y = k/x \ (\text{inverse relation});$$
$$y = k/x^2 \ (\text{inverse-square relation}).$$

In all these forms, k is a constant or a product of constants, and the numerical value of k may or may not be known. Figure 23 shows graphs of these four forms of relationship; for simplicity, we have taken the constant k equal to unity in all of them.

Let's see how the preceding relational forms can be applied to Problem 1. From our analysis in this chapter, we know that when an object starts from rest at the point $x = 0$ on the x axis and moves along the axis with constant acceleration a_x, its position x at any time t is given by the simple relation

$$x = \tfrac{1}{2}a_x t^2.$$

We call the two cars A and B; they have the same acceleration a_x. If car A accelerates for a time t_A, it travels a distance x_A given by

$$x_A = \tfrac{1}{2}a_x t_A^2,$$

and if car B accelerates for a time t_B, it travels a distance x_B given by

$$x_B = \tfrac{1}{2}a_x t_B^2.$$

We'd like to get a general relationship between the two distances and the two times that doesn't contain the common acceleration, which may or may not be known. There are two ways to do this: We can divide one of the preceding equations by the other. When we do, the factor $a_x/2$ divides out, and we obtain

$$\frac{x_A}{x_B} = \frac{\tfrac{1}{2}a_x t_A^2}{\tfrac{1}{2}a_x t_B^2} = \frac{t_A^2}{t_B^2} = \left(\frac{t_A}{t_B}\right)^2.$$

Dr. Kevin Eggan

▲ **BIO Application A long time coming.**
Proportional reasoning may not make sense for two variables with a non-linear relationship. Albert Einstein's seminal work on Brownian motion showed that the distance that molecules diffuse is related to the time of diffusion by a quadratic relation $x = kt^2$, where k incorporates information about the diffusing molecule and the medium through which the molecules are moving. Proteins and informational molecules can diffuse from the center of a typical spherical biological cell (diameter $20\ \mu m$) to the cell's periphery in about 1 s. In the case of a motor neuron, in which the cell nucleus (in red) is in the spinal cord, an extension of the cell called the axon is sent to the target muscle and may be 1 m long in humans. Proportional reasoning shows that the time required for molecules to diffuse from the nucleus to the end of the cell where they are used would be 10^{10} s or about 300 years. This is an impossibly long time, so neurons have evolved sophisticated mechanisms for moving materials around much more rapidly.

Or we can put all the variables in each equation on one side and all the constants on the other side, equate the two resulting equations, and obtain the same result:

$$\frac{x_A}{t_A^2} = \frac{1}{2}a_x \quad \text{and} \quad \frac{x_B}{t_B^2} = \frac{1}{2}a_x, \quad \text{so}$$

$$\frac{x_A}{t_A^2} = \frac{x_B}{t_B^2}, \quad \text{or} \quad \frac{x_A}{x_B} = \left(\frac{t_A}{t_B}\right)^2 \quad (\text{as before}).$$

Either of these procedures can be used to yield a relation that contains only the values of x and t.

Now let's get back to the original problem: If car A travels for twice as much time as car B, then $t_A = 2t_B$, or $t_A/t_B = 2$. This equation becomes

$$\frac{x_A}{x_B} = (2)^2 = 4,$$

and we see that $x_A = 4x_B$; Car A, with twice as much time to accelerate as car B, travels four times as far.

Now let's summarize what we've done:

1. First, we choose the quantities we want to consider as our variables (in this case, x and t) and find an equation relating them (in this case, $x = a_x t^2/2$).
2. Next, we write this equation for two different values of each of the chosen variables (t_A, x_A and t_B, x_B in our example) and then use one of the procedures described above to eliminate the constants and obtain an equation containing only the two values of each variable.
3. Finally, we specify a relation between two values of one variable (in this case, t_A and t_B) and solve for the relation between the corresponding values of the other variable (in this case, x_A and x_B). We don't need the numerical value of a_x (or k in the generic examples in Figure 23); everything is done with ratios and proportions. Note, incidentally, that this relation is *quadratic* in form, the second example in the figure.

Here's another example: The same two cars, A and B, have just finished a speed run; they cross the finish line at the same time, with different speeds v_A and v_B. They both apply their brakes as they cross the line, giving them the same (negative) acceleration, and they come to a stop at distances x_A and x_B, respectively, beyond the finish line. If car A has $1\frac{1}{2}$ times the speed of car B at the finish line, by what factor does its stopping distance exceed that of car B?

For Step 1, we choose v and x as our variables; we need to find a relation between them. No times are mentioned in the statement of the problem; this suggests that we use Equation 13. Dropping the subscript x to simplify our notation, we write this equation as

$$v^2 = v_0^2 + 2a(x - x_0).$$

We place the origin of coordinates at the finish line (the starting point for our analysis), so that $x_0 = 0$ for both cars. The final velocity is zero (i.e., $v = 0$) for both cars. Thus, the relationship we need is simply

$$v_0^2 = -2ax.$$

That is, a car that crosses the finish line with speed v_0 and brakes with constant (negative) acceleration a travels a distance x before stopping.

For Step 2, we rewrite the preceding equation, placing the variables on the left side and the constants on the right:

$$\frac{v_0^2}{x} = -2a, \quad \text{so} \quad \frac{v_{0A}^2}{x_A} = -2a \quad \text{and} \quad \frac{v_{0B}^2}{x_B} = -2a.$$

Hence $\dfrac{x_A}{x_B} = \left(\dfrac{v_{0A}}{v_{0B}}\right)^2$.

The relationship is again quadratic, but now our variables are x and v instead of x and t.

Finally, for Step 3, if car A is initially moving $1\frac{1}{2}$ times as fast as car B, it travels a distance $\left(\frac{3}{2}\right)^2 = \frac{9}{4}$ as great as car B before stopping.

Here's an alternative language for the relationships we've discovered: In our first example, in which the variables were x and t, we say that x is proportional to t^2; in the second, x is proportional to v^2. The special symbol $\propto$ is often used to represent proportionality; thus, in the above examples, we would write $x \propto t^2$ and $x \propto v^2$, read as "x is proportional to t^2" and "x is proportional to v^2."

Quantitative Analysis 4

Brakes on a wet road

When you are driving your car on wet pavement and need to stop suddenly, the maximum (negative) acceleration you can apply to the car without skidding is about one-third as much as on dry pavement. For a given initial velocity, how does your stopping distance x_w on wet pavement differ from your stopping distance x_d on dry pavement?

A. $x_w = x_d$
B. $x_w = 3x_d$
C. $x_w = 9x_d$

SOLUTION As in the previous example, the variables are related by $v_0^2 = -2ax$. This time we consider the variables to be x and a, and the initial velocity v_0 is constant. Separating constants and variables, we find that

$$xa = -\tfrac{1}{2}v_0^2, \quad \text{so} \quad x_d a_d = -\tfrac{1}{2}v_0^2, \quad x_w a_w = -\tfrac{1}{2}v_0^2,$$

$$x_d a_d = x_w a_w, \quad \frac{x_w}{x_d} = \frac{a_d}{a_w}, \quad \text{and} \quad x \propto \frac{1}{a}.$$

This result confirms our intuition that x varies *inversely* with a: If $a_w = \frac{1}{3}a_d$, then $x_w = 3x_d$, and choice B is the correct one. The relation of x to a is shown by the graph in Figure 23c.

6 Freely Falling Objects

The most familiar example of motion with (nearly) constant acceleration is that of an object falling under the influence of the earth's gravitational attraction. Such motion has held the attention of philosophers and scientists since ancient times. Aristotle thought (erroneously) that heavy objects fall faster than light objects, in proportion to their weight. Galileo argued that an object should fall with an acceleration that is constant and *independent* of its weight. We mentioned in Section 1 that, according to legend, Galileo experimented by dropping musket balls and cannon balls from the Leaning Tower of Pisa.

The motion of falling bodies has since been studied with great precision. When air resistance is absent, as in a vacuum chamber or on the moon, Galileo is right: All objects at a particular location fall with the same acceleration, regardless of their size or weight. Figure 24 shows an apple and a feather falling in a vacuum chamber; they are released at the same time and fall at the same rate. If the distance of the fall is small compared with the radius of the earth (or of the moon, planet, or other astronomical body on which the fall occurs), the acceleration is constant. In the discussion that follows, we'll use an idealized model in which we neglect air resistance, the earth's rotation, and the decrease in an object's acceleration with increasing altitude. We call this idealized motion **free fall,** although it includes rising as well as falling motion.

The constant acceleration of a freely falling object is called the **acceleration due to gravity,** or the *acceleration of free fall;* we denote its magnitude with the letter g. At or near the earth's surface, the value of g is approximately 9.80 m/s^2, 980 cm/s^2, or 32.2 ft/s^2. Because g is the magnitude of a vector quantity, it is always a *positive* number. On the surface of the moon, the acceleration due to gravity is caused by the attractive force of the moon rather than the earth, and $g = 1.62 \text{ m/s}^2$. Near the surface of the sun, $g = 274 \text{ m/s}^2$.

Mastering**PHYSICS**

PhET: Lunar Lander
ActivPhysics 1.7: Balloonist Drops Lemonade
ActivPhysics 1.10: Pole-Vaulter Lands

▲ **FIGURE 24** In vacuum, objects with different weights fall with the same acceleration and thus fall side by side.

James Sugar/Stock Photo/Black Star

In the examples that follow, we use the constant-acceleration equations developed in Section 4. We suggest that you review the problem-solving strategy discussed in that section before you study these examples.

EXAMPLE 10 Falling euro in Pisa

A 2-euro coin is dropped from the Leaning Tower of Pisa. It starts from rest and falls freely. Compute its position and velocity after 1.0, 2.0, and 3.0 s.

SOLUTION

SET UP Figure 25 shows the diagram we sketch. Because the motion is downward, we choose a vertical axis; by convention, we call it the y axis rather than the x axis. Choosing this axis means that we will replace all the x's in the constant-acceleration equations by y's. We choose the upward direction to be positive, and we place the origin at the starting point. The position, velocity, and acceleration have only y components. The initial value y_0 of the coordinate y and the initial y component of velocity v_{0y} are both zero. The acceleration is downward (in the negative y direction), so the constant y component of acceleration is $a_y = -g = -9.8 \text{ m/s}^2$. (Remember that, by definition, g itself is *always* positive.)

SOLVE From Equations 12 and 8, with x replaced by y, we get

$$y = v_0t + \tfrac{1}{2}a_yt^2 = 0 + \tfrac{1}{2}(-g)t^2 = (-4.9 \text{ m/s}^2)t^2,$$

$$v_y = v_{0y} + a_yt = 0 + (-g)t = (-9.8 \text{ m/s}^2)t.$$

Using subscripts 1, 2, and 3 for the three times, we find that when $t = t_1 = 1.0 \text{ s}$, $y_1 = (-4.9 \text{ m/s}^2)(1.0 \text{ s})^2 = -4.9 \text{ m}$ and $v_{1y} = (-9.8 \text{ m/s}^2)(1.0 \text{ s}) = -9.8 \text{ m/s}$. The coin is therefore 4.9 m below the origin (because y is negative) and has a downward velocity (v_y is negative) with magnitude 9.8 m/s.

The position and velocity at 2.0 and 3.0 s are found in the same way. The results are -19.6 m and -19.6 m/s at $t = 2.0$ s and -44.1 m and -29.4 m/s at $t = 3.0$ s.

REFLECT All of our values of y and v_y are negative because we have chosen the positive y axis to be upward. We could just as well have chosen the downward direction to be positive. In that case, the y component of acceleration would have been $a_y = g = +9.8 \text{ m/s}^2$. The crucial point is that you *must* decide

The Leaning Tower   Our sketch for the problem

▲ **FIGURE 25**

at the start which direction is positive, and then stick with your decision.

Practice Problem: The coin is released 47 m above the ground. How much time is required for the coin to fall to the ground? What is its velocity just before it strikes the ground? *Answers:* 3.1 s, -30 m/s.

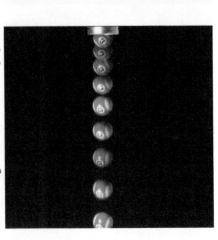

▲ **FIGURE 26** Strobe photo of a freely falling ball.

Figure 26 is a strobe photograph of a falling ball taken with a light source that produces a series of intense, brief flashes. The flashes occur at equal time intervals, so this photograph records the position of the ball at equal time intervals. Therefore, the average velocity of the ball between successive flashes is proportional to the distance between the corresponding images of the ball in the photograph. The increasing distances between images show that the ball's velocity increases continuously; in other words, the ball accelerates. Careful measurement shows that the change in velocity is the same in each time interval; thus the acceleration is constant.

EXAMPLE 11　A ball on the roof

Suppose you throw a ball vertically upward from the flat roof of a tall building. The ball leaves your hand at a point even with the roof railing, with an upward velocity of 15.0 m/s. On its way back down, it just misses the railing. Find **(a)** the position and velocity of the ball 1.00 s and 4.00 s after it leaves your hand; **(b)** the velocity of the ball when it is 5.00 m above the railing; and **(c)** the maximum height reached and the time at which it is reached. Ignore the effects of the air.

SOLUTION

SET UP As shown in Figure 27, we place the origin at the level of the roof railing, where the ball leaves your hand, and we take the positive direction to be upward. Here's what we know: The initial position y_0 is zero, the initial velocity v_{0y} (y component) is $+15.0$ m/s, and the acceleration (y component) is $a_y = -9.80$ m/s^2.

SOLVE What equations do we have to work with? The velocity v_y at any time t is

$$v_y = v_{0y} + a_y t = 15.0 \text{ m/s} + (-9.80 \text{ m/s}^2)t.$$

The position y at any time t is

$$y = v_{0y}t + \tfrac{1}{2}a_y t^2 = (15.0 \text{ m/s})t + \tfrac{1}{2}(-9.80 \text{ m/s}^2)t^2.$$

The velocity v_y at any position y is given by

$$\begin{aligned} v_y^2 &= v_{0y}^2 + 2a_y(y - y_0) \\ &= (15.0 \text{ m/s})^2 + 2(-9.80 \text{ m/s}^2)(y - 0). \end{aligned}$$

Part (a): When $t = 1.00$ s, the first two equations give $y = +10.1$ m, $v_y = +5.20$ m/s.
The ball is 10.1 m above the origin (y is positive), and it has an upward velocity (v is positive) of 5.20 m/s (less than the initial velocity of 15.0 m/s, as expected).

When $t = 4.00$ s, the same equations give

$$y = -18.4 \text{ m}, \qquad v_y = -24.2 \text{ m/s}.$$

Thus, at time $t = 4.00$ s, the ball has passed its highest point and is 18.4 m *below* the origin (y is negative). It has a *downward* velocity (v_y is negative) with magnitude 24.2 m/s (greater than the initial velocity, as we should expect). Note that, to get these results, we don't need to find the highest point the ball reaches or the time at which it was reached. The equations of motion give the position and velocity at *any* time, whether the ball is on the way up or on the way down.

Part (b): When the ball is 5.00 m above the origin, $y = +5.00$ m. Now we use our third equation to find the velocity v_y at this point:

$$v_y^2 = (15.0 \text{ m/s})^2 + 2(-9.80 \text{ m/s}^2)(5.00 \text{ m}) = 127 \text{ m}^2/\text{s}^2,$$
$$v_y = \pm 11.3 \text{ m/s}.$$

We get two values of v_y, one positive and one negative. That is, the ball passes the point $y = +5.00$ m *twice*, once on the way up and again on the way down. The velocity on the way up is $+11.3$ m/s, and on the way down it is -11.3 m/s.

▲ **FIGURE 27**

Part (c): At the highest point, the ball's velocity is momentarily zero ($v_y = 0$); it has been going up (positive v_y) and is about to start going down (negative v_y). From our third equation, we have

$$0 = (15.0 \text{ m/s})^2 - (19.6 \text{ m/s}^2)y,$$

and the maximum height (where $v_y = 0$) is $y = 11.5$ m.

We can now find the time t when the ball reaches its highest point from Equation 8, setting $v_y = 0$:

$$0 = 15.0 \text{ m/s} + (-9.80 \text{ m/s}^2)t,$$
$$t = 1.53 \text{ s}.$$

Alternative Solution: Alternatively, to find the maximum height, we may ask first *when* the maximum height is reached. That is, at what value of t is $v_y = 0$? As we just found, $v_y = 0$ when $t = 1.53$ s. Substituting this value of t back into the equation for y, we find that

$$y = (15 \text{ m/s})(1.53 \text{ s}) + \tfrac{1}{2}(-9.8 \text{ m/s}^2)(1.53 \text{ s})^2 = 11.5 \text{ m}.$$

REFLECT Although at the highest point the velocity is momentarily zero, the *acceleration* at that point is still -9.8 m/s^2. The ball stops for an instant, but its velocity is continuously changing, from positive values through zero to negative values.

Continued

The acceleration is constant throughout; it is *not* zero when $v_y = 0$!

Figure 28 shows graphs of position and velocity as functions of time for this problem. Note that the graph of v_y versus t has a constant negative slope. Thus, the acceleration is negative on the way up, at the highest point, and on the way down.

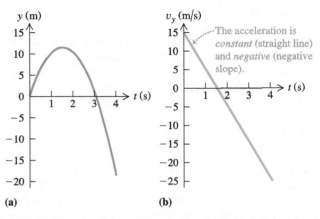

(a) (b)

▲ **FIGURE 28** (a) Position and (b) velocity as functions of time for a ball thrown upward with an initial velocity of 15 m/s.

Conceptual Analysis 5

A pop fly

In a baseball game, a batter hits a pitched ball that goes straight up in the air above home plate. At the top of its motion, the ball is momentarily motionless. At this point,

A. the acceleration is zero because the ball is motionless at that instant.
B. the acceleration is zero because the motion is changing from slowing down to speeding up.
C. the acceleration is zero because at that instant the force from the impact with the bat is balanced by the pull of the earth.
D. the acceleration is 9.8 m/s² downward.

SOLUTION A nonzero acceleration means that an object is either speeding up or slowing down. If an object has no acceleration, its speed does not change. Since a ball at the top of its motion is about to move downward, it must have acceleration, even though it is motionless at that instant. This argument rules out A, B, and C; the ball's acceleration cannot be zero. But is D correct? When velocity and acceleration are in opposite directions, the velocity is decreasing in magnitude. When they are in the same direction, the velocity is increasing in magnitude. At the top, the velocity is about to increase in the downward direction (i.e., becomes more and more negative), and its direction becomes the same as that of the acceleration. So D is correct.

Conceptual Analysis 6

Tossing two stones

Suppose you throw two identical stones from the top of a tall building. You throw one directly upward with a speed of 10 m/s and the other directly downward with the same speed. When they hit the street below, how do their speeds compare? (Neglect air friction.)

A. The one thrown upward is traveling faster.
B. The one thrown downward is traveling faster.
C. Both are traveling at the same speed.

SOLUTION The stone thrown upward decreases its speed by 9.8 m/s every second as it goes upward and increases its speed by 9.8 m/s every second as it comes back down. Thus, when it returns to the point (at the top of the building) from which it was thrown, it has exactly its original speed; but it is moving downward instead of upward. Since it now has the same downward velocity as the stone that was originally thrown downward, the two stones must have the same velocity when they hit the ground.

7 Relative Velocity along a Straight Line

We always describe the position and velocity of an object with reference to a particular coordinate system. When we speak of the velocity of a moving car, we usually mean its velocity with respect to an observer who is stationary on the earth. But when two observers measure the velocity of a moving object, they get different results if one observer is moving relative to the other. The velocity seen by a particular observer is called the velocity *relative* to that observer, or simply the **relative velocity.**

Figure 29 shows an example of the concept of relative velocity in action. In this example we'll assume that all the motions are along the same straight line, the *x* axis. A woman walks in a straight line with a velocity (*x* component) of

1.0 m/s along the aisle of a train that is moving along the same line with a velocity of 3.0 m/s. What is the woman's velocity? This seems like a simple enough question, but in reality it has no single answer. As seen by a passenger sitting in the train, she is moving at 1.0 m/s. A person on a bicycle standing beside the train sees the woman moving at 1.0 m/s + 3.0 m/s = 4.0 m/s. An observer in another train going in the opposite direction would give still another answer. The velocity is different for different observers. We have to specify which observer we mean, and we speak of the velocity *relative* to a particular observer. The woman's velocity relative to the train is 1.0 m/s, her velocity relative to the cyclist is 4.0 m/s, and so on. Each observer, equipped in principle with a meterstick and a stopwatch, forms what we call a **frame of reference.** Thus, a frame of reference is a coordinate system plus a timer.

Let's generalize this analysis. In Figure 29, we call the cyclist's frame of reference (at rest with respect to the ground) C and we call the frame of reference of the moving train T (Figure 29b). The woman's position at any time, relative to a reference point O_T in the moving train (i.e, in frame of reference T), is given by the distance $x_{W/T}$. Her position at any time, relative to a reference point O_C that is stationary on the ground (i.e, in the cyclist's frame C), is given by the distance $x_{W/C}$, and the position of the train's reference point O_T relative to the stationary one O_C is $x_{T/C}$. We choose the reference points so that at time $t = 0$ all these x's are zero. Then we can see from the figure that at any later time they are related by the equation

$$x_{W/C} = x_{W/T} + x_{T/C}. \tag{15}$$

That is, the total distance from the origin of C to the woman at point W is the sum of the distance from the origin O_C of the cyclist's frame to the origin O_T of the train's frame, plus the distance from O_T to the position of the woman.

Because Equation 15 is true at any instant, it must also be true that the *rate of change* of $x_{W/C}$ is equal to the sum of the rates of change of $x_{W/T}$ and $x_{T/C}$. But the rate of change of $x_{W/C}$ is just the velocity of W with respect to C, which we'll denote as $v_{W/C}$, and similarly for $x_{W/T}$ and $x_{T/C}$. Thus, we arrive at the velocity relation

$$v_{W/C} = v_{W/T} + v_{T/C}. \tag{16}$$

Remember that C is the cyclist's frame of reference, T is the frame of reference of the train, and point W represents the woman. Using the preceding notation, we have

$$v_{W/T} = 1.0 \text{ m/s}, \qquad v_{T/C} = 3.0 \text{ m/s}.$$

From Equation 16, the woman's velocity $v_{W/C}$ relative to the cyclist on the ground is

$$v_{W/C} = 1.0 \text{ m/s} + 3.0 \text{ m/s} = 4.0 \text{ m/s},$$

as we already knew.

In this example both velocities are toward the right, and we have implicitly taken that as the positive direction. If the woman walks toward the *left* relative to the train, then $v_{W/T} = -1.0$ m/s, and her velocity relative to the cyclist is 2.0 m/s. The sum in Equation 16 is always an *algebraic* sum, and any or all of the velocities may be negative.

When the woman looks out the window, the stationary cyclist on the ground appears to her to be moving backward; we can call the cyclist's velocity relative to the woman on the train $v_{C/W}$. Clearly, this is just the negative of $v_{W/C}$. In general, if A and B are any two points or frames of reference,

$$v_{A/B} = -v_{B/A}. \tag{17}$$

(a)

(b)

▲ **FIGURE 29** (a) A woman walks in a moving train while observed by a cyclist on the ground outside. (b) The woman's position W, at the instant shown, in two frames of reference: that of the train (T) and that of the cyclist (C).

PROBLEM-SOLVING STRATEGY 2 **Relative velocity**

Note the order of the double subscripts on the velocities in our discussion; $v_{A/B}$ always means "the velocity of A (first subscript) relative to B (second subscript)." These subscripts obey an interesting kind of algebra, as Equation 16 shows. If we regard each one as a fraction, then the fraction on the left side is the *product* of the fractions on the right sides: For a point P relative to frames A and B, $P/A = (P/B)(B/A)$. This is a handy rule to use when you apply Equation 16. If there are *three* different frames of reference, A, B, and C, we can write immediately

$$v_{P/A} = v_{P/C} + v_{C/B} + v_{B/A},$$

and so on.

EXAMPLE 12 Relative velocity on the highway

Suppose you are driving north on a straight two-lane road at a constant 88 km/h (Figure 30). A truck traveling at a constant 104 km/h approaches you (in the other lane, fortunately). **(a)** What is the truck's velocity relative to you? **(b)** What is your velocity with respect to the truck?

SOLUTION

SET UP Let you be Y, the truck be T, the earth be E, and let the positive direction be north (Figure 30). Then $v_{Y/E} = +88$ km/h.

SOLVE Part **(a):** The truck is approaching you, so it must be moving south, giving $v_{T/E} = -104$ km/h. We want to find $v_{T/Y}$. Modifying Equation 16, we have

$$v_{T/E} = v_{T/Y} + v_{Y/E},$$
$$v_{T/Y} = v_{T/E} - v_{Y/E}$$
$$= -104 \text{ km/h} - 88 \text{ km/h} = -192 \text{ km/h}.$$

The truck is moving 192 km/h south relative to you.

Part (b): From Equation 17,

$$v_{Y/T} = -v_{T/Y} = -(-192 \text{ km/h}) = +192 \text{ km/h}.$$

You are moving 192 km/h north relative to the truck.

REFLECT How do the relative velocities of Example 9 change after you and the truck have passed? They don't change at all! The relative positions of the objects don't matter. The velocity of

▲ **FIGURE 30** Velocities of you and the truck, relative to the ground.

the truck relative to you is still -192 km/h, but it is now moving away from you instead of toward you.

Theory of Relativity

When we derived the relative-velocity relations, we assumed that all the observers use the same time scale. This assumption may seem so obvious that it isn't even worth mentioning, but it is precisely the point at which Einstein's special theory of relativity departs from the physics of Galileo and Newton. When any of the speeds approach the speed of light in vacuum, denoted by c, the velocity-addition equation has to be modified. It turns out that if the woman could walk down the aisle at $0.30c$ and the train could move at $0.90c$, then her speed relative to the ground would be not $1.20c$ but $0.94c$. No material object can travel faster than c.

CHAPTER SUMMARY

Displacement and Velocity

(Sections 1 and 2) When an object moves along a straight line, we describe its position with respect to an origin O by means of a coordinate such as x. If the object starts at position x_1 at time t_1 and arrives at position x_2 at time t_2, the object's **displacement** is a vector quantity whose x component is $\Delta x = x_2 - x_1$. The displacement doesn't depend on the details of how the object travels between x_1 and x_2.

The rate of change of position with respect to time is given by the **average velocity,** a vector quantity whose x component is

$$v_{av,x} = \frac{x_2 - x_1}{t_2 - t_1} = \frac{\Delta x}{\Delta t}. \tag{3}$$

On a graph of x versus t, $v_{av,x}$ is the slope of the line connecting the starting point (x_1, t_1) and the ending point (x_2, t_2). As the average velocity is calculated for progressively smaller intervals of time Δt, the average velocity approaches the **instantaneous velocity v_x:** $v_x = \lim_{\Delta t \to 0} (\Delta x / \Delta t)$ (Equation 4).

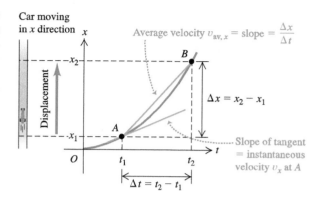

Acceleration

(Section 3) When the velocity of an object changes with time, we say that the object has an **acceleration.** Just as velocity describes the rate of change of *position* with time, acceleration is a vector quantity that describes rate of change of *velocity* with time. For an object with velocity v_{1x} at time t_1 and velocity v_{2x} at time t_2, the x component of average acceleration is

$$a_{av,x} = \frac{v_{2x} - v_{1x}}{t_2 - t_1} = \frac{\Delta v}{\Delta t}. \tag{5}$$

The average acceleration (x component) between two points can also be found on a graph of v_x versus t: $a_{av,x}$ is the slope of the line connecting the first point (v_{1x} at time t_1) and the second point (v_{2x} at time t_2). As with velocity, when the average acceleration is calculated for smaller and smaller intervals of time Δt, the average acceleration approaches the **instantaneous acceleration a_x.**

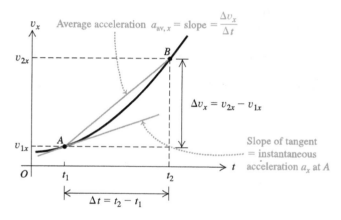

Motion with Constant Acceleration

(Section 4) When an object moves with constant acceleration in a straight line, the following two equations describe its position and velocity as functions of time: $x = x_0 + v_{0x}t + \frac{1}{2}a_x t^2$ (Equation 12), and $v_x = v_{0x} + a_x t$ (Equation 8).

In these equations, x_0 and v_{0x} are, respectively, the position and velocity at an initial time $t = 0$, and x and v_x are, respectively, the position and velocity at any later time t. The final position x is the sum of three terms: the initial position x_0, plus the distance $v_0 t$ that the body would move if its velocity were constant, plus an additional distance $\frac{1}{2}at^2$ caused by the constant acceleration.

The following equation relates velocity, acceleration, and position without explicit reference to time: $v_x^2 = v_{0x}^2 + 2a_x(x - x_0)$ (Equation 13).

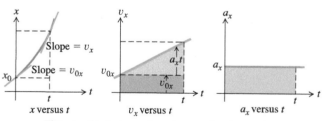

Three graphical views of constant-acceleration motion.

Continued

Proportional Reasoning

(Section 5) Many problems have two variables that are related in a simple way. One variable may be a constant times the other, or a constant times the square of the other, or a similar simple relationship. In such problems, a change in the value of one variable is related in a simple way to the corresponding change in the value of the other. This relation can be expressed as a relation between the quotient of two values of one variable and the quotient of two values of the other, even when the constant proportionality factors are not known.

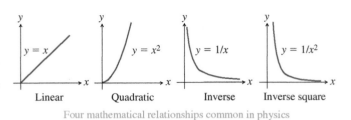

Four mathematical relationships common in physics

Freely Falling Objects

(Section 6) A freely falling object is an object that moves under the influence of a constant gravitational force. The term *free fall* includes objects that are initially at rest, as well as objects that have an initial upward or downward velocity. When the effects of air resistance are excluded, all bodies at a particular location fall with the same acceleration, regardless of their size or weight. The constant acceleration of freely falling objects is called the **acceleration due to gravity,** and we denote its magnitude with the letter g. At or near the earth's surface, the value of g is approximately 9.8 m/s^2.

The motion of an object tossed up and allowed to fall. (For clarity, we show a U-shaped path.) The object is in free fall throughout.

$a_y = -g$
$= -9.80 \text{ m/s}^2$

Relative Velocity along a Straight Line

(Section 7) When an object P moves relative to an object (or reference frame) B, and B moves relative to a second reference frame A, we denote the velocity of P relative to B by $v_{P/B}$, the velocity of P relative to A by $v_{P/A}$, and the velocity of B relative to A by $v_{B/A}$. These velocities are related by this modification of Equation 16:

$$v_{P/A} = v_{P/B} + v_{B/A}.$$

Motion Along a Straight Line: Problem Set

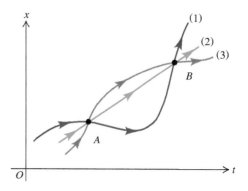

For instructor-assigned homework, go to www.masteringphysics.com

Conceptual Questions

1. Give an example or two in which the magnitude of the displacement of a moving object is (a) equal to the distance the object travels and (b) less than the distance the object travels. (c) Can the magnitude of the displacement ever be greater than the distance the object travels?

2. Does the speedometer of a car measure speed or velocity?

3. Under what conditions is average velocity equal to instantaneous velocity?

4. If an automobile is traveling north, can it have an acceleration toward the south? Under what circumstances?

5. True or false? (a) If an object's average speed is zero, its average velocity must also be zero. (b) If an object's average velocity is zero, its average speed must also be zero. Explain the reasoning behind your answers. If the statement is false, give several examples to show that it is false.

6. Is it possible for an object to be accelerating even though it has stopped moving? How? Illustrate your answer with a simple example.

7. Can an object with constant acceleration reverse its direction of travel? Can it reverse its direction *twice*? In each case, explain your reasoning.

8. Under constant acceleration the average velocity of a particle is half the sum of its initial and final velocities. Is this still true if the acceleration is *not* constant? Explain your reasoning.

9. If the graph of the velocity of an object as a function of time is a straight line, what can you find out about the acceleration of this object? Consider cases in which the slope is positive, negative, and zero.

10. If the graph of the position of an object as a function of time is a straight line, what can you find out about the velocity of this object? Consider cases in which the slope is positive, negative, and zero.

11. The following table shows an object's position x as a function of time t:

x (in m)	6.50	6.75	7.00	7.25	7.50	7.75
t (in s)	2.00	4.00	6.00	8.00	10.0	12.0

(a) Just by looking at the table, what can you conclude about this object's velocity and acceleration? (b) To see if you are correct, calculate this object's average velocity and acceleration for a few time intervals. (c) How far did the object move between $t = 2.00$ s and $t = 12.0$ s?

12. The following table shows an object's velocity v as a function of time t:

v (in cm/s)	3.40	3.80	4.20	4.60	5.00	5.40
t (in s)	5.00	8.00	11.0	14.0	17.0	20.0

(a) Just by looking at the table, what can you conclude about this object's acceleration? (b) To see if you are correct, calculate the object's average acceleration for several time intervals.

13. A dripping water faucet steadily releases drops 1.0 s apart. As these drops fall, will the distance between them increase, decrease, or stay the same? Prove your answer.

14. Figure 31 shows graphs of the positions of three different moving objects as a function of time. All three graphs pass through points A and B. (a) What can you conclude about the average velocities of these three objects between points A and B? Why? b) At point B, what characteristics of the motion do the three objects have in common? That is, are they in the same place, do they have the same velocity or speed, and do they have the same acceleration?

▲ **FIGURE 31** Question 14.

15. Figure 32 shows graphs of the velocities of three different moving objects as a function of time. All three graphs pass through points A and B. (a) What can you conclude about the average accelerations of these three objects between points A and B? Why? (b) At point A, what characteristics

From Chapter 2 of *College Physics*, Ninth Edition, Hugh D. Young. Copyright © 2012 by Pearson Education, Inc. Published by Pearson Addison-Wesley. All rights reserved.

of the motion do the three objects have in common? That is, are they in the same place, do they have the same velocity or speed, and do they have the same acceleration?

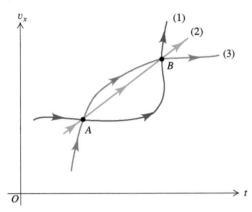

▲ **FIGURE 32** Question 15.

16. Figure 33 shows the graph of an object's position x as a function of time t. (a) Does this object ever reverse its direction of motion? If so, where? (b) Does the object ever return to its starting point? (c) Is the velocity of the object constant? (d) Is the object's speed ever zero? If so, where? (e) Does the object have any acceleration?

▲ **FIGURE 33** Question 16.

17. Figure 34 shows the graph of an object's velocity v_x as a function of time t. (a) Does this object ever reverse its direction of motion? b) Does the object ever return to its starting point? (c) Is the object's speed ever zero? If so, where? (d) Does the object have any acceleration?

▲ **FIGURE 34** Question 17.

18. A ball is dropped from rest from the top of a building of height h. At the same instant, a second ball is projected vertically upward from the ground level, such that it has zero speed when it reaches the top of the building. When the two balls pass each other, which ball has the greater speed, or do they have the same speed? Explain. Where will the two balls be when they are alongside each other: at height $h/2$ above the ground, below this height, or above this height? Explain.

Multiple-Choice Problems

1. Which of the following statements about average speed is correct? (More than one statement may be correct.)
   A. The average speed is equal to the magnitude of the average velocity.
   B. The average speed can never be greater than the magnitude of the average velocity.
   C. The average speed can never be less than the magnitude of the average velocity.

D. If the average speed is zero, then the average velocity must be zero.
   E. If the average velocity is zero, then the average speed must be zero.

2. A ball is thrown directly upwards with a velocity of $+20$ m/s. At the end of 4 s, its velocity will be closest to
   A. -50 m/s.   B. -30 m/s.   C. -20 m/s.   D. -10 m/s.

3. Two objects start at the same place at the same time and move along the same straight line. Figure 35 shows the position x as a function of time t for each object. At point A, what must be true about the motion of these objects? (More than one statement may be correct.)

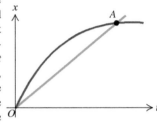

▲ **FIGURE 35** Multiple-choice problem 3.

   A. Both have the same speed.
   B. Both have the same velocity.
   C. Both are at the same position.
   D. Both have traveled the same distance.

4. Based *only* on dimensional analysis, which formulas could *not* be correct? In each case, x is position, v is velocity, a is acceleration, and t is time. (More than one choice may be correct.)
   A. $v^2 = v_0^2 + 2at$
   B. $x = v_0 + 1/2\,at^2$
   C. $a = v^2/x$
   D. $v = v_0 + 2at$

5. An object starts from rest and accelerates uniformly. If it moves 2 m during the first second, then, during the first 3 seconds, it will move
   A. 6 m.   B. 9 m.   C. 10 m.   D. 18 m.

6. If a car moving at 80 mph takes 400 ft to stop with uniform acceleration after its brakes are applied, how far will it take to stop under the same conditions if its initial velocity is 40 mph?
   A. 20 ft   B. 50 ft   C. 100 ft   D. 200 ft

7. Figure 36 shows the velocity of a jogger as a function of time. What statements must be true about the jogger's motion? (More than one statement may be correct.)
   A. The jogger's speed is increasing.
   B. The jogger's speed is decreasing.

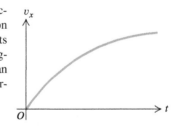

▲ **FIGURE 36** Multiple-choice problem 7.

   C. The jogger's acceleration is increasing.
   D. The jogger's acceleration is decreasing.

8. A certain airport runway of length L allows planes to accelerate uniformly from rest to takeoff speed using the full length of the runway. Because of newly designed planes, the takeoff speed must be doubled, again using the full length of the runway and having the same acceleration as before. In terms of L, what must be the length of the new runway?
   A. $4L$ B. $2L$ C. $L/2$ D. L^2

9. A ball rolls off a horizontal shelf a height h above the floor and takes 0.5 s to hit. For the ball to take 1.0 s to reach the floor, the shelf's height above the floor would have to be
   A. $2h$ B. $3h$ C. $\sqrt{2}h$ D. $4h$

10. A frog leaps vertically into the air and encounters no appreciable air resistance. Which statement about the frog's motion is correct?
    A. On the way up its acceleration is 9.8 m/s² upward, and on the way down its acceleration is 9.8 m/s² downward.
    B. On the way up and on the way down its acceleration is 9.8 m/s² downward, and at the highest point its acceleration is zero.
    C. On the way up, on the way down, and at the highest point its acceleration is 9.8 m/s² downward.
    D. At the highest point, it reverses the direction of its acceleration.

11. You slam on the brakes of your car in a panic and skid a distance X on a straight, level road. If you had been traveling half as fast under the same road conditions, you would have skidded a distance
    A. $\frac{X}{4}$.   B. $\frac{X}{2}$.   C. X.   D. $\frac{X}{\sqrt{2}}$.

12. A cat runs in a straight line. Figure 37 shows a graph of the cat's position as a function of time. Which of the following statements about the cat's motion must be true? (There may be more than one correct choice.)

    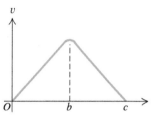

    ▲ FIGURE 37 Multiple-choice problem 12.

    A. At point c, the cat has returned to the place where it started.
    B. The cat's speed is zero at points a and c.
    C. The cat's velocity is zero at point b.
    D. The cat reverses the direction of its velocity at point b.

13. A wildebeest is running in a straight line, which we shall call the x axis, with the positive direction to the right. Figure 38 shows this animal's velocity as a function of time. Which of the following statements about the animal's motion must be true? (There may be more than one correct choice.)

    A. Its acceleration is increasing.
    B. Its speed is decreasing from a to b and increasing from b to c.
    C. It is moving to the right between a and c.
    D. It is moving to the left between a and b and to the right between b and c.

    ▲ FIGURE 38 Multiple-choice problem 13.

14. A brick falling freely from a helicopter drops 40 meters during a certain 1-second time interval. The distance it will fall in the *next* second is
    A. 45 m   B. 50 m   C. 56 m   D. 80 m

15. A bullet is dropped into a river from a very high bridge. At the same time, another bullet is fired from a gun straight down towards the water. If air resistance is negligible, the acceleration of the bullets just before they strike the water
    A. is greater for the dropped bullet.
    B. is greater for the fired bullet.
    C. is the same for both bullets.
    D. depends on how high they started.

Problems

1 Displacement and Average Velocity

1. • An ant is crawling along a straight wire, which we shall call the x axis, from A to B to C to D (which overlaps A), as shown in Figure 39. O is the origin. Suppose you take measurements and find that AB is 50 cm, BC is 30 cm, and AO is 5 cm. (a) What is the ant's position at points A, B, C, and D? (b) Find the displacement of the ant and the distance it has moved over each of the following intervals: (i) from A to B, (ii) from B to C, (iii) from C to D, and (iv) from A to D.

▲ FIGURE 39 Problem 1.

2. •• A person is walking briskly in a straight line, which we shall call the x axis. Figure 40 shows a graph of the person's position x along this axis as a function of time t. (a) What is the person's displacement during each of the following time intervals: (i) between t = 1.0 s and t = 10.0 s, (ii) between t = 3.0 s and t = 10.0 s, (iii) between t = 2.0 s and t = 3.0 s, and (iv) between t = 2.0 s and t = 4.0 s? (b) What distance did the person move from (i) t = 0 s to t = 4.0 s, (ii) t = 2.0 s to t = 4.0 s, and (iii) t = 8.0 s to t = 10.0 s?

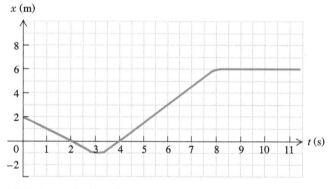

▲ FIGURE 40 Problem 2.

3. • A dog runs from points A to B to C in 3.0 s. (See Figure 41.) Find the dog's average velocity and average speed over this 3-second interval.

▲ FIGURE 41 Problem 3.

4. • In an experiment, a shearwater (a seabird) was taken from its
   BIO nest, flown 5150 km away, and released. The bird found its way back to its nest 13.5 days after release. If we place the origin in the nest and extend the +x-axis to the release point, what was the bird's average velocity in m/s (a) for the return flight, and (b) for the whole episode, from leaving the nest to returning?

5. ●● Figure 42 shows the position of a moving object as a function of time. (a) Find the average velocity of this object from points A to B, B to C, and A to C. (b) For the intervals in part (a), would the average speed be less than, equal to, or greater than the values you found in that part? Explain your reasoning.

▲ **FIGURE 42** Problem 5.

6. ●● An object moves along the x axis. Figure 43 shows a graph of its position x as a function of time. (a) Find the average velocity of the object from points A to B, B to C, and A to C. (b) For the intervals in part (a), would the average speed be less than, equal to, or greater than the values you found in that part? Explain your reasoning.

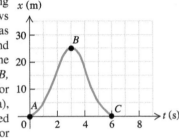

▲ **FIGURE 43** Problem 6.

7. ●● A boulder starting from rest rolls down a hill in a straight line, which we shall call the x axis. A graph of its position x as a function of time t is shown in Figure 44. Find (a) the distance the boulder rolled between the end of the first second and the end of the third second and (b) the boulder's average speed during (i) the first second, (ii) the second second, (iii) the third second, (iv) the fourth second, and (v) the first 4 seconds.

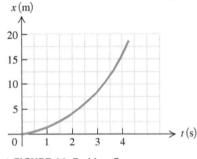

▲ **FIGURE 44** Problem 7.

8. ●● Each graph in Figure 45 shows the position of a running cat, called Mousie, as a function of time. In each case, sketch a clear *qualitative* (no numbers) graph of Mousie's velocity as a function of time.

▲ **FIGURE 45** Problem 8.

9. ● In 1954, Roger Bannister became the first human to run a mile in less than 4 minutes. Suppose that a runner on a straight track covers a distance of 1.00 mi in exactly 4.00 min. What is his average speed in (a) mi/h, (b) ft/s, and (c) m/s?

10. ● **Hypersonic scramjet.** On March 27, 2004, the United States successfully tested the hypersonic X-43A scramjet, which flew at Mach 7 (seven times the speed of sound) for 11 seconds. (A scramjet gets its oxygen directly from the air, rather than from fuel.) (a) At this rate, how many minutes would it take such a scramjet to carry passengers the approximately 5000 km from San Francisco to New York? (Use 331 m/s for the speed of sound in air.) (b) How many kilometers did the scramjet travel during its 11 second test?

11. ● **Plate tectonics.** The earth's crust is broken up into a series of more-or-less rigid plates that slide around due to motion of material in the mantle below. Although the speeds of these plates vary somewhat, they are typically about 5 cm/yr. Assume that this rate remains constant over time. (a) If you and your neighbor live on opposite sides of a plate boundary at which one plate is moving northward at 5.0 cm/yr with respect to the other plate, how far apart do your houses move in a century? (b) Los Angeles is presently 550 km south of San Francisco, but is on a plate moving northward relative to San Francisco. If the 5.0 cm/yr velocity continues, how many years will it take before Los Angeles has moved up to San Francisco?

12. ● A runner covers one lap of a circular track 40.0 m in diameter in 62.5 s. (a) For that lap, what were her average speed and average velocity? (b) If she covered the first half-lap in 28.7 s, what were her average speed and average velocity for that half-lap?

13. ● Sound travels at a speed of about 344 m/s in air. You see a distant flash of lightning and hear the thunder arrive 7.5 seconds later. How many miles away was the lightning strike? (Assume the light takes essentially no time to reach you.)

14. ● **Ouch!** Nerve impulses travel at different speeds, depending
BIO on the type of fiber through which they move. The impulses for touch travel at 76.2 m/s, while those registering pain move at 0.610 m/s. If a person stubs his toe, find (a) the time for each type of impulse to reach his brain, and (b) the time *delay* between the pain and touch impulses. Assume that his brain is 1.85 m from his toe and that the impulses travel directly from toe to brain.

15. ●● While driving on the freeway at 110 km/h, you pass a truck whose total length you estimate at 25 m. (a) If it takes you, in the driver's seat, 5.5 s to pass from the rear of the truck to its front, what is the truck's speed relative to the road? (b) How far does the truck travel while you're passing it?

16. ●● A mouse travels along a straight line; its distance x from the origin at any time t is given by the equation $x = (8.5 \text{ cm} \cdot \text{s}^{-1})t - (2.5 \text{ cm} \cdot \text{s}^{-2})t^2$. Find the average velocity of the mouse in the interval from $t = 0$ to $t = 1.0$ s and in the interval from $t = 0$ to $t = 4.0$ s.

17. ●● **The freeway blues!** When you normally drive the freeway between Sacramento and San Francisco at an average speed of 105 km/hr (65 mph), the trip takes 1.0 hr and 20 min. On a Friday afternoon, however, heavy traffic slows you down to an average of 70 km/hr (43 mph) for the same distance. How much longer does the trip take on Friday than on the other days?

18. ●● Two runners start simultaneously at opposite ends of a 200.0 m track and run toward each other. Runner A runs at a steady 8.0 m/s and runner B runs at a constant 7.0 m/s. When and where will these runners meet?

2 Instantaneous Velocity

19. •• A physics professor leaves her house and walks along the sidewalk toward campus. After 5 min, she realizes that it is raining and returns home. The distance from her house as a function of time is shown in Figure 46. At which of the labeled points is her velocity (a) zero? (b) constant and positive? (c) constant and negative? (d) increasing in magnitude? and (e) decreasing in magnitude?

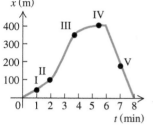
▲ **FIGURE 46** Problem 19.

20. •• A test car travels in a straight line along the x axis. The graph in Figure 47 shows the car's position x as a function of time. Find its instantaneous velocity at points A through G.

▲ **FIGURE 47** Problem 20.

21. •• Figure 48 shows the position x of a crawling spider as a function of time. Use this graph to draw a *numerical* graph of the spider's velocity as a function of time over the same time interval.

▲ **FIGURE 48** Problem 21.

3 Average and Instantaneous Acceleration

22. •• The graph in Figure 49 shows the velocity of a motorcycle police officer plotted as a function of time. Find the instantaneous acceleration at times $t = 3$ s, at $t = 7$ s, and at $t = 11$ s.

23. •• A test driver at Incredible Motors, Inc., is testing a new model car having a speedometer calibrated to read m/s rather than mi/h. The following series of speedometer readings was obtained during a test run:

▲ **FIGURE 49** Problem 22.

Time (s)	0	2	4	6	8	10	12	14	16
Velocity (m/s)	0	0	2	5	10	15	20	22	22

(a) Compute the average acceleration during each 2 s interval. Is the acceleration constant? Is it constant during any part of

the test run? (b) Make a velocity–time graph of the data shown, using scales of 1 cm = 1 s horizontally and 1 cm = 2 m/s vertically. Draw a smooth curve through the plotted points. By measuring the slope of your curve, find the magnitude of the instantaneous acceleration at times $t = 9$ s, 13 s, and 15 s.

24. • (a) The pilot of a jet fighter will black out at an acceleration greater than approximately $5g$ if it lasts for more than a few seconds. Express this acceleration in m/s^2 and ft/s^2. (b) The acceleration of the passenger during a car crash with an air bag is about $60g$ for a very short time. What is this acceleration in m/s^2 and ft/s^2? (c) The acceleration of a falling body on our moon is 1.67 m/s^2. How many g's is this? (d) If the acceleration of a test plane is 24.3 m/s^2, how many g's is it?

25. •• For each graph of velocity as a function of time in Figure 50, sketch a qualitative graph of the acceleration as a function of time.

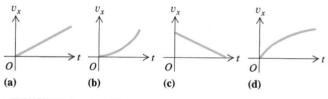
▲ **FIGURE 50** Problem 25.

26. •• A little cat, Bella, walks along a straight line, which we shall call the x axis, with the positive direction to the right. As an observant scientist, you make measurements of her motion and construct a graph of the little feline's velocity as a function of time. (See Figure 51.) (a) Find Bella's velocity at $t = 4.0$ s and at $t = 7.0$ s. (b) What is her acceleration at $t = 3.0$ s? at $t = 6.0$ s? at $t = 7.0$ s? (c) Sketch a clear graph of Bella's acceleration as a function of time.

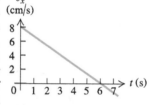
▲ **FIGURE 51** Problem 26.

4 Motion with Constant Acceleration

27. • A car driving on the turnpike accelerates uniformly in a straight line from 88 ft/s (60 mph) to 110 ft/s (75 mph) in 3.50 s. (a) What is the car's acceleration? (b) How far does the car travel while it accelerates?

28. • **Animal motion.** Cheetahs, the fastest of the great cats, can **BIO** reach 45 mph in 2.0 s starting from rest. Assuming that they have constant acceleration throughout that time, find (a) their acceleration (in ft/s^2 and m/s^2) and (b) the distance (in m and ft) they travel during that time.

29. •• A cat drops from a shelf 4.0 ft above the floor and lands on **BIO** all four feet. His legs bring him to a stop in a distance of 12 cm. Calculate (a) his speed when he first touches the floor (ignore air resistance), (b) how long it takes him to stop, and (c) his acceleration (assumed constant) while he is stopping, in m/s^2 and g's.

30. •• **Blackout?** A jet fighter pilot wishes to accelerate from rest
BIO at 5g to reach Mach 3 (three times the speed of sound) as quickly as possible. Experimental tests reveal that he will black out if this acceleration lasts for more than 5.0 s. Use 331 m/s for the speed of sound. (a) Will the period of acceleration last long enough to cause him to black out? (b) What is the greatest speed he can reach with an acceleration of 5g before blacking out?

31. •• **A fast pitch.** The fastest measured pitched baseball left
BIO the pitcher's hand at a speed of 45.0 m/s. If the pitcher was in contact with the ball over a distance of 1.50 m and produced constant acceleration, (a) what acceleration did he give the ball, and (b) how much time did it take him to pitch it?

32. • If a pilot accelerates at more than 4g, he begins to "gray
BIO out," but not completely lose consciousness. (a) What is the shortest time that a jet pilot starting from rest can take to reach Mach 4 (four times the speed of sound) without graying out? (b) How far would the plane travel during this period of acceleration? (Use 331 m/s for the speed of sound in cold air.)

33. • **Air-bag injuries.** During an auto accident, the vehicle's air
BIO bags deploy and slow down the passengers more gently than if they had hit the windshield or steering wheel. According to safety standards, the bags produce a maximum acceleration of 60 g, but lasting for only 36 ms (or less). How far (in meters) does a person travel in coming to a complete stop in 36 ms at a constant acceleration of 60 g?

34. •• Starting from rest, a boulder rolls down a hill with constant acceleration and travels 2.00 m during the first second. (a) How far does it travel during the second second? (b) How fast is it moving at the end of the first second? at the end of the second second?

35. • **Faster than a speeding bullet!** The Beretta Model 92S (the standard-issue U.S. army pistol) has a barrel 127 mm long. The bullets leave this barrel with a muzzle velocity of 335 m/s. (a) What is the acceleration of the bullet while it is in the barrel, assuming it to be constant? Express your answer in m/s^2 and in g's. (b) For how long is the bullet in the barrel?

36. •• An airplane travels 280 m down the runway before taking off. Assuming that it has constant acceleration, if it starts from rest and becomes airborne in 8.00 s, how fast (in m/s) is it moving at takeoff?

37. **Entering the freeway.** A car sits in an entrance ramp to a freeway, waiting for a break in the traffic. The driver accelerates with constant acceleration along the ramp and onto the freeway. The car starts from rest, moves in a straight line, and has a speed of 20 m/s (45 mi/h) when it reaches the end of the 120-m-long ramp. (a) What is the acceleration of the car? (b) How much time does it take the car to travel the length of the ramp? (c) The traffic on the freeway is moving at a constant speed of 20 m/s. What distance does the traffic travel while the car is moving the length of the ramp?

38. •• The "reaction time" of the average automobile driver is about 0.7 s. (The reaction time is the interval between the perception of a signal to stop and the application of the brakes.) If an automobile can slow down with an acceleration of 12.0 ft/s^2, compute the total distance covered in coming to a stop after a signal is observed (a) from an initial velocity of 15.0 mi/h (in a school zone) and (b) from an initial velocity of 55.0 mi/h.

39. •• According to recent typical test data, a Ford Focus travels 0.250 mi in 19.9 s, starting from rest. The same car, when braking from 60.0 mph on dry pavement, stops in 146 ft. Assume constant acceleration in each part of its motion, but not necessarily the same acceleration when slowing down as when speeding up. (a) Find this car's acceleration while braking and while speeding up. (b) If its acceleration is constant while speeding up, how fast (in mph) will the car be traveling after 0.250 mi of acceleration? (c) How long does it take the car to stop while braking from 60.0 mph?

40. •• A subway train starts from rest at a station and accelerates at a rate of 1.60 m/s^2 for 14.0 s. It runs at constant speed for 70.0 s and slows down at a rate of 3.50 m/s^2 until it stops at the next station. Find the *total* distance covered.

5 Proportional Reasoning

41. •• If the radius of a circle of area A and circumference C is doubled, find the new area and circumference of the circle in terms of A and C.

42. •• In the redesign of a machine, a metal cubical part has each of its dimensions tripled. By what factor do its surface area and volume change?

43. • You have two cylindrical tanks. The tank with the greater volume is 1.20 times the height of the smaller tank. It takes 218 gallons of water to fill the larger tank and 150 gallons to fill the other. What is the ratio of the radius of the larger tank to the radius of the smaller one?

44. • A speedy basketball point guard is 5 ft 10 inches tall; the
BIO center on the same team is 7 ft 2 inches tall. Assuming their bodies are similarly proportioned, if the point guard weighs 175 lb, what would you expect the center to weigh?

45. •• Two rockets having the same acceleration start from rest, but rocket A travels for twice as much time as rocket B. (a) If rocket A goes a distance of 250 km, how far will rocket B go? (b) If rocket A reaches a speed of 350 m/s, what speed will rocket B reach?

46. •• Two cars having equal speeds hit their brakes at the same time, but car A has three times the acceleration as car B. (a) If car A travels a distance D before stopping, how far (in terms of D) will car B go before stopping? (b) If car B stops in time T, how long (in terms of T) will it take for car A to stop?

47. •• Airplane A, starting from rest with constant acceleration, requires a runway 500 m long to become airborne. Airplane B requires a takeoff speed twice as great as that of airplane A, but has the same acceleration, and both planes start from rest. (a) How long must the runway be for airplane B? (b) If airplane A takes time T to travel the length of its runway, how long (in terms of T) will airplane B take to travel the length of its runway?

6 Freely Falling Bodies

48. • (a) If a flea can jump straight up to a height of 22.0 cm, what is its initial speed (in m/s) as it leaves the ground, neglecting air resistance? (b) How long is it in the air? (c) What are the magnitude and direction of its acceleration while it is (i) moving upward? (ii) moving downward? (iii) at the highest point?

49. • A brick is released with no initial speed from the roof of a building and strikes the ground in 2.50 s, encountering no appreciable air drag. (a) How tall, in meters, is the building?

(b) How fast is the brick moving just before it reaches the ground? (c) Sketch graphs of this falling brick's acceleration, velocity, and vertical position as functions of time.

50. • **Loss of power!** In December of 1989, a KLM Boeing 747 airplane carrying 231 passengers entered a cloud of ejecta from an Alaskan volcanic eruption. All four engines went out, and the plane fell from 27,900 ft to 13,300 ft before the engines could be restarted. It then landed safely in Anchorage. Neglecting any air resistance and aerodynamic lift, and assuming that the plane had no vertical motion when it lost power, (a) for how long did it fall before the engines were restarted, and (b) how fast was it falling at that instant? c) In reality, why would the plane not be falling nearly as fast?

51. •• A tennis ball on Mars, where the acceleration due to gravity is 0.379g and air resistance is negligible, is hit directly upward and returns to the same level 8.5 s later. (a) How high above its original point did the ball go? (b) How fast was it moving just after being hit? (c) Sketch clear graphs of the ball's vertical position, vertical velocity, and vertical acceleration as functions of time while it's in the Martian air.

52. • **Measuring g.** One way to measure g on another planet or moon by remote sensing is to measure how long it takes an object to fall a given distance. A lander vehicle on a distant planet records the fact that it takes 3.17 s for a ball to fall freely 11.26 m, starting from rest. (a) What is the acceleration due to gravity on that planet? Express your answer in m/s^2 and in earth g's. b) How fast is the ball moving just as it lands?

53. •• **That's a lot of hot air!** A hot-air balloonist, rising vertically with a constant speed of 5.00 m/s, releases a sandbag at the instant the balloon is 40.0 m above the ground. (See Figure 52.) After it is released, the sandbag encounters no appreciable air drag. (a) Compute the position and velocity of the sandbag at 0.250 s and 1.00 s after its release. (b) How many seconds after its release will the bag strike the ground? (c) How fast is it moving as it strikes the ground? (d) What is the greatest height above the ground that the sandbag reaches? (e) Sketch graphs of this bag's acceleration, velocity, and vertical position as functions of time.

$v = 5.00$ m/s

40.0 m to ground

▲ **FIGURE 52**
Problem 53.

54. **Look out below.** Sam heaves a 16-lb shot straight upward, giving it a constant upward acceleration from rest of 45.0 m/s^2 for 64.0 cm. He releases it 2.20 m above the ground. You may ignore air resistance. (a) What is the speed of the shot when Sam releases it? (b) How high above the ground does it go? (c) How much time does he have to get out of its way before it returns to the height of the top of his head, 1.83 m above the ground?

55. •• **Astronauts on the moon.** Astronauts on our moon must function with an acceleration due to gravity of 0.170g. (a) If an astronaut can throw a certain wrench 12.0 m vertically upward on earth, how high could he throw it on our moon if he gives it the same starting speed in both places? (b) How much *longer* would it be in motion (going up and coming down) on the moon than on earth?

56. • A student throws a water balloon vertically downward from the top of a building. The balloon leaves the thrower's hand with a speed of 15.0 m/s. (a) What is its speed after falling freely for 2.00 s? (b) How far does it fall in 2.00 s? (c) What is the magnitude of its velocity after falling 10.0 m?

57. • A rock is thrown vertically upward with a speed of 12.0 m/s from the roof of a building that is 60.0 m above the ground. (a) In how many seconds after being thrown does the rock strike the ground? (b) What is the speed of the rock just before it strikes the ground? Assume free fall.

58. •• **Physiological effects of large acceleration.** The rocket-driven sled *Sonic Wind No. 2,* used for investigating the physiological effects of large accelerations, runs on a straight, level track that is 1080 m long. Starting from rest, it can reach a speed of 1610 km/h in 1.80 s. (a) Compute the acceleration in m/s^2 and in g's. (b) What is the distance covered in 1.80 s? (c) A magazine article states that, at the end of a certain run, the speed of the sled decreased from 1020 km/h to zero in 1.40 s and that, during this time, its passenger was subjected to more than 40g. Are these figures consistent?

BIO

59. •• Two stones are thrown vertically upward from the ground, one with three times the initial speed of the other. (a) If the faster stone takes 10 s to return to the ground, how long will it take the slower stone to return? (b) If the slower stone reaches a maximum height of *H,* how high (in terms of *H*) will the faster stone go? Assume free fall.

60. •• Two coconuts fall freely from rest at the same time, one from a tree twice as high as the other. (a) If the coconut from the taller tree reaches the ground with a speed *V,* what will be the speed (in terms of *V*) of the coconut from the other tree when it reaches the ground? (b) If the coconut from the shorter tree takes time *T* to reach the ground, how long (in terms of *T*) will it take the other coconut to reach the ground?

*7 Relative Velocity along a Straight Line

61. • A Toyota Prius driving north at 65 mph and a VW Passat driving south at 42 mph are on the same road heading toward each other (but in different lanes). What is the velocity of each car relative to the other (a) when they are 250 ft apart, just before they meet, and (b) when they are 525 ft apart, after they have passed each other?

62. • The wind is blowing from west to east at 35 mph, and an eagle in that wind is flying at 22 mph relative to the air. What is the velocity of this eagle relative to a person standing on the ground if the eagle is flying (a) from west to east relative to the air and (b) from east to west relative to the air?

63. •• A helicopter 8.50 m above the ground and descending at 3.50 m/s drops a package from rest (relative to the helicopter). Just as it hits the ground, find (a) the velocity of the package relative to the helicopter and (b) the velocity of the helicopter relative to the package. The package falls freely.

64. •• A jetliner has a cruising air speed of 600 mph relative to the air. How long does it take this plane to fly round-trip from San Francisco to Chicago, an east–west flight of 2,000 mi each way, (a) if there is no wind blowing and (b) if the wind is blowing at 150 mph from the west to the east?

General Problems

65. • **Life from space?** One rather controversial suggestion for
BIO the origin of life on the earth is that the seeds of life arrived
here from outer space in tiny spores—a theory called *pan-spermia*. Of course, any life in such spores would have
to survive a long journey through the frigid near vacuum
of outer space. If these spores originated at the distance of
our nearest star, Alpha Centauri, and traveled at a constant
1000 km/s, how many years would it take for them to make
the journey here? (Alpha Centauri is approximately $4\frac{1}{4}$ light
years away, and the light year is the distance light travels in
1 year.)

66. •• At the instant the traffic light turns green, an automobile
that has been waiting at an intersection starts ahead with a constant acceleration of 2.50 m/s^2. At the same instant, a truck,
traveling with a constant speed of 15.0 m/s, overtakes and
passes the automobile. (a) How far beyond its starting point
does the automobile overtake the truck? (b) How fast is the
automobile traveling when it overtakes the truck?

67. •• On a 20-mile bike ride, you ride the first 10 miles at an
average speed of 8 mi/h. What must your average speed over
the next 10 miles be to have your average speed for the total
20 miles be (a) 4 mi/h? (b) 12 mi/h? (c) Given this average
speed for the first 10 miles, can you possibly attain an average
speed of 16 mi/h for the total 20-mile ride? Explain.

68. • You and a friend start out at the same time on a 10-km run.
Your friend runs at a steady 2.5 m/s. How fast do you have to
run if you want to finish the run 15 minutes before your
friend?

69. •• Two rocks are thrown directly upward with the same initial
speeds, one on earth and one on our moon, where the acceleration due to gravity is one-sixth what it is on earth. (a) If the
rock on the moon rises to a height *H*, how high, in terms of *H*,
will the rock rise on the earth? (b) If the earth rock takes 4.0 s
to reach its highest point, how long will it take the moon rock
to do so?

70. • **Prevention of hip fractures.** Falls resulting in hip fractures
BIO are a major cause of injury and even death to the elderly. Typically, the hip's speed at impact is about 2.0 m/s. If this can be
reduced to 1.3 m/s or less, the hip will usually not fracture.
One way to do this is by wearing elastic hip pads. (a) If a typical pad is 5.0 cm thick and compresses by 2.0 cm during the
impact of a fall, what acceleration (in m/s^2 and in *g*'s) does the
hip undergo to reduce its speed to 1.3 m/s? (b) The acceleration you found in part (a) may seem like a rather large acceleration, but to fully assess its effects on the hip, calculate how
long it lasts.

71. • **Are we Martians?** It has been suggested, and not face-
BIO tiously, that life might have originated on Mars and been carried to Earth when a meteor hit Mars and blasted pieces of
rock (perhaps containing primitive life) free of the surface.
Astronomers know that many Martian rocks have come to
Earth this way. (For information on one of these, search the
Internet for "ALH 84001".) One objection to this idea is that
microbes would have to undergo an enormous, lethal acceleration during the impact. Let us investigate how large such an
acceleration might be. To escape Mars, rock fragments would
have to reach its escape velocity of 5.0 km/s, and this would
most likely happen over a distance of about 4.0 m during the
impact. (a) What would be the acceleration, in m/s^2 and *g*'s,
of such a rock fragment? (b) How long would this acceleration
last? (c) In tests, scientists have found that over 40% of *Bacillus
subtilis* bacteria survived after an acceleration of 450,000*g*. In
light of your answer to part (a), can we rule out the hypothesis
that life might have been blasted from Mars to Earth?

72. •• **Raindrops.** If the effects of the air acting on falling raindrops are ignored, then we can treat raindrops as freely falling
objects. (a) Rain clouds are typically a few hundred meters
above the ground. Estimate the speed with which raindrops
would strike the ground if they were freely falling objects.
Give your estimate in m/s, km/h, and mi/h. (b) Estimate (from
your own personal observations of rain) the speed with which
raindrops actually strike the ground. (c) Based on your
answers to parts (a) and (b), is it a good approximation to neglect the effects of the air on falling raindrops? Explain.

73. •• **Egg drop.** You are on the
roof of the physics building
of your school, 46.0 m above
the ground. (See Figure 53.)
Your physics professor, who
is 1.80 m tall, is walking
alongside the building at a
constant speed of 1.20 m/s.
If you wish to drop an egg on
your professor's head, where
should the professor be when
you release the egg, assuming that the egg encounters
no appreciable air drag.

▲ **FIGURE 53** Problem 73.

74. •• A 0.525 kg ball starts
from rest and rolls down a hill with uniform acceleration, traveling 150 m during the second 10.0 s of its motion. How far did
it roll during the first 5.0 s of motion?

75. •• A large boulder is ejected vertically upward from a volcano with an initial speed of 40.0 m/s. Air resistance may be
ignored. (a) At what time after being ejected is the boulder
moving at 20.0 m/s upward? (b) At what time is it moving at
20.0 m/s downward? (c) When is the displacement of the boulder from its initial position zero? (d) When is the velocity of
the boulder zero? (e) What are the magnitude and direction
of the acceleration while the boulder is (i) moving upward?
(ii) Moving downward? (iii) At the highest point? (f) Sketch
a_y-*t*, v_y-*t*, and *y*-*t* graphs for the motion.

76. •• **Freeway ramps.** In designing a freeway on-ramp, you
must make it long enough for cars to be able to accelerate and
merge safely with traffic traveling at speeds of 70 mph. For an
off-ramp, the cars must be able to come to a stop from 70 mph
over the length of the ramp. Your traffic engineers provide the
following data: Powerful cars can accelerate from rest to
60 mph in 5.0 s, while less powerful cars take twice as long to
do this. When slowing down from 60 mph, a car with good
tire treads will take 12.0 s to stop, whereas one with bald tires
takes 20.0 s. In order to safely accommodate all the types of
vehicles, what should be the minimum length (in meters) of
on-ramps and off-ramps? Assume constant acceleration.

77. • A healthy heart pumping at a rate of 72 beats per minute
BIO increases the speed of blood flow from 0 to 425 cm/s with each
beat. Calculate the acceleration of the blood during this process.

78. •• You decide to take high-speed strobe light photos of your
little dog Holly as she runs along. Figure 54 shows some of

these photos. The strobe flashes at a uniform rate, which means that the time interval between adjacent images is the same in all the photos. For each case, sketch clear *qualitative* (no numbers) graphs of Holly's position as a function of time and her velocity as a function of time.

(a)

(b)

(c)

(d)

▲ **FIGURE 54** Problem 78.

79. •• A rocket blasts off vertically from rest on the launch pad with a constant upward acceleration of 2.50 m/s². At 20.0 s after blastoff, the engines suddenly fail, and the rocket begins free fall. (a) How high above the launch pad will the rocket eventually go? (b) Find the rocket's velocity and acceleration at its highest point. (c) How long after it was launched will the rocket fall back to the launch pad, and how fast will it be moving when it does so?

80. •• **Mouse at play, I.** A little mouse runs in a straight line, which we shall call the *x* axis. As an eager scientist, you record its position as a function of time and use the information you obtain to construct the graph plotted in Figure 55, which shows the mouse's position *x* as a function of time *t*. You have adopted the usual sign convention according to which quantities to the right are positive and those to the left are negative. Use the information on the graph to answer the following questions: (a) When is the mouse to the right of the origin? to the left of the origin? at the origin? (b) What are the magnitude and direction of the mouse's initial velocity? (c) Does the mouse move with constant acceleration throughout the 10 seconds? (d) What is the mouse's maximum speed? In which direction is it moving with that speed? (e) When is the mouse moving to the right? moving to the left? not moving? (f) Through what total distance has the mouse moved during the first 3 s? during the first 10 s? (g) When is the mouse speeding up? slowing down? (h) Do the kinematics formulas $v_x = v_{0x} + a_x t$ and $x = x_0 + v_{0x} t + \frac{1}{2} a_x t^2$ apply to this mouse's motion throughout the 10 s? Why or why not?

▲ **FIGURE 55** Problem 80.

81. •• **Earthquake waves.** Earthquakes produce several types of shock waves. The best known are the P-waves (P for *primary* or *pressure*) and the S-waves (S for *secondary* or *shear*). In the earth's crust, P-waves travel at around 6.5 km/s while S-waves move at about 3.5 km/s. (The actual speeds vary with the type of material the waves are going through.) The time delay between the arrival of these two types of waves at a seismic recording station tells geologists how far away the earthquake that produced the waves occurred. (a) If the time delay at a seismic station is 33 s, how far from that station did the earthquake occur? (b) One form of earthquake warning system detects the faster (but less damaging) P-waves and sounds an alarm when they first arrive, giving people a short time to seek cover before the more dangerous S-waves arrive. If an earthquake occurs 375 km away from such a warning device, how much time would people have to take cover between the alarm and the arrival of the S-waves?

82. • An elite human sprinter reaches his top speed of 11.8 m/s at **BIO** a time of 7.02 s after the starting gun. In the first 1.40 s, however, he reaches a speed of 8.00 m/s, with a nearly constant acceleration. Calculate (a) his maximum acceleration during the starting phase and (b) his average acceleration to top speed. (c) Assuming constant acceleration for the first 1.40 s, how far does he travel during that time?

83. •• **How high is the cliff?** Suppose you are climbing in the High Sierra when you suddenly find yourself at the edge of a fog-shrouded cliff. To find the height of this cliff, you drop a rock from the top and, 10.0 s later, hear the sound of it hitting the ground at the foot of the cliff. (a) Ignoring air resistance, how high is the cliff if the speed of sound is 330 m/s? (b) Suppose you had ignored the time it takes the sound to reach you. In that case, would you have overestimated or underestimated the height of the cliff? Explain your reasoning.

Passage Problems

BIO Blood flow in the heart. The human circulatory system is closed; that is, the blood that is pumped out of the left ventricle of the heart into the arteries is constrained to a series of continuous, branching vessels as it passes through the capillaries and then into the veins as it returns to the heart. The blood in each of the four chambers of the heart comes briefly to rest after entering and before ejection by the contraction of the heart muscle.

84. If the contraction of the left ventricle of the heart lasts 250 ms and the rate of flow of the blood in the aorta (the large artery leaving the heart) is 1.0 m/s, what is the average acceleration of a red blood cell as it leaves the heart?
    A. 250 m/s²
    B. 25 m/s²
    C. 40 m/s²
    D. 4.0 m/s²

85. If the aorta (diameter of d_a) branches into two equal-sized arteries with a combined area equal to the aorta, what is the diameter of one of the branches?
    A. $\sqrt{d_a}$
    B. $d_a/\sqrt{2}$
    C. $2d_a$
    D. $d_a/2$

86. After its journey to the head, arms, and legs, a round trip distance of about 3 m, the red blood cell returns to the left ventricle after 1 minute. What is the average velocity for the trip?
    A. 0.05 m/s, downward
    B. 0.5 m/s, downward
    C. 0 m/s, round trip
    D. 0.05 m/s, upward

ANSWERS TO SELECTED PROBLEMS

Conceptual Questions

1. (a) The magnitude of the displacement equals the distance traveled only when the motion is always in the same direction and lies along a straight line in space. An example is a car traveling due east on a straight, level road. (b) A car travels due east for 0.4 mi and then due west for 0.1 mi. The displacement has magnitude 0.3 mi, while the distance traveled is 0.5 mi. (c) No.

3. The average velocity equals the instantaneous velocity if the velocity is constant.

5. (a) True. The average speed can be zero only if the object is not moving. (b) False. If the object returns to its starting point, then its displacement is zero and its average velocity is zero; however, the distance it traveled is not zero, and thus its average speed is nonzero. An example is a car that travels 50 m north for 5 s and then 50 m south for 5 s. For the 10-second interval, the average velocity is zero, but the average speed is $(100 \text{ m})/(10 \text{ s}) = 10 \text{ m/s}$.

9. In each of these cases, the slope of velocity versus time is the acceleration. The sign of the slope gives the sign of the acceleration, in terms of the direction taken to be positive for plotting the velocity. Consequently, a positive slope indicates that the object is either speeding up in the positive x direction or slowing down in the negative x direction. Similarly, a negative slope indicates an increasing speed in the negative x direction or a decreasing speed in the positive x direction. A zero slope implies constant speed and thus no acceleration.

11. (a) The velocity must be positive, since x is increasing in the positive x direction. The intervals between time values, Δt, and between displacements, Δx, are both constants for all five intervals; thus, the velocity is constant and the acceleration is zero. (b) For each time interval, the average velocity is $v_{av,x} = \Delta x/\Delta t = (0.25 \text{ m})/(2.00 \text{ s}) = 0.125 \text{ m/s}$. Since the velocity does not change, $a_{av,x} = \Delta v_x/\Delta t = (0.0 \text{ m/s})/(2.00 \text{ s}) = 0.0 \text{ m/s}^2$

for each time interval. (c) The displacement is 7.75 m − 6.50 m = 1.25 m.

15. (a) Since all three objects have the same v at A and at B, Δv is the same for all three. And given that $a_{av} = \Delta v/\Delta t$, a_{av} is the same for all three objects. (b) At A, they all have the same velocity. By comparing the slope of a tangent line drawn to the v–t graph for each object at point A, we can conclude that the acceleration is different for all three objects.

17. (a) Since the object's velocity is always positive, the object does not reverse its direction of motion. (b) No, the object is always moving away from its starting point; the velocity is always in the same direction. (c) Yes, $v = 0$ at the beginning and at the end of the motion. (d) Yes, initially the object has a positive acceleration; however, the acceleration subsequently decreases in magnitude, passes through zero, and then becomes increasingly negative (increasing in magnitude).

Multiple-Choice Problems

1. C, D
3. C, D
5. D
7. A, D
9. D
11. A
13. B, D
15. C

Problems

1. (a) $x_A = -5$ cm, $x_B = +45$ cm, $x_C = +15$ cm, $x_D = -5$ cm
   (b) (i) +50 cm; 50 cm (ii) −30 cm; 30 cm (iii) −20 cm; 20 cm
   (iv) 0; 100 cm
3. 1.3 m/s; 2.0 m/s
5. (a) 3.0 m/s; 1.5 m/s; 1.8 m/s (b) same
7. (a) 7.0 m (b) (i) 1.0 m/s (ii) 3.0 m/s (iii) 5.0 m/s (iv) 7.0 m/s (v) 4.0 m/s
9. (a) 15.0 mi/h (b) 22.0 ft/s (c) 6.70 m/s
11. (a) 5.0 m (b) 1.1×10^7 yr
13. 1.6 mi
15. (a) 26 m/s (b) 140 m
17. 40 min

19. (a) IV (b) I (c) V (d) II (e) III
23. (a) (in m/s^2) 0, 1.0, 1.5, 2.5, 2.5, 2.5, 1.0, 0; no; yes (b) 2.5 m/s^2; 1.0 m/s^2; 0
27. (a) 6.3 ft/s^2 (b) 347 ft
29. (a) 4.9 m/s (b) 0.049 s (c) 100 m/s^2, 10 g's
31. (a) 675 m/s^2 (b) 0.067 s
33. 38 cm
35. (a) 4.42×10^5 m/s$^2 = 4.51 \times 10^4 g$
   (b) 0.758 ms
37. (a) 1.67 m/s^2 (b) 12 s (c) 240 m
39. (a) braking: −26.5 ft/s^2; speeding up: 6.67 ft/s^2 (b) 90.4 mph, (c) 3.32 s
41. 4A; 2C
43. $R_{large}/R_{small} = 1.10$
45. (a) 62.5 km (b) 175 m/s
47. (a) 2000 m (b) 2T
49. (a) 30.6 m (b) 24.5 m/s
51. (a) 33.5 m (b) 15.8 m/s
53. (a) 0.250 s: 40.9 m aboveground; 2.55 m/s upward. 1.00 s: 40.1 m aboveground; 4.80 m/s downward (b) 3.41 s (c) 28.4 m/s (d) 41.2 m
55. (a) 70.6 m (b) 15.3 s
57. (a) 4.93 s (b) 36.3 m/s
59. (a) 3.3 s (b) 9H
61. (a) 107 mph (b) 107 mph
63. (a) 9.9 m/s, downward
   (b) 9.9 m/s, upward
65. 1300 yr
67. (a) 2.7 mi/h (b) 24 mi/h (c) no
69. (a) $H/6$ (b) 24.0 s
71. (a) 3.1×10^6 m/s$^2 = 3.2 \times 10^5 g$
   (b) 1.6 ms (c) no
73. 3.60 m from point directly below the drop
75. (a) 2.04 s (b) 6.12 s (c) 8.16 s (d) 4.08 s
   (e) 9.8 m/s^2 downward at all points
77. 510 cm/s^2
79. (a) 628 m (b) 0; 9.8 m/s^2 downward
   (c) 36.4 s; 111 m/s
81. (a) 250 km (b) 49 s
83. (a) 383 m (b) overestimated

Passage Problems

84. D
85. B
86. C

Motion in a Plane

From Chapter 3 of *College Physics*, Ninth Edition, Hugh D. Young. Copyright © 2012 by Pearson Education, Inc.
Published by Pearson Addison-Wesley.

Motion in a Plane

Daisy Gilardini/The Image Bank/Getty Images

A Navy F14 Tomcat jet fighter roars off from the deck of an aircraft carrier, moving 55 m/s relative to the deck. It quickly accelerates into the sky. The instruments in the cockpit tell the pilot the speed and altitude of the plane and warn of other airplanes nearby. Pilots must constantly be aware of the three-dimensional nature of their motion.

In the straight-line problems, we could describe the position of a particle with a single coordinate. But to understand the curved flight of a baseball, the orbital motion of a satellite, or the path of the water from a fire hose, we need to extend our descriptions of motion to more than one dimension. We'll focus on motion in two dimensions—that is, in a plane—but the principles also apply to three-dimensional motion. For two-dimensional motion, the vector quantities displacement, velocity, and acceleration now have two components and lie in a plane rather than along a line. We'll also generalize the concept of relative velocity to motion in a plane, such as an airplane flying in a crosswind.

This chapter represents a merging of vector language with kinematic language. We're concerned with *describing* motion, not with analyzing its causes. But the language you learn here will be an essential tool when you use Newton's laws of motion to study the relation between force and motion.

1 Velocity in a Plane

To describe the *motion* of an object in a plane, we first need to be able to describe the object's *position*. (In this chapter, as in the preceding one, we assume that the objects we describe can be modeled as particles.) Often, it's useful to use a familiar x-y axis system (Figure 1a). For example, when a football player kicks a

When you see a cat jump, you probably don't think, "projectile!" However, except for the effects of air resistance and a couple of other minor factors, all objects that jump or are launched above the surface and then travel passively until they land move in exactly the same way and can be called projectiles. Projectile motion is a classic example of motion in a plane—the topic of this chapter.

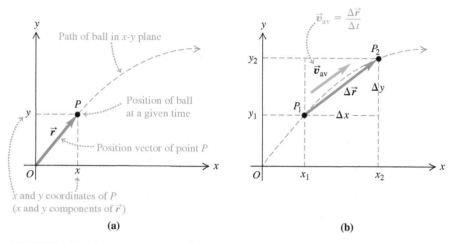

(a)   **(b)**

▲ **FIGURE 1** Position vectors can specify the location and displacement of a point in an *x-y* coordinate system. A position vector points from the origin to the point.

AP Photo/Toby Talbot

field goal, the ball (represented by point P) moves in a vertical plane. The ball's horizontal distance from the origin O at any time is x, and its vertical distance above the ground at any time is y. The numbers x and and y are called the *coordinates* of point P. The vector $\vec{r}$ from the origin O to point P is called the **position vector** of point P, and the Cartesian coordinates x and y of point P are the x and y components, respectively, of vector $\vec{r}$. The *distance* of point P from the origin is the magnitude of vector $\vec{r}$:

$$r = |\vec{r}| = \sqrt{x^2 + y^2}.$$

Figure 1b shows the ball at two points in its curved path. At time t_1, it is at point P_1 with position vector $\vec{r}_1$; at the later time t_2, it is at point P_2 with position vector $\vec{r}_2$. The ball moves from P_1 to P_2 during the time interval $\Delta t = t_2 - t_1$. The change in position (the displacement) during this interval is the vector $\Delta\vec{r} = \vec{r}_2 - \vec{r}_1$. We define the **average velocity** $\vec{v}_{\text{av}}$ during the interval in the same way we did for straight-line motion:

Definition of average velocity
The average velocity of a particle is the displacement $\Delta\vec{r}$, divided by the time interval Δt:

$$\vec{v}_{\text{av}} = \frac{\vec{r}_2 - \vec{r}_1}{t_2 - t_1} = \frac{\Delta\vec{r}}{\Delta t}. \tag{1}$$

That is, the average velocity is a vector quantity having the same direction as $\Delta\vec{r}$ and a magnitude equal to the magnitude of $\Delta\vec{r}$, divided by the time interval Δt. The magnitude of $\Delta\vec{r}$ is always the straight-line distance from P_1 to P_2, regardless of the actual shape of the path taken by the object. Thus, the average velocity would be the same for *any* path that would take the particle from P_1 to P_2 in the same time interval Δt.

Figure 1b also shows that, during any displacement $\Delta\vec{r}$, Δx and Δy are the components of the vector $\Delta\vec{r}$; it follows that the components $v_{\text{av},x}$ and $v_{\text{av},y}$ of the average velocity vector are

$$v_{\text{av},x} = \frac{\Delta x}{\Delta t} \quad \text{and} \quad v_{\text{av},y} = \frac{\Delta y}{\Delta t}. \tag{2}$$

▲ **Application Not your parents' yo-yo.**
The yo-yo may seem like a child's toy, but looks can often be deceiving. Knowledge of basic principles of physics and engineering design has sparked the creation of a new generation of high-performance yo-yos. Some can be made to spin at the end of the string for up to 14 minutes, the current world record set in 2003. In the photo shown here, 1998 world champion Jennifer Baybrook is demonstrating a classic yo-yo trick. When the center of the spinning yo-yo remains at the same position, its displacement and average velocity are zero.

We define the **instantaneous velocity** $\vec{v}$ as follows:

Definition of instantaneous velocity $\vec{v}$ in a plane

The instantaneous velocity is the limit of the average velocity as the time interval Δt approaches zero:

$$\vec{v} = \lim_{\Delta t \to 0} \frac{\Delta \vec{r}}{\Delta t}. \tag{3}$$

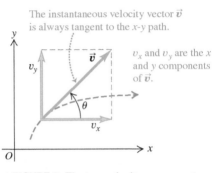

The instantaneous velocity vector $\vec{v}$ is always tangent to the x-y path.

v_x and v_y are the x and y components of $\vec{v}$.

▲ **FIGURE 2** The two velocity components for motion in the x-y plane.

As $\Delta t \to 0$, points P_1 and P_2 move closer and closer together. In the limit, the vector $\Delta \vec{r}$ becomes *tangent* to the curve, as shown in Figure 2. The direction of $\Delta \vec{r}$ in the limit is also the direction of the instantaneous velocity $\vec{v}$. This analysis leads to an important conclusion:

At every point along the path, the instantaneous velocity vector is tangent to the path.

During any displacement $\Delta \vec{r}$, the changes Δx and Δy in the coordinates x and y are the *components* of $\Delta \vec{r}$. It follows that the components v_x and v_y of the instantaneous velocity $\vec{v}$ are

$$v_x = \lim_{\Delta t \to 0} \frac{\Delta x}{\Delta t} \qquad \text{and} \qquad v_y = \lim_{\Delta t \to 0} \frac{\Delta y}{\Delta t}.$$

The instantaneous *speed* of the object is the *magnitude* v of the instantaneous velocity vector $\vec{v}$. This is given by the Pythagorean relation

$$|\vec{v}| = v = \sqrt{v_x^2 + v_y^2}. \quad \text{(speed of a particle in a plane)}$$

The direction of $\vec{v}$ is given by the angle θ in the figure. We see that when we measure θ in the usual way (counterclockwise from the $+x$ axis),

$$\theta = \tan^{-1} \frac{v_y}{v_x}.$$

NOTE ▶ In this text, we always use Greek letters for angles; we'll use θ (theta) for the directions of vectors measured counterclockwise from the $+x$ axis and ϕ (phi) for most other angles. ◀

Because velocity is a vector quantity, we may represent it either in terms of its components or in terms of its magnitude and direction. The *direction* of an object's instantaneous velocity at any point is *always* tangent to the path at that point. But in general, the position vector $\vec{r}$ does *not* have the same direction as the instantaneous velocity $\vec{v}$. (The direction of the position vector depends on where you place the origin, while the direction of $\vec{v}$ is determined by the shape of the path.)

EXAMPLE 1   A model car

Suppose you are operating a radio-controlled model car on a vacant tennis court. The surface of the court represents the x-y plane, and you place the origin at your own location. At time $t_1 = 2.00$ s the car has x and y coordinates $(4.0 \text{ m}, 2.0 \text{ m})$, and at time $t_2 = 2.50$ s it has coordinates $(7.0 \text{ m}, 6.0 \text{ m})$. For the time interval from t_1 to t_2, find **(a)** the components of the average velocity of the car and **(b)** the magnitude and direction of the average velocity.

Continued

SOLUTION

SET UP Figure 3 shows the sketch we draw. We see that $\Delta x = 7.0 \text{ m} - 4.0 \text{ m} = 3.0 \text{ m}$, $\Delta y = 6.0 \text{ m} - 2.0 \text{ m} = 4.0 \text{ m}$, and $\Delta t = 0.50 \text{ s}$.

SOLVE Part (a): To find the components of $\vec{v}_{av}$, we use their definitions (Equations 2):

$$v_{av,x} = \frac{\Delta x}{\Delta t} = \frac{3.0 \text{ m}}{0.50 \text{ s}} = 6.0 \text{ m/s},$$

$$v_{av,y} = \frac{\Delta y}{\Delta t} = \frac{4.0 \text{ m}}{0.50 \text{ s}} = 8.0 \text{ m/s}.$$

Part (b): The magnitude of $\vec{v}_{av}$ is obtained from the Pythagorean theorem:

$$|\vec{v}_{av}| = \sqrt{v_{av,x}{}^2 + v_{av,y}{}^2}$$
$$= \sqrt{(6.0 \text{ m/s})^2 + (8.0 \text{ m/s})^2} = 10.0 \text{ m/s}.$$

The direction of $\vec{v}_{av}$ is most easily described by its angle, measured counterclockwise from the positive x axis. Calling this angle θ, we have

$$\theta = \tan^{-1}\frac{v_{av,y}}{v_{av,x}} = \tan^{-1}\frac{8.0 \text{ m/s}}{6.0 \text{ m/s}} = 53°.$$

Alternative Solution: Alternatively, the magnitude of $\vec{v}_{av}$ is the distance between the points $(4.0 \text{ m}, 2.0 \text{ m})$ and $(7.0 \text{ m}, 6.0 \text{ m})$ (i.e., 5.0 m, found using Pythagoras's theorem), divided by the time interval (0.5 s):

$$|\vec{v}_{av}| = \frac{5.0 \text{ m}}{0.50 \text{ s}} = 10.0 \text{ m/s}.$$

$\vec{v}_{av}$ points from P_1 toward P_2. It doesn't matter how long you make it; its magnitude will be found mathematically.

▲ **FIGURE 3** Our sketch for this problem.

Since the direction of $\vec{v}_{av}$ is the same as the direction of the displacement $\Delta \vec{r}$ between the two points, we can calculate it from Δx and Δy rather than $v_{av,x}$ and $v_{av,y}$:

$$\theta = \tan^{-1}\frac{\Delta y}{\Delta x} = \tan^{-1}\frac{4.0 \text{ m}}{3.0 \text{ m}} = 53°.$$

REFLECT Be sure you understand the relation between the two solutions to part (b). In the first, we calculated the magnitude and direction of $\vec{v}_{av}$ from the components of this vector quantity. In the alternative solution, we used the fact that the average velocity $\vec{v}_{av}$ and the displacement $\Delta \vec{r}$ have the same direction.

Practice Problem: Suppose you reverse the car's motion, so that it retraces its path in the opposite direction in the same time. Find the components of the average velocity of the car and the magnitude and direction of the average velocity. *Answers:* -6.0 m/s, -8.0 m/s, 10.0 m/s, 233°.

2 Acceleration in a Plane

Now let's consider the acceleration of an object moving on a curved path in a plane. In Figure 4, the vector $\vec{v}_1$ represents the particle's instantaneous velocity at point P_1 at time t_1, and the vector $\vec{v}_2$ represents the particle's instantaneous velocity at point P_2 at time t_2. In general, the two velocities differ in both magnitude and direction.

We define the **average acceleration** $\vec{a}_{av}$ of the particle as follows:

MasteringPHYSICS

PhET: Maze Game

Definition of average acceleration $\vec{a}_a$

As an object undergoes a displacement during a time interval Δt, its average acceleration is its change in velocity, $\Delta \vec{v}$, divided by Δt:

$$\text{Average acceleration} = \vec{a}_{av} = \frac{\vec{v}_2 - \vec{v}_1}{t_2 - t_1} = \frac{\Delta \vec{v}}{\Delta t}. \qquad (4)$$

Average acceleration is a vector quantity in the same direction as the vector $\Delta \vec{v}$. Acceleration is a quantitative description of the way an object's motion is

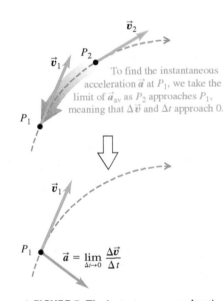

As this car slows while rounding a curve, its instantaneous velocity changes in both magnitude and direction. Thus, it accelerates.

(a)

To find the car's average acceleration between P_1 and P_2, we first find the change in velocity $\Delta \vec{v}$ by subtracting $\vec{v}_1$ from $\vec{v}_2$. (Notice that $\vec{v}_1 + \Delta \vec{v} = \vec{v}_2$.)

(b)

The average acceleration has the same direction as the change in velocity, $\Delta \vec{v}$.

(c)

▲ **FIGURE 4** Finding the average acceleration between two points in the *x-y* plane.

changing with time. Figure 4b shows that the **final velocity $\vec{v}_2$ (at time t_2) is the vector sum of the original velocity $\vec{v}_1$ (at time t_1) and the change in velocity, $\Delta \vec{v}$, during the interval Δt.**

We define the **instantaneous acceleration $\vec{a}$** at point P_1 as follows (Figure 5):

Definition of instantaneous acceleration $\vec{a}$

When the velocity of a particle changes by an amount $\Delta \vec{v}$ as the particle undergoes a displacement $\Delta \vec{r}$ during a time interval Δt, the instantaneous acceleration is the limit of the average acceleration as Δt approaches zero:

$$\text{Instantaneous acceleration} = \vec{a} = \lim_{\Delta t \to 0} \frac{\Delta \vec{v}}{\Delta t}. \tag{5}$$

To find the instantaneous acceleration $\vec{a}$ at P_1, we take the limit of $\vec{a}_{av}$ as P_2 approaches P_1, meaning that $\Delta \vec{v}$ and Δt approach 0.

$$\vec{a} = \lim_{\Delta t \to 0} \frac{\Delta \vec{v}}{\Delta t}$$

▲ **FIGURE 5** The instantaneous acceleration of a point in the *x-y* plane.

The instantaneous acceleration vector at point P_1 in Figure 5 does *not* have the same direction as the instantaneous velocity vector $\vec{v}$ at that point; in general, there is no reason it should. (Recall that the velocity and acceleration components of a particle moving along a line could have opposite signs.) The construction in Figure 5 shows that the acceleration vector must always point toward the *concave* side of the curved path. **When a particle moves in a curved path, it *always* has nonzero acceleration, even when it moves with constant speed.** More generally, acceleration is associated with change of speed, change of direction of velocity, or both.

◀ **Application Can you spot the three accelerators?** Almost anyone will recognize the gas pedal as an accelerator—pressing it makes the car speed up. As a physics student, you probably also recognize the brake pedal as an accelerator—it slows the car. The third accelerator is the steering wheel, which changes the *direction* of the car's velocity.

Cindy Lewis/Carphotos/Alamy

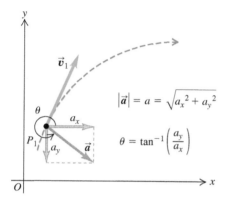

Components of $\Delta\vec{v}$ and $\vec{a}_{av}$.

(a) Components of average acceleration for the interval from P_1 to P_2.

(b) Components of instantaneous acceleration at P_1.

▲ **FIGURE 6** Components of average and instantaneous acceleration.

We often represent the acceleration of a particle in terms of the components of this vector quantity. Like Figure 2, Figure 6 shows the motion of a particle as described in a rectangular coordinate system. During a time interval Δt, the velocity of the particle changes by an amount $\Delta\vec{v}$, with components Δv_x and Δv_y. So we can represent the average acceleration $\vec{a}_{av}$ in terms of its x and y components:

$$a_{av,x} = \frac{\Delta v_x}{\Delta t}, \qquad a_{av,y} = \frac{\Delta v_y}{\Delta t}. \tag{6}$$

Similarly, the x and y components of instantaneous acceleration, a_x and a_y, are

$$a_x = \lim_{\Delta t \to 0} \frac{\Delta v_x}{\Delta t}, \qquad a_y = \lim_{\Delta t \to 0} \frac{\Delta v_y}{\Delta t}.$$

If we know the components a_x and a_y, we can find the magnitude and direction of the acceleration vector $\vec{a}$, just as we did with velocity:

$$|\vec{a}| = a = \sqrt{a_x^2 + a_y^2}, \qquad \theta = \tan^{-1}\frac{a_y}{a_x}. \tag{7}$$

The angle θ gives the direction of $\vec{a}$, measured counterclockwise from the $+x$ axis.

Mark Boulton/Alamy

▲ **BIO Application Knowing up from down.** Plant roots have exquisitely developed mechanisms for sensing gravity and growing downward. If the direction of a root is changed, say by running into a rock in the soil, the root is forced to grow horizontally; however, as soon as it can, it again turns downward. This ability involves a number of cellular signals, but the primary sensor detects acceleration. The sensing cells contain statoliths, specialized starch-containing granules that are denser than the fluid in the cells and, in response to changes in the direction of gravity, fall (are accelerated) to a different location within the cells. This triggers an active localized response of the cells and causes the growth direction of the root to re-orient so that the root once again grows down.

EXAMPLE 2 **The model car again**

Let's look again at the radio-controlled model car in Example 1. Suppose that at time $t_1 = 2.00$ s the car has components of velocity $v_x = 1.0$ m/s and $v_y = 3.0$ m/s and that at time $t_2 = 2.50$ s the components are $v_x = 4.0$ m/s and $v_y = 3.0$ m/s. Find **(a)** the components and **(b)** the magnitude and direction of the average acceleration during this interval.

SOLUTION

SET UP Figure 7 shows our sketch.

SOLVE Figure 6a outlines the relations we'll use.

Part (a): To find the components of average acceleration, we need the components of the change in velocity, Δv_x and Δv_y, and the time interval, which is $\Delta t = 0.50$ s. The change in v_x is $\Delta v_x = v_{2x} - v_{1x} = (4.0 \text{ m/s} - 1.0 \text{ m/s}) = 3.0$ m/s, so the x component of average acceleration in the interval $\Delta t = 0.50$ s is

$$a_{\text{av},x} = \frac{\Delta v_x}{\Delta t} = \frac{3.0 \text{ m/s}}{0.50 \text{ s}} = 6.0 \text{ m/s}^2.$$

The change in v_y is zero, so $a_{\text{av},y}$ in this interval is also zero.

Part (b): The vector $\vec{a}_{\text{av}}$ has only an x component. The vector points in the $+x$ direction and has magnitude 6.0 m/s^2.

REFLECT We can always represent a vector quantity (such as displacement, velocity, or acceleration) either in terms of its components or in terms of its magnitude and direction.

▲ **FIGURE 7** Our sketch for this problem.

An acceleration parallel to an object's velocity changes the magnitude, but not the direction, of the velocity; the object moves in a straight line with changing speed.

(a)

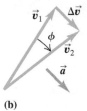

An acceleration perpendicular to an object's velocity changes the direction, but not the magnitude, of the velocity; the object follows a curved path at constant speed.

(b)

▲ **FIGURE 8** Two special cases: acceleration (a) parallel and (b) perpendicular to an object's velocity.

Figure 8 shows two special cases. In Figure 8a, the acceleration vector $\vec{a}$ is *parallel* to the velocity vector $\vec{v}_1$. (In Fig. 8a, $\vec{a}$ points in the same direction as $\vec{v}$; it could alternatively point in the opposite direction.) Then, because $\vec{a}$ gives the rate of change of velocity, the *change* in $\vec{v}$ during a small time interval Δt is a vector $\Delta \vec{v}$ that has the same direction as $\vec{a}$ and hence the same direction as $\vec{v}_1$. As a result, the velocity $\vec{v}_2$ at the end of Δt, given by $\vec{v}_2 = \vec{v}_1 + \Delta \vec{v}$, is a vector having the *same direction* as $\vec{v}_1$ but somewhat greater (or smaller) magnitude.

In Figure 8b, the acceleration $\vec{a}$ is *perpendicular* to the velocity $\vec{v}$. In a small time interval Δt, the change $\Delta \vec{v}$ in the velocity vector $\vec{v}$ is a vector very nearly perpendicular to $\vec{v}_1$, as shown. Again, $\vec{v}_2 = \vec{v}_1 + \Delta \vec{v}$, but in this case $\vec{v}_1$ and $\vec{v}_2$ have different directions. As the time interval Δt approaches zero, the angle ϕ in the figure also approaches zero. In this limit, $\Delta \vec{v}$ becomes perpendicular to *both* $\vec{v}_1$ and $\vec{v}_2$, and the two vectors have the same magnitude.

We conclude that when $\vec{a}$ is *parallel* (or antiparallel) to $\vec{v}$, its effect is to change the magnitude of $\vec{v}$, but not its direction. When $\vec{a}$ is *perpendicular* to $\vec{v}$, its effect is to change the direction of $\vec{v}$, but not its magnitude. In general, $\vec{a}$ may have components *both* parallel and perpendicular to $\vec{v}_1$, but the preceding statements are still valid for the individual components. In particular, when an object travels along a curved path with constant speed, its acceleration is *not* zero, even though the magnitude of $\vec{v}$ does not change. In this case, the acceleration is always perpendicular to $\vec{v}$ at each point. For example, when a particle moves in a circle with constant speed, the acceleration at each instant is directed toward the center of the circle. We'll consider this special case in detail in Section 4.

3 Projectile Motion

A **projectile** is any object that is given an initial velocity and then follows a path determined entirely by the effects of gravitational acceleration and air resistance. A batted baseball, a thrown football, and a package dropped from an airplane are all examples of projectiles. The path followed by a projectile is called its *trajectory.*

To analyze this common type of motion, we'll start with an idealized model. We represent the projectile as a single particle with an acceleration (due to the earth's gravitational pull) that is constant in both magnitude and direction. We'll neglect the effects of air resistance and the curvature and rotation of the earth. Like all models, this one has limitations. The curvature of the earth has to be considered in the flight of long-range ballistic missiles, and air resistance is of crucial importance to a skydiver. Nevertheless, we can learn a lot by analyzing this simple model.

We first notice that projectile motion is always confined to a vertical plane determined by the direction of the initial velocity. We'll call this plane the x-y *coordinate plane,* with the x axis horizontal and the y axis directed vertically upward. Figure 9 shows a view of this plane from the side, along with a typical trajectory.

The key to analyzing projectile motion is the fact that *we can treat the x and y coordinates separately.* Why is this so? Anticipating a relation that we'll study in detail, we note that the instantaneous acceleration of an object is proportional to (and in the same direction as) the net *force* acting on the object. Because of the assumptions made in our model, the only force acting on the projectile is the earth's gravitational attraction; we assume that this is constant in magnitude and always vertically downward in direction. Thus the vertical component of acceleration is the same as if the projectile moved only in the y direction. Figure 10 shows two trajectories; the vertical displacements of the two objects at any time are the same, even though their horizontal displacements are different.

We conclude that the x component of acceleration, a_x, is zero and the y component a_y is constant and equal in magnitude to the acceleration of free fall:

$$a_x = 0; \qquad a_y = -g = -9.80 \text{ m/s}^2.$$

NOTE ▶ Remember that, by definition, g is always positive (because it is the magnitude of the acceleration vector due to gravity), but with our choice of coordinate directions, a_y is negative. ◀

So we can think of projectile motion as a combination of horizontal motion with constant velocity and vertical motion with constant acceleration. We can then express all the vector relationships in terms of separate equations for the horizontal and vertical components. The actual motion is a combination of these separate motions. Figure 11 shows the horizontal and vertical components of motion for a projectile that starts at (or passes through) the origin of coordinates at time $t = 0$. As in Figure 10, the projectile is shown at equal time intervals.

The horizontal (x) and vertical (y) components of $\vec{a}$ for a projectile are

$$a_x = 0, \qquad a_y = -g.$$

We'll usually use $g = 9.80 \text{ m/s}^2$, but occasionally we'll use $g = 10 \text{ m/s}^2$ for approximate calculations.

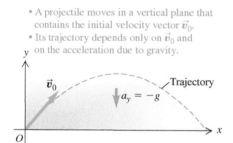

• A projectile moves in a vertical plane that contains the initial velocity vector $\vec{v}_0$.
• Its trajectory depends only on $\vec{v}_0$ and on the acceleration due to gravity.

▲ **FIGURE 9** The trajectory of a projectile.

Richard Megna/Fundamental Photographs

▲ **FIGURE 10** Independence of horizontal and vertical motion: At any given time, both balls have the same y position, velocity, and acceleration, despite having different x positions and velocities. Successive images are separated by equal time intervals.

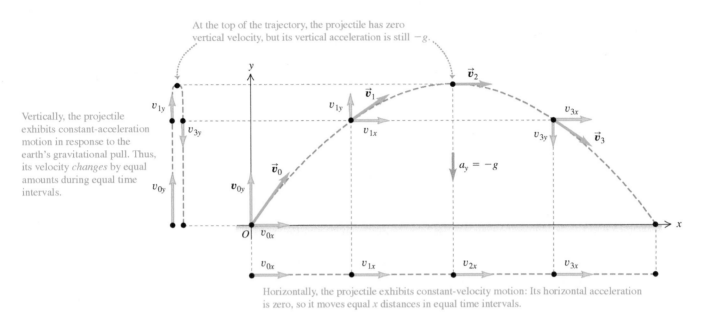

At the top of the trajectory, the projectile has zero vertical velocity, but its vertical acceleration is still $-g$.

Vertically, the projectile exhibits constant-acceleration motion in response to the earth's gravitational pull. Thus, its velocity *changes* by equal amounts during equal time intervals.

Horizontally, the projectile exhibits constant-velocity motion: Its horizontal acceleration is zero, so it moves equal x distances in equal time intervals.

▲ **FIGURE 11** Independence of horizontal and vertical motion. In the vertical direction, a projectile behaves like a freely falling object; in the horizontal direction, it moves with constant velocity.

 Conceptual Analysis 1

Horizontal stone throw

If you throw a stone horizontally out over the surface of a lake, the time it is in the air (i.e., before it hits the water) is determined *only* by

A. the height from which you throw it.
B. the height from which you throw it and its initial speed.
C. its initial speed and the horizontal distance to the point where it splashes down.

SOLUTION As we've just learned, the horizontal and vertical components of a projectile's motion are independent. Therefore, the stone reaches the water at the same time as a rock that was dropped vertically from the same starting height. The time required for the stone to reach the water depends only on the height from which it is thrown, so answer A is the correct one. The *distance* the stone travels before splashing down, however, depends on both the height from which it is thrown and the speed with which it is thrown.

In projectile motion, the vertical and horizontal coordinates both vary with constant-acceleration motion. (The horizontal component of acceleration is constant at zero.) Therefore, we can use the same equations we derived for constant-acceleration motion. Here's a reminder of these relationships:

$$v_x = v_{0x} + a_x t, \quad \text{(velocity as a function of time)}$$
$$x = x_0 + v_{0x}t + \tfrac{1}{2}a_x t^2, \quad \text{(position as a function of time)}$$
$$v_x^2 = v_{0x}^2 + 2a_x(x - x_0). \quad \text{(velocity as a function of position)}$$

Our procedure will be to use this set of equations separately for each coordinate. That is, we use this set of equations for the x coordinate, and then we use a second set with all the x's replaced by y's for the y coordinate. Next, we have to choose the appropriate components of the constant acceleration $\vec{a}$ and the initial velocity $\vec{v}_0$. At time $t = 0$, the particle is at the point (x_0, y_0), and its velocity components have the initial values v_{0x} and v_{0y}. The components of acceleration are constant: $a_x = 0$, $a_y = -g$. When we put all the pieces together, here's what we get:

Equations for projectile motion (assuming that $a_x = 0$, $a_y = -g$)

Considering the x motion, we substitute $a_x = 0$

$$v_x = v_{0x}, \tag{8}$$
$$x = x_0 + v_{0x}t. \tag{9}$$

For the y motion, we substitute y for x, v_y for v_x, v_{0y} for v_{0x}, and $-g$ for a to get

$$v_y = v_{0y} - gt \tag{10}$$
$$y = y_0 + v_{0y}t - \tfrac{1}{2}gt^2 \tag{11}$$

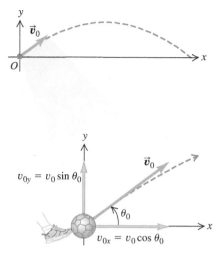

Usually it is simplest to take the initial position (at time $t = 0$) as the origin; in this case, $x_0 = y_0 = 0$. The initial position might be, for example, the position of a ball at the instant it leaves the thrower's hand or the position of a bullet at the instant it leaves the barrel of the gun.

As shown in Figure 11, the x component of acceleration for a projectile is zero, so v_x is constant, but v_y changes by equal amounts in equal times, corresponding to a constant y component of acceleration. At the highest point in the trajectory, $v_y = 0$. But a_y is still equal to $-g$ at this point. Make sure you understand why!

We can also represent the initial velocity $\vec{v}_0$ by its magnitude v_0 (the initial speed) and its angle θ_0 with the positive x axis, as shown in Figure 12. In terms of these quantities, the components v_{0x} and v_{0y} of initial velocity are

$$v_{0x} = v_0\cos\theta_0, \qquad v_{0y} = v_0\sin\theta_0.$$

Using these relations in Equations 8 through 11 and setting $x_0 = y_0 = 0$, we obtain the following alternative formulation for projectile motion:

Position and velocity of a projectile as functions of time t

$$x = (v_0\cos\theta_0)t \tag{12}$$
$$y = (v_0\sin\theta_0)t - \tfrac{1}{2}gt^2 \tag{13}$$
$$v_x = v_0\cos\theta_0 \tag{14}$$
$$v_y = v_0\sin\theta_0 - gt \tag{15}$$

We can get a lot of information from these equations. For example, the distance r of the projectile from the origin at any time (the magnitude of the position vector $\vec{r}$) is given by

$$r = \sqrt{x^2 + y^2}.$$

The projectile's speed v (the magnitude of its velocity) at any time is

$$v = \sqrt{v_x^2 + v_y^2}.$$

The *direction* of the velocity at any time, in terms of the angle θ it makes with the positive x axis, is given by

$$\theta = \tan^{-1}\frac{v_y}{v_x}.$$

The velocity vector $\vec{v}$ is tangent to the trajectory at each point. Note that v_x is constant, but that the *direction* of the velocity changes because v_y changes continuously.

The formulation just described gives us the coordinates and velocity components of a projectile as functions of time. The actual *shape* of the trajectory is a graph of y as a function of x. We can derive an equation for this relationship from Equations 12 and 13. First we solve Equation 12 for t, and then we

▲ **FIGURE 12** The initial velocity of a projectile, showing the components and the launch angle θ_0.

Ken Davies/Masterfile

▲ **Application Which is accelerating the most?** If you answered "none of the above," you are correct. In the photo, one apple and one orange are moving up while the other two fruits are moving down. Despite their different positions and velocities, all four have the same rate of change of velocity. Like all freely falling objects near the earth's surface, they are accelerating downward at 9.8 m/s². The apple and orange moving up are losing upward velocity at exactly the same rate the other two fruits are gaining downward velocity. Even at the highest point of their path, where for an instant they move neither upward nor downward, they have the same acceleration, a rate of change in velocity of 9.8 m/s² toward the center of the earth.

▲ **FIGURE 13** Strobe photo of a bouncing ball; the images are separated by equal time intervals. The ball follows a parabolic trajectory after each bounce. It rises a little less after each bounce because it loses energy during each collision with the floor.

substitute the resulting expression for t into Equation 13 and simplify the result. We find that $t = x/(v_0\cos\theta_0)$ and

$$y = v_0\sin\theta_0\left(\frac{x}{v_0\cos\theta_0}\right) - \tfrac{1}{2}g\left(\frac{x}{v_0\cos\theta_0}\right)^2,$$

$$y = (\tan\theta_0)x - \left(\frac{g}{2v_0^2\cos^2\theta_0}\right)x^2.$$

Don't worry about the details of this equation; the important point is its general form. The quantities v_0, $\tan\theta_0$, $\cos\theta_0$, and g are all constants, so the equation is a relation between the variables x and y, with the general form

$$y = bx - cx^2,$$

where b and c are positive constants. This is the equation of a *parabola*. With projectile motion, for our simple model, the trajectory is always a parabola (Figure 13).

 Quantitative Analysis 2 **Horizontal paintball shot**

A paintball is shot horizontally in the positive x direction. At time Δt after the ball is shot, it is 3 cm to the right and 3 cm below its starting point. Over the next interval Δt, the *changes* in horizontal and vertical position are

A. $\Delta x = 3$ cm, $\Delta y = -3$ cm;
B. $\Delta x = 3$ cm, $\Delta y = -9$ cm;
C. $\Delta x = 6$ cm, $\Delta y = -6$ cm.

SOLUTION The ball is a projectile, so we assume that its horizontal component of velocity is constant. Therefore, the changes Δx in horizontal position during equal time intervals are equal. This result rules out choice C. Because the ball speeds up as it falls, the second Δy must be larger than the first, eliminating answer A. However, is answer B correct? With constant acceleration, the distance of fall from rest is proportional to t^2. This means that, as time increases from 1 to 2 to 3 in units of t, the distance fallen will be y, $4y$, and $9y$, or -3 cm, -12 cm, and -27 cm, in vertical height. The change in y from one time interval to the next is -3 cm, -9 cm $[= -12$ cm $- (-3$ cm$)]$, and -15 cm $[= -27$ cm $- (-12$ cm$)]$. The ratio of these numbers is $1:3:5$, the sequence of odd integers. Answer B is correct.

EXAMPLE 3 **Paintball gun**

The contestant in Figure 14 shoots a paintball horizontally at a speed of 75.0 m/s from a point 1.50 m above the ground. The ball misses its target and hits the ground. **(a)** For how many seconds is the ball in the air? **(b)** Find the maximum horizontal displacement (which we'll call the *range* of the ball). Ignore air resistance.

SOLUTION

SET UP We choose to place the origin of the coordinate system at ground level, directly below the end of the gun barrel, as shown in Figure 15. (This choice of position of the origin avoids having to deal with negative values of y, a modest convenience.) Then $x_0 = 0$ and $y_0 = 1.50$ m. The gun is fired horizontally, so

$v_{0x} = 75.0$ m/s and $v_{0y} = 0$. The final position of the ball, at ground level, is $y = 0$.

SOLVE Part (a): We're asked to find the total time the paintball is in the air. This is equal to the time it would take the paintball to fall vertically from its initial height to the ground. In each case, the vertical position is given as a function of time by Equation 11,

▲ **FIGURE 14**

▲ **FIGURE 15** Our sketch for this problem.

Continued

$y = y_0 + v_{0y}t - \frac{1}{2}gt^2$. In this problem, $y_0 = 1.5$ m, $y = 0$, and $v_{0y} = 0$, so that equation becomes simply

$$0 = y_0 - \tfrac{1}{2}gt^2.$$

We need to find the time t. Solving for t, and substituting numerical values, we obtain

$$t = \sqrt{\frac{2y_0}{g}} = \sqrt{\frac{2(1.50\text{ m})}{9.80\text{ m/s}^2}} = 0.553 \text{ s}.$$

Part (b): Now that we know the time t of the ball's flight through the air, we can find the range—that is, the horizontal dis-tance x it travels during time t. We use Equation 9: $x = x_0 + v_{0x}t$. Setting $x_0 = 0$, we find that

$$x = x_0 + v_{0x}t = 0 + (75.0\text{ m/s})(0.553\text{ s}) = 41.5 \text{ m}.$$

REFLECT Actual ranges of paintballs are less than this, typically about 30 m. The difference is due primarily to air resistance, which decreases the horizontal component of velocity.

Practice Problem: If air resistance is neglected, what initial speed is required for a range of 20 m? *Answer:* 36.1 m/s.

PROBLEM-SOLVING STRATEGY 1 **Projectile motion**

The strategies that we used for solving straight-line, constant-acceleration motion problems are equally useful for projectile motion.

SET UP

1. Define your coordinate system and make a sketch showing your axes. Usually, it is easiest to place the origin at the initial $(t = 0)$ position of the projectile, with the x axis horizontal and the y axis upward. Then $x_0 = 0$, $y_0 = 0$, $a_x = 0$, and $a_y = -g$.
2. List the known and unknown quantities. In some problems, the components (or magnitude and direction) of initial velocity will be given, and you can use Equations 12 through 15 to find the coordinates and velocity components at some later time. In other problems, you might be given two points on the trajectory and be asked to find the initial velocity. Be sure you know which quantities are given and which are to be found.
3. It often helps to state the problem in prose and then translate into symbols. For example, *when* does the particle arrive at a certain point (i.e, at what value of t)? *Where* is the particle when a velocity component has a certain value? (That is, what are the values of x and y when v_x or v_y has the specified value?)

SOLVE

4. At the highest point in a trajectory, $v_y = 0$. So the question "When does the projectile reach its highest point?" translates into "What is the value of t when $v_y = 0$?" Similarly, if $y_0 = 0$, then "When does the projectile return to its initial elevation?" translates into "What is the value of t when $y = 0$?" and so on.
5. Resist the temptation to break the trajectory into segments and analyze each one separately. You don't have to start all over, with a new axis system and a new time scale, when the projectile reaches its highest point. It is usually easier to set up Equations 8 through 11 (or Equations 12 through 15) at the start and use the same axes and time scale throughout the problem.

REFLECT

6. Try to make rough estimates as to what your answers should be, and then ask whether your calculations confirm your estimates. Ask, "Does this result make sense?"

Pascal Ribollet

▲ **BIO Application Ballistic spores.**
Animals generally depend on muscles to move about while other organisms such as plants and fungi are relatively immobile and require specialized mechanisms for seed and spore dispersal. Among the fungi, some of those living on animal dung have compartments called asci (shown) that contain spores (inset) and generate substantial hydrostatic pressure. The asci rupture and behave as "squirt guns," propelling the spores into the air. The initial acceleration of the spores has only recently been measured with specialized video cameras capturing up to 250,000 frames per second. These data reveal that the spores are ejected with accelerations of up to 1,800,000 m/s^2, or about 180,000 g. These are the largest natural accelerations ever measured.

EXAMPLE 4   A home-run hit

A home-run baseball is hit with an initial speed $v_0 = 37.0$ m/s at an initial angle $\theta_0 = 53.1°$. **(a)** Find the ball's position, and the magnitude and direction of its velocity, when $t = 2.00$ s. **(b)** Find the time when the ball reaches the highest point of its flight, and find its height h at that point. **(c)** Find the horizontal range R (the horizontal distance from the starting point to the point where the ball hits the ground).

SOLUTION

SET UP The ball is probably struck a meter or so above ground level, but we'll neglect this small distance and assume that it starts at ground level $(y_0 = 0)$. Figure 16 shows our sketch. We place the origin of coordinates at the starting point, so $x_0 = 0$. The components of initial velocity are

$$v_{0x} = v_0\cos\theta_0 = (37.0 \text{ m/s})(0.600) = 22.2 \text{ m/s},$$
$$v_{0y} = v_0\sin\theta_0 = (37.0 \text{ m/s})(0.800) = 29.6 \text{ m/s}.$$

SOLVE Part (a): We ignore the effects of the air. We want to find x, y, v_x, and v_y at time $t = 2.00$ s. We substitute these values into Equations 8 through 11, along with the value $t = 2.00$ s. The coordinates at $t = 2.00$ s are

$$x = v_{0x}t = (22.2 \text{ m/s})(2.00 \text{ s}) = 44.4 \text{ m},$$
$$y = v_{0y}t - \tfrac{1}{2}gt^2$$
$$= (29.6 \text{ m/s})(2.00 \text{ s}) - \tfrac{1}{2}(9.80 \text{ m/s}^2)(2.00 \text{ s})^2 = 39.6 \text{ m}.$$

The components v_x and v_y of the velocity vector $\vec{v}$ at time $t = 2.00$ s are

$$v_x = v_{0x} = 22.2 \text{ m/s},$$
$$v_y = v_{0y} - gt = 29.6 \text{ m/s} + (-9.80 \text{ m/s}^2)(2.00 \text{ s})$$
$$= 10.0 \text{ m/s}.$$

The magnitude and direction of the velocity vector $\vec{v}$ at time $t = 2.00$ s are, respectively,

$$v = \sqrt{v_x^2 + v_y^2} = \sqrt{(22.2 \text{ m/s})^2 + (10.0 \text{ m/s})^2} = 24.3 \text{ m/s},$$
$$\theta = \tan^{-1}\frac{10.0 \text{ m/s}}{22.2 \text{ m/s}} = \tan^{-1}0.450 = 24.2°.$$

Part (b): At the highest point in the ball's path, the vertical velocity component v_y is zero. When does this happen? Call that time t_1; then, using $v_y = v_{0y} - gt$, we find that

$$v_y = 0 = 29.6 \text{ m/s} - (9.80 \text{ m/s}^2)t_1,$$
$$t_1 = 3.02 \text{ s}.$$

The height h at this time is the value of y when $t = 3.02$ s. We use Equation 11,

$$y = y_0 + v_{0y}t + \tfrac{1}{2}(-g)t^2,$$

to obtain

$$h = 0 + (29.6 \text{ m/s})(3.02 \text{ s}) + \tfrac{1}{2}(-9.80 \text{ m/s}^2)(3.02 \text{ s})^2$$
$$= 44.7 \text{ m}.$$

Alternatively, we can use the constant-acceleration formula

$$v_y^2 = v_{0y}^2 + 2a(y - y_0) = v_{0y}^2 + 2(-g)(y - y_0).$$

At the highest point, $v_y = 0$ and $y = h$. Substituting these in, along with $y_0 = 0$, we find that

$$0 = (29.6 \text{ m/s})^2 - 2(9.80 \text{ m/s}^2)h,$$
$$h = 44.7 \text{ m}.$$

This is roughly half the height of the Toronto Skydome above the playing field.

Part (c): To find the range R, we start by asking *when* the ball hits the ground. This occurs when $y = 0$. Call that time t_2; then, from Equation 11,

$$y = 0 = (29.6 \text{ m/s})t_2 + \tfrac{1}{2}(-9.80 \text{ m/s}^2)t_2^2.$$

This is a quadratic equation for t_2; it has two roots:

$$t_2 = 0 \qquad \text{and} \qquad t_2 = 6.04 \text{ s}.$$

There are two times at which $y = 0$: $t_2 = 0$ is the time the ball *leaves* the ground, and $t_2 = 6.04$ s is the time of its return. The latter is exactly twice the time taken to reach the highest point, so the time of descent equals the time of ascent. (This is *always* true if the starting and ending points are at the same elevation and air resistance is neglected. We'll prove it in Example 5.)

The range R is the value of x when the ball returns to the ground—that is, when $t = 6.04$ s:

$$R = v_{0x}t_2 = (22.2 \text{ m/s})(6.04 \text{ s}) = 134 \text{ m}.$$

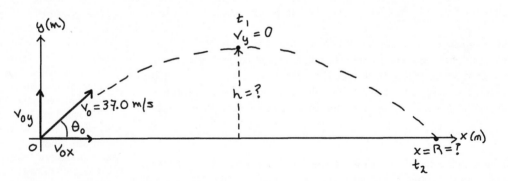

▲ **FIGURE 16** Our sketch for this problem.

Continued

For comparison, the distance from home plate to center field at Pittsburgh's PNC Park is 399 ft (about 122 m). If we could neglect air resistance, the ball really would be a home run.

At the instant the ball returns to $y = 0$, its vertical component of velocity is

$$v_y = 29.6 \text{ m/s} + (-9.80 \text{ m/s}^2)(6.04 \text{ s}) = -29.6 \text{ m/s}.$$

That is, v_y has the same magnitude as the initial vertical velocity v_{0y}, but the opposite sign. Since v_x is constant, the angle $\theta = -53.1°$ (below the horizontal) at this point is the negative of the initial angle $\theta_0 = 53.1°$.

REFLECT The actual values of the maximum height h and the range R are substantially less than the values we've found, because air resistance is *not* negligible. In fact, the range of a batted ball is substantially greater (on the order of 10 m for a home-run ball) in Denver than in Pittsburgh, because the density of air is almost 20% less in Denver.

Practice Problem: If the ball could continue to travel *below* its original level (through an appropriately shaped hole in the ground), then negative values of y corresponding to times greater than 6.04 s would be possible. Compute the ball's position and velocity 8.00 s after the start of its flight. *Answers:* $x = 178$ m, $y = -76.8$ m, $v_x = 22.2$ m/s, $v_y = -48.8$ m/s.

EXAMPLE 5   **Range and maximum height of a home-run ball**

For the situation of Example 4, derive general expressions for the maximum height h and the range R of a ball hit with an initial speed v_0 at an angle θ_0 above the horizontal (between 0 and 90°). For a given v_0, what value of θ_0 gives the maximum height? The maximum horizontal range?

SOLUTION

SET UP We can use the same coordinate system and diagram as for Example 4, so $y_0 = 0$.

SOLVE The basic relations are Equations 12 through 15. The solution will follow the same pattern as in Example 4, but now no numerical values are given. Thus the results won't be numbers, but rather symbolic expressions from which we can extract general relationships and proportionalities.

First, for a given θ_0, *when* does the projectile reach its highest point? At this point, $v_y = 0$, so, from Equation 15, the time t_1 at the highest point $(y = h)$ is given by

$$v_y = v_0 \sin\theta_0 - gt_1 = 0, \qquad t_1 = \frac{v_0 \sin\theta_0}{g}.$$

Next, in terms of v_0 and θ_0, what is the value of y at this time? From Equations 10 and 13,

$$h = v_{0y}t - \tfrac{1}{2}gt^2 = v_0\sin\theta_0\left(\frac{v_0\sin\theta_0}{g}\right) - \tfrac{1}{2}g\left(\frac{v_0\sin\theta_0}{g}\right)^2,$$

$$h = \frac{v_0^2 \sin^2\theta_0}{2g}.$$

To derive a general expression for the range R, we again follow the procedure we used in Example 4. First we find an expression for the time t_2 when the projectile returns to its initial elevation, At that time, $y = 0$; from Equation 13,

$$t_2(v_0\sin\theta_0 - \tfrac{1}{2}gt_2) = 0.$$

The two roots of this quadratic equation for t_2 are $t_2 = 0$ (the launch time) and $t_2 = 2v_0\sin\theta_0/g$. The range R is the value of x at the *second* time. Substituting this expression for t_2 into Equation 12, we find that

$$R = (v_0\cos\theta_0)\frac{2v_0\sin\theta_0}{g}.$$

We now use the trigonometric identity $2\sin\theta_0\cos\theta_0 = \sin 2\theta_0$ to rewrite this equation as

$$R = \frac{v_0^2 \sin 2\theta_0}{g}.$$

REFLECT If we vary θ_0, the *maximum* value of h occurs when $\sin\theta_0 = 1$ and $\theta_0 = 90°$, in other words, when the ball is hit straight up. That's what we should expect. In that case, $h = v_0^2/2g$. If the ball is launched horizontally, then $\theta_0 = 0$, and the maximum height is zero! The maximum range R occurs when $\sin 2\theta_0$ has its greatest value, namely, unity. That occurs when $2\theta_0 = 90°$, or $\theta_0 = 45°$. This angle gives the maximum range for a given initial speed.

Note that both h and R are proportional to the *square* of the initial speed v_0; this relationship may be a little surprising. If we double the initial speed, the range and maximum height increase by a factor of four! We can also use proportional-reasoning methods, along with the equations for h and R just derived, to confirm that both of these quantities are proportional to v_0^2 and inversely proportional to g.

Practice Problem: Show that the range is the same when the launch angle is 30° as when it is 60° and that it is the same for any launch angle θ_0 as for the complementary angle $(90° - \theta_0)$. *Answer:* $\sin\phi = \sin(180° - \phi)$, so $\sin 2\theta_0 = \sin 2(90° - \theta_0)$.

A 45° launch angle gives the greatest range; other angles fall shorter.

▲ FIGURE 17 A firing angle of 45° gives the maximum horizontal range (based on a strobe photo).

◀ **Application** **Faster than a speeding bullet?** In a human cannonball act, the cannon must be angled so that the human projectile lands in the net. If the available space is short, this angle will be higher than 45°. Also, allowance must be made for the level of the net—it may be higher or lower than the level of the muzzle. Finally, a human cannonball is *not* an ideal projectile—air resistance has to be taken into account.

NOTE ▶ We don't recommend memorizing the equations for h and R. They are applicable only in the special circumstances that we have described. In particular, they are valid *only* when the launch and landing heights are equal. You may encounter problems to which these equations are *not* applicable. ◀

Figure 17 is based on a composite photograph of three trajectories of a ball projected from a spring gun at angles of $< 45°$, $45°$, and $> 45°$. The initial speed v_0 is approximately the same in all three cases. The horizontal ranges are nearly the same for the smallest and largest angles, and the range for $45°$ is greater than either.

Symmetry in Projectile Motion

Comparing the expressions for t_1 and t_2 in Example 5, we see that $t_2 = 2t_1$; that is, the total flight time is twice the time required to reach the highest point. It follows that the time required to reach the highest point equals the time required to fall from there back to the initial elevation, as we asserted in Example 4. More generally, Figure 11 shows that the path of the particle is symmetric about the highest point.

 Conceptual Analysis 3 **Throwing stones**

Two stones are launched from the top of a tall building. One stone is thrown in a direction 20° above the horizontal with a speed of 10 m/s; the other is thrown in a direction 20° below the horizontal with the same speed. How do their speeds compare just before they hit the ground below? (Neglect air friction.)

A. The one thrown upward is traveling faster.
B. The one thrown downward is traveling faster.
C. Both are traveling at the same speed.

SOLUTION We've just learned that the portion of a projectile's trajectory that lies above the initial height will be symmetric about its highest point. Thus, when the stone launched upward comes back to the level of the building's top, it is moving at 10 m/s in a direction 20° below the horizontal (symmetric to its launch velocity). At this point, it has the same speed and angle as the stone launched downward. The velocities of the two stones therefore match exactly at any position below the top of the building. So answer C is correct.

EXAMPLE 6 **Kicking a field goal**

For a field goal attempt, a football is kicked from a point on the ground that is a horizontal distance s from the goalpost. For the attempt to be successful, the ball must clear the crossbar, 10 ft (about 3.05 m) above the ground, as shown in Figure 18.

The ball leaves the kicker's foot with an initial speed of 20.0 m/s at an angle of 30° above the horizontal. What is the distance d between kicker and goalpost if the ball barely clears the crossbar?

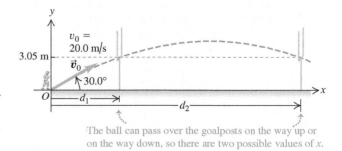

The ball can pass over the goalposts on the way up or on the way down, so there are two possible values of x.

▲ FIGURE 18 Kicking a field goal.

Continued

SOLUTION

SET UP We use our idealized model of projectile motion, in which we assume level ground, neglect effects of air resistance, and treat the football as a point particle. We place the origin of coordinates at the point where the ball is kicked. Then $x_0 = y_0 = 0$,

$$v_{0x} = v_0 \cos 30.0° = (20.0 \text{ m/s})(0.866) = 17.3 \text{ m/s}, \quad \text{and}$$
$$v_{0y} = v_0 \sin 30.0° = (20.0 \text{ m/s})(0.500) = 10.0 \text{ m/s}.$$

SOLVE We first ask *when* (i.e., at what value of t) the ball is at a height of 3.05 m above the ground; then we find the value of x at that time. When that value of x is equal to the distance d, the ball is just barely passing over the crossbar.

To find the time t when $y = 3.05$ m, we use the equation $y = y_0 + v_{0y}t - \frac{1}{2}gt^2$. Substituting numerical values, we obtain

$$3.05 \text{ m} = (10.0 \text{ m/s})t - (4.90 \text{ m/s}^2)t^2.$$

This is a quadratic equation; to solve it, we first write it in standard form: $(4.90 \text{ m/s}^2)t^2 - (10.0 \text{ m/s})t + 3.05 \text{ m} = 0$. Then we use the quadratic formula. We get

$$t = \frac{1}{2(4.9 \text{ m/s}^2)}$$
$$\times \left(10.0 \text{ m/s} \pm \sqrt{(10.0 \text{ m/s})^2 - 4(4.90 \text{ m/s}^2)(3.05 \text{ m})}\right)$$
$$= 0.373 \text{ s}, 1.67 \text{ s}.$$

There are two roots: $t = 0.373$ s and $t = 1.67$ s. The ball passes the height 3.05 m twice, once on the way up and once on the way down. We need to find the value of x at each of these times, using the equation for x as a function of time. Because $x_0 = 0$, we have simply $x = v_{0x}t$. For $t = 0.373$ s, we get $x = d_1 = (17.3 \text{ m/s})(0.373 \text{ s}) = 6.45$ m, and for $t = 1.67$ s, we get $x = d_2 = (17.3 \text{ m/s})(1.67 \text{ s}) = 28.9$ m. So if the goalpost is located between 6.45 m and 28.9 m from the initial point, the ball will pass over the crossbar; otherwise it will pass under it.

REFLECT The distance of 28.9 m is about 32 yards; field goal attempts are often successful at that distance. The ball passes the height $y = 10$ ft twice, once on the way up (when $t = 0.373$ s) and once on the way down (when $t = 1.67$ s). To verify this, we could calculate v_y at both times; when we do, we find that it is positive (upward) at $t = 0.373$ s and negative (downward) with the same magnitude at $t = 1.67$ s.

Practice Problem: If the kicker gives the ball the same initial speed and angle, but the ball is kicked from a point 25 m from the goalpost, what is the height of the ball above the crossbar as it crosses over the goalpost? *Answer: 1.2 m.*

EXAMPLE 7   Robin Hood shoots a pear

In a festival competition, the great archer Robin Hood is challenged to hit a falling pear with an arrow. At the sound of a horn, he is to shoot his arrow, and at the same instant the pear will be dropped from the top of a tall tower. As shown in Figure 19, Robin Hood aims *directly* at the initial position of the pear, seemingly making no allowance for the fact that the pear is dropping as the arrow moves toward it. His rivals assume that this is a mistake, but to their shock, he hits the pear. Show that if the arrow is aimed directly at the initial position of the pear, it will *always* hit the pear, regardless of the pear's initial location or initial speed (assuming that neither pear nor arrow hits the ground first).

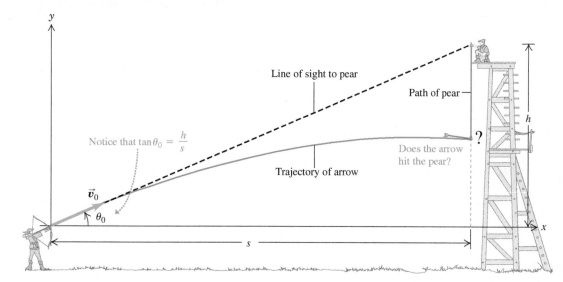

▲ **FIGURE 19** Robin Hood's shot.

Continued

SOLUTION

SET UP To show that the arrow hits the pear, we have to prove that there is some time when the arrow and the pear have the same x and y coordinates. We place the origin at the point from which Robin Hood shoots the arrow. Figure 19 shows that, initially, the pear is a horizontal distance s and a vertical distance $h = s\tan\theta_0$ from this point. First, we derive an expression for the time when the x coordinates are the same. Then we ask whether the y coordinates are *also* the same at this time; if they are, the arrow hits the pear.

SOLVE The pear drops straight down, so for it, $x_{\text{pear}} = s$ at *all* times. For the arrow, x_{arrow} is given by Equation 12: $x_{\text{arrow}} = (v_0\cos\theta_0)t$. The time when the x coordinates of the arrow and pear are equal (i.e., $x_{\text{pear}} = x_{\text{arrow}}$) is given by $s = (v_0\cos\theta_0)t$, or

$$t = \frac{s}{v_0\cos\theta_0}.$$

Now we ask whether y_{arrow} and y_{pear} are also equal at this time; if they are, we have a hit. The pear is in one-dimensional free fall, and its position at *any* time t is given by Equation 11, that is, $y = y_0 + v_{0y}t - \frac{1}{2}gt^2$. The initial height is $y_0 = s\tan\theta_0$, the initial y component of velocity v_y is zero, and we find that

$$y_{\text{pear}} = s\tan\theta_0 - \frac{1}{2}gt^2.$$

For the arrow, we use Equation 13:

$$y_{\text{arrow}} = (v_0\sin\theta_0)t - \frac{1}{2}gt^2.$$

If the y coordinates are equal ($y_{\text{pear}} = y_{\text{arrow}}$) at the same time that $t = s/v_0\cos\theta_0$, the time when their x coordinates are equal, we have a hit. We see that this happens if $s\tan\theta_0 = (v_0\sin\theta_0)t$ at time $t = s/v_0\cos\theta_0$ (the time when the x coordinates are equal).

When we substitute this expression for t into the preceding equation, the right side becomes

$$(v_0\sin\theta_0)t = (v_0\sin\theta_0)\frac{s}{v_0\cos\theta_0} = s\tan\theta_0.$$

We see that the right side is indeed equal to the left side, showing that, at the time when the x coordinates of pear and arrow are equal, their y coordinates are also equal. Robin Hood wins the contest!

REFLECT We have established the fact that, at the time the x coordinates are equal, the y coordinates are also equal. Thus, an arrow aimed at the initial position of the pear *always* hits it, no matter what v_0 is. With no gravity ($g = 0$), the pear would remain motionless, and the arrow would travel in a straight line to hit it. With gravity, both objects "fall" the same additional distance $\left(-\frac{1}{2}gt^2\right)$ below their $g = 0$ positions, and the arrow still hits the pear. We can see this explicitly in the expressions for the y positions of the two objects, where the effects of gravity are highlighted:

Arrow: $\qquad\qquad\qquad\qquad$ Pear:

$$y_{\text{arrow}} = v_{0y}\,t - \frac{1}{2}gt^2 \quad \text{and} \quad y_{\text{pear}} = y_{0,\text{pear}} - \frac{1}{2}gt^2$$

Effect of gravity is the same for both.

Figure 20 shows a comparison of the situations with and without gravity.

Practice Problem: Suppose the pear is released from a height of 6.00 m above Robin's arrow, the arrow is shot at a speed of 30.0 m/s, and the distance between Robin Hood and the base of the tower is 15.0 m. Find the time at which the arrow hits the pear, the distance the pear has fallen, and the height of the arrow above its release point. *Answers:* 0.54 s, 1.4 m, and 4.6 m.

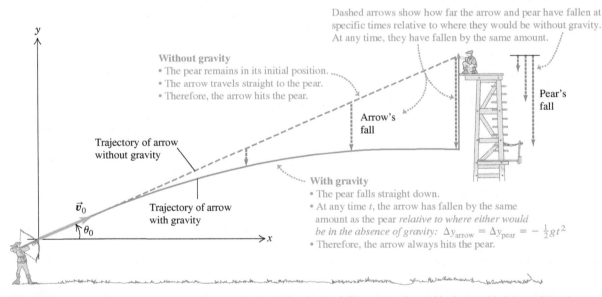

▲ **FIGURE 20** An explanation of why an arrow that is aimed directly at a falling target always hits it (provided that neither the arrow nor the target hits the ground first).

We mentioned at the beginning of this section that air resistance isn't always negligible. When it has to be included, the calculations become a lot more complicated, because the air-resistance forces depend on velocity and the acceleration is no longer constant. Figure 21 shows a computer simulation of the trajectory of the baseball in Example 4 for 10 s of flight, with an air-resistance force proportional to the square of the particle's speed. We see that air resistance decreases the maximum height and range substantially, and the trajectory becomes asymmetric. In this case, the initial angle θ_0 that gives maximum range (for a given value of v_0) is less than 45°.

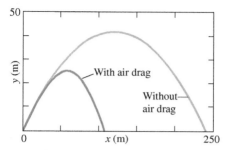

▲ **FIGURE 21** Computer-generated trajectories of a baseball with and without air resistance. Air resistance has a large cumulative effect on the flight of a baseball.

Quantitative Analysis 4

Shooting at a cliff

Suppose you shoot an arrow across a ravine at the vertical cliff opposite you, a distance d away, as shown in Figure 22. On your first try, you aim your arrow 15° above the horizontal, directly toward point A; it strikes the cliff a distance h below point A. On your next try, you aim the arrow 15° below the horizontal, toward point B, shooting it with the same speed. It will strike the cliff

A. the same distance h below point B.
B. less than distance h below point B.
C. more than distance h below point B.

SOLUTION If there were no gravitational force on the arrows, they would travel in straight lines, hitting the cliff at points A and B, respectively. The earth's gravitational attraction causes each arrow to fall below its straight-line path by an amount $\Delta y = -\frac{1}{2}gt^2$ for any time interval t. So, if the two arrows take the same time to reach the cliff, they will have fallen below their aiming points by the same amount $|\Delta y| = h$ when they strike, and answer A will be correct. Do they take the same time to reach the cliff? Remember that the time it takes a projectile to reach a given horizontal position x (the cliff, in this problem) depends on the projectile's horizontal component of velocity v_{0x}: $x - x_0 = v_{0x}t$ (where $x_0 = 0$ in this problem). Because the two arrows are shot at the same initial speed and at angles of 15° with respect to the horizontal, this component of velocity is the same for both. Therefore, the two arrows do in fact take the same time to reach the cliff and strike at equal distances below their aiming points.

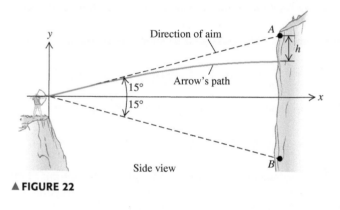

▲ **FIGURE 22**

4 Uniform Circular Motion

We discussed components of acceleration in Section 2. When a particle moves along a curved path, the direction of its velocity changes. Thus it *must* have a component of acceleration perpendicular to the path, even if its speed is constant.

When a particle moves in a circle with constant speed, the motion is called **uniform circular motion.** A car rounding a curve with a constant radius at constant speed, a satellite moving in a circular orbit, and an ice skater skating in a circle with constant speed are all examples of uniform circular motion. There is no component of acceleration parallel (tangent) to the path; otherwise, the speed would change (Figure 23). The component of acceleration perpendicular to the path, which causes the direction of the velocity to change, is related in a simple way to the speed v of the particle and the radius R of the circle. Our next project is to derive that relation.

First we note that this is a different problem from the projectile-motion situation in Section 3, in which the acceleration was always straight down and was constant in both magnitude and direction. Here the acceleration is perpendicular

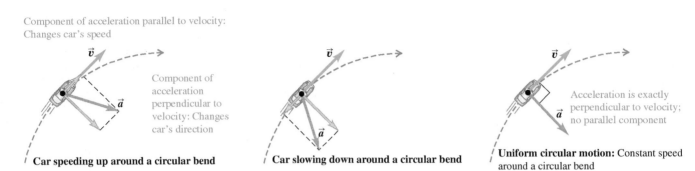

Component of acceleration parallel to velocity: Changes car's speed

$\vec{v}$

$\vec{a}$

Component of acceleration perpendicular to velocity: Changes car's direction

Car speeding up around a circular bend

$\vec{v}$

$\vec{a}$

Car slowing down around a circular bend

$\vec{v}$

$\vec{a}$

Acceleration is exactly perpendicular to velocity; no parallel component

Uniform circular motion: Constant speed around a circular bend

▲ **FIGURE 23** In uniform circular motion, an object moves at constant speed in a circular path, and its acceleration is perpendicular to its velocity.

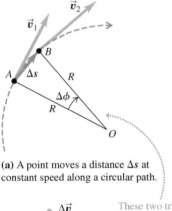

(a) A point moves a distance Δs at constant speed along a circular path.

These two triangles are similar.

(b) The corresponding change in velocity.

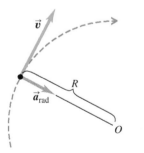

(c) The acceleration in uniform circular motion always points toward the center of the circle.

▲ **FIGURE 24** Finding the change in velocity $\vec{v}$ of an object moving in a circle at constant speed.

to the velocity at each instant; as the direction of the velocity changes, the direction of the acceleration also changes. As we will see, the acceleration vector at each point in the circular path is directed toward the *center* of the circle.

Figure 24a shows an object (represented by a dot) moving with constant speed in a circular path with radius R and center at O. The object moves from A to B, a distance Δs, in a time Δt. The vector change in velocity $\Delta \vec{v}$ during this time is shown in Figure 24b.

The two triangles, one in Figure 24a, the other in Figure 24b, are *similar,* because both are isosceles triangles and the angles $\Delta \phi$ are the same. From geometry, the ratios of corresponding sides of similar triangles are equal, so

$$\frac{|\Delta \vec{v}|}{v_1} = \frac{\Delta s}{R}, \quad \text{or} \quad |\Delta \vec{v}| = \frac{v_1}{R} \Delta s.$$

The magnitude a_{av} of the average acceleration $\vec{a}_{av}$ during Δt is therefore

$$a_{av} = \frac{|\Delta \vec{v}|}{\Delta t} = \frac{v_1}{R} \frac{\Delta s}{\Delta t}.$$

The magnitude a of the instantaneous acceleration $\vec{a}$ at point A is the limit of this expression as Δt approaches zero and point B gets closer and closer to point A:

$$a = \lim_{\Delta t \to 0} \frac{v_1}{R} \frac{\Delta s}{\Delta t} = \frac{v_1}{R} \lim_{\Delta t \to 0} \frac{\Delta s}{\Delta t}.$$

But the limit of $\Delta s/\Delta t$ is just the *speed* v_1 at point A. Also, A can be any point on the path, and the speed is the same at every point on the path. So we can drop the subscript and let v represent the speed at *any* point. Then we obtain the following relationship:

Acceleration in uniform circular motion

The acceleration of an object in uniform circular motion is *radial,* meaning that it always points toward the center of the circle and is perpendicular to the object's velocity $\vec{v}$. We denote it as $\vec{a}_{rad}$; its magnitude a_{rad} is given by

$$a_{rad} = \frac{v^2}{R}. \tag{16}$$

That is, the magnitude a_{rad} is proportional to the square of the speed $(a_{rad} \propto v^2)$ and inversely proportional to the radius $(a_{rad} \propto 1/R)$.

Because the acceleration of an object in uniform circular motion is always directed toward the center of the circle, it is sometimes called **centripetal acceleration.**

▶ **Application Where am I?** If you've ever used a global positioning system (GPS) unit for navigating or geocaching, you've used an application of uniform circular motion. This system uses a group of 24 satellites to pinpoint locations anywhere on the earth's surface or in the air, often to within as little as 3 meters. Although these satellites are moving at speeds of over 11,000 km/h, their orbits are precisely known, and their exact positions at any instant can be determined. In the field, distance readings taken simultaneously from several of the satellites to a GPS unit provide position vectors that are used to determine precise positions anywhere on the earth.

The word *centripetal* is derived from two Latin words meaning "seeking the center."

Figure 25 shows the directions of the velocity and acceleration vectors at several points for an object moving with uniform circular motion. Compare the motion shown in this figure with the projectile motion in Figure 11, in which the acceleration is always directed straight down and is *not* perpendicular to the path, except at the highest point in the trajectory.

It may seem odd that the centripetal acceleration is proportional to the *square* of the object's speed, rather simply proportional to the speed. Here's a way to make that relationship more plausible. Suppose that in Figure 24 we double the object's speed. This doubles the magnitude of the velocity vector, which would seem to double its rate of change when its direction changes. But note that the direction is also changing twice as rapidly, an effect that, by itself, would double the magnitude of the acceleration. So each of the two effects separately would double a_{rad}, and the combined effect is to increase a_{rad} by a factor of four when v is doubled. Hence we say that a_{rad} is proportional to v^2.

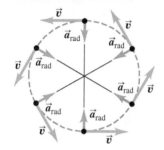

▲ **FIGURE 25** For an object in uniform circular motion, the velocity at each point is tangent to the circle, and the acceleration is directed toward the center of the circle.

EXAMPLE 8   Fast car, flat curve

The 2005 Corvette claims a "lateral acceleration" of 0.92 g, which is $(0.92)(9.8 \text{ m/s}^2) = 8.9 \text{ m/s}^2$. If this represents the maximum centripetal acceleration that can be attained without skidding out of the circular path, and if the car is traveling at a constant 45 m/s (about 101 mi/h), what is the minimum radius of curve the car can negotiate? (Assume that the curve is unbanked.)

SOLUTION

SET UP AND SOLVE Figure 26 shows our diagram. The solution is a straightforward application of Equation 16. We find that

$$R = \frac{v^2}{a_{rad}} = \frac{(45 \text{ m/s})^2}{8.9 \text{ m/s}^2} = 230 \text{ m} \quad \left(\text{about } \tfrac{1}{7} \text{ mi}\right).$$

REFLECT Don't try this at home! The acceleration given represents an absolute maximum with smooth, dry pavement and very grippy tires. If the curve is banked, the radius can be smaller.

Practice Problem: A more reasonable maximum acceleration for varying pavement conditions is 5.0 m/s². Under these condi-

▲ **FIGURE 26** Our diagram for this problem.

tions, what is the maximum speed at which a car can negotiate a flat curve with radius 230 m? *Answer:* 34 m/s = 76 mi/h.

EXAMPLE 9 A high-speed carnival ride

The passengers in a carnival ride travel in a circle with radius 5.0 m (Figure 27). They make one complete circle in a time $T = 4.0$ s. What is their acceleration?

SOLUTION

SET UP Figure 28 shows our diagram.

SOLVE We again use Equation 16: $a = v^2/R$. To find the speed v, we use the fact that a passenger travels a distance equal to the circumference of the circle $(2\pi R)$ in the time T for one revolution:

$$v = \frac{2\pi R}{T} = \frac{2\pi(5.0\text{ m})}{4.0\text{ s}} = 7.9\text{ m/s}.$$

The centripetal acceleration is

$$a_{rad} = \frac{v^2}{R} = \frac{(7.9\text{ m/s})^2}{5.0\text{ m}} = 12\text{ m/s}^2.$$

REFLECT As in Example 8, the direction of $\vec{a}$ is always toward the center of the circle. The magnitude of $\vec{a}$ is greater than g, the acceleration due to gravity, so this is not a ride for the faint-hearted. (But some roller coasters subject their passengers to accelerations as great as $4g$.)

Practice Problem: If the ride increases in speed so that $T = 2.0$ s, what is a_{rad}? (This question can be answered by using proportional reasoning, without much arithmetic.) *Answer:* 49 m/s²

► **FIGURE 27**

Shutterstock

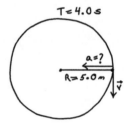

▲ **FIGURE 28** Our diagram for this problem.

5 Relative Velocity in a Plane

We have introduced the concept of *relative velocity* for motion along a straight line. We can extend this concept to include motion in a plane by using vector addition to combine velocities.

Suppose that woman is walking, not down the aisle of the railroad car, but from one side of the car to the other, with a speed of 1.0 m/s, as shown in Figure 29a. We can again describe the woman's position in two different frames of reference: that of the railroad car and that of the ground. Instead of coordinates x, we use position vectors $\vec{r}$. Let W represent the woman's position, C the frame of reference of the stationary ground observer (the cyclist), and T the frame of reference of the moving train. Then, as Figure 29b shows, the velocities are related by

$$\vec{v}_{W/C} = \vec{v}_{W/T} + \vec{v}_{T/C}.$$

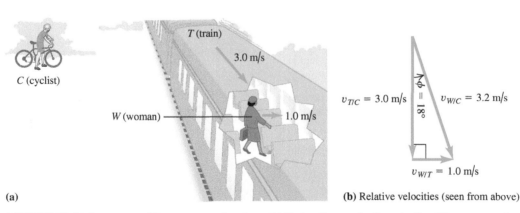

(a)

(b) Relative velocities (seen from above)

▲ **FIGURE 29** (a) A woman walking across a railroad car. (b) Vector diagram for the velocity of the woman relative to the cyclist. Recall that vector addition is commutative.

Relative motion in a plane

When an object W is moving with velocity $\vec{v}_{W/T}$ relative to an object (or observer) T, and T is moving with velocity $\vec{v}_{T/C}$ with respect to an object (or observer) C, the velocity $\vec{v}_{W/C}$ of W with respect to C is given by

$$\vec{v}_{W/C} = \vec{v}_{W/T} + \vec{v}_{T/C}. \qquad (17)$$

If the train's velocity relative to the cyclist has magnitude $v_{T/C} = 3.0 \text{ m/s}$ and the woman's velocity relative to the train has magnitude $v_{W/T} = 1.0 \text{ m/s}$, then her velocity $\vec{v}_{W/C}$ relative to the cyclist is as shown in the vector diagram of Figure 29b. The Pythagorean theorem then gives us

$$v_{W/C} = \sqrt{(3.0 \text{ m/s})^2 + (1.0 \text{ m/s})^2} = \sqrt{10 \text{ m}^2/\text{s}^2} = 3.2 \text{ m/s}.$$

We can also see from the diagram that the *direction* of her velocity relative to the cyclist makes an angle ϕ with the train's velocity vector $\vec{v}_{T/C}$, where

$$\tan\phi = \frac{v_{W/T}}{v_{T/C}} = \frac{1.0 \text{ m/s}}{3.0 \text{ m/s}}, \qquad \phi = 18°.$$

We have the general rule that if A and B are any two points or frames of reference, then

$$\vec{v}_{A/B} = -\vec{v}_{B/A}. \qquad (18)$$

The velocity of the woman relative to the train is the negative of the velocity of the train relative to the woman, and so on.

PROBLEM-SOLVING STRATEGY 2 **Relative velocity**

The strategy for relative velocity in a straight line is also useful here. The essential difference is that now the $\vec{v}$'s aren't all along the same line, so they have to be treated explicitly as vectors. For the double subscripts on the velocities, $\vec{v}_{A/B}$ always means "velocity of A relative to B." A useful rule for keeping the order of things straight is to regard each double subscript as a fraction. Then the fraction on the left side is the *product* of the fractions on the right sides: $P/A = (P/B)(B/A)$. This is helpful when you apply Equation 18. If there are *three* different frames of reference A, B, and C, you can write immediately

$$\vec{v}_{P/A} = \vec{v}_{P/C} + \vec{v}_{C/B} + \vec{v}_{B/A},$$

and so on. This is a *vector* equation, and you should always draw a vector diagram to show the addition of velocity vectors.

EXAMPLE 10 **Flying in a crosswind**

The compass of an airplane indicates that it is headed due north, and the airspeed indicator shows that the plane is moving through the air at 240 km/h. If there is a wind of 100 km/h from west to east, what is the velocity of the aircraft relative to the earth?

SOLUTION

SET UP Figure 30 shows the appropriate vector diagram. We choose subscript P to refer to the plane and subscript A to the moving air (which now plays the role of the railroad car in Figure 29). Subscript E refers to the earth. The information given is

$$\vec{v}_{P/A} = 240 \text{ km/h} \qquad \text{due north,}$$
$$\vec{v}_{A/E} = 100 \text{ km/h} \qquad \text{due east,}$$

and we want to find the magnitude and direction of $\vec{v}_{P/E}$.

Continued

SOLVE We adapt Equation 17 to the notation of this situation:

$$\vec{v}_{P/E} = \vec{v}_{P/A} + \vec{v}_{A/E}.$$

The three relative velocities and their relationship are shown in Figure 30. From this diagram, we find that

$$v_{P/E} = \sqrt{(240 \text{ km/h})^2 + (100 \text{ km/h})^2} = 260 \text{ km/h},$$

$$\alpha = \tan^{-1}\frac{100 \text{ km/h}}{240 \text{ km/h}} = 23° \text{ E of N}.$$

REFLECT The plane's velocity with respect to the air is straight north, but the air's motion relative to earth gives the plane's velocity with respect to earth a component toward the east.

Practice Problem: If the plane maintains its airspeed of 240 km/h, but the wind decreases, what is the wind speed if the plane's velocity with respect to earth is 15° east of north? *Answer:* 64 km/h

▲ **FIGURE 30** The plane is pointed north, but the wind blows east, giving the resultant velocity $\vec{v}_{P/E}$ relative to the earth.

EXAMPLE 11   Compensating for a crosswind

In what direction should the pilot in Example 10 head in order for the plane to travel due north? What will be her velocity relative to the earth then? (Assume that the wind velocity and the magnitude of her airspeed are the same as in Example 10.)

SOLUTION

SET UP Now the information given is

$$\vec{v}_{P/A} = 240 \text{ km/h} \qquad \text{direction unknown,}$$
$$\vec{v}_{A/E} = 100 \text{ km/h} \qquad \text{due east.}$$

Figure 31 shows the appropriate vector diagram. Be sure you understand why this is not the same diagram as that in Figure 30.

SOLVE We want to find $\vec{v}_{P/E}$; its magnitude is unknown, but we know that its direction is due north. Note that both this and the preceding example require us to determine two unknown quantities. In Example 10, these were the magnitude and direction of $\vec{v}_{P/E}$; in this example, the unknowns are the direction of $\vec{v}_{P/A}$ and the *magnitude* of $\vec{v}_{P/E}$.

The three relative velocities must still satisfy the vector equation

$$\vec{v}_{P/E} = \vec{v}_{P/A} + \vec{v}_{A/E}.$$

We find that

$$\beta = \sin^{-1}\frac{100 \text{ km/h}}{240 \text{ km/h}} = 25°,$$

$$v_{P/E} = \sqrt{(240 \text{ km/h})^2 - (100 \text{ km/h})^2} = 218 \text{ km/h}.$$

The pilot should head 25° west of north; her ground speed will then be 218 km/h.

REFLECT When a plane flies in a crosswind that is at right angles to the plane's velocity relative to the ground, its speed relative to

▲ **FIGURE 31** The pilot must point the plane in the direction of the vector $\vec{v}_{P/A}$ in order to travel due north relative to the earth.

the ground is always less than the airspeed; the trip takes longer than in calm air.

Practice Problem: Prove that if the wind speed is greater than or equal to 240 km/h, the plane can't fly straight north relative to the ground, no matter how hard it tries. Hurricanes often have wind speeds of greater than 240 km/h (about 150 mi/h).

CHAPTER SUMMARY

Position, Velocity, and Acceleration Vectors

(Sections 1 and 2) The position vector $\vec{r}$ of an object in a plane is the displacement vector from the origin to that object. Its components are the coordinates x and y. The average velocity $\vec{v}_{av}$ of the object during a time interval Δt is its displacement $\Delta \vec{r}$ (the change in the position vector $\vec{r}$), divided by Δt:

$$\vec{v}_{av} = \frac{\vec{r}_2 - \vec{r}_1}{t_2 - t_1} = \frac{\Delta \vec{r}}{\Delta t}. \tag{1}$$

Because Δt is a scalar quantity, the direction of average velocity vector $\vec{v}_{av}$ is determined entirely by the direction of the vector displacement $\Delta \vec{r}$.

The instantaneous velocity $\vec{v}$ is $\vec{v} = \lim_{\Delta x \to 0} (\Delta \vec{r}/\Delta t)$; its components are $v_x = \lim_{\Delta t \to 0}(\Delta x/\Delta t)$ and $v_y = \lim_{\Delta t \to 0}(\Delta y/\Delta t)$.

The average acceleration $\vec{a}_{av}$ during the time interval Δt is the change in velocity, $\Delta \vec{v}$, divided by the time interval Δt:

$$\vec{a}_{av} = \frac{\vec{v}_2 - \vec{v}_1}{t_2 - t_1} = \frac{\Delta \vec{v}}{\Delta t}. \tag{4}$$

Instantaneous acceleration $\vec{a}$ is $\vec{a} = \lim_{\Delta t \to 0}(\Delta \vec{v}/\Delta t)$; its components are $a_x = \lim_{\Delta t \to 0}(\Delta v_x/\Delta t)$, $a_y = \lim_{\Delta t \to 0}(\Delta v_y/\Delta t)$. An object has acceleration if *either* its speed or its direction of motion changes—that is, if either the magnitude or direction of its velocity changes.

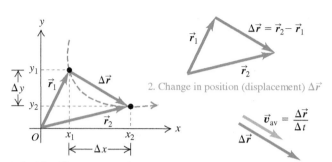

2. Change in position (displacement) $\Delta \vec{r}$

1. Position $\vec{r}$ in an x-y coordinate system

3. Average velocity $\vec{v}_{av}$ over a displacement

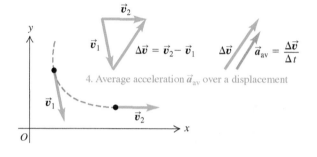

4. Average acceleration $\vec{a}_{av}$ over a displacement

Projectile Motion

(Section 3) Projectile motion occurs when an object is given an initial velocity and then follows a path determined entirely by the effect of a constant gravitational force. The path, called a **trajectory,** is a parabola in the x-y plane. The vertical motion of a projectile is independent of its horizontal motion.

In projectile motion, $a_x = 0$ (there is no horizontal component of acceleration) and $a_y = -g$ (a constant vertical component of acceleration due to a constant gravitational force). The coordinates and velocity components, as functions of time, are

$$x = (v_0 \cos\theta_0)t, \tag{12}$$
$$y = (v_0 \sin\theta_0)t - \frac{1}{2}gt^2, \tag{13}$$
$$v_x = v_0 \cos\theta_0, \tag{14}$$
$$v_y = v_0 \sin\theta_0 - gt. \tag{15}$$

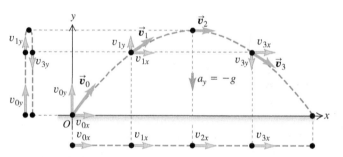

The vertical and horizontal components of a projectile's motion are independent.

Uniform Circular Motion

(Section 4) When a particle moves in a circular path with radius R and with constant speed v, it has an acceleration with magnitude

$$a_{rad} = \frac{v^2}{R} \tag{16}$$

always directed toward the center of the circle and perpendicular to the instantaneous velocity v at each instant.

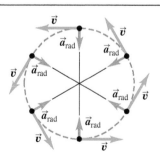

Continued

Relative Velocity

(Section 5) When an object P moves relative to another object (or reference frame) B, and B moves relative to a third object (or reference frame) A, we denote the velocity of P relative to B by $\vec{v}_{P/B}$, the velocity of P relative to A by $\vec{v}_{P/A}$, and the velocity of B relative to A by $\vec{v}_{B/A}$. These velocities are related by this variation of Equation 17:

$$\vec{v}_{P/A} = \vec{v}_{P/B} + \vec{v}_{B/A}.$$

$\vec{v}_{P/A}$
$\vec{v}_{B/A}$ Wind relative to ground
$\vec{v}_{P/B}$

Plane relative to ground

Plane relative to wind

$\vec{v}_{P/A} = \vec{v}_{P/B} + \vec{v}_{B/A}$

A (ground observer) B (wind) P (plane)

Motion in a Plane: Problem Set

Conceptual Questions

1. A football is thrown in a parabolic path. Is there any point at which the acceleration is parallel to the velocity? Perpendicular to the velocity?

2. When a rifle is fired at a stationary distant target, the barrel is not lined up exactly with the target. Why not?

3. A physicist measures the acceleration of a falling body in an elevator traveling at a constant speed of 9.8 m/s. What result does she obtain if the elevator is traveling (a) upward and (b) downward?

4. Intrigued by her result in the previous question, the physicist now measures the acceleration of a falling body in an elevator accelerating at a constant 9.8 m/s^2. What result does she obtain if the elevator is accelerating (a) upward and (b) downward?

5. A package falls from an airplane in level flight at constant speed. If air resistance can be neglected, how does the motion of the package look to the pilot? To a person on the ground?

6. If an athlete can give himself the same initial speed regardless of the direction in which he jumps, how is his maximum vertical jump (high jump) related to his maximum horizontal jump (long jump)?

7. The maximum range of a projectile occurs when it is aimed at a 45° angle if air resistance is neglected. At what angle should you launch it so that it will achieve the maximum time in the air? What would be its range in that case?

8. If an artificial earth satellite is in an orbit around the earth's equator with a period of exactly 1 day, how does its motion look to an observer on the rotating earth if it orbits in the same direction as the earth turns? (Such an orbit is said to be *geosynchronous;* most communications satellites are placed in geosynchronous orbits.)

9. A projectile is fired at an angle above the horizontal from the edge of a vertical cliff. (a) Is its velocity ever only horizontal? If so, when? (b) Is its velocity ever only vertical? If so, why?

10. An archer shoots an arrow from the top of a vertical cliff at an angle θ above the horizontal. When the arrow reaches the level ground at the bottom of the cliff, will its speed depend on the angle θ at which it was shot?

11. An observer draws the path of a stone thrown into the air, as shown in the Figure 32. What is wrong with the path shown? (There are *two* things wrong with it; can you spot both of them?)

▲ **FIGURE 32** Problem 11.

12. A frisky grasshopper leaps into the air with an initial speed of 1.5 m/s at an angle of 60° above the level ground. The insect feels no air resistance. (a) Using the given information, what could you calculate regarding the grasshopper's motion? (Do not actually calculate it; just decide what things you *could* calculate.) (b) What information could you calculate if you knew only the grasshopper's initial speed, but not the angle at which it jumped?

13. In uniform circular motion, how does the acceleration change when the speed is increased by a factor of 3? When the radius is decreased by a factor of 2?

14. Suppose a space capsule with an astronaut inside is launched from the top of a tower at some angle above the horizontal. (a) While the capsule is in free fall, what are the acceleration of the astronaut and the capsule? (b) If the astronaut measures his acceleration compared with that of the capsule, what value will he get? (c) In what sense can we say that the astronaut is "weightless" in the capsule? Is he "weightless" because the gravity of the earth has gone away?

15. A hunter shoots a bullet from the top of a cliff. What is wrong with the drawing of the bullet's path in Figure 33?

16. According to what we have seen about circular motion, the earth is accelerating toward the sun, yet it is not getting any closer to the sun. To many people, this situation would seem like a contradiction. Explain why it really is *not* a contradiction.

▲ **FIGURE 33** Problem 15.

Multiple-Choice Problems

1. A cannonball is fired toward a vertical building 400 m away with an initial velocity of 100 m/s at 36.9° above the horizontal. The ball will hit the building in
   A. 4.0 s.   B. 5.0 s.
   C. less than 4.0 s.   D. more than 5.0 s.

2. If the cannonball in the previous question is fired horizontally from a 150-m-high cliff, but still 400 m from the building, then the ball will hit the building in
   A. 4.0 s.   B. 5.0 s.
   C. less than 4.0 s.   D. more than 5.0 s.

3. A ball thrown horizontally from the top of a building hits the ground in 0.50 s. If it had been thrown with twice the speed in the same direction, it would have hit the ground in
   A. 4.0 s.   B. 1.0 s.   C. 0.50 s.
   D. 0.25 s.   E. 0.125 s.

4. Two balls are dropped from the top of the Leaning Tower of Pisa. The second ball is dropped a fraction of a second after the first ball. As they continue to accelerate to the ground, the distance between them will
   A. remain constant.
   B. decrease.
   C. increase.

5. Two balls are dropped at the same time from different heights. As they accelerate toward the ground, the distance between them will
   A. remain constant.
   B. decrease.
   C. increase.

6. A rock dropped from a small bridge encounters no air resistance and hits the pond below 1.0 s later. If it had been thrown horizontally with a speed of 10 m/s, then it would have hit the water
   A. more than 1.0 s later, since it has a greater distance to travel.
   B. 1.0 s later, since the vertical motion is not affected by the horizontal motion.
   C. less than 1.0 s later, since the higher speed would tend to get the ball to the ground more quickly.

7. An airplane flying at a constant horizontal velocity drops a package of supplies to a scientific mission in the Antarctic. If air resistance is negligibly small, the path of this package, *as observed by a person in the plane,* is
   A. a parabola.
   B. a straight line downward.
   C. a straight line pointing ahead of the plane.
   D. a straight line pointing behind the plane.

8. Your boat departs from the bank of a river that has a swift current parallel to its banks. If you want to cross this river in the shortest amount of time, you should direct your boat
   A. perpendicular to the current.
   B. upstream.
   C. downstream.
   D. so that it drifts with the current.

9. A car is driving toward a building at 10 mph. On the roof of the car, an insect is scurrying away from the building at 15 mph relative to the car's roof. To a person sitting in the building, the insect's velocity is
   A. 25 mph away from the building.
   B. 25 mph toward the building.
   C. 5 mph away from the building.
   D. 5 mph toward the building.

10. A ball is thrown horizontally from the top of a building and lands a distance d from the foot of the building after having been in the air for a time T and encountering no significant air resistance. If the building were twice as tall, the ball would have
    A. landed a distance $2d$ from the foot of the building.
    B. been in the air a time $2T$.
    C. been in the air a time $T\sqrt{2}$.
    D. reached the ground with twice the speed it did from the shorter building.

11. A child standing on a rotating carousel at a distance R from the center walks slowly inward until she's a distance $R/2$ from the center. Compared to her original centripetal acceleration, her acceleration is now
    A. half as great
    B. twice as great
    C. $\sqrt{2}$ times as great
    D. unchanged

12. An airplane whose air speed is 600 mi/h is flying perpendicular to a jet stream whose speed relative to the earth's surface is 100 mi/h. The airplane's speed relative to the earth's surface is
    A. 600 mi/h
    B. somewhat less than 600 mi/h
    C. somewhat more than 600 mi/h
    D. 100 mi/h

13. A golf ball is hit into the air, but not straight up, and encounters no significant air resistance. Which statements accurately describe its motion while it is in the air? (More than one choice may be correct.)
    A. On the way up it is accelerating upward, and on the way down it is accelerating downward.
    B. On the way up, both its horizontal and vertical velocity components are decreasing; on the way down, they are both increasing.
    C. Its vertical acceleration is zero at the highest point.
    D. Its horizontal velocity does not change once it is in the air, but its vertical velocity does change.

14. You shoot a bullet at a tasty apple high up in a tree some feet in front of you, hoping to knock it loose so you can catch it and eat it. In order to hit this apple, you should aim
    A. directly at it.
    B. above it.
    C. below it.

15. At the same time that rock A is dropped from rest from the top of a building, rock B is thrown horizontally away from the building, also starting at the top. Air resistance is not large enough to worry about. Which of the following statements are correct? (More than one choice may be correct.)
    A. Rock B hits the ground before rock A does.
    B. Both rocks have the same speed just as they reach the ground.
    C. Rock B has more acceleration than rock A.
    D. Both rocks reach the ground at the same time.

16. A stone is thrown horizontally with a speed of 15 m/s from the top of a vertical cliff at the edge of a lake. If the stone hits the water 2.0 s later, the height of the cliff is closest to
    A. 10 m.   B. 20 m.   C. 30 m.   D. 50 m.

17. An object traveling at constant speed V in a circle of radius R has an acceleration a. If *both* R and V are doubled, the new acceleration will be
    A. a.   B. $2a$.   C. $4a$.   D. $8a$.

Problems

1 Velocity in a Plane

2 Acceleration in a Plane

1. • A meteor streaking through the night sky is located with radar. At point A its coordinates are $(5.00 \text{ km}, 1.20 \text{ km})$, and 1.14 s later it has moved to point B with coordinates $(6.24 \text{ km}, 0.925 \text{ km})$. Find (a) the x and y components of its average velocity between A and B and (b) the magnitude and direction of its average velocity between these two points.

2. • At an air show, a jet plane has velocity components $v_x = 625 \text{ km/h}$ and $v_y = 415 \text{ km/h}$ at time 3.85 s and $v_x = 838 \text{ km/h}$ and $v_y = 365 \text{ km/h}$ at time 6.52 s. For this time interval, find (a) the x and y components of the plane's average acceleration and (b) the magnitude and direction of its average acceleration.

3. •• A dragonfly flies from point A to point B along the path shown in Figure 34 in 1.50 s. (a) Find the x and y components of its position vector at point A. (b) What are the magnitude and direction of its position vector at A? (c) Find the x and y components of the dragonfly's average velocity between A and B. (d) What are the magnitude and direction of its average velocity between these two points?

▲ FIGURE 34 Problem 3.

4. • A coyote chasing a rabbit is moving 8.00 m/s due east at one moment and 8.80 m/s due south 4.00 s later. Find (a) the x and y components of the coyote's average acceleration during that time and (b) the magnitude and direction of the coyote's average acceleration during that time.

5. •• An athlete starts at point A and runs at a constant speed of 6.0 m/s around a round track 100 m in diameter, as shown in Figure 35. Find the x and y components of this runner's average velocity and average acceleration between points (a) A and B, (b) A and C, (c) C and D, and (d) A and A (a full lap). (e) Calculate the magnitude of the runner's average velocity between A and B. Is his average speed equal to the magnitude of his average velocity? Why or why not? (f) How can his velocity be changing if he is running at constant speed?

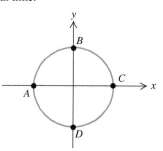

▲ FIGURE 35 Problem 5.

3 Projectile Motion

6. • A stone is thrown horizontally at 30.0 m/s from the top of a very tall cliff. (a) Calculate its horizontal position and vertical position at 2-s intervals for the first 10.0 s. (b) Plot your positions from part (a) to scale. Then connect your points with a smooth curve to show the trajectory of the stone.

7. • A baseball pitcher throws a fastball horizontally at a speed of 42.0 m/s. Ignoring air resistance, how far does the ball drop between the pitcher's mound and home plate, 60 ft 6 in away?

8. • A physics book slides off a horizontal tabletop with a speed of 1.10 m/s. It strikes the floor in 0.350 s. Ignore air resistance. Find (a) the height of the tabletop above the floor, (b) the horizontal distance from the edge of the table to the point where the book strikes the floor, and (c) the horizontal and vertical components of the book's velocity, and the magnitude and direction of its velocity, just before the book reaches the floor.

9. • A tennis ball rolls off the edge of a tabletop 0.750 m above the floor and strikes the floor at a point 1.40 m horizontally from the edge of the table. (a) Find the time of flight of the ball. (b) Find the magnitude of the initial velocity of the ball. (c) Find the magnitude and direction of the velocity of the ball just before it strikes the floor.

10. • A military helicopter on a training mission is flying horizontally at a speed of 60.0 m/s when it accidentally drops a bomb (fortunately, not armed) at an elevation of 300 m. You can ignore air resistance. (a) How much time is required for the bomb to reach the earth? (b) How far does it travel horizontally while falling? (c) Find the horizontal and vertical components of the bomb's velocity just before it strikes the earth. (d) Draw graphs of the horizontal distance vs. time and the vertical distance vs. time for the bomb's motion. (e) If the velocity of the helicopter remains constant, where is the helicopter when the bomb hits the ground?

11. •• Inside a starship at rest on the earth, a ball rolls off the top of a horizontal table and lands a distance D from the foot of the table. This starship now lands on the unexplored Planet X. The commander, Captain Curious, rolls the same ball off the same table with the same initial speed as on earth and finds that it lands a distance $2.76D$ from the foot of the table. What is the acceleration due to gravity on Planet X?

12. •• A daring 510 N swimmer dives off a cliff with a running horizontal leap, as shown in Figure 36. What must her minimum speed be just as she leaves the top of the cliff so that she will miss the ledge at the bottom, which is 1.75 m wide and 9.00 m below the top of the cliff?

▲ FIGURE 36 Problem 12.

13. •• **Leaping the river, I.** A 10,000 N car comes to a bridge during a storm and finds the bridge washed out. The 650 N driver must get to the other side, so he decides to try leaping it with his car. The side the car is on is 21.3 m above the river, while the opposite side is a mere 1.80 m above the river. The river itself is a raging torrent 61.0 m wide. (a) How fast should the car be traveling just as it leaves the cliff in order to clear the river and land safely on the opposite side? (b) What is the speed of the car just before it lands safely on the other side?

14. • A football is thrown with an initial upward velocity component of 15.0 m/s and a horizontal velocity component of 18.0 m/s. (a) How much time is required for the football to reach the highest point in its trajectory? (b) How high does it get above its release point? (c) How much time after it is

thrown does it take to return to its original height? How does this time compare with what you calculated in part (b)? Is your answer reasonable? (d) How far has the football traveled horizontally from its original position?

15. • A tennis player hits a ball at ground level, giving it an initial velocity of 24 m/s at 57° above the horizontal. (a) What are the horizontal and vertical components of the ball's initial velocity? (b) How high above the ground does the ball go? (c) How long does it take the ball to reach its maximum height? (d) What are the ball's velocity and acceleration at its highest point? (e) For how long a time is the ball in the air? (f) When this ball lands on the court, how far is it from the place where it was hit?

16. •• (a) A pistol that fires a signal flare gives it an initial velocity (muzzle velocity) of 125 m/s at an angle of 55.0° above the horizontal. You can ignore air resistance. Find the flare's maximum height and the distance from its firing point to its landing point if it is fired (a) on the level salt flats of Utah, and (b) over the flat Sea of Tranquility on the moon, where $g = 1.67$ m/s^2.

17. •• A major leaguer hits a baseball so that it leaves the bat at a speed of 30.0 m/s and at an angle of 36.9° above the horizontal. You can ignore air resistance. (a) At what two times is the baseball at a height of 10.0 m above the point at which it left the bat? (b) Calculate the horizontal and vertical components of the baseball's velocity at each of the two times you found in part (a). (c) What are the magnitude and direction of the baseball's velocity when it returns to the level at which it left the bat?

18. •• A balloon carrying a basket is descending at a constant velocity of 20.0 m/s. A person in the basket throws a stone with an initial velocity of 15.0 m/s horizontally perpendicular to the path of the descending balloon, and 4.00 s later this person sees the rock strike the ground. (See Figure 37.) (a) How high was the balloon when the rock was thrown out? (b) How far horizontally does the rock travel before it hits the ground? (c) At the instant the rock hits the ground, how far is it from the basket?

▲ **FIGURE 37** Problem 18.

19. •• A batted baseball leaves the bat at an angle of 30.0° above the horizontal and is caught by an outfielder 375 ft from home plate at the same height from which it left the bat. (a) What was the initial speed of the ball? (b) How high does the ball rise above the point where it struck the bat?

20. •• A man stands on the roof of a 15.0-m-tall building and throws a rock with a velocity of magnitude 30.0 m/s at an angle of 33.0° above the horizontal. You can ignore air resistance. Calculate (a) the maximum height above the roof reached by the rock, (b) the magnitude of the velocity of the rock just before it strikes the ground, and (c) the horizontal distance from the base of the building to the point where the rock strikes the ground.

21. • **The champion jumper of the insect world.** The froghopper, *Philaenus spumarius*, holds the world record for insect jumps. When leaping at an angle of 58.0° above the horizontal, some of the tiny critters have reached a maximum height of 58.7 cm above the level ground. (See *Nature*, Vol. 424, 31 July 2003, p. 509.) (a) What was the takeoff speed for such a leap? (b) What horizontal distance did the froghopper cover for this world-record leap?

22. •• A grasshopper leaps into the air from the edge of a vertical cliff, as shown in Figure 38. Use information from the figure to find (a) the initial speed of the grasshopper and (b) the height of the cliff.

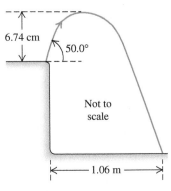

▲ **FIGURE 38** Problem 22.

23. •• Firemen are shooting a stream of water at a burning building. A high-pressure hose shoots out the water with a speed of 25.0 m/s as it leaves the hose nozzle. Once it leaves the hose, the water moves in projectile motion. The firemen adjust the angle of elevation of the hose until the water takes 3.00 s to reach a building 45.0 m away. You can ignore air resistance; assume that the end of the hose is at ground level. (a) Find the angle of elevation of the hose. (b) Find the speed and acceleration of the water at the highest point in its trajectory. (c) How high above the ground does the water strike the building, and how fast is it moving just before it hits the building?

24. •• Show that a projectile achieves its maximum range when it is fired at 45° above the horizontal if $y = y_0$.

25. •• A water balloon slingshot launches its projectiles essentially from ground level at a speed of 25.0 m/s. (a) At what angle should the slingshot be aimed to achieve its maximum range? (b) If shot at the angle you calculated in part (a), how far will a water balloon travel horizontally? (c) For how long will the balloon be in the air? (You can ignore air resistance.)

26. •• A certain cannon with a fixed angle of projection has a range of 1500 m. What will be its range if you add more powder so that the initial speed of the cannonball is tripled?

27. •• The nozzle of a fountain jet sits in the center of a circular pool of radius 3.50 m. If the nozzle shoots water at an angle of 65°, what is the maximum speed of the water at the nozzle that will allow it to land within the pool? (You can ignore air resistance.)

28. •• Two archers shoot arrows in the same direction from the same place with the same initial speeds but at different angles. One shoots at 45° above the horizontal, while the other shoots at 60.0°. If the arrow launched at 45° lands 225 m from the archer, how far apart are the two arrows when they land? (You can assume that the arrows start at essentially ground level.)

29. • A bottle rocket can shoot its projectile vertically to a height of 25.0 m. At what angle should the bottle rocket be fired to reach its maximum horizontal range, and what is that range? (You can ignore air resistance.)

30. •• An airplane is flying with a velocity of 90.0 m/s at an angle of 23.0° above the horizontal. When the plane is 114 m directly above a dog that is standing on level ground, a suitcase drops out of the luggage compartment. How far from the dog will the suitcase land? You can ignore air resistance.

4 Uniform Circular Motion

31. • You swing a 2.2 kg stone in a circle of radius 75 cm. At what speed should you swing it so its centripetal acceleration will be 9.8 m/s^2?

32. •• Calculate the radial acceleration (in m/s^2 and g's) of an object (a) on the ground at the earth's equator and (b) at the equator of Jupiter (which takes 0.41 day to spin once), turning with the planet.

33. •• Assume circular orbits. (a) What is the magnitude of the orbital velocity, in m/s, of the earth around the sun? (b) What is the radial acceleration, in m/s, of the earth toward the sun? (c) Repeat parts (a) and (b) for the motion of the planet Mercury.

34. • A model of a helicopter rotor has four blades, each 3.40 m in length from the central shaft to the tip of the blade. The model is rotated in a wind tunnel at 550 rev/min. (a) What is the linear speed, in m/s, of the blade tip? (b) What is the radial acceleration of the blade tip, expressed as a multiple of the acceleration g due to gravity?

35. •• A wall clock has a second hand 15.0 cm long. What is the radial acceleration of the tip of this hand?

36. • A curving freeway exit has a radius of 50.0 m and a posted speed limit of 35 mi/h. What is your radial acceleration (in m/s^2) if you take this exit at the posted speed? What if you take the exit at a speed of 50 mi/h?

37. •• **Dizziness.** Our balance is maintained, at least in part, by
BIO the endolymph fluid in the inner ear. Spinning displaces this fluid, causing dizziness. Suppose a dancer (or skater) is spinning at a very high 3.0 revolutions per second about a vertical axis through the center of his head. Although the distance varies from person to person, the inner ear is approximately 7.0 cm from the axis of spin. What is the radial acceleration (in m/s^2 and in g's) of the endolymph fluid?

38. • **Pilot blackout in a power dive.** A jet plane comes in for a
BIO downward dive as shown in Figure 39. The bottom part of the path is a quarter circle having a radius of curvature of 350 m. According to medical tests, pilots lose consciousness at an acceleration of 5.5g. At what speed (in m/s and mph) will the pilot black out for this dive?

▲ **FIGURE 39** Problem 38.

5 Relative Velocity in a Plane

39. •• A canoe has a velocity of 0.40 m/s southeast relative to the earth. The canoe is on a river that is flowing 0.50 m/s east relative to the earth. Find the velocity (magnitude and direction) of the canoe relative to the river.

40. •• **Crossing the river, I.** A river flows due south with a speed of 2.0 m/s. A man steers a motorboat across the river; his velocity relative to the water is 4.2 m/s due east. The river is 800 m wide. (a) What is his velocity (magnitude and direction) relative to the earth? (b) How much time is required for the man to cross the river? (c) How far south of his starting point will he reach the opposite bank?

41. •• **Crossing the river, II.** (a) In which direction should the motorboat in the previous problem head in order to reach a point on the opposite bank directly east from the starting point? (The boat's speed relative to the water remains 4.2 m/s.) (b) What is the velocity of the boat relative to the earth? (c) How much time is required to cross the river?

42. • You're standing outside on a windless day when raindrops begin to fall straight down. You run for shelter at a speed of 5.0 m/s, and you notice while you're running that the raindrops appear to be falling at an angle of about 30° from the vertical. What's the vertical speed of the raindrops?

43. •• **Bird migration.** Canadian geese migrate essentially along
BIO a north–south direction for well over a thousand kilometers in some cases, traveling at speeds up to about 100 km/h. If one such bird is flying at 100 km/h relative to the air, but there is a 40 km/h wind blowing from west to east, (a) at what angle relative to the north–south direction should this bird head so that it will be traveling directly southward relative to the ground? (b) How long will it take the bird to cover a ground distance of 500 km from north to south? (*Note:* Even on cloudy nights, many birds can navigate using the earth's magnetic field to fix the north–south direction.)

General Problems

44. •• A test rocket is launched by accelerating it along a 200.0-m incline at 1.25 m/s^2 starting from rest at point A (Figure 40.) The incline rises at 35.0° above the horizontal, and at the instant the rocket

▲ **FIGURE 40** Problem 44.

leaves it, its engines turn off and it is subject only to gravity (air resistance can be ignored). Find (a) the maximum height above the ground that the rocket reaches, and (b) the greatest horizontal range of the rocket beyond point A.

45. •• A player kicks a football at an angle of 40.0° from the horizontal, with an initial speed of 12.0 m/s. A second player standing at a distance of 30.0 m from the first (in the direction of the kick) starts running to meet the ball at the instant it is kicked. How fast must he run in order to catch the ball just before it hits the ground?

46. •• **Dynamite!** A demolition crew uses dynamite to blow an old building apart. Debris from the explosion flies off in all directions and is later found at distances as far as 50 m from the explosion. Estimate the maximum speed at which debris was blown outward by the explosion. Describe any assumptions that you make.

47. •• **Fighting forest fires.** When fighting forest fires, airplanes work in support of ground crews by dropping water on the fires. A pilot is practicing by dropping a canister of red dye, hoping to hit a target on the ground below. If the plane is flying in a horizontal path 90.0 m above the ground and with a speed of 64.0 m/s (143 mi/h), at what horizontal distance from the target should the pilot release the canister? Ignore air resistance.

48. •• **An errand of mercy.** An airplane is dropping bales of hay to cattle stranded in a blizzard on the Great Plains. The pilot releases the bales at 150 m above the level ground when the plane is flying at 75 m/s 55° above the horizontal. How far in front of the cattle should the pilot release the hay so that the bales will land at the point where the cattle are stranded?

49. •• A cart carrying a vertical missile launcher moves horizontally at a constant velocity of 30.0 m/s to the right. It launches a rocket vertically upward. The missile has an initial vertical velocity of

▲ **FIGURE 41** Problem 49.

40.0 m/s relative to the cart. (a) How high does the rocket go? (b) How far does the cart travel while the rocket is in the air? (c) Where does the rocket land relative to the cart?

50. •• **The longest home run.** According to the *Guinness Book of World Records,* the longest home run ever measured was hit by Roy "Dizzy" Carlyle in a minor-league game. The ball traveled 188 m (618 ft) before landing on the ground outside the ballpark. (a) Assuming that the ball's initial velocity was 45° above the horizontal, and ignoring air resistance, what did the initial speed of the ball need to be to produce such a home run if the ball was hit at a point 0.9 m (3.0 ft) above ground level? Assume that the ground was perfectly flat. (b) How far would the ball be above a fence 3.0 m (10 ft) in height if the fence were 116 m (380 ft) from home plate?

51. • A professional golfer can hit a ball with a speed of 70.0 m/s. What is the maximum distance a golf ball hit with this speed could travel on Mars, where the value of g is 3.71 m/s²? (The distances golf balls travel on earth are greatly shortened by air resistance and spin, as well as by the stronger force of gravity.)

52. •• A baseball thrown at an angle of 60.0° above the horizontal strikes a building 18.0 m away at a point 8.00 m above the point from which it is thrown. Ignore air resistance. (a) Find the magnitude of the initial velocity of the baseball (the velocity with which the baseball is thrown). (b) Find the magnitude and direction of the velocity of the baseball just before it strikes the building.

53. •• A boy 12.0 m above the ground in a tree throws a ball for his dog, who is standing right below the tree and starts running the instant the ball is thrown. If the boy throws the ball horizontally at 8.50 m/s, (a) how fast must the dog run to catch the ball just as it reaches the ground, and (b) how far from the tree will the dog catch the ball?

54. •• Suppose the boy in the previous problem throws the ball upward at 60.0° above the horizontal, but all else is the same. Repeat parts (a) and (b) of that problem.

55. •• A firefighting crew uses a water cannon that shoots water at 25.0 m/s at a fixed angle of 53.0° above the horizontal. The firefighters want to direct the water at a blaze that is 10.0 m above ground level. How far from the building should they position their cannon? There are *two* possibilities; can you get them both? (*Hint:* Start with a sketch showing the trajectory of the water.)

56. • A gun shoots a shell into the air with an initial velocity of 100.0 m/s, 60.0° above the horizontal on level ground. Sketch quantitative graphs of the shell's horizontal and vertical velocity components as functions of time for the complete motion.

57. ••• **Look out!** A snowball rolls off a barn roof that slopes downward at an angle of 40.0°. (See Figure 42.) The edge of the roof is 14.0 m above the ground, and the snowball has a speed of 7.00 m/s as it rolls off the roof. Ignore air resistance. How far from the edge of the barn does the snowball strike the ground if it doesn't strike anything else while falling?

▲ **FIGURE 42** Problem 57.

58. •• **Spiraling up.** It is common to see birds of prey rising upward on thermals. The paths they take may be spiral-like. **BIO** You can model the spiral motion as uniform circular motion combined with a constant upward velocity. Assume a bird completes a circle of radius 8.00 m every 5.00 s and rises vertically at a rate of 3.00 m/s. Determine: (a) the speed of the bird relative to the ground; (b) the bird's acceleration (magnitude and direction); and (c) the angle between the bird's velocity vector and the horizontal.

59. •• A water hose is used to fill a large cylindrical storage tank of diameter D and height $2D$ The hose shoots the water at 45° above the horizontal from the same level as the base of the tank and is a distance $6D$ away (Fig. 43). For what *range* of launch speeds (v_0) will the water enter the tank? Ignore air resistance, and express your answer in terms of D and g.

▲ **FIGURE 43** Problem 59.

60. •• **A world record.** In the shot put, a standard track-and-**BIO** field event, a 7.3 kg object (the shot) is thrown by releasing it at approximately 40° over a straight left leg. The world record for distance, set by Randy Barnes in 1990, is 23.11 m. Assuming that Barnes released the shot put at 40.0° from a height of 2.00 m above the ground, with what speed, in m/s and mph, did he release it?

61. •• A Ferris wheel with radius 14.0 m is turning about a horizontal axis through its center, as shown in Figure 44. The linear speed of a passenger on the rim is constant and equal to 7.00 m/s. What are the magnitude and direction of the passenger's acceleration as she passes through (a) the lowest point in her circular motion and (b) the highest point in her circular motion? (c) How much time does it take the Ferris wheel to make one revolution?

▲ **FIGURE 44** Problem 61.

62. ••• **Leaping the river, II.** A physics professor did daredevil stunts in his spare time. His last stunt was an attempt to jump across a river on a motorcycle. (See Figure 45.) The takeoff ramp was inclined at 53.0°, the river was 40.0 m wide, and the far bank was 15.0 m lower than the top of the ramp. The river itself was 100 m below the ramp. You can ignore air resistance. (a) What should his speed have been at the top of the ramp for him to have just made it to the edge of the far bank? (b) If his speed was only half the value found in (a), where did he land?

▲ **FIGURE 45** Problem 62.

63. •• A 76.0 kg boulder is rolling horizontally at the top of a vertical cliff that is 20.0 m above the surface of a lake, as shown in Figure 46. The top of the vertical face of a dam is located 100.0 m from the foot of the cliff, with the top of the dam level with the surface of the water in the lake. A level plain is 25.0 m below the top of the dam. (a) What must the minimum speed of the rock be just as it leaves the cliff so that it will travel to the plain without striking the dam? (b) How far from the foot of the dam does the rock hit the plain?

▲ **FIGURE 46** Problem 63.

64. •• A batter hits a baseball at a speed of 35.0 m/s and an angle of 65.0° above the horizontal. At the same instant, an outfielder 70.0 m away begins running away from the batter in the line of the ball's flight, hoping to catch it. How fast must the outfielder run to catch the ball? (Ignore air resistance, and assume the fielder catches the ball at the same height at which it left the bat.)

65. •• A shell is launched at 150 m/s 53° above the horizontal. When it has reached its highest point, it launches a projectile at a velocity of 100.0 m/s 30.0° above the horizontal relative to the *shell*. Find (a) the maximum height about the ground that the projectile reaches and (b) its distance from the place where the shell was fired to its landing place when it eventually falls back to the ground.

66. If the astronaut tosses the ball straight up on the moon, it will reach a height of
   A. 5 m
   B. 10 m
   C. 30 m
   D. 50 m

If the astronaut throws the ball at an angle of 45° (see figure 11) what can you say about the path of the ball compared to the path that it would have followed had it been thrown on the earth instead?

67. The ball will travel
   A. the same distance as on the earth
   B. farther
   C. not as far

68. The ball will stay aloft
   A. the same amount of time as on the earth
   B. a shorter amount of time
   C. a longer amount of time

69. The maximum height of the ball will be
   A. the same as on earth
   B. higher
   C. lower

70. If the time of flight of the ball is t seconds, at what point in time will the ball have zero vertical velocity?
   A. 0 s
   B. $t/4$ s
   C. $t/2$ s
   D. t s
   E. There is no place on the path where the vertical velocity is zero.

Passage Problems

BIO Throwing a ball on the moon. The acceleration due to gravity on the moon is approximately 1.6 m/s^2, or 1/6th that of the acceleration due to gravity on the earth. An astronaut who can throw a ball 5 m straight up on earth is now on the moon with the same ball. (Assume that air resistance on the earth is negligible.)

ANSWERS TO SELECTED PROBLEMS

Conceptual Questions

1. The acceleration is downward at all points in the motion. The football's velocity has a constant nonzero horizontal component, so the velocity is never vertical and therefore never parallel to the acceleration. At the highest point in the trajectory, the vertical component of the velocity is zero; thus, the velocity is horizontal, and the acceleration and velocity are perpendicular at this point.

3. The constant speed of the elevator does not affect the rate at which the object falls relative to the elevator. She obtains $a = 9.8$ m/s^2 downward for either direction of the elevator's motion.

5. As it falls, the package retains the same horizontal component of velocity that it had in the airplane. The package and air-

plane travel horizontally at the same speed; thus, relative to the pilot, the package falls straight downward. A person at rest on the ground sees the package move with constant horizontal velocity and with a vertical velocity of increasing magnitude. Relative to this person, the path of the package is a parabola.

7. The time in the air is governed solely by the vertical component of the motion: $t = 2v_{0y}/g = 2v_0\sin\theta_0/g$. To achieve the maximum time in the air, maximize $\sin\theta_0$ by launching the projectile straight upward at a launch angle of 90° with respect to the horizontal. Since the horizontal component of velocity would be zero, the range would be zero $(x = (v_0\cos 90°)t)$.

9. (a) Yes, at the maximum height of the projectile's motion, the vertical component of its velocity is zero and thus its velocity is purely horizontal. (b) No, since the projectile's velocity has a constant nonzero horizontal component, the velocity is never vertical.

11. Two aspects of this path violate the physical principles of projectile motion: (1) The horizontal component of the velocity must be constant; this path provides for a varying horizontal velocity component that equals zero at the path's endpoints. (2) The shape of the path must be parabolic; this path is a semicircle.

15. The trajectory does not allow for a constant horizontal velocity component; the horizontal component varies from zero, to a maximum nonzero value at the peak

of travel, and back to zero. Also, this path does not have the requisite parabolic shape that results from motion having a constant downward acceleration and a constant horizontal velocity component.

Multiple-Choice Problems

1. B
3. C
5. A
7. B
9. C
11. A
13. D
15. D
17. B

Problems

1. (a) 1.09 km/s; −0.24 km/s
   (b) 1.12 km/s; 12.4° below +x axis
3. (a) 2.0 m, 1.0 m (b) 2.2 m, 26.6° counterclockwise from +x axis (c) 5.3 m/s; 3.3 m/s (d) 6.2 m/s; 32° counterclockwise from +x axis
5. (a) $(v_x)_{av} = 3.8$ m/s; $(v_y)_{av} = 3.8$ m/s; $(a_x)_{av} = 0.46$ m/s²; $(a_y)_{av} = -0.46$ m/s²
   (b) $(v_x)_{av} = 3.8$ m/s; $(v_y)_{av} = 0$;
   $(a_x)_{av} = 0$; $(a_y)_{av} = -0.46$ m/s²
   (c) $(v_x)_{av} = -3.8$ m/s;
   $(v_y)_{av} = -3.8$ m/s;
   $(a_x)_{av} = -0.46$ m/s²;
   $(a_y)_{av} = 0.46$ m/s²
   (d) $(v_x)_{av} = (v_y)_{av} = 0$;
   $(a_x)_{av} = (a_y)_{av} = 0$ (e) 5.4 m/s; no; distance traveled is larger than displacement
7. (a) 0.945 m
9. (a) 0.391 s (b) 3.58 m/s (c) 5.24 m/s at 46.9° below horizontal
11. 1.28 m/s²
13. (a) 30.6 m/s (b) 36.3 m/s
15. (a) 13 m/s, 20 m/s (b) 20 m (c) 2.0 s (d) 13 m/s, horizontal; 9.80 m/s², downward (e) 4.0 s (f) 52 m
17. (a) 0.682 s, 2.99 s (b) 24.0 m/s, 11.3 m/s; 24.0 m/s, −11.3 m/s (c) 30.0 m/s at 36.9° below the horizontal
19. (a) 118 ft/s (b) 54.4 ft
21. (a) 4.00 m/s (b) 1.47 m
23. (a) 53.1° (b) 15.0 m/s; 9.80 m/s², downward (c) 15.9 m; 17.7 m/s
25. (a) 45° (b) 63.8 m (c) 3.61 s
27. 6.69 m/s
29. 45°; 50.0 m
31. 2.7 m/s

33. (a) 2.97×10^4 m/s
    (b) 5.91×10^{-3} m/s²
    (c) 4.78×10^4 m/s; 3.97×10^{-2} m/s²
35. 1.64×10^{-3} m/s²
37. 25 m/s² = 2.5g
39. 0.36 m/s, 38° west of south
41. (a) 28° north of east
    (b) 3.7 m/s, east
    (c) 217 s
43. (a) 24° west of south (b) 5.5 hr
45. 9.87 m/s
47. 275 m
49. (a) 81.6 m (b) 8.16 s (c) in the cart
51. (a) 9.16 m/s² (b) 2.72 s (c) 8.45 m
53. (a) 8.50 m/s (b) 13.3 m
55. 8.8 m; 52.4 m
57. 6.91 m
59. $3\sqrt{gD}$ min; $3.13\sqrt{gD}$ max
61. (a) 3.50 m/s², upward
    (b) 3.50 m/s², downward
    (c) 12.6 s
63. (a) 49 m/s (b) 50 m
65. (a) 863 m (b) 4360 m

Passage Problems

67. B
69. B

Newton's Laws of Motion

Ulrich Doering/Alamy

How can a tugboat push a cruise ship that's much heavier than the tug? Why is a long distance needed to stop the ship once it is in motion? Why does your foot hurt more when you kick a big rock than when you kick an empty cardboard box? Why is it harder to control a car on wet ice than on dry concrete? The answers to these and similar questions take us into the subject of **dynamics,** the relationship of motion to the forces associated with it. In the two preceding chapters we studied *kinematics,* the language for describing motion. Now we are ready to think about what makes objects move the way they do. In this chapter, we will use the kinematic quantities of displacement, velocity, and acceleration, along with two new concepts: *force* and *mass*.

All the principles of dynamics can be wrapped up in a neat package containing three statements called **Newton's laws of motion.** These laws, the cornerstone of mechanics, are based on experimental studies of moving objects. They are fundamental laws of nature; they cannot be deduced or proved from any other principles. They were clearly stated for the first time by Sir Isaac Newton (1642–1727), who published them in 1686 in his *Principia,* or *Mathematical Principles of Natural Philosophy.* Many other scientists before Newton contributed to the foundations of mechanics, especially Galileo Galilei (1564–1642), who died the same year Newton was born. Indeed, Newton himself said, "If I have been able to see a little farther than other men, it is because I have stood on the shoulders of giants."

Ordinarily we'd say that the elephant pushes the tree, not that the tree pushes the elephant. Yet the forces they exert on each other are equal in magnitude, so both statements are true. In this chapter we'll learn why.

1 Force

The concept of **force** gives us a quantitative description of the interaction between two objects or between an object and its environment (Figure 1). When you push on a car that is stuck in the snow, you exert a force on it. A locomotive exerts a force

From Chapter 4 of *College Physics*, Ninth Edition, Hugh D. Young. Copyright © 2012 by Pearson Education, Inc. Published by Pearson Addison-Wesley. All rights reserved.

- A force is a push or a pull.
- A force is an interaction between two objects or between an object and its environment.
- A force is a vector quantity, with magnitude and direction.

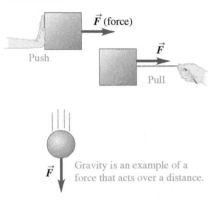

Push

$\vec{F}$ (force)

$\vec{F}$

Pull

$\vec{F}$

Gravity is an example of a force that acts over a distance.

▲ **FIGURE 1** The concept of a force.

$\vec{n}$

$\vec{n}$

Normal force $\vec{n}$: When an object rests or pushes on a surface, the surface exerts a push on it that is directed perpendicular to the surface.

$\vec{n}$

$\vec{f}$

Friction force $\vec{f}$: In addition to the normal force, a surface may exert a frictional force on an object, directed parallel to the surface.

$\vec{T}$

Tension force $\vec{T}$: A pulling force exerted on an object by a rope, cord, etc.

$\vec{w}$

Weight $\vec{w}$: The pull of gravity on an object.

▲ **FIGURE 2** Some types of forces.

on the train it is pulling or pushing, a steel cable exerts a force on the beam it is lifting at a construction site, and so on. Each of these examples shows that force is a push or a pull acting on an object. In this chapter, we'll encounter several kinds of forces.

Types of Forces

When a force involves direct contact between two objects, we call it a **contact force.** When an object rests on a surface, there is always a component of force perpendicular to the surface; we call this component a **normal force,** denoted by $\vec{n}$ (Figure 2). There may also be a component of force parallel to the surface; we call this a **friction force,** denoted by $\vec{f}$. This force often (though not always) acts to resist sliding of the object on the surface.

When a rope or cord is attached to an object and pulled, the corresponding force applied to the object is referred to as a **tension,** denoted by $\vec{T}$.

A familiar force that we'll work with often is the gravitational attraction that the earth (or some other astronomical body) exerts on an object. This force is the object's **weight,** denoted by $\vec{w}$. You may be used to thinking of your weight as a property of your body, but actually it is a force exerted on you by the earth. The gravitational attraction of two objects acts even when the objects are not in contact. We'll discuss this concept at greater length in Section 4.

Measuring Force

Force is a vector quantity; to describe a force, we need to describe the direction in which it acts as well as its magnitude—the quantity that tells us "how much" or "how strongly" the force pushes or pulls. The SI unit of the magnitude of force is the *newton,* abbreviated N. (We haven't yet given a precise definition of the newton. The official definition is based on the standard kilogram; we'll get into that in Section 3.) The weight of a medium-sized apple is about 1 N; the pulling force of a diesel locomotive can be as much as 10^6 N.

When forces act on a solid object, they usually deform the object. For example, a coil spring stretches or compresses when forces act on its ends. This property forms the basis for a common instrument for *measuring* forces, called a *spring balance.* The instrument consists of a coil spring, enclosed in a case for protection, with a pointer attached to one end. When forces are applied to the ends of the spring, it stretches; the amount of stretch depends on the force. We can make a scale for the pointer and calibrate it by using a number of identical objects with weights of exactly 1 N each. When two, three, or more of these are suspended simultaneously from the balance, the total stretching force on each end of the spring is 2 N, 3 N, and so on, and we can label the corresponding positions of the pointer 2 N, 3 N, and so on. Then we can use our spring balance to measure the magnitude of an unknown force. We can also make a similar instrument that measures pushes instead of pulls.

Suppose we pull or push a box, as shown in Figure 3. As with other vector quantities, we can represent the force we exert on the box by a vector arrow. The arrow points in the direction of the force, and its length represents the magnitude

10 N

30°

(a) A 10 N pull directed 30° above the horizontal

10 N

45°

(b) A 10 N push directed 45° below the horizontal

▲ **FIGURE 3** Forces can be represented with vector arrows.

of the force. For example, we might scale the diagram so that an arrow 1 cm long represents a 5 N force.

Resultant of Forces

Experiment shows that when two forces $\vec{F}_1$ and $\vec{F}_2$ act at the same time on the same point of an object (Figure 4), the effect is the same as the effect of a single force equal to the vector sum of the original forces. This vector sum is often called the **resultant** of the forces or the *net force,* denoted by $\vec{R}$. That is, $\vec{R} = \vec{F}_1 + \vec{F}_2$. More generally, the effect of *any number* of forces applied at a point on an object is the same as the effect of a single force equal to the vector sum of the original forces. This important principle goes by the name **superposition of forces.**

The discovery that forces combine according to vector addition is of the utmost importance, and we'll use this fact many times throughout our study of physics. In particular, it allows us to represent a force by means of components, as we've done with displacement, velocity, and acceleration. In Figure 5a, for example, a force $\vec{F}$ acts on an object at a point that we'll designate as the origin of coordinates, O. The component vectors of $\vec{F}$ in the x and y directions are $\vec{F}_x$ and $\vec{F}_y$, and the corresponding components are F_x and F_y. As Figure 5b shows, if we apply two forces $\vec{F}_x$ and $\vec{F}_y$ to the object, the effect is exactly the same as applying the original force. **Any force can be replaced by its components, acting at the same point.**

In general, a force can have components in all three (x, y, and z) directions. It will usually be clear how to extend this discussion to three-dimensional situations, but we'll limit our discussion here to situations in which only x and y components are needed.

The x and y coordinate axes don't have to be vertical and horizontal. Figure 6 shows a stone block being pulled up a ramp by a force $\vec{F}$, represented by its components F_x and F_y with respect to axes parallel and perpendicular, respectively, to the sloping surface of the ramp. We draw a wiggly line through the force vector $\vec{F}$ to show that we have replaced it by its x and y components. Otherwise, the diagram would include the same force twice.

We'll often need to find the vector sum (resultant) of several forces acting on an object. We'll use the Greek letter Σ (capital sigma, equivalent to an S) as a shorthand notation for a sum. If the forces are labeled $\vec{F}_1$, $\vec{F}_2$, $\vec{F}_3$, and so on, we abbreviate the vector sum operation as

$$\vec{R} = \vec{F}_1 + \vec{F}_2 + \vec{F}_3 + \cdots = \Sigma\vec{F}, \quad \text{(resultant, or vector sum, of forces)} \quad (1)$$

where $\Sigma\vec{F}$ is read as "the vector sum of the forces" or "the net force." The component version of Equation 1 is the pair of component equations

$$R_x = \Sigma F_x, \qquad R_y = \Sigma F_y, \qquad \text{(components of vector sum of forces)} \quad (2)$$

Two forces $\vec{F}_1$ and $\vec{F}_2$ acting on a point have the same effect as a single force $\vec{R}$ equal to their vector sum (resultant).

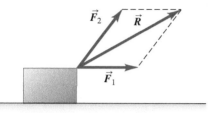

▲ **FIGURE 4** Superposition of forces.

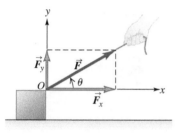

(a) Component vectors: $\vec{F}_x$ and $\vec{F}_y$
Components: $F_x = F \cos \theta$ and $F_y = F \sin \theta$

(b) Component vectors $\vec{F}_x$ and $\vec{F}_y$ together have the same effect as original force $\vec{F}$.

▲ **FIGURE 5** A force can be represented by its components.

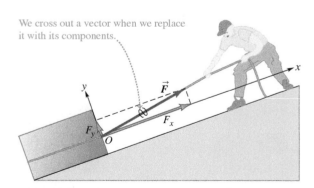

We cross out a vector when we replace it with its components.

▲ **FIGURE 6** The pull exerted by the mason can be replaced by components parallel and perpendicular to the direction of motion.

where $\sum F_x$ is the sum of the x components, and so on. Each component may be positive or negative; be careful with signs when you evaluate the sums in Equations 2.

Once we have the components R_x and R_y, we can find the magnitude and direction of the vector $\vec{R}$. The magnitude is

$$R = \sqrt{R_x^2 + R_y^2}, \qquad \text{(magnitude of vector sum of forces)}$$

and the angle θ between $\vec{R}$ and the x axis can be found from the relation $\tan\theta = R_y/R_x$. The components R_x and R_y may be positive or negative, and the angle θ may be in any of the four quadrants. As usual, we measure θ counterclockwise from the x axis.

▲ **Application** **An object in motion.**
Catapults are founded on Newton's first law. When the catapult arm is released from its cocked position, it accelerates rapidly, carrying the projectile with it. When the arm hits the crossbar, it comes to a sudden stop—but the projectile keeps going. Once in flight, the projectile experiences no forward force; it flies on because objects in motion tend to stay in motion. It *does* experience the downward force of gravity and a retarding force due to air resistance; these forces will end its flight if it doesn't hit a wall first. Today, a modern version of the catapult is used on aircraft carriers to help launch airplanes, which can reach speeds of 250 kilometers per hour in less than 3 seconds.

2 Newton's First Law

The fundamental role of a force is to change the state of motion of the object on which the force acts. The key word is "change." Newton's first law of motion, translated from the Latin of the *Principia* and put into modern language, is as follows:

Newton's first law
Every object continues either at rest or in constant motion in a straight line, unless it is forced to change that state by forces acting on it.

When *no* force acts on an object, or when the vector sum of forces on it is zero, the object either remains at rest or moves with constant velocity in a straight line. Once an object has been set in motion, no net force is needed to keep it moving. In other words, **an object acted on by no net force moves with constant velocity (which may be zero) and thus with zero acceleration.**

Everyday experience may seem to contradict this statement. Suppose you give a push to a hockey puck on a table, as shown in Figure 7a. After you stop pushing and take your hand away, the puck *does not* continue to move indefinitely; it slows down and stops. To keep it moving, you have to keep pushing. This is because, as the puck slides, the tabletop applies a frictional force to it in a direction *opposite* that of its motion.

But now imagine pushing the puck across the smooth ice of a skating rink (Figure 7b). Here, it will move a lot farther after you quit pushing before it stops. Put it on an air-hockey table, where it floats on a thin cushion of air, and it slides still farther (Figure 7c). The more slippery the surface, the less friction there is. The first law states that if we could eliminate friction completely, we would need *no forward force at all* to keep the puck moving with constant velocity once it had been started moving.

(a) Table: puck stops short   **(b)** Ice: puck slides farther   **(c)** Air-hockey table: puck slides even farther

▲ **FIGURE 7** An experimental approach to Newton's first law. As we reduce friction, the puck's motion comes closer and closer to constant velocity and the net force acting on the puck approaches zero, as predicted by Newton's first law.

▶ **Application** **Objects at rest?** This trick photo was taken an instant after a super-smooth table was very rapidly yanked out from underneath the dinner setting. The table was removed so rapidly that it exerted a force on the place setting only for a very short time. We can visualize the concept of inertia as described by Newton's first law. The objects at rest tend to stay at rest—but the force of gravity causes them to accelerate rapidly downward!

Loomis Dean/Time & Life Picrures/Getty Images

Inertia

The tendency of an object to remain at rest, or to keep moving once it is set in motion, results from a property called *inertia.* That's what you feel when you're behind home plate trying to catch a fastball pitch. That baseball really "wants" to keep moving. The tendency of an object at rest to remain at rest is also due to inertia. You may have seen a tablecloth yanked out from under the china without anything being broken. As the tablecloth slides, the force it exerts on the china isn't great enough to make the china move appreciably.

The quantitative measure of inertia is the physical quantity called **mass,** which we'll discuss in detail in the next section.

Conceptual Analysis 1

Science or fiction?

In a 1950s TV science fiction show, the hero is cruising the vacuum of outer space when the engine of his spaceship dies and his ship drifts to a stop. Will rescue arrive before his air runs out? What do you think about the physics of this plot?

SOLUTION The engine creates a force that accelerates the ship by ejecting mass out of its stern. When the engine dies and this

process stops, there is no force on the ship (assuming that the gravitational forces exerted by planets and stars are negligible). The ship doesn't come to a stop, but continues to move in a straight line with constant speed. Science fiction sometimes contains more fiction than science!

When a single force acts on an object, it changes the object's state of motion. An object that is initially at rest starts to move. If the object is initially moving, a force in the direction opposite that of the motion causes the object to slow down. (If the force is maintained, eventually the object stops and reverses direction.) Suppose a hockey puck rests on a horizontal surface with negligible friction, such as an air-hockey table or a slab of ice. If the puck is initially at rest and a single horizontal force $\vec{F}_1$ acts on it (Figure 8a), the puck starts to move. If the puck is in motion at the start, the force makes it speed up, slow down, or change direction, depending on the direction of the force.

Now suppose we apply a second force $\vec{F}_2$ (Figure 8b), equal in magnitude to $\vec{F}_1$, but opposite in direction. The two forces are negatives of each other $(\vec{F}_2 = -\vec{F}_1)$, and their vector sum $\vec{R}$ is zero:

$$\vec{R} = \vec{F}_1 + \vec{F}_2 = 0.$$

We find that if the puck is at rest at the start, it remains at rest. If it is initially moving, it continues to move in the same direction with constant speed. These results show that, in Newton's first law, **zero resultant force is equivalent to no force at all.**

When an object is acted on by no forces or by several forces whose vector sum (resultant) is zero, we say that the object is in **equilibrium.** For an object in equilibrium,

$$\vec{R} = \Sigma\vec{F} = 0. \quad \text{(equilibrium under zero resultant force)} \quad (3)$$

For Equation 3 to be true, each component of $\vec{R}$ must be zero, so

$$\Sigma F_x = 0, \quad \Sigma F_y = 0. \quad \text{(object in equilibrium)} \quad (4)$$

A puck on a frictionless surface accelerates when acted on by a single horizontal force.

(a)

An object acted on by forces whose vector sum is zero behaves as though no forces act on it.

(b)

▲ **FIGURE 8** A puck responding to a nonzero net force (a) and to two forces whose vector sum is zero (b).

When Equations 4 are satisfied, the object is in equilibrium; that is, it has no acceleration. (We are assuming that the object can be modeled adequately as a particle. For an object with finite size, we also have to consider *where* on the object the forces are applied.

Conceptual Analysis 2

Air hockey

Your team decides to play leaf-blower ice hockey. You use your blower to apply a constant force that accelerates the puck in a straight line. An opponent skates up and uses her blower to apply an equally strong, constant force directed opposite to yours. Her force, acting together with yours, will cause the puck to

A. slow down and eventually stop.
B. stop immediately.
C. slow somewhat and then move with constant velocity.
D. continue to move, but with constant velocity.

SOLUTION The force from your blower alone causes the puck to accelerate. The force from your opponent's blower is equal in magnitude and opposite in direction to yours, so the vector sum of the two forces is zero. A puck that is acted upon by zero net force has no acceleration. Thus, the puck does not slow down or halt (which would be acceleration), but instead moves with constant velocity in accordance with Newton's first law. Thus, the answer is D.

Inertial Frames of Reference

In our discussions of relative velocity, we stressed the concept of a *frame of reference.* This concept also plays a central role in Newton's laws of motion. Suppose you are sitting in an airplane as it accelerates down the runway during takeoff. You feel a forward force pushing on your back, but you don't start moving forward relative to the airplane. If you could stand in the aisle on roller skates, you would accelerate *backward* relative to the plane. In either case, it looks as though Newton's first law is not obeyed. Forward net force but no acceleration, or zero net force and backward acceleration. What's wrong?

The point is that the plane, accelerating with respect to the earth, is not a suitable frame of reference for Newton's first law. This law is valid in some frames of reference and not in others. A frame of reference in which Newton's first law *is* valid is called an **inertial frame of reference.** The earth is approximately an inertial frame of reference, but the airplane is not.

This may sound as though there's only one inertial frame of reference in the whole universe. On the contrary, if Newton's first law is obeyed in one particular reference frame, it is also valid in every other reference frame that moves with constant velocity relative to the first. All such frames are therefore inertial. For instance, Figure 9 shows three frames of reference: that of a person standing beside the runway, that of a truck driving at constant speed in a straight line, and that of the accelerating airplane. The stationary person's frame of reference is inertial. The truck moves with constant velocity relative to the person, so its frame of reference is also inertial. In both of these frames, Newton's first law is obeyed. However, the airplane, which is accelerating with respect to both of these observers, is in a non-inertial frame.

Thus, there is no single inertial frame of reference that is preferred over all others for formulating Newton's laws. If one frame is inertial, then every other frame moving relative to it with constant velocity is also inertial. Both the state of rest and the state of uniform motion (with constant velocity) can occur when the vector sum of forces acting on the object is zero. Because Newton's first law can be used to define what we mean by an inertial frame of reference, it is sometimes called the *law of inertia.*

The truck moves with constant velocity relative to the person on the ground. Newton's first law is obeyed in both frames, so they are **inertial**.

$\vec{v}_T$ = constant

$\vec{a}$

Constant velocity

Accelerating

In the accelerating airplane, Newton's first law is not obeyed, so the frame of the airplane is **not inertial**.

▲ **FIGURE 9** Inertial and non-inertial frames of reference.

3 Mass and Newton's Second Law

Qualitatively, we've learned that when an object is acted on by a nonzero net force, it accelerates. We now want to know the relation of the acceleration to the force; this is what Newton's second law of motion is all about.

Mastering**PHYSICS**

ActivPhysics 2.1.3: Tension Change

Let's look at several fundamental experiments. Consider a small object moving on a flat, level, frictionless surface. The object could be a puck on an air-hockey table, as we described in Section 2. Initially, it is moving to the right along the x axis of a coordinate system (Figure 10a). We apply a constant horizontal force $\vec{F}$ to the object, using the spring balance we described in Section 1, with the spring stretched a constant amount. We find that during the time the force is acting, the velocity of the object changes at a constant rate; that is, the object moves with *constant acceleration.* If we change the magnitude of the force, the acceleration changes in the same proportion. Doubling the force doubles the acceleration, halving the force halves the acceleration, and so on (Figures 10b and 10c). When we take away the force, the acceleration becomes zero and the object moves with constant velocity. We conclude that, for any given object, the acceleration is *directly proportional* to the force acting on it.

In another experiment (Figure 11), we give the object the same initial velocity as before. With no force, the velocity is constant (Figure 11a). With a constant force directed to the right (Figure 11b), the acceleration is constant and to the right. But when we reverse the direction of the force (Figure 11c), we find that the object moves more and more slowly to the right. (If we continue the experiment, the object stops and then moves toward the left with increasing speed.) The direction of the acceleration is toward the *left,* in the same direction as the force $\vec{F}$. We conclude that the *magnitude* of the acceleration is proportional to that of the force, and the *direction* of the acceleration is the same as that of the force, regardless of the direction of the velocity. If there is *no* force, the object has zero acceleration; no force is required to maintain motion with constant velocity.

A constant force $\vec{F}$ causes a constant acceleration $\vec{a}$.

(a)

Doubling the force doubles the acceleration.

(b)

Halving the force halves the acceleration.

(c)

▲ **FIGURE 10** Experiments demonstrating the direct proportion between an applied force and the resulting acceleration.

A puck moving with constant velocity: $\Sigma\vec{F} = 0$, $\vec{a} = 0$

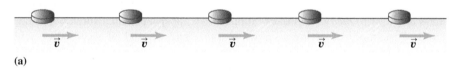

(a)

A constant force in the direction of motion causes a constant acceleration in the same direction as the force.

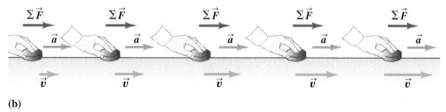

(b)

A constant force opposite to the direction of motion causes a constant acceleration in the same direction as the force.

(c)

▲ **FIGURE 11** Experiments showing that an object's acceleration has the same direction as the net force acting on the object.

For a given object, the ratio of the magnitude F of the force to the magnitude a of the acceleration is constant. We call this ratio the inertial mass, or simply the **mass,** of the object and denote it as m. That is, $m = F/a$.

An equivalent statement is that when a force with magnitude F acts on an object with mass m, the magnitude a of the object's acceleration is

$$a = \frac{F}{m}. \tag{5}$$

The concept of mass is a familiar one. If you hit a table-tennis ball with a paddle and then hit a basketball with the same force, the basketball has a much smaller acceleration because it has a much greater mass. When a large force is needed to give an object a certain acceleration, the mass of the object is large. When only a small force is needed for the same acceleration, the mass is small. The greater the mass, the more the object "resists" being accelerated. Thus, mass is a quantitative measure of inertia, which we discussed in Section 2.

The SI unit of mass is the **kilogram.** The kilogram is officially defined to be the mass of a chunk of platinum–iridium alloy kept in a vault near Paris. We can use this standard kilogram, along with Equation 5, to define the fundamental SI unit of force, the **newton,** abbreviated N:

Definition of the newton
One newton is the amount of force that gives an acceleration of 1 meter per second squared to an object with a mass of 1 kilogram. That is,

$$1 \text{ N} = (1 \text{ kg})(1 \text{ m/s}^2).$$

We can use this definition to calibrate the spring balances and other instruments that we use to measure forces.

We can also use Equation 5 to compare a particular mass with the standard mass and thus to *measure* masses. Suppose we apply a constant force with magnitude F to an object having a known mass m_1 and we find an acceleration with magnitude a_1, as shown in Figure 12a. We then apply the *same* force to another object having an unknown mass m_2, and we find an acceleration with magnitude a_2 (Figure 12b). Then, according to Equation 5,

$$m_1 a_1 = m_2 a_2,$$

or

$$\frac{m_2}{m_1} = \frac{a_1}{a_2}. \tag{6}$$

The ratio of the masses is the inverse of the ratio of the accelerations. In principle, we could use this relation to measure an unknown mass m_2, but it is usually easier to determine an object's mass indirectly by measuring the object's weight. We'll return to this point in Section 4.

When two objects with masses m_1 and m_2 are fastened together, we find that the mass of the composite object is always $m_1 + m_2$ (Figure 12c). This additive property of mass may seem obvious, but it has to be verified experimentally. Ultimately, the mass of an object is related to the numbers of protons, electrons, and neutrons it contains. This wouldn't be a good way to *define* mass, because there is no practical way to count these particles. But the concept of mass is the most fundamental way to characterize the quantity of matter in an object.

A known force $\Sigma\vec{F}$ causes an object with mass m_1 to have an acceleration $\vec{a}_1$.

(a)

Applying the same force $\Sigma\vec{F}$ to a second object and noting the acceleration allows us to measure the mass.

(b)

When the two objects are fastened together, the same method shows that their composite mass is the sum of their individual masses.

(c)

▲ **FIGURE 12** For a constant force, the magnitude of acceleration is inversely proportional to the mass of an object. The mass of a composite object is the sum of the masses of its parts.

We need to generalize Equation 5 in two ways. First, the object doesn't necessarily have to move along a straight line; its path may be a curve. Its velocity, its acceleration, and the force acting on it can then all change directions, so they have to be treated as vector quantities. Second, there may be several forces $(\vec{F}_1, \vec{F}_2, \cdots)$ acting on the object. As discussed earlier, we can combine the forces by using vector addition; the effect of the forces acting together is the same as the effect of a single force equal to their vector sum, which we usually write as $\sum \vec{F}$ or $\vec{R}$.

Newton wrapped up all these relationships and experimental results in a single concise statement that we now call **Newton's second law of motion:**

Newton's second law of motion (vector form)

The vector sum (resultant) of all the forces acting on an object equals the object's mass times its acceleration (the rate of change of its velocity):

$$\sum \vec{F} = m\vec{a}. \tag{7}$$

The acceleration $\vec{a}$ has the same direction as the resultant force $\sum \vec{F}$.

Newton's second law is a fundamental law of nature, the basic relation between force and motion. Most of the remainder of this chapter and all of the next are devoted to learning how to apply this principle in various situations.

Equation 7 is a *vector* equation. We'll usually use it in component form:

Newton's second law of motion (component form)

For an object moving in a plane, each component of the total force equals the mass times the corresponding component of acceleration:

$$\sum F_x = ma_x, \qquad \sum F_y = ma_y. \tag{8}$$

Equations 7 and 8 are valid only when the mass m is *constant.* It's easy to think of systems whose masses change, such as a leaking tank truck, a rocket ship, or a moving railroad car being loaded with coal. Such systems are better handled by using the concept of momentum.

Like the first law, Newton's second law is valid only in inertial frames of reference. We'll usually assume that the earth is an adequate approximation to an inertial frame, even though it is not precisely inertial because of its rotation and orbital motion.

Remember that we defined the newton as $1 \text{ N} = 1 \text{ kg} \cdot \text{m/s}^2$. Notice that the newton *must* be defined this way for $\sum \vec{F} = m\vec{a}$ to be dimensionally consistent.

In this chapter, as we learn how to apply Newton's second law, we'll begin with problems involving only motion along a straight line, and we'll always take this line to be a coordinate axis, often the x axis. In these problems, $\vec{v}$ and $\vec{a}$ have components only along this axis. Individual forces may have components along directions other than the x axis, but the *sum* of those components will always be zero.

▲ **Application** **Too small to measure?** Bubble chamber images like the one shown here are used both to study characteristics of known subatomic particles and to search for new types of matter and antimatter particles. For example, the linked spiral tracks indicate the simultaneous creation of an electron–positron pair from a photon. Using such images, we can apply Newton's second law ($F = ma$) or its relativistic generalization to determine the masses of particles so minute that they cannot be measured directly.

EXAMPLE 1 A box on ice

A worker with spikes on his shoes pulls with a constant horizontal force of magnitude 20 N on a box with mass 40 kg resting on the flat, frictionless surface of a frozen lake. What is the acceleration of the box?

SOLUTION

SET UP Figure 13 shows our sketch. We take the $+x$ axis in the direction of the horizontal force. "Frictionless" means that the ice doesn't supply any force that opposes the motion (such as the friction force mentioned in Section 1). Thus, the only horizontal force is the one due to the rope that the worker is pulling. Because the box has no vertical acceleration, we know that the sum of the vertical components of force is zero. However, two vertical forces do act on the box: the downward force of the earth's gravitational attraction and the upward normal force exerted by the ice on the box. For completeness, we show these two vertical forces in our sketch; their vector sum must be zero because $a_y = 0$.

SOLVE The acceleration is given by Newton's second law. There is only one horizontal component of force, so we have

$$\Sigma F_x = ma_x,$$
$$a_x = \frac{F_x}{m} = \frac{20\ \text{N}}{40\ \text{kg}} = \frac{20\ \text{kg} \cdot \text{m/s}^2}{40\ \text{kg}} = 0.5\ \text{m/s}^2.$$

The force is constant, so the acceleration is also constant. If we are given the initial position and velocity of the box, we can find

The box has no vertical acceleration, so the vertical components of the net force sum to zero. Nevertheless, for completeness, we show the vertical forces acting on the box.

▲ **FIGURE 13** Our sketch for this problem.

the position and velocity at any later time from the equations of motion with constant acceleration.

REFLECT Two vertical (y) components of force act on the box—its weight $\vec{w}$ and an upward normal force $\vec{n}$ exerted on the bottom of the box by the ice—but their vector sum is zero.

Practice Problem: If the box starts from rest, what is its speed after it has been pulled a distance of 0.36 m? *Answer:* 0.6 m/s.

EXAMPLE 2 The ketchup slide

A counter attendant in a diner shoves a ketchup bottle with mass 0.20 kg along a smooth, level lunch counter. The bottle leaves her hand with an initial velocity of 2.8 m/s. As it slides, it slows down because of the horizontal friction force exerted on it by the countertop. The bottle slides a distance of 1.0 m before coming to rest. What are the magnitude and direction of the friction force acting on it?

SOLUTION

SET UP Figure 14 shows our diagrams—one for the bottle's motion and one for the forces on the bottle. We place the origin at the point where the waitress releases the bottle and point the $+x$ axis in the direction the bottle moves. Because the bottle has no vertical acceleration, we know that the vertical forces on it (the weight $\vec{w}$ and the upward normal force $\vec{n}$) must sum to zero. The only horizontal force on the bottle is the friction force $\vec{f}$. Because the bottle is slowing down (a_x is negative in our coordinate system), we know that this force points in the $-x$ direction.

SOLVE We need to find the relation between v_x and a_x; to do this, we can use the constant-acceleration equation $v_x^2 - v_{0x}^2 =$

$2a_x(x - x_0)$. The initial x component of velocity is $v_{0x} = 2.8$ m/s, and the final value is $v_x = 0$. Also, $x_0 = 0$ and $x = 1.0$ m. Once a_x is known, we can use the component form of Newton's second law, Equation 8 $(\Sigma F_x = ma_x)$, to find the magnitude f of the friction force. Because f is the only horizontal component of force, $\Sigma F_x = -f$. Using the numerical values in Equation 2.13, we first find the bottle's acceleration:

$$v_x^2 - v_0^2 = 2a_x(x - x_0),$$
$$0 - (2.8\ \text{m/s})^2 = 2a_x(1.0\ \text{m} - 0),$$
$$a_x = -3.9\ \text{m/s}^2.$$

We draw one diagram for the bottle's motion and one showing the forces on the bottle.

▲ **FIGURE 14** Our sketch for this problem.

Continued

We can now find the net force acting on the bottle.

$$\Sigma F_x = -f = ma_x$$
$$-f = (0.20 \text{ kg})(-3.9 \text{ m/s}^2) = -0.78 \text{ kg} \cdot \text{m/s}^2 = -0.78 \text{ N}.$$

Since the frictional force is the *only* horizontal force acting on the bottle, this answer gives us its magnitude (0.78 N) and also the fact that it acts in the $-x$ direction (which we already knew).

REFLECT Notice that we did most of the physics before doing any math. We knew that the vertical forces on the bottle summed to zero, and we knew the direction of the friction force. We did math only to find the magnitude of that force.

Practice Problem: Suppose the bottle travels 1.5 m before stopping, instead of 1.0 m. What is its initial velocity? *Answer:* 3.4 m/s.

EXAMPLE 3   A TV picture tube

In a color TV picture tube, an electric field exerts a net force with magnitude 1.60×10^{-13} N on an electron ($m = 9.11 \times 10^{-31}$ kg). What is the electron's acceleration?

SOLUTION

SET UP Figure 15 shows our simple diagram. The statement of the problem tells us that the *net force* on the electron is due to the electric field, so we consider only the electric-field force. (If other forces act on the electron, they are negligible or sum to zero.) The direction of the acceleration must be the same as that of the force; we designate this direction as the $+x$ direction.

SOLVE We use Newton's second law in component form, rearranging it slightly to solve for acceleration:

$$a_x = \frac{\Sigma F_x}{m} = \frac{1.60 \times 10^{-13} \text{ N}}{9.11 \times 10^{-31} \text{ kg}} = \frac{1.60 \times 10^{-13} \text{ kg} \cdot \text{m/s}^2}{9.11 \times 10^{-31} \text{ kg}}$$
$$= 1.76 \times 10^{17} \text{ m/s}^2.$$

▲ **FIGURE 15** Even for a simple problem, a quick sketch helps us to see the situation and avoid mistakes.

REFLECT Notice that the magnitudes of these quantities are far outside the range of everyday experience. Because the mass of the electron is miniscule, a tiny force produces a huge acceleration.

Practice Problem: If the electron starts from rest, what time is required for it to travel 0.20 m from its source to the screen of the picture tube? *Answer:* 1.51×10^{-9} s.

Raising a toolbox

Suppose you use a rope to hoist a box of tools vertically at a constant speed v. The rope exerts a constant upward force of magnitude F_{up} on the box, and gravity exerts a constant downward force (the weight of the box). No other forces act on the box. To raise the box twice as fast, the force of the rope on the box would have to have

A. the same magnitude F_{up}.
B. a magnitude of $2F_{up}$.

SOLUTION The key is that the box moves at constant velocity in both cases; it is in equilibrium. Thus, by Newton's first law, no *net* force acts on it; the vector sum of the upward and downward forces is zero. Since the downward force (the box's weight) is always the same, the upward force must be the same, too, regardless of the box's speed. Note that this is true only while the box is moving at constant speed, not during the initial acceleration from rest.

4 Mass and Weight

We've mentioned that the weight of an object is a force—the force of gravitational attraction of the earth (or whatever astronomical body the object is near, such as the moon or Mars). The terms *mass* and *weight* are often misused and interchanged in everyday conversation. It's absolutely essential for you to understand clearly the distinctions between these two physical quantities.

Mass characterizes the *inertial* properties of an object. Mass is what keeps the china on the table when you yank the tablecloth out from under it. The greater the mass, the greater is the force needed to cause a given acceleration; this meaning is reflected in Newton's second law, $\Sigma \vec{F} = m\vec{a}$. Weight, on the other hand, is a *force* exerted on an object by the gravitational pull of the earth or some other astronomical body (Figure 16). Everyday experience shows us that objects that have large mass also have large weight. A cart loaded with bricks is hard to get started rolling because of its large *mass*, and it is also hard to lift off the ground

The relation of mass to net force: $\Sigma \vec{F} = m\vec{a}$

The relation of mass to weight: $\vec{w} = m\vec{g}$

▲ **FIGURE 16** The relation of mass to net force and to weight.

because of its large *weight*. On the moon, the cart would be just as hard to get rolling, but it would be easier to lift. So what exactly *is* the relationship between mass and weight?

The answer to this question, according to legend, came to Newton as he sat under an apple tree watching the apples fall. A freely falling object has an acceleration $\vec{a}$ with magnitude equal to g—that is, the acceleration due to gravity (also called the acceleration of free fall). Because of Newton's second law, this acceleration requires a force. If a 1 kg object falls with an acceleration of magnitude $g = 9.8 \text{ m/s}^2$, the required force $\vec{F}$ must have magnitude

$$F = ma = (1 \text{ kg})(9.8 \text{ m/s}^2) = 9.8 \text{ kg} \cdot \text{m/s}^2 = 9.8 \text{ N}.$$

But the force that makes the object accelerate downward is the gravitational pull of the earth—that is, the *weight* of the object. Any object near the surface of the earth that has a mass of 1 kg *must* have a weight with magnitude 9.8 N in order for it to have the acceleration we observe when it is in free fall. More generally, the relation of mass to weight must be as follows:

Relation of mass to weight

The weight of an object with mass m must have a magnitude w equal to the mass times the magnitude of acceleration due to gravity, g:

$$w = mg. \tag{9}$$

Because weight is a force, we can write this equation as a vector relation:

$$\vec{w} = m\vec{g}. \tag{10}$$

NOTE ▶ Remember that g is the *magnitude* of $\vec{g}$, the acceleration due to gravity, so, by definition, g is always a positive number, Thus, w, given by Equation 9, is the *magnitude* of the weight, and it, too, is always positive. In the discussion that follows, we'll sometimes call w "the weight" and F "the force," even though, strictly speaking, we should call w "the magnitude of the weight" and F "the magnitude of the force." ◀

We'll use the value $g = 9.80 \text{ m/s}^2$ for problems dealing with the earth. The value of g actually varies somewhat from point to point on the earth's surface, from about 9.78 to 9.82 m/s², because the earth is not perfectly spherical and because of effects due to its rotation, orbital motion, and composition. At a point where $g = 9.80 \text{ m/s}^2$, the weight of a standard kilogram is $w = 9.80 \text{ N}$. At a different point, where $g = 9.78 \text{ m/s}^2$, the weight is $w = 9.78 \text{ N}$, but the mass is still 1 kg. The weight of an object varies from one location to another; the mass does not. If we take a standard kilogram to the surface of the moon, where the acceleration of free fall is 1.62 m/s², the weight of the standard kilogram is 1.62 N, but its mass is still 1 kg (Figure 17). An 80 kg man has a weight on earth of $(80.0 \text{ kg})(9.80 \text{ m/s}^2) = 784 \text{ N}$, but on the moon his weight is only $(80.0 \text{ kg})(1.62 \text{ m/s}^2) = 130 \text{ N}$.

The following brief excerpt from Astronaut Buzz Aldrin's book *Men from Earth* offers some interesting insights into the distinction between mass and weight (Figure 18):

> Our portable life-support system backpacks looked simple, but they were hard to put on and tricky to operate. On earth the portable life-support system and space suit combination weighed 190 pounds, but on the moon it was only 30. Combined with my own body weight, that brought me to a total lunar-gravity weight of around 60 pounds.

Mass = 1.00 kg

$w = 9.80 \text{ N}$ $g = 9.80 \text{ m/s}^2$

The *mass* of an object is constant, but its *weight* changes with location.

(a) On earth

Mass = 1.00 kg

$w = 1.62 \text{ N}$ $g = 1.62 \text{ m/s}^2$

(b) On the moon

▲ **FIGURE 17** Mass and weight for a 1 kg object on the earth and on the moon.

NASA

▲ **FIGURE 18** Astronaut Buzz Aldrin on the surface of the moon, trying to cope with his own inertia.

▶ **BIO Application** **No brakes needed.** When considering the deceleration of massive objects such as a car, air friction doesn't matter because inertial considerations dominate. However, small objects living in more viscous fluids such as water have vastly different experiences. Under those circumstances, inertia is unimportant and the force of viscous drag dominates. Astonishingly, if a bacterium propelling itself through water stops beating its flagellum (the oar that propels it), it will come to rest in about 0.01 nm, a dimension that is small on the scale of atoms. It lives in a very different world than we do.

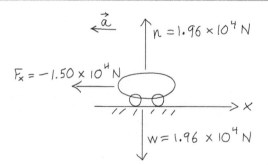

Shutterstock

One of my tests was to jog away from the lunar module to see how maneuverable an astronaut was on the surface. I remembered what Isaac Newton had taught us two centuries before: Mass and weight are not the same. I weighed only 60 pounds, but my *mass* was the same as it was on Earth. Inertia was a problem. I had to plan ahead several steps to bring myself to a stop or to turn without falling.

NOTE ▶ As indicated by Buzz Aldrin's words, the pound is actually a unit of force, not mass. In fact, 1 pound is defined officially as exactly 4.448221615260 newtons. It's handy to remember that a pound is about 4.4 N and a newton is about 0.22 pound. Next time you want to order a "quarter-pounder," try asking for a "one-newtoner" and see what happens. ◀

Here's another useful fact: An object with a mass of 1 kg has a weight of about 2.2 lb at the earth's surface. In the British system, the unit of force is the *pound* (or pound-force), and the unit of mass is the *slug.* The unit of acceleration is 1 foot per second squared, so 1 pound = 1 slug · ft/s². In the cgs metric system (not used in this text), the unit of mass is the gram, equal to 10^{-3} kg, and the unit of distance is the centimeter, equal to 10^{-2} m. The corresponding unit of force is called the *dyne:* 1 dyne = 1 g · cm/s² = 10^{-5} N.

It's important to understand that the weight of an object, as given by Equation 10, acts on the object *all the time,* whether it is in free fall or not. When a 10-kg flowerpot hangs suspended from a chain, it is in equilibrium, and its acceleration is zero. But its 98 N weight is still pulling down on it. In this case the chain pulls up on the pot, applying a 98 N upward force. The *vector sum* of the two 98 N forces is zero, and the pot is in equilibrium.

Mastering**PHYSICS**

ActivPhysics 2.9: Pole-Vaulter Vaults

EXAMPLE 4 **Quick stop of a heavy car**

A big luxury car weighing 1.96×10^4 N (about 4400 lb), traveling in the $+x$ direction, makes a fast stop; the x component of the net force acting on it is -1.50×10^4 N. What is its acceleration?

SOLUTION

SET UP Figure 19 shows our diagram. We draw the weight as a force with magnitude w. Because the car does not accelerate in the y direction, the road exerts an upward normal force of equal magnitude on the car; for completeness, we include that force in our diagram.

SOLVE To find the acceleration, we'll use Newton's second law, $\Sigma F_x = ma_x$. First, however, we need the car's mass. Since we know the car's weight, we can find its mass m from Equation 9, $w = mg$. We obtain

$$m = \frac{w}{g} = \frac{1.96 \times 10^4 \, \text{N}}{9.80 \, \text{m/s}^2} = \frac{1.96 \times 10^4 \, \text{kg} \cdot \text{m/s}^2}{9.80 \, \text{m/s}^2} = 2000 \, \text{kg}.$$

▲ **FIGURE 19** Our diagram for this problem.

Continued

Then, $\sum F_x = ma_x$ gives

$$a_x = \frac{F_x}{m} = \frac{-1.50 \times 10^4 \text{ N}}{2000 \text{ kg}} = \frac{-1.50 \times 10^4 \text{ kg} \cdot \text{m/s}^2}{2000 \text{ kg}}$$
$$= -7.5 \text{ m/s}^2.$$

REFLECT This acceleration can be written as $-0.77g$. Note that -0.77 is also the ratio of -1.50×10^4 N to 1.96×10^4 N. An

acceleration of this magnitude is possible only on a dry paved road. Don't expect it on a wet or icy road!

Practice Problem: If passenger comfort requires that the acceleration should be no greater in magnitude than $0.10g$, what distance is required to stop the car if its speed is initially 30 m/s (roughly 60 mi/h)? What force is required? *Answers:* 459 m, 1960 N.

▲ **FIGURE 20** An equal-arm balance determines the mass of an object by comparing its weight to a known weight.

Usually, the easiest way to measure the mass of an object is to measure its weight, often by comparison with a standard weight. In accordance with Equation 10, two objects that have the same weight at a particular location also have the same mass. We can compare weights very precisely; the familiar equal-arm balance (Figure 20) can determine with great precision (to one part in 10^6) when the weights of two objects are equal and hence when their masses are equal. This method doesn't work, however, in the "zero-gravity" environment of outer space. Instead, we have to use Newton's second law directly: We apply a known force to the object, measure its acceleration, and compute the mass as the ratio of force to acceleration. This method, or a variation of it, is used to measure the masses of astronauts in orbiting space stations and also the masses of atomic and subatomic particles.

The concept of mass plays two rather different roles in mechanics. On the one hand, the weight of an object (the gravitational force acting on it) is proportional to its mass; we may therefore call the property related to gravitational interactions *gravitational mass*. On the other hand, we can call the inertial property that appears in Newton's second law the *inertial mass*. If these two quantities were different, the acceleration of free fall might well be different for different objects. However, extraordinarily precise experiments have established that, in fact, the two *are* the same, to a precision of better than one part in 10^{12}. Recent efforts to find departures from this equivalence, possibly showing evidence of a previously unknown force, have been inconclusive.

Finally, we remark that the SI units for mass and weight are often misused in everyday life. Incorrect expressions such as "This box weighs 6 kg" are nearly universal. What is meant is that the *mass* of the box, probably determined indirectly by *weighing,* is 6 kg. This usage is so common that there's probably no hope of straightening things out, but be sure you recognize that the term *weight* is often used when *mass* is meant. To keep your own thinking clear, be careful to avoid this kind of mistake! In SI units, weight (a force) is always measured in newtons, mass always in kilograms. (However, we'll often refer to the weight of an object when, strictly speaking, we mean the *magnitude* of its weight.)

5 Newton's Third Law

At the beginning of this chapter, we noted that force is a quantitative description of the interaction between two objects. A force acting on an object is always the result of that object's interaction with another object, so forces always come in pairs. As my hand pushes your shoulder, your shoulder pushes back on my hand. When you kick a football, the force your foot exerts on the ball launches it into its trajectory, but you also feel the force the ball exerts on your foot.

Experiments show that whenever two objects interact, the two forces they exert on each other are equal in magnitude and opposite in direction. This fact is called *Newton's third law.* In Figure 21, $\vec{F}_{\text{foot on ball}}$ is the force applied by the foot to the ball, and $\vec{F}_{\text{ball on foot}}$ is the force applied by the ball to the foot. The directions of the forces in this example correspond to a *repulsive* interaction, tending

▲ **FIGURE 21** An interacting ball and foot exert forces on each other that are equal in magnitude and opposite in direction.

▶ **Application An action shot.** This Olympic biathlon competitor knows her physics: Every action has an equal and opposite reaction. When she fires her rifle, the force propelling the bullet forward is matched by an equal and opposite force pushing against the rifle and her. If she had her skis pointed in the direction in which she is firing, she would be pushed backward on the slippery mat and maybe end up flat on her back. By keeping her back ski firmly planted sideways on the mat, she can avoid the possible consequences of ignoring Newton's third law.

Agence Zoom/Getty Images

to push the objects apart. However, interactions can also be *attractive,* such as the gravitational attraction of two masses or the electrical attraction of two particles with opposite charges.

Newton's third law

For two interacting objects A and B, the formal statement of Newton's third law is

$$\vec{F}_{A \text{ on } B} = -\vec{F}_{B \text{ on } A}. \tag{11}$$

Newton's own statement, translated from the Latin of the *Principia,* is

> To every action there is always opposed an equal reaction; or, the mutual actions of two objects upon each other are always equal, and directed to contrary parts.

NOTE ▶ In the preceding statement, "action" and "reaction" are the two opposite forces. This terminology is not meant to imply any cause-and-effect relationship: We can consider either force as the action and the other the reaction. We often say simply that the forces are "equal and opposite" meaning that they have equal magnitudes and opposite directions. ◀

EXAMPLE 5 **Newton's apple on a table**

An apple sits in equilibrium on a table. What forces act on the apple? What is the reaction force to each of the forces acting on it? What are the action–reaction pairs?

SOLUTION

SET UP First, in Figure 22a, we diagram the situation and the two forces that act on the apple. $\vec{F}_{\text{earth on apple}}$ is the weight of the apple—the downward gravitational force exerted *by* the earth *on* the apple. Similarly, $\vec{F}_{\text{table on apple}}$ is the upward normal force exerted *by* the table *on* the apple.

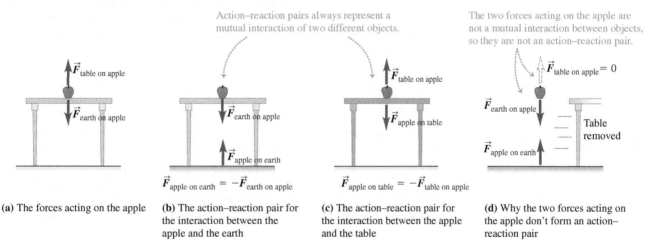

Action–reaction pairs always represent a mutual interaction of two different objects.

The two forces acting on the apple are not a mutual interaction between objects, so they are not an action–reaction pair.

$$\vec{F}_{\text{apple on earth}} = -\vec{F}_{\text{earth on apple}}$$

$$\vec{F}_{\text{apple on table}} = -\vec{F}_{\text{table on apple}}$$

(a) The forces acting on the apple

(b) The action–reaction pair for the interaction between the apple and the earth

(c) The action–reaction pair for the interaction between the apple and the table

(d) Why the two forces acting on the apple don't form an action–reaction pair

▲ **FIGURE 22** The two forces in an action–reaction pair always act on different objects.

Continued

SOLVE The two forces acting on the apple are $\vec{F}_{\text{earth on apple}}$ and $\vec{F}_{\text{table on apple}}$. Because the apple is in equilibrium, it follows from Newton's first law that the vector sum of these two forces on the apple must be zero: $\vec{F}_{\text{earth on apple}} + \vec{F}_{\text{table on apple}} = 0$.

What is the reaction force for $\vec{F}_{\text{earth on apple}}$? As the earth pulls down on the apple, the apple exerts an equally strong upward pull $\vec{F}_{\text{apple on earth}}$ on the earth, as shown in Figure 22b. The two forces are

$$\vec{F}_{\text{apple on earth}} = -\vec{F}_{\text{earth on apple}}. \qquad \text{(action and reaction for earth and apple)}$$

These forces represent the mutual interaction between the apple and the earth; one force cannot exist without the other.

Also, as the table pushes up on the apple with force $\vec{F}_{\text{table on apple}}$, the corresponding reaction is the downward force $\vec{F}_{\text{apple on table}}$ exerted on the table by the apple (Figure 22c), and we have

$$\vec{F}_{\text{table on apple}} = -\vec{F}_{\text{apple on table}}. \qquad \text{(action and reaction for apple and table)}$$

The two forces acting on the apple are $\vec{F}_{\text{table on apple}}$ and $\vec{F}_{\text{earth on apple}}$. Are they an action–reaction pair? No, they aren't, despite the fact that they are "equal and opposite" (a consequence of Newton's *first* law, not the third). They do not represent the mutual interaction between two objects; they are two different forces acting on the same object. **The two forces in an action–reaction pair *never* act on the same object.** Figure 22d shows another way to look at this situation. Suppose we suddenly yank the table out from under the apple. The two forces $\vec{F}_{\text{table on apple}}$ and $\vec{F}_{\text{apple on table}}$ then become zero. But $\vec{F}_{\text{earth on apple}}$ and $\vec{F}_{\text{apple on earth}}$ are still there, and they *do* form an action–reaction pair. Thus, $\vec{F}_{\text{table on apple}}$ can't possibly be the negative of $\vec{F}_{\text{earth on apple}}$ with the table removed.

REFLECT Interaction forces always come in pairs; if you can't find both members of the pair, your diagrams aren't complete. Also, remember that the two forces in an action–reaction pair *never* act on the same object.

EXAMPLE 6 Sliding a stone across the floor

A stonemason drags a marble block across a floor by pulling on a rope attached to the block (Figure 23a). The block has just started to move, and it may not be in equilibrium. How are the various forces related? What are the action–reaction pairs?

SOLUTION

SET UP We have three interacting objects: the block, the rope, and the mason. First we draw separate diagrams showing the horizontal forces acting on each object (Figure 23b). Instead of writing out "block on rope," etc., we designate the block as B, the rope R, and the mason M.

SOLVE Vector $\vec{F}_{\text{M on R}}$ represents the force exerted *by* the mason *on* the rope. The reaction to $\vec{F}_{\text{M on R}}$ is the "equal and opposite" force $\vec{F}_{\text{R on M}}$ exerted *on* the mason *by* the rope. Vector $\vec{F}_{\text{R on B}}$ represents the force exerted on the block by the rope. The reaction to it is the equal and opposite force $\vec{F}_{\text{B on R}}$ exerted on the rope by the block. From Newton's third law,

$$\vec{F}_{\text{R on M}} = -\vec{F}_{\text{M on R}}$$

and

$$\vec{F}_{\text{B on R}} = -\vec{F}_{\text{R on B}}. \qquad \text{(action–reaction pairs)}$$

The forces $\vec{F}_{\text{M on R}}$ and $\vec{F}_{\text{B on R}}$ are *not* an action–reaction pair (Figure 23c). Both of these forces act on the *same* object (the rope); an action and its reaction *must* always act on *different* objects. Furthermore, the forces $\vec{F}_{\text{M on R}}$ and $\vec{F}_{\text{B on R}}$ are not necessarily equal in magnitude (Figure 23d). Applying Newton's second law to the rope (mass m_R, acceleration $\vec{a}_R$), we get

$$\vec{F}_{\text{M on R}} + \vec{F}_{\text{B on R}} = m_R \vec{a}_R.$$

If block and rope are accelerating to the right, the rope is not in equilibrium, and $\vec{F}_{\text{M on R}}$ must have greater magnitude than

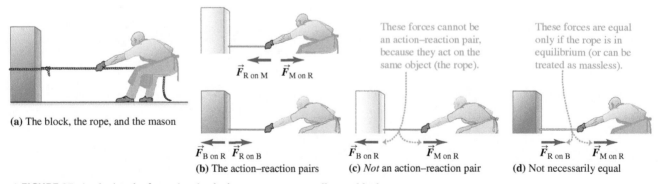

(a) The block, the rope, and the mason

$\vec{F}_{\text{R on M}}$ $\vec{F}_{\text{M on R}}$

$\vec{F}_{\text{B on R}}$ $\vec{F}_{\text{R on B}}$
(b) The action–reaction pairs

These forces cannot be an action–reaction pair, because they act on the same object (the rope).

$\vec{F}_{\text{B on R}}$ $\vec{F}_{\text{M on R}}$
(c) *Not* an action–reaction pair

These forces are equal only if the rope is in equilibrium (or can be treated as massless).

$\vec{F}_{\text{R on B}}$ $\vec{F}_{\text{M on R}}$
(d) Not necessarily equal

▲ FIGURE 23 Analyzing the forces involved when a stonemason pulls on a block.

Continued

$\vec{F}_{\text{B on R}}$. In the special case in which the rope is in equilibrium, the forces $\vec{F}_{\text{M on R}}$ and $\vec{F}_{\text{B on R}}$ are equal in magnitude, but this is an example of Newton's *first* law, not his *third.* Newton's third law holds whether the rope is accelerating or not. The action–reaction forces $\vec{F}_{\text{M on R}}$ and $\vec{F}_{\text{R on M}}$ are always equal in magnitude to *each other,* as are $\vec{F}_{\text{R on B}}$ and $\vec{F}_{\text{B on R}}$. But $\vec{F}_{\text{M on R}}$ is *not* equal in magnitude to $\vec{F}_{\text{B on R}}$ when the rope is accelerating.

REFLECT If you feel as though you're drowning in subscripts at this point, take heart. Go over this discussion again, comparing the symbols with the vector diagrams, until you're sure you see what's going on.

In the special case in which the rope is in equilibrium, or when we can consider it as massless, then the total force on the rope is zero, and $\vec{F}_{\text{B on R}}$ equals $-\vec{F}_{\text{M on R}}$ because of Newton's *first* or *second* law. Also, $\vec{F}_{\text{B on R}}$ always equals $-\vec{F}_{\text{R on B}}$ by Newton's *third* law, so in this special case, $\vec{F}_{\text{R on B}}$ also equals $\vec{F}_{\text{M on R}}$. We can then think of the rope as "transmitting" to the block, without change, the force that the stonemason exerts on it (Figure 23d). This is a useful point of view, but you have to remember that it is valid only when the rope has negligibly small mass or is in equilibrium.

▶ **Application Out of this world.** This photo shows the liftoff of a Delta Two rocket carrying the *Pathfinder* probe bound for the surface of Mars. A common misconception is that a rocket is propelled by the exhaust gases pushing against the earth. As we know from Newton's third law, the explosive force on the gases being rapidly expelled from the tail of the rocket is matched by an equal and opposite forward force on the rocket itself. It is this second force that pushes the rocket upward and allows it to continue accelerating toward Mars long after it is away from the ground. If the rocket's motion did depend on its gases pressing against the earth, it would be unable to maneuver in outer space and the *Pathfinder* could never reach the Red Planet.

NASA

An object, such as the rope in Figure 23, that has pulling forces applied at its ends is said to be in **tension,** as we mentioned in Section 1. The tension at any point is the magnitude of force acting at that point. In Figure 23c, the tension at the right-hand end of the rope is the magnitude of $\vec{F}_{\text{M on R}}$ (or of $\vec{F}_{\text{R on M}}$), and the tension at the left-hand end equals the magnitude of $\vec{F}_{\text{B on R}}$ (or of $\vec{F}_{\text{R on B}}$). If the rope is in equilibrium and if no forces act except at its ends, the tension is the same at both ends and throughout the rope. If the magnitudes of $\vec{F}_{\text{B on R}}$ and $\vec{F}_{\text{M on R}}$ are 50 N each, the tension in the rope is 50 N (*not* 100 N). Resist the temptation to add the two forces; remember that the total force $\vec{F}_{\text{B on R}} + \vec{F}_{\text{M on R}}$ on the rope in this case is zero!

NOTE ▶ Finally, we emphasize once more a fundamental truth: The two forces in an action–reaction pair *never* act on the same object. Remembering this simple fact can often help you avoid confusion about action–reaction pairs and Newton's third law. ◀

Conceptual Analysis 4

Giving a push

You use your car to push a friend's pickup truck that has broken down. To bring both of you to a stop, your friend applies the brakes in the truck. Then, in magnitude,

A. the force of the car on the truck is greater than the force of the truck on the car.
B. the force of the car on the truck is equal to the force of the truck on the car.
C. the force of the car on the truck is less than the force of the truck on the car.

SOLUTION Whenever two objects interact with each other, the interaction is described by an action–reaction pair. From Newton's third law, the two forces in this pair are always equal in magnitude and opposite in direction (even though in this case the car and truck may have different masses). So the answer is B. Also, Newton's third law is still obeyed when the objects are accelerating, as they are in this example. Unequal masses and accelerations of the objects don't alter the validity of the third law.

Rensselaer County Historical Society

◀ **Application Wet-body diagram?** This 1921 tug-of-war between the Rensselaer Polytechnic Institute sophomore and freshman classes started with the two teams centered on either side of the fire hose. As you can see, the system has not remained in equilibrium. Averaged over time, the forces exerted by the team on the left have exceeded those exerted by the team on the right, which is now, inch by inch, getting very wet.

6 Free-Body Diagrams

Newton's three laws of motion are a beautifully wrapped package containing the basic principles we need to solve a wide variety of problems in mechanics. They are very simple in form, but the process of applying them to specific situations can pose real challenges.

Let's talk about some useful techniques. When you apply Newton's first or second law ($\Sigma \vec{F} = 0$ for an equilibrium situation or $\Sigma \vec{F} = m\vec{a}$ for a non-equilibrium situation), you *must* apply it to some specific object. It is absolutely essential to decide at the beginning what object you're talking about. This statement may sound trivial, but it isn't. Once you have chosen an object, then you have to identify all the forces acting on it. These are the forces that are included in $\Sigma \vec{F}$. As you may have noticed in Section 5, it is easy to get confused between the forces acting *on* an object and the forces exerted *by* that object *on* some other object. Only the forces acting *on* the object go into $\Sigma \vec{F}$.

(a) The force of the starting block on the runner has a vertical component that counteracts her weight and a large horizontal component that accelerates her.

(b) This player is a freely falling object.

To jump up, this player will push down against the floor, increasing the upward reaction force of the floor on him.

(c) Kicking causes the water to exert a forward reaction force, or thrust, on the swimmer.

The water exerts a buoyancy force that counters the swimmer's weight.

Thrust is countered by drag forces exerted by the water on the moving swimmer.

▲ **FIGURE 24** Some examples of free-body diagrams.

To help identify the relevant forces, draw a **free-body diagram.** What's that? It is a diagram showing the chosen object by itself, "free" of its surroundings, with vectors drawn to show the forces applied to it by the various other objects that interact with it. We have already shown free-body diagrams in some previously worked-out examples. Be careful to include *all* the forces acting on the object, but be equally careful *not* to include any forces that the object exerts on any other object. In particular, the two forces in an action–reaction pair must *never* appear in the same free-body diagram, because they never act on the same object. Figure 24 shows some examples of free-body diagrams.

When you have a complete free-body diagram, you should be able to answer, for each force shown, the question "What other object is applying this force?" If you can't answer that question, you may be dealing with a nonexistent force. Sometimes you will have to take the problem apart and draw a separate free-body diagram for each part.

Dribble

A boy bounces a basketball straight down against the floor of the court. To answer the following question, it's helpful to draw a free-body diagram and consider the acceleration of the ball.

During the time the ball is in contact with the floor,

A. the force of the floor on the ball becomes much larger than the force of the ball on the floor.
B. the force of the ball on the floor plus the force of the floor on the ball equals the force of acceleration of the ball.
C. the force of the floor on the ball is equal to the force of gravity on the ball plus the force of inertia of the ball.
D. the force of the floor on the ball becomes much larger than the force of gravity on the ball.

SOLUTION First, there is no such thing as "force of acceleration" or "force of inertia." These are erroneous and misleading concepts, so answers B and C should be eliminated immediately from consideration. During the very short time the ball is touching the floor, the upward force exerted by the floor quickly becomes greater in magnitude than the ball's weight. The ball continues to move downward, but with decreasing speed (and upward acceleration), stops for an instant, then begins to move upward with increasing speed (again upward acceleration). For upward acceleration, the upward force exerted by the floor on the ball must be greater in magnitude than the weight of the ball. Thus, answer D is correct. But Newton's third law requires the force of the floor on the ball and the force of the ball on the floor to be equal and opposite; therefore, answer A cannot be correct. Forces by the ball on other objects have no effect on the acceleration of the ball. The floor pushes up on the ball, and the earth pulls down on it. Because the direction of acceleration is upward as the ball slows, stops, and then accelerates upward, the larger force must be directed upward to produce this upward acceleration. The answer is D.

Relating graphs and free-body diagrams

An object moves along the x axis. Assuming that the positive coordinate is to the right and that the forces are constant, which of the following graphs of v_x as a function of time is consistent with the forces shown in the free-body diagram in Figure 25?

▶ **FIGURE 25**

SOLUTION The force diagram shows the larger force to the right, the positive direction. Hence, the acceleration must be to the right also; a_x is positive. This means that the object is either (a) moving toward the left (the negative direction) and slowing down or (b) moving toward the right and speeding up. None of the graphs show leftward, slowing motion. D shows rightward, slowing motion, while A shows a constant velocity. Both B and C show rightward and speeding-up motion, but only C has a constant slope (corresponding to constant acceleration). Since the forces are constant, the acceleration is constant also, as indicated by the straight line in answer C.

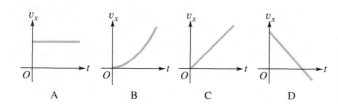

PROBLEM-SOLVING STRATEGY 1 Newton's laws

SET UP

1. Always define your coordinate system. A diagram showing the positive axis direction is essential. If you know the direction of the acceleration, it's often convenient to take that as your positive direction. If you will need to calculate displacements of the moving object, you also need to specify the location of the origin of your coordinate system.

2. Be consistent with signs. Once you define the x axis and its positive direction, velocity, acceleration, and force components in that direction are also positive.

3. In applying Newton's laws, always concentrate on a specific object. Draw a free-body diagram showing all the forces (magnitudes and directions) acting *on* this object, but *do not* include forces that the object exerts on any other object. The acceleration of the object is determined by the forces acting on it, not by the forces it exerts on something else. Represent the object as a dot or by a simple sketch; you don't have to be an artist.

SOLVE

4. Identify the known and unknown quantities, and give each unknown quantity an algebraic symbol. If you know the direction of a force at the start, use a symbol to represent the *magnitude* of the force (always a positive quantity). Keep in mind that the *component* of this force along a particular axis direction may still be either positive or negative.

5. Always check units for consistency. When appropriate, use the conversion $1\ \text{N} = 1\ \text{kg} \cdot \text{m/s}^2$.

REFLECT

6. Check to make sure that your forces obey Newton's third law. When you can guess the direction of the net force, make sure that its direction is the same as that of the acceleration, as required by Newton's second law.

We'll expand this strategy to deal with more complex problems, but it's important for you to use it consistently from the very start, to develop good habits in the systematic analysis of problems.

EXAMPLE 7 **Tension in a massless chain**

To improve the acoustics in an auditorium, a sound reflector with a mass of 200 kg is suspended by a chain from the ceiling. What is its weight? What force (magnitude and direction) does the chain exert on it? What is the tension in the chain? Assume that the mass of the chain itself is negligible.

SOLUTION

SET UP The reflector is in equilibrium, so we use Newton's first law, $\Sigma \vec{F} = 0$. We draw separate free-body diagrams for the reflector and the chain (Figure 26). We take the positive y axis to be upward, as shown. Each force has only a y component. We give symbolic labels to the magnitudes of the unknown forces, using T to represent the tension in the chain.

SOLVE The magnitude of the weight $\vec{w}$ of the reflector is given by Equation 9:

$$w = mg = (200\ \text{kg})(9.80\ \text{m/s}^2) = 1960\ \text{N}.$$

Armed with this number and Newton's first law, we can compute the unknown force magnitudes.

The weight $\vec{w}$ of the reflector is a force pointing in the negative y direction, so its y component is -1960 N. The upward force $\vec{T}$ exerted on the reflector by the chain has unknown magnitude T. Because the reflector is in equilibrium, the sum of the y components of force on it must be zero:

$$\Sigma F_y = T + (-1960\ \text{N}) = 0, \quad \text{so} \quad T = 1960\ \text{N}.$$

The chain pulls *up* on the reflector with a force $\vec{T}$ of magnitude 1960 N. By Newton's third law, the reflector pulls *down* on the chain with a force of magnitude 1960 N.

Continued

The chain is also in equilibrium, so the vector sum of forces on it must equal zero. For this to be true, an upward force with magnitude 1960 N must act on it at its top end. The tension in the chain is $T = 1960$ N.

REFLECT Note that we have defined T to be the *magnitude* of a force, so it is always positive. But the y component of force acting on the chain at its lower end is $-T = -1960$ N. The tension is the same at every point in the chain; imagine cutting a link and then pulling the cut ends together. To hold them together requires a force with magnitude T on each cut end. If the chain isn't massless, the situation is different, as the next example shows.

Practice Problem: The weight of the reflector (the earth's gravitational pull) and the force the reflector exerts on the earth form an action–reaction pair. Determine the magnitude and direction of each of these forces. *Answers:* 1960 N down, 1960 N up.

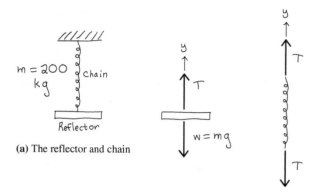

(a) The reflector and chain

(b) Free-body diagrams for the reflector and the chain

▲ **FIGURE 26** The diagrams we draw for this problem.

EXAMPLE 8   Tension in a chain with mass

Suppose the mass of the chain in Example 7 is not negligible, but is 10.0 kg. Find the forces at the ends of the chain.

SOLUTION

SET UP Again we draw separate free-body diagrams for the reflector and the chain (Figure 27); each is in equilibrium. We take the y axis to be vertically upward. The weight w_C of the chain is $w_C = m_C g = (10.0\ \text{kg})(9.8\ \text{m/s}^2) = 98$ N. The free-body diagrams are different from those in Figure 26 because the magnitudes of the forces acting on the two ends of the chain are no longer equal. (Otherwise the chain couldn't be in equilibrium.) We label these two forces T_1 and T_2.

SOLVE Note that the two forces labeled T_2 form an action–reaction pair; that's how we know that they have the same magnitude. The equilibrium condition $\sum F_y = 0$ for the reflector is

$$T_2 + (-1960\ \text{N}) = 0, \quad \text{so} \quad T_2 = 1960\ \text{N}.$$

There are now three forces acting on the chain: its weight and the forces at the two ends. The equilibrium condition $\sum F_y = 0$ for the chain is

$$T_1 + (-T_2) + (-98\ \text{N}) = 0.$$

Note that the y component of T_1 is positive because it points in the $+y$ direction, but the y components of both T_2 and 98 N are negative. When we substitute the value $T_2 = 1960$ N and solve for T_1, we find that

$$T_1 = 2058\ \text{N}.$$

Alternative Solution: An alternative procedure is to draw a free-body diagram for the composite object consisting of the reflector and the chain together (Figure 27b). The two forces on this composite object are the upward force T_1 at the top of the chain and the total weight, with magnitude 1960 N + 98 N =

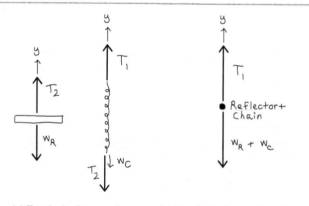

(a) Free-body diagrams for reflector and chain.

(b) Free-body diagram for reflector and chain treated as a unit.

▲ **FIGURE 27** Two alternative diagrams we could draw for this problem.

2058 N. Again, we find that $T_1 = 2058$ N. Note that we cannot find T_2 by this method; we still need a separate free-body diagram for one of the objects.

REFLECT When a composite object can be broken into two or more component parts, there are usually several alternative solutions. Often, the calculations can be simplified by a clever choice of subsystems. Also, solving a problem in two or more alternative ways provides a consistency check that's useful in finding errors.

Practice Problem: Solve the problem described in this example by using two free-body diagrams, one for the composite reflector–chain object, and one for the reflector alone.

EXAMPLE 9   **Weighing yourself in an elevator**

You stand on a bathroom scale that rests on the floor of an elevator. (Don't ask why!) Standing on the scale compresses internal springs and activates a dial that indicates your weight in newtons. When the elevator is at rest, the scale reads 600 N. Then the elevator begins to move upward with a constant acceleration $a_y = 2.00 \text{ m/s}^2$. **(a)** Determine your mass. **(b)** Determine the scale reading while the elevator is accelerating. **(c)** If you read the scale without realizing that the elevator is accelerating upward, what might you *think* your mass is?

SOLUTION

SET UP All the forces are vertical; we take the y axis to be vertically upward. We neglect the weight of the scale itself. When the scale is in equilibrium (not accelerating), the total force acting on it must be zero. When it reads 600 N, forces of magnitude 600 N (with opposite directions) are applied to its top and bottom surfaces. Using this analysis, we draw separate free-body diagrams for you and the scale (Figure 28).

SOLVE Part (a):   At first, you, the scale, and the elevator are at rest in an inertial system; all three objects are in equilibrium. You push down on the scale with a force of magnitude 600 N, and (from Newton's third law) the scale applies an equal and opposite upward force to your feet. The only other force on you is your weight; you are in equilibrium, so the *total* y component of force on you is zero. Your weight is 600 N, and your mass is

$$m = \frac{w}{g} = \frac{600 \text{ N}}{9.80 \text{ m/s}^2} = 61.2 \text{ kg} \qquad \text{(about 135 lb)}.$$

Part (b):   When the system accelerates upward at 2.00 m/s^2, your weight is still 600 N, but now the upward force the scale applies to your feet is different because you are no longer in equilibrium. We'll call the magnitude of the upward force F (Figure 28b). We use Newton's second law to relate the acceleration to the net force:

$$F - 600 \text{ N} = ma = (61.2 \text{ kg})(2.00 \text{ m/s}^2)$$

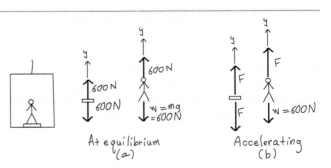

▲ **FIGURE 28** Our diagrams for this problem.

and

$$F = 722 \text{ N}.$$

Part (c):   If you think your weight is 722 N, then you are likely to conclude that your mass is $m = w/g = (722 \text{ N})/(9.8 \text{ m/s}^2) = 73.7 \text{ kg}$, instead of the actual value of 61.2 kg.

REFLECT Relate what we've said here to your own feeling of being lighter or heavier in an elevator. Do these feelings occur only when the elevator is accelerating?

Practice Problem: Suppose the elevator is accelerating *downward* at 2.00 m/s^2. What does the scale read during the acceleration? *Answer:* 478 N.

CHAPTER SUMMARY

Force

(Section 1) Force, a vector quantity, is a quantitative measure of the mechanical interaction between two objects. When several forces act on an object, the effect is the same as when a single force, equal to the vector sum, or resultant, of the forces, acts on the object.

Two forces acting on a point have the same effect as a single force $\vec{R}$ equal to their vector sum.

A force may be treated as the vector sum of its component vectors.

Newton's First Law

(Section 2) Newton's first law states that when no force acts on an object or when the vector sum of all forces acting on it is zero, the object is in equilibrium. If the object is initially at rest, it remains at rest; if it is initially in motion, it continues to move with constant velocity. This law is valid only in inertial frames of reference.

If the vector sum of the forces acting on an object is zero, the object remains at rest or (as here) in motion with constant velocity.

Mass and Newton's Second Law

(Section 3) The inertial properties of an object are characterized by its *mass*. The acceleration of an object under the action of a given set of forces is directly proportional to the vector sum of the forces and inversely proportional to the mass of the object. This relationship is Newton's second law:

$$\Sigma \vec{F} = m\vec{a}, \qquad (7)$$

or, in component form, $\Sigma F_x = ma_x$ and $\Sigma F_y = ma_y$ (Equations 8).

An object's acceleration depends on its mass and on the net force acting on it.

Mass and Weight

(Section 4) The weight of an object is the gravitational force exerted on it by the earth (or whatever other object exerts the gravitational force). Weight is a force and is therefore a vector quantity. The magnitude of the weight of an object at any specific location is equal to the product of the mass m of the object and the magnitude of the acceleration due to gravity, g, at that location:

$$w = mg. \qquad (9)$$

The weight of an object depends on its location, but the mass is independent of location.

An object's weight depends on its mass and on the acceleration due to gravity at its location.

Newton's Third Law

(Section 5) Newton's third law states that "action equals reaction"; when two bodies interact, they exert forces on each other that, at each instant, are equal in magnitude and opposite in direction. The two forces in an action–reaction pair always act on two different bodies; they never act on the same object.

An action–reaction pair: $\vec{F}_{\text{ball on foot}} = -\vec{F}_{\text{foot on ball}}$. The two forces represent a *mutual interaction* of two objects, and each acts on a *different* object.

Free-Body Diagrams

(Section 6) In Newton's second law, only the forces acting on an object go into $\Sigma \vec{F}$. To help identify the relevant forces, draw a free-body diagram. Such a diagram shows the chosen object by itself, "free" of its surroundings, with vectors drawn to show the forces applied to it by the various other objects that interact with it. Be careful to include *all* the forces acting on the object, but be equally careful *not* to include any forces that the object exerts on any other object. In particular, the two forces in an action–reaction pair must *never* appear in the same free-body diagram, because they never act on the same object.

A free-body diagram of a man dragging a crate. The diagram shows *all* the forces acting on the man, and *only* forces acting on the man.

Man (treated as particle)

Newton's Laws of Motion: Problem Set

For instructor-assigned homework, go to www.masteringphysics.com

Conceptual Questions

1. When a car accelerates starting from rest, where is the force applied to the car in order to cause its acceleration? What object exerts this force on the car?

2. When a car stops suddenly, the passengers are "thrown forward" out of their seats (if they are not wearing seat belts). What causes this to happen? Are they really *thrown* forward?

3. For medical reasons, it is important for astronauts in outer space to determine their body mass at regular intervals. Devise a scheme for measuring body mass in a zero-gravity environment.

4. Although in everyday life the earth seems to be an inertial frame of reference, the paths of objects moving freely across the earth's surface, such as air masses, artillery shells, and even thrown baseballs, have a tendency to curve slightly to their right (in the Northern Hemisphere) as seen by an observer on the surface. Can you explain why this is?

5. A passenger in a bus notices that a ball which has been at rest in the aisle suddenly starts to roll toward the front of the bus. What can the passenger conclude about the motion of the bus from this observation?

6. If you hit the sidewalk with a hammer, the hammer bounces back at you. How does this process involve Newton's third law?

7. In a head-on collision between a compact hybrid car and a gas-guzzling SUV, which vehicle is acted upon by the greater force? So why are people in the smaller car more likely to get injured than those in the large one, assuming that both cars are equally strong?

8. Suppose you are in a car in a very dense fog and cannot see the meters on your dashboard or anything outside the car. (Maybe you should not be driving under these conditions!) (a) How can you tell if your car is speeding up or slowing down? (b) Can you tell if your car is at rest or is moving with uniform velocity?

9. It would be much easier to lift a bowling ball on the moon than on the earth. Would it be similarly easier to *catch* the bowling ball on the moon, if someone threw it to you? Explain.

10. You are in a spaceship far from any stars or planets when you notice that if you release an object, it accelerates toward your feet at 9.8 m/s². (a) What can you conclude about the motion of the spaceship? (b) What force, if any, do you feel on your feet from the floor? (c) Explain how your observations in parts (a) and (b) lead you to believe that gravity is present. (d) Is gravity *really* present in the spaceship? How has the ship generated artificial gravity?

11. When a car is hit from behind, people in that car can receive a whiplash injury to their necks. Use Newton's laws of motion to explain why this occurs.

12. If your hands are wet and no towel is handy, you can remove excess water by shaking them. Use Newton's laws to explain why doing this gets rid of the water.

13. It is possible to play catch with a softball in an airplane in level flight just as though the plane were at rest. Is this still possible when the plane is making a turn?

14. Newton's third law tells us that if you push a box with a 15 N force, it pushes back on you with a 15 N force. How can you ever accelerate this box if it always pushes back with the same force you exert on it?

15. If you drop a 10 lb rock and a 10 lb pillow from the same height with no air resistance, which one is moving faster when they reach the ground? So why would you rather be hit by the pillow than the rock?

16. Which "feels" a greater pull due to gravity, a heavy object or a light object? So why do heavy objects *not* accelerate faster than light objects?

17. If you step hard on the accelerator pedal of your car, your body feels "pushed back" in the seat. (a) Why do you feel this? Are you really pushed back? (b) Make a free-body diagram of your body under these circumstances.

Multiple-Choice Problems

1. A force F is required to push a crate along a rough horizontal floor at a constant speed V with friction present. What force is needed to push this crate along the same floor at a constant speed $3V$ if friction is the same as before?
   A. A constant force $3F$ is needed.
   B. A force that gradually increases from F to $3F$ is needed.
   C. A constant force F is needed.
   D. No force is needed, since the crate has no acceleration.

2. When you're driving on the freeway it's necessary to keep your foot on the accelerator to keep the car moving at a constant speed. In this situation
   A. the net force on the car is in the forward direction.
   B. the net force on the car is toward the rear.
   C. the net force on the car is zero.
   D. the net force on the car depends on your speed.

3. Assuming you like chocolate cake, which would you rather have:
   A. a piece of cake that weighs 1 N on earth.
   B. a piece of cake that weighs 1 N on the moon.
   C. a piece of cake that weighs 1 N on Jupiter.
   D. The weight doesn't matter; the amount of cake is the same in all three cases.

4. A golfer tees off and hits the ball with a mighty swing. During the brief time the golf club is in contact with the ball,
   A. the ball pushes just as hard on the club as the club pushes on the ball.
   B. the push of the club on the ball is much greater than the push of the ball on the club, since the club makes the ball move.
   C. the push of the ball on the club would be equal to the push of the club on the ball only if the ball did not move.
   D. the club pushes harder on the ball than the ball does on the club because the club has a greater mass than the ball.

5. Three books are at rest on a horizontal table, as shown in Figure 29. The *net* force on the middle book is
   A. 5 N downward.
   B. 15 N upward.
   C. 15 N downward.
   D. 0 N.

▲ **FIGURE 29** Multiple-choice problem 5.

6. In outer space, where there is no gravity or air, an astronaut pushes with an equal force of 12 N on a 2 N moon rock and on a 4 N moon rock.
   A. Since both rocks are weightless, they will have the same acceleration.
   B. The 4 N rock pushes back on the astronaut twice as hard as the 2 N rock.
   C. Both rocks push back on the astronaut with 12 N.
   D. Since both rocks are weightless, they do not push back on the astronaut.

7. A rocket firing its engine and accelerating in outer space (no gravity, no air resistance) suddenly runs out of fuel. Which of the following best describes its motion after burnout?
   A. It continues to accelerate at the same rate.
   B. It continues to accelerate but at a gradually decreasing rate, until it reaches a constant velocity.
   C. It immediately stops accelerating, and continues moving at the velocity it had when burnout occurred.
   D. It immediately begins slowing down and gradually approaches zero velocity.

8. A 3 lb physics book rests on an ordinary scale that is placed on a horizontal table. The reaction force to the downward 3 lb force on the book is
   A. an upward 3 lb force on the scale due to the table.
   B. an upward 3 lb force on the book due to the scale.
   C. an upward 3 lb force on the table due to the floor.
   D. an upward 3 lb force on the earth due to the book.

9. A person pushes horizontally with constant force P on a 250 N box resting on a frictionless horizontal floor. Which of the following statements about this box is correct?
   A. The box will accelerate no matter how small P is.

B. The box will not accelerate unless $P > 250$ N.
   C. The box will move with constant velocity because P is constant.
   D. Once the box is set moving, it will come to rest after P is removed.

10. Suppose the sun, including its gravity, suddenly disappeared. Which of the following statements best describes the subsequent motion of the earth?
    A. The earth would continue moving in a straight line tangent to its original direction, but would gradually slow down.
    B. The earth would speed up because the sun's gravity would not be able to slow it down.
    C. The earth would continue moving in a straight line tangent to its original direction and would not change its speed.
    D. The earth would move directly outward with constant speed away from the sun's original position.

11. Three weights hang by very light wires as shown in Figure 30. What must be true about the tensions in these wires? (There may be more than one correct choice.)
    A. The tension in A is the greatest.
    B. The tension in C is the greatest.
    C. All three wires have the same tension because the system is in equilibrium.
    D. The tension in C is the least.

▲ **FIGURE 30** Multiple-choice problem 11.

12. A woman normally weighs 125 lb. If she is standing on a spring scale in an elevator that is traveling *downward,* but slowing up, the scale will read
    A. more than 125 lb.
    B. 125 lb.
    C. less than 125 lb.
    D. It is impossible to answer this question without knowing the acceleration of the elevator.

13. A worker pushes horizontally on a 2000 N refrigerator on a kitchen floor with a force of 25 N.
    A. If the refrigerator moves forward, this person feels it pushing back with less than 25 N.
    B. The person always feels a 25 N push from the refrigerator.
    C. The person feels a 25 N push from the refrigerator only if it does not move.
    D. The person feels a 2000 N push from the refrigerator.

14. Far from any gravity, an astronaut accidentally releases a metal wrench inside a spaceship that is traveling at a constant velocity of 250 km/s away from earth in outer space. What will be the subsequent behavior of that wrench as observed by the astronaut?
    A. It will fall to the floor with constant velocity.
    B. It will fall to the floor with constant acceleration.
    C. It will fall to the back of the spaceship with constant velocity.
    D. It will fall to the back of the spaceship with constant acceleration.
    E. It will remain right where the astronaut released it.

15. A worker pulls horizontally on a crate on a rough horizontal floor, causing it to move forward with constant velocity. In Figure 31, force A is the pull of the worker and force B is the force of friction due to the floor. Which one of the following statements about these forces is correct?
A. $A < B$ B. $A = B$ C. $A > B$

▲ **FIGURE 31** Multiple-choice problem 15.

16. A person pushes two boxes with a horizontal 100 N force on a frictionless floor, as shown in Figure 32. Box A is heavier than box B. Which of the following statements about these boxes is correct?
A. Box A pushes on box B with a force of 100 N, and box B pushes on box A with a force of 100 N.
B. Box A pushes on box B harder than box B pushes on box A.
C. Boxes A and B push on each other with equal forces of less than 100 N.
D. The boxes will not begin to move unless the total weight of the two boxes is less than 100 N.

▲ **FIGURE 32** Multiple-choice problem 16.

Problems

1 Force

1. ● A warehouse worker pushes a crate along the floor, as shown in Figure 33, by a force of 10 N that points downward at an angle of 45° below the horizontal. Find the horizontal and vertical components of the push.

▲ **FIGURE 33** Problem 1.

2. ● Two dogs pull horizontally on ropes attached to a post; the angle between the ropes is 60.0°. If dog A exerts a force of 270 N and dog B exerts a force of 300 N, find the magnitude of the resultant force and the angle it makes with dog A's rope.

3. ● A man is dragging a trunk up the loading ramp of a mover's truck. The ramp has a slope angle of 20.0°, and the man pulls upward with a force $\vec{F}$ of magnitude 375 N whose direction makes an angle of 30.0° with the ramp. (See Figure 34.) Find the horizontal and vertical components of the force $\vec{F}$.

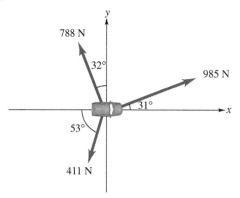

▲ **FIGURE 34** Problem 3.

4. ● **Jaw injury.** Due to a jaw injury, a patient must wear a strap (see Figure 35) that produces a net upward force of 5.00 N on his chin. The tension is the same throughout the strap. To what tension must the strap be adjusted to provide the necessary upward force?

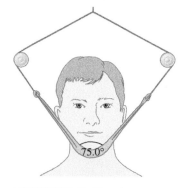

▲ **FIGURE 35** Problem 4.

5. ● Workmen are trying to free an SUV stuck in the mud. To extricate the vehicle, they use three horizontal ropes, producing the force vectors shown in Figure 36. (a) Find the x and y components of each of the three pulls. (b) Use the components to find the magnitude and direction of the resultant of the three pulls.

▲ **FIGURE 36** Problem 5.

3 Mass and Newton's Second Law

6. ● A box rests on a frozen pond, which serves as a frictionless horizontal surface. If a fisherman applies a horizontal force with magnitude 48.0 N to the box and produces an acceleration of magnitude 3.00 m/s², what is the mass of the box?

7. ● In outer space, a constant net force of magnitude 140 N is exerted on a 32.5 kg probe initially at rest. (a) What acceleration does this force produce? (b) How far does the probe travel in 10.0 s?

8. ●● A 68.5 kg skater moving initially at 2.40 m/s on rough horizontal ice comes to rest uniformly in 3.52 s due to friction from the ice. What force does friction exert on the skater?

9. ●● **Animal dynamics.** An adult 68 kg cheetah can accelerate from rest to 20.1 m/s (45 mph) in 2.0 s. Assuming constant acceleration, (a) find the net external force causing this acceleration. (b) Where does the force come from? That is, what exerts the force on the cheetah?

10. •• A hockey puck with mass 0.160 kg is at rest on the horizontal, frictionless surface of a rink. A player applies a force of 0.250 N to the puck, parallel to the surface of the ice, and continues to apply this force for 2.00 s. What are the position and speed of the puck at the end of that time?

11. •• A dock worker applies a constant horizontal force of 80.0 N to a block of ice on a smooth horizontal floor. The frictional force is negligible. The block starts from rest and moves 11.0 m in the first 5.00 s. What is the mass of the block of ice?

4 Mass and Weight

12. • (a) What is the mass of a book that weighs 3.20 N in the laboratory? (b) In the same lab, what is the weight of a dog whose mass is 14.0 kg?

13. • Superman throws a 2400-N boulder at an adversary. What horizontal force must Superman apply to the boulder to give it a horizontal acceleration of 12.0 m/s^2?

14. • (a) How many newtons does a 150 lb person weigh?
BIO (b) Should a veterinarian be skeptical if someone said that her adult collie weighed 40 N? (c) Should a nurse question a medical chart which showed that an average-looking patient had a mass of 200 kg?

15. • (a) An ordinary flea has a mass of 210 μg. How many new-
BIO tons does it weigh? (b) The mass of a typical froghopper is 12.3 mg. How many newtons does it weigh? (c) A house cat typically weighs 45 N. How many pounds does it weigh and what is its mass in kilograms?

16. • Calculate the mass (in SI units) of (a) a 160-lb human being;
BIO (b) a 1.9-lb cockatoo. Calculate the weight (in English units) of (c) a 2300-kg rhinoceros; (d) a 22-g song sparrow.

17. •• An astronaut's pack weighs 17.5 N when she is on earth but only 3.24 N when she is at the surface of an asteroid. (a) What is the acceleration due to gravity on this asteroid? (b) What is the mass of the pack on the asteroid?

18. • **Interpreting a medical chart.** You, a resident physician,
BIO are reading the medical chart of a normal adult female patient. Carelessly, one of the nurses has entered this woman's weight as a number without units. Another nurse has offered a suggestion for what the units might be. In each of the following cases, decide whether this nurse's suggestion is physically reasonable: (a) The number is 150, and the nurse suggests that the units are kilograms. (b) The number is 25, and the nurse suggests that the units are slugs. (c) The number is 65,000, and the nurse suggests that the units are grams.

19. • What does a 138 N rock weigh if it is accelerating (a) upward at 12 m/s^2, (b) downward at 3.5 m/s^2? (c) What would be the answers to parts (a) and (b) if the rock had a mass of 138 kg? (d) What would be the answers to parts (a) and (b) if the rock were moving with a constant upward velocity of 23 m/s?

20. •• At the surface of Jupiter's moon Io, the acceleration due to gravity is 1.81 m/s^2. If a piece of ice weighs 44.0 N at the surface of the earth, (a) what is its mass on the earth's surface? (b) What are its mass and weight on the surface of Io?

21. •• A scientific instrument that weighs 85.2 N on the earth weighs 32.2 N at the surface of Mercury. (a) What is the acceleration due to gravity on Mercury? (b) What is the instrument's mass on earth and on Mercury?

22. •• **Planet X!** When venturing forth on Planet X, you throw a 5.24 kg rock upward at 13.0 m/s and find that it returns to the same level 1.51 s later. What does the rock weigh on Planet X?

23. •• The driver of a 1750 kg car traveling on a horizontal road at 110 km/h suddenly applies the brakes. Due to a slippery pavement, the friction of the road on the tires of the car, which is what slows down the car, is 25% of the weight of the car. (a) What is the acceleration of the car? (b) How many meters does it travel before stopping under these conditions?

5 Newton's Third Law

24. • You drag a heavy box along a rough horizontal floor by a horizontal rope. Identify the reaction force to each of the following forces: (a) the pull of the rope on the box, (b) the friction force on the box, (c) the normal force on the box, and (d) the weight of the box.

25. • Imagine that you are holding a book weighing 4 N at rest on the palm of your hand. Complete the following sentences: (a) A downward force of magnitude 4 N is exerted on the book by _____. (b) An upward force of magnitude _____ is exerted on _____ by the hand. (c) Is the upward force in part (b) the reaction to the downward force in part (a)? d) The reaction to the force in part (a) is a force of magnitude _____, exerted on _____ by _____. Its direction is _____. (e) The reaction to the force in part (b) is a force of magnitude _____, exerted on _____ by _____. Its direction is _____. (f) The forces in parts (a) and (b) are "equal and opposite" because of Newton's _____ law. (g) The forces in parts (b) and (e) are "equal and opposite" because of Newton's _____ law.

26. • Suppose now that you exert an upward force of magnitude 5 N on the book in the previous problem. (a) Does the book remain in equilibrium? (b) Is the force exerted on the book by your hand equal and opposite to the force exerted on the book by the earth? (c) Is the force exerted on the book by the earth equal and opposite to the force exerted on the earth by the book? (d) Is the force exerted on the book by your hand equal and opposite to the force exerted on your hand by the book? Finally, suppose that you snatch your hand away while the book is moving upward. (e) How many forces then act on the book? (f) Is the book in equilibrium?

27. • The upward normal force exerted by the floor is 620 N on an elevator passenger who weighs 650 N. What are the reaction forces to these two forces? Is the passenger accelerating? If so, what are the magnitude and direction of the acceleration?

6 Free-Body Diagrams

28. • A person throws a 2.5 lb stone into the air with an initial upward speed of 15 ft/s. Make a free-body diagram for this stone (a) after it is free of the person's hand and is traveling upward, (b) at its highest point, (c) when it is traveling downward, and (d) while it is being thrown upward, but is still in contact with the person's hand.

29. • The driver of a car traveling at 65 mph suddenly hits his brakes on a horizontal highway. (a) Make a free-body diagram of the car while it is slowing down. (b) Make a free-body diagram of a passenger in a car that is accelerating on a freeway entrance ramp.

30. • A tennis ball traveling horizontally at 22 m/s suddenly hits a vertical brick wall and bounces back with a horizontal velocity of 18 m/s. Make a free-body diagram of this ball (a) just before it hits the wall, (b) just after it has bounced free of the wall, and (c) while it is in contact with the wall.

31. •• Two crates, A and B, sit at rest side by side on a frictionless horizontal surface. The crates have masses m_A and m_B. A horizontal force $\vec{F}$ is applied to crate A and the two crates move off to the right. (a) Draw clearly labeled free-body diagrams for crate A and for crate B. Indicate which pairs of forces, if any, are third-law action–reaction pairs. (b) If the magnitude of force $\vec{F}$ is less than the total weight of the two crates, will it cause the crates to move? Explain.

32. •• A ball is hanging from a long string that is tied to the ceiling of a train car traveling eastward on horizontal tracks. An observer inside the train car sees the ball hang motionless. Draw a clearly labeled free-body diagram for the ball if (a) the train has a uniform velocity, and (b) the train is speeding up uniformly. Is the net force on the ball zero in either case? Explain.

33. • A person drags her 65 N suitcase along the rough horizontal floor by pulling upward at 30° above the horizontal with a 50 N force. Make a free-body diagram of this suitcase.

34. •• A factory worker pushes horizontally on a 250 N crate with a force of 75 N on a horizontal rough floor. A 135 N crate rests on top of the one being pushed and moves along with it. Make a free-body diagram of *each* crate if the friction force exerted by the floor is less than the worker's push.

35. •• A dock worker pulls two boxes connected by a rope on a horizontal floor, as shown in Figure 37. All the ropes are horizontal, and there is some friction with the floor. Make a free-body diagram of each box.

▲ **FIGURE 37** Problem 35.

36. •• A hospital orderly pushes horizontally on two boxes of equipment on a rough horizontal floor, as shown in Figure 38. Make a free-body diagram of each box.

▲ **FIGURE 38** Problem 36.

37. • A uniform 25.0 kg chain 2.00 m long supports a 50.0 kg chandelier in a large public building. Find the tension in (a) the bottom link of the chain, (b) the top link of the chain, and (c) the middle link of the chain.

38. • An acrobat is hanging by his feet from a trapeze, while supporting with his hands a second acrobat who hangs below him. Draw separate free-body diagrams for the two acrobats.

39. • A 275 N bucket is lifted with an acceleration of 2.50 m/s² by a 125 N uniform vertical chain. Start each of the following parts with a free-body diagram. Find the tension in (a) the top link of the chain, (b) the bottom link of the chain, and (c) the middle link of the chain.

40. •• **Human biomechanics.** World-class sprinters can spring **BIO** out of the starting blocks with an acceleration that is essentially horizontal and of magnitude 15 m/s². (a) How much horizontal force must a 55-kg sprinter exert on the starting blocks during a start to produce this acceleration? (b) What exerts the force that propels the sprinter, the blocks or the sprinter himself?

41. •• A chair of mass 12.0 kg is sitting on the horizontal floor; the floor is not frictionless. You push on the chair with a force $F = 40.0$ N that is directed at an angle of 37.0° below the horizontal, and the chair slides along the floor. (a) Draw a clearly labeled free-body diagram for the chair. (b) Use your diagram and Newton's laws to calculate the normal force that the floor exerts on the chair.

42. •• **Human biomechanics.** The fastest pitched baseball was **BIO** measured at 46 m/s. Typically, a baseball has a mass of 145 g. If the pitcher exerted his force (assumed to be horizontal and constant) over a distance of 1.0 m, (a) what force did he produce on the ball during this record-setting pitch? (b) Make free-body diagrams of the ball during the pitch and just *after* it has left the pitcher's hand.

43. •• You walk into an elevator, step onto a scale, and push the "up" button. You also recall that your normal weight is 625 N. Start each of the following parts with a free-body diagram. (a) If the elevator has an acceleration of magnitude 2.50 m/s², what does the scale read? (b) If you start holding a 3.85 kg package by a light vertical string, what will be the tension in this string once the elevator begins accelerating?

44. •• A truck is pulling a car on a horizontal highway using a horizontal rope. The car is in neutral gear, so we can assume that there is no appreciable friction between its tires and the highway. As the truck is accelerating to highway speeds, draw a free-body diagram of (a) the car and (b) the truck. (c) What force accelerates this system forward? Explain how this force originates.

45. •• **The space shuttle.** During the first stage of its launch, a space shuttle goes from rest to 4973 km/h while rising a vertical distance of 45 km. Assume constant acceleration and no variation in g over this distance. (a) What is the acceleration of the shuttle? (b) If a 55.0 kg astronaut is standing on a scale inside the shuttle during this launch, how hard will the scale push on her? Start with a free-body diagram of the astronaut. (c) If this astronaut did not realize that the shuttle had left the launch pad, what would she think were her weight and mass?

46. •• A woman is standing in an elevator holding her 2.5-kg briefcase by its handles. Draw a free-body diagram for the briefcase if the elevator is accelerating downward at 1.50 m/s², and calculate the downward pull of the briefcase on the woman's arm while the elevator is accelerating.

General Problems

47. •• An advertisement claims that a particular automobile can "stop on a dime." What net force would actually be necessary to stop a 850-kg automobile traveling initially at 45.0 km/h in a distance equal to the diameter of a dime, which is 1.8 cm?

48. •• A rifle shoots a 4.20 g bullet out of its barrel. The bullet has a muzzle velocity of 965 m/s just as it leaves the barrel. Assuming a constant horizontal acceleration over a distance of 45.0 cm starting from rest, with no friction between the bullet and the barrel, (a) what force does the rifle exert on the bullet while it is in the barrel? (b) Draw a free-body diagram of the bullet (i) while it is in the barrel and (ii) just *after* it has left the barrel. (c) How many g's of acceleration does the rifle give this bullet? (d) For how long a time is the bullet in the barrel?

49. •• A parachutist relies on air resistance (mainly on her parachute) to decrease her downward velocity. She and her parachute have a mass of 55.0 kg, and at a particular moment air resistance exerts a total upward force of 620 N on her and her parachute. (a) What is the weight of the parachutist? (b) Draw a free-body diagram for the parachutist (see Section 6). Use that diagram to calculate the net force on the parachutist. Is the net force upward or downward? (c) What is the acceleration (magnitude and direction) of the parachutist?

50. •• A spacecraft descends vertically near the surface of Planet X. An upward thrust of 25.0 kN from its engines slows it down at a rate of 1.20 m/s^2, but it speeds up at a rate of 0.80 m/s^2 with an upward thrust of 10.0 kN. (a) In each case, what is the direction of the acceleration of the spacecraft? (b) Draw a free-body diagram for the spacecraft. In each case, speeding up or slowing down, what is the direction of the net force on the spacecraft? (c) Apply Newton's second law to each case, slowing down or speeding up, and use this to find the spacecraft's weight near the surface of Planet X.

51. •• **A standing vertical jump.** Basketball player Darrell Griffith is on record as attaining a standing vertical jump of 1.2 m (4 ft). (This means that he moved upward by 1.2 m after his feet left the floor.) Griffith weighed 890 N (200 lb). (a) What was his speed as he left the floor? (b) If the time of the part of the jump before his feet left the floor was 0.300 s, what were the magnitude and direction of his acceleration (assuming it to be constant) while he was pushing against the floor? (c) Draw a free-body diagram of Griffith during the jump. (d) Use Newton's laws and the results of part (b) to calculate the force he applied to the ground during his jump.

52. •• You leave the doctor's office after your annual checkup and recall that you weighed 683 N in her office. You then get into an elevator that, conveniently, has a scale. Find the magnitude and direction of the elevator's acceleration if the scale reads (a) 725 N, (b) 595 N.

53. •• **Human biomechanics.** The fastest served tennis ball, served by "Big Bill" Tilden in 1931, was measured at 73.14 m/s. The mass of a tennis ball is 57 g, and the ball is typically in contact with the tennis racquet for 30.0 ms, with the ball starting from rest. Assuming constant acceleration, (a) what force did Big Bill's tennis racquet exert on the tennis ball if he hit it essentially horizontally? (b) Make free-body diagrams of the tennis ball during the serve and just after it has moved free of the racquet.

54. •• **Extraterrestrial physics.** You have landed on an unknown planet, Newtonia, and want to know what objects will weigh there. You find that when a certain tool is pushed on a frictionless horizontal surface by a 12.0 N force, it moves 16.0 m in the first 2.00 s, starting from rest. You next observe that if you release this tool from rest at 10.0 m above the ground, it takes 2.58 s to reach the ground. What does the tool weigh on Newtonia and what would it weigh on Earth?

55. •• An athlete whose mass is 90.0 kg is performing weight-lifting exercises. Starting from the rest position, he lifts, with constant acceleration, a barbell that weighs 490 N. He lifts the barbell a distance of 0.60 m in 1.6 s. (a) Draw a clearly labeled free-body force diagram for the barbell and for the athlete. (b) Use the diagrams in part (a) and Newton's laws to find the total force that the ground exerts on the athlete's feet as he lifts the barbell.

56. •• **Jumping to the ground.** A 75.0 kg man steps off a platform 3.10 m above the ground. He keeps his legs straight as he falls, but at the moment his feet touch the ground his knees begin to bend, and, treated as a particle, he moves an additional 0.60 m before coming to rest. (a) What is his speed at the instant his feet touch the ground? (b) Treating him as a particle, what are the magnitude and direction of his acceleration as he slows down if the acceleration is constant? (c) Draw a free-body diagram of this man as he is slowing down. (d) Use Newton's laws and the results of part (b) to calculate the force the ground exerts on him while he is slowing down. Express this force in newtons and also as a multiple of the man's weight. (e) What are the magnitude and direction of the reaction force to the force you found in part (c)?

57. •• An electron $(\text{mass} = 9.11 \times 10^{-31} \text{ kg})$ leaves one end of a TV picture tube with zero initial speed and travels in a straight line to the accelerating grid, which is 1.80 cm away. It reaches the grid with a speed of 3.00×10^6 m/s. If the accelerating force is constant, compute (a) the acceleration of the electron, (b) the time it takes the electron to reach the grid, and (c) the net force that is accelerating the electron, in newtons. (You can ignore the gravitational force on the electron.)

Passage Problems

BIO Bacterial motion. A bacterium using its flagellum as propulsion can move through liquids at a rate of 0.003 m/s. For a 50 μm-long bacterium, that is the equivalent of 60 cell lengths per second. Bacteria of that size have a mass of approximately 1×10^{-12} g.

The viscous drag on a swimming bacterium is so great that if it stops beating its flagellum it will stop within a distance of 0.01 nm.

58. What is the acceleration that stops the bacterium?
   A. $1.2 \times 10^4 \text{ m/s}^2$
   B. $5 \times 10^5 \text{ m/s}^2$
   C. $6 \times 10^5 \text{ m/s}^2$
   D. $9 \times 10^5 \text{ m/s}^2$

59. What is average magnitude of this viscous force?
   A. 4×10^{-7} N
   B. 1.7×10^{-8} N
   C. 9×10^{-9} N
   D. 5×10^{-10} N

60. What amount of force must the flagellum generate to propel the bacterium at a constant velocity of 0.003 m/s?
    A. 1.5×10^{-10} N
    B. 5×10^{-10} N
    C. 9×10^{-7} N
    D. 1.8×10^{-7} N

61. If the bacterium wished to accelerate at a rate of 0.001 m/s², how much additional force would be necessary?
    A. 1×10^{-18} N
    B. 3×10^{-18} N
    C. 1×10^{-15} N
    D. 4×10^{-15} N

ANSWERS TO SELECTED PROBLEMS

Conceptual Questions

1. The force is applied at the wheels by the surface of the road.

3. Use Newton's second law. Apply a known force that imparts rectilinear motion, and measure the acceleration that is produced. If the person is initially at rest and the force is applied for time t, the acceleration is $a = v/t$, where v is the final speed of the person. The mass is then calculated as $m = F/a$.

5. The bus must be slowing down (braking). The friction force on the ball is small; consequently, the ball continues to move with its initial velocity: the velocity of the bus prior to braking.

7. By Newton's third law, the magnitude of the force the compact exerts on the SUV equals the magnitude of the force the SUV exerts on the compact. The effect of the force on the motion—the acceleration that is produced—is greater for the compact, and thus for its passengers, since the compact has less mass.

9. The bowling ball weighs less on the moon than on the earth, but it has the same mass. It would therefore be just as hard to stop the thrown bowling ball as it is on earth.

11. The impact force gives the car a large forward acceleration. Consequently, the car seat imparts a forward force, proportional to the forward acceleration, on the passenger's torso. However, if the car does not have a headrest, or if the headrest is improperly adjusted, the motion of the passenger's unsupported head follows Newton's first law. The head, which was not acted upon by an outside force, initially maintains the speed of the car and thus moves backward *relative* to the passenger's torso. Next, the head is rapidly thrust forward. This back-and-forth or "whipping" motion can cause injury to the neck.

13. While the ball is in the air, there is no horizontal force on it, and it travels in a straight line in accordance with Newton's first law. If the plane turns, the ball no longer travels in a straight line relative to the passenger to whom the ball was thrown. There is now a net horizontal force on the passenger, causing him to accelerate in the new direction of the plane; but there is no corresponding force on the ball. The passenger thus cannot catch the ball.

15. With no air resistance, all objects fall with the same acceleration and thus have identical speeds when they reach the ground. The pillow is softer, so it travels through a greater distance as it comes to rest. The pillow therefore has a smaller magnitude of acceleration than the rock, and the stopping force on the pillow is less. By Newton's third law, since your head exerts less force on the pillow than on the rock, the pillow exerts less force on your head.

17. (a) You feel this because the seat exerts a forward force on you, while your body exerts a backward reaction force on the seat. You feel as though you are being pushed back, but you are actually being pushed forward. (b) The free-body diagram is sketched in the figure below. $\vec{F}_1$ and $\vec{F}_2$ are the horizontal and vertical components, respectively, of the force the car seat exerts on you. F_2 equals the weight mg of the person, while F_1 produces the horizontal acceleration.

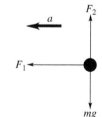

Multiple-Choice Problems

1. C
3. B
5. D

7. C
9. A
11. A, D
13. B
15. B

Problems

1. 7.1 N to the right; 7.1 N downward
3. 241 N; 287 N
5. (a) $F_{1x} = 844$ N, $F_{1y} = 507$ N; $F_{2x} = -418$ N, $F_{2y} = 668$ N; $F_{3x} = -248$ N, $F_{3y} = -328$ N (b) 866 N; 78.1°
7. (a) 4.31 m/s² (b) 215 m
9. (a) 680 N (b) the ground
11. 90.9 kg
13. 2940 N
15. (a) 2.06×10^{-6} N (b) 1.21×10^{-4} N (c) 10.1 lb; 4.6 kg
17. (a) 1.81 m/s² (b) 1.79 kg
19. (a) 138 N (b) 138 N (c) 1350 N for both (a) and (b) (d) the same, 138 N
21. (a) 3.71 m/s² (b) 8.69 kg
23. (a) 2.45 m/s² (b) 191 m
25. (a) earth (b) 4 N; the book (c) no (d) 4 N; the earth; the book; upward (e) 4 N; the hand; the book; downward (f) second (g) third
27. 0.452 m/s², downward
31. (b) yes
37. (a) 490 N (b) 735 N (c) 612 N
39. (a) 502 N (b) 345 N (c) 424 N
41. (b) 142 N
43. (a) 784 N (b) 47.4 N
45. (a) 21.2 m/s² (b) 1700 N (c) 1700 N; 173 kg
47. 3.7×10^6 N
49. (b) upward (c) 1.5 m/s², upward
51. (a) 4.8 m/s (b) 16 m/s² (d) 2360 N
53. (a) 140 N
57. (a) 539 N (b) 81 N, upward (c) 1.47 m/s², upward

Passage Problems

59. D
61. A

Applications of Newton's Laws

From Chapter 5 of *College Physics*, Ninth Edition, Hugh D. Young. Copyright © 2012 by Pearson Education, Inc.
Published by Pearson Addison-Wesley. All rights reserved.

Applications of Newton's Laws

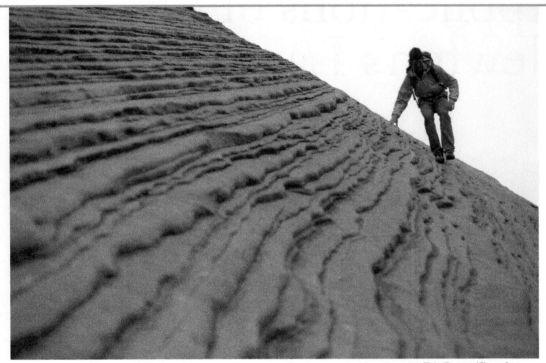

Eric Draper/Getty Images

Newton's three laws of motion, the foundation of classical mechanics, can be stated very simply, as we have seen. But applying these laws to situations such as a locomotive, a suspension bridge, a car rounding a banked curve, or a toboggan sliding down a hill requires some analytical skills and some problem-solving technique. In this chapter we introduce no new principles, but we'll try to help you develop some of the problem-solving skills you'll need to analyze such situations.

We begin with equilibrium problems, concentrating on systems at rest. Then we generalize our problem-solving techniques to include systems that are not in equilibrium, for which we need to deal precisely with the relationships between forces and motion. We'll learn how to describe and analyze the contact force that acts on an object when it rests or slides on a surface, as well as the elastic forces that are present when a solid object is deformed. Finally, we take a brief look at the fundamental nature of force and the kinds of forces found in the physical universe.

The soles of hiking boots are designed to stick, not slip, on rocky surfaces. In this chapter we'll learn about the interactions that give good traction.

1 Equilibrium of a Particle

An object is in **equilibrium** when it is at rest or moving with constant velocity in an inertial frame of reference. A hanging lamp, a rope-and-pulley setup for hoisting heavy loads, a suspension bridge—all these are examples of equilibrium situations. In this section, we consider only the equilibrium of an object that can be modeled as a particle. The essential physical principle is Newton's first law: **When an object is at rest or is moving with constant velocity in an inertial** frame of reference, the vector sum of all the forces acting on it must be zero. That is, we have the following principle:

Necessary condition for equilibrium of an object

For an object to be in equilibrium, the vector sum of the forces acting on it must be zero:

$$\sum \vec{F} = 0. \qquad \text{(A)}$$

This condition is sufficient only if the object can be treated as a particle, which we assume in the next principle and throughout the remainder of the chapter.

We'll usually use this equation in component form:

Equilibrium conditions in component form

An object is in equilibrium if the sum of the components of force in each axis direction is zero:

$$\sum F_x = 0, \qquad \sum F_y = 0. \qquad \text{(B)}$$

This chapter is about solving problems. We strongly recommend that you study carefully the strategies that follow, look for their applications in the worked-out examples, and then try to apply them when you solve problems.

PROBLEM-SOLVING STRATEGY 1 Solving problems involving an object in equilibrium

SET UP

1. Draw a simple sketch of the apparatus or structure, showing all relevant dimensions and angles.
2. Identify the object or objects in equilibrium that you will consider.
3. Draw a free-body diagram for each object identified in step 2.
   a. Assuming that the object can be modeled as a particle, you can represent it by a large dot. Do not include other objects (such as a surface the object may be resting on or a rope pulling on it) in your free-body diagram.
   b. Identify all the ways in which other things interact with the object, either by touching it or via a noncontact force such as gravity. Draw a force vector to represent each force *acting on the object.* Do not include forces exerted *by* the object. For each force, make sure that you can answer the question "What other object interacts with the chosen object to cause that force?" If you can't answer that question, you may be imagining a force that isn't there.
   c. Label each force with a symbol representing the *magnitude* of the force (*w* for the object's weight; *n* for a normal force; *T* for a tension force, etc.); indicate the directions with appropriate angles. (If the object's mass is given, use $w = mg$ to find its weight.)
4. Choose a set of coordinate axes, and represent each force acting on the object in terms of its components along those axes. Cross out each force that has been replaced by its components, so that you don't count it twice. You can often simplify the problem by using a particular choice of coordinate axes. For example, when an object rests or slides on a plane surface, it is usually simplest to take the axes in the directions parallel and perpendicular to this surface, even when the plane is tilted.

Continued

European Southern Observatory

▲ **Application Easy does it!** This crane is unloading a 50 ton, 8.2 meter mirror for the European Southern Observatory in Antofagasta, Chile. It is one of four such mirrors that make up an instrument known as the Very Large Telescope, one of the world's biggest, most advanced optical telescopes. The crane moves the mirror steadily, so that it remains nearly in equilibrium—the vector sum of the forces on it is almost zero. However, that does not ensure the mirror's safety, because it is not a particle. The forces acting on different *parts* of it are not the same. Warping or deforming would be disastrous. The mirror is heavy in part because it is heavily reinforced.

SOLVE

5. For each object, set the algebraic sum of all x components of force equal to zero. In a separate equation, set the algebraic sum of all y components equal to zero. (Never add x and y components in a single equation.) You can then solve these equations for up to two unknown quantities, which may be force magnitudes, components, or angles.

6. If you are dealing with two or more objects that interact with each other, use Newton's third law to relate the forces they exert on each other. You need to find as many independent equations as the number of unknown quantities. Then solve these equations to obtain the values of the unknowns. This part is algebra, not physics, but it's an essential step.

REFLECT

7. Whenever possible, look at your results and ask whether they make sense. When the result is a symbolic expression or formula, try to think of special cases (particular values or extreme cases for the various quantities) for which you can guess what the results ought to be. Check to see that your formula works in these particular cases. Think about what the problem has taught you that you can apply to other problems in the future.

EXAMPLE 1 **One-dimensional equilibrium**

A gymnast has just begun climbing up a rope hanging from a gymnasium ceiling. She stops, suspended from the lower end of the rope by her hands. Her weight is 500 N, and the weight of the rope is 100 N. Analyze the forces on the gymnast and on the rope.

SOLUTION

SET UP First we sketch the situation (Figure 1a). Then we draw two free-body diagrams, one for the gymnast and the other for the rope (Figures 1b and c). (We'll explain Figure 1d below.) The forces acting on the gymnast are her weight (magnitude 500 N) and the upward force (magnitude T_1) exerted on her by the rope. We *don't* include the downward force she exerts on the rope, because it isn't a force that acts *on* her. We take the y axis to be directed vertically upward, the x axis horizontally. There are no x components of force; that's why we call this a one-dimensional problem.

SOLVE The gymnast is motionless, so we know that she is in equilibrium. Since we know her weight, we can use Equation B, $\Sigma F_y = 0$, to find the magnitude of the upward tension T_1 on her. This force pulls in the positive y direction. Her weight acts in the negative y direction, so its y component is the *negative* of the magnitude—that is, -500 N. Thus,

$$\Sigma F_y = 0,$$
$$T_1 + (-500\,\text{N}) = 0, \qquad \text{(equilibrium of gymnast)}$$
$$T_1 = 500\,\text{N}.$$

The two forces acting on the gymnast are *not* an action–reaction pair, because they act on the same object.

Next we need to consider the forces acting on the rope (Figure 1c). Newton's third law tells us that the gymnast exerts a force on the rope that is equal and opposite to the force it exerts on her. In other words, she pulls down on the rope with a force

These are action–reaction pairs

(a) (b) (c) (d)

▲ **FIGURE 1** Our diagrams for this problem. We sketch the situation (a), plus free-body diagrams for the gymnast (b) and rope (c). (d) A partial free-body diagram for the ceiling. (See "Reflect.")

whose magnitude T_1 is 500 N. As you probably expect, this force equals the gymnast's weight.

The other forces on the rope are its own weight (magnitude 100 N) and the upward force (magnitude T_2) exerted on its upper end by the ceiling. The equilibrium condition $\Sigma F_y = 0$ for the rope gives

$$\Sigma F_y = T_2 + (-100\,\text{N}) + (-500\,\text{N}) = 0, \qquad \text{(equilibrium}$$
$$T_2 = 600\,\text{N}. \qquad\qquad\qquad\qquad\qquad \text{of rope)}$$

Continued

REFLECT The tension is 100 N greater at the top of the rope (where it must support the weights of both the rope and the gymnast) than at the bottom (where it supports only the gymnast).

Figure 1d is a partial free-body diagram of the ceiling, showing that the rope exerts a downward force with magnitude T_2 on the ceiling. From Newton's third law, the magnitude of this force is also 600 N.

Practice Problem: Determine the tension at the midpoint of the rope. *Answer:* 550 N.

The strength of the rope in Example 1 probably isn't a major concern. The breaking strength of a string, rope, or cable is described by the maximum tension it can withstand without breaking. A few typical breaking strengths are shown in Table 1.

TABLE 1   Approximate breaking strengths

Thin white string	50 N
$\frac{1}{4}''$ nylon clothesline rope	4000 N
11 mm Perlon mountaineering rope	3×10^4 N
$1\frac{1}{4}''$ manila climbing rope	6×10^4 N
$\frac{1}{4}''$ steel cable	6×10^4 N

EXAMPLE 2   Two-dimensional equilibrium

In Figure 2a, a car engine with weight w hangs from a chain that is linked at point O to two other chains, one fastened to the ceiling and the other to the wall. Find the tension in each of the three chains, assuming that w is given and the weights of the chains themselves are negligible.

(a)

▶ **FIGURE 2**

(b) Free-body diagram of engine

(c) Free-body diagram of ring O

SOLUTION

SET UP Figure 2b is our free-body diagram for the engine. Without further ceremony, we can conclude that $T_1 = w$. (Because we neglect the weights of the chains, the tension is the same throughout the length of each chain.) The horizontal and slanted chains do not exert forces on the engine itself, because they are not attached to it, but they do exert forces on the ring (point O), where three chains join. So let's consider the *ring* as a particle in equilibrium; the weight of the ring itself is negligible.

In our free-body diagram for the ring (Figure 2c), T_1, T_2, and T_3 are the *magnitudes* of the forces; their directions are shown by the vectors in the diagram. We add an x-y coordinate system and resolve the force with magnitude T_3 into its x and y components. Note that the downward force with magnitude T_1 of the chain acting on the ring and the upward force with magnitude T_1 of the chain acting on the engine are not an action–reaction pair.

SOLVE We now apply the equilibrium conditions *for the ring,* writing separate equations for the x and y components. (Note that

x and y components are *never* added together in a single equation.) We find that

$$\sum F_x = 0, \qquad T_3 \cos 60° + (-T_2) = 0,$$
$$\sum F_y = 0, \qquad T_3 \sin 60° + (-T_1) = 0.$$

Because $T_1 = w$, we can rewrite the second equation as

$$T_3 = \frac{T_1}{\sin 60°} = \frac{w}{\sin 60°} = 1.155w.$$

We can now use this result in the first equation:

$$T_2 = T_3 \cos 60° = (1.155w) \cos 60° = 0.577w.$$

So we can express all three tensions as multiples of the weight w of the engine, which we assume is known. To summarize, we have

$$T_1 = w,$$
$$T_2 = 0.577w,$$
$$T_3 = 1.155w.$$

If the engine's weight is $w = 2200$ N (about 500 lb), then

$$T_1 = 2200 \text{ N},$$
$$T_2 = (0.577)(2200 \text{ N}) = 1270 \text{ N},$$
$$T_3 = (1.155)(2200 \text{ N}) = 2540 \text{ N}.$$

Continued

REFLECT Each of the three tensions is proportional to the weight w; if we double w, all three tensions double. Note that T_3 is greater than the weight of the engine. If this seems strange, observe that T_3 must be large enough for its vertical component to be equal in magnitude to w, so T_3 itself must have a magnitude *larger* than w.

Practice Problem: If we change the angle of the upper chain from 60° to 45°, determine the new expressions for the three tensions. *Answers:* $T_1 = w$, $T_2 = w\cos 45°/\sin 45° = w$, $T_3 = w/\sin 45° = \sqrt{2}w$.

EXAMPLE 3 **Car on a ramp**

A car with a weight of 1.76×10^4 N rests on the ramp of a trailer (Figure 3a). The car's brakes and transmission lock are released; only the cable prevents the car from rolling backward off the trailer. The ramp makes an angle of 26.0° with the horizontal. Find the tension in the cable and the force with which the ramp pushes on the car's tires.

We replace the weight by its components.

▶ **FIGURE 3**   (a) Car on ramp   (b) Free-body diagram for car

---

SOLUTION

SET UP Figure 3b shows our free-body diagram for the car. The three forces exerted on the car are its weight (magnitude w), the tension in the cable (magnitude T), and the normal force with magnitude n exerted by the ramp. (Because we treat the car as a particle, we can lump the normal forces on the four wheels together as a single force.) We orient our coordinate axes parallel and perpendicular to the ramp, and we replace the weight force by its components.

SOLVE The car is in equilibrium, so we first find the components of each force in our axis system and then apply Newton's first law. To find the components of the weight, we note that the angle α between the ramp and the horizontal is equal to the angle α between the weight vector and the normal to the ramp, as shown. The angle α is *not* measured in the usual way, counterclockwise from the $+x$ axis. To find the components of the weight $(w_x$ and $w_y)$, we use the right triangles in Figure 3b. We find that $w_x = -w\sin\alpha$ and $w_y = -w\cos\alpha$. The equilibrium conditions then give us

$$\Sigma F_x = 0, \quad T + (-w\sin\alpha) = 0,$$
$$\Sigma F_y = 0, \quad n + (-w\cos\alpha) = 0.$$

Be sure you understand how the signs are related to our choice of coordinate axis directions. Remember that, by defini-

tion, T, w, and n are *magnitudes* of vectors and are therefore positive.

Solving these equations for T and n, we find that

$$T = w\sin\alpha,$$
$$n = w\cos\alpha.$$

Finally, inserting the numerical values $w = 1.76 \times 10^4$ N and $\alpha = 26°$, we obtain

$$T = (1.76 \times 10^4 \text{ N})(\sin 26°) = 7.72 \times 10^3 \text{ N},$$
$$n = (1.76 \times 10^4 \text{ N})(\cos 26°) = 1.58 \times 10^3 \text{ N}.$$

REFLECT To check some special cases, note that if the angle α is zero, then $\sin\alpha = 0$ and $\cos\alpha = 1$. In this case, the ramp is horizontal; no cable tension T is needed to hold the car, and the magnitude of the total normal force n is equal to the car's weight. If the angle is 90° (the ramp is vertical), then $\sin\alpha = 1$ and $\cos\alpha = 0$. In that case, the cable tension T equals the weight w and the normal force n is zero.

We also note that these results would still be correct if the car were on a ramp on a car transport trailer traveling down a straight highway at a constant speed of 65 mi/h. Do you see why?

Practice Problem: What ramp angle would be needed in order for the cable tension to equal one-half of the car's weight? *Answer:* 30°.

EXAMPLE 4 **Lifting granite and dumping dirt**

Blocks of granite, each with weight w_1, are being hauled up a 15° slope out of a quarry (Figure 4). For environmental reasons, dirt is also being dumped into the quarry to fill up old holes. You have been asked to find a way to use this dirt to move the granite out more easily. You design a system that lets the dirt (weight w_2, including the weight of the bucket) that drops vertically into the quarry pull out a granite block on a cart with steel wheels (total weight w_1), rolling on steel rails. Ignoring the weight of the cable and friction in the pulley and wheels, determine how the weights w_1 and w_2 must be related for the system to move with constant speed.

Cart

Bucket

15°

▲ **FIGURE 4**

Continued

SOLUTION

SET UP Figure 5a shows an idealized model for the system. We draw two free-body diagrams, one for the dirt and bucket (Figure 5b) and one for the granite block on its cart (Figure 5c). In drawing the coordinate axes for each object, we're at liberty to orient them differently for the two objects; the choices shown are the most convenient ones. (But we must *not* change the orientation of the objects themselves.) We represent the weight of the granite block in terms of its components in the chosen axis system. The tension T in the cable is the same throughout, because we are assuming that the cable's weight is negligible. (The pulley changes the *directions* of the cable forces, but if it is frictionless and massless, it can't change their *magnitudes*.)

SOLVE Each object is in equilibrium. Applying $\Sigma F_y = 0$ to the bucket (Figure 5b), we find that

$$T + (-w_2) = 0, \qquad T = w_2.$$

Applying ΣF_x to the cart (Figure 5c), we get

$$T + (-w_1 \sin 15°) = 0, \qquad T = w_1 \sin 15°.$$

Equating the two expressions for T yields

$$w_2 = w_1 \sin 15° = 0.26 w_1.$$

REFLECT If the weight w_2 of the dirt and bucket totals 26% of the weight w_1 of the granite block and cart, the system can move in either direction with constant speed. In the real world, where friction tends to hold back the motion, would w_2 need to be more or less than $0.26w_1$ for the granite block to move up with constant speed?

Practice Problem: Determine the total normal force n that the tracks apply to the wheels of the granite cart, as a fraction of w_1. *Answer:* $n = w_1 \cos 15° = 0.97 w_1$.

(a) Idealized model

(b) Free-body diagram of bucket

(c) Free-body diagram of cart

▲ **FIGURE 5**

2 Applications of Newton's Second Law

MasteringPHYSICS

We're now ready to discuss problems in **dynamics,** showing applications of Newton's second law to systems that are *not* in equilibrium. Here's a restatement of that law:

PhET: Lunar Lander
ActivPhysics 2.1.5: Car Race
ActivPhysics 2.2: Lifting a Crate
ActivPhysics 2.3: Lowering a Crate
ActivPhysics 2.4: Rocket Blasts Off
ActivPhysics 2.11: Modified Atwood Machine

Newton's second law

An object's acceleration equals the vector sum of the forces acting on it, divided by its mass. In vector form, we rewrite this statement as

$$\Sigma \vec{F} = m\vec{a}. \tag{C}$$

However, we'll usually use this relation in its component form:

$$\Sigma F_x = ma_x, \qquad \Sigma F_y = ma_y. \tag{D}$$

Richard Megna/Fundamental Photographs

▲ Application **Gravity-defying liquid?**
Although this container is on a level table-top, the liquid inside forms a slant. How can that be? You may have guessed that the photo shows a demonstration of a simple liquid-filled accelerometer. As the container is accelerated to the left, the surface of the liquid forms an angle with the horizontal. The tangent of the angle is proportional to the acceleration. Can you verify that if the container is 19.6 cm wide, the height of the liquid at the right end (in cm) above its level when the apparatus is at rest will give the acceleration of the container itself, in meters per second squared?

The following problem-solving strategy is similar to our strategy for solving equilibrium problems, presented in Section 1:

PROBLEM-SOLVING STRATEGY 2 **Using Newton's second law**

SET UP

1. Draw a sketch of the physical situation, and identify the moving object or objects to which you will apply Newton's second law.
2. Draw a free-body diagram for each chosen object, showing all the forces acting *on* that object, as described in the strategy for Newton's first law (Problem-Solving Strategy 1). Label the magnitudes of unknown forces with algebraic symbols. Usually, one of the forces will be the object's weight; it is generally best to label this as *mg*. If a numerical value of mass is given, you can compute the corresponding weight.
3. Show your coordinate axes explicitly in each free-body diagram, and then determine components of forces with reference to these axes. If you know the direction of the acceleration, it is usually best to take that direction as one of the axes. When you represent a force in terms of its components, cross out the original force so as not to include it twice. When there are two or more objects, you can use a separate axis system for each object; you don't have to use the same axis system for all the objects. But in the equations for each object, the signs of the components *must* be consistent with the axes you have chosen for that object.

SOLVE

4. Write the equations for Newton's second law in component form: $\sum F_x = ma_x$ and $\sum F_y = ma_y$ (Equation D). Be careful not to add x and y components in the same equation.

5. If more than one object is involved, repeat step 4 for each object. In addition, the motions of the bodies may be related. For example, the objects may be connected by a rope. Express these relations in algebraic form as relations between the accelerations of the various bodies. Then solve the equations to find the required unknowns.

REFLECT

6. Check particular cases or extreme values of quantities, when possible, and compare the results for these particular cases with your intuitive expectations. Ask yourself, "Does this result make sense?" Think about what the problem has taught you that you can apply to other problems in the future.

Quantitative Analysis 1

A two-cart train

The carts in Figure 6 are speeding up as they are pulled to the right with increasing speed across a frictionless surface. The ropes have negligible mass. We can conclude that

A. The pull of rope 1 on cart *A* has greater magnitude than the pull of rope 1 on cart *B*.
B. The pull of rope 2 on cart *B* has greater magnitude than the pull of rope 1 on cart *B*.
C. The pull of rope 1 on cart *A* has greater magnitude than the pull of rope 2 on cart *B*.

SOLUTION Answer B is correct: For cart *B* to accelerate, there must be a net force to the right. Answer A cannot be right; if the

▲ **FIGURE 6**

rope is massless, the forces acting on its two ends must add to zero. Nor can answer C be right: The two carts have the same acceleration; therefore, the tension in rope 2 must be great enough to give this acceleration to both carts, while the tension in rope 1 is just great enough to give cart *A* the same acceleration.

EXAMPLE 5   A simple accelerometer

You tape one end of a piece of string to the ceiling light of your car and hang a key with mass m to the other end (Figure 7). A protractor taped to the light allows you to measure the angle the string makes with the vertical. Your friend drives the car while you make measurements. When the car has a constant acceleration with magnitude a toward the right, the string hangs at rest (relative to the car), making an angle β with the vertical. (a) Derive an expression for the acceleration a in terms of the mass m and the measured angle β. (b) In particular, what is a when $\beta = 45°$? When $\beta = 0$?

(a) Low-tech accelerometer

▲ **FIGURE 7**

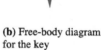

(b) Free-body diagram for the key

SOLUTION

SET UP Our free-body diagram is shown in Figure 7b. The forces acting on the key are its weight $w = mg$ and the string tension T. We direct the x axis to the right (in the direction of the acceleration) and the y axis vertically upward.

SOLVE **Part (a):** This problem may look like an equilibrium problem, but it isn't. The string and the key are at rest with respect to the car, but car, string, and key are all accelerating in the $+x$ direction. Thus, there must be a horizontal component of force acting on the key. Therefore, we use Newton's second law in component form: $\Sigma F_x = ma_x$ and $\Sigma F_y = ma_y$.

We find the components of the string tension, as shown in Figure 7b. The sum of the horizontal components of force is

$$\Sigma F_x = T\sin\beta,$$

and the sum of the vertical components is

$$\Sigma F_y = T\cos\beta + (-mg).$$

The x component of acceleration is the acceleration a_x of the car, string, and key, and the y component of acceleration is zero, so

$$\Sigma F_x = T\sin\beta = ma_x,$$
$$\Sigma F_y = T\cos\beta + (-mg) = ma_y = 0.$$

Rearranging terms, we obtain

$$T\sin\beta = ma_x, \qquad T\cos\beta = mg.$$

When we divide the first equation by the second, we get

$$a_x = g\tan\beta.$$

The acceleration a_x is thus proportional to the tangent of the angle β.

Part (b): When $\beta = 0$, the key hangs vertically and the acceleration is zero; when $\beta = 45°$, $a_x = g$, and so on.

REFLECT We note that β can never be 90°, because that would require an infinite acceleration. We note also that the relation between a_x and β doesn't depend on the mass of the key, but it *does* depend on the acceleration due to gravity.

Practice Problem: What is the angle β if the acceleration is $g/2$? *Answer:* 26.6°.

EXAMPLE 6   Acceleration down a hill

A toboggan loaded with vacationing students (total weight w) slides down a long, snow-covered slope. The hill slopes at a constant angle α, and the toboggan is so well waxed that there is virtually no friction at all. Find the toboggan's acceleration and the magnitude n of the normal force the hill exerts on the toboggan.

SOLUTION

SET UP As a reminder of the importance of drawing sketches, we'll show the diagrams we draw in pencil, rather than in printed style (Figure 8). The only forces acting on the toboggan are its weight w and the normal force n (Figure 8b). The direction of the weight is straight down, but the direction of the normal force is perpendicular to the surface of the hill, at an angle α with the vertical. We take axes parallel and perpendicular to the surface of the hill and resolve the weight into x and y components.

Continued

SOLVE There is only one x component of force, so

$$\Sigma F_x = w\sin\alpha.$$

From $\Sigma F_x = ma_x$, we have

$$w\sin\alpha = ma_x,$$

and since $w = mg$, the acceleration is

$$a_x = g\sin\alpha.$$

The y-component equation gives $\Sigma F_y = n + (-mg\cos\alpha)$. We know that the y component of acceleration is zero, because there is no motion in the y direction. So $\Sigma F_y = 0$ and $n = mg\cos\alpha$.

REFLECT The mass m does not appear in the expression for a_x; this means that *any* toboggan, regardless of its mass or number of passengers, slides down a frictionless hill with an acceleration of $g\sin\alpha$. In particular, when $\alpha = 0$ (a flat surface with no slope at all), the acceleration is $a_x = 0$, as we should expect. When the surface is vertical, $\alpha = 90°$ and $a_x = g$ (free fall).

Note that the magnitude n of the normal force exerted on the toboggan by the surface of the hill $(n = mg\cos\alpha)$ is *propor-*

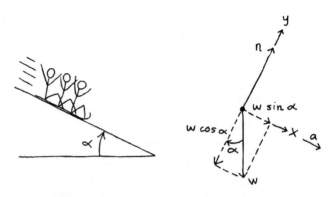

(a) The situation   **(b)** Free-body diagram for toboggan

▲ **FIGURE 8** Our diagrams for this problem.

tional to the magnitude mg of the toboggan's weight; the two are *not* equal, except in the special case where $\alpha = 0$.

Practice Problem: At what angle does the hill slope if the acceleration is $g/2$? *Answer:* $30°$.

EXAMPLE 7 **An air track in a physics lab**

Figure 9 shows a glider with mass m_1 that moves on a level, frictionless air track in a physics lab. It is connected by a string passing over a small frictionless pulley to a hanging weight with total mass m_2. The string is light and flexible, and it doesn't stretch. Find the acceleration of each object and the tension in the string.

SOLUTION

SET UP The two objects have different motions, so we need to draw a separate free-body diagram and coordinate system for each, as shown in Figure 9b and c. We are free to use different coordinate axes for the two objects; in this case, it's convenient to take the $+x$ direction to the right for the glider and the $+y$ direction downward for the hanging weight. Then the glider has only an x component of acceleration a_{1x} (i.e., $a_{1y} = 0$), and the weight hanger has only a y component a_{2y} (i.e., $a_{2x} = 0$). There is no fric-

tion in the pulley, and we consider the string to be massless, so the tension T in the string is the same throughout; it applies a force with magnitude T to each object. The weights are m_1g and m_2g.

SOLVE We apply Newton's second law, in component form, to each object in turn.

For the glider on the track, Newton's second law gives

$$\Sigma F_x = T = m_1 a_{1x}$$
$$\Sigma F_y = n + (-m_1g) = m_1 a_{1y} = 0,$$

(a) Apparatus

▲ **FIGURE 9**

(b) Free-body diagram for glider

(c) Free-body diagram for weight

Continued

and for the hanging weight,

$$\Sigma F_y = m_2 g + (-T) = m_2 a_{2y}.$$

Now, because the string doesn't stretch, the two objects must move equal distances in equal times, and their *speeds* at any instant must be equal. When the speeds change, they change by equal amounts in a given time, so the accelerations of the two bodies must have the same magnitude a. We can express this relation as

$$a_{1x} = a_{2y} = a.$$

(The directions of the two accelerations are different, of course.) The two Newton's-second-law equations are then

$$T = m_1 a,$$
$$m_2 g + (-T) = m_2 a.$$

We'd like to get separate expressions for T and a, in terms of the masses and g.

An easy way to get an expression for a is to replace $-T$ in the second equation by $-m_1 a$ and rearrange the result; when we do so, we obtain $m_2 g + (-m_1 a) = m_2 a$, $m_2 g = (m_1 + m_2)a$, and, finally,

$$a = \frac{m_2}{m_1 + m_2} g.$$

Then, to get an expression for T, we substitute this expression for a back into the first equation. The result is

$$T = \frac{m_1 m_2}{m_1 + m_2} g = \frac{m_1}{m_1 + m_2} m_2 g.$$

REFLECT It's always a good idea to check general symbolic results such as this for particular cases where we can guess what the answer ought to be. For example, if the mass of the glider is zero $(m_1 = 0)$, we expect that the hanging weight (mass m_2) would fall freely with acceleration g and there would be no tension in the string. When we substitute $m_1 = 0$ into the preceding expressions for T and a, they do give $T = 0$ and $a = g$, as expected. Also, if $m_2 = 0$, there is nothing to create tension in the string or accelerate either mass. For this case, the equations give $T = 0$ and $a = 0$. Thus, in these two special cases, the results agree with our intuitive expectations.

We also note that, in general, the tension T is *not* equal to the weight $m_2 g$ of the hanging mass m_2, but is *less* by a factor of $m_1/(m_1 + m_2)$. If T *were* equal to $m_2 g$, then m_2 would be in equilibrium, but it isn't.

3 Contact Forces and Friction

We've seen several problems in which an object rests or slides on a surface that exerts forces on the object. We introduced the terms *normal force* and *friction force* to describe these forces. Whenever two objects interact by direct contact (touching) of their surfaces, we call the interaction forces *contact forces*. Normal and friction forces are both contact forces. Friction is important in many aspects of everyday life, for both facilitating and preventing the slipping of an object in contact with a surface. For example, the oil in a car engine facilitates sliding between moving parts, but friction between the tires and the road prevents slipping. Similarly, air drag decreases automotive fuel economy, but makes parachutes work. Without friction, nails would pull out, light bulbs and bottle caps would unscrew effortlessly, and riding a bicycle would be hopeless. A "frictionless surface" is a useful concept in idealized models of mechanical systems in which the friction forces are negligibly small. In the real world, such an idealization is unattainable, although driving a car on wet ice comes fairly close!

Let's consider an object sliding across a surface. When you try to slide a heavy box of books across the floor, the box doesn't move at all until you reach a certain critical force. Then the box starts moving, and you can usually keep it moving with less force than you needed to get it started. If you take some of the books out, you need less force than before to get it started or keep it moving. What general statements can we make about this behavior?

First, when an object rests or slides on a surface, we can always represent the contact force exerted by the surface on the object in terms of components of force perpendicular and parallel to the surface (Figure 10). We call the perpendicular component the *normal force,* denoted by $\vec{n}$. (*Normal* is a synonym for *perpendicular.*) The component parallel to the surface is the *friction force,* denoted

The frictional and normal forces are really components of a single contact force.

▲ **FIGURE 10** The frictional and normal forces for a block sliding on a rough surface.

▲ **Application Friction can be fun.** As this rock climber shows, frictional forces can be important. Without them, a climber could not move or maintain an equilibrium position. Notice how the climber is demonstrating one of the key concepts of frictional forces: The frictional force is proportional to the normal force. Therefore, even in a narrow crack, a good climber tries to contact the rock at an angle as close as feasible to 90°. This maximizes the normal force and therefore also maximizes the frictional force.

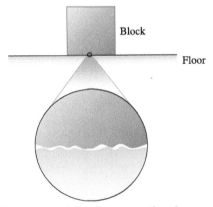

On a microscopic level, even smooth surfaces are rough; they tend to catch and cling.

▲ **FIGURE 11** The origin of frictional forces.

by $\vec{f}$. By definition, $\vec{n}$ and $\vec{f}$ are always perpendicular to each other. When an object is sliding with respect to a surface, the associated friction force is called a *kinetic-friction* force, with magnitude f_k. When there is no relative motion, we speak of a *static-friction* force, with magnitude f_s. We'll discuss these two possibilities separately.

When one object is moving relative to a surface, the *direction* of the kinetic-friction force on the object is always opposite to the direction of motion of that object relative to the surface. For example, when a book slides from left to right along a tabletop, the friction force on it acts to the left, as in Figure 10. According to Newton's third law, the book simultaneously applies a force to the table that is equal in magnitude, but directed to the right; in effect, the book tries to drag the table along with it.

The *magnitude* f_k of a kinetic-friction force usually increases when the normal force magnitude n increases. Thus, more force is needed to slide a box full of books across the floor than to slide the same box when it is empty. This principle is also used in automotive braking systems: The harder the brake pads are squeezed against the rotating brake disks, the greater is the braking effect. In some cases, the magnitude of the sliding friction force f_k is found to be approximately *proportional* to the magnitude n of the normal force. In such cases, we call the ratio f_k/n the **coefficient of kinetic friction,** denoted as μ_k:

Relation between kinetic-friction force and normal force

When the magnitude of the sliding friction force f_k is roughly proportional to the magnitude n of the normal force, the two are related by a constant μ_k called the coefficient of kinetic friction:

$$f_k = \mu_k n. \tag{1}$$

Because μ_k is the ratio of two force magnitudes, it has no units.

The more slippery the surface, the smaller the coefficient of friction is. Because it is a quotient of two force magnitudes, μ_k is a pure number, without units.

NOTE ▶ The friction force and the normal force are always perpendicular, so Equation 1 is *not* a vector equation, but a relation between the *magnitudes* of the two forces. ◀

The numerical value of the coefficient of kinetic friction for any two surfaces depends on the materials and the surfaces. For Teflon on steel, μ_k is about 0.04. For rubber tires on rough dry concrete (or sneakers on a dry gym floor), μ_k can be as large as 1.0 to 1.2. For two smooth metal surfaces, it is typically 0.4 to 0.8.

Although these numbers are given to two significant figures, they are only approximate values; indeed, Equation 1 is just an *approximate* representation of a complex phenomenon. On a microscopic level, friction and normal forces result from the intermolecular forces (fundamentally electrical in nature) between two rough surfaces at high points where they come into contact. Figure 11 suggests the nature of the interaction. The actual area of contact is usually much smaller than the total surface area. When two smooth surfaces of the same metal are brought together, these forces can cause a "cold weld"; a similar effect occurs with aluminum pistons in an unlubricated aluminum cylinder. Indeed, the success of lubricating oils depends on the fact that they maintain a film between the surfaces that prevents them from coming into actual contact. Friction forces can also depend on the *velocity* of the object relative to the surface. We'll ignore that complication for now in order to concentrate on the simplest cases.

Friction forces may also act when there is *no* relative motion between the surfaces of contact. If you try to slide that box of books across the floor, the box may not move at all if you don't push hard enough, because the floor exerts an equal and opposite friction force on the box. This force is called a **static-friction force** $\vec{f}_s$. In Figure 12a, the box is at rest, in equilibrium, under the action of its weight $\vec{w}$ and the upward normal force $\vec{n}$, which is equal in magnitude to the weight and exerted on the box by the floor. Now we tie a rope to the box (Figure 12b) and gradually increase the tension T in the rope. At first the box remains at rest, because, as T increases, the force of static friction f_s also increases (staying equal in magnitude to T).

At some point, however, T becomes greater than the maximum friction force f_s that the surface can exert; the box then "breaks loose" and starts to slide. Figure 12c shows the force diagram when T is at this critical value, and Figure 12d is the case when T exceeds this value and the box begins to move. Figure 12e shows how the friction force varies if we start with no applied force ($T = 0$) and gradually increase the force until the object starts to slide. Note that the force f_k of kinetic friction is somewhat less than the maximum force $f_{s,\text{max}}$ of static friction: Less force is needed to keep the box sliding with constant speed than to start it moving initially.

For a given pair of surfaces, the maximum value of f_s depends on the normal force. In some cases, the maximum value of f_s is approximately *proportional* to n;

Dean Conger/Corbis

▲ Application **Friction can be a problem.** If you're trying to saw stone, friction is not necessarily a good thing. If this saw blade were not lubricated, friction would make it hard to draw the saw through the cut, and the heat from friction could warp or melt the blade. Therefore, the blade of this "wet saw" in a commercial stone quarry is continuously showered with water to minimize frictional forces and carry away heat. Even so, a cut like this will take time to complete.

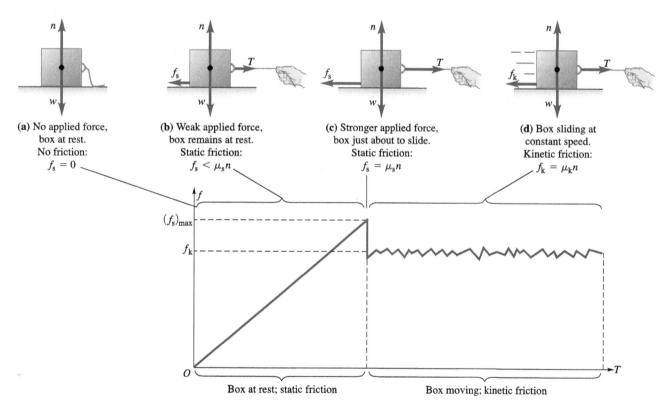

(e)

▲ **FIGURE 12** Static and kinetic friction for a box subjected to a gradually increasing pulling force.

Dr. Paul Selvin

▲ **BIO** Application **Molecular motors.**
Nature has engineered a small number of
molecular motors that convert the chemical
energy of an ATP molecule into mechanical
force. These nanomachines rely on a kind
of friction to direct this force to their loads.
A two-headed motor protein called myosin
(in blue) binds to a structural track called
actin (in red), along which it applies force
through electrical interactions that are the
small-scale version of friction. During the
power stroke, when the myosin is applying
force to the actin, each myosin head applies
1-10 pN of force to the actin, depending on
the type of myosin. The aggregate force of
many such molecules working in concert is
the basis of the forces generated by animal
skeletal muscles.

we call the proportionality factor μ_s the **coefficient of static friction.** In a particular situation, the actual force of static friction can have any magnitude between
zero (when there is no other force parallel to the surface) and a maximum value
$f_{s,\text{max}}$ given by $f_{s,\text{max}} = \mu_s n$. Like μ_k, μ_s has no unit.

Relation between normal force and maximum static-friction force

When the maximum magnitude of the static-friction force can be represented
as proportional to the magnitude of the normal force, the two are related by a
constant μ_s called the coefficient of static friction:

$$f_s \leq \mu_s n. \tag{2}$$

The equality sign holds only when the applied force T, parallel to the surface, has
reached the critical value at which motion is about to start (Figure 12c). When T is
less than this value (Figure 12b), the inequality sign holds. In that case, we have to
use the equilibrium conditions $\sum \vec{F} = 0$ to find f_s. For any given pair of surfaces,
the coefficient of kinetic friction is usually *less* than the coefficient of static friction. As a result, when sliding starts, the friction force usually *decreases,* as
Figure 12e shows.

In some situations, the surfaces will alternately stick (static friction is opera-
tive) and slip (kinetic friction arises); this alternation is what causes the horrible
squeak made by chalk held at the wrong angle while you're writing on the black-
board. Another slip-and-stick phenomenon is the squeaky noise your windshield-
wiper blades make when the glass is nearly dry; still another is the outraged
shriek of tires sliding on asphalt pavement. A more positive example is the sound
produced by the motion of a violin bow against the string.

Liquids and gases also show frictional effects. Friction between two solid surfaces separated by a layer of liquid or gas is determined primarily by the *viscosity*
of the fluid. In a car engine, the pistons are separated from the cylinder walls by a
thin layer of oil. When an object slides on a layer of gas, friction can be made
very small. In the familiar linear air track (like the one in Example 7), the gliders
are supported on a layer of air. The frictional force is velocity dependent, but at
typical speeds the effective coefficient of friction is on the order of 0.001. A
device similar to the air track is the frictionless air table, on which pucks are supported by an array of small air jets about 2 cm apart.

For a wheeled vehicle, we can define a **coefficient of rolling friction,** μ_r, which
is the horizontal force needed for constant speed on a flat surface, divided by the
upward normal force exerted by the surface. Typical values of μ_r are 0.002 to
0.003 for steel wheels on steel rails and 0.01 to 0.02 for rubber tires on concrete.
These values are one reason that railroad trains are, in general, much more fuel efficient than highway trucks.

Quantitative Analysis 2

A friction experiment

A block is pulled along a horizontal surface (with
friction) by a constant force with magnitude F_x, and the acceleration a_x is measured. The experiment is repeated several times,
with different values of F_x, and a graph of acceleration as a
function of force is plotted. For the various trials, which of the
graphs of acceleration versus force shown at right is most nearly
correct?

SOLUTION No motion occurs unless the force F_x exceeds the
maximum static-friction force; when it does, the block starts to

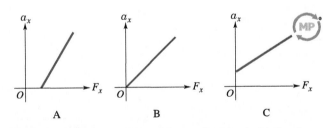

A   B   C

move under the action of F_x and the smaller kinetic-friction force.
Only answer A shows no acceleration at small values of the
applied force.

Conceptual Analysis 3

Turning things over

You are pushing the heavy plastic block in Figure 13 across the room with constant velocity. You decide to turn the block on end, reducing the surface area in contact with the floor by half. In this new orientation, to push this same block across the same floor with the same speed as before, the magnitude of force that you must apply is

A. twice as great as before.
B. the same as before.
C. half as great as before.

SOLUTION For many surfaces, dry sliding friction depends only on the normal force with which the object presses against the sur-

▲ **FIGURE 13**

face, in this case a force equal to the weight of the block. The frictional force does not depend on the area of contact. Since the frictional force is the same in both orientations, the applied force needed is the same. The correct answer is B.

EXAMPLE 8 **Delivering the goods**

A delivery company has just unloaded a 500 N crate full of home exercise equipment in your level driveway. You find that to get it started moving toward your garage, you have to pull with a horizontal force of magnitude 230 N. Once it "breaks loose" and starts to move, you can keep it moving at constant velocity with only 200 N of force. What are the coefficients of static and kinetic friction?

SOLUTION

SET UP As shown in Figure 14, the forces acting on the crate are its weight (magnitude w), the force applied by the rope (magnitude T), and the normal and frictional components (magnitudes n and f, respectively) of the contact force the driveway surface exerts on the crate. We draw free-body diagrams for the crate at the instant it starts to move (when the static frictional force is maximum) and while it is in motion.

SOLVE Whether the crate is moving or not, the friction force opposes your pull because it tends to prevent the crate from sliding relative to the surface. An instant before the crate starts to move, the static-friction force has its maximum possible value, $f_{s,max} = \mu_s n$. The state of rest and the state of motion with constant velocity are both equilibrium conditions. Remember that w, n, and f are the *magnitudes* of the forces; some of the components have negative signs. For example, the magnitude of the weight is 500 N, but its y component is -500 N. We write Newton's second law in component form, $\Sigma F_x = 0$ and $\Sigma F_y = 0$, for the crate. Then

$$\Sigma F_y = n + (-w) = n - 500 \text{ N} = 0, \qquad n = 500 \text{ N},$$
$$\Sigma F_x = T + (-f_s) = 230 \text{ N} - f_s = 0, \qquad f_s = 230 \text{ N},$$
$$f_{s,max} = \mu_s n \qquad \text{(motion about to start)},$$
$$\mu_s = \frac{f_{s,max}}{n} = \frac{230 \text{ N}}{500 \text{ N}} = 0.46.$$

After the crate starts to move, the friction force becomes that of kinetic friction (Figure 14c). The crate moves with constant velocity, so it is still in equilibrium. Thus, the vector sum of the forces is still zero, and we have

$$\Sigma F_y = n + (-w) = n - 500 \text{ N} = 0, \qquad n = 500 \text{ N},$$
$$\Sigma F_x = T + (-f_k) = 200 \text{ N} - f_k = 0, \qquad f_k = 200 \text{ N},$$
$$f_k = \mu_k n \qquad \text{(moving)}.$$

The coefficient of kinetic friction is

$$\mu_k = \frac{f_k}{n} = \frac{200 \text{ N}}{500 \text{ N}} = 0.40.$$

REFLECT There is no vertical motion, so $a_y = 0$ and $n = w$. It is easier to keep the crate moving than to start it moving from rest, because $\mu_k < \mu_s$. Note, however, that just as the crate begins to move, the acceleration is nonzero while the velocity changes from zero to its final, constant value.

Practice Problem: On a different part of the driveway, $\mu_s = 0.30$ and $\mu_k = 0.25$. What horizontal force is required to start the crate moving? What force is required to keep it sliding at constant velocity? *Answers:* 150 N, 125 N.

(a)

▶ **FIGURE 14**

(b) Crate just as it starts to move

$f_{s,max}$ $T = 230 \text{ N}$

$w = 500 \text{ N}$

(c) Crate moving at constant speed

f_k $T = 200 \text{ N}$

$w = 500 \text{ N}$

EXAMPLE 9 Not pulling hard enough

What is the friction force if the crate in Example 8 is at rest on the surface and a horizontal force of 50 N is applied to it?

SOLUTION

SET UP AND SOLVE The setup is the same as for Example 8. From the equilibrium conditions, we have

$$\Sigma F_x = T + (-f_s) = 50\,\text{N} - f_s = 0,$$
$$f_s = 50\,\text{N}.$$

REFLECT In this case, $f_s < \mu_s n$. The frictional force can prevent motion for any horizontal force less than 230 N.

Quantitative Analysis 4 — Pushing too hard

A baggage handler applies a constant horizontal force with magnitude F to push a box across a rough horizontal surface with a very small constant acceleration, starting from rest. Then he pushes a second box, identical to the first, with a force twice as great in magnitude. How does the acceleration of the second box compare with that of the first?

A. It is more than double the first acceleration.
B. It is exactly double the first acceleration.
C. It is less than double the first acceleration.

SOLUTION From Newton's second law, $F - f_k = ma_x$. In the first case, the acceleration is small, so F is only a little greater than f_k, and the net horizontal component of force $(F - f_k)$ is much smaller than F. Therefore, if F is doubled, the net horizontal force is much larger than before. Thus the acceleration is also much larger than before. Answer A is correct.

EXAMPLE 10 Moving the exercise equipment again

Suppose you try to move the crate full of exercise equipment in Example 8 by pulling upward on the rope at an angle of 30° above the horizontal. How hard do you have to pull to keep the crate moving with constant velocity? Is this easier or harder than pulling horizontally? Recall that $w = 500\,\text{N}$ and $\mu_k = 0.40$ for this crate.

(a)

(b) Free-body diagram for moving crate

▲ FIGURE 15

SOLUTION

SET UP Figure 15 shows the situation and our free-body diagram. We use the same coordinate system as in Example 8. The magnitude f_k of the friction force is still equal to $\mu_k n$, but now the magnitude n of the normal force is *not* equal in magnitude to the weight of the crate. Instead, the force exerted by the rope has an additional vertical component that tends to lift the crate off the floor; this component makes n less than w.

SOLVE The crate is moving with constant velocity, so it is still in equilibrium. Applying $\Sigma \vec{F} = 0$ in component form, we find that

$$\Sigma F_x = T\cos 30° + (-f_k) = T\cos 30° - 0.40n = 0,$$
$$\Sigma F_y = T\sin 30° + n + (-500\,\text{N}) = 0.$$

These are two simultaneous equations for the two unknown quantities T and n. To solve them, we can eliminate one unknown and

Continued

solve for the other. There are many ways to do this. Here is one way: Rearrange the second equation to the form

$$n = 500 \text{ N} - T\sin 30°.$$

Then substitute this expression for n back into the first equation:

$$T\cos 30° - 0.40(500 \text{ N} - T\sin 30°) = 0.$$

Finally, solve this equation for T, and then substitute the result back into either of the original equations to obtain n. The results are

$$T = 188 \text{ N}, \qquad n = 406 \text{ N}.$$

REFLECT The normal-force magnitude n is *less* than the weight $(w = 500 \text{ N})$ of the box, and the tension required is a little less than the force needed (200 N) when you pulled horizontally.

Practice Problem: Try pulling at 22°; you'll find that you need even less force. (In fact, this angle gives the smallest possible value of T.) *Answers:* $T = 186 \text{ N}, n = 430 \text{ N}$.

EXAMPLE 11   **Toboggan ride with friction**

Let's go back to the toboggan we studied in Example 6. The wax has worn off, and there is now a coefficient of kinetic friction μ_k. The slope has just the right angle to make the toboggan slide with constant velocity. Derive an expression for the slope angle in terms of w and μ_k.

SOLUTION

SET UP Figure 16 shows our sketch and free-body diagram. The slope angle is α. The forces on the toboggan are identified by their magnitudes: its weight (w) and the normal (n) and frictional (f_k) components of the contact force exerted on it by the sloping surface. We take axes perpendicular and parallel to the surface and represent the weight in terms of its components in these two directions as shown.

SOLVE The toboggan is moving with constant velocity and is therefore in equilibrium. The equilibrium conditions are

$$\Sigma F_x = w\sin\alpha + (-f_k) = w\sin\alpha - \mu_k n = 0,$$
$$\Sigma F_y = n + (-w\cos\alpha) = 0.$$

Rearranging terms, we get

$$\mu_k n = w\sin\alpha, \qquad n = w\cos\alpha.$$

Note that the normal force n is less than the weight w. When we divide the first of these equations by the second, we find that

$$\mu_k = \frac{\sin\alpha}{\cos\alpha} = \tan\alpha.$$

▲ **FIGURE 16** Our diagrams for this problem.

REFLECT The normal force is *not* equal in magnitude to the weight; it is always smaller. The weight w doesn't appear in the expression for μ_k; *any* toboggan, regardless of its weight, slides down an incline with constant speed if the tangent of the slope angle of the hill equals the coefficient of kinetic friction. The greater the coefficient of friction, the steeper the slope has to be for the toboggan to slide with constant velocity. This behavior is just what we should expect.

EXAMPLE 12   **A steeper hill**

Suppose the toboggan in Example 11 goes down a steeper hill. The coefficient of friction is the same, but this time the toboggan accelerates. Derive an expression for the acceleration in terms of g, α, μ_k, and w.

SOLUTION

SET UP Our free-body diagram (Figure 17) is almost the same as for Example 11, but the toboggan is no longer in equilibrium: a_y is still zero, but a_x is not.

SOLVE We apply Newton's second law in component form. From $\Sigma F_x = ma_x$ and $\Sigma F_y = ma_y$, we get the two equations

$$\Sigma F_x = mg\sin\alpha + (-f_k) = ma_x,$$
$$\Sigma F_y = n + (-mg\cos\alpha) = 0.$$

From the second equation, we find that $n = mg\cos\alpha$; then, from Equation 1 $(f_k = \mu_k n)$, we get $f_k = \mu_k n = \mu_k mg\cos\alpha$.

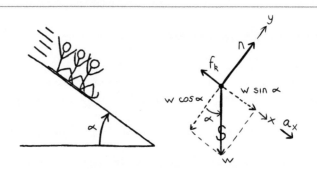

▲ **FIGURE 17** Our diagrams for the toboggan on a steeper hill.

Continued

That is, the magnitude of the friction force equals μ_k times the component of the weight normal to the surface. We substitute this expression for f_k back into the x-component equation. The result is

$$mg\sin\alpha + (-\mu_k mg\cos\alpha) = ma_x,$$
$$a_x = g(\sin\alpha - \mu_k\cos\alpha).$$

REFLECT Does this result make sense? Let's check some special cases. First, if the hill is *vertical*, $\alpha = 90°$; then $\sin\alpha = 1$, $\cos\alpha = 0$, and $a_x = g$. This is free fall, just what we would expect. Second, on a hill with angle α with *no* friction, $\mu_k = 0$. Then $a_x = g\sin\alpha$. The situation is the same as in Example 6, and

we get the same result; that's encouraging! Next, suppose that $a_x = 0$. Then there is just enough friction to make the toboggan move with constant velocity. In that case, $a_x = 0$, and it follows that

$$\sin\alpha = \mu_k\cos\alpha \quad \text{and} \quad \mu_k = \tan\alpha.$$

This agrees with our result from Example 11; good! Finally, note that there may be *so much* friction that $\mu_k\cos\alpha$ is actually greater than $\sin\alpha$. In that case, a_x is negative. If we give the toboggan an initial downhill push, it will slow down and eventually stop.

We have pretty much beaten the toboggan problem to death, but there is an important lesson to be learned. We started out with a simple problem and then extended it to more and more general situations. Our most general result includes all the previous ones as special cases, and that's a nice, neat package! Don't memorize this package; it is useful only for this one set of problems. But do try to understand how we obtained it and what it means.

One final variation that you may want to try out is the case in which we give the toboggan an initial push *up* the hill. The direction of the friction force is now reversed, so the acceleration is different from the downhill value. It turns out that the expression for a_x is the same as before, except that the minus sign becomes a plus sign.

EXAMPLE 13 **Fluid friction**

When an object moves through a fluid (such as water or air), it exerts a force on the fluid to push it out of the way. By Newton's third law, the fluid pushes back on the object, in a direction opposite to the object's velocity relative to the fluid, always opposing the object's motion and usually increasing with speed. In high-speed motion through air, the resisting force is approximately proportional to the square of the object's speed v; it's called a *drag force*, or simply *drag*. We can represent its magnitude F_D by

$$F_D = Dv^2,$$

where D is a proportionality constant that depends on the shape and size of the object and the density of air.

When an object falls vertically through air, the drag force opposing the object's motion increases, and the downward acceleration decreases. Eventually, the object reaches a *terminal velocity:* its acceleration approaches zero and the velocity becomes nearly constant. Derive an expression for the terminal velocity magnitude v_T in terms of D and the weight mg of the object.

SOLUTION

SET UP As shown in Figure 18, we take the positive y direction to be downward, and we neglect any force associated with buoyancy in the fluid. The net vertical component of force is $mg - Dv^2$.

SOLVE Newton's second law gives

$$mg - Dv_y^2 = ma_y.$$

When the object has reached terminal velocity v_T, the acceleration a_y is zero, and

$$mg - Dv_T^2 = 0, \quad \text{or} \quad v_T = \sqrt{\frac{mg}{D}}.$$

REFLECT For a skydiver in the spread-eagled position, the value of the constant D is found experimentally to be about 0.25 kg/m.

▲ **FIGURE 18** An object falling through air, before and after reaching its terminal velocity.

Continued

(Does this number have the correct units?) If the skydiver's mass is 80 kg, the terminal velocity magnitude is

$$v_T = \sqrt{\frac{mg}{D}} = \sqrt{\frac{(80 \text{ kg})(9.8 \text{ m/s}^2)}{0.25 \text{ kg/m}}} = 56 \text{ m/s}.$$

This terminal velocity magnitude is about 125 mi/h. Does this seem reasonable?

Practice Problem: For an average-sized cat, the constant D is approximately one-fourth that for a human, or about $D = 0.062 \text{ kg/m}$. Find the terminal velocity magnitude of a 4.5 kg cat. *Answer: 27 m/s.*

Quantitative Analysis 5

Skydivers everywhere

As we just saw, objects falling through the air at high speeds are acted upon by a drag force proportional in magnitude to v^2. A falling object speeds up until the magnitude of the force from air drag equals the magnitude of the object's weight. If a 120 lb woman using a parachute falls with terminal velocity v, a 240 lb man using an identical chute will fall with terminal velocity

A. v.   B. $\sqrt{2}v$.   C. $2v$.

SOLUTION Since both people use the same chute, the constant D is the same for both. The mass of the man is twice the mass of the woman, so he requires twice the drag force to produce zero acceleration. The drag force is proportional to v^2; hence, it doubles if the velocity increases by a factor of $\sqrt{2}$. The correct answer is B.

Rolling vehicles also experience air drag, which usually increases proportionally to the square of the speed. Air drag is often negligible at low speeds, but at highway speeds it is comparable to or greater than rolling friction.

Mastering PHYSICS

ActivPhysics 2.1.2: Skydiver

4 Elastic Forces

When we introduced the concept of *force,* we mentioned that when forces are applied to a solid object, they usually deform the object. In particular, we discussed the use of a coil spring in a device called a spring balance that can be used to measure the magnitudes of forces.

Let's look at the relation of force to deformation in a little more detail. Figure 19 shows a coil spring with one end attached to an anchor point and the other end attached to an object that can slide without friction along the x axis. The coordinate x describes the position of the right end of the spring. When $x = 0$, the spring is neither stretched nor compressed. When the object is moved a distance x to the right, the spring is stretched by an amount x. It then exerts a force with magnitude F_{spr} on the object and an "equal and opposite" force on the anchor point. When the string is stretched more, greater forces are required. For many common materials, such as steel coil springs, experiments show that stretching the spring an amount $2x$ requires forces with magnitude $2F_{spr}$; that is, the magnitude of force required is *directly proportional* to the amount of stretch.

If the spring has spaces between its coils, as in the figure, then it can be compressed as well as stretched (Figure 19d). Again, experiments show that the amount of compression is directly proportional to the magnitude of the force. In both stretching and compressing, the sign of the x coordinate of the right end of the spring is always opposite the sign of the x component of force the spring applies to the object at its right end. When x is positive, the spring is stretched and applies a force that pulls to the left (the negative x direction) on the object. When x is negative, the spring is compressed and pushes to the right (the positive x direction) on the object.

This proportionality of force to stretching and compressing can be summarized in a simple equation called *Hooke's law* (after Robert Hooke, a contemporary of Newton):

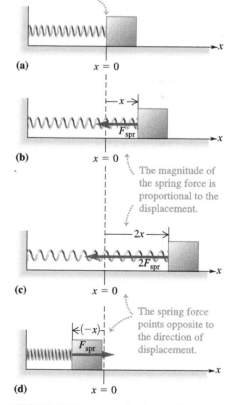

At the equilibrium position $x = 0$, the spring is neither stretched nor compressed.

(a) $x = 0$

(b) $x = 0$

The magnitude of the spring force is proportional to the displacement.

(c) $x = 0$

The spring force points opposite to the direction of displacement.

(d) $x = 0$

▲ **FIGURE 19** Some experiments exploring spring forces.

Elastic behavior of springs (Hooke's law)

For springs, the spring force F_{spr} is approximately proportional to the distance x by which the spring is stretched or compressed:

$$F_{spr} = -kx. \tag{3}$$

In this equation, k is a positive proportionality constant called the **force constant,** or sometimes the *spring constant,* of the spring. If force is measured in newtons and x in meters, the units of k are N/m. The negative sign indicates that the spring force on the object is always opposite to the displacement.

A very stiff spring requires a large force for a little deformation, corresponding to a large value of the constant k; a weak spring, made with thin wire, requires only a small force for the same deformation, corresponding to a smaller value of k.

Although this relationship is called Hooke's *law,* it is only an approximate relation. Most metallic springs obey it quite well for deformations that are small compared with the overall length of the spring, but rubber bands don't obey it even for small deformations. So it would be safer to call it "Hooke's rule of thumb" (without intending any disparagement of Hooke, one of the great pioneers of late 17th-century science).

EXAMPLE 14   Fishy business

A spring balance used to weigh fish is built with a spring that stretches 1.00 cm when a 12.0 N weight is placed in the pan. When the 12.0 N weight is replaced with a 1.50 kg fish, what distance does the spring stretch?

SOLUTION

SET UP Figure 20a and b show how the spring responds to the 12.0 N weight and to the 1.50 kg fish. The spring and fish are in equilibrium. We draw a free-body diagram for the fish (Figure 20c), showing the downward force of gravity and the upward force exerted by the stretched spring. We point the x axis vertically downward, so x is zero with no fish and positive when the fish is attached and the spring stretches.

SOLVE We want to use Hooke's law $(F_{spr} = -kx)$ to relate the stretch of the spring to the force, but first we need to find the force constant k. The problem states that forces of magnitude 12.0 N are required to stretch the spring 1.00 cm $(= 1.00 \times 10^{-2}\text{ m})$, so

$$k = -\frac{-12.0\text{ N}}{1.00 \times 10^{-2}\text{ m}} = 1200\text{ N/m}.$$

The weight of the 1.50 kg fish is $w = mg = (1.50\text{ kg}) \cdot (9.80\text{ m/s}^2) = 14.7\text{ N}$. The equilibrium condition for the fish is

$$\Sigma F_x = 0, \qquad mg + F_{spr} = 0,$$
$$14.7\text{ N} - (1200\text{ N/m})x = 0,$$

and finally, $x = 0.0123\text{ m} = 1.23\text{ cm}$.

REFLECT The weight of the fish is greater than the amount of force needed to stretch the spring 1.00 cm, so we expect the fish to stretch the spring more than 1.00 cm. We've used the fact that x can stand for any length change of a Hooke's law spring and F_{spr} for the corresponding change in the component of the spring force.

Practice Problem: If, instead of the fish, we place a 3.00 kg rock in the pan, how much does the spring stretch? *Answer:* Twice as much, 2.45 cm.

▶ **FIGURE 20** Weighing a fish.

(a) The scale stretched by a known weight

(b) The scale stretched by a known mass

(c) Free-body diagram for the fish

EXAMPLE 15   An innerspring mattress

You have just bought an innerspring mattress that contains coil springs in a rectangular array 20 coils wide and 40 coils long. You estimate that when you lie on the mattress, your weight is supported by about 200 springs (about one-fourth of the total number of springs in the mattress). Lacking further funds for a foundation spring, you lay the mattress directly on the floor. You observe that the springs compress about 2.6 cm when you lie on the mattress. Assuming that your weight of 800 N is supported equally by 200 springs, find the force constant of each spring.

SOLUTION

SET UP You are the object in equilibrium, so start with a free-body diagram of yourself (Figure 21). Observe that the spring forces are *additive,* in the sense that the total upward force they exert on your body is just 200 times the force of each individual spring. Your body is in equilibrium under the action of the total spring force and your weight.

SOLVE For equilibrium, the total upward force of all the supporting springs must be 800 N, so $(200)k(2.6 \times 10^{-2}\,\text{m}) = 800\,\text{N}$, and

$$k = 154\,\text{N/m} = 1.54\,\text{N/cm}.$$

REFLECT To borrow a term from electric circuit analysis, the springs are *in parallel;* the deformation is the same for each, and the total force is the sum of the individual spring forces. Of course, the assumption that all the deformations are the same is probably not realistic.

▲ **FIGURE 21** Free-body diagram of yourself on the mattress.

Practice Problem: Suppose you lay a thin, lightweight sheet of plywood on top of the mattress, so that your weight is spread over all 800 springs. How much does each spring compress? *Answer:* 0.65 cm.

5 Forces in Nature

The historical development of our understanding of the forces (or interactions) found in nature has traditionally placed them into four distinct classes (Figure 22). Two are familiar in everyday experience. The other two involve fundamental particle interactions that we cannot observe with the unaided senses.

Of the two familiar classes, **gravitational interactions** were the first to be studied in detail. The *weight* of an object results from the earth's gravitational pull acting on it. The sun's gravitational attraction for the earth keeps the earth in its nearly circular orbit around the sun. Newton recognized that the motions of the planets around the sun and the free fall of objects on earth are both the result of gravitational forces. In the next chapter, we'll study gravitational interactions in greater detail and we'll analyze their vital role in the motions of planets and satellites.

The second familiar class of forces, **electromagnetic interactions,** includes electric and magnetic forces. When you run a comb through your hair, you can then use the comb to pick up bits of paper or fluff; this interaction is the result of an *electric* charge on the comb, which also causes the infamous "static cling." *Magnetic* forces occur in interactions between magnets or between a magnet and a piece of iron. These forces may seem to form a different category, separate from electric forces, but magnetic interactions are actually the result of electric charges in motion. In an electromagnet, an electric current in a coil of wire causes magnetic interactions. One of the great achievements of 19th-century physics was the *unification* of theories of electric and magnetic interactions into a single theoretical framework. We'll study these interactions in detail in the second half of this text.

Gravitational and electromagnetic interactions differ enormously in their strength. The electrical repulsion between two protons at a given distance is

NASA

(a)

Helen Hansma

(b)

◄ **FIGURE 22** Instances of the four fundamental forces. (a) Gravitational interactions hold the earth and moon in orbit around each other. (b) Electromagnetic interactions hold together the atoms of a DNA molecule. (c) The strong nuclear interaction is involved in the nuclear reactions that release energy in stars, such as our sun. (d) The weak nuclear interaction plays a role in the release of energy in supernovae, which partly involves the decay of unstable nuclei. (The arrow in the left image indicates the star that has become a supernova in the right image.)

stronger than their gravitational attraction by a factor on the order of 10^{35}. Gravitational forces play no significant role in atomic or molecular structure. But in bodies of astronomical size, positive and negative charge are usually present in nearly equal amounts, and the resulting electrical interactions nearly cancel out. Gravitational interactions are the dominant influence in the motion of planets and also in the internal structure of stars.

The other two classes of interactions are less familiar. One, the **strong interaction,** is responsible for holding the nucleus of an atom together. Nuclei contain electrically neutral and positively charged particles. The charged particles repel each other, and a nucleus could not be stable if it were not for the presence of an *attractive* force of a different kind that counteracts the repulsive electrical interactions. In this context, the strong interaction is also called the *nuclear force.* It has a much shorter range than electrical interactions, but within its range it is much stronger. The strong interaction is also responsible for the creation of unstable particles in high-energy particle collisions.

Finally, there is the **weak interaction.** This force plays no direct role in the behavior of ordinary matter, but it is of vital importance in the behavior of fundamental particles. The weak interaction is responsible for beta decay (one kind of nuclear radiation), as well as the decay of many unstable particles produced in high-energy collisions of fundamental particles. It also plays a significant role in the evolution of stars.

During the 1970s, a unified theory of the electromagnetic and weak interactions was developed. This interaction is now called the *electroweak interaction.* In a sense, it reduces the number of classes of forces from four to three. Similar attempts have been made to understand all strong, electromagnetic, and weak interactions on the basis of a single unified theory called *quantum chromodynamics* (QCD), or a *grand unified theory* (GUT), in which only two forces are postulated. The most promising of the GUT theories make use of vibrating entities called *strings,* whose description requires a space with many more dimensions than our familiar three-dimensional space.

Finally, the ultimate goal is to include gravitational forces in the unification, to produce a *theory of everything* (TOE). Theories of this nature are intimately related to the very early history of the universe, following the Big Bang. Such theories are still highly speculative and raise many unanswered questions. The entire field is in much ferment today. Recent research has had the remarkable effect of connecting our understanding of the *smallest* objects in the universe—that is, fundamental particles—with our understanding of the *largest* objects—the universe itself and its evolution in time since the Big Bang.

Shutterstock

(c)

Anglo-Australian Observatory/
David Malin

(d)

CHAPTER SUMMARY

Equilibrium of a Particle

(**Section 1**) When an object is in equilibrium, the vector sum of the forces acting on it must be zero: $\Sigma \vec{F} = 0$. (Equation A). In component form,

$$\Sigma F_x = 0, \qquad \Sigma F_y = 0. \qquad \text{(B)}$$

Free-body diagrams are useful in identifying the forces acting on the object being considered. Newton's third law is also frequently needed in equilibrium problems. The two forces in an action–reaction pair never act on the same object.

An object moving at constant velocity down a frictionless ramp is in equilibrium: $\Sigma \vec{F} = 0$.

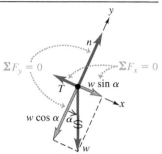

A free-body diagram and coordinate system for the object. The weight vector is replaced by its components.

Applications of Newton's Second Law

(**Section 2**) When the vector sum of the forces on an object is not zero, the object has an acceleration determined by Newton's second law, $\Sigma \vec{F} = m\vec{a}$ (Equation C). In component form,

$$\Sigma F_x = ma_x, \qquad \Sigma F_y = ma_y. \qquad \text{(D)}$$

$\Sigma \vec{F} = m\vec{a}$.

A free-body diagram for the object.

Contact Forces and Friction

(**Section 3**) The contact force between two objects can always be represented in terms of a normal component n perpendicular to the surface of interaction and a frictional component f parallel to the surface. When sliding occurs, the kinetic-friction force f_k is often approximately proportional to n. Then the proportionality constant is μ_k, the coefficient of kinetic friction: $f_k = \mu_k n$ (Equation 1).

When there is no relative motion, the maximum possible friction force is approximately proportional to the normal force, and the proportionality constant is μ_s, the coefficient of static friction. The governing equation is $f_s \leq \mu_s n$ (Equation 2).

The actual static-friction force may be anything from zero to the maximum value given by the equality in Equation 2, depending on the situation. Usually, μ_k is less than μ_s for a given pair of surfaces.

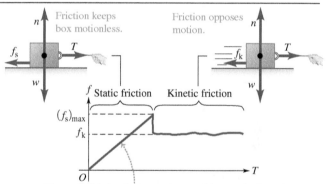

The static-friction force remains equal in magnitude to the tension force until its maximum value $(f_s)_{max}$ is exceeded.

Elastic Forces

(**Section 4**) When forces act on a solid object, the object usually deforms. In some cases, such as a stretched or compressed spring, the deformation is approximately proportional to the magnitude of the applied force. This proportionality is called Hooke's law:

$$F_{spr} = -kx. \qquad \text{(3)}$$

When stretched or compressed from equilibrium, the spring exerts a force $\vec{F}_{spr}$ whose magnitude is approximately proportional to the displacement.

Forces in Nature

(**Section 5**) Historically, forces have been classified as strong, electromagnetic, weak, and gravitational. Present-day research includes intensive efforts to create a unified description of forces in all these categories.

Applications of Newton's Laws: Problem Set

(MP) For instructor-assigned homework, go to www.masteringphysics.com

Conceptual Questions

1. Can a body be in equilibrium when only one force acts on it?
2. A clothesline is hung between two poles, and then a shirt is hung near the center of the line. No matter how tightly the line is stretched, it always sags a little at the center. Show why.
3. A man sits in a seat that is suspended from a rope. The rope passes over a pulley suspended from the ceiling, and the man holds the other end of the rope in his hands. What is the tension in the rope, and what force does the seat exert on the man? Draw a free-body force diagram for the man.
4. Is it physically possible for the coefficient of friction ever to be greater than one? What would this mean?
5. Why is it so much more difficult to walk on icy pavement than dry pavement?
6. A car accelerates gradually to the right with power on the two rear wheels. What is the direction of the friction force on these wheels? Show why. Is it static or kinetic friction?
7. Without doing any calculations, decide whether the tension T in Figure 23 will be equal to, greater than, or less than the weight of the suspended object.

▲ **FIGURE 23** Question 7.

8. A box slides up an incline, comes to rest, and then slides down again, accelerating in both directions. Answer the following questions, using only a free-body diagram and *without* doing any calculations: (a) If there is no friction on the incline, how will the box's acceleration going up compare in magnitude *and* direction with its acceleration going down? (b) If there is kinetic friction on the incline, how will the box's acceleration going up compare in magnitude *and* direction with its acceleration going down? (c) What will be the box's acceleration at its highest point?
9. For the objects shown in Figure 24, will the tension in the wire be greater than, equal to, or less than the weight W? Decide *without* doing any calculations.

▲ **FIGURE 24** Question 9.

10. A woman is pushing horizontally on two boxes on a factory floor, as shown in Figure 25. Which is greater, the force the woman exerts on the 10 lb box or the force the 10 lb box exerts on the 250 lb box? Decide without doing any calculations.

▲ **FIGURE 25** Question 10.

11. In a world *without* friction, could you (a) walk on a horizontal sidewalk, (b) climb a ladder, (c) climb a vertical pole, (d) jump into the air, (e) ride your bike, and (f) drive around a curve on a flat roadway? Explain your reasoning.
12. How could you measure the acceleration of a spaceship by using only simple instruments (such as springs, strings, and rulers) located *within* the ship?
13. You can classify scales for weighing objects as those that use springs and those that use standard masses to balance unknown masses. Which group would be more accurate when you use it in an accelerating spaceship? When you use it on the moon?
14. (a) Show that, in terms of the fundamental quantities, the units of the force constant k for a spring reduce to kg/s^2. (b) Why is it physically more sensible to express k in N/m instead of in its fundamental units of kg/s^2?
15. When you stand with bare feet in a wet bathtub, the grip feels fairly secure, and yet a catastrophic slip is quite possible. Explain this in terms of the two coefficients of friction.
16. True or false? The minus sign in Hooke's law ($F_{spr} = -kx$) means that the spring's force always points in the negative direction. If the statement is false, what *does* the minus sign mean?

Multiple-Choice Problems

1. A horizontal force accelerates a box across a rough horizontal floor with friction present, producing an acceleration a. If the force is now tripled, but all other conditions remain the same, the acceleration will become
   A. greater than $3a$.
   B. equal to $3a$.
   C. less than $3a$.
2. You slide an 800-N table across the kitchen floor by pushing with a force of 100 N. If the table moves at a constant speed, the friction force with the floor must be
   A. 100 N   B. more than 100 N
   C. 800 N   D. more than 800 N
3. An artist wearing spiked shoes pushes two crates across her frictionless horizontal studio floor. (See Figure 26.) If she

exerts a horizontal 36 N force on the smaller crate, then the smaller crate exerts a force on the larger crate that is closest to

A. 36 N.   B. 30 N.
C. 200 N.   D. 240 N.

▲ FIGURE 26 Multiple-choice problem 3.

4. A horizontal pull P pulls two wagons over a horizontal frictionless floor, as shown in Figure 27. The tension

▲ FIGURE 27 Multiple-choice problem 4.

in the light horizontal rope connecting the wagons is

A. equal to P, by Newton's third law.
B. equal to 2000 N.
C. greater than P.
D. less than P.

5. A horizontal pull P drags two boxes connected by a horizontal rope having tension T, as shown in Figure 28. The floor is horizontal and frictionless. Decide which of the following statements is true *without* doing any calculations:

A. $P > T$ B. $P = T$ C. $P < T$
D. We need more information to decide which is greater.

▲ FIGURE 28 Multiple-choice problem 5.

6. A crate slides up an inclined ramp and then slides down the ramp after momentarily stopping near the top. This crate is acted upon by friction on the ramp and accelerates both ways. Which statement about this crate's acceleration is correct?

A. The acceleration going up the ramp is greater than the acceleration going down.
B. The acceleration going down the ramp is greater than the acceleration going up.
C. The acceleration is the same in both directions.

7. A bungee cord with a normal length of 2 ft requires a force of 30 lb to stretch it to a total length of 5 ft. The force constant of the bungee cord is

A. 6 lb/ft   B. 10 lb/ft   C. 15 lb/ft   D. 30 lb/ft

8. A weightless spring scale is attached to two equal weights as shown in Figure 29. The reading in the scale will be

A. 0.   B. W.
C. $2W$.

▲ FIGURE 29 Multiple-choice problem 8.

9. Two objects are connected by a light wire as shown in Figure 30, with the wire pulling horizontally on the 400 N object. After this system is released from rest, the tension in the wire will be

A. less than 300 N.
B. 300 N.
C. 200 N.
D. 100 N.

$\mu_s = \dfrac{1}{2}, \ \mu_k = \dfrac{1}{4}$

300 N

▲ FIGURE 30 Multiple-choice problem 9.

10. A 100 N weight is supported by two weightless wires A and B as shown in Figure 31. What can you conclude about the tensions in these wires?

A. The tensions are equal to 50 N each.
B. The tensions are equal, but less than 50 N each.
C. The tensions are equal, but greater than 50 N each.
D. The tensions are equal to 100 N each.

▲ FIGURE 31 Multiple-choice problem 10.

11. The two blocks in Figure 32 are in balance, and there is no friction on the surface of the incline. If a slight vibration occurs, what will M do after that?

A. It will accelerate up the ramp.
B. It will accelerate down the ramp.
C. It will not accelerate.

▲ FIGURE 32 Multiple-choice problem 11.

▲ FIGURE 33 Multiple-choice problem 12.

12. The system shown in Figure 33 is released from rest, there is no friction between B and the tabletop, and all of the objects move together. What must be true about the friction force on A?

A. It is zero.
B. It acts to the right on A.
C. It acts to the left on A.
D. We cannot tell whether there is any friction force on A because we do not know the coefficients of friction between A and B.

13. In the system shown in Figure 34, $M > m$, the surface of the bench is horizontal and frictionless, and the connecting string pulls horizontally on m. As more and more weight is gradually added to m, which of the following statements best describes the behavior of the system after it is released?

▲ FIGURE 34 Multiple-choice problem 13.

A. The acceleration remains the same in all cases, since there is no friction and the pull of gravity on M is the same.
B. The acceleration becomes zero when enough weight is added so that $m = M$.
C. The velocity becomes zero when $m = M$.
D. None of the preceding statements is correct.

Problems

1 Equilibrium of a Particle

1. • A 15.0 N bucket is to be raised at a constant speed of 50.0 cm/s by a rope. According to the information in Table 1, how many kilograms of cement can be put into this bucket without breaking the rope if it is made of (a) thin white string, (b) $\frac{1}{4}$ in. nylon clothesline, (c) $1\frac{1}{4}$ in. manila climbing rope?

2. • In a museum exhibit, three equal weights are hung with identical wires, as shown in Figure 35. Each wire can support a tension of no more than 75.0 N without breaking. Start each of the following parts with an appropriate free-body diagram. (a) What is the maximum value that W can be without breaking any wires? (b) Under these conditions, what is the tension in each wire?

▲ FIGURE 35
Problem 2.

▲ FIGURE 36
Problem 3.

3. • Two 25.0 N weights are suspended at opposite ends of a rope that passes over a light, frictionless pulley. The pulley is attached to a chain that is fastened to the ceiling. (See Figure 36.) Start solving this problem by making a free-body diagram of each weight. (a) What is the tension in the rope? (b) What is the tension in the chain?

4. • Two weights are hanging as shown in Figure 37. (a) Draw a free-body diagram of each weight. (b) Find the tension in cable A. (c) Find the tension in cables B and C.

5. • An adventurous archaeologist crosses between two rock cliffs by slowly going hand over hand along a rope stretched between the cliffs. He stops to rest at the middle of the rope (Figure 38). The rope will break if the tension in it exceeds 2.50×10^4 N. Our hero's mass is 90.0 kg. (a) If the angle θ is 10.0°, find the tension in the rope. Start with a free-body diagram of the archaeologist. (b) What is the smallest value the angle θ can have if the rope is not to break?

▲ FIGURE 38 Problem 5.

6. •• A 1130-kg car is held in place by a light cable on a very smooth (frictionless) ramp, as shown in Fig. 39. The cable makes an angle of 31.0° above the surface of the ramp, and the

ramp itself rises at 25.0° above the horizontal. (a) Draw a free-body diagram for the car. (b) Find the tension in the cable. (c) How hard does the surface of the ramp push on the car?

▲ FIGURE 39 Problem 6.

7. •• **Tension in a muscle.** Muscles are attached to bones by
   BIO means of tendons. The maximum force that a muscle can exert is directly proportional to its cross-sectional area A at the widest point. We can express this relationship mathematically as $F_{\max} = \sigma A$, where σ (sigma) is a proportionality constant. Surprisingly, σ is about the same for the muscles of all animals and has the numerical value of 3.0×10^5 in SI units. (a) What are the SI units of σ in terms of newtons and meters and also in terms of the fundamental quantities (kg, m, s)? (b) In one set of experiments, the average maximum force that the gastrocnemius muscle in the back of the lower leg could exert was measured to be 755 N for healthy males in their midtwenties. What does this result tell us was the average cross-sectional area, in cm^2, of that muscle for the people in the study?

8. •• **Muscles and tendons.** The gas-
   BIO trocnemius muscle, in the back of the leg, has two portions, known as the medial and lateral heads. Assume that they attach to the Achilles tendon as shown in Figure 40. The cross-sectional area of each of these two muscles is typically 30 cm^2 for many adults. What is the maximum tension they can produce in the Achilles tendon? (See the previous problem for some useful information.)

▲ FIGURE 40
Problem 8.

9. • **Traction apparatus.** In
   BIO order to prevent muscle contraction from misaligning bones during healing (which can cause a permanent limp), injured or broken legs must be supported horizontally and at the same time kept under tension (traction) directed along the leg. One version of a device to accomplish this aim, the Russell traction apparatus, is shown in Figure 41. This system allows the apparatus to support the full weight of the injured leg and at the same time provide the traction along the leg. If the leg to be

▲ FIGURE 41 Problem 9.

supported weighs 47.0 N, (a) what must be the weight of W and (b) what traction force does this system produce along the leg?

10. • **A broken thigh bone.** When the thigh is fractured, the BIO patient's leg must be kept under traction. One method of doing so is a variation on the Russell traction apparatus. (See Figure 42.) If the physical therapist specifies that the traction force directed along the leg must be 25 N, what must W be?

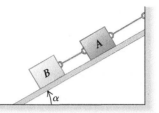

▲ FIGURE 43
Problem 11.

▲ FIGURE 42 Problem 10.

11. •• Two artifacts in a museum display are hung from vertical walls by very light wires, as shown in Figure 43. (a) Draw a free-body diagram of each artifact. (b) Find the tension in each of the three wires. (c) Would the answers be different if each wire were twice as long, but the angles were unchanged? Why or why not?

12. •• In a rescue, the 73 kg police officer is suspended by two cables, as shown in Figure 44. (a) Sketch a free-body diagram of him. (b) Find the tension in each cable.

▲ FIGURE 44 Problem 12.

13. •• A tetherball leans against the smooth, frictionless post to which it is attached. (See Figure 45.) The string is attached to the ball such that a line along the string passes through the center of the ball. If the string is 1.40 m long and the ball has a radius of 0.110 m with mass 0.270 kg, (a) make a free-body diagram of the ball. (b) What is the tension in the rope? (c) What is the force the pole exerts on the ball?

14. •• Find the tension in each cord in Figure 46 if the weight of the suspended object is 250 N.

▲ FIGURE 45
Problem 13.

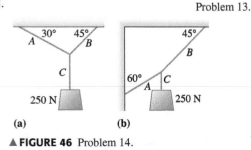

(a)   (b)

▲ FIGURE 46 Problem 14.

15. •• Two blocks, each with weight w, are held in place on a frictionless incline as shown in Figure 47. In terms of w and the angle α of the incline, calculate the tension in (a) the rope connecting the blocks and (b) the rope that connects block A to the wall. (c) Calculate the magnitude of the force that the incline exerts on each block. (d) Interpret your answers for the cases $\alpha = 0$ and $\alpha = 90°$.

▲ FIGURE 47 Problem 15.

16. •• A man pushes on a piano of mass 180 kg so that it slides at a constant velocity of 12.0 cm/s *down* a ramp that is inclined at 11.0° above the horizontal. No appreciable friction is acting on the piano. Calculate the magnitude and direction of this push (a) if the man pushes parallel to the incline, (b) if the man pushes the piano *up* the plane instead, also at 12.0 cm/s parallel to the incline, and (c) if the man pushes horizontally, but still with a speed of 12.0 cm/s.

2 Applications of Newton's Second Law

17. •• **Air-bag safety.** According to safety standards for air bags, BIO the maximum acceleration during a car crash should not exceed $60g$ and should last for no more than 36 ms. (a) In such a case, what force does the air bag exert on a 75 kg person? Start with a free-body diagram. (b) Express the force in part (a) in terms of the person's weight.

18. •• **Forces during chin-ups.** People who do chin-ups raise BIO their chin just over a bar (the chinning bar), supporting themselves only by their arms. Typically, the body below the arms is raised by about 30 cm in a time of 1.0 s, starting from rest. Assume that the entire body of a 680 N person who is chinning is raised this distance and that half the 1.0 s is spent accelerating upward and the other half accelerating downward, uniformly in both cases. Make a free-body diagram of the person's body, and then apply it to find the force his arms must exert on him during the accelerating part of the chin-up.

19. •• **Force on a tennis ball.** The record speed for a tennis ball that is served is 73.14 m/s. During a serve, the ball typically starts from rest and is in contact with the tennis racquet for 30 ms. Assuming constant acceleration, what was the average force exerted on the tennis ball during this record serve, expressed in terms of the ball's weight W?

20. •• A 75,600 N spaceship comes in for a vertical landing. From an initial speed of 1.00 km/s, it comes to rest in 2.00 min with uniform acceleration. (a) Make a free-body diagram of this ship as it is coming in. (b) What braking force must its rockets provide? Ignore air resistance.

21. •• **Force during a jump.** An average person can reach a BIO maximum height of about 60 cm when jumping straight up from a crouched position. During the jump itself, the person's body from the knees up typically rises a distance of around 50 cm. To keep the calculations simple and yet get a reasonable result, assume that the *entire body* rises this much during the jump. (a) With what initial speed does the person leave the ground to reach a height of 60 cm? (b) Make a free-body diagram of the person during the jump. (c) In terms of this

jumper's weight W, what force does the ground exert on him or her during the jump?

22. •• A short train (an engine plus four cars) is accelerating at 1.10 m/s^2. If the mass of each car is 38,000 kg, and if each car has negligible frictional forces acting on it, what are (a) the force of the engine on the first car, (b) the force of the first car on the second car, (c) the force of the second car on the third car, and (d) the force of the third car on the fourth car? In solving this problem, note the importance of selecting the correct set of cars to isolate as your object.

23. •• A large fish hangs from a spring balance supported from the roof of an elevator. (a) If the elevator has an upward acceleration of 2.45 m/s^2 and the balance reads 60.0 N, what is the true weight of the fish? (b) Under what circumstances will the balance read 35.0 N? (c) What will the balance read if the elevator cable breaks?

24. •• A 750.0-kg boulder is raised from a quarry 125 m deep by a long uniform chain having a mass of 575 kg. This chain is of uniform strength, but at any point it can support a maximum tension no greater than 2.50 times its weight without breaking. (a) What is the maximum acceleration the boulder can have and still get out of the quarry, and (b) how long does it take to be lifted out at maximum acceleration if it started from rest?

25. •• The TGV, France's high-speed train, pulls out of the Lyons station and is accelerating uniformly to its cruising speed. Inside one of the cars, a 3.00 N digital camera is hanging from the luggage compartment by a light, flexible strap that makes a 12.0° angle with the vertical. (a) Make a free-body diagram of this camera. (b) Apply Newton's second law to the camera, and find the acceleration of the train and the tension in the strap.

26. •• Which way and by what angle does the accelerometer in Figure 48 deflect under the following conditions? (a) The cart is moving toward the right with speed increasing at 3.0 m/s^2. (b) The cart is moving toward the left with speed decreasing at 4.5 m/s^2. (c) The cart is moving toward the left with a constant speed of 4.0 m/s.

▲ FIGURE 48 Problem 26.

27. • A skier approaches the base of an icy hill with a speed of 12.5 m/s. The hill slopes upward at 24° above the horizontal. Ignoring all friction forces, find the acceleration of this skier (a) when she is going up the hill, (b) when she has reached her highest point, and (c) after she has started sliding down the hill. In each case, start with a free-body diagram of the skier.

28. • At a construction site, a 22.0 kg bucket of concrete is connected over a very light frictionless pulley to a 375 N box on the roof of a building. (See Figure 49.) There is no appreciable friction on the box, since it is on roller bearings. The box starts from rest. (a) Make free-body diagrams of the bucket and the box. (b) Find the acceleration of the bucket. (c) How fast is the bucket moving after it has fallen 1.50 m (assuming that the box has not yet reached the edge of the roof)?

▲ FIGURE 49 Problem 28.

29. •• Two boxes are connected by a light string that passes over a light, frictionless pulley. One box rests on a frictionless ramp that rises at 30.0° above the horizontal (see Figure 50), and the system is released from rest. (a) Make free-body diagrams of each box. (b) Which way will the 50.0 kg box move, up the plane or down the plane? Or will it even move at all? Show why or why not. (c) Find the acceleration of each box.

▲ FIGURE 50 Problem 29.

3 Frictional Forces

30. • An 80 N box initially at rest is pulled by a horizontal rope on a horizontal table. The coefficients of kinetic and static friction between the box and the table are $\frac{1}{4}$ and $\frac{1}{2}$, respectively. What is the friction force on this box if the pull is (a) 0 N, (b) 25 N, (c) 39 N, (d) 41 N, (e) 150 N?

31. • A box of bananas weighing 40.0 N rests on a horizontal surface. The coefficient of static friction between the box and the surface is 0.40, and the coefficient of kinetic friction is 0.20. (a) If no horizontal force is applied to the box and the box is at rest, how large is the friction force exerted on the box? (b) What is the magnitude of the friction force if a monkey applies a horizontal force of 6.0 N to the box and the box is initially at rest? (c) What minimum horizontal force must the monkey apply to start the box in motion? (d) What minimum horizontal force must the monkey apply to keep the box moving at constant velocity once it has been started?

32. • **Friction at the hip joint.** Figure
BIO 51 shows the bone structure at the hip joint. The bones are normally not in direct contact, but instead are covered with cartilage to reduce friction. The space between them is filled with waterlike synovial fluid, which further decreases friction. Due to this fluid, the coefficient of kinetic friction between the bones can range from 0.0050 to 0.020. (The wide range of values is due to the fact that motion such as running causes more fluid to squirt

▲ FIGURE 51
Problem 32.

between the bones, thereby reducing friction when they strike each other.) Typically, approximately 65% of a person's weight is above the hip—we'll call this the *upper weight*. (a) Show that when a person is simply standing upright, each hip supports half of his upper weight. (b) When a person is walking, each hip now supports up to 2.5 times his upper weight, depending on how fast he is walking. (Recall that when you walk, your weight shifts from one leg to the other and your body comes down fairly hard on each leg.) For a 65 kg person, what is the maximum kinetic friction force at the hip joint if μ_k has its minimum value of 0.0050? (c) As a person gets older, the aging process, as well as osteoarthritis, can alter the composition of the synovial fluid. In the worst case, this fluid could disappear, leaving bone-on-bone contact with a coefficient of kinetic friction of 0.30. What would be the greatest friction force for the walking person in part (b)? The increased friction causes pain and, in addition, wears down the joint even more.

33. ● At a construction site, a pallet of bricks is to be suspended by attaching a rope to it and connecting the other end to a couple of heavy crates on the roof of a building, as shown in Figure 52. The rope pulls horizontally on the lower crate, and the coefficient of static friction between the lower crate and the roof is 0.666. (a) What is the weight of the heaviest pallet of bricks that can be supported this way? Start with appropriate free-body diagrams. (b) What is the friction force on the upper crate under the conditions of part (a)?

▲ **FIGURE 52** Problem 33.

34. ●● Two crates connected by a rope of negligible mass lie on a horizontal surface. (See Figure 53.) Crate A has mass m_A and crate B has mass m_B. The coefficient of kinetic friction between each crate and the surface is μ_k. The crates are pulled to the right at a constant velocity of 3.20 cm/s by a horizontal force $\vec{F}$. In terms of m_A, m_B, and μ_k, calculate (a) the magnitude of the force $\vec{F}$ and (b) the tension in the rope connecting the blocks. Include the free-body diagram or diagrams you used to determine each answer.

▲ **FIGURE 53** Problem 34.

35. ●● A hockey puck leaves a player's stick with a speed of 9.9 m/s and slides 32.0 m before coming to rest. Find the coefficient of friction between the puck and the ice.

36. ●● **Stopping distance of a car.** (a) If the coefficient of kinetic friction between tires and dry pavement is 0.80, what is the shortest distance in which you can stop an automobile by locking the brakes when traveling at 29.1 m/s (about 65 mi/h)? (b) On wet pavement, the coefficient of kinetic friction may be only 0.25. How fast should you drive on wet pavement in order to be able to stop in the same distance as in part (a)? (*Note:* Locking the brakes is *not* the safest way to stop.)

37. ●● An 85-N box of oranges is being pushed across a horizontal floor. As it moves, it is slowing at a constant rate of 0.90 m/s each second. The push force has a horizontal component of 20 N and a vertical component of 25 N downward. Calculate the coefficient of kinetic friction between the box and floor.

38. ●● **Rolling friction.** Two bicycle tires are set rolling with the same initial speed of 3.50 m/s on a long, straight road, and the distance each travels before its speed is reduced by half is measured. One tire is inflated to a pressure of 40 psi and goes 18.1 m; the other is at 105 psi and goes 92.9 m. What is the coefficient of rolling friction μ_r for each? Assume that the net horizontal force is due to rolling friction only.

39. ●● A stockroom worker pushes a box with mass 11.2 kg on a horizontal surface with a constant speed of 3.50 m/s. The coefficients of kinetic and static friction between the box and the surface are 0.200 and 0.450, respectively. (a) What horizontal force must the worker apply to maintain the motion of the box? (b) If the worker stops pushing, what will be the acceleration of the box?

40. ●● The coefficients of static and kinetic friction between a 476 N crate and the warehouse floor are 0.615 and 0.420, respectively. A worker gradually increases his horizontal push against this crate until it just begins to move and from then on

maintains that same maximum push. What is the acceleration of the crate after it has begun to move? Start with a free-body diagram of the crate.

41. ●● **Measuring the coefficients of friction.** One straightforward way to measure the coefficients of friction between a box and a wooden surface is illustrated in Figure 54. The sheet of wood can be raised by pivoting it about one edge. It is first raised to an angle θ_1 (which is measured) for which the box just begins to slide downward. The sheet is then immediately lowered to an angle θ_2 (which is also measured) for which the box slides with constant speed down the sheet. Apply Newton's second law to the box in both cases to find the coefficients of kinetic and static friction between it and the wooden sheet in terms of the measured angles θ_1 and θ_2.

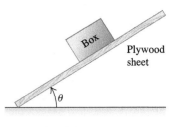

▲ **FIGURE 54** Problem 41.

42. With its wheels locked, a van slides down a hill inclined at 40.0° to the horizontal. Find the acceleration of this van a) if the hill is icy and frictionless, and b) if the coefficient of kinetic friction is 0.20.

43. ● **The Trendelberg position.** In emergencies with major **BIO** blood loss, the doctor will order the patient placed in the Trendelberg position, which is to raise the foot of the bed to get maximum blood flow to the brain. If the coefficient of static friction between the typical patient and the bedsheets is 1.2, what is the maximum angle at which the bed can be tilted with respect to the floor before the patient begins to slide?

44. ●● **Injuries to the spinal column.** In treating spinal injuries, **BIO** it is often necessary to provide some tension along the spinal column to stretch the backbone. One device for doing this is the Stryker frame, illustrated in part (a) of Figure 55. A weight W is attached to the patient (sometimes around a neck collar, as shown in part (b) of the figure), and friction between the person's body and the bed prevents sliding. (a) If the coefficient of static friction between a 78.5 kg patient's body and the bed is 0.75, what is the maximum traction force along the spinal column that W can provide without causing the patient to slide? (b) Under the conditions of maximum traction, what is the tension in each cable attached to the neck collar?

(a)

W

(b)

▲ **FIGURE 55** Problem 44.

45. •• A winch is used to drag a 375 N crate up a ramp at a constant speed of 75 cm/s by means of a rope that pulls parallel to the surface of the ramp. The rope slopes upward at 33° above the horizontal, and the coefficient of kinetic friction between the ramp and the crate is 0.25. (a) What is the tension in the rope? (b) If the rope were suddenly to snap, what would be the acceleration of the crate immediately after the rope broke?

46. •• A toboggan approaches a snowy hill moving at 11.0 m/s. The coefficients of static and kinetic friction between the snow and the toboggan are 0.40 and 0.30, respectively, and the hill slopes upward at 40.0° above the horizontal. Find the acceleration of the toboggan (a) as it is going up the hill and (b) after it has reached its highest point and is sliding down the hill.

47. •• A 25.0-kg box of textbooks rests on a loading ramp that makes an angle α with the horizontal. The coefficient of kinetic friction is 0.25, and the coefficient of static friction is 0.35. (a) As the angle α is increased, find the minimum angle at which the box starts to slip. (b) At this angle, find the acceleration once the box has begun to move. (c) At this angle, how fast will the box be moving after it has slid 5.0 m along the loading ramp?

48. •• A person pushes on a stationary 125 N box with 75 N at 30° below the horizontal, as shown in Figure 56. The coefficient of static friction between the box and the horizontal floor is 0.80. (a) Make a free-body diagram of the box. (b) What is the normal force on the box? (c) What is the friction force on the box? (d) What is the largest the friction force could be? (e) The person now replaces his push with a 75 N pull at 30° above the horizontal. Find the normal force on the box in this case.

▲ FIGURE 56 Problem 48.

49. •• A crate of 45.0-kg tools rests on a horizontal floor. You exert a gradually increasing horizontal push on it and observe that the crate just begins to move when your force exceeds 313 N. After that you must reduce your push to 208 N to keep it moving at a steady 25.0 cm/s. (a) What are the coefficients of static and kinetic friction between the crate and the floor? (b) What push must you exert to give it an acceleration of 1.10 m/s²? (c) Suppose you were performing the same experiment on this crate but were doing it on the moon instead, where the acceleration due to gravity is 1.62 m/s². (i) What magnitude push would cause it to move? (ii) What would its acceleration be if you maintained the push in part (b)?

50. •• You are working for a shipping company. Your job is to stand at the bottom of an 8.0-m-long ramp that is inclined at 37° above the horizontal. You grab packages off a conveyor belt and propel them up the ramp. The coefficient of kinetic friction between the packages and the ramp is $\mu_k = 0.30$. (a) What speed do you need to give a package at the bottom of the ramp so that it has zero speed at the top of the ramp? (b) Your coworker is supposed to grab the packages as they arrive at the top of the ramp, but she misses one and it slides back down. What is its speed when it returns to you?

51. •• The drag coefficient for a spherical raindrop with a radius of 0.415 cm falling at its terminal velocity is 2.43×10^{-5} kg/m. Calculate the raindrop's terminal velocity in m/s.

52. What is the acceleration of a raindrop that has reached half of its terminal velocity? Give your answer in terms of g.

53. •• An object is dropped from rest and encounters air resistance that is proportional to the square of its speed. Sketch qualitative graphs (no numbers) showing (a) the air resistance on this object as a function of its speed, (b) the *net* force on the object as a function of its speed, (c) the *net* force on the object as a function of time, (d) the speed of the object as a function of time, and (e) the acceleration of the object as a function of time.

4 Elastic Forces

54. • You find that if you hang a 1.25 kg weight from a vertical spring, it stretches 3.75 cm. (a) What is the force constant of this spring in N/m? (b) How much mass should you hang from the spring so it will stretch by 8.13 cm from its original, unstretched length?

55. • An unstretched spring is 12.00 cm long. When you hang an 875 g weight from it, it stretches to a length of 14.40 cm. (a) What is the force constant (in N/m) of this spring? (b) What total mass must you hang from the spring to stretch it to a total length of 17.72 cm?

56. • **Heart repair.** A surgeon is using material from a donated
BIO heart to repair a patient's damaged aorta and needs to know the elastic characteristics of this aortal material. Tests performed on a 16.0 cm strip of the donated aorta reveal that it stretches 3.75 cm when a 1.50 N pull is exerted on it. (a) What is the force constant of this strip of aortal material? (b) If the maximum distance it will be able to stretch when it replaces the aorta in the damaged heart is 1.14 cm, what is the greatest force it will be able to exert there?

57. • An "extreme" pogo stick utilizes a spring whose uncompressed length is 46 cm and whose force constant is 1.4×10^4 N/m. A 60-kg enthusiast is jumping on the pogo stick, compressing the spring to a length of only 5.0 cm at the bottom of her jump. Calculate (a) the net upward force on her at the moment the spring reaches its greatest compression and (b) her upward acceleration, in m/s² and g's at that moment.

58. •• A student measures the force required to stretch a spring by various amounts and makes the graph shown in Figure 57, which plots this force as a function of the distance the spring has stretched. (a) Does this spring obey Hooke's law? How do you know? (b) What is the force constant of the spring, in N/m? (c) What force would be needed to stretch the spring a distance of 17 cm from its unstretched length, assuming that it continues to obey Hooke's law?

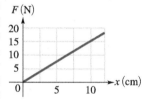

▲ FIGURE 57 Problem 58.

59. •• A student hangs various masses from a spring and records the resulting distance the spring has stretched. She then uses her data to construct the graph shown in Figure 58, which plots the mass hung from the spring as a function of the distance the mass

▲ FIGURE 58 Problem 59.

caused the spring to stretch beyond its unstretched length. (a) Does this spring obey Hooke's law? How do you know? (b) What is the force constant of the spring, in N/m? (c) By how much will the spring have stretched if you hang a 2.35 kg mass from it, assuming that it continues to obey Hooke's law?

60. • Three identical 6.40 kg masses are hung by three identical springs, as shown in Figure 59. Each spring has a force constant of 7.80 kN/m and was 12.0 cm long before any masses were attached to it. (a) Make a free-body diagram of each mass. (b) How long is each spring when hanging as shown? (*Hint:* First isolate only the bottom mass. Then treat the bottom two masses as a system. Finally, treat all three masses as a system.)

▲ **FIGURE 59** Problem 60.

61. • A light spring having a force constant of 125 N/m is used to pull a 9.50 kg sled on a horizontal frictionless ice rink. If the sled has an acceleration of 2.00 m/s², by how much does the spring stretch if it pulls on the sled (a) horizontally, (b) at 30.0° above the horizontal?

62. •• In the previous problem, what would the answers in both cases be if there were friction and the coefficient of kinetic friction between the sled and the ice were 0.200?

General Problems

63. •• **Prevention of hip injuries.** People (especially the elderly) **BIO** who are prone to falling can wear hip pads to cushion the impact on their hip from a fall. Experiments have shown that if the speed at impact can be reduced to 1.3 m/s or less, the hip will usually not fracture. Let us investigate the worst-case scenario, in which a 55 kg person completely loses her footing (such as on icy pavement) and falls a distance of 1.0 m, the distance from her hip to the ground. We shall assume that the person's entire body has the same acceleration, which, in reality, would not quite be true. (a) With what speed does her hip reach the ground? (b) A typical hip pad can reduce the person's speed to 1.3 m/s over a distance of 2.0 cm. Find the acceleration (assumed to be constant) of this person's hip while she is slowing down and the force the pad exerts on it. (c) The force in part (b) is very large. To see if it is likely to cause injury, calculate how long it lasts.

64. •• **Modeling elastic hip pads.** In the previous problem, we **BIO** assumed constant acceleration (and hence a constant force) due to the hip pad. But of course, such a pad would most likely be somewhat elastic. Assuming that the force you found in the previous problem was the maximum force over the period of impact with the ground, and that the hip pad is elastic enough to obey Hooke's law, calculate the force constant of this pad, using appropriate data from the previous problem.

65. •• You've attached a bungee cord to a wagon and are using it to pull your little sister while you take her for a jaunt. The bungee's unstretched length is 1.3 m, and you happen to know that your little sister weighs 220 N and the wagon weighs 75 N. Crossing a street, you accelerate from rest to your normal walking speed of 1.5 m/s in 2.0 s, and you notice that while you're accelerating, the bungee's length increases to about 2.0 m. What's the force constant of the bungee cord, assuming it obeys Hooke's law?

66. •• **Atwood's Machine.** A 15.0-kg load of bricks hangs from one end of a rope that passes over a small, frictionless pulley. A 28.0-kg counterweight is suspended from the other end of the

rope, as shown in Fig. 60. The system is released from rest. (a) Draw two free-body diagrams, one for the load of bricks and one for the counterweight. (b) What is the magnitude of the upward acceleration of the load of bricks? (c) What is the tension in the rope while the load is moving? How does the tension compare to the weight of the load of bricks? To the weight of the counterweight?

28.0 kg

15.0 kg

▲ **FIGURE 60** Problem 66.

67. • **Mountaineering.** Figure 61 shows a technique called *rappelling*, used by mountaineers for descending vertical rock faces. The climber sits in a rope seat, and the rope slides through a friction device attached to the seat. Suppose that the rock is perfectly smooth (i.e., there is no friction) and that the climber's feet push horizontally onto the rock. If the climber's weight is 600.0 N, find (a) the tension in the rope and (b) the force the climber's feet exert on the rock face. Start with a free-body diagram of the climber.

15°

▲ **FIGURE 61** Problem 67.

68. •• Two identical, perfectly smooth 71.2 N bowling balls 21.7 cm in diameter are hung together from the same hook in the ceiling by means of two thin, light wires, as shown in Figure 62, find (a) the tension in each wire and (b) the force the balls exert on each other.

69. •• **Stay awake!** An astro- **BIO** naut is inside a 2.25 × 10⁶ kg rocket that is blasting off vertically from the launch pad. You want this rocket to reach the speed of sound (331 m/s) as quickly as possible, but you also do not want the astronaut to black out. Medical tests have shown that astronauts are in danger of blacking out for an acceleration greater than 4g. (a) What is the maximum thrust the engines of the rocket can have to just barely avoid blackout? Start with a free-body diagram of the rocket. (b) What force, in terms of her weight W, does the rocket exert on the astronaut? Start with a free-body diagram of the astronaut. (c) What is the shortest time it can take the rocket to reach the speed of sound?

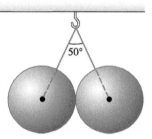

50°

▲ **FIGURE 62** Problem 68.

70. •• The stretchy silk of a certain species of spider has a force **BIO** constant of 1.10 mN/cm. The spider, whose mass is 15 mg,

has attached herself to a branch as shown in Figure 63. Calculate (a) the tension in each of the three strands of silk and (b) the distance each strand is stretched beyond its normal length.

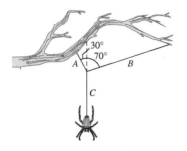

▲ **FIGURE 63** Problem 70.

71. •• Block *A* in Figure 64 weighs 60.0 N. The coefficient of static friction between the block and the surface on which it rests is 0.25. The weight *w* is 12.0 N and the system remains at rest. (a) Find the friction force exerted on block *A*. (b) Find the maximum weight *w* for which the system will remain at rest.

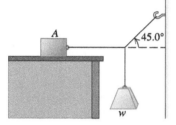

▲ **FIGURE 64** Problem 71.

72. •• **Friction in an elevator.** You are riding in an elevator on the way to the 18th floor of your dormitory. The elevator is accelerating upward with $a = 1.90 \text{ m/s}^2$. Beside you is the box containing your new computer; the box and its contents have a total mass of 28.0 kg. While the elevator is accelerating upward, you push horizontally on the box to slide it at constant speed toward the elevator door. If the coefficient of kinetic friction between the box and the elevator floor is $\mu_k = 0.32$, what magnitude of force must you apply?

73. •• A student attaches a series of weights to a tendon and
BIO measures the *total length* of the tendon for each weight. He then uses the data he has gathered to construct the graph shown in Figure 65, giving the weight as a function of the length of the tendon. (a) Does this tendon obey Hooke's law? How do you know? (b) What is the force constant (in N/m) for the tendon? (c) What weight should you hang from the tendon to make it stretch by 8.0 cm from its unstretched length?

▲ **FIGURE 65** Problem 73.

74. •• A 65.0-kg parachutist falling vertically at a speed of
BIO 6.30 m/s impacts the ground, which brings him to a complete stop in a distance of 0.92 m (roughly half of his height).

Assuming constant acceleration after his feet first touch the ground, what is the average force exerted on the parachutist by the ground?

75. •• **Mars Exploration Rover landings.** In January 2004 the Mars Exploration Rover spacecraft landed on the surface of the Red Planet, where the acceleration due to gravity is 0.379 what it is on earth. The descent of this 827 kg vehicle occurred in several stages, three of which are outlined here. In Stage I, friction with the Martian atmosphere reduced the speed from 19,300 km/h to 1600 km/h in a 4.0 min interval. In Stage II, a parachute reduced the speed from 1600 km/h to 321 km/h in 94 s, and in Stage III, which lasted 2.5 s, retrorockets fired to reduce the speed from 321 km/h to zero. As part of your solution to this problem, make a free-body diagram of the rocket during each stage. Assuming constant acceleration, find the force exerted on the spacecraft (a) by the atmosphere during Stage I, (b) by the parachute during Stage II, and (c) by the retrorockets during Stage III.

76. •• Block *A* in Figure 66 weighs 1.20 N and block *B* weighs 3.60 N. The coefficient of kinetic friction between all surfaces is 0.300. Find the magnitude of the horizontal force $\vec{F}$ necessary to drag block *B* to the left at a constant speed of 2.50 cm/s (a) if *A* rests on *B* and moves with it (Figure 66a); (b) if *A* is held at rest by a string (Figure 66b). (c) In part (a), what is the friction force on block *A*?

(a)   (b)

▲ **FIGURE 66** Problem 76.

77. •• **Crash of the Genesis Mission.** You are assigned the task of designing an accelerometer to be used inside a rocket ship in outer space. Your equipment consists of a very light spring that is 15.0 cm long when no forces act to stretch or compress it, plus a 1.10 kg weight. One end of this spring will be attached to a friction-

▲ **FIGURE 67** Problem 77.

free tabletop, while the 1.10 kg weight is attached to the other end, as shown in Figure 67. (Such a spring-type accelerometer system was actually used in the ill-fated Genesis Mission, which collected particles of the solar wind. Unfortunately, because it was installed *backward,* it did not measure the acceleration correctly during the craft's descent to earth. As a result, the parachute failed to open and the capsule crashed on Sept. 8, 2004.) (a) What should be the force constant of the spring so that it will stretch by 1.10 cm when the rocket accelerates forward at 2.50 m/s²? Start with a free-body diagram of the weight. (b) What is the acceleration (magnitude *and* direction) of the rocket if the spring is *compressed* by 2.30 cm?

78. •• A block with mass m_1 is placed on an inclined plane with slope angle α and is connected to a second hanging block with mass m_2 by a cord passing over a small, frictionless pulley (Fig. 68). The coefficient of static friction is μ_s and the coefficient of kinetic friction is μ_k. (a) Find the mass m_2 for which block m_1 moves up the plane at constant speed once it is set in motion. (b) Find the mass m_2 for which block m_1 moves down the plane at constant speed once it is set in motion. (c) For what range of values of m_2 will the blocks remain at rest if they are released from rest?

▲ **FIGURE 68** Problem 78.

79. •• A pickup truck is carrying a toolbox, but the rear gate of the truck is missing, so the box will slide out if it is set moving. The coefficients of kinetic and static friction between the box and the bed of the truck are 0.355 and 0.650, respectively. Starting from rest, what is the shortest time this truck could accelerate uniformly to 30.0 m/s ($\approx$ 60 mph) without causing the box to slide. Include a free-body diagram of the toolbox as part of your solution. (*Hint:* First use Newton's second law to find the maximum acceleration that static friction can give the box, and then solve for the time required to reach 30.0 m/s.)

80. •• **Accident analysis.** You have been called to testify as an expert witness in a trial involving an automobile accident. The speed limit on the highway where the accident occurred was 40 mph. The driver of the car slammed on his brakes, locking his wheels, and left skid marks as the car skidded to a halt. You measure the length of these skid marks to be 219 ft, 9 in., and determine that the coefficient of kinetic friction between the wheels and the pavement at the time of the accident was 0.40. How fast was this car traveling (to the nearest number of mph) just before the driver hit his brakes? Was he guilty of speeding?

81. •• A window washer pushes his scrub brush up a vertical window at constant speed by applying a force $\vec{F}$ as shown in Fig. 69. The brush weighs 12.0 N and the coefficient of kinetic friction is $\mu_k = 0.150$. Calculate (a) the magnitude of the force $\vec{F}$ and (b) the normal force exerted by the window on the brush.

82. • **A fractured tibia.** While a
BIO fractured tibia (the larger of the two major lower leg bones in mammals) is healing, it must be held horizontal and kept under some tension so that the bones will heal properly to prevent a permanent limp. One way to do this is to support the leg by using a variation of the Russell traction apparatus. (See Figure 70.) The lower leg

▲ **FIGURE 69** Problem 81.

(including the foot) of a particular patient weighs 51.5 N, all of which must be supported by the traction apparatus. (a) What must be the mass of W, shown in the figure? (b) What traction force does the apparatus provide along the direction of the leg?

83. • You push with a horizontal force of 50 N against a 20 N box, pressing it against a rough vertical wall to hold it in place. The coefficients of kinetic and static friction between this box and the wall are 0.20 and 0.50, respectively. (a) Make a free-body diagram of this box. (b) What is the friction force on the box? (c) How hard would you have to press for the box to slide downward with a uniform speed of 10.5 cm/s?

▲ **FIGURE 70** Problem 82.

84. •• Some sliding rocks approach the base of a hill with a speed of 12 m/s. The hill rises at 36° above the horizontal and has coefficients of kinetic and static friction of 0.45 and 0.65, respectively, with these rocks. Start each part of your solution to this problem with a free-body diagram. (a) Find the acceleration of the rocks as they slide up the hill. (b) Once a rock reaches its highest point, will it stay there or slide down the hill? If it stays there, show why. If it slides down, find its acceleration on the way down.

85. •• **Elevator design.** You are designing an elevator for a hospital. The force exerted on a passenger by the floor of the elevator is not to exceed 1.60 times the passenger's weight. The elevator accelerates upward with constant acceleration for a distance of 3.0 m and then starts to slow down. What is the maximum speed of the elevator?

86. •• At night while it is dark, a driver inadvertently parks his car on a drawbridge. Some time later, the bridge must be raised to allow a boat to pass through. The coefficients of friction between the bridge and the car's tires are $\mu_s = 0.750$ and $\mu_k = 0.550$. Start each part of your solution to this problem with a free-body diagram of the car. (a) At what angle will the car just start to slide? (b) If the bridge attendant sees the car suddenly start to slide and immediately turns off the bridge's motor, what will be the car's acceleration after it has begun to move?

87. •• A block is placed against the vertical front of a cart as shown in Figure 71. What acceleration must the cart have in order that block A does not fall? The coefficient of static friction between the block and the cart is μ_s.

▲ **FIGURE 71** Problem 87.

88. •• **The monkey and her bananas.** A 20 kg monkey has a firm hold on a light rope that passes over a frictionless pulley and is attached to a 20 kg bunch of bananas (Figure 72). The monkey looks up, sees the bananas, and starts to climb the rope to get them. (a) As the monkey climbs, do the bananas move up, move down, or remain at rest? (b) As the monkey climbs, does the distance between the monkey and the bananas decrease, increase, or remain constant? (c) The monkey releases her hold on the rope. What happens to the distance between the monkey and the bananas while she is falling? (d) Before reaching the ground, the monkey grabs the rope to stop her fall. What do the bananas do?

▲ FIGURE 72
Problem 88.

Passage Problems

BIO Back to the toboggan! Consider the motion of a toboggan filled with students flying down a hill. Our clever physics students have now designed a sail system that they attach to the toboggan. The sail uses the force of the wind, which blows up the hill at a constant speed to allow them to ride up the hill as well as down. The slope of the hill is the angle α; the combined weight of the students, the toboggan, and the sail is w.

89. If the toboggan is well waxed so that there is no friction, what force does the sail have to provide to move the student-filled toboggan up the hill at a constant velocity (once it gets started)?
 A. $g\sin\alpha$
 B. $w\sin\alpha$
 C. w
 D. $wg\sin\alpha$

90. If the wind were to change direction and blow downhill, what would be the acceleration of the toboggan?
 A. $2w\sin\alpha$
 B. $w\sin\alpha$
 C. $2g\sin\alpha$
 D. $g\sin\alpha$

91. The wax wears off so that the coefficient of kinetic friction is now μ_k. How much force does the sail now have to provide for a constant velocity ride back up the hill (once it gets started)?
 A. $\mu_k g\sin\alpha$
 B. $\mu_k w\sin\alpha$
 C. $\mu_k w\cos\alpha$
 D. $w\sin\alpha + \mu_k w\cos\alpha$
 E. $w\sin\alpha - \mu_k w\cos\alpha$

ANSWERS TO SELECTED PROBLEMS

Conceptual Questions

1. No, the object is in equilibrium only if the vector sum of all of the forces on it is zero. With only one applied force, the net force cannot be zero.
5. The coefficient of static friction is much less for icy pavement.
7. The vertical component of the vector $\vec{T}$ must equal the weight of the object. Since the magnitude of any vector is greater than either of its components, T must be greater than the weight of the object.
9. With no friction, the weight W will accelerate downward when the system is released. This downward acceleration is possible only if a net downward force exists. The downward force W on the weight must therefore be greater than the upward tensile force in the wire. The tension will be less than W.
11. (a) No, without friction, there would be no horizontal force on you. (b) Yes, you could push down on the rung of a ladder, and the ladder would exert an upward normal force on you. (c) No, the pole could not exert a vertical force, parallel to the pole, without friction. (d) Yes, you could push down on the ground, and the ground would push up on you. (e) No, without friction, the ground could not exert the horizontal force on the wheels necessary for traction. (f) No, without friction, there would be no horizontal force on the car; therefore, the car could travel only in a straight line.

Multiple-Choice Problems

1. A
3. B
5. A
7. B
9. A
11. C
13. D

Problems

1. (a) 3.6 kg (b) 410 kg (c) 6×10^3 kg
3. (a) 25.0 N (b) 50.0 N
5. (a) 2.54×10^3 N (b) $1.01°$
7. (a) N/m^2; $kg/(m \cdot s^2)$ (b) 25 cm^2
9. (a) 47.0 N (b) 85.2 N
11. (b) 649 N; 314 N; 813 N (c) no
13. (b) 2.65 N (c) 0.193 N
15. (a) $w\sin\alpha$ (b) $2w\sin\alpha$ (c) $w\cos\alpha$ for each block
17. (a) 4.41×10^4 N (b) 60 times the weight
19. $250W$
21. (a) 3.4 m/s (c) $2.2W$
23. (a) 48.0 N (b) $a = 2.65$ m/s², downward (c) 0
25. (b) 2.08 m/s²; 3.07 N
27. (a) 4.0 m/s², down the slope (b) 4.0 m/s², down the slope (c) 4.0 m/s², down the slope
29. (b) up the ramp (c) 50.0 kg box: 0.612 m/s² up the ramp; 30.0 kg box: 0.612 m/s² downward
31. (a) 0 (b) 6.0 N (c) 16.0 N (d) 8.0 N
33. (a) 266 lb (b) 0
35. 0.16
37. 0.25

39. (a) 22.0 N (b) 1.96 m/s², opposite to the motion
41. $\mu_s = \tan\theta_1$; $\mu_k = \tan\theta_2$
43. 50°
45. (a) 283 N (b) 7.39 m/s²
47. (a) 19.3° (b) 0.92 m/s² (c) 3 m/s
49. (a) 0.710, 0.472 (b) 258 N (c) (i) 51.8 N (ii) 4.97 m/s²
55. (a) 357 N/m (b) 2.08 kg
57. (a) 5100 N (b) 85 m/s², 8.70,
59. (a) yes; graph of m versus x is a straight line (b) 24.5 N/m (c) 94 cm
61. (a) 15.2 cm (b) 17.6 cm
63. (a) 4.4 m/s (b) 440 m/s², upward; 2.5×10^4 N (c) 7.0 ms
65. 32 N/m
67. (a) 621 N (b) 161 N
69. (a) 1.10×10^8 N (b) $5W$ (c) 8.4 s
71. (a) 12.0 N (b) 15.0 N
73. (a) yes; the graph of W versus L is a straight line (b) 50.0 N/m (c) 4.0 N
75. (a) 2.0×10^4 N (b) 6.19×10^3 N (c) 3.26×10^4 N
77. (a) 250 N/m (b) 5.23 m/s²; in the backward direction
79. 4.71 s
81. (a) 16.9 N (b) 10.1 N
83. (b) 20 N (c) 100 N
85. 5.9 m/s
87. g/μ_s

Passage Problems

89. B
91. D

171

Circular Motion and Gravitation

Clive Mason/Getty Images

In this chapter, we'll continue our study of dynamics, concentrating especially on *circular motion*. Objects move in circular paths in a wide variety of situations, such as cars on racetracks, rotating machine parts, and the motions of planets and satellites, so it's worthwhile to study this special class of motions in detail. We also return to *gravitational* interactions for a detailed study of Newton's law of gravitation. This law plays a central role in planet and satellite motion, and it also provides a fuller understanding of the concept of weight than does the formula $w = mg$ by itself.

Why do these skaters lean deeply into their turn? They do it so that the force of the ice on their skates has a large component directed inward toward the center of the turn. In this chapter, we will learn why turning motions require inward-directed forces.

1 Force in Circular Motion

Here's a brief summary of what we know about the kinematics of circular motion. When a particle moves along any curved path, the direction of its velocity must change. Thus, it *must* have a component of acceleration perpendicular to its path, even if its speed is constant.

In particular, when a particle moves in a circular path with constant speed, there is *no* component of acceleration parallel to the instantaneous velocity (tangent to the path); otherwise the speed would change. Motion with constant speed in a circular path (either a complete circle or a fraction of a circle) is called *uniform circular motion*. In this motion, the particle's acceleration at each instant is directed toward the center of the circle (perpendicular to the instantaneous velocity), as shown in Figure 1. The magnitude a_{rad} of the acceleration is constant

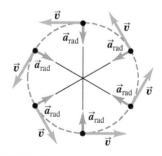

▲ **FIGURE 1** The kinematics of uniform circular motion.

From Chapter 6 of *College Physics*, Ninth Edition, Hugh D. Young. Copyright © 2012 by Pearson Education, Inc. Published by Pearson Addison-Wesley. All rights reserved.

Cornell University Press

and is given in terms of the speed v and the radius R of the circle by the following equation:

Acceleration in uniform circular motion

When an object moves at constant speed around a circle (or an arc of a circle) the magnitude of its acceleration (a_{rad}) is proportional to the square of its speed v and inversely proportional to the radius R of the circle:

$$a_{\text{rad}} = \frac{v^2}{R}.$$

ActivPhysics 4.1: Magnitude of Centripetal Acceleration
ActivPhysics 4.5: Car Circles a Track

The subscript "rad" is a reminder that at each point the direction of the acceleration is radially inward toward the center of the circle, perpendicular to the instantaneous velocity. This acceleration is sometimes called *centripetal acceleration.*

We can also express the centripetal acceleration a_{rad} in terms of the **period** T, the time for one revolution. The speed v is equal to the distance ($2\pi R$) the particle travels in one revolution (i.e., the circumference of the circle), divided by the time T, so

$$v = \frac{2\pi R}{T}. \qquad \text{(relation of period to speed)} \qquad (1)$$

Expressed in terms of the period,

$$a_{\text{rad}} = \frac{4\pi^2 R}{T^2}. \qquad (2)$$

A ball whirls on a string attached to a rotating peg in the center of a frictionless table (viewed from above). Suddenly, the string breaks, releasing the radial force on the ball.

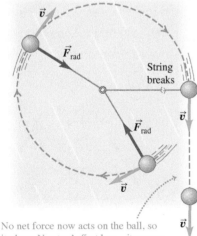

No net force now acts on the ball, so it obeys Newton's first law—it moves straight at constant velocity.

▲ **FIGURE 2** An object moves in a circle because of a centripetal net force.

NOTE ▶ In earlier chapters, we've used T to denote tension in a rope or string. Here we use T to denote the period of a periodic motion, including uniform circular motion. From here on, we'll usually denote tension by F_T. ◄

Like all other motions of an object that can be modeled as a particle, circular motion is governed by Newton's second law. The object's acceleration toward the center of the circle must be caused by a force, or several forces, such that their vector sum $\Sigma \vec{F}$ is a vector that is always directed toward the center, with constant magnitude. The magnitude of the radial acceleration is given by $a_{\text{rad}} = v^2/R$, so the magnitude of the net inward radial force F_{net} on an object with mass m must be equal to the object's mass m, multiplied by this acceleration:

$$F_{\text{net}} = m\frac{v^2}{R}. \qquad \text{(relation of net force to acceleration)} \qquad (3)$$

Here's a familiar example: We fasten a small object, such as a ball, to a string and whirl it in a horizontal circle (Figure 2). To keep the ball moving in a circle,

▶ Application **Slip slidin' away.** When a car rounds a curve on a level surface, the centripetal force that keeps it moving in a circle is provided by the friction force of the road on the tires. For a bobsledder racing on a frozen track, friction is minimal, and level turns are impossible. Therefore, the curves are steeply and precisely banked. The normal force of the track presses on the sled, providing the necessary horizontal centripetal force. This force allows sharp, nearly frictionless turns at speeds of over 120 km/hr and helped Jill Bakken and Vonetta Flowers win the gold medal at the 2002 Winter Olympics—the first USA bobsledding medal since 1956.

Jed Jacobsohn/Getty Images

the string has to pull constantly toward the center. If the string breaks, then the inward force no longer acts, and the ball moves off in a direction tangent to the circle—not radially outward.

When several forces act on an object in uniform circular motion, their *vector sum* must be a vector with magnitude given by Equation 3 and direction always toward the center of the circle. The net force magnitude in Equation 3 is sometimes called *centripetal force.* This term tends to imply that such a force is somehow different from ordinary forces, and it really isn't. The term *centripetal* refers to the fact that, in uniform circular motion, the direction of the net force that causes the acceleration toward the center must also point toward the center. In the equation $\sum \vec{F} = m\vec{a}$, the sum of the forces must include only the real physical forces—pushes or pulls exerted by strings, rods, gravitation, and so on. The quantity $m(v^2/R)$ does *not* appear in $\sum \vec{F}$, but rather in the $m\vec{a}$ side of the equation.

Two cars on a curving road

A small car with mass m and a large car with mass $2m$ drive around a highway curve of radius R with the same speed v. As they travel around the curve, their accelerations are

A. equal.
B. along the direction of motion.
C. in the ratio of 2 to 1.
D. zero.

SOLUTION The equation $a_{rad} = \dfrac{v^2}{R}$ gives the acceleration of an object moving with uniform speed v in a circular path of radius R. The acceleration depends only on the speed and the radius. Both cars have the *same* speed and radius, so both must have the same acceleration. The correct answer is A. Because their masses are different, different forces are required for the two cars, even though their accelerations are the same. Answers B and D are certainly not right: The acceleration is not zero (otherwise the cars would move in a straight line), nor is it along the direction of motion (otherwise the speed would increase or decrease).

Skateboarder takes the hills

The following pictures show a skateboarder (seen from the side) moving along a straight or curved track.

Which picture is consistent with the free-body diagram shown in Figure 3?

SOLUTION Force $\vec{F}$ is the net normal force of the track on the skateboard wheels. Force $\vec{w}$ has a larger magnitude than force $\vec{F}$. The net force is directed downward, so the acceleration must also

▲ **FIGURE 3**

be downward. In A, there is no vertical component of acceleration, so this choice cannot be correct. In B, the acceleration is upward, toward the center of the circular path. This would require a net upward force, not downward. The center of the circular path in C is downward from the ball. The acceleration is downward (toward the center), requiring a net downward force, as in Figure 3. The correct picture is C.

PROBLEM-SOLVING STRATEGY 1 Circular motion

The strategies for dynamics problems are equally applicable here, and we suggest that you reread them before studying the examples that follow.

NOTE ▶ A serious peril in circular-motion problems is the temptation to regard $m(v^2/R)$ as a *force*, as though the object's circular motion somehow generates an extra force in addition to the real physical forces exerted by strings, contact with other bodies, gravitation, or whatever. *Resist this temptation!* The quantity $m(v^2/R)$ is *not* a force; it corresponds to the $m\vec{a}$ side of $\Sigma\vec{F} = m\vec{a}$ and *must not* appear in $\Sigma\vec{F}$. It may help to draw the free-body diagram with colored pencils, using one color for the forces and a different color for the acceleration. Then, in the $\Sigma\vec{F} = m\vec{a}$ equations, write the force terms in the force color and the $m(v^2/R)$ term in the acceleration color. This may sound silly, but if it helps, do it! ◀

EXAMPLE 1 Model airplane on a string

Suppose you fly a propeller-driven model airplane on a 5.00 m string in a horizontal circle. The airplane, which has a mass of 0.500 kg, flies level and at constant speed and makes one revolution every 4.00 seconds. How hard must you pull on the string to keep the plane flying in a circle?

SOLUTION

SET UP Figure 4 shows our sketches. For the free-body diagram, we assume that the string has negligible mass, so that the force you exert on it equals the tension force it exerts on the plane (which keeps the plane moving in a circle). The plane flies horizontally, so its weight must be countered by an upward lift force from its wings. Thus, the net force is the tension from the string. (The plane also encounters drag from the air and thrust from its propeller, neither of which is shown in the plane of our free-body diagram. However, since the plane travels at constant speed, these forces also sum to zero.)

SOLVE We first find the airplane's centripetal acceleration and then use Newton's second law to find the tension force F_T. We begin by calculating the plane's speed v, using Equation 1 and the period T and radius R given:

$$v = \frac{2\pi R}{T} = \frac{2(3.14)(5.00 \text{ m})}{(4.00 \text{ s})}$$
$$= 7.85 \text{ m/s}, \quad \text{(speed of airplane in circular path)}$$

We now use this value to calculate the centripetal acceleration:

$$a_{\text{rad}} = \frac{v^2}{R} = \frac{(7.85 \text{ m/s})^2}{(5.00 \text{ m})} = 12.3 \text{ m/s}^2. \quad \text{(acceleration in circular motion)}$$

Alternatively, we could use Equation 2 to find a_{rad}:

$$a_{\text{rad}} = \frac{4\pi^2 R}{T^2} = \frac{4\pi^2(5.00 \text{ m})}{(4.00 \text{ s})^2} = 12.3 \text{ m/s}^2.$$

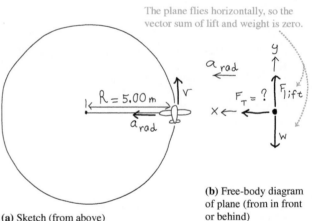

The plane flies horizontally, so the vector sum of lift and weight is zero.

(a) Sketch (from above)

(b) Free-body diagram of plane (from in front or behind)

▲ **FIGURE 4** Our diagrams for this problem.

Finally, we use Newton's second law to calculate the radial force necessary to produce this centripetal acceleration:

$$\Sigma F_x = F_T = ma_{\text{rad}} = (0.500 \text{ kg})(12.3 \text{ m/s}^2) = 6.15 \text{ N}.$$

This is the magnitude of force exerted by the string on the airplane; it is also the magnitude of force you have to exert on the string to keep the airplane flying in its circular path.

REFLECT The free-body diagram shows that the force on an object moving in a circle at constant speed is inward (toward the center of the circle), *not* outward.

Practice Problem: What if the string you are using is rated for no more than 50 N (approx 10 lb). How fast could you fly your model plane before the string breaks? *Answer:* 22.4 m/s.

EXAMPLE 2 **At the end of the tether**

A tetherball is attached to a swivel in the ceiling by a light cord of length L. When the ball is hit by a paddle, it swings in a horizontal circle with constant speed v, and the cord makes a constant angle β with the vertical direction. The ball goes through one revolution in time T. Assuming that T, the mass m, and the length L of rope are known, derive algebraic expressions for the tension F_T in the cord and the angle β.

SOLUTION

SET UP Figure 5 shows our diagrams. Two forces act on the ball: its weight $\vec{w}$ and the tension force $\vec{F}_T$ exerted by the cord. In our free-body diagram, we point the x axis toward the center of the circle (in the direction of the centripetal acceleration a_{rad}), and we replace the tension force by its x and y components: $F_x = F_T\sin\beta$ and $F_y = F_T\cos\beta$, respectively. The y components of force sum to zero, so the net force on the ball is the x component of tension, which acts toward the center of the ball's circular path.

SOLVE Because the period T is known, we express a_{rad} in terms of T and the radius R of the circle, using Equation 2: $a_{rad} = 4\pi^2 R/T^2$. (Note that the radius of the circular path is $L\sin\beta$, not L.)

To find F_T, we use Newton's second law for the x component of net force:

$$\Sigma F_x = ma_x = ma_{rad}, \qquad F_T\sin\beta = m\frac{4\pi^2 R}{T^2}.$$

Next, we substitute the expression for the radius R of the circle $(R = L\sin\beta)$ into the preceding equation:

$$F_T\sin\beta = m\frac{4\pi^2(L\sin\beta)}{T^2}.$$

The factor $\sin\beta$ divides out, and we get

$$F_T = m\frac{4\pi^2 L}{T^2}.$$

We're halfway home; the foregoing equation gives the rope tension F_T in terms of known quantities. To obtain an expression for the angle β, we use Newton's second law for the y component of net force. (Remember that this component must be zero $(\Sigma F_y = 0)$, because there is no y component of acceleration.) Newton's second law yields

$$\Sigma F_y = F_T\cos\beta + (-mg) = 0.$$

We substitute our expression for F_T into this equation to get

$$m\frac{4\pi^2 L}{T^2}\cos\beta + (-mg) = 0, \qquad \cos\beta = \frac{gT^2}{4\pi^2 L}.$$

So we've succeeded in expressing the tension F_T and the cosine of the angle β in terms of known quantities.

REFLECT For a given length L, $\cos\beta$ decreases and β increases as T becomes smaller and the ball makes more revolutions per second. The angle can never be 90°, however; that would require that $T = 0$, $F_T = \infty$, and $v = \infty$. The relationship between T and β doesn't contain the *mass* of the ball, but the force magnitude F_T is directly proportional to m. When β is small, F_T is approximately equal to the ball's weight, $\cos\beta$ is approximately unity, and the expressions we found above give the approximate expression $T = 2\pi\sqrt{(L/g)}$.

Practice Problem: What is the speed v of the ball if $T = 2.0$ s and $L = 2.0$ m? *Answer:* 5.5 m/s.

(a) The situation (b) The forces on the ball (c) Free-body diagram of the ball

▲ **FIGURE 5**

NOTE ▶ You may be tempted to add an extra outward force to the forces in Figure 5b, to "keep the object out there" at angle β or to "keep it in equilibrium." You may have heard the term *centrifugal force;* "centrifugal means" "fleeing from the center." Resist that temptation! First, the object *doesn't* stay "out there"; it is in constant motion around its circular path. Its velocity is constantly changing in direction—it accelerates—so it is *not* in equilibrium. Second, if there *were* an additional outward ("centrifugal") force to balance the inward force, there would then be *no* net inward force to cause the circular motion, and the object would move in a straight line, not a circle. In an inertial frame of reference, there is no such thing as centrifugal force, and we promise not to mention this term again. ◄

EXAMPLE 3   **Rounding a flat curve**

A car rounds a flat, unbanked curve with radius R. **(a)** If the coefficient of static friction between tires and road is μ_s, derive an expression for the maximum speed v_{max} at which the driver can take the curve without sliding. **(b)** What is the maximum speed if $R = 250$ m and $\mu_s = 0.90$?

SOLUTION

SET UP Figure 6 shows the situation, plus a free-body diagram for the car. As in the preceding example, we point the x axis toward the center. Note that the friction between a rolling wheel and the pavement is *static* friction, because the portion of the wheel in contact with the pavement doesn't slide relative to the pavement. (If the wheel slides or skids, however, the friction force is kinetic.) This friction force f_s is responsible for the car's centripetal acceleration $a_{rad} = v^2/R$; it points toward the center of the circle, in the x direction. In the y direction, the car's weight and the normal force on the car sum to zero.

SOLVE Part (a): The component equations from Newton's second law are

$$f_s = m\frac{v^2}{R}, \qquad n + (-mg) = 0.$$

In the first equation, f_s is the force *needed* to keep the car moving in its circular path at a given speed v; this force increases with v. But the maximum friction force *available* is $f_s = \mu_s n = \mu_s mg$; this limitation determines the car's maximum speed v_{max}. When we equate the maximum friction force available to the force mv^2/R required for the circular motion, we find that

$$\mu_s mg = m\frac{v_{max}^2}{R} \quad \text{and} \quad v_{max} = \sqrt{\mu_s gR}.$$

Part (b): If $\mu_s = 0.90$ and $R = 250$ m, then

$$v_{max} = \sqrt{(0.90)(9.8 \text{ m/s}^2)(250 \text{ m})} = 47 \text{ m/s},$$

or about 105 mi/h.

REFLECT If the car travels around the curve at less than v_{max}, f_s is less than $\mu_s n$, but it is still true that $f_s = mv^2/R$. If the car is moving at more than v_{max}, not enough friction is available to provide the needed centripetal acceleration. Then the car skids. Because the kinetic friction acting on skidding tires is less than the static friction acting before the car skids, a car always skids toward the outside of the curve.

It's possible to bank a curve so that at one certain speed no friction at all is needed. Then a car moving at just the right speed can round the curve even on wet ice with Teflon® tires. Airplanes *always* bank at this angle when making turns, and bobsled racing depends on the same idea. We'll explore the banking of curves in Example 4.

Practice Problem: What is the friction force on a 1200 kg car if it rounds a curve with radius 150 m at a speed of 25 m/s? What minimum coefficient of friction is needed?

Answers: 5000 N, 0.43.

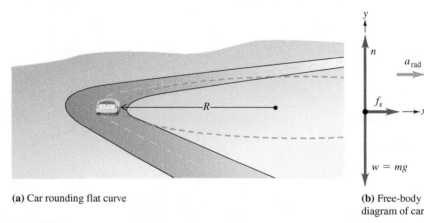

(a) Car rounding flat curve

(b) Free-body diagram of car

▲ FIGURE 6

Quantitative Analysis 3

Speeding up on the curves

A frictional force f_s provides the centripetal force as a car goes around an unbanked curve of radius R at speed v. If the driver speeds up on this curve until the speed of the car is tripled to $3v$, and if the car still follows the curved path, the frictional force must now be

A. $3f_s$.   B. $\frac{1}{3}f_s$.   C. $9f_s$.   D. $\frac{1}{9}f_s$.

SOLUTION The centripetal acceleration, and therefore the frictional force needed, is proportional to v^2. When the speed increases by a factor of 3, the force needed increases by a factor of $3^2 = 9$. Thus, C is the correct answer. Note that both m and R are constant. If this isn't clear, you may want to review Example 3.

EXAMPLE 4   Rounding a banked curve

An engineer proposes to rebuild the curve in Example 3, banking it so that, at a certain speed v, *no* friction at all is needed for the car to make the curve. At what angle β should it be banked if $v = 25$ m/s (56 mi/h)?

SOLUTION

SET UP Figure 7 shows the free-body diagram for a car following a horizontal, circular path around the curve at the designated speed. We use the same coordinate system as in Example 3. The car's centripetal acceleration is now due to the horizontal component of the normal force exerted by the banked pavement. No friction force is needed.

SOLVE The horizontal component of $\vec{n}$ must now cause the acceleration v^2/R; there is no vertical component of acceleration. The component equations from Newton's second law are

$$n\sin\beta = \frac{mv^2}{R}, \qquad n\cos\beta + (-mg) = 0.$$

Dividing $n\sin\beta$ by $n\cos\beta$, we find that

$$\tan\beta = \frac{v^2}{gR}.$$

As in Example 3, $R = 250$ m. For the specified speed $v = 25$ m/s,

$$\beta = \tan^{-1}\frac{(25 \text{ m/s})^2}{(9.8 \text{ m/s}^2)(250 \text{ m})} = 14°$$

REFLECT The banking angle depends on the speed as well as the radius, but *not* on the mass of the vehicle. (Mass does not appear in the equation.) That's why it's possible to make banked curves that work for both cars and trucks, provided that the vehicles do not drive too fast. Highway designers assume friction will be available under good driving conditions and bank curves at angles less than β.

Practice Problem: In this example, what is the magnitude of the normal force on the 1200 kg car as it rounds the curve? *Answer:* 12,000 N.

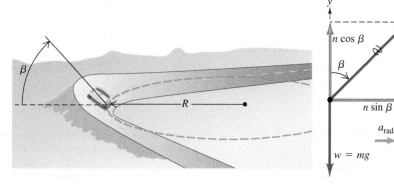

(a) Car rounding banked curve

(b) Free-body diagram of car

▲ **FIGURE 7**

2 Motion in a Vertical Circle

In all the examples in Section 1, the object moved in a horizontal circle. Motion in a *vertical* circle is no different in principle, but the weight of the object has to be treated carefully. The next example shows what we mean.

EXAMPLE 5 Dynamics of a Ferris wheel ride

A passenger on a Ferris wheel moves in a vertical circle of radius R with constant speed v. **(a)** Assuming that the seat remains upright during the motion, derive expressions for the magnitude of the upward force the seat exerts on the passenger at the top and bottom of the circle if the passenger's mass is m. **(b)** What are these forces if the passenger's mass is 60.0 kg, the radius of the circle is $R = 8.00$ m, and the wheel makes one revolution in 10.0 s? How do they compare with the passenger's actual weight?

SOLUTION

SET UP Figure 8 shows the Ferris wheel, with free-body diagrams for the passenger at the top and at the bottom. All the vector quantities (forces and accelerations) have only vertical components. We take the positive y direction as upward in both cases. We use n_T and n_B to denote the magnitude of force the seat applies to the passenger at the top and bottom of the wheel, respectively.

SOLVE Part (a): To derive expressions for the magnitudes n_T and n_B, we use Newton's second law for the y component of net force: $\Sigma F_y = ma_y$. Notice that the sign of a_y is negative at the top of the wheel, but positive at the bottom, although its magnitude is v^2/R at both places. Also, the y component of weight (magnitude mg) is negative, but the y components of both n_T and n_B are positive.

Thus, at the top of the Ferris wheel,

$$n_{T,y} + w_y = ma_y, \quad n_T + (-mg) = m\left(-\frac{v^2}{R}\right),$$

$$\text{or} \quad n_T = m\left(g - \frac{v^2}{R}\right) = mg\left(1 - \frac{v^2}{gR}\right).$$

This means that, at the top of the Ferris wheel, the upward force the seat applies to the passenger is *smaller* in magnitude than the passenger's weight.

At the bottom of the circle (Figure 8c) the acceleration is upward, and Newton's second law gives

$$n_B + (-mg) = +m\frac{v^2}{R}, \quad \text{or}$$

$$n_B = m\left(g + \frac{v^2}{R}\right) = mg\left(1 + \frac{v^2}{gR}\right).$$

At this point, the upward force provided by the seat is always *greater than* the passenger's weight. You feel the seat pushing up on you more firmly than when you are at rest.

Part (b): We want to calculate n_T and n_B for a 60.0 kg passenger riding a Ferris wheel with radius $R = 8.00$ m and a period of 10.0 s. The speed v is the circumference $2\pi R$, divided by the time T for one revolution:

$$v = \frac{2\pi R}{T} = \frac{2\pi(8.00\text{ m})}{10.0\text{ s}} = 5.03\text{ m/s}.$$

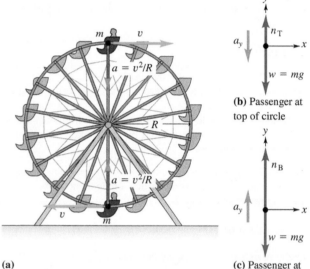

(b) Passenger at top of circle

(c) Passenger at bottom of circle

▲ **FIGURE 8** A passenger on a Ferris wheel.

The magnitude of the radial acceleration is

$$a_{\text{rad}} = \frac{v^2}{R} = \frac{(5.03\text{ m/s})^2}{(8.00\text{ m})} = 3.16\text{ m/s}^2.$$

The two forces (the apparent weights at top and bottom) are

$$n_T = (60.0\text{ kg})(9.80\text{ m/s}^2 - 3.16\text{ m/s}^2) = 398\text{ N}$$
$$n_B = (60.0\text{ kg})(9.80\text{ m/s}^2 + 3.16\text{ m/s}^2) = 778\text{ N}.$$

The passenger's weight is 588 N, and n_T and n_B are, respectively, about 30% less than and greater than the weight.

REFLECT If the Ferris wheel turned so fast that v^2/R were equal to g, the seat would apply *no* force to the passenger at the top of the ride. If the wheel went still faster, n_T would become negative, so that a *downward* force would be needed to keep the passenger in the seat. We could supply a seat belt, or we could glue the passenger to the seat.

Some military aircraft are capable of an apparent gravitational acceleration of $9g$ when pulling out of a dive. (That is, $g + v^2/R = 9g$.) However, even wearing special flight suits, human pilots black out quickly at such accelerations.

NOTE ▶ When we tie a string to an object and whirl it in a vertical circle, the preceding analysis isn't directly applicable. The speed v isn't constant in this case, because, at every point except the top and bottom, there is a component of force (and therefore of acceleration) tangent to the circle. Even worse, we can't use the constant-acceleration formulas to relate the speeds at various points, since *neither* the magnitude nor the direction of the acceleration is constant. The speed relations we need are best obtained by using energy relations. ◀

A stone-age toy

A stone of mass m is attached to a strong string and whirled in a vertical circle of radius R. At the lowest point of the path, the tension in the string is six times the stone's weight. The stone's speed at this point is given by

A. $5\sqrt{gR}$ B. $\sqrt{gR}$ C. $\sqrt{5gR}$

SOLUTION At the lowest point of the circle, the forces acting on the stone are its weight (downward, with magnitude mg) and the string tension force (upward, with magnitude $6mg$). The net upward force has magnitude $5mg$ and must equal the mass m times the magnitude of the centripetal acceleration v^2/R. Thus, $5mg = mv^2/R$, and it follows that $v = \sqrt{5gR}$. The correct answer is C.

Conceptual Analysis 5

A very slippery ramp

A box slides down a circular, frictionless ramp, as shown in Figure 9. The forces on the box at the instant it reaches point A, and their relative magnitudes, are

A. the upward push of the ramp, which is greater than the inertial force ma of the box.
B. the upward push of the ramp, which equals the downward pull of the earth.
C. the upward push of the ramp, which is greater than the downward pull of the earth.

SOLUTION The quantity ma is not a force; there is no such thing as an inertial force. Answer A is wrong both quantitatively and

▲ **FIGURE 9**

conceptually. If B were correct, the net force on the box would be zero and it would have to move in a straight line, not a circle. For circular motion at point A, there must be a net upward force; the correct answer is C.

Walking and Circular Motion

The swinging motion of your legs when you walk can be modeled approximately as circular motion, and this model can be used to find the maximum speed a person of a given leg length can walk. Humans keep the weight-bearing leg straight while walking. Consequently, as shown in Figure 10, each hip in turn moves in a circular arc with a radius R equal to the length of the leg and with the weight-bearing foot at the center of the circle. In the simplest model, we imagine the person's entire mass M to be concentrated near the hip. In this model, when a person walks with speed v, the force required to keep the hips in circular motion is

$$F_{\text{rad}} = \frac{Mv^2}{R}.$$

Gravity provides this force, so the maximum available force is the person's weight Mg. Thus, in this simple model, the maximum speed v_{max} a person can walk is given by

$$Mg = \frac{M(v_{\text{max}})^2}{R}, \quad \text{or} \quad v_{\text{max}} = \sqrt{gR}.$$

The average adult leg length is about 1 m long; assuming this length, we get

$$v_{\text{max}} = \sqrt{(9.8\,\text{m/s}^2)(1.0\,\text{m})} = 3.1 \text{ m/s, or } 7.0 \text{ mi/h}.$$

We assume that the person's mass is all located at the hip.

In each stride, the hip follows a circular arc around the planted foot.

Path of hip

▲ **FIGURE 10** A simple model of human walking.

David P. Hall/Masterfile

This number is quite realistic. Adults can walk at speeds up to about 2.7 m/s, although usual walking speeds are below 2.0 m/s. Race walkers use a special motion that flattens the arc followed by the hip and allows them to walk at up to 4.0 m/s.

3 Newton's Law of Gravitation

About 300 years ago, Newton discovered that gravitation—the force that makes an apple fall out of a tree—also keeps the planets in their nearly circular orbits around the sun. Gravitation is one of the four classes of forces found in nature, and it was the earliest one of the four to be studied extensively.

Our most familiar encounter with the gravitational force is the *weight* of an object—the force that attracts it toward the earth (or toward whatever astronomical body it is near, such as a moon, planet, or star). Newton discovered the **law of gravitation** during his study of the motions of planets around the sun, and he published it in 1686.

▲ BIO Application An earth-moving experience? In walking, a person has at least one foot on the ground at all times. When we model walking as a circular motion of the body, pivoting about the grounded foot, we find that physics imposes a speed limit of about 3 m/s for normal walking (for a foot-to-hip distance of about 1 m). However, this limit does not hold in running, in which the feet are off the ground for part of each stride. In either case—walking or running—you use your leg muscles to press backwards on the earth. The reaction force pushes forward to propel you forward. As Newton's third law tells us, the forward acceleration of a runner times the runner's mass equals the backward acceleration of the earth times its mass. So if you want to move the earth, just go for a run!

Newton's law of gravitation

Newton's law of gravitation may be stated as follows:

> Every particle of matter in the universe attracts every other particle with a force that is directly proportional to the product of the masses of the particles and inversely proportional to the square of the distance between them.

For two particles with masses m_1 and m_2, separated by a distance r (Figure 11), Newton's law of gravitation can be expressed as

$$F_g = G\frac{m_1 m_2}{r^2}, \tag{4}$$

where F_g is the magnitude of the gravitational force on either particle and G is a fundamental physical constant called the **gravitational constant.** Gravitational forces are always attractive; gravitation always pulls objects toward each other.

Gravitational forces between two particles always obey Newton's third law; they always act along the line joining the two particles, and they form an action–reaction pair. Even when the masses of the particles are different, the two interaction forces have equal magnitude. The attractive force that your body exerts on the earth has the same magnitude as the force it exerts on you.

We've stated the law of gravitation in terms of the interaction forces between two *particles*. It turns out that the interaction between any two objects having *spherically symmetric* mass distributions (such as solid spheres or spherical shells) is the same as though all the mass of each were concentrated at its center, as in Figure 12. In effect, we can replace each spherically symmetric object with a particle at its center. Thus, if we model the earth as a solid sphere with mass m_E, then the force exerted by it on a particle or a spherically symmetric object with mass m at a distance r between the two centers is

$$F_g = G\frac{m m_E}{r^2}, \tag{5}$$

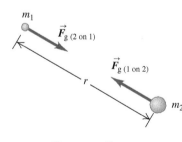

$$F_{g\,(1\text{ on }2)} = F_{g\,(2\text{ on }1)}$$

▲ FIGURE 11 Two particles exert attractive gravitational forces of equal magnitude on each other, even if their masses are quite different.

provided that the object lies outside the earth. A force of the same magnitude is exerted *on* the earth by the object.

NOTE ▶ Notice that r is the distance between the *centers* of the two objects, not between their surfaces. ◀

At points *inside* the earth, the situation is different. If we could drill a hole to the center of the earth and measure the gravitational force on a particle at various depths, we would find that the force *decreases* as we approach the center, rather than increasing as $1/r^2$. As the object entered the interior of the earth (or another spherical object), some of the earth's mass would be on the side of the object opposite from the center and would pull in the opposite direction. Exactly at the center, the gravitational force on the object would be zero.

To determine the value of the gravitational constant G, we have to *measure* the gravitational force between two objects with known masses m_1 and m_2 at a known distance r. For bodies of reasonable size, the force is extremely small, but it can be measured with an instrument called a *torsion balance,* used by Sir Henry Cavendish in 1798 to determine G.

The Cavendish balance consists of a light, rigid rod shaped like an inverted T (Figure 13) and supported by a very thin vertical quartz fiber. Two small spheres, each of mass m_1, are mounted at the ends of the horizontal arms of the T. When we bring two large spheres, each of mass m_2, to the positions shown, the attractive gravitational forces twist the T through a small angle. To measure this angle, we shine a beam of light on a mirror fastened to the T; the reflected beam strikes a scale, and as the T twists, the beam moves along the scale.

After calibrating the instrument, we can measure gravitational forces and thus determine G. The currently accepted value (in SI units) is

$$G = 6.674 \times 10^{-11} \, \text{N} \cdot \text{m}^2/\text{kg}^2.$$

Because $1 \, \text{N} = 1 \, \text{kg} \cdot \text{m/s}^2$, the units of G can also be expressed (in fundamental SI units) as $\text{m}^3/(\text{kg} \cdot \text{s}^2)$.

Gravitational forces combine vectorially. If each of two masses exerts a force on a third, the *total* force on the third mass is the vector sum of the individual forces due to the first two. That is, gravitational forces obey the principle of superposition.

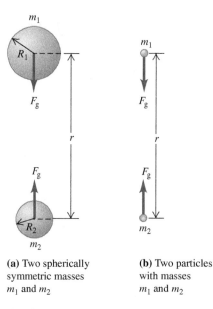

(a) Two spherically symmetric masses m_1 and m_2

(b) Two particles with masses m_1 and m_2

▲ **FIGURE 12** Spherically symmetric objects interact gravitationally as though all the mass of each were concentrated at its center.

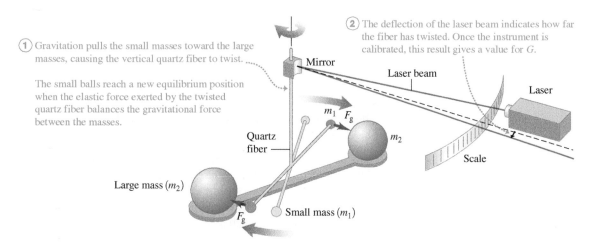

① Gravitation pulls the small masses toward the large masses, causing the vertical quartz fiber to twist.

The small balls reach a new equilibrium position when the elastic force exerted by the twisted quartz fiber balances the gravitational force between the masses.

② The deflection of the laser beam indicates how far the fiber has twisted. Once the instrument is calibrated, this result gives a value for G.

Mirror

Laser beam

Laser

m_1 F_g

m_2

Quartz fiber

Scale

Large mass (m_2)

F_g

Small mass (m_1)

▲ **FIGURE 13** The principle of the Cavendish balance. The angle of deflection is exaggerated for clarity.

EXAMPLE 6 **Gravitational forces in a Cavendish balance**

The mass m_1 of one of the small spheres of a Cavendish balance is 10.0 g ($=0.0100$ kg), the mass m_2 of one of the large spheres is 0.500 kg, and the center-to-center distance between each large sphere and the nearer small one is 0.0500 m. Find the magnitude of the gravitational force F_g on each sphere due to the nearest other sphere.

SOLUTION

SET UP AND SOLVE Figure 14 shows our sketch. Assuming that the spheres have spherically symmetric mass distributions, we can apply Newton's law of gravitation, taking the distance r to be the distance between centers of the spheres. The magnitude of each force is

$$F_g = G\frac{m_1 m_2}{r^2}$$

$$= (6.67 \times 10^{-11}\,\text{N} \cdot \text{m}^2/\text{kg}^2)\frac{(0.0100\,\text{kg})(0.500\,\text{kg})}{(0.0500\,\text{m})^2}$$

$$= 1.33 \times 10^{-10}\,\text{N}.$$

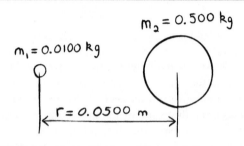

▲ **FIGURE 14** Our sketch for this problem.

REFLECT Gravitational forces between objects of familiar sizes are extremely small. Also, gravitational forces obey Newton's third law: The force that mass m_1 exerts on mass m_2 is equal in magnitude to the force that m_2 exerts on m_1, even though their masses are very different.

Practice Problem: What is the force magnitude F_g if the separation between centers of the spheres is doubled to 0.100 m? *Answer:* One-fourth as much: 3.34×10^{-11} N.

EXAMPLE 7 **Accelerations of Cavendish spheres**

Suppose one large and one small sphere in Example 6 are detached from the apparatus and placed 0.0500 m (between centers) from each other at a point in space far removed from all other objects. What is the magnitude of the acceleration of each sphere relative to an inertial system?

SOLUTION

SET UP AND SOLVE The force on each sphere has the same magnitude that we found in Example 6. From Newton's second law, the acceleration magnitude a_1 of the smaller sphere is

$$a_1 = \frac{F_g}{m_1} = \frac{1.33 \times 10^{-10}\,\text{N}}{0.0100\,\text{kg}} = 1.33 \times 10^{-8}\,\text{m/s}^2.$$

The acceleration magnitude a_2 of the larger sphere is

$$a_2 = \frac{F_g}{m_2} = \frac{1.33 \times 10^{-10}\,\text{N}}{0.500\,\text{kg}} = 2.66 \times 10^{-10}\,\text{m/s}^2.$$

REFLECT Although the forces on the objects are equal in magnitude, the two accelerations are *not* equal in magnitude. Also, they are not constant, because the gravitational forces increase in magnitude as the spheres start to move toward each other.

4 Weight

We tentatively defined your *weight* as the attractive gravitational force exerted on you by the earth. We can now broaden our definition:

> **The weight of an object is the *total* gravitational force exerted on the object by all other objects in the universe.**

When the object is near the surface of the earth, we can neglect all other gravitational forces and consider the weight as just the gravitational force exerted on the object by the earth. At the surface of the *moon* we can consider an object's weight to be the gravitational force exerted on it by the moon, and so on.

If we again model the earth as a spherically symmetric object with radius R_E and mass m_E, then the weight w of a small object of mass m at the earth's surface (a distance R_E from its center) is

$$w = F_g = \frac{Gmm_E}{R_E^2}. \tag{6}$$

But we also know that the weight w of an object is its mass m times the acceleration g of free fall at the location of the object: $w = mg$; weight is the force that causes the acceleration of free fall. Thus, Equation 6 must be equal to mg:

$$mg = \frac{Gmm_E}{R_E^2}.$$

Dividing by m, we find

$$g = \frac{Gm_E}{R_E^2}. \qquad (7)$$

Because this result does not contain m, the acceleration due to gravity g is independent of the mass m of the object. We already knew that, but we can now see how it follows from the law of gravitation.

Furthermore, we can *measure* all the quantities in Equation 7 except for m_E, so this relation allows us to compute the mass of the earth. We first solve Equation 7 for m_E, obtaining

$$m_E = \frac{gR_E^2}{G}.$$

Taking $R_E = 6380$ km $= 6.38 \times 10^6$ m and $g = 9.80$ m/s^2, we find that

$$m_E = 5.98 \times 10^{24} \text{ kg}.$$

Once Cavendish had measured G, he could compute the mass of the earth! He described his measurement of G with the grandiose phrase "weighing the earth." That's not really what he did; he certainly didn't hang our planet from a spring balance. But after he had determined G, he carried out the preceding calculation and determined the mass (not the weight) of the earth.

The weight of an object decreases inversely with the square of its distance from the earth's center. At a radial distance $r = 2R_E$ from earth's center, the weight is one-quarter of its value at the earth's surface. Figure 15 shows how weight varies with height above the earth for an astronaut who weighs 700 N on earth.

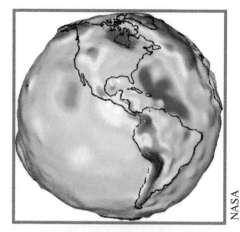

▲ Application **Falling with style.** This is a gravity map of the earth. Protrusions represent areas of stronger gravity (because of nonuniform mass distribution), and dips show areas of weaker gravity. For example, the Andes represent an area of strong gravity because of the extra mass of the mountain range. The map was made by the Gravity Recovery and Climate Experiment (GRACE) project. To measure gravity, GRACE employs a pair of satellites that orbit the earth in formation while precisely monitoring the distance between them. For instance, as the pair approaches a mountain range, the lead satellite will speed up in response to the mountains' gravitational pull, increasing the distance between the two satellites. As the satellites straddle the mountains, the pull of the extra mass then shrinks the distance between them, and as they pass the mountains, the distance increases again.

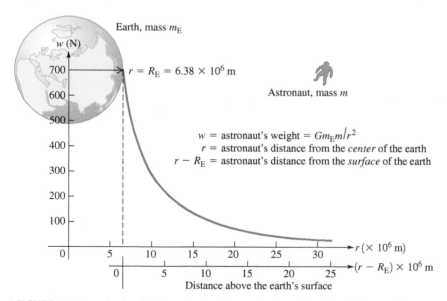

▲ **FIGURE 15** A graph of weight (gravitational interaction) as a function of distance from the earth's surface.

EXAMPLE 8   Density of the earth

Using the values of m_E and R_E quoted above, determine the average *density* (mass per unit volume) of the earth.

SOLUTION

SET UP The volume, assuming a spherical earth is

$$V = \frac{4}{3}\pi R_E^3 = \frac{4}{3}\pi (6.38 \times 10^6 \text{ m})^3 = 1.09 \times 10^{21} \text{ m}^3.$$

SOLVE The average density ρ of the earth is the total mass divided by the total volume:

$$\rho = \frac{M}{V} = \frac{5.98 \times 10^{24} \text{ kg}}{1.09 \times 10^{21} \text{ m}^3} = 5500 \text{ kg/m}^3 = 5.50 \text{ g/cm}^3.$$

REFLECT For comparison, the density of water is $1.00 \text{ g/cm}^3 = 1000 \text{ kg/m}^3$. The density of igneous rock near the earth's surface, such as basalt, is about $3 \text{ g/cm}^3 = 3000 \text{ kg/m}^3$. So the interior of the earth must be much more dense than the surface. In fact, the maximum density at the center, where the pressure is enormous, is thought to be nearly 15 g/cm^3. Figure 16 is a graph of density as a function of distance from the earth's center.

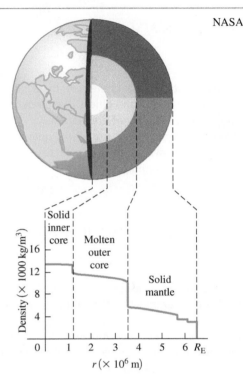
NASA

▶ **FIGURE 16** The density of the earth decreases with increasing distance from its center. The "steps" in the graph represent major changes in composition or in phase (solid versus liquid).

EXAMPLE 9   Gravity on Mars

You're involved in the design of a mission carrying humans to the surface of the planet Mars, which has a radius $R_{Mars} = 3.38 \times 10^6$ m and a mass $m_{Mars} = 6.42 \times 10^{23}$ kg. The earth weight of the Mars lander is 39,200 N. Calculate the weight F_g of the Mars lander and the acceleration due to Mars's gravity, g_{Mars}, **(a)** at the surface of Mars, and **(b)** at 6.00×10^6 m above the surface of Mars (corresponding to the orbit of the Martian moon Phobos).

SOLUTION

SET UP Figure 17 diagrams the problem. Notice that the altitude given is 6.00×10^6 m above the *surface* of Mars. To find the gravitational forces, we need to translate that altitude to the distance from the *center* of Mars: $r = 6.00 \times 10^6$ m $+ 3.38 \times 10^6$ m $= 9.38 \times 10^6$ m.

SOLVE **Part (a):** In Equations 6 and 7 we replace m_E with m_{Mars} and R_E with R_{Mars}. The value of G is the same everywhere; it is a fundamental physical constant. The mass m of the lander is its *earth* weight w, divided by the acceleration due to gravity, g, on the earth:

$$m = \frac{w}{g} = \frac{3.92 \times 10^4 \text{ N}}{9.80 \text{ m/s}^2} = 4.00 \times 10^3 \text{ kg}.$$

The mass is the same whether the lander is on the earth, on Mars, or in between. From Equation 6,

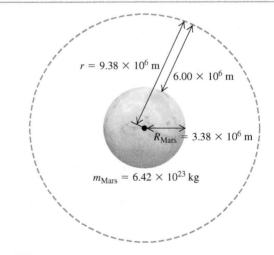

▲ **FIGURE 17**

Continued

$$F_g = \frac{Gmm_{\text{Mars}}}{r^2}$$

$$= \frac{(6.67 \times 10^{-11}\,\text{N}\cdot\text{m}^2/\text{kg}^2)(4.00 \times 10^3\,\text{kg})(6.42 \times 10^{23}\,\text{kg})}{(3.38 \times 10^6\,\text{m})^2}$$

$$= 1.50 \times 10^4\,\text{N}.$$

The acceleration due to the gravity of Mars at its surface is

$$g_{\text{Mars}} = \frac{F_g}{m} = \frac{1.50 \times 10^4\,\text{N}}{4.00 \times 10^3\,\text{kg}} = 3.75\,\text{m/s}^2.$$

We can also obtain g_{Mars} directly from Equation 7:

$$g_{\text{Mars}} = \frac{Gm_{\text{Mars}}}{R_{\text{Mars}}{}^2}$$

$$= \frac{(6.67 \times 10^{-11}\,\text{N}\cdot\text{m}^2/\text{kg}^2)(6.42 \times 10^{23}\,\text{kg})}{(3.38 \times 10^6\,\text{m})^2}$$

$$= 3.75\,\text{m/s}^2.$$

Part (b): To find F_g and g at a point 6.0×10^6 m above the surface of Mars, we repeat the preceding calculations, replacing $R_{\text{Mars}} = 3.38 \times 10^6$ m with $r = 9.38 \times 10^6$ m. At that altitude, both F_g and g are smaller than they are at the surface, by a factor of

$$\left(\frac{3.38 \times 10^6\,\text{m}}{9.38 \times 10^6\,\text{m}} \right)^2 = 0.130,$$

and we find that $F_g = 1.95 \times 10^3$ N and $g = 0.487$ m/s^2. The latter is also the acceleration of Phobos in its orbit due to Mars's gravity, even though Phobos has far more mass than our lander.

REFLECT On the surface of Mars, F_g and g are roughly 40% as large as they are on the surface of the earth. At a point in the orbit of Phobos, they are 13% as large as they are on the surface of Mars.

5 Satellite Motion

Satellites orbiting the earth are a familiar fact of contemporary life. We know that they differ only in scale, not in principle, from the motion of our moon around the earth or the motion of the moons of Jupiter. But we still have to deal with questions such as "What holds that thing up there anyway?" So let's see how we can use Newton's laws and the law of gravitation for a detailed analysis of satellite motion.

To begin, think back to the discussion of projectile motion. We fired a paintball horizontally from some distance above the ground; it followed a parabolic path until it struck the ground. In a similar situation, a motorcycle rider rides horizontally off the edge of a cliff, launching himself into a parabolic path that ends on the flat ground at the base of the cliff (Figure 18).

If he survives and repeats the experiment with an increased launch speed, he will land farther from the starting point. We can imagine him launching himself with great enough speed that the earth's curvature becomes significant. As he falls, the earth curves away beneath him. If he is going fast enough, and if his launch point is high enough that he clears the mountaintops, he may be able to go right on around the earth without ever landing.

Figure 19 shows a variation on this theme. We launch a projectile from point A in a direction tangent to the earth's surface (i.e., horizontally). Trajectories

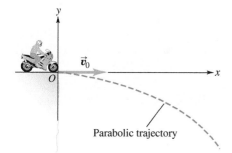

▲ FIGURE 18 The trajectory of a biker launching himself horizontally from a cliff.

PhET: My Solar System
ActivPhysics 4.6: Satellites Orbit

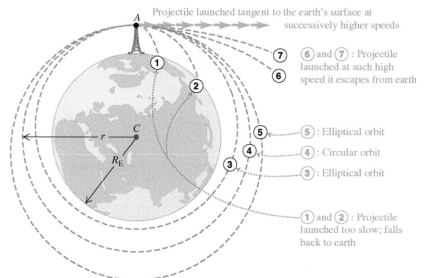

◄ FIGURE 19 An orbit is not fundamentally different from familiar trajectories on earth. If you launch a projectile slowly, it falls back to earth. If you launch it fast enough, the earth curves away from it as it falls, and it goes into orbit.

Corbis

1 through 7 show the effect of increasing the initial speed. Trajectory 3 just misses the earth, and the projectile has become an earth satellite. If there is no retarding force (such as air resistance), its speed when it returns to point A is the same as its initial speed, and it repeats its motion indefinitely.

Trajectories 1 through 5 are ellipses or segments of ellipses; trajectory 4 is a circle (a special case of an ellipse). Trajectories 6 and 7 are not closed orbits; in these trajectories, the projectile never returns to its starting point, but travels farther and farther away from the earth.

A circular orbit is the simplest case and is the only one we'll analyze in detail. Artificial satellites often have nearly circular orbits, and the orbits of most of the planets around the sun are also nearly circular. As we learned in Section 3.4, a particle in uniform circular motion with speed v and radius r has an acceleration with magnitude $a_{rad} = v^2/r$, always directed toward the center of the circle. For a satellite with mass m, the *force* that provides this acceleration is the gravitational attraction of the earth (mass m_E), as shown in Figure 20. If the radius of the circular orbit, measured from the *center* of the earth, is r, then the gravitational force is given by the law of gravitation: $F_g = Gmm_E/r^2$.

The principle governing the motion of the satellite is Newton's second law; the force is F_g, and the acceleration is v^2/r, so the equation $\sum \vec{F} = m\vec{a}$ becomes

$$\frac{Gmm_E}{r^2} = \frac{mv^2}{r}.$$

Solving this equation for v, we find that

$$v = \sqrt{\frac{Gm_E}{r}}. \tag{8}$$

Equation 8 shows that we can't choose the radius r of the orbit and the speed v of the satellite independently; if we choose a value of r, then v is determined. Equation 8 also shows that the satellite's motion *does not* depend on its mass m, because m doesn't appear in the equation. If we could cut a satellite in half without changing its speed, each half would continue on with the original motion.

We can also derive a relation between the radius r of the orbit and the period T of the satellite—the time for one revolution. The speed v is equal to the distance $2\pi r$ (the circumference of the orbit) traveled in one revolution, divided by the time T for one revolution. Thus,

$$v = \frac{2\pi r}{T}. \tag{9}$$

To get an expression for T, we solve Equation 9 for T and combine the resulting equation with Equation 8:

$$T = \frac{2\pi r}{v} = 2\pi r\sqrt{\frac{r}{Gm_E}} = \frac{2\pi r^{3/2}}{\sqrt{Gm_E}}. \tag{10}$$

Equations 8 and 10 show that larger orbits correspond to slower speeds and longer periods.

▲ **FIGURE 20** The force F_g due to the earth's gravitational attraction provides the centripetal force that keeps a satellite in orbit.

Conceptual Analysis 6 | **Orbital speed of a satellite**

A satellite in a circular orbit travels at constant speed because

A. the net force acting on it is zero.
B. the pull of gravity is balanced by the centrifugal force.
C. there is no component of force along its direction of motion.

SOLUTION The net force is not zero; if it were, the satellite would travel in a straight line, not a circle. Thus, A can't be right. There is no such thing as a balancing centrifugal force; if the pull of gravity were balanced by some mythical outward force, the satellite would move in a mythical straight line! So B is wrong, too. The net force on the satellite is the pull of the earth's gravity on the satellite. This pull is always directed toward the center of the orbit, and it provides the centripetal acceleration to maintain the satellite in circular motion. The net force is perpendicular to the satellite's velocity and therefore acts only to change the direction of the velocity. It has no component along the direction of the satellite's motion; if it, did, the speed of the satellite would change. The correct answer is C.

Conceptual Analysis 7 | **Why doesn't the moon fall?**

The moon is pulled directly toward the earth by the earth's gravity, yet it does not fall to the earth because

A. the net force on it is zero.
B. the pull of earth's gravity is balanced by the centrifugal force.
C. the moon pulls back on the earth with an equal and opposite force.
D. . . . but it *is* constantly falling!

SOLUTION The correct answer is D. Recall our earlier discussion about the daredevil motorcyclist going off the cliff. If he goes fast enough, the earth curves away beneath him. At one very high speed, he falls at just the right rate to stay on a circular path. This same argument applies to the moon. Without gravity, it would shoot away from earth in a straight line. The moon does fall, but just enough to keep it on a circular path around the earth. Concerning answer A, the net force is certainly *not* zero. With respect to answer B, a balancing centrifugal force is a mythical "beast," like the unicorn and the free lunch. Answer C tries to bring in an additional force that doesn't act *on* the moon. It is a misuse of Newton's second law!

EXAMPLE 10   A weather satellite

Suppose we want to place a weather satellite into a circular orbit 300 km above the earth's surface. What speed, period, and radial acceleration must it have? The earth's radius is 6380 km = 6.38×10^6 m, and its mass is 5.98×10^{24} kg.

SOLUTION

SET UP AND SOLVE Figure 21 shows our sketch. The radius of the satellite's orbit is

$$r = 6380 \text{ km} + 300 \text{ km} = 6680 \text{ km} = 6.68 \times 10^6 \text{ m}.$$

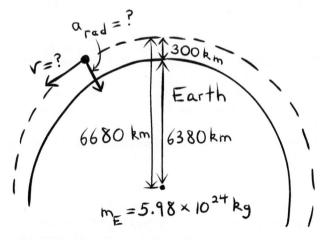

▲ **FIGURE 21** Our sketch for this problem.

From Equation 8,

$$\frac{Gmm_E}{r^2} = \frac{mv^2}{r},$$

$$v = \sqrt{\frac{Gm_E}{r}} = \sqrt{\frac{(6.67 \times 10^{-11} \text{ N} \cdot \text{m}^2/\text{kg}^2)(5.98 \times 10^{24} \text{ kg})}{6.68 \times 10^6 \text{ m}}}$$

$$= 7730 \text{ m/s}.$$

From Equation 10,

$$T = \frac{2\pi r}{v} = \frac{2\pi(6.68 \times 10^6 \text{ m})}{7730 \text{ m/s}}$$

$$= 5430 \text{ s} = 90.5 \text{ min}.$$

The radial acceleration is

$$a_{rad} = \frac{v^2}{r} = \frac{(7730 \text{ m/s})^2}{6.68 \times 10^6 \text{ m}}$$

$$= 8.95 \text{ m/s}^2.$$

Continued

REFLECT The radial acceleration of the satellite is somewhat less than the value of the free-fall acceleration $g = 9.8 \text{ m/s}^2$ at the earth's surface; it is equal to the value of g at a height of 300 km above the earth's surface. The value of T we obtained is only a little larger than the smallest possible period for an earth satellite (corresponding to the smallest possible orbit radius, i.e., the radius of earth itself).

Practice Problem: Find the speed and orbit radius for an earth satellite with a period of 1 day (86,400 s). *Answer:* 3.07×10^3 m/s, 4.23×10^7 m (from the center of the earth).

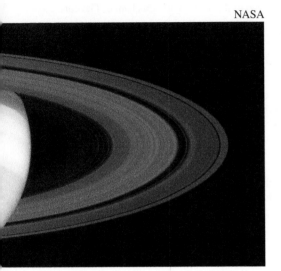
NASA

▲ **FIGURE 22** Saturn's rings consist of myriad separate particles orbiting the planet independently.

Masses of Astronomical Objects

We've talked mostly about artificial earth satellites, but we can apply the same analysis to the circular motion of *any* object acted upon by a gravitational force from a stationary object. Other familiar examples are our moon, the moons of other planets, and the planets orbiting the sun in nearly circular paths. The rings of Saturn (Figure 22), Jupiter, and Neptune are composed of small pieces of matter traveling in circular orbits around those planets.

Observations of satellite motions have been used to determine the masses of the planets in our solar system and of many other astronomical objects. For example, Jupiter has over 30 moons; the orbit radii and periods of many of them have been measured by astronomical observations. The appropriate relationship is Equation 10; we replace m_E with m_{Jupiter} and then solve for m_{Jupiter}:

$$T^2 = \frac{4\pi^2 r^3}{Gm_{\text{Jupiter}}}, \qquad m_{\text{Jupiter}} = \frac{4\pi^2 r^3}{GT^2}.$$

If the orbit radius r and period T of a satellite of Jupiter can be measured, we can calculate the mass of Jupiter.

Black Holes

A more dramatic example of the sort of analysis just described is the discovery of **black holes**—aggregations of matter that are so massive and so dense that nothing (not even light) can escape from their gravitational field. In 1916, Karl Schwarzschild predicted, on the basis of Einstein's general theory of relativity, that if an aggregation of matter with total mass M has a radius less than a critical value R_S, called the **Schwarzschild radius,** then nothing (not even light) can escape from its gravitational field. The value of R_S is given by

$$R_S = \frac{2GM}{c^2},$$

where G is the gravitational constant and c is the speed of light. The surface of a sphere with radius R_S surrounding a black hole is called the **event horizon;** because light can't escape from within that sphere, we can't see events that occur inside. All we can know about a black hole is its mass (from its gravitational field), its charge (from its electric field, expected to be zero), and its rotational characteristics.

At points far from a black hole, its gravitational effects are the same as those of any normal object with the same mass. But any object moving close to a black hole is acted upon by huge forces, causing the object to become so hot that it emits not just visible light (as in "red-hot" or "white-hot" light), but x rays. Astronomers look for these x rays (emitted *before* the object crosses the event horizon) to signal the presence of a black hole (Figure 23). Black holes have also been observed indirectly by the effects their gravitational fields have on the motions of nearby astronomical objects.

(a)   (b)

▲ **FIGURE 23** (a) When a spherical object with mass M has a radius R greater than the Schwarzschild radius R_S, matter and energy can escape from its gravitational attraction. (b) When the radius is less than R_S, the object is a black hole. No matter or energy at a distance less than R_S from its center (the event horizon) can escape, because the escape speed would need to be greater than the speed of light.

The concept of a black hole is one of the most interesting and startling products of modern gravitational theory. Experimental and theoretical studies of black holes are a vital and exciting area of research in contemporary physics.

Weightlessness

What does it mean to say that an astronaut orbiting the earth in a spacecraft is *weightless?* The earth's gravitation still acts on the spacecraft and its occupants, as it must to provide the centripetal acceleration that keeps the craft in orbit. Yet, to the occupants, the environment *seems* to have no gravity. How can we understand this apparent paradox?

To answer this question, let's return to the example of a person standing in an accelerating elevator. We learned there that if the person stands on a spring scale, the scale doesn't read the true weight of the person during the acceleration. Now let's consider an implausible, though instructive, extreme. Suppose the elevator cables have all been broken and all the safety brakes have failed, so that both the elevator and its contents are in free fall, with a downward acceleration of magnitude $g = 9.8 \text{ m/s}^2$. What does the spring scale read now? The scale can't exert any upward force on the person; otherwise her acceleration would be less than g. So the scale must read zero, and the passenger *seems* to be weightless, even though the earth's gravitation still acts on her and her actual weight hasn't changed. If, in the excitement of the moment, she lets go of her purse, it doesn't fall to the floor, because it is already accelerating downward with the same acceleration as the elevator!

The same discussion is applicable to astronauts in a spacecraft orbiting the earth (Figure 24). The earth's gravity acts on both the spacecraft and its occupants, giving them the same acceleration. Thus, when an object is released inside the spacecraft, it doesn't fall relative to the craft, so it *appears* to be weightless.

The physiological effects of prolonged apparent weightlessness afford an interesting medical problem that is being actively explored. Gravity plays an important role in distributing blood in the body; one reaction to apparent weightlessness is a decrease in blood volume through increased excretion of water. In some cases, astronauts returning to earth have experienced temporary impairment of their sense of balance, a greater tendency toward motion sickness, and decalcification of their bones.

NASA

▲ **FIGURE 24** Astronauts appear to be weightless as they orbit the earth, because their acceleration is the same as that of their spacecraft. They still interact gravitationally with the earth, however, and thus have weight in the true sense; this weight is the force that holds them in orbit.

Historical Footnote

We close this chapter with a bit of historical perspective about the role of gravitation and orbital motion in the evolution of scientific thought. The study of planetary motion played a pivotal role in the early development of physics. Johannes Kepler (1571–1630) spent several painstaking years analyzing the motions of the planets, basing his work on remarkably precise measurements made by the Danish astronomer Tycho Brahe (1546–1601) *without the aid of a telescope.* (The telescope was invented in 1608.) Kepler discovered that the orbits of the planets are (nearly circular) ellipses and that the period of a planet in its orbit is proportional to the three-halves power of the radius of the orbit, as Equation 10 shows.

But it remained for Isaac Newton (1642–1727) to show, with his laws of motion and law of gravitation, that this celestial behavior of the planets could be understood on the basis of the very same physical principles he had developed to analyze *terrestrial* motion. Newton recognized that the falling apple was pulled to the earth by gravitational attraction. But to arrive at the $1/r^2$ form of the law of gravitation, he had to do something much subtler than this qualitative observation: He had to take Brahe's observations of planetary motions, as systematized by Kepler, and show that Kepler's rules demanded a $1/r^2$ force law.

From our historical perspective more than 300 years later, there is absolutely no doubt that this **Newtonian synthesis,** as it has come to be called, is one of the greatest achievements in the entire history of science, certainly comparable in significance to the development of quantum mechanics, the theory of relativity, and the understanding of DNA in the 20th century. It was an astonishing leap in understanding, made by a giant intellect!

CHAPTER SUMMARY

Circular Motion Dynamics

(**Sections 1 and 2**) For an object in uniform circular motion, the acceleration vector $\vec{a}_{\text{rad}}$ is directed toward the center of the circle and has constant magnitude $a_{\text{rad}} = v^2/R$. The period T is the time required for the object to make one complete circle; the magnitude of the acceleration vector can also be written $a_{\text{rad}} = 4\pi^2 R/T^2$ (Equation 2). Provided that the object can be treated as a particle, circular motion (like other motions) is governed by Newton's second law, $\Sigma\vec{F} = m\vec{a}$. Because the net force vector points in the same direction as the acceleration vector, an object in uniform circular motion is acted upon by a net force directed toward the center of the circle, with magnitude $F_{\text{net}} = m(v^2/R)$ (Equation 3).

Newton's Law of Gravitation

(**Section 3**) Two particles with masses m_1 and m_2, a distance r apart, attract each other gravitationally with forces of magnitude

$$F_{\text{g}} = G\frac{m_1 m_2}{r^2}. \tag{4}$$

These forces form an action–reaction pair in accordance with Newton's third law. If the objects cannot be treated as particles, but are spherically symmetric, this law is still valid; then, r is the distance between their centers. The gravitational interaction of a spherically symmetric object, from any point outside the object, is just the same as though all its mass were concentrated at the object's center.

Weight

(**Section 4**) The weight w of a body is the total gravitational force exerted on it by all other bodies in the universe. Near the surface of the earth, an object's weight is very nearly equal to the gravitational force exerted by the earth alone. If the earth's mass is m_{E}, the weight of an object of mass m is

$$w = F_{\text{g}} = \frac{Gmm_{\text{E}}}{R_{\text{E}}^2} \tag{6}$$

and the acceleration due to gravity g is

$$g = \frac{Gm_{\text{E}}}{R_{\text{E}}^2}. \tag{7}$$

Satellite Motion

(**Section 5**) When a satellite moves in a circular orbit, the centripetal acceleration is provided by the gravitational attraction of the astronomical body it orbits. If the satellite orbits the earth in an orbit of radius r, its speed v and period T are, respectively,

$$v = \sqrt{\frac{Gm_{\text{E}}}{r}}, \tag{8}$$

$$T = \frac{2\pi r}{v} = 2\pi r\sqrt{\frac{r}{Gm_{\text{E}}}} = \frac{2\pi r^{3/2}}{\sqrt{Gm_{\text{E}}}}. \tag{10}$$

A black hole is an aggregation of matter that is so dense that nothing can escape its gravitational attraction. A nonrotating spherical distribution of mass is a black hole if its total mass M is contained within a radius of less than $R_{\text{s}} = 2GM/c^2$ (the Schwarzschild radius), where c is the speed of light.

Circular Motion and Gravitation: Problem Set

(MP) For instructor-assigned homework, go to www.masteringphysics.com

Conceptual Questions

1. If there is a net force on a particle in uniform circular motion, why doesn't the particle's speed change?
2. As a car rounds a banked circular curve at constant speed, several forces are acting on it: for example, air resistance toward the rear, friction from the pavement in the forward direction, gravity, and the normal force from the tilted road surface. In what direction does the *net* force point? Explain.
3. A student wrote, "The reason an apple falls downward to meet the earth instead of the earth falling upward to meet the apple is that the earth is much more massive than the apple and therefore exerts a much greater pull than the apple does." Is this explanation correct? If not, what is the correct one?
4. In discussions of satellites by laymen, one often hears questions such as "What keeps the satellite moving in its orbit?" and "What keeps the satellite up?" How do you answer these questions? Are your answers also applicable to the moon?
5. Suppose you are sealed inside a lab on the planet Vulcan. After some time, you notice that objects do not fall to the floor when released. Without looking outside the lab, could you determine whether you and the lab are in free fall or whether the Vulcans have somehow found a way to turn off the force of gravity?
6. During an actual interview for a college teaching position in physics, several candidates said that the earth does not fall into the sun because the gravitational pull from the outer planets prevents it from doing so. If you were on the interview committee, would you hire any of these candidates? Explain your reasoning.
7. If two planets have the same mass, will they *necessarily* produce the same gravitational pull on 1.0 kg objects that are (a) at their surfaces; (b) the same center-to-center distance from both planets (but above their surfaces)? Explain.
8. True or false? Astronauts in satellites orbiting around the earth are weightless because the earth's gravity is so weak up there that it is negligible. Explain.
9. True or false? If a rock is acted upon by a gravitational force F from the earth when it is a distance d above the surface of our planet, it will be acted upon by a force $F/4$ if it is raised to twice the height $(2d)$ above the surface. Explain your reasoning.
10. On an icy road, you approach a curve that has the banking angle calculated for 55 mph. Your passenger suggests you slow down below 55 mph, just to be on the safe side, but you say that you should maintain your speed at 55 mph. (a) Who is correct, you or your passenger? (b) What would happen if you were to slow down (or speed up)? (c) Would your passenger's suggestion be a good one on an *unbanked* road?
11. When you're riding a slow Ferris wheel, you may feel slightly lighter at the top of the wheel, and a little heavier at the bottom. If the wheel keeps accelerating, however, at a certain speed of rotation you'll feel weightless at the top, and double your normal weight at the bottom. What's special about this particular rotation speed?
12. The moon is accelerating toward the earth. Does this mean that it is getting closer to our planet? Explain your reasoning.
13. A passenger in a car rounding a sharp curve feels "thrown" toward the outside of the curve. (a) What causes this to happen? Is the person really *thrown* away from the center of the curve? (b) Make a free-body diagram of the person.
14. How does a lettuce spinner remove water from lettuce?
15. What is *wrong* with this statement? "A satellite stays in orbit because the outward centrifugal force just balances the inward centripetal force." Make a free-body diagram of the satellite.

Multiple-Choice Problems

1. Objects in orbiting satellites are apparently weightless because
   A. they are too far from earth to feel its gravity.
   B. earth's gravitational pull is balanced by the outward centrifugal force.
   C. earth's gravitational pull is balanced by the centripetal force.
   D. both they and the satellite are in free fall toward the earth.
2. If the earth had twice its present mass, its orbital period around the sun (at our present distance from the sun) would be
   A. $\sqrt{2}$ years.   B. 1 year.
   C. $\dfrac{1}{\sqrt{2}}$ year.   D. $\frac{1}{2}$ year.
3. An astronaut is floating happily outside her spaceship, which is orbiting the earth at a distance above the earth's surface equal to 1 earth radius. The astronaut's weight is
   A. zero
   B. equal to her normal weight on earth
   C. half her normal weight on earth
   D. one-fourth her normal weight on earth
4. A stone of mass m is attached to a strong string and whirled in a vertical circle of radius R. At the exact top of the path, the tension in the string is three times the stone's weight. At this point, the stone's speed is

A. $2\sqrt{gR}$.   B. $\sqrt{2gR}$.
C. $3\sqrt{gR}$.   D. $\sqrt{3gR}$.

5. A frictional force f provides the centripetal force as a car goes around an unbanked curve of radius R at speed V. Later, the car encounters a similar curve, except of radius $2R$, and the driver continues around this curve at the same speed V. In order to make this second curve, the frictional force on the car must be equal to
A. $2f$.   B. f.   C. $\frac{1}{2}f$.   D. $\frac{1}{4}f$.

6. In the 1960s, during the Cold War, the Soviet Union put a rocket into a nearly circular orbit around the earth. One U.S. senator expressed concern that a nuclear bomb could be dropped on our nation if it were released when the rocket was over the United States. If such a bomb were, in fact, released when the rocket was directly over the United States, where would it land?
A. Directly below, on the United States.
B. It would follow a curved path and most likely land somewhere in the ocean.
C. It would not hit the United States, because it would remain in orbit with the rocket.
D. It would move in a straight line out into space.

7. Two masses m and $2m$ are each forced to go around a curve of radius R at the same constant speed. If, as they move around this curve, the smaller mass is acted upon by a net force F, then the larger one is acted upon by a net force of
A. $\frac{1}{2}F$.   B. F.   C. $2F$.   D. $4F$.

8. A weight W is swung in a vertical circle at constant speed at the end of a rigid bar that pivots about the opposite end (like the spoke of a wheel). If the tension in this bar is equal to $2W$ when the weight is at its lowest point, then the tension when the weight is at the highest point will be
A. 0.   B. W.
C. $2W$.   D. $3W$.

9. If a planet had twice the earth's radius, but only half its mass, the acceleration due to gravity at its surface would be
A. G.   B. $\frac{1}{2}g$.
C. $\frac{1}{4}g$.   D. $\frac{1}{8}g$.

10. When a mass goes in a horizontal circle with speed V at the end of a string of length L on a frictionless table, the tension in the string is T. If the speed of this mass were doubled, but all else remained the same, the tension would be
A. $2T$.   B. $4T$.
C. $T\sqrt{2}$.   D. $\dfrac{T}{\sqrt{2}}$.

11. In the previous problem, if *both* the speed and the length were doubled, the tension in the string would be
A. T.   B. $2T$.
C. $4T$.   D. $T\sqrt{2}$.

12. Two 1.0 kg point masses a distance D apart each exert a gravitational attraction F on the other one. If 1.0 kg is now added to each mass, the gravitational attraction exerted by each would be
A. $2F$.   B. $3F$.   C. $4F$.

13. Two massless bags contain identical bricks, each brick having a mass M. Initially, each bag contains four bricks, and the bags mutually exert a gravitational attraction F_1 on each other. You now take two bricks from one bag and add them to the other bag, causing the bags to attract each other with a force F_2. What is the closest expression for F_2 in terms of F_1?

A. $F_2 = \frac{3}{4}F_1$.
B. $F_2 = \frac{1}{2}F_1$.
C. $F_2 = \frac{1}{4}F_1$.
D. $F_2 = F_1$ because neither the total mass nor the distance between the bags has changed.

14. When two point masses are a distance D apart, each exerts a gravitational attraction F on the other mass. To reduce this force to $\frac{1}{3}F$, you would have to separate the masses to a distance of
A. $D\sqrt{3}$.   B. $3D$.
C. $9D$.   D. $\frac{1}{3}D$.

15. If human beings ever travel to a planet whose mass and radius are both twice that of the earth, their weight on that planet will be
A. equal to their weight on earth
B. twice their weight on earth
C. half their weight on earth
D. one-fourth their weight on earth

Problems

1 Force in Circular Motion

1. • A racing car drives at *constant speed* around the horizontal track shown in Figure 25. At points A, B, and C, draw a vector showing the magnitude and direction of the net force on this car. Make sure that the lengths of your arrows represent the relative magnitudes of the three forces.

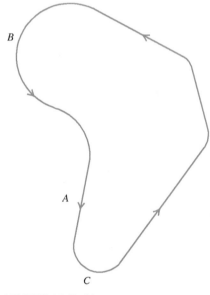

▲ **FIGURE 25** Problem 1.

2. • A stone with a mass of 0.80 kg is attached to one end of a string 0.90 m long. The string will break if its tension exceeds 60.0 N. The stone is whirled in a horizontal circle on a frictionless tabletop; the other end of the string remains fixed. (a) Make a free-body diagram of the stone. (b) Find the maximum speed the stone can attain without breaking the string.

3. •• **Force on a skater's wrist.** A 52 kg ice skater spins about a
BIO vertical axis through her body with her arms horizontally outstretched, making 2.0 turns each second. The distance from one hand to the other is 1.50 m. Biometric measurements indicate

that each hand typically makes up about 1.25% of body weight. (a) Draw a free-body diagram of one of her hands. (b) What horizontal force must her wrist exert on her hand? (c) Express the force in part (b) as a multiple of the weight of her hand.

4. ● A flat (unbanked) curve on a highway has a radius of 220 m. A car rounds the curve at a speed of 25.0 m/s. (a) Make a free-body diagram of the car as it rounds this curve. (b) What is the minimum coefficient of friction that will prevent sliding?

5. ●● The "Giant Swing" at a county fair consists of a vertical central shaft with a number of horizontal arms attached at its upper end. (See Figure 26.) Each arm supports a seat suspended from a 5.00-m-long rod, the upper end of which is fastened to the arm at a point 3.00 m from the central shaft. (a) Make a free-body diagram of the seat, including the person in it. (b) Find the time of one revolution of the swing if the rod supporting the seat makes an angle of 30.0° with the vertical. (c) Does the angle depend on the weight of the passenger for a given rate of revolution?

▲ FIGURE 26 Problem 5.

6. ● A small button placed on a horizontal rotating platform with diameter 0.320 m will revolve with the platform when it is brought up to a speed of 40.0 rev/min, provided the button is no more than 0.150 m from the axis. (a) What is the coefficient of static friction between the button and the platform? (b) How far from the axis can the button be placed, without slipping, if the platform rotates at 60.0 rev/min?

7. ● Calculate (a) the speed of the planet Venus in its essentially circular orbit around the sun and (b) the gravitational force that the sun must be exerting on Venus. Start with a free-body diagram of Venus.

8. ● A highway curve with radius 900.0 ft is to be banked so that a car traveling 55.0 mph will not skid sideways even in the absence of friction. (a) Make a free-body diagram of this car. (b) At what angle should the curve be banked?

9. ●● **The Indy 500.** The Indianapolis Speedway (home of the Indy 500) consists of a 2.5 mile track having four turns, each 0.25 mile long and banked at 9°12′. What is the no-friction-needed speed (in m/s and mph) for these turns? (Do you think drivers actually take the turns at that speed?)

2 Motion in a Vertical Circle

10. ● A bowling ball weighing 71.2 N is attached to the ceiling by a 3.80 m rope. The ball is pulled to one side and released; it then swings back and forth like a pendulum. As the rope swings through its lowest point, the speed of the bowling ball is measured at 4.20 m/s. At that instant, find (a) the magnitude and direction of the acceleration of the bowling ball and (b) the tension in the rope. Be sure to start with a free-body diagram.

11. ●● The Cosmoclock 21 Ferris wheel in Yokohama City, Japan, has a diameter of 100 m. Its name comes from its 60 arms, each of which can function as a second hand (so that it makes one revolution every 60.0 s). (a) Find the speed of the passengers when the Ferris wheel is rotating at this rate. (b) A passenger weighs 882 N at the weight-guessing booth on the ground. What is his apparent weight at the highest and at the lowest point on the Ferris wheel? (c) What would be the time for one revolution if the passenger's apparent weight at the highest point were zero? (d) What then would be the passenger's apparent weight at the lowest point?

12. ●● A 50.0 kg stunt pilot who has been diving her airplane vertically pulls out of the dive by changing her course to a circle in a vertical plane. (a) If the plane's speed at the lowest point of the circle is 95.0 m/s, what should the minimum radius of the circle be in order for the centripetal acceleration at this point not to exceed 4.00g? (b) What is the apparent weight of the pilot at the lowest point of the pullout?

13. ●● **Effect on blood of walking.** While a person is walking, **BIO** his arms swing through approximately a 45° angle in $\frac{1}{2}$ s. As a reasonable approximation, we can assume that the arm moves with constant speed during each swing. A typical arm is 70.0 cm long, measured from the shoulder joint. (a) What is the acceleration of a 1.0 gram drop of blood in the fingertips at the bottom of the swing? (b) Make a free-body diagram of the drop of blood in part (a). (c) Find the force that the blood vessel must exert on the drop of blood in part (b). Which way does this force point? (d) What force would the blood vessel exert if the arm were not swinging?

14. ● **Stay dry!** You tie a cord to a pail of water, and you swing the pail in a vertical circle of radius 0.600 m. What minimum speed must you give the pail at the highest point of the circle if no water is to spill from it? Start with a free-body diagram of the water at its highest point.

15. ● Stunt pilots and fighter pilots who fly at high speeds in a **BIO** downward-curving arc may experience a "red out," in which blood is forced upward into the flier's head, potentially swelling or breaking capillaries in the eyes and leading to a reddening of vision and even loss of consciousness. This effect can occur at centripetal accelerations of about 2.5g's. For a stunt plane flying at a speed of 320 km/h, what is the minimum radius of downward curve a pilot can achieve without experiencing a red out at the top of the arc? (*Hint:* Remember that gravity provides part of the centripetal acceleration at the top of the arc; it's the acceleration required *in excess of gravity* that causes this problem.)

3 Newton's Law of Gravitation

16. ● If two tiny identical spheres attract each other with a force of 3.0 nN when they are 25 cm apart, what is the mass of each sphere?

17. ● What gravitational force do the two protons in the helium nucleus exert on each other? Their separation is approximately 1.0 fm.

18. • **Rendezvous in space!** A couple of astronauts agree to rendezvous in space after hours. Their plan is to let gravity bring them together. One of them has a mass of 65 kg and the other a mass of 72 kg, and they start from rest 20.0 m apart. (a) Make a free-body diagram of each astronaut, and use it to find his or her initial acceleration. As a rough approximation, we can model the astronauts as uniform spheres. (b) If the astronauts' acceleration remained constant, how many days would they have to wait before reaching each other? (Careful! They *both* have acceleration toward each other.) (c) Would their acceleration, in fact, remain constant? If not, would it increase or decrease? Why?

19. • What is the ratio of the gravitational pull of the sun on the moon to that of the earth on the moon? (Assume that the distance of the moon from the sun is approximately the same as the distance of the earth from the sun.) Use the data in Appendix E. Is it more accurate to say that the moon orbits the earth or that the moon orbits the sun? Why?

20. • A 2150 kg satellite used in a cellular telephone network is in a circular orbit at a height of 780 km above the *surface* of the earth. What is the gravitational force on the satellite? What fraction is this force of the satellite's weight at the surface of the earth?

21. • An interplanetary spaceship passes through the point in space where the gravitational forces from the sun and the earth on the ship exactly cancel. (a) How far from the center of the earth is it? Use the data in Appendix E. (b) Once it reached the point found in part (a), could the spaceship turn off its engines and just hover there indefinitely? Explain.

22. •• Find the magnitude and direction of the net gravitational force on mass *A* due to masses *B* and *C* in Figure 27. Each mass is 2.00 kg.

▲ **FIGURE 27** Problem 22.

23. • How far from a very small 100-kg ball would a particle have to be placed so that the ball pulled on the particle just as hard as the earth does? Is it reasonable that you could actually set up this as an experiment? Why?

24. •• Each mass in Figure 28 is 3.00 kg. Find the magnitude and direction of the net gravitational force on mass *A* due to the other masses.

(a) Equilateral triangle of side 10 cm

(b) Square of side 10 cm

▲ **FIGURE 28** Problem 24.

25. •• An 8.00-kg point mass and a 15.0-kg point mass are held in place 50.0 cm apart. A particle of mass *m* is released from a point between the two masses 20.0 cm from the 8.00-kg mass along the line connecting the two fixed masses. Find the magnitude and direction of the acceleration of the particle.

4 Weight

26. • How many kilometers would you have to go above the *surface* of the earth for your weight to decrease to half of what it was at the surface?

27. •• Your spaceship lands on an unknown planet. To determine the characteristics of this planet, you drop a 1.30 kg wrench from 5.00 m above the ground and measure that it hits the ground 0.811 s later. You also do enough surveying to determine that the circumference of the planet is 62,400 km. (a) What is the mass of the planet, in kilograms? (b) Express the planet's mass in terms of the earth's mass.

28. •• If an object's weight is *W* on the earth, what would be its weight (in terms of *W*) if the earth had (a) twice its present mass, but was the same size, (b) half its present radius, but the same mass, (c) half its present radius and half its present mass, (d) twice its present radius and twice its present mass?

29. •• **Huygens probe on Titan.** In January 2005 the *Huygens* probe landed on Saturn's moon Titan, the only satellite in the solar system having a thick atmosphere. Titan's diameter is 5150 km, and its mass is 1.35×10^{23} kg. The probe weighed 3120 N on the earth. What did it weigh on the surface of Titan?

30. •• The mass of the moon is about 1/81 the mass of the earth, its radius is $\frac{1}{4}$ that of the earth, and the acceleration due to gravity at the earth's surface is 9.80 m/s². Without looking up either body's mass, use this information to compute the acceleration due to gravity on the moon's surface.

31. •• Neutron stars, such as the one at the center of the Crab Nebula, have about the same mass as our sun, but a *much* smaller diameter. If you weigh 675 N on the earth, what would you weigh on the surface of a neutron star that has the same mass as our sun and a diameter of 20.0 km?

32. •• The asteroid 234 Ida has a mass of about 4.0×10^{16} kg and an average radius of about 16 km (it's not spherical, but you can assume it is). (a) Calculate the acceleration of gravity on 234 Ida. (b) What would an astronaut whose earth weight is 650 N weigh on 234 Ida? (c) If you dropped a rock from a height of 1.0 m on 234 Ida, how long would it take to reach the ground? (d) If you can jump 60 cm straight up on earth, how high could you jump on 234 Ida? (Assume the asteroid's gravity doesn't weaken significantly over the distance of your jump.)

5 Satellite Motion

33. • An earth satellite moves in a circular orbit with an orbital speed of 6200 m/s. (a) Find the time of one revolution of the satellite. (b) Find the radial acceleration of the satellite in its orbit. (c) Make a free-body diagram of the satellite.

34. • What is the period of revolution of a satellite with mass *m* that orbits the earth in a circular path of radius 7880 km (about 1500 km above the surface of the earth)?

35. • What must be the orbital speed of a satellite in a circular orbit 780 km above the surface of the earth?

36. •• **Planets beyond the solar system.** On October 15, 2001, a planet was discovered orbiting around the star HD68988. Its orbital distance was measured to be 10.5 million kilometers from the center of the star, and its orbital period was estimated

at 6.3 days. What is the mass of HD68988? Express your answer in kilograms and in terms of our sun's mass.

37. •• **Communications satellites.** Communications satellites are used to bounce radio waves from the earth's surface to send messages around the curvature of the earth. In order to be available all the time, they must remain above the same point on the earth's surface and must move in a circle above the equator. (a) How long must it take for a communications satellite to make one complete orbit around the earth? (Such an orbit is said to be *geosynchronous.*) (b) Make a free-body diagram of the satellite in orbit. (c) Apply Newton's second law to the satellite and find its altitude above the earth's *surface.* (d) Draw the orbit of a communications satellite to scale on a sketch of the earth.

38. • (a) Calculate the speed with which you would have to throw a rock to put it into orbit around the asteroid 234 Ida, near the surface (see Problem 32; assume 234 Ida is spherical, with the given radius and mass). (b) How long would it take for your rock to return and hit you in the back of the head?

39. •• In March 2006, two small satellites were discovered orbiting Pluto, one at a distance of 48,000 km and the other at 64,000 km. Pluto already was known to have a large satellite Charon, orbiting at 19,600 km with an orbital period of 6.39 days. Assuming that the satellites do not affect each other, find the orbital periods of the two small satellites *without* using the mass of Pluto.

40. •• **Apparent weightlessness in a satellite.** You have probably seen films of astronauts floating freely in orbiting satellites. People often think the astronauts are weightless because they are free of the gravity of the earth. Let us see if that explanation is correct. (a) Typically, such satellites orbit around 400 km above the *surface* of the earth. If an astronaut weighs 750 N on the ground, what will he weigh if he is 400 km above the surface? (b) Draw the orbit of the satellite in part (a) to scale on a sketch of the earth. (c) In light of your answers to parts (a) and (b), are the astronauts weightless because gravity is so weak? Why are they apparently weightless?

41. •• **Baseball on Deimos!** Deimos, a moon of Mars, is about 12 km in diameter, with a mass of 2.0×10^{15} kg. Suppose you are stranded alone on Deimos and want to play a one-person game of baseball. You would be the pitcher, and you would be the batter! With what speed would you have to throw a baseball so that it would go into orbit and return to you so you could hit it? Do you think you could actually throw it at that speed?

General Problems

42. •• **International Space Station.** The International Space Station, launched in November 1998, makes 15.65 revolutions around the earth each day in a circular orbit. (a) Draw a free-body diagram of this satellite. (b) Apply Newton's second law to the space station and find its height (in kilometers) above the earth's surface.

43. •• **Artificial gravity.** One way to create artificial gravity in a space station is to spin it. If a cylindrical space station 275 m in diameter is to spin about its central axis, at how many revolutions per minute (rpm) must it turn so that the outermost points have an acceleration equal to g?

44. •• **Hip wear on the moon.** (a) Calculate the acceleration due
BIO to gravity on the moon. (b) Calculate the friction force on a walking 65 kg astronaut carrying a 43 kg instrument pack on the moon if the coefficient of kinetic friction at her hip joint is

0.0050. (Recall that approximately 65% of the body weight is above the hip.) (c) What would be the friction force on earth for this astronaut?

45. •• **Volcanoes on Io.** Jupiter's moon Io has active volcanoes (in fact, it is the most volcanically active body in the solar system) that eject material as high as 500 km (or even higher) above the surface. Io has a mass of 8.94×10^{22} kg and a radius of 1815 km. Ignore any variation in gravity over the 500 km range of the debris. How high would this material go on earth if it were ejected with the same speed as on Io?

46. •• You are driving with a friend who is sitting to your right on the passenger side of the front seat of your car. You would like to be closer to your friend, so you decide to use physics to achieve your romantic goal by making a quick turn. (a) Which way (to the left or to the right) should you turn the car to get your friend to slide toward you? (b) If the coefficient of static friction between your friend and the car seat is 0.55 and you keep driving at a constant speed of 15 m/s, what is the maximum radius you could make your turn and still have your friend slide your way?

47. •• On the ride "Spindletop" at the amusement park Six Flags Over Texas, people stood against the inner wall of a hollow vertical cylinder with radius 2.5 m. The cylinder started to rotate, and when it reached a constant rotation rate of 0.60 rev/s, the floor on which the people were standing dropped about 0.5 m. The people remained pinned against the wall. (a) Draw a free-body diagram for a person on this ride after the floor has dropped. (b) What minimum coefficient of static friction is required if the person on the ride is not to slide downward to the new position of the floor? (c) Does your answer in part (b) depend on the mass of the passenger? (*Note:* When the ride is over, the cylinder is slowly brought to rest. As it slows down, people slide down the walls to the floor.)

48. •• **Physical training.** As part of a training program, an athlete
BIO runs while holding 8.0 kg weights in each hand. As he runs, the weights swing through a 30.0° arc in $\frac{1}{3}$ s at essentially constant speed. His hands are 72 cm from his shoulder joint, and they are light enough that we can neglect their weight compared with that of the 8.0 kg weight he is carrying. (a) Make a free-body diagram of one of the 8.0 kg weights at the bottom of its swing. (b) What force does the runner's hand exert on each weight at the bottom of the swing?

49. •• The asteroid Toro has a radius of about 5.0 km. (a) Assuming that the density of Toro is the same as that of the earth (5.5 g/cm^3), find its total mass and find the acceleration due to gravity at its surface. (b) Suppose an object is to be placed in a circular orbit around Toro, with a radius just slightly larger than the asteroid's radius. What is the speed of the object? Could you launch yourself into orbit around Toro by running?

50. •• A 1125-kg car and a 2250-kg pickup truck approach a curve on the expressway that has a radius of 225 m. (a) At what angle should the highway engineer bank this curve so that vehicles traveling at 65.0 mi/h can safely round it regardless of the condition of their tires? Should the heavy truck go slower than the lighter car? (b) As the car and truck round the curve at 65.0 mi/h, find the normal force on each one due to the highway surface.

51. •• **Exploring Europa.**

BIO Europa, a satellite of Jupiter, is believed to have an ocean of liquid water (with the possibility of life) beneath its icy surface. (See Figure 29.) Europa is 3130 km in diameter and has a mass of 4.78×10^{22} kg. In the future, we will surely want to send astronauts to investigate Europa. In planning such a future mission, what is the fastest that such an astronaut could walk on the surface of Europa if her legs are 1.0 m long?

▲ **FIGURE 29** Problem 51.

52. • The star Rho[1] Cancri is 57 light-years from the earth and has a mass 0.85 times that of our sun. A planet has been detected in a circular orbit around Rho[1] Cancri with an orbital radius equal to 0.11 times the radius of the earth's orbit around the sun. What are (a) the orbital speed and (b) the orbital period of the planet of Rho[1] Cancri?

53. •• **Catch a piece of a comet.** The *Stardust* spacecraft was designed to visit a comet and bring samples of its material back to the earth. The craft is 1.7 m across and has a mass of 385 kg. In January 2004, from a distance of 237 km, it took the photograph of the nucleus of comet Wild2, shown in Figure 30. The distance across this nucleus

▲ **FIGURE 30** Problem 53.

is 5 km, and we can model it as an approximate sphere. Since astronomers think that comets have a composition similar to that of Pluto, we can assume a density the same as Pluto's, which is 2.1 g/cm³. The samples taken were returned to earth on Jan. 15, 2006. (a) What gravitational force did the comet exert on the spacecraft when it took the photo in the figure? (b) Compare this force with the force that the earth's gravity exerted on it when the spacecraft was on the launch pad.

54. •• The 4.00 kg block in the figure is attached to a vertical rod by means of two strings. When the system rotates about the axis of the rod, the strings are extended as shown in Figure 31 and the tension in the upper string is 80.0 N. (a) What is the tension in the lower cord? Start with a free-body diagram of the block. (b) What is the speed of the block?

▲ **FIGURE 31** Problem 54.

1.25 m

2.00 m   4.00 kg

1.25 m

55. •• As your bus rounds a flat curve at constant speed, a package with mass 0.500 kg, suspended from the luggage compartment of the bus by a string 45.0 cm long, is found to hang at rest relative to the bus, with the string making an angle of 30.0° with the vertical. In this position, the package is 50.0 m from the center of curvature of the curve. What is the speed of the bus?

56. •• **Artificial gravity in space stations.** One problem for humans living in outer space is that they are apparently weightless. One way around this problem is to design a cylindrical space station that spins about an axis through its center at a constant rate. (See Figure 32.) This spin creates "artificial gravity" at the outside rim of the station. (a) If the diameter of the space station is 800.0 m, how fast must the rim be moving in order for the "artificial gravity" acceleration to be *g* at the outer rim? (b) If the space station is a waiting area for travelers going to Mars, it might be desirable to simulate the acceleration due to gravity on the Martian surface. How fast must the rim move in this case? (c) Make a free-body diagram of an astronaut at the outer rim.

800.0 m

▲ **FIGURE 32** Problem 56.

Passage Problems

BIO **Weightlessness and artificial gravity.** Astronauts who live under weightless (zero gravity) conditions for a prolonged time can experience health risks as a result. One way to avoid these adverse physiological effects is to provide an artificial gravity to simulate what is naturally experienced on the earth.

In one design a space station is constructed in the shape of a long cylinder that spins at a constant rate about its longitudinal axis. Astronauts standing on the inside lateral surface of the cylinder experience a centripetal acceleration (due to their circular motion about the axis of the cylinder) that simulates the effect of gravity. The magnitude of the simulated gravity can be increased or decreased to the desired value by changing the rotation rate of the cylinder.

57. If the diameter of the space station is 1000 m, how fast must the outer edge of the space station move to give an astronaut the experience of a reduced "gravity" of 5 m/s² (roughly ½ earth normal)? You may assume that the astronaut is standing on the inner wall at a distance of nearly 1000 m from the axis of the space station.

A. 5000 m/s
B. 2500 m/s
C. 71 m/s
D. 50 m/s

58. What would be the resulting period of rotation of the space station? You may assume that the space station has a circumference of approximately 3000 m.
    A. 0.6 s
    B. 3 s
    C. 42 s
    D. 60 s
    E. 380 s

59. Under these same conditions, how much force would an astronaut need to exert on a 2-kg space helmet that she is holding to keep it moving on the same circular path that she follows? *Note:* This force is known as the "effective weight" of the space helmet.
    A. 20 N
    B. 10 N
    C. 5 N
    D. 0 N

ANSWERS TO SELECTED PROBLEMS

Conceptual Questions

3. This is incorrect. The magnitude of the force of the earth on the apple equals the magnitude of the force of the apple on the earth. Equal forces have different effects on the two objects because the mass of the earth is much greater than the mass of the apple. The same magnitude of force produces a much larger acceleration for the apple.

5. No, there is no way to tell the difference without making observations outside the laboratory.

7. (a) No. The gravitational pull on the 1.0 kg object is $F_g = G \dfrac{(1.0 \text{ kg}) m_p}{R_p^2}$,
   where m_p is the mass of the planet and R_p is its radius. If the planets have different radii, then the gravitational pulls will be different; the planet of smaller radius exerts a greater pull. (b) Yes. The gravitational pull is $F_g = G \dfrac{(1.0 \text{ kg}) m_p}{r^2}$,
   where r is the distance of the object from the center of the planet. At the same r and for planets of the same m_p, the force F_g will be the same.

9. False. F_g is proportional to $1/r^2$, where r is the distance of the object from the center of the earth. Doubling the height above the surface does not double the distance from the center of the earth.

11. At one particular speed, the size of the centripetal force needed to keep you moving in a circle of the Ferris wheel's radius is exactly equal to your weight. At that speed, gravity provides all the centripetal force at the top, but with nothing "left over" to hold you to the seat, which therefore exerts no upward force on you. At the same speed, at the bottom, the seat must not only support your normal weight, but must also provide a centripetal force equal

to your weight. The seat therefore pushes upward on you with a force equal to twice your weight at that point in the ride.

13. (a) The car turns while the person tends to continue traveling in a straight line. There is no outward force on the person. (b) The free-body diagram is given in the figure below. The acceleration $\vec{a}_{rad}$ is inward toward the center of the curve. $\vec{F}$ is the force exerted by the car on the person.

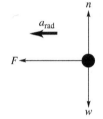

15. First, there is no outward force on the satellite. Second, the forces on the satellite do not balance. There is, however, a net inward force (gravity) that produces the inward acceleration associated with the circular motion. The free-body diagram is given in the figure below.

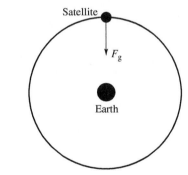

Multiple-Choice Problems

1. D
3. D
5. C
7. C
9. D
11. B
13. A
15. C

Problems

3. (b) 77 N (c) 12 times weight of hand
5. (b) 6.19 s (c) no
7. (a) 35.0 km/s (b) 5.50 × 10²² N
9. 20.0 m/s = 44.7 mph
11. (a) 5.24 m/s (b) highest: 833 N; lowest: 931 N (c) 14.2 s (d) 1760 N
13. (a) 1.73 m/s² (c) 0.0115 N, upward (d) 9.8 × 10⁻³ N
15. 230 m
17. 1.87 × 10⁻³⁴ N
19. 2.18
21. (a) 2.59 × 10⁸ m (b) no
23. 0.0261 mm; no
25. 2.2 × 10⁻⁹ m/s², toward the 8.00 kg mass
27. (a) 2.25 × 10²⁵ kg (b) 3.76m_E
29. 433 N
31. 9.16 × 10¹³ N
33. (a) 175 min (b) 3.71 m/s²
35. 7.46 × 10³ m/s
37. (a) 86,400 s = 24 h (c) 3.58 × 10⁷ m
39. 37.7 days
41. 4.7 m/s
43. 2.55 rpm
45. 92 km
47. (b) 0.28 (c) no
49. (a) 2.9 × 10¹⁵ kg; 7.7 × 10⁻³ m/s² (b) 6.2 m/s; yes
51. 1.1 m/s
53. (a) 6.28 × 10⁻⁵ N (b) 3.77 × 10³ N
55. 16.8 m/s

Passage Problems

57. D
59. B

Work and Energy

Work and Energy

Audio-kinetic ball machine by George Rhoads

By now we have developed an understanding of mechanics as embodied in Newton's three laws of motion. In principle, these laws provide a complete description of the relation between the motion of an object and the forces that act on it. But some problems aren't as simple as they look. Suppose you try to find the speed of a toy glider launched by a compressed spring that applies a varying force. You apply Newton's laws and all the problem-solving techniques that we've learned, but you find that the acceleration isn't constant and the simple methods we've learned can't be implemented directly. As we'll see, there are powerful alternative methods for dealing with such problems.

In this chapter, we'll introduce a new concept—*energy*—that is one of the most important unifying concepts in all of physical science. Its importance stems from the principle of *conservation of energy*. We'll concentrate on mechanical energy, which is associated with the motions and positions of mechanical systems. In the opening section of the chapter, we'll tour the main ideas associated with energy on a qualitative level. Then we'll develop the concepts of work and kinetic energy (energy of motion) and the relationship between them. In the remainder of the chapter, we'll learn how to apply these concepts to the analysis of problems.

1 An Overview of Energy

The concept of **energy** appears throughout every area of physics, yet it's not easy to define just what energy is. This concept is the cornerstone of a fundamental law of nature called **conservation of energy,** which states that the total energy in any isolated system is constant, no matter what happens within the system. (Later in the chapter, we'll explain what an *isolated system* is.) Energy can be converted from one form to another, but it cannot be created or destroyed.

Conservation laws, including conservation of mass, energy, momentum, angular momentum, electric charge, and other quantities, play vital roles in every area of physics and provide unifying threads that run through the whole fabric of the subject. Every conservation law says that the total amount of some physical quantity in every isolated system is constant.

An example is the conservation of mass in chemical reactions. The total mass of the material participating in a chemical reaction is always the same (within the limits of experimental precision) before and after the reaction. This generalization is called the principle of *conservation of mass,* and it is obeyed in all chemical reactions.

Something analogous happens in collisions between objects. For a particle with mass m moving with speed v, we define a quantity $\frac{1}{2}mv^2$ called the **kinetic energy** of the particle. When two hard, springy objects, such as steel ball bearings, collide, we find that the individual speeds change, but that the total kinetic energy (the sum of the $\frac{1}{2}mv^2$ quantities for the two balls) is very nearly the same after the collision as before. When it is *exactly* the same, we say that kinetic energy is *conserved.* We haven't really said what kinetic energy *is,* only that this product of half the mass and the square of the speed is useful in representing a conservation principle in a particular class of interactions.

When two soft, deformable objects (such as two balls of putty or chewing gum) collide, we find that kinetic energy is *not* conserved, but the bodies become warmer. It turns out that there is a definite relationship between the rise in temperature and the loss of kinetic energy. We can define a new quantity, *internal energy,* that increases with temperature in a definite way such that the *sum* of the kinetic energy and the internal energy *is* conserved in these collisions. We can also define additional forms of energy that enable us to extend the principle of conservation of energy to broader classes of phenomena.

Energy is transformed from one form to another, but it is not created or destroyed. There is energy associated with heat, elastic deformations, electric and magnetic fields, and, according to the theory of relativity, even with mass itself. Newtonian mechanics has its limitations; it doesn't work for very fast motion, for which we have to use the theory of relativity, or for atomic or subatomic systems, for which we need quantum mechanics. But conservation of energy holds even in these realms. It is a *universal* conservation principle; no exception has ever been found. Studying conservation of energy is like studying a snowflake under a microscope, or the finer and finer details of a fractal pattern, or the structure of a Bach fugue. The more closely you look, the richer the subject becomes.

Figure 1 conveys a sense of energy transfer and transformation. A little of the sun's nuclear energy is successively transformed into other forms and eventually appears as energy you spend when exercising. This energy is not created spontaneously, and it is not "used up"; instead, it is transformed from one form to another.

Forms of Mechanical Energy

In this chapter, we'll be concerned only with **mechanical energy**—the energy associated with motion, position, and deformation of objects. We'll find that, in some interactions, mechanical energy is conserved; in others, there is a conversion of mechanical energy to or from other forms.

As we mentioned at the beginning of this chapter, the energy associated with motion of an object is called kinetic energy. For an object with constant mass, kinetic energy depends only on its speed v and mass m. When a moving object

Nuclear energy in the sun's core …

Becomes energy of the sun's hot gas …

Becomes energy of sunlight …

Which is converted by plants to the chemical energy of grains and other foods …

Which you may consume as calories …

Which can be used to lift weights …

And the story goes on.

▲ **FIGURE 1** A typical sequence of energy transfers and transformations—one that sustains life on earth.

▲ **FIGURE 2** Elastic potential energy stored in a stretched rubber band.

The gravitational potential energy is larger when the skateboarder is at this higher position.

Gravitational potential energy in the process of becoming kinetic energy

▲**FIGURE 3** Transformation of gravitational potential energy to kinetic energy.

TABLE 1   The analogy between energy and money

How money is like energy:

- It can take multiple forms (coins, bills, checks, bank accounts).
- You can transform it (e.g., by cashing a check) or transfer it to others.
- These transfers and transformations do not change its total amount.
- It can be stored or spent.

How money is not like energy:

- Money can be created or destroyed, whereas energy cannot be.

such as a kicked football or a speeding car interacts with another object, obvious changes (such as broken windows or bent fenders) result, and associated with these changes are transfers of kinetic energy to other forms of energy.

The other class of mechanical energy we'll consider is energy that is not directly associated with motion, but rather a quantity that is *stored* as a result of the position or elastic deformation of an object. Consider a stretched rubber band (Figure 2). You have to expend energy to stretch it, and as soon as it is released, physical changes occur; for instance, it may fly across the room. An unstretched rubber band lacks this capability. The act of stretching the rubber band stores energy in it, and releasing the rubber band allows this stored energy to be transformed to other types of energy, such as kinetic energy. We call this stored energy **potential energy.** Energy that is stored in an elastic object when you stretch, compress, twist, or otherwise deform it is called **elastic potential energy.**

Another example of potential energy is provided by the skateboarder in Figure 3. When he descends from the top edge of the quarter-pipe, he speeds up and gains kinetic energy. While he momentarily stops at the top of the opposite edge, he has no kinetic energy. As soon as he begins his descent, he gains kinetic energy as the gravitational force (his weight) pulls him downward. Thus, his initial elevated position represents a form of *stored energy;* we call it **gravitational potential energy.** Whenever an object moves vertically while a gravitational force (its weight) acts on it, the gravitational potential energy changes. The greater the change in height, the greater is the change in gravitational potential energy.

Kinetic energy, elastic potential energy, and gravitational potential energy are all forms of mechanical energy.

Energy and Money

Earlier, we remarked that even physicists have a hard time defining what energy *is.* You may now feel that same difficulty. What *is* this entity that goes from object to object and from one form to another? An analogy that you're probably familiar with is *money.* Money takes many forms, such as a coin, a bill, and an electronic number in a bank's computer. You can store money, or you can spend it to buy things. Even though money is real, it is also in a sense a pure abstraction. Energy, similarly, is both an abstract idea and a very real quantity that is involved in changes and transformations of physical systems. Table 1 sums up this analogy between money and energy.

Conservation of Energy

In discussing energy relations, we'll often use the concept of a **system.** A system usually consists of one or more objects that can interact, move, and undergo deformations. In general, a system can interact with its surroundings. In the special case where a system has *no* interaction with its surroundings, we call it an **isolated system.** As we mentioned earlier, the principle of conservation of energy states that **the total energy in any isolated system is constant, no matter what happens within the system.** Energy cannot be created or destroyed. This statement is believed to be an *absolute* conservation law; no exception has ever been observed. It is one of the core principles of physics.

Here's another example of energy relations: Suppose we use a slingshot to shoot a rock straight upward (Figure 4). For the present, we'll ignore air resistance. Initially, the rock sits in the pouch of the stretched sling (Figure 4a). At this time, the sling's stretched elastic bands hold elastic potential energy. When the pouch is released, the sling propels the rock upward. The sequence in Figure 4b begins where the rock has just lost contact with the pouch. Most of the elastic potential energy that was stored in the sling has now become kinetic energy of the

Karlene V. Schwartz

rock. As the rock rises, it slows; the gravitational potential energy of the system increases as the rock's kinetic energy decreases. The total energy of the system is constant, but there is a transformation from kinetic energy to gravitational potential energy. At the highest point in the rock's path, it comes to rest momentarily and has zero kinetic energy. At this point, all of the energy is gravitational potential energy. As the rock falls, the gravitational potential energy again becomes kinetic energy. Every change in the system represents a transformation or transfer of energy, but *the total* mechanical energy (kinetic plus potential) remains the same.

Dissipation of Mechanical Energy

Real-world systems often include interactions that allow mechanical energy to be transformed into *non*mechanical types of energy. In the case of the slingshot, for instance, we ignored air drag, which would remove kinetic energy from the system without any compensating increase in potential energy. And when the rock hits the ground, all its kinetic energy disappears, and we have a rock sitting on the ground. What became of this lost mechanical energy?

Most of the mechanical energy of this system goes into slightly warming the rock, the air through which it passes, and the ground the rock strikes. To understand this transformation, think about a brick kicked across the floor. As the brick slides, friction eventually brings it to a halt. On a microscopic level, the brick consists of molecules vibrating randomly, held together by a web of springlike bonds (Figure 5). *The hotter an object, the more strongly its molecules vibrate.* This random, atomic-scale vibration is a form of energy called **internal energy.** On a microscopic scale, internal energy consists of the kinetic and potential energies of individual molecules, but it is useful to distinguish it from energy of position and motion of macroscopic (large-scale) objects.

When two objects slide against each other, they catch and tug on each other. These interactions cause the surface molecules of each object to vibrate more strongly. As shown in Figure 6, when friction slows a sliding block, the block's kinetic energy is transformed into internal energy of random vibrations of molecules in the block, the floor, and the surrounding air.

In our slingshot example, the rock may lose kinetic energy to air drag (a form of friction). Figure 7 shows the effect of air drag on a tennis ball. As the ball passes through air, some of its kinetic energy is transferred to the air, increasing the random motion of the air molecules. Thus, air drag converts some of an object's kinetic energy to internal energy of both the air and the surface of the moving object.

Any force, such as friction, that turns mechanical energy into nonmechanical forms of energy, is called a **dissipative** force, because it dissipates (reduces) the mechanical energy in a system, converting it to other forms of energy.

▶ **BIO Application Efficient locomotion through springs.** The hopping gait of kangaroos is exceptionally energy efficient. Much of this efficiency comes from the fact that kangaroo's hind legs are, in effect, big pogo sticks. The massive tendons you see in the photo are elastic, like stiff rubber bands. At the end of each hop, the impact stretches these tendons, transforming energy of motion into elastic potential energy. This stored energy helps to launch the animal on its next hop, thus transforming back to kinetic energy. Because most of the kinetic energy from each hop is saved and reused, the kangaroo's muscles need to add only a little kinetic energy at the start of each hop.

Stretched sling stores elastic potential energy.

(a) Before release

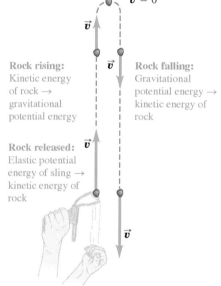

Top of trajectory:
Gravitational potential energy only

$\vec{v} = 0$

$\vec{v}$

Rock rising: $\vec{v}$ Rock falling:
Kinetic energy Gravitational
of rock → potential energy →
gravitational kinetic energy of
potential energy rock

Rock released: $\vec{v}$
Elastic potential
energy of sling →
kinetic energy of
rock

$\vec{v}$

(b) After release

▲ **FIGURE 4** Energy is conserved as it is first transferred from a slingshot to a rock and then transformed between kinetic energy and gravitational potential energy during the rock's flight.

Martin Harvey/Photo Researchers, Inc.

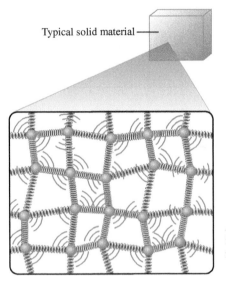

Typical solid material

The atoms and molecules of a solid can be thought of as particles vibrating randomly on springlike bonds. This random vibration is an example of **internal energy**. The stronger the vibration, the hotter is the object.

▲ **FIGURE 5** A simple model of internal energy in a solid.

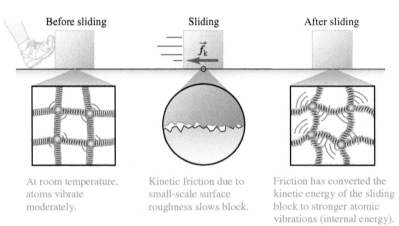

Before sliding   Sliding   After sliding

$\vec{f}_k$

At room temperature, atoms vibrate moderately.

Kinetic friction due to small-scale surface roughness slows block.

Friction has converted the kinetic energy of the sliding block to stronger atomic vibrations (internal energy).

▲ **FIGURE 6** How friction converts kinetic energy to internal energy. The "atomic-scale" view in the square insets represents a far higher level of magnification than the small-scale roughness in the middle inset.

NOTE ▶ When we speak of "dissipation of mechanical energy," we really mean conversion of mechanical energy into other forms. Physicists and engineers sometimes say that a system "loses" mechanical energy. The energy isn't really lost; mechanical energy is transformed into nonmechanical energy, but the total energy (mechanical and nonmechanical) doesn't change. ◀

Let's summarize the key points we've established in this section:

- Energy can take various forms. In this chapter, we'll concentrate on kinetic energy, gravitational potential energy, and elastic potential energy, all of which are forms of mechanical energy.
- The total energy (mechanical plus nonmechanical) of an isolated system is *always* conserved. It can be transferred between objects or transformed into different forms, but its total amount remains the same.
- Mechanical energy can be dissipated to nonmechanical forms of energy. For instance, friction dissipates kinetic energy, converting it to internal energy.

Undisturbed air ahead of the ball. The lines are thin smoke streams.

In the ball's wake, the air's motion is stronger and more random.

NASA

▲ **FIGURE 7** The motion of air in the wake of a tennis ball. This photo is from a wind-tunnel study of the aerodynamics of tennis balls at typical court speeds of over 100 mi/hr. The wind tunnel blows air past a fixed ball, but the effects are exactly the same as for a ball moving through still air. The lines in the air are due to thin smoke streams that are used to make the air's motion visible.

2 Work

In everyday usage, *work* is any activity that requires muscular or mental exertion. Physicists have a much more specific definition, involving a force acting on an object while the object undergoes a displacement. The importance of the concept of work stems from the fact that, in any motion of a particle, the change in *kinetic energy* of the particle equals the total work done by the forces acting on it. We'll develop this relationship in Section 3; but first, let's learn how to calculate work in a variety of situations.

The simplest case is straight-line motion of an object acted on by a constant force $\vec{F}$. When the displacement $\vec{s}$ and force $\vec{F}$ have the same direction (Figure 8), we define the work W done by the force as the product of the magnitudes of these two quantities ($W = Fs$). More generally, if the force makes an angle ϕ with the displacement (Figure 9), then the component of the force along the direction of the displacement is $F_\parallel = F\cos\phi$ (where the subscript $\parallel$ means *parallel,* indicating that this component is parallel to the direction of displacement). We can now define work as the product of the *component* of force in the direction of displacement and the magnitude s of the displacement.

$\vec{F}$

x

$\vec{s}$

▲ **FIGURE 8** Work is the product of the magnitudes of a displacement $\vec{s}$ and a constant force $\vec{F}$ in the direction of $\vec{s}$.

▲ **FIGURE 9** The work done by a constant force $\vec{F}$ during a straight-line displacement $\vec{s}$ is $(F\cos\phi)s$.

Definition of work

When an object undergoes a displacement $\vec{s}$ with magnitude s along a straight line, while a constant force $\vec{F}$ with magnitude F, making an angle ϕ with $\vec{s}$ (Figure 9), acts on the object, the **work** done by the force on the object is

$$W = F_{\parallel}s = (F\cos\phi)s. \tag{1}$$

Unit: joule (J). In SI units, the unit of force is the newton, the unit of distance is the meter, and their product is the *newton-meter* $(\text{N} \cdot \text{m})$. This combination appears so often in mechanics that we give it a special name, the **joule** (abbreviated J and pronounced "jewel"). It was named in honor of the English physicist James Prescott Joule:

$$1 \text{ joule} = 1 \text{ newton-meter} \quad \text{or} \quad 1 \text{ J} = 1 \text{ N} \cdot \text{m}.$$

In the British system, the unit of force is the pound (lb), the unit of distance is the foot, and the unit of work is the *foot-pound* $(\text{ft} \cdot \text{lb})$. The following conversions are useful:

$$1 \text{ J} = 0.7376 \text{ ft} \cdot \text{lb}, \qquad 1 \text{ ft} \cdot \text{lb} = 1.356 \text{ J}.$$

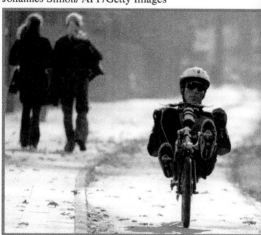

▲ **Application Low and sleek.** Many engineering problems boil down to reducing dissipative forces. For instance, a standard bicycle places the rider in a position that catches a lot of wind, creating significant air drag. On a recumbent bicycle, the rider's low profile causes much less air drag. The real-life difference is so great that, in 1933, a second-string racer rode a recumbent at nearly 30 miles an hour, smashing by 10% a record almost 20 years old. After that, recumbent bicycles were banned from racing. A *fairing*—an aerodynamic shell—further reduces air drag and thus increases speed even more; faired recumbent bicycles can travel 36 mph and can break 65 mph for short distances.

EXAMPLE 1 **Pushing a stalled car**

Steve is trying to impress Elaine with his new car, but the engine dies in the middle of an intersection. While Elaine steers, Steve pushes the car 19 m to clear the intersection. If he pushes with a constant force with magnitude 210 N (about 47 lb), how much work does he do on the car **(a)** if he pushes in the direction the car is heading and **(b)** if he pushes at 30° to that direction?

SOLUTION

SET UP AND SOLVE From Equation 1, $W = F\cos\phi \, s$.

Part (a): When Steve pushes in the direction the car is headed, $\phi = 0$, $\cos\phi = 1$, and

$$W = (F\cos\phi)s = (210 \text{ N})(1)(19 \text{ m}) = 4.0 \times 10^3 \text{ J}.$$

Part (b): In this case, $\phi = 30°$, $\cos\phi = 0.866$, and

$$W = (F\cos\phi)s = (210 \text{ N})(0.866)(19 \text{ m}) = 3.5 \times 10^3 \text{ J}.$$

REFLECT In part (a), Steve pushed the car in the direction he wanted it to go. In (b), he pushed at an angle of 30° to that direction. Only the component of force in the direction of the car's motion, $F\cos\phi$ is effective in moving the car.

Practice Problem: What force would be required for Steve to do as much work when he pushes at $\phi = 30°$ as when he pushed in the $\phi = 0$ direction? *Answer:* 240 N.

It's important to understand that work is a *scalar* quantity, even though it is calculated by using two vector quantities (force and displacement). A 5 N force toward the east acting on an object that moves 6 m to the east does exactly the same 30 J of work as a 5 N force toward the north acting on an object that moves 6 m to the north. Work can be positive or negative. When the force has a component in the *same direction* as the displacement (ϕ between zero and 90°), $\cos\phi$ in

MasteringPHYSICS

ActivPhysics 5.1: Work Calculations

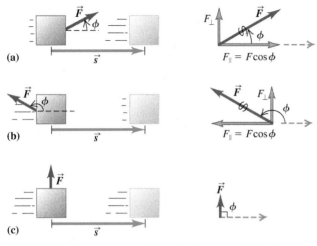

The force has a component in the direction of displacement:
• The work on the object is positive. (The object speeds up.)
• $W = F_\parallel s = (F\cos\phi)s$

The force has a component opposite to the direction of displacement:
• The work on the object is negative. (The object slows down.)
• $W = F_\parallel s = (F\cos\phi)s$
• Mathematically, $W < 0$ because $F\cos\phi$ is negative for $90° < \phi < 270°$.

The force is perpendicular to the direction of displacement:
• The force does *no* work on the object.
• More generally, if a force acting on an object has a component $F_\perp$ perpendicular to the object's displacement, that component does no work on the object.

▲ **FIGURE 10** Three cases in which a single constant force does work on an object.

Equation 1 is positive, and the work W is *positive* (Figure 10a). When the force has a component *opposite* to the displacement (ϕ between $90°$ and $270°$), $\cos\phi$ is negative, and the work is *negative* (Figure 10b). When the force is *perpendicular* to the displacement, $\phi = 90°$, and the work done by the force is *zero* (Figure 10c).

Conceptual Analysis 1

Work and orbital motion

A communications satellite moves in a circular orbit at constant speed in response to gravity, as shown in Figure 11. Which of the following statements is correct?

A. The earth does positive work on the satellite.
B. The earth does negative work on the satellite.
C. The earth does no work on the satellite.
D. Once a coordinate system is specified, the work changes sign every half orbit, so that the average work is zero.

▲ **FIGURE 11** A satellite in a circular orbit.

SOLUTION In circular gravitational orbits, the force on the orbiting object is always perpendicular to the object's velocity, as indicated in the figure. The displacement of the object is always along the direction of the velocity, so the force is always perpendicular to the displacement. Therefore, $F_\parallel = 0$, and the work is zero for any displacement along the orbit. This result still might seem confusing, since your intuition may correctly guess that orbiting objects have energy. But remember that *work is the transfer of energy that changes an object's speed.* Since the speed of an object is constant in uniform circular motion, $W = 0$, and all answers other than choice C can be rejected. As we'll see later, energy is required to set an object in orbital motion, and the orbital system holds onto this energy, but no additional energy needs to be supplied to maintain the object in its orbit. Our solar system has been executing orbital motion for about 5 billion years and does not require an energy source to maintain its orbits.

We always speak of work done *by* a specific force *on* a particular object. Always be sure to specify exactly what force is doing the work you are talking about. When a spring is stretched, the work done on the spring by the stretching force is positive. When an object is lifted, the work done on the object by the lifting force is positive. However, the work done by the *gravitational* force on an object being lifted is *negative* because the (downward) gravitational force is opposite to the (upward) displacement. You might think it is "hard work" to hold this book out at arm's length for five minutes, but you aren't actually doing any work at all on the book, because there is no displacement. Even when you walk with constant velocity on a level floor while carrying the book, you do no work on it, because the (vertical) supporting force you exert on the book has no component in the direction of the (horizontal) motion. In this case, in Equation 1, $\phi = 90°$ and $\cos\phi = 0$. When an object slides along a surface, the work done by the normal force acting on the object is zero; and when an object moves in a circle, the work done by the centripetal force on the object is also zero. (See Figure 11.).

How do we calculate work when several forces act on an object? One way is to use Equation 1 to compute the work done by each separate force. Then, because work is a scalar quantity, the *total* work W_{total} done on the object by all the forces is the algebraic sum of the quantities of work done by the individual forces. An alternative route to finding the total work is to compute the vector sum (resultant) of the forces and then use this vector sum as $\vec{F}$ in Equation 1.

EXAMPLE 2   **Sliding down a ramp**

A package with mass m is unloaded from a truck with an inclined ramp, as shown in Figure 12. The ramp has rollers that eliminate friction, and the truck unloads the package from an initial height h. The ramp is inclined at an angle β. Find an algebraic expression in terms of these quantities for the work done on the package during its trip down the ramp.

▲ **FIGURE 12** A package sliding down a friction-less ramp.

SOLUTION

SET UP Figure 13 shows our sketches. We diagram the situation, indicating the package's displacement $\vec{s}$ and the height h. Then we draw a free-body diagram for the package, pointing the x axis in the direction of the displacement. Only the weight has a component parallel to the direction of displacement, so only this force does work on the package. The normal force $\vec{n}$ is perpendicular to the displacement, so it does no work on the package.

SOLVE We solve for the work done on the package by the x (parallel) component of weight. Notice, however, that the angle we are given, β, is *not* the angle between the direction of displacement and the weight force (ϕ in Figure 13b). To use Equation 1 directly, we could define $\phi = 90 - \beta$. Instead, we choose to use β directly, modifying the trigonometry to fit. Because weight is the only force doing work on the package, the work done on the package is

$$W = (F\sin\beta)s$$
$$= (mg\sin\beta)s.$$

The statement of the problem gives the height h rather than the distance s measured along the ramp, but we can solve for h by recognizing from the geometry in Figure 13 that $s\sin\beta = h$. Therefore,

$$W = (mg\sin\beta)s = mgh.$$

REFLECT Because we are neglecting friction, the only force that does work on the package is its weight mg. We've found that the work W is the product of the weight mg and the vertical distance h through which the package falls. In Section 5, we'll restate this result in terms of potential energy, which we haven't yet defined precisely. We'll find that the work done on the package is the negative of the change in the potential energy. When the force of gravity does a positive amount of work $W = mgh$ on the package, the potential energy must decrease by the same amount. The work done on the package by gravity depends only on the change in the package's vertical position h.

(a) Sketch of situation

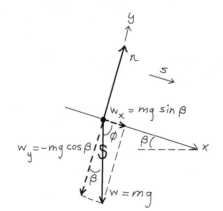

(b) Free-body diagram of package

▲ **FIGURE 13** Our sketches for this problem.

EXAMPLE 3   **Work done by several forces**

Farmer Johnson hitches his tractor to a sled loaded with firewood and pulls it a distance of 20.0 m along level frozen ground (Figure 14a). The total weight of sled and load is 14,700 N. The tractor exerts a constant force $\vec{F}_T$ with magnitude 5000 N at an angle of $\phi = 36.9°$ above the horizontal, as shown. A constant 3500 N friction force opposes the motion. Find the work done on the sled by each force individually and the total work done on the sled by all the forces.

SOLUTION

SET UP Figure 14b shows a free-body diagram and a coordinate system, identifying all the forces acting on the sled. As in the preceding example, we point the x axis in the direction of displacement.

SOLVE The work W_w done by the weight is zero because its direction is perpendicular to the displacement. (The angle between the two directions is 90°, and the cosine of the angle is zero.) For the same reason, the work W_n done by the normal force $\vec{n}$ (which, incidentally, is *not* equal in magnitude to the weight) is also zero. So $W_w = W_n = 0$.

That leaves F_T and f. From Equation 1, the work W_T done by the tractor is (with $\cos \phi = \cos 36.9° = 0.800$)

$$W_T = (F_T \cos\phi)s$$
$$= (5000\ N)(0.800)(20.0\ m) = 80,000\ N \cdot m = 80.0\ kJ.$$

The friction force f is opposite to the displacement, so, for this force, $\phi = 180°$ and $\cos\phi = -1$. The work W_f done by the friction force is

$$W_f = fs \cos 180° = -(3500\ N)(20.0\ m)$$
$$= -70,000\ N \cdot m = -70.0\ kJ.$$

The total work W_{total} done by all of the forces on the sled is the algebraic sum (*not* the vector sum) of the work done by the individual forces:

$$W_{total} = W_T + W_w + W_n + W_f$$
$$= 80.0\ kJ + 0 + 0 + (-70.0\ kJ) = 10.0\ kJ.$$

Alternative Solution: In the alternative approach, we first find the vector sum (resultant) of the forces and then use it to compute the total work. The vector sum is best found by using components. From Figure 14b,

$$\Sigma F_x = (5000\ N) \cos 36.9° - 3500\ N = 500\ N,$$
$$\Sigma F_y = (5000\ N) \sin 36.9° + n + (-14,700\ N).$$

We don't really need the second equation; we know that the y component of force is perpendicular to the displacement, so it does no work. Besides, there is no y component of acceleration, so ΣF_y has to be zero anyway. The work done by the total x component is therefore the total work:

$$W_{total} = (500\ N)(20.0\ m) = 10,000\ J = 10.0\ kJ.$$

This is the same result that we found by computing the work of each force separately.

REFLECT Be sure you understand why the two solution methods are equivalent and give the same result.

Practice Problem: Suppose the tractor pulls horizontally on the sled instead of at an angle of 36.9°. As a result, the magnitude of the friction force increases to 4400 N. What is the total work done on the sled? *Answer:* $1.20 \times 10^4\ J$.

(a)

(b) Free-body diagram of sled

▲ **FIGURE 14** (a) A tractor pulls a sled. (b) Our sketch for this problem.

3 Work and Kinetic Energy

Now we're ready to develop the relation between the work done on an object and that object's change in kinetic energy. This important relationship is called the *work–energy theorem* (more precisely, the work–kinetic energy theorem).

Let's consider a particle with mass m moving along the x axis under the action of a constant net force with magnitude F_{total} directed along the x axis. The particle's acceleration is constant and is given by Newton's second law, $F_{total} = ma$. Suppose the particle's speed increases from v_i to v_f while the particle undergoes a displacement s from point x_i to x_f. Using the constant-acceleration equation and replacing v_{0x} by v_i, v_x by v_f, and $(x - x_0)$ by s, we have

$$v_f^2 = v_i^2 + 2as,$$
$$a = \frac{v_f^2 - v_i^2}{2s}.$$

When we multiply the last equation by m and replace ma with F_{total}, we obtain

$$F_{total} = ma = m\frac{v_f^2 - v_i^2}{2s}$$

and

$$F_{total}s = \tfrac{1}{2}mv_f^2 - \tfrac{1}{2}mv_i^2. \tag{2}$$

The product $F_{total}s$ is the work done by the net force F_{total} and thus is equal to the total work W_{total} done by all the forces. In Section 1, we defined the quantity $\tfrac{1}{2}mv^2$ as kinetic energy. We'll denote this quantity as K. Then

$$K = \tfrac{1}{2}mv^2. \tag{3}$$

The first term on the right side of Equation 2 is the final kinetic energy of the particle, $K_f = \tfrac{1}{2}mv_f^2$ (after the displacement). The second term is the initial kinetic energy, $K_i = \tfrac{1}{2}mv_i^2$, and the difference between these terms is the *change* in the particle's kinetic energy during the displacement s. So Equation 2 relates the particle's change in kinetic energy to the work done by the forces that act on the particle.

Work–energy theorem

The kinetic energy K of a particle with mass m moving with speed v is $K = \tfrac{1}{2}mv^2$. During any displacement of the particle, the work done by the net external force on it is equal to its change in kinetic energy, or

$$W_{total} = K_f - K_i = \Delta K. \tag{4}$$

This theorem is the foundation for most of what follows in this chapter.

Kinetic energy, like work, is a scalar quantity. It can never be negative, although work can be either positive or negative. The kinetic energy of a moving particle depends only on its speed (the magnitude of its velocity), not on the direction of its motion. A car (viewed as a particle) has the same kinetic energy when going north at 5 m/s as when going east at 5 m/s. The *change* in kinetic energy during any displacement is determined by the total work W_{total} done by all the forces acting on the particle. When W_{total} is *positive,* the particle speeds up during the displacement, K_f is greater than K_i, and the kinetic energy *increases.* When W_{total} is *negative,* the kinetic energy and speed *decrease;* and when $W_{total} = 0$, K is *constant.*

In SI units, m is measured in kilograms and v in meters per second, so the quantity $\tfrac{1}{2}mv^2$ (kinetic energy) has the units $kg \cdot m^2/s^2$. From Equation 2 or Equation 4, kinetic energy must have the same units as work, which we saw is measured in joules (newton-meters). To confirm that these units are the same, we recall from Newton's second law that $1\,N = 1\,kg \cdot m/s^2$, so

$$1\,J = 1\,N \cdot m = 1(kg \cdot m/s^2) \cdot m = 1\,kg \cdot m^2/s^2.$$

The joule is the SI unit of both work and kinetic energy and, indeed, as we will see later, of all kinds of energy. In the British system,

$$1 \text{ ft} \cdot \text{lb} = 1 \text{ ft} \cdot \text{slug} \cdot \text{ft}/\text{s}^2 = 1 \text{ slug} \cdot \text{ft}^2/\text{s}^2.$$

NOTE ▶ In calculating W_{total} for Equation 4, remember what we learned in Section 2: First, only the component of net force parallel to the displacement does work on the particle; second, W_{total} can be calculated either as the work done by the net force or as the algebraic sum of the amounts of work done by the individual forces. ◄

Conceptual Analysis 2

Work and kinetic energy

Two blocks of ice, one twice as heavy as the other, are at rest on a frozen lake. A person pushes each block a distance of 5 m with a constant force (the same magnitude of force for each block). Assume that friction may be neglected. The kinetic energy of the light block after the push is

A. smaller than that of the heavy block.
B. equal to that of the heavy block.
C. larger than that of the heavy block.

SOLUTION Three forces act on each block: its weight, the normal force exerted by the surface, and the push applied by the person. The weight and the normal force are perpendicular to the displacement, so they do no work on the block. Only the person's push does work on each block. Both this force and the displacement are the same for the two blocks, so the amounts of work done on them are equal. The work–energy theorem, $W_{\text{total}} = K_{\text{f}} - K_{\text{i}} = \Delta K$, says that the change in each block's kinetic energy equals the net work done on it. Both blocks have the same initial kinetic energy ($K_{\text{i}} = 0$) and have equal amounts of work done on them. Therefore, they must have equal final kinetic energies K_{f}. Answer B is correct.

PROBLEM-SOLVING STRATEGY 1 **Work and kinetic energy**

SET UP

1. Draw a free-body diagram; make sure you show all the forces that act on the object. List the forces; represent any unknown forces by algebraic symbols.
2. List the initial and final kinetic energies K_{i} and K_{f}. If a quantity such as v_{i} or v_{f} is unknown, express it in terms of an algebraic symbol. When you calculate kinetic energies, make sure you use the *mass* of the object, not its *weight*.

SOLVE

3. Calculate the total work done on the object. You can do this in either of two ways: by calculating the work done by each individual force and taking the algebraic sum (usually the easiest method) or by finding the net force and then calculating the work it does on the object. Be sure to check signs. When a force has a component in the same direction as the displacement, its work is positive; when the direction is opposite to the displacement, the work is negative. When force and displacement are perpendicular, the work is zero.
4. Use the relationship $W_{\text{total}} = K_{\text{f}} - K_{\text{i}} = \Delta K$; insert the results from the preceding steps and solve for whatever unknown is required.

REFLECT

5. Remember that kinetic energy can never be negative. If you come up with a negative K, you've made a mistake. Maybe you interchanged subscripts i and f or made a sign error in one of the calculations of work.

EXAMPLE 4 **Using work and energy to calculate speed**

Let's revisit the sled from Example 3. The free-body diagram is shown again in Figure 15. We found that the total work done on the sled by all the forces is $10{,}000 \text{ J} = 10.0 \text{ kJ}$, so the kinetic energy of the sled must increase by 10.0 kJ. The mass of the sled is $m = (14{,}700 \text{ N})/(9.80 \text{ m/s}^2) = 1500 \text{ kg}$. Suppose the sled's initial speed v_{i} is 2.00 m/s. What is its final speed?

Continued

SOLUTION

SET UP Steps 1 and 2 of the problem-solving strategy were done in Example 3, where we found that $W_{total} = 10.0$ kJ. The initial kinetic energy K_i is

$$K_i = \tfrac{1}{2}mv_i^2$$
$$= \tfrac{1}{2}(1500 \text{ kg})(2.00 \text{ m/s})^2 = 3000 \text{ kg} \cdot \text{m}^2/\text{s}^2 = 3000 \text{ J}.$$

The final kinetic energy K_f is

$$K_f = \tfrac{1}{2}(1500 \text{ kg})v_f^2,$$

where v_f is the unknown final speed that we want to find.

SOLVE Equation 4 gives

$$K_f = K_i + W_{total},$$
$$\tfrac{1}{2}(1500 \text{ kg})v_f^2 = 3000 \text{ J} + 10,000 \text{ J} = 13,000 \text{ J}.$$

Solving for v_f, we find

$$v_f = 4.16 \text{ m/s}.$$

REFLECT This problem can also be done without the work–energy theorem. We can find the acceleration from $F = ma$ and then use the equations of motion with constant acceleration to find v_f. (Recall from Example 3 that the sled moves through a displacement of 20.0 m.) We have

$$a = \frac{F}{m} = \frac{4000 \text{ N} - 3500 \text{ N}}{1500 \text{ kg}} = 0.333 \text{ m/s}^2,$$

and

$$v_f^2 = v_i^2 + 2as = (2.0 \text{ m/s})^2 + 2(0.333 \text{ m/s}^2)(20 \text{ m})$$
$$= 17.3 \text{ m}^2/\text{s}^2,$$
$$v_f = 4.16 \text{ m/s}.$$

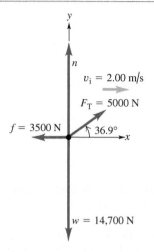

▲ **FIGURE 15** The free-body diagram from Example 3.

The work–energy approach lets us avoid the intermediate step of finding the acceleration. You'll find several other examples and problems in this chapter and the next that *can* be done without using energy considerations, but that are easier when energy methods are used. Also, when a problem can be done by two different methods, doing it both ways is always a good way to check your work.

Practice Problem: If the tractor pulls horizontally and the friction force again has magnitude 4400 N, find the magnitude of the force the tractor must exert to make the sled move with constant speed. Verify that in this case the kinetic energy of the sled doesn't change. *Answer:* 4400 N.

EXAMPLE 5 **Forces on a hammerhead**

In a pile driver, a steel hammerhead with mass 200 kg is lifted 3.00 m above the top of a vertical I-beam being driven into the ground (Figure 16a). The hammer is then dropped, driving the I-beam 40 cm farther into the ground. The vertical rails that guide the hammerhead exert a constant 60.0 N friction force on it. Use the work–energy theorem to find **(a)** the speed of the hammerhead just as it hits the I-beam and **(b)** the average force the hammerhead exerts on the I-beam.

SOLUTION

SET UP Figures 16b and 16c are free-body diagrams for the hammerhead during two intervals: first, while it falls (from point 1 to point 2 in Figure 16a) and second, while it pushes the I-beam (from point 2 to point 3). Because the displacement is vertical, any horizontal forces that may be present do no work. Therefore, our free-body diagrams show only the vertical forces on the hammerhead.

SOLVE The forces on the hammerhead during the 3.00 m drop are its weight, with magnitude $mg = (200 \text{ kg})(9.80 \text{ m/s}^2) = 1960$ N and the upward friction force, with magnitude 60.0 N. The net

downward force on the hammerhead has magnitude 1900 N, and the total work done on it during the 3.00 m drop is

$$W_{total} = (1900 \text{ N})(3.00 \text{ m}) = 5700 \text{ J}.$$

Part (a): In place of our usual subscripts i and f, we'll use 1 and 2, referring to points 1 and 2 in Figure 16. The hammerhead is initially at rest (point 1), so its initial kinetic energy K_1 is zero. Equation 4 gives

$$W_{total} = K_2 - K_1,$$
$$5700 \text{ J} = \tfrac{1}{2}(200 \text{ kg})v_2^2 - 0,$$
$$v_2 = 7.55 \text{ m/s}.$$

Continued

This is the hammerhead's speed at point 2, just as it hits the beam.

Part (b): We now consider the interval from point 2 to point 3, during which the hammerhead pushes the I-beam through a downward displacement of 7.40 cm. As shown in Figure 16c, the hammerhead now also is acted upon by an upward normal force $\vec{n}$ (which we assume is constant). At point 3, where the hammerhead comes to rest, its kinetic energy K_3 is again zero. The work W_n done by the normal force is

$$W_n = (F\cos\phi)s$$
$$= (n\cos 180°)(0.0740 \text{ m}) = n(-1)(0.0740 \text{ m}).$$

The total work done on the hammerhead during its displacement of 0.0740 m is the sum of the work done by the weight, the friction force, and the normal force. We already know that the vector sum of the weight and friction forces has a magnitude of 1900 N, so we sum the work done by that resultant force and by the normal force:

$$W_{\text{total}} = (1900 \text{ N})(0.0740 \text{ m}) + n(0.0740 \text{ m})(-1).$$

The total work is equal to the change in kinetic energy, $K_3 - K_2 = 0 - 5700$ J, so we have

$$(1900 \text{ N} - n)(0.0740 \text{ m}) = 0 - 5700 \text{ J},$$
$$n = 79,000 \text{ N}.$$

The force *on* the I-beam is the equal, but opposite, *downward* reaction force of 79,000 N (about 9 tons).

REFLECT The total change in the hammerhead's kinetic energy during the whole process is zero; a relatively small force does positive work over a large distance, and then a much larger force does negative work over a much smaller distance. The same thing happens if you speed your car up gradually and then drive it into a brick wall. The very large force needed to reduce the kinetic energy to zero over a short distance is what does the damage to your car—and possibly to you!

Practice Problem: Suppose the pile is driven 15.0 cm instead of 7.4 cm. What force (assumed constant) is exerted on it? *Answer:* 39,900 N.

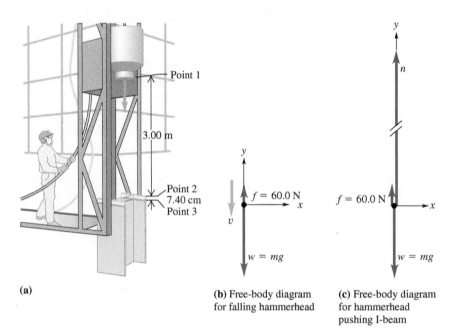

(a)

Point 1

3.00 m

Point 2
7.40 cm
Point 3

y

$f = 60.0$ N

x

v

$w = mg$

(b) Free-body diagram for falling hammerhead

y

n

$f = 60.0$ N

x

$w = mg$

(c) Free-body diagram for hammerhead pushing I-beam

▲ **FIGURE 16**

NOTE ▶ Because we used Newton's laws in deriving the work–kinetic energy theorem, we must use the theorem only in an inertial frame of reference. The speeds we use to compute the kinetic energies and the distances we use to compute work *must* be measured in an inertial frame. But the work–energy theorem is valid in *all* inertial frames. For a given situation, the work and kinetic energies will be different in different frames of reference because the speed of an object is different in different frames. ◀

4 Work Done by a Varying Force

In Section 2, we defined work done by a *constant* force. But what happens when you stretch a spring? The more you stretch it, the harder you have to pull, so the force is *not* constant as the spring is stretched. You can think of many other situations in which a force that varies, in both magnitude and direction, acts on an

▶ **BIO Application Nature's rubber bands.** Biologists used to believe that tendons and ligaments were simple straps, without significant elasticity. We now know that they are often elastic, like very stiff rubber bands, and that their elasticity is central to their function in the body. The photo shows the microscopic basis of tendon and ligament elasticity. The fibers you see consist of collagen, a tough, fibrous protein that is the main constituent of tendon and ligament tissue. Notice that the collagen fibers are wavy. As the tissue stretches, these wavy fibers straighten out; then they pull back to their equilibrium wavy configuration when released.

Biology Media/Photo Researchers, Inc.

object moving along a curved path. We need to be able to compute the work done by the force in these more general situations.

To add only one complication at a time, let's consider straight-line motion under the influence of a force that is directed along the line, but that may change in magnitude as the object moves. For example, imagine a train on a straight track, with the engineer constantly changing the locomotive's throttle setting or applying the brakes. Suppose a particle moves along the x axis from point x_i to point x_f, as shown in Figure 17a. Figure 17b is a graph of the x component of force as a function of the particle's coordinate x. To find the work done by this force, we divide the total displacement into small segments Δx_1, Δx_2, and so on (Figure 17c). We approximate the work done by the force during segment Δx_1 as the average force F_{1x} in that segment, multiplied by its length Δx_1. We do this for each segment and then add the results for all the segments. The work done by the force in the total displacement from x_i to x_f is approximately

$$W = F_{1x}\,\Delta x_1 + F_{2x}\,\Delta x_2 + F_{3x}\,\Delta x_3 + \cdots.$$

We see that $F_{1x}\,\Delta x_1$ represents the *area* of the first vertical strip in Figure 17c, $F_{2x}\,\Delta x_2$ the area of the second, and so on. The sum represents the area under the curve of Figure 17b between x_i and x_f. **On a graph of force as a function of position, the total work done by the force is represented by the area under the curve between the initial and final positions.**

Now let's apply this analysis to a stretched spring. To keep a spring stretched an amount x beyond its unstretched length, we have to apply a force with magnitude F at each end (Figure 18). If the elongation is not too great, the spring obeys Hooke's law; that is, F is directly proportional to x, or

$$F = kx, \tag{5}$$

where k is a constant called the force constant (or spring constant) of the spring. Equation 5 shows that the units of k are force divided by distance. In SI, the units are N/m.

Suppose we apply forces with equal magnitude and opposite direction to the ends of the spring and gradually increase the forces, starting from zero. We hold the left end stationary; the force at this end does no work on the spring. The force at the moving end *does* do work. Figure 19 is a graph of the x component of force, F_x, as a function of x (the elongation of the spring). The total work done on the spring by the force F_x when the elongation goes from zero to a maximum value X is represented by the area under the graph (the shaded triangle in the figure). The area is equal to half the product of the base (X) and altitude (kX), or

$$W = \tfrac{1}{2}(X)(kX) = \tfrac{1}{2}kX^2. \tag{6}$$

This result also says that the work is equal to the *average* force $kX/2$, multiplied by the total displacement X. Thus, the total work is proportional to the *square* of the final elongation X. When the elongation is doubled, the total work needed increases by a factor of four.

The spring also exerts a force on the hand, which moves during the stretching process. The displacement of the hand is the same as that of the

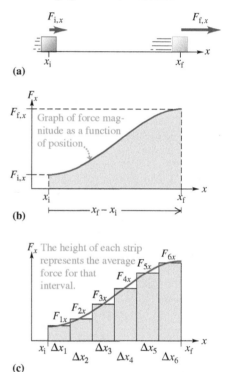

Particle moving from x_i to x_f in response to a changing force in the x direction

(a)

(b)

(c)

▲ **FIGURE 17** Graphs of force as a function of displacement for a particle moving in response to a varying force.

▲ **FIGURE 18** The force needed to stretch an ideal spring is proportional to the elongation: $F_x = kx$ (Hooke's law).

The area under the curve represents the work done on the spring as the spring is stretched from $x = 0$ to a maximum value X:

$$W = \tfrac{1}{2}kX^2$$

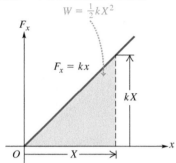

▲ FIGURE 19 The work done in stretching a spring is equal to the area of the shaded triangle.

moving end of the spring, but the force on it is opposite in direction to the force on the spring, because the two forces form an action–reaction pair. Thus, the work done *on* the hand *by* the spring is the negative of the work done on the spring, namely, $-\tfrac{1}{2}kX^2$. In problems involving work and its relation to kinetic energy, we will nearly always want to find the work done *by* a force *on* the object under study, and we have to be careful to write work quantities with the correct sign.

Now, suppose the spring is stretched a distance x_i at the start. Then the work we have to do on it to stretch it to a greater elongation x_f is

$$W = \tfrac{1}{2}kx_f^2 - \tfrac{1}{2}kx_i^2. \tag{7}$$

If the spring has spaces between the coils when it is unstretched, then it can be compressed as well as stretched, and Hooke's law holds for compression as well as stretching. In this case, F and x in Equation 5 are both negative, the force again has the same direction as the displacement, and the work done by F is again positive. So the total work is still given by Equation 6 or 7, even when X or either or both of x_i and x_f are negative.

 Quantitative Analysis 3   **Stretching a spring**

A spring is stretched from $x = 0$ to $x = 2a$, as shown in Figure 20a. Is more energy required to stretch the spring through the first half of this displacement (from $x = 0$ to $x = a$) or through the second half (from $x = a$ to $x = 2a$)?

SOLUTION Hooke's law $(F_x = kx)$ tells us that the force required to stretch a spring increases with increasing elongation. Thus, more energy is required to stretch the spring through the second half of its displacement. The graph in Figure 20b shows how much more. As we've seen, the area under a graph of force versus displacement for an object represents the work done by the force on the object. In this case, the area under the curve for the second half of the displacement can be divided into three triangles, each of which has an area equal to that under the curve for the first half. Thus, three times as much energy is needed to stretch the spring through the second half of the displacement than through the first half.

(a) Stretching a spring through two equal halves of a total displacement $2a$

This half of the area can be divided into three triangles, each equal in area to the triangle under the first half of the curve.

(b) Force-versus-distance curve for the two halves of the displacement

▲ FIGURE 20

EXAMPLE 6   **Work done on a spring scale**

A woman weighing 600 N steps on a bathroom scale containing a heavy spring (Figure 21). The spring compresses by 1.0 cm under her weight. Find the force constant of the spring and the total work done on it during the compression.

Because of our choice of axis, both the force component and displacement are negative. The work on the spring is positive.

► FIGURE 21 Compressing the spring of a bathroom scale.

Continued

SOLUTION

SET UP AND SOLVE If positive values of x correspond to elongation, then $x = -0.010$ m when $F_x = -600$ N. We need to use Equation 5 (Hooke's law) to find the force constant k and then use Equation 6 to find the work W done on the spring. We have

$$k = \frac{F_x}{x} = \frac{-600 \text{ N}}{-0.010 \text{ m}} = 6.0 \times 10^4 \text{ N/m},$$

$$W = \tfrac{1}{2}kX^2 = \tfrac{1}{2}(6.0 \times 10^4 \text{ N/m})(-0.010 \text{ m})^2$$
$$= 3.0 \text{ N} \cdot \text{m} = 3.0 \text{ J}.$$

REFLECT The force of gravity is the woman's weight, a constant 600 N. As she steps on the scale, the force pushing down on the top of the spring varies from 0 to 600 N, with an average value of 300 N, as it is compressed 0.010 m. The total work done on the spring is the average force (300 N) multiplied by the displacement (0.010 m), or 3.0 J.

Practice Problem: Suppose we want to modify the scale to permit a weight of 900 N when the spring is compressed 1.00 cm. What should the force constant of the spring be? *Answer:* $9.0 \times 10^4 \text{ N/m}$.

5 Potential Energy

An object gains or loses kinetic energy because it interacts with other objects that exert forces on it. We've learned that, during any interaction, the change in a particle's kinetic energy is equal to the total work done on the particle by the forces that act on it during the interaction.

But there are many situations in which it seems as though kinetic energy has been *stored* in a system, to be recovered later. It's like a savings account in a bank: You deposit money, and then you can draw it out later. When we raise the steel hammerhead of Example 5 into the air, we're storing energy in the system, energy that is later converted into kinetic energy as the hammer is released and falls back down. Or consider the humble pogo stick, in which a spring is compressed as you jump on the stick and then rebounds, launching you into the air. Or a mousetrap, in which the spring stores energy that is released when the trigger is tripped. And so on.

All these examples point to the idea of an energy associated with the *position* of bodies in a system. In some cases, changes in this energy may accompany opposite changes in kinetic energy in such a way that the *total* energy remains constant, or is *conserved*. Energy associated with position is called potential energy, and forces that can be associated with a potential energy are called **conservative forces.** A system in which the total mechanical energy, kinetic and potential, is constant, is called a **conservative system.** As we'll see, there is potential energy associated with an object's weight and its height above the ground. There is also potential energy associated with *elastic* deformations of an object, such as stretching or compressing a spring (Figure 21).

Another way to look at potential energy is that "potential" refers to the potential for a force to do work on an object. When the pile-driver hammer is raised, the earth's gravitational force (the hammer's weight) gains the *opportunity* to do work on the hammer as it falls. When we set a mousetrap, we give it the opportunity to do work on whatever is in its way when the spring snaps back. So potential energy is associated with the opportunity, or potential, to do work.

The kinetic energy of a falling object increases as it drops because a force (the earth's gravity, or, in other words, the object's weight) is doing positive work on it. Remember, $W_{\text{total}} = \Delta K$. Another way to say this is that the kinetic energy increases because the potential energy decreases. When the force we are considering (such as the pile-driver's weight) does positive work, the potential energy must decrease. So we can think of potential energy as a shorthand way to calculate the work done by some of the forces in a system.

Gravitational Potential Energy

To begin our detailed study of potential energy, let's apply the work–energy theorem to the work done on an object when it moves under the action of the earth's

Michael Yamashita/Corbis

▲ **BIO Application Energy-efficient transport.** In Indonesia and other countries, some women are known to carry loads of up to 70% of their body weight in baskets on their heads. Westerners who attempt to carry a load in this way expend almost twice as much energy as people who do it normally. This puzzling difference prompted an additional study, which found that, when Westerners walk, they have more up-and-down motion than do women accustomed to carrying baskets. For larger vertical motion, more work is done by gravity on the load; thus, more energy is required to raise the load a higher distance against the force of gravity.

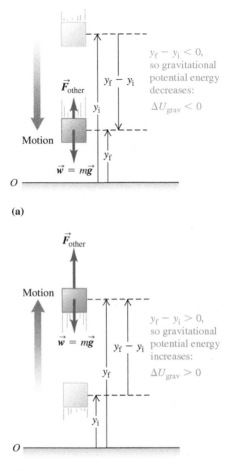

(a)

(b)

▲ **FIGURE 22** The work done by the gravitational force w as an object moves downward or upward changes the gravitational potential energy.

gravitational force (again, the object's weight). This will lead directly to the concept of *gravitational potential energy*—energy associated with the *position* of the object relative to the earth.

Let's consider an object with mass m that moves along the (vertical) y axis (Figure 22). The forces acting on the object are its weight, with magnitude $w = mg$, and possibly some other forces; we call the resultant of all the other forces $\vec{F}_{\text{other}}$. We'll assume that the object stays close enough to earth's surface that the weight is constant. We want to find the work done by the weight when the object drops from a height y_i above the origin to a smaller height y_f (Figure 22a). The weight and displacement are in the same direction, so the work W_{grav} done on the object by its weight is positive and is given by

$$W_{\text{grav}} = Fs = mg(y_i - y_f) = mgy_i - mgy_f. \tag{8}$$

This expression also gives the correct work when the object moves upward and y_f is greater than y_i (Figure 22b). In that case, the quantity $(y_i - y_f)$ is negative, and W_{grav} is negative because the weight and displacement are opposite in direction.

Equation 8 shows that we can express W_{grav} in terms of the values of the quantity mgy at the beginning and at the end of the displacement. This quantity, the product of the weight mg and the height y above the origin of coordinates, is called the gravitational potential energy and is denoted by U_{grav}.

Definition of gravitational potential energy

When an object with mass m is a vertical distance y above the origin of coordinates, in a uniform gravitational field g, the gravitational potential energy U_{grav} of the system is

$$U_{\text{grav}} = mgy. \tag{9}$$

Like work and all forms of energy, gravitational potential energy is measured in joules.

In Figure 22, the initial value of U_{grav} is $U_{\text{grav,i}} = mgy_i$, and its final value is $U_{\text{grav,f}} = mgy_f$. We can express the work W_{grav} done by the gravitational force during the displacement from y_i to y_f as

$$W_{\text{grav}} = U_{\text{grav,i}} - U_{\text{grav,f}} = -\Delta U_{\text{grav}}. \tag{10}$$

The negative sign in front of ΔU_{grav} is essential. Remember that ΔU_{grav} always means the final value minus the initial value. When the object moves down, y decreases, the gravitational force does *positive* work, and the potential energy *decreases* (Figure 22a). It's like drawing some money out of the bank (decreasing U) and spending it (doing positive work). When the object moves up (Figure 22b), the work done by the gravitational force is *negative,* and the potential energy *increases*—you put money into the bank.

> **NOTE** ► We use the subscript "grav" to distinguish gravitational potential energy from other forms of potential energy we'll introduce later. But in problems where the *only* potential energy is gravitational, we'll sometimes drop this subscript to simplify the notation. ◄

Here's a simple example of the usefulness of the concept of potential energy. An object moves along a straight vertical line. Suppose the object's weight is the *only* force acting on it, so that $\vec{F}_{\text{other}} = 0$. The object may be in free fall, or perhaps we throw it upward. Let its speed at point y_i be v_i and its speed at y_f be v_f. The work–energy theorem, Equation 4, says that $W_{\text{total}} = K_f - K_i$, and in this case, $W_{\text{total}} = W_{\text{grav}} = U_i - U_f$. Putting these equations together, we get

$$U_i - U_f = K_f - K_i,$$

which we can rewrite as

$$K_i + U_i = K_f + U_f,$$

or

$$\tfrac{1}{2}mv_i^2 + mgy_i = \tfrac{1}{2}mv_f^2 + mgy_f. \tag{11}$$

We now define $K + U$ to be the **total mechanical energy** (kinetic plus potential) of the system; let's call it E. Then $E_i = (K_i + U_i)$ is the total energy when the object is at position y_i, and $E_f = (K_f + U_f)$ is the total energy at y_f. Equation 11 says that when the object's weight is the only force doing work on it, $E_i = E_f$. That is, E is constant; it has the same value at y_i and at all points during the motion. **When $\vec{F}_{other} = 0$, the total mechanical energy is constant or conserved.** This is our first example of the principle of **conservation of energy.**

When we throw a ball straight upward, it slows down on the way up as kinetic energy is converted to potential energy. On the way back down, potential energy is converted back to kinetic energy, and the ball speeds up. But the total energy, kinetic plus potential, is the same at every point in the motion. (We're assuming, of course, that air resistance and other frictional effects are negligible.)

EXAMPLE 7 Height of a baseball from energy conservation

You throw a 0.150 kg baseball straight up in the air, giving it an initial upward velocity with magnitude 20.0 m/s. Use conservation of energy to find how high it goes, ignoring air resistance.

SOLUTION

SET UP The only force doing work on the ball after it leaves your hand is its weight, and we can use Equation 11. We place the origin at the starting (initial) point, (point i), where the ball leaves your hand; then $y_i = 0$ (Figure 23). At this point, $v_i = 20.0$ m/s. We want to find the height at the final point (point f), where the ball stops and begins to fall back to earth. At this point, $v_f = 0$ and y_f is unknown.

SOLVE Equation 11 says that $K_i + U_i = K_f + U_f$, or

$$\tfrac{1}{2}mv_i^2 + mgy_i = \tfrac{1}{2}mv_f^2 + mgy_f,$$
$$\tfrac{1}{2}(0.150\text{ kg})(20.0\text{ m/s})^2 + (0.150\text{ kg})(9.80\text{ m/s}^2)(0)$$
$$= \tfrac{1}{2}(0.150\text{ kg})(0)^2 + (0.150\text{ kg})(9.80\text{ m/s}^2)y_f,$$
$$y_f = 20.4\text{ m.}$$

The mass divides out, as we should expect; the motion of an object in free fall doesn't depend on its mass.

REFLECT We could have substituted the values $y_i = 0$ and $v_f = 0$ in Equation 11 and then solved algebraically for y_f to get

$$y_f = \frac{v_i^2}{2g}.$$

▲ **FIGURE 23**

Practice Problem: You throw the same baseball up from the surface of the moon (where the acceleration due to gravity is 1.62 m/s²) with the same speed as before. Find how high the ball goes. *Answer:* 123 m.

An important point about gravitational potential energy is that it doesn't matter where we put the origin of coordinates. If we shift the origin for y, both y_i and y_f change, but the *difference* $(y_f - y_i)$ does not. It follows that, although the potential energies U_i and U_f depend on where we place the origin, their difference $(U_f - U_i)$ does not. The physically significant quantity is not the value of U at a particular point, but only the *difference* in U between two points. We can define U

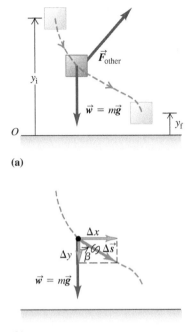

(a)

(b)

▲ **FIGURE 24** (a) A displacement along a curved path. (b) The work done by the gravitational force w depends only on the vertical component of the displacement Δy.

to be zero at any point we choose (in this case, at the origin); the difference in the value of U between any two points is independent of this choice.

In the preceding examples, the object moved along a straight vertical line. What happens when the path is slanted or curved, as in Figure 24a? The forces include the gravitational force $w = mg$ and possibly an additional force $\vec{F}_{\text{other}}$. The work done by the gravitational force during the displacement of the object is still given by Equation 10:

$$W_{\text{grav}} = U_i - U_f = mgy_i - mgy_f. \qquad (12)$$

To prove that this equation is valid, we divide the path into small segments Δs; a typical segment is shown in Figure 24b. The work done in this segment by the gravitational force is the magnitude of the force, multiplied by the vertical component of the displacement, $\Delta y = -\Delta s \cos\beta$. (The negative sign is needed because Δs is positive, while Δy is negative.) As the figure shows, the angle between the force and displacement vectors is β. The work done during the displacement is therefore $mg\,\Delta s \cos\beta$. But $\Delta s \cos\beta$ is equal to Δy, so the work done by w is

$$mg\,\Delta s \cos\beta = -mg\,\Delta y.$$

The work is the same as though the object had been displaced vertically a distance Δy. This is true for every segment, so the *total* work done by the gravitational force depends only on the *total* vertical displacement $(y_f - y_i)$. The total work is $-mg(y_f - y_i)$; this work is independent of any horizontal motion that may occur.

We haven't spoken about the gravitational potential energy *of an object* moving in the earth's gravitational field because the energy belongs not just to the object, but rather to the *system* consisting of the object and the earth. The earth has much more mass than the objects we've been considering. However, when the masses of the objects are more comparable, it is more obvious that the gravitational potential energy cannot be given to one of them.

Elastic Potential Energy

When a railroad car runs into a spring bumper at the end of the track, the spring is compressed as the car is brought to a stop. If there is no friction, the bumper springs back, and the car rolls away in the opposite direction. During the interaction with the spring, the car's kinetic energy is "stored" in the elastic deformation of the spring. Something similar happens in a spring gun. Work is done on the spring by the force that compresses it; that work is stored in the spring until you pull the trigger and the spring gives kinetic energy to the projectile.

This is the same pattern that we saw with the pile driver: Do work on the system to store energy; then this energy can later be converted to kinetic energy. We can apply the concept of elastic potential energy to the storage process. We proceed just as we did for gravitational potential energy. We begin with the work done by the force that the spring exerts on an object (which we will call the **spring force**) and then combine this work with the work–energy theorem.

In Section 4, we discussed work associated with stretching or compressing a spring. Figure 25 shows the spring from Figure 18, with its left end held stationary and its right end attached to an object with mass m that can move along the x axis. The object is at $x = 0$ when the spring is neither stretched nor compressed (Figure 25a). An external force $\vec{F}_{\text{ext}}$ acts on the object to make it undergo a displacement (Figure 25b), while the spring force $\vec{F}_{\text{spring}}$ pulls on it in the other direction. How much work does the spring force do on the object?

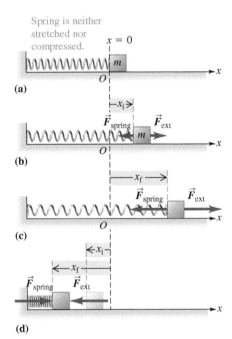

(a)

(b)

(c)

(d)

▲ **FIGURE 25** A block and spring on a horizontal surface. Both the spring force $\vec{F}_{\text{spring}}$ and the external force $\vec{F}_{\text{ext}}$ do work on the block.

We found in Section 4 that the work we must do *on* the spring to stretch it from an elongation x_i to a greater elongation x_f is $\frac{1}{2}kx_f^2 - \frac{1}{2}kx_i^2$, where k is the force constant of the spring. Now we need to find the work done *by* the spring *on* the object. From Newton's third law, the two quantities of work are just negatives of each other. Changing the signs in the expression on the right-hand side of Equation 7, we find that, in a displacement from x_i to x_f, the spring does an amount of work W_{el} given by

$$W_{el} = \tfrac{1}{2}kx_i^2 - \tfrac{1}{2}kx_f^2,$$

where the subscript "el" stands for *elastic*. When x_f is greater than x_i (Figure 25c), this quantity is negative because the object moves in the $+x$ direction while the spring pulls on it in the $-x$ direction. If the spring can be compressed as well as stretched, then x_i, x_f, or both may be negative (Figure 25d), and the expression for W_{el} is still valid.

Following the same procedure as for gravitational work, we define **elastic potential energy** as follows:

Definition of elastic potential energy

When a spring that obeys Hooke's law, $F = kx$, is stretched or compressed a distance x from its undistorted state, the associated potential energy U_{el} is given by

$$U_{el} = \tfrac{1}{2}kx^2. \tag{13}$$

The units of k are N/m, so the units of U_{el} are J. (Remember that $1\ \text{J} = 1\ \text{N} \cdot \text{m}$.) The joule is the unit used for *all* energy and work quantities.

NOTE ▶ In the expression $U_{el} = \frac{1}{2}kx^2$, x *must* be the displacement of the spring from its *unstretched* length (because we have used $F = kx$ to derive the expression). ◀

We can use Equation 13 to express the work W_{el} done on the object by the spring force in terms of the change in potential energy:

$$W_{el} = \tfrac{1}{2}kx_i^2 - \tfrac{1}{2}kx_f^2 = U_{el,i} - U_{el,f} = -\Delta U_{el}. \tag{14}$$

When x increases, W_{el} is *negative* and the stored energy U_{el} *increases;* when x decreases, W_{el} is *positive* and U_{el} *decreases*. If the spring can be compressed as well as stretched, then x is negative for compression. But, as Equation 13 shows, U_{el} is positive for both positive and negative x, and Equations 13 and 14 are valid in both cases. When $x = 0$, $U_{el} = 0$, and the spring is neither stretched nor compressed.

The work–energy theorem says that $W_{total} = K_f - K_i$, no matter what kind of forces are acting. If the spring force is the *only* force that does work on the object, then

$$W_{total} = W_{el} = U_i - U_f.$$

The work–energy theorem then gives us

$$K_i + U_{el,i} = K_f + U_{el,f} \quad \text{and} \quad \tfrac{1}{2}mv_i^2 + \tfrac{1}{2}kx_i^2 = \tfrac{1}{2}mv_f^2 + \tfrac{1}{2}kx_f^2 \tag{15}$$

In this case, the total energy $E = K + U_{el}$ is *conserved*.

▲ **BIO** Application **Climbing El Capitan.** One of the world's most famous climbing rocks is the 884 m El Capitan in Yosemite National Park. The red line shows a common climbing route, which involves an overnight stay on a ledge. For a typical 75 kg male climber, the change in gravitational potential energy from the bottom to the top of El Capitan is about 6.5×10^5 J. That sounds like a lot, but in fact, it's less than the energy you get from eating a typical candy bar! The work that results in the net change in gravitational potential energy represents just a small part of the total energy expended on such a climb.

▲ **BIO** Application **Miniature machines.** The inner ears of vertebrates contain "hair cells" which convert the mechanical energy of fluid motion to electrical signals that are sent to the brain. Each hair cell has a bundle of cross-linked cilia that flex in response to fluid movement. The stiffness of these bundles is due to the mechanical properties of the molecule actin. Direct microscopic measurement of bundle stiffness reveals a force constant of about $600\ \mu\text{N/m}$. From that measurement, we can estimate the structural rigidity of actin molecules, because the number of cilia per hair cell is easily determined and each cilium has about 30 actin molecules. The physical principles derived from the study of the macroscopic world apply with remarkably little modification to the micro- and nano-scale world.

EXAMPLE 8 **Potential energy on an air track**

A glider with mass $m = 0.200$ kg sits on a frictionless, horizontal air track, connected to a spring of negligible mass with force constant $k = 5.00$ N/m. You pull on the glider, stretching the spring 0.100 m, and then release it with no initial velocity. The glider begins to move back toward its equilibrium position $(x = 0)$. What is its speed when $x = 0.0800$ m?

SOLUTION

SET UP Figure 26 shows our diagram. We mark the $x = 0$ position at which the spring is relaxed, and we show the initial and final positions we will use. As the glider starts to move, potential energy is converted into kinetic energy. The spring force is the only force doing work on the glider, so $W_{other} = 0$, the total mechanical energy is constant, and we may use Equation 15. The energy quantities are

$$K_i = \tfrac{1}{2}(0.200 \text{ kg})(0)^2 = 0,$$
$$U_i = \tfrac{1}{2}(5.00 \text{ N/m})(0.100 \text{ m})^2 = 0.0250 \text{ J},$$
$$K_f = \tfrac{1}{2}(0.200 \text{ kg})v_f^2,$$
$$U_f = \tfrac{1}{2}(5.00 \text{ N/m})(0.0800 \text{ m})^2 = 0.0160 \text{ J}.$$

SOLVE From Equation 15,

$$\tfrac{1}{2}mv_i^2 + \tfrac{1}{2}kx_i^2 = \tfrac{1}{2}mv_f^2 + \tfrac{1}{2}kx_f^2,$$
$$0 + 0.0250 \text{ J} = \tfrac{1}{2}(0.200 \text{ kg})v_f^2 + 0.0160 \text{ J},$$
$$v_f = \pm\, 0.300 \text{ m/s}.$$

REFLECT The quadratic equation for v_f has two roots. The object doesn't stop at $x = 0$, but overshoots; when it returns to $x = 0$, the direction of its motion is reversed. Note that this problem

▲ **FIGURE 26** Our sketch for this problem. We show the initial and final states we will use in solving the problem.

cannot be solved by using the equations of motion with constant acceleration, because the spring force varies with position. The energy method, in contrast, offers a simple and elegant solution.

Practice Problem: What is the value of x when the object's speed is 0.15 m/s? *Answer:* ± 0.095 m.

Stephen Dalton/Photo Researchers, Inc.

▲ **BIO Application Catapult legs.** To jump, a grasshopper must straighten its hind legs faster than its leg muscles can contract. It does so by using a catapult mechanism. The black swelling on the first joint of each jumping leg marks a spot where the insect's exoskeleton has been modified into a pair of stiff springs shaped like flattened C's. Before a jump, the limb muscles build up elastic potential energy by compressing these springs while the joint is flexed. To jump, the animal releases the springs, which cause the legs to snap straight. Such mechanisms rely on conservation of mechanical energy.

6 Conservation of Energy

In the examples of the preceding section, we classified the forces acting on an object as gravitational, elastic, and "other." The general form of the work–energy theorem is

$$\Delta K = K_f - K_i = W_{total} = W_{grav} + W_{el} + W_{other}.$$

We've learned that the work done by the gravitational and elastic forces can be represented in terms of changes in their associated potential energy U_{grav} and U_{el}:

$$W_{grav} = U_{grav,i} - U_{grav,f} = -\Delta U_{grav} \quad \text{and} \quad W_{el} = U_{el,i} - U_{el,f} = -\Delta U_{el}.$$

When we substitute these expressions into the general work–energy theorem, we find that

$$K_f - K_i = U_{grav,i} - U_{grav,f} + U_{el,i} - U_{el,f} + W_{other},$$

or

$$K_f + U_{grav,f} + U_{el,f} = K_i + U_{grav,i} + U_{el,i} + W_{other}. \tag{16}$$

This equation bristles with subscripts and may seem complicated. But when we look at the individual terms, we recognize the quantity $K + U_{grav} + U_{el}$, with subscript i (initial) or f (final), as representing the total mechanical energy of the system. Therefore, Equation 16 states that the total mechanical energy of a system at the end (f) of any process equals the total mechanical energy at the beginning (i), plus the work W_{other} done by the forces *other than* gravitational and elastic forces. If we abbreviate the total potential energy as $U = U_{grav} + U_{el}$, we can say, more simply, that

$$K_f + U_f = K_i + U_i + W_{other}.$$

If there are no forces other than gravitational and elastic forces, or if the vector sum of all other forces is zero, then $\vec{F}_{other} = 0$, $W_{other} = 0$, and *all* the work can be represented in terms of changes in potential energy. In this special case, the *total* mechanical energy, $E = K + U_{grav} + U_{el}$, is constant, or *conserved*. Earlier, we mentioned that such a system is called a *conservative system* because mechanical energy is conserved. In this section, we'll discuss several examples of conservative systems.

ActivPhysics 5.2: Upward-Moving Elevator Stops
ActivPhysics 5.3: Stopping a Downward-Moving Elevator
ActivPhysics 5.4: Inverse Bungee Jumper

Conceptual Analysis 4

Mass-and-pulley system

Two unequal masses are connected by a massless cord passing over a frictionless pulley as shown in Figure 27. Considering the two masses as a system, which of the following statements is true about the gravitational potential energy U_{grav} and kinetic energy K after the masses are released from rest?

A. U_{grav} increases and K increases.
B. U_{grav} decreases and K increases.
C. Both U_{grav} and K remain constant.

SOLUTION The total kinetic energy K of the system is the sum of the two objects' individual kinetic energies, and the total gravitational potential energy U_{grav} is the sum of the individual gravitational potential energies.

Because both objects start from rest and end up moving, the total kinetic energy of the system increases. (Remember that kinetic energy depends on speed, not velocity, so the *direction* of motion has no effect on the kinetic energy.)

Now let's consider the change in gravitational potential energy. The downward motion of the heavy block decreases the

Before release   **After release**
▲ **FIGURE 27**

U_{grav} associated with this block. The upward motion of the light block increases the associated U_{grav}. However, since U_{grav} depends directly on mass, the decrease due to the heavy block dominates, so the total gravitational potential energy decreases. Thus, choice B is correct.

Quantitative Analysis 5

Total mechanical energy

In Figure 28, two blocks with masses m_A and m_B, where $m_A > m_B$, are attached to a thin string that passes over a frictionless pulley. The larger mass is resting on a spring that is compressed a distance s from its equilibrium position. The spring's compression is maintained by a trigger mechanism. What is the total mechanical energy for this system?

A. $m_A g h_A + m_B g h_B + \frac{1}{2}kh_A^2$
B. $m_A g h_A + m_B g h_B + \frac{1}{2}ks^2$
C. $m_A g h_A - m_B g h_B + \frac{1}{2}ks^2$

SOLUTION The total mechanical energy E is the sum of the energies for the individual parts of the system and is given by $E = K + U$, where $K = \frac{1}{2}m_B v_B^2 + \frac{1}{2}m_A v_A^2$ and $U = U_{grav} + U_{el}$. Using the tabletop for the reference level as shown in Figure 28, we find that $U_{grav} = m_A g h_A + m_B g h_B$. The spring is compressed a distance s, so $U_{el} = \frac{1}{2}ks^2$. With the trigger in place,

The spring is compressed a distance s from its uncompressed length.

▲ **FIGURE 28**

neither block is moving, and $K = 0$. Thus, $E = U_{grav} + U_{el} = m_A g h_A + m_B g h_B + \frac{1}{2}ks^2$ (choice B).

PROBLEM-SOLVING STRATEGY 2 **Conservation of energy with conservative forces**

SET UP

1. Identify the system you will analyze, and decide on the initial and final states (positions and velocities) you will use in solving the problem. Use the subscript i for the initial state and f for the final state. Draw one or more sketches showing the initial and final states.

2. Define your coordinate system, particularly the zero points for gravitational and elastic potential energies (the point at which $y = 0$ in the case of gravitational potential energy or at which the spring or other elastic object is relaxed in the case of elastic potential energy). For gravitational potential energy, Equation 9 assumes that the positive direction for y is upward; we suggest that you use this choice consistently.

3. List the initial and final kinetic and potential energies—that is, K_i, K_f, U_i, and U_f. Some of these will be known and some unknown. Use algebraic symbols for any unknown coordinates or velocities. In general, U includes both gravitational and elastic potential energy.

SOLVE

4. Write expressions for the total initial mechanical energy and for the total final mechanical energy, equate them, and solve to find whatever unknown quantity is required.

REFLECT

5. Check to make sure there are no forces other than gravitational and elastic forces that do work on the system. If there are additional forces, W_{other} is not zero, and you need to use the method we'll discuss in the next section (Problem-Solving Strategy 3).

EXAMPLE 9   **Maximum height of a home-run ball**

The expression for the maximum height h of a projectile launched with initial speed v_0 at initial angle θ_0 (neglecting air resistance) is:

$$h = \frac{v_0^2 \sin^2 \theta_0}{2g}.$$

Derive this expression now by using energy considerations.

SOLUTION

SET UP There are no nonconservative forces; the work done by gravity is accounted for in the potential-energy terms. As shown in Figure 29, we choose the launch point as the initial point and the highest point on the trajectory as the final point. We place $y = 0$ at the launch level; then $U_i = 0$ and $U_f = mgh$, where h is unknown. We can express the kinetic energy at each point in terms of the components of velocity, using the fact that, at each point, $v^2 = v_x^2 + v_y^2$:

$$K_i = \tfrac{1}{2}m(v_{i,x}^2 + v_{i,y}^2)$$
$$K_f = \tfrac{1}{2}m(v_{f,x}^2 + v_{f,y}^2)$$

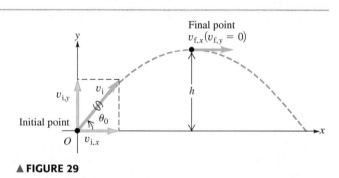

▲ **FIGURE 29**

Continued

SOLVE Conservation of energy gives $K_i + U_i = K_f + U_f$, so

$$\tfrac{1}{2}m(v_{i,x}^2 + v_{i,y}^2) + 0 = \tfrac{1}{2}m(v_{f,x}^2 + v_{f,y}^2) + mgh.$$

To simplify this equation, we multiply through by $2/m$ to obtain

$$v_{i,x}^2 + v_{i,y}^2 = v_{f,x}^2 + v_{f,y}^2 + 2gh.$$

Now for the *coup de grace:* We recall that, in projectile motion, the x component of acceleration is zero, so the x component of velocity is constant, and $v_{i,x} = v_{f,x}$. Also, because the final point is the highest point, the vertical component of velocity is zero at that point: $v_{f,y} = 0$. Subtracting the v_x^2 terms from both sides, we get

$$v_{i,y}^2 = 2gh.$$

But $v_{i,y}$ is just the y component of initial velocity, which is equal to $v_0 \sin\theta_0$. Making this substitution and solving for h, we find that

$$h = \frac{v_0^2 \sin^2\theta_0}{2g}.$$

REFLECT This result is correct. The energy approach has the advantage that we don't have to solve for the time when the maximum height is reached.

Practice Problem: Use the energy method to show that, for a given initial speed, the maximum height is greatest when $\theta_0 = 90°$.

EXAMPLE 10 Calculating speed along a vertical circle

Your cousin Throckmorton skateboards down a quarter-pipe with radius $R = 3.0$ m (Figure 30). The total mass of Throcky and the skateboard is 25.0 kg. If he starts from rest and there is no friction, derive an algebraic expression for his speed at the bottom of the ramp. Evaluate this expression with the values given. (Throcky's center of mass moves in a circle with radius somewhat smaller than R; neglect this small difference.)

SOLUTION

SET UP This is a conservative system. We can't use the equations of motion with constant acceleration; the acceleration isn't constant, because the slope decreases as Throcky descends. However, if there is no friction, the only force other than his weight is the normal force $\vec{n}$ exerted by the ramp (Figure 30b). The work done by this force is zero because, at each point, it is perpendicular to his velocity at that point. Thus, $W_{\text{other}} = 0$, and mechanical energy is conserved. We take his starting point as the initial point and the lowest point in the pipe as the final point. Then $y_i = R$ and $y_f = 0$. Throcky starts from rest at the top, so $v_i = 0$. The various energy quantities are

$$K_i = 0, \qquad K_f = \tfrac{1}{2}mv_f^2,$$
$$U_i = mgR, \qquad U_f = 0.$$

SOLVE From conservation of energy,

$$K_i + U_i = K_f + U_f,$$
$$0 + mgR = \tfrac{1}{2}mv_f^2 + 0,$$
$$v_f = \sqrt{2gR} = \sqrt{2(9.80 \text{ m/s}^2)(3.00 \text{ m})} = 7.67 \text{ m/s}.$$

REFLECT Throcky's speed at the bottom is the same as if he had fallen vertically through a height R, and it is independent of his mass.

Practice Problem: Find Throcky's speed at the bottom of the pipe if he is given a push at the top edge, so that he has an initial downward speed of 2.00 m/s. *Answer:* 7.93 m/s.

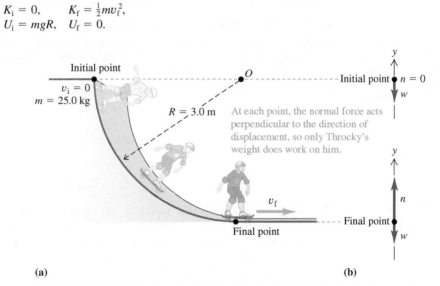

Initial point

$v_i = 0$
$m = 25.0$ kg

$R = 3.0$ m

At each point, the normal force acts perpendicular to the direction of displacement, so only Throcky's weight does work on him.

v_f

Final point

Initial point $n = 0$
w

n

Final point
w

(a)

(b)

▲ **FIGURE 30** (a) Motion showing initial and final points. (b) Free-body diagrams for initial and final points.

EXAMPLE 11 Elevator safety (or not)

In a "worst-case" design scenario, a 2000 kg elevator with broken cables is falling at 8.00 m/s when it first contacts a cushioning spring at the bottom of the shaft. The spring is supposed to stop the elevator, compressing 3.00 m as it does so (Figure 31). As an energy consultant, you are asked to determine what the force constant of the spring should be. Ignore air resistance and friction in the elevator guides.

SOLUTION

SET UP AND SOLVE We take the initial point as the elevator's position when it first contacts the spring $(y_i = 3.00 \text{ m})$ and the final point as its position when the spring is fully compressed $(y_f = 0)$. The elevator's initial speed is $v_i = 8.00 \text{ m/s}$, so

$$K_i = \tfrac{1}{2}mv_i^2 = \tfrac{1}{2}(2000 \text{ kg})(8.00 \text{ m/s})^2 = 64{,}000 \text{ J}.$$

The elevator stops at the final point; thus, $K_f = 0$. The elastic potential energy at the initial point is zero because the spring isn't yet compressed. The initial gravitational potential energy is

$$U_i = mgy_i = (2000 \text{ kg})(9.80 \text{ m/s}^2)(3.00 \text{ m}) = 58{,}800 \text{ J}.$$

At the final point, the gravitational potential energy is zero (because $y_f = 0$) and the elastic potential energy is

$$U_f = \tfrac{1}{2}kx^2 = \tfrac{1}{2}k(-3.00 \text{ m})^2,$$

where the force constant k is to be determined.

Inserting all these values in Equation 16, we find that

$$K_i + U_i = K_f + U_f,$$
$$64{,}000 \text{ J} + 58{,}800 \text{ J} = 0 + \tfrac{1}{2}k(-3.00 \text{ m})^2,$$
$$k = 2.73 \times 10^4 \text{ N/m}.$$

REFLECT You still have to explain to the client that the elevator won't stay at the bottom of the shaft, but will bounce back up and

▲ FIGURE 31

then return to hit the spring again and again until enough energy has been removed by friction for it to stop.

Practice Problem: If the mass of the elevator (with four fewer passengers than before) is 1600 kg, what should the spring constant be for a maximum compression of 3.00 m? *Answer:* $2.18 \times 10^4 \text{ N/m}$.

7 Conservative and Nonconservative Forces

In the preceding section, we discussed several problems involving work done on an object by conservative forces. In these problems, the work could be described completely in terms of changes in mechanical energy, and the *total* mechanical energy (kinetic plus potential) was conserved. We also hinted at methods for dealing with problems involving forces that do work W_{other} that can't be described in terms of a potential energy. We called these forces $\vec{F}_{other}$. Let's now return to this more general class of problem.

The key to dealing with problems involving nonconservative forces is Equation 16:

$$K_f + U_{grav,f} + U_{el,f} = K_i + U_{grav,i} + U_{el,i} + W_{other}. \tag{16}$$

Translated into words, this equation says that the total mechanical energy $(K + U_{grav} + U_{el})$ at the end of any process equals the total mechanical energy at the beginning, plus the work done by "other" forces whose work is not (or cannot be) included in the potential-energy terms. In such systems, mechanical energy is *not* conserved, but the initial and final values of total mechanical energy are related simply to the work done by the "other" forces.

Following are several examples of this more general class of problems and of the application of Equation 16. Then we'll close this section with a more general discussion of the nature of conservative and nonconservative forces.

MasteringPHYSICS

PhET: The Ramp
ActivPhysics 5.5: Spring-Launched Bowler
ActivPhysics 5.6: Skier Speed
ActivPhysics 5.7: Modified Atwood Machine

PROBLEM-SOLVING STRATEGY 3 **Conservation of energy with nonconservative forces**

The strategy outlined in Section 6 is equally useful here. In the list of kinetic and potential energies in Step 3, you should include both gravitational and elastic potential energies when appropriate. Remember that every force that does work must be represented *either* in U or in W_{other}, but *never* in both places. The work done by the gravitational and elastic forces is accounted for by the potential energies; the work of the other forces, W_{other}, has to be included separately. In some cases there will be "other" forces that do no work, as we mentioned in Section 2. Remember that, in the expression $U = \frac{1}{2}kx^2$, the coordinate x must be the displacement of the spring from its *unstretched* length (because we have used $F = -kx$ to derive U).

EXAMPLE 12   Work and energy on an air track

For the system of Example 8, suppose the glider is initially at rest at $x = 0$, with the spring unstretched. Then you apply a constant force $\vec{F}$ with magnitude 0.610 N to the glider. What is the glider's speed when it has moved to $x = 0.100$ m?

SOLUTION

SET UP Figure 32 shows our sketch. Mechanical energy is not conserved, because of the work W_{other} done by the force $\vec{F}$, but we can still use the energy relation of Equation 16. Let the initial point be $x = 0$ and the final point be $x = 0.100$ m. The energy quantities are

$$K_i = 0, \quad K_f = \frac{1}{2}(0.200\text{ kg})v_f^2,$$
$$U_i = 0, \quad U_f = \frac{1}{2}(5.00\text{ N/m})(0.100\text{ m})^2 = 0.0250\text{ J},$$
$$W_{other} = (0.610\text{ N})(0.100\text{ m}) = 0.0610\text{ J}.$$

SOLVE Putting the pieces into Equation 16, we obtain

$$K_f + U_f = K_i + U_i + W_{other},$$
$$\frac{1}{2}(0.200\text{ kg})v_f^2 + 0.0250\text{ J} = 0 + 0 + 0.0610\text{ J},$$
$$v_f = 0.600\text{ m/s}.$$

REFLECT The total mechanical energy of the system changes by an amount equal to the work W_{other} done by the applied force. Even

▲ **FIGURE 32** Our sketch for this problem.

though mechanical energy isn't conserved, energy considerations simplify this problem greatly.

Practice Problem: If the 0.610 N force is removed when the glider reaches the 0.100 m point, at what distance from the starting point does the glider come to rest? *Answer:* 0.156 m.

EXAMPLE 13   Throcky on the half-pipe again

Suppose the ramp in Example 10 is not frictionless and that Throcky's speed at the bottom is only 7.00 m/s . What work was done by the frictional force acting on him?

SOLUTION

SET UP We choose the same initial and final points and reference level as in Example 10 (Figure 30). In this case, $W_{other} = W_f$. The energy quantities are

$$K_i = 0,$$
$$U_i = mgR = (25.0\text{ kg})(9.80\text{ m/s}^2)(3.00\text{ m}) = 735\text{ J},$$
$$K_f = \frac{1}{2}mv_f^2 = \frac{1}{2}(25.0\text{ kg})(7.00\text{ m/s})^2 = 613\text{ J},$$
$$U_f = 0.$$

SOLVE From Equation 16,

$$W_{other} = K_f + U_f - K_i - U_i$$
$$= 613\text{ J} + 0 - 0 - 735\text{ J} = -122\text{ J}.$$

The work done by the friction force is -122 J, and the total mechanical energy *decreases* by 122 J.

REFLECT W_{other} has to be negative because, at each point, the friction force is opposite in direction to Throcky's velocity. In this problem, as in several others in this chapter, Throcky's motion is

Continued

determined by Newton's second law, $\Sigma \vec{F} = m\vec{a}$. But it would be very difficult to apply that law here because the acceleration is continuously changing, in both magnitude and direction, as Throcky skates down. The energy approach, in contrast, relates the motions at the top and bottom of the ramp without involving the details of what happens in between. This simplification is typical of many problems that are easy if we use energy considerations, but very complex if we try to use Newton's laws directly.

The work W_f done by the nonconservative friction forces is -122 J. As Throcky rolls down, the wheels, the bearings, and the ramp all get a little warmer. The same temperature changes could have been produced by adding 122 J of heat to these objects. Their *internal* energy increases by 122 J; the sum of this energy and the final mechanical energy equals the initial mechanical energy, and the total energy of the system (including nonmechanical forms of energy) is conserved.

Practice Problem: If Throcky's speed at the bottom of the quarter-pipe is exactly half of what it would be without friction, how much work does the friction force do? *Answer:* -551 J.

EXAMPLE 14   Loading a crate onto a truck

A crate full of machine parts sits on the floor; the total mass is 8.0 kg. The crate must be raised to the floor of a truck by sliding it up a ramp 2.5 m long, inclined at 30°. The shop foreman, giving no thought to the force of friction, calculates that he can get the crate up the ramp by giving it an initial speed of 5.0 m/s at the bottom and letting it go. Unfortunately, friction is *not* negligible; the crate slides 1.6 m up the ramp, stops, and slides back down. Figure 33 shows the situation. **(a)** Assuming that the friction force acting on the crate is constant, find its magnitude. **(b)** How fast is the crate moving when it reaches the bottom of the ramp?

SOLUTION

SET UP We have three critical points: ground level (point 1 in Figure 33a), the point where the crate stops on the ramp (point 2), and the point where it reaches the ground again (point 3 in Figure 33b). (We count points 1 and 3 separately because the crate's velocity is different on the return trip.) For part (a), point 1 is the initial point and point 2 is the final point; for part (b), point 1 is the initial point and point 3 is the final point.

SOLVE Part (a):   For this part of the problem, the final point is $(1.6 \text{ m})(\sin 30°) = 0.80$ m above the floor. If we take $U = 0$ at floor level, we have $y_1 = 0$, $y_2 = 0.80$ m. The energy quantities are

$$K_1 = \tfrac{1}{2}(8.0 \text{ kg})(5.0 \text{ m/s})^2 = 100 \text{ J}, \qquad K_2 = 0,$$
$$U_1 = 0, \qquad U_2 = (8.0 \text{ kg})(9.8 \text{ m/s}^2)(0.80 \text{ m}) = 62.7 \text{ J},$$
$$W_{\text{other}} = -fs = -f(1.6 \text{ m}),$$

where f is the magnitude of the unknown friction force. Using Equation 16, we find that

$$K_1 + U_1 + W_{\text{other}} = K_2 + U_2,$$
$$100 \text{ J} + 0 - f(1.6 \text{ m}) = 0 + 62.7 \text{ J},$$
$$f = 23 \text{ N}.$$

Part (b):   This time we use points 1 and 3 as our initial and final points, respectively. The friction force reverses direction for the return trip, so the frictional work is negative for both halves of the trip, and the total work done by friction is twice the previous amount. The total gravitational work for the round-trip is zero, so the total work is

$$W_{\text{other}} = W_f = -2(1.6 \text{ m})(23.3 \text{ N}) = -74.6 \text{ J}.$$

The other energy quantities are

$$K_1 = 100 \text{ J}, \qquad U_1 = U_3 = 0, \qquad K_3 = \tfrac{1}{2}(8.0 \text{ kg})v_3^2,$$

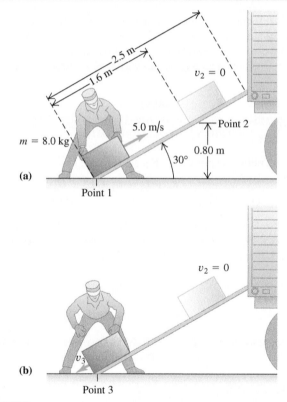

(a)

Point 1

(b)

Point 3

▲ FIGURE 33

Continued

where v_3 is the unknown final speed. Substituting these values into Equation 16, we get

$$100\,\text{J} + 0 + (-74.6\,\text{J}) = \tfrac{1}{2}(8.0\,\text{kg})v_3^2 + 0,$$
$$v_3 = 2.5\,\text{m/s}.$$

REFLECT The crate's speed and kinetic energy when it returns to the bottom of the ramp are less than when it left that point;

mechanical energy is lost to friction. We could have applied Equation 16 to points 2 and 3, considering the second half of the trip by itself.

Practice Problem: Follow the suggestion to apply Equation 16 to points 2 and 3 to verify that you get the same result for v_3 as before.

Nonconservative Forces

In our discussions of potential energy, we've talked about "storing" kinetic energy by converting it to potential energy. When you throw a ball up in the air, it slows down as kinetic energy is converted into potential energy. On the way down, the conversion is reversed, and potential energy is converted completely back to kinetic energy (if air resistance is neglected.).

Similarly, when a glider moving on a frictionless, horizontal air track runs into a spring bumper at the end of the track, the spring compresses and the glider stops. But then the glider bounces back with the same speed and kinetic energy that it had before the collision. Again, there is a two-way conversion from kinetic to potential energy and back.

A force that permits two-way conversion between kinetic and potential energies is called a **conservative force.** The work of a conservative force is always *reversible:* Anything that we deposit in the energy "bank" can later be withdrawn without loss. In some cases (including gravitational forces), an object may move from an initial to a final point by various paths (Figure 34), but if the force is conservative, the work done by the force is the same for all of these paths. If an object moves around a *closed* path, ending at the same point where it started, the *total* work done by the gravitational force is always zero.

The work done by a conservative force has these properties:

1. It can always be expressed as the difference between the initial and final values of a *potential-energy* function.
2. It is reversible.
3. It is independent of the path of the object and depends only on the starting and ending points.
4. When the starting and ending points are the same, the total work is zero.

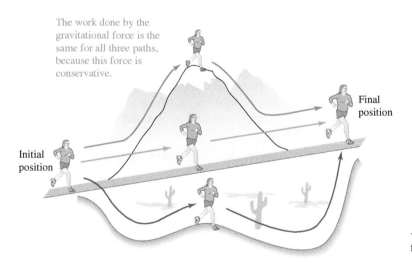

The work done by the gravitational force is the same for all three paths, because this force is conservative.

Initial position

Final position

◀ **FIGURE 34** The work done by a conservative force is independent of the path taken.

When all the work done on an object is done by conservative forces, the total mechanical energy $E = K + U$ is constant.

Not all forces are conservative. Consider the friction force acting on the crate sliding on a ramp in Example 14. There is no potential-energy function for this force. When the object slides up and then back down to the starting point, the total work done on it by the friction force is *not* zero. When the direction of motion reverses, so does the friction force, and it does *negative* work in *both* directions. When a car with its brakes locked skids across the pavement with decreasing speed (and decreasing kinetic energy), the lost kinetic energy cannot be recovered by reversing the motion (or, for that matter, in any other way), and mechanical energy is *not* conserved.

Such a force is called a **nonconservative force** or a **dissipative force.** To describe the associated energy relations, we have to introduce additional kinds of energy and a more general energy-conservation principle. When an object slides on a rough surface, such as tires on pavement or a box dropped on a conveyer belt, the surfaces become hotter; the energy associated with this change in the state of the materials is called *internal energy*. In later chapters, we'll study the relation of internal energy to temperature changes, heat, and work. This is the heart of the area of physics called *thermodynamics*.

8 Power

Time considerations aren't involved directly in the definition of work. If you lift a barbell weighing 400 N through a vertical distance of 0.5 m at constant velocity, you do 200 J of work on it, whether it takes you 1 second, 1 hour, or 1 year to do it. Often, though, we need to know how quickly work is done. The time rate at which work is done or energy is transferred is called **power.** Like work and energy, power is a scalar quantity. We define **average power** as follows:

Definition of average power P_{av}
When a quantity of work ΔW is done during a time interval Δt, the average power P_{av}, or work per unit time, is defined as

$$P_{av} = \frac{\Delta W}{\Delta t}. \tag{17}$$

Unit: watt (W), where 1 watt is defined as 1 joule per second (J/s).

The rate at which work is done isn't necessarily constant. Even when it varies, however, we can define the **instantaneous power** P as the limit of this quotient as Δt approaches zero:

$$P = \lim_{\Delta t \to 0} \frac{\Delta W}{\Delta t}.$$

For many applications, power is measured in kilowatts or megawatts $(1\,MW = 10^6\,W)$. In the British system, in which work is expressed in foot-pounds, the unit of power is the foot-pound per second. A larger unit called the *horsepower* (hp) is also used:

$$1\,hp = 550\,ft \cdot lb/s = 33,000\,ft \cdot lb/min.$$

That is, a 1 hp motor running at full load does 33,000 ft · lb of work every minute. A useful conversion factor is

$$1\,hp = 746\,W = 0.746\,kW.$$

Note that 1 horsepower equals about $\frac{3}{4}$ of a kilowatt, a useful figure to remember.

Thomas, D. D., D. Kast, and V. Korman. 2009. Site-Directed Spectroscopic Probes of Actomyosin Structural Dynamics. Annu Rev Biophys. 38:347–369.

Actin   Myosin

▲ **BIO Application Work at the molecular scale.** Ultimately, everything a living organism does, including doing work, depends on the aggregate actions of organized molecules. High-resolution pictures of molecules, such as those provided by x-ray crystallography, provide insight into the workings of molecular machines. When a muscle contracts, the force generated is due to the interaction of a motor protein called myosin, and a structural track called actin. The head of the myosin molecule attaches to the actin and rotates about a pivot point, as shown. The force applied by the myosin to the actin in a skeletal muscle is in the range of 1–10 pN and the distance moved in a single power stroke is perhaps 5 nm. The work done in a single power stroke ($\frac{1}{2}\,kx^2$) derives its energy from a single ATP molecule, the body's energy currency. One ATP molecule can do up to 60 pN · nm of work, consistent with the force constant of the elastic element of the myosin of 5 pN · nm. This work represents about half the energy available from one ATP molecule.

The watt is a familiar unit of *electrical* power; a 100 W lightbulb converts 100 J of electrical energy into light and heat each second. But there is nothing inherently electrical about the watt; a lightbulb could be rated in horsepower, and some automobile manufacturers rate their engines in kilowatts as well as horsepower.

Power units can be used to define new units of work or energy. The *kilowatt-hour* (kWh) is the usual commercial unit of electrical energy. One kilowatt-hour is the total work done in 1 hour (3600 s) when the power is 1 kilowatt (10^3 J/s), so

$$1 \text{ kWh} = (10^3 \text{ J/s})(3600 \text{ s}) = 3.6 \times 10^6 \text{ J} = 3.6 \text{ MJ}.$$

The kilowatt-hour is a unit of *work* or *energy,* not power.

When a force acts on a moving object, it does work on the object (unless the force and velocity are always perpendicular). The corresponding power can be expressed in terms of force and velocity. Suppose a force $\vec{F}$ acts on an object while it undergoes a vector displacement $\Delta \vec{s}$. If $F_{\parallel}$ is the component of $\vec{F}$ tangent to the path (parallel to $\Delta \vec{s}$), then the work is $\Delta W = F_{\parallel} \Delta s$, where Δs is the magnitude of the displacement $\Delta \vec{s}$, and the average power is

$$P_{av} = \frac{F_{\parallel} \Delta s}{\Delta t} = F_{\parallel} \frac{\Delta s}{\Delta t} = F_{\parallel} v_{av}.$$

Instantaneous power P is the limit of P_{av} as $\Delta t \to 0$:

$$P = F_{\parallel} v, \tag{18}$$

where v is the magnitude of the instantaneous velocity.

It's a curious fact of modern life that although energy is an abstract physical quantity, it is bought and sold. We don't buy a newton of force or a meter per second of velocity, but a kilowatt-hour of electrical energy usually costs from 2 to 10 cents, depending on one's location and the amount purchased.

EXAMPLE 15 Power in a jet engine

A jet airplane engine develops a thrust (a forward force on the plane) of 15,000 N (roughly 3000 lb). When the plane is flying at 300 m/s (roughly 670 mi/h), what horsepower does the engine develop?

SOLUTION

SET UP AND SOLVE From Equation 18,

$$P = Fv = (1.50 \times 10^4 \text{ N})(300 \text{ m/s}) = 4.50 \times 10^6 \text{ W}$$
$$= (4.50 \times 10^6 \text{ W})\left(\frac{1 \text{ hp}}{746 \text{ W}}\right) = 6030 \text{ hp}.$$

REFLECT This power is comparable to the power developed by a Diesel railroad locomotive. The airplane travels 10 times as fast as the locomotive, with a much smaller cargo weight.

Practice Problem: Suppose the airplane carries 150 passengers with an average mass of 55 kg each. After disembarking, all these passengers get on a freight elevator, which itself has a mass of 750 kg. How fast can the elevator's 6000 hp motor lift the loaded elevator? (That is, at what speed is 6000 hp just enough to keep the elevator rising?) *Answer:* 51 m/s.

EXAMPLE 16 A marathon stair climb

As part of a charity fund-raising drive, a Chicago marathon runner with mass 50.0 kg runs up the stairs to the top of the Willis Tower, the tallest building in Chicago (443 m), in 15.0 minutes (Figure 35). What is her average power output in watts? In kilowatts? In horsepower?

Continued

▲ **FIGURE 35** Climbing the Willis Tower.

Shutterstock

SOLUTION

SET UP AND SOLVE The runner's total work W is her weight mg, multiplied by the height h she climbs:

$$W = mgh = (50.0 \text{ kg})(9.80 \text{ m/s}^2)(443 \text{ m}) = 2.17 \times 10^5 \text{ J}.$$

The time is 15 min = 900 s, so the average power is

$$P_{av} = \frac{2.17 \times 10^5 \text{ J}}{900 \text{ s}} = 241 \text{ W} = 0.241 \text{ kW} = 0.323 \text{ hp}.$$

Alternative Solution: The average vertical component of velocity is $(443 \text{ m})/(900 \text{ s}) = 0.492 \text{ m/s}$, so the average power is

$$P_{av} = Fv_{av} = (mg)v_{av}$$
$$= (50.0 \text{ kg})(9.80 \text{ m/s}^2)(0.492 \text{ m/s}) = 241 \text{ W}.$$

REFLECT A horse can supply considerably more than 1 hp for short periods of time.

Practice Problem: If all the runner's work output could be collected and sold at the rate of 10 cents per kilowatt-hour, what would be the cash value of the work? *Answer:* 0.603 cents.

CHAPTER SUMMARY

Overview of Energy

(Section 1) Energy is one of the most important unifying concepts in all of physical science. Its importance stems from the principle of conservation of energy. Energy is exchanged and transformed during interactions of systems, but the total energy in a closed system is constant. This chapter is concerned with mechanical energy of three types: kinetic energy, associated with the motion of objects that have mass; gravitational potential energy, associated with gravitational interactions; and elastic potential energy, associated with elastic deformations of objects. Potential energy can be viewed as a stored quantity that represents the potential for doing work.

Work

(Section 2) When a force acts on an object that undergoes a displacement, the force does work on the object and transfers energy to it. For a constant force, $W = F_\parallel s$ (Equation 1), where $F_\parallel$ is the component of force parallel to the object's displacement (of magnitude s). This component can be positive, negative, or zero. Work is a scalar quantity, not a vector. If $F_\parallel$ points opposite to the displacement, then $W < 0$. When several forces act on an object, the total work done by all the forces is the sum of the amounts of work done by the individual forces.

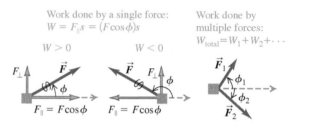

Work done by a single force:
$$W = F_\parallel s = (F\cos\phi)s$$

$W > 0$ $W < 0$

$F_\parallel = F\cos\phi$ $F_\parallel = F\cos\phi$

Work done by multiple forces:
$$W_{\text{total}} = W_1 + W_2 + \cdots$$

Work and Kinetic Energy

(Section 3) The kinetic energy K of an object is defined in terms of the object's mass m and speed v as $K = \frac{1}{2}mv^2$. When forces act on an object, the change in its kinetic energy is equal to the total work done by all the forces acting on it: $W_{\text{total}} = K_f - K_i = \Delta K$ (Equation 4). When W is positive, the object speeds up; when W is negative, it slows down.

$v = 2.0$ m/s $v = 1.0$ m/s

Honda, mass 1300 kg   Mercedes, mass 2600 kg

$K = \frac{1}{2}mv^2 = 2600$ J $K = \frac{1}{2}mv^2 = 1300$ J

Work Done by a Varying Force

(Section 4) When an object moves under the action of a varying force parallel to the displacement, the work done by the force is represented graphically as the area under a graph of the force as a function of displacement. If the magnitude of force F required to stretch a spring a distance x beyond its natural length is proportional to x, then $F = kx$, where k is a constant for the spring, called its force constant or spring constant. The total work W needed to stretch the spring from $x = 0$ to $x = X$ is $W = \frac{1}{2}kX^2$.

Potential Energy

(Section 5) Potential energy can be thought of as *stored* energy. For an object with mass m at a height y above a chosen origin (where $y = 0$), the gravitational potential energy is $U_{\text{grav}} = mgy$ (Equation 9). When a spring is stretched or compressed a distance x from its uncompressed length, the spring stores elastic potential energy $U_{\text{el}} = \frac{1}{2}kx^2$ (Equation 13). Potential energy is associated only with conservative forces, not with nonconservative forces such as friction.

$U_{\text{grav,i}} = mgy_i$

$F = mg$

$U_{\text{grav,f}} = mgy_f$

$x = 0$

Gravitational potential energy: For an object at vertical position y,
$$U_{\text{grav}} = mgy$$
For a change in vertical position,
$$\Delta U_{\text{grav}} = U_{\text{grav,f}} - U_{\text{grav,i}}$$

Elastic potential energy: For a spring stretched or compressed by a distance x from equilibrium,
$$U_{\text{el}} = \frac{1}{2}kx^2$$

Continued

Conservation of Energy

(Sections 6 and 7) When only conservative forces act on an object, the total mechanical energy (kinetic plus potential) is constant; that is, $K_i + U_i = K_f + U_f$, where U may include both gravitational and elastic potential energies. If some of the forces are nonconservative, we label their work as W_{other}. The change in total energy (kinetic plus potential) of an object during any motion is equal to the work W_{other} done by the nonconservative forces: $K_i + U_i + W_{\text{other}} = K_f + U_f$ (Equation 16). Nonconservative forces include friction forces, which usually act to decrease the total mechanical energy of a system.

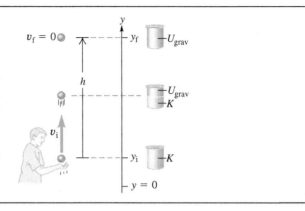

Power

(Section 8) Power is the time rate of doing work or the rate at which energy is transferred or transformed. For mechanical systems, power is the time rate at which work is done by or on an object or a system. When an amount of work ΔW is done during a time interval Δt, the average power is $P_{\text{av}} = \frac{\Delta W}{\Delta t}$ (Equation 17).

Work and Energy: Problem Set

(MP) For instructor-assigned homework, go to www.masteringphysics.com

Conceptual Questions

1. How does friction produce internal energy? Explain what is happening at the molecular level to produce this form of energy.
2. True or false? If hydrogen molecules and oxygen molecules have the same kinetic energy, then they have the same speed. Explain your answer.
3. Can the *total* work done on an object during a displacement be negative? Explain. If the total work is negative, can its magnitude be greater than the initial kinetic energy of the object? Explain.
4. An elevator is hoisted by its cables at constant speed. Is the *total* work done on the elevator positive, negative, or zero? Explain your reasoning.
5. A rope tied to an object is pulled, causing the object to accelerate. According to Newton's third law, the object pulls back on the rope with an equal and opposite force. Is the total net work done on the object then zero? If so, how can the object's kinetic energy change?
6. If a projectile is fired upward at various angles above the horizontal, it has the same initial kinetic energy in each case. Why does it *not* then rise to the same maximum height in each case?
7. When you use a jack to lift a car, the force you exert on the jack is much less than the weight of the car. Does this mean that less work is done on the car than if the car were lifted directly?
8. An advertisement for a portable electrical generating unit claims that the unit's diesel engine produces 28,000 hp to drive an electrical generator that produces 30 MW of electrical power. Is this possible? Explain.
9. A compressed spring is clamped in its compressed position and is then dissolved in acid. What becomes of the spring's potential energy?
10. You bounce on a trampoline, going a little higher with each bounce. Explain how you increase your total mechanical energy.
11. When you jump from the ground into the air, where does your kinetic energy come from? What force does work on you to lift you into the air? Could you jump if you were floating in outer space?
12. Hydroelectric energy comes from gravity pulling down water through dams in rivers. Explain how such energy is really just a form of solar energy by tracing how the sun's energy is able to get the water from the ocean to the reservoir behind the dam.
13. Does the kinetic energy of a car change more when the car speeds up from 10 mph to 15 mph or from 15 mph to 20 mph?

14. Does an object's speed at the bottom of a frictionless ramp depend on the shape of the ramp or just on its height? Explain. What if the ramp is *not* frictionless?
15. You often hear that the energy we use on the earth comes from the sun. Explain how this is true. For example, how does the kinetic energy of a running person come from the sun?
16. On your electrical "power" bill, you are charged for kilowatt-hours (kWh). Is this really a power bill? What kind of quantity is the kilowatt-hour?

Multiple-Choice Problems

1. A spiral spring is compressed so as to add U units of potential energy to it. When this spring is instead stretched two-thirds of the distance it was compressed, its remaining potential energy in the same units will be
   A. $2U/3$ B. $4U/9$ C. $U/3$ D. $U/9$
2. A block slides a distance d down a frictionless plane and then comes to a stop after sliding a distance s across a rough horizontal plane, as shown in the accompanying figure. What fraction of the distance s does the block slide before its speed is reduced to one-third of the maximum speed it had at the bottom of the ramp?
   A. $s/3$ B. $2s/3$ C. $s/9$ D. $8s/9$

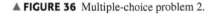

▲ FIGURE 36 Multiple-choice problem 2.

3. You slam on the brakes of your car in a panic and skid a distance d on a straight and level road. If you had been traveling twice as fast, what distance would the car have skidded under the same conditions?
   A. $4d$ B. $2d$ C. $\sqrt{2}d$ D. $d/2$
4. You wish to accelerate your car from rest at a constant acceleration. Assume that there is negligible air drag. To create a constant acceleration, the car's engine must
   A. maintain a constant power output.
   B. develop ever-decreasing power.
   C. develop ever-increasing power.

5. Consider two frictionless inclined planes with the same vertical height. Plane 1 makes an angle of 30° with the horizontal, and plane 2 makes an angle of 60° with the horizontal. Mass m_1 is placed at the top of plane 1, and mass m_2 is placed at the top of plane 2. Both masses are released at the same time. At the bottom, which mass is going faster?
   A. m_1
   B. m_2
   C. Neither; they both have the same speed at the bottom.

6. A brick is dropped from the top of a building through the air (friction is present) to the ground below. How does the brick's kinetic energy (K) just before striking the ground compare with the gravitational potential energy (U_{grav}) at the top of the building? Set $y = 0$ at the ground level.
   A. K is equal to U_{grav}.
   B. K is greater than U_{grav}.
   C. K is less than U_{grav}.

7. Which of the following statements about work is or are true? (More than one statement may be true.)
   A. Negative net work done on an object always reduces the object's kinetic energy.
   B. If the work done on an object by a force is zero, then either the force or the displacement must have zero magnitude.
   C. If a force acts downward, it does negative work.
   D. The formula $W = Fd\cos\theta$ can be used only if the force is constant over the distance d.

8. A 10 kg stone and a 100 kg stone are released from rest at the same height above the ground. There is no appreciable air drag. Which of the following statements is or are true? (More than one statement may be true.)
   A. Both stones have the same initial gravitational potential energy.
   B. Both stones will have the same acceleration as they fall.
   C. Both stones will have the same speed when they reach the ground.
   D. Both stones will have the same kinetic energy when they reach the ground.
   E. Both stones will reach the ground at the same time.

9. Two *identical* objects are pressed against two different springs so that each spring stores 50 J of potential energy. The objects are then released from rest. One spring is quite stiff (hard to compress), while the other one is quite flexible (easy to compress). Which of the following statements is or are true? (More than one statement may be true.)
   A. Both objects will have the same maximum speed after being released.
   B. The object pressed against the stiff spring will gain more kinetic energy than the other object.
   C. Both springs are initially compressed by the same amount.
   D. The stiff spring has a larger spring constant than the flexible spring.
   E. The flexible spring must have been compressed more than the stiff spring.

10. For each of two objects with *different* masses, the gravitational potential energy is 100 J. They are released from rest and fall to the ground. Which of the following statements is or are true? (More than one statement may be true.)
    A. Both objects are released from the same height.
    B. Both objects will have the same kinetic energy when they reach the ground.

C. Both objects will have the same speed when they reach the ground.
   D. Both objects will accelerate toward the ground at the same rate.
   E. Both objects will reach the ground at the same time.

11. Two objects with *different* masses are launched vertically into the air by identical springs. The two springs are compressed by the same amount before launching. Which of the following statements is or are true? (More than one statement may be true.)
    A. Both masses reach the same maximum height.
    B. Both masses leave the springs with the same energy.
    C. Both masses leave the springs with the same speed.
    D. Both masses leave the springs with the same kinetic energy.
    E. The lighter mass will gain more gravitational potential energy than the heavier mass.

12. Two objects with *unequal* masses are released from rest from the *same height*. They slide without friction down a slope and then encounter a rough horizontal region, as shown in the accompanying figure. The coefficient of kinetic friction in the rough region is the same for both masses. Which of the following statements is or are true? (More than one statement may be true.)
    A. Both masses start out with the same gravitational potential energy.
    B. Both objects have the same speed when they reach the base of the slope.
    C. Both masses have the same kinetic energy at the bottom of the slope.
    D. Both masses travel the same distance on the rough horizontal surface before stopping.
    E. Both masses will generate the same amount of thermal energy due to friction on the rough surface.

▲ **FIGURE 37** Multiple-choice problem 12.

13. Spring #1 has a force constant of k, and spring #2 has a force constant of $2k$. Both springs are attached to the ceiling, identical weights are hooked to their ends, and the weights are allowed to stretch the springs. The ratio of the energy stored by spring #1 to that stored by spring #2 is
    A. 1:1   B. 1:2   C. 2:1
    D. $1:\sqrt{2}$ E. $\sqrt{2}:1$

14. Two balls having *different* masses reach the same height when shot into the air from the ground. If there is no air drag, which of the following statements must be true? (More than one statement may be true.)
    A. Both balls left the ground with the same speed.
    B. Both balls left the ground with the same kinetic energy.
    C. Both balls will have the same gravitational potential energy at the highest point.
    D. The heavier ball must have left the ground with a greater speed than the lighter ball.
    E. Both balls have no acceleration at their highest point.

15. The stone in the accompanying figure can be carried from the bottom to the top of a cliff by various paths. Which path requires more work?
    A. *AC*
    B. *ABC*
    C. The work is the same for both paths.

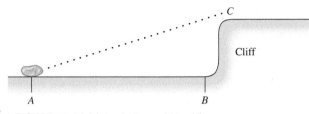

▲ FIGURE 38 Multiple-choice problem 15.

Problems

2 Work

1. ● A fisherman reels in 12.0 m of line while landing a fish, using a constant forward pull of 25.0 N. How much work does the tension in the line do on the fish?

2. ● A tennis player hits a 58.0 g tennis ball so that it goes straight up and reaches a maximum height of 6.17 m. How much work does gravity do on the ball on the way up? On the way down?

3. ● A boat with a horizontal tow rope pulls a water skier. She skis off to the side, so the rope makes an angle of 15.0° with the forward direction of motion. If the tension in the rope is 180 N, how much work does the rope do on the skier during a forward displacement of 300.0 m?

4. ● A constant horizontal pull of 8.50 N drags a box along a horizontal floor through a distance of 17.4 m. (a) How much work does the pull do on the box? (b) Suppose that the same pull is exerted at an angle above the horizontal. If this pull now does 65.0 J of work on the box while pulling it through the same distance, what angle does the force make with the horizontal?

5. ● You push your physics book 1.50 m along a horizontal tabletop with a horizontal push of 2.40 N while the opposing force of friction is 0.600 N. How much work does each of the following forces do on the book? (a) your 2.40 N push, (b) the friction force, (c) the normal force from the table, and (d) gravity? (e) What is the net work done on the book?

6. ● A 128.0 N carton is pulled up a frictionless baggage ramp inclined at 30.0° above the horizontal by a rope exerting a 72.0 N pull parallel to the ramp's surface. If the carton travels 5.20 m along the surface of the ramp, calculate the work done on it by (a) the rope, (b) gravity, and (c) the normal force of the ramp. (d) What is the net work done on the carton? (e) Suppose that the rope is angled at 50.0° above the horizontal, instead of being parallel to the ramp's surface. How much work does the rope do on the carton in this case?

7. ● A factory worker moves a 30.0 kg crate a distance of 4.5 m along a level floor at constant velocity by pushing horizontally on it. The coefficient of kinetic friction between the crate and the floor is 0.25. (a) What magnitude of force must the worker apply? (b) How much work is done on the crate by the worker's push? (c) How much work is done on the crate by friction? (d) How much work is done by the normal force? By gravity? (e) What is the net work done on the crate?

8. ●● An 8.00 kg package in a mail-sorting room slides 2.00 m down a chute that is inclined at 53.0° below the horizontal. The coefficient of kinetic friction between the package and the chute's surface is 0.40. Calculate the work done on the package by (a) friction (b) gravity, and (c) the normal force. (d) What is the net work done on the package?

9. ●● Two tugboats pull a disabled supertanker. Each tug exerts a constant force of 1.80×10^6 N, one 14° west of north and the other 14° east of north, as they pull the tanker 0.75 km toward the north. What is the total work they do on the supertanker?

10. ●● A tow truck pulls a car 5.00 km along a horizontal roadway using a cable having a tension of 850 N. (a) How much work does the cable do on the car if it pulls horizontally? If it pulls at 35.0° above the horizontal? (b) How much work does the cable do on the tow truck in both cases of part (a)? (c) How much work does gravity do on the car in part (a)?

11. ●● A boxed 10.0 kg computer monitor is dragged by friction 5.50 m up along the moving surface of a conveyor belt inclined at an angle of 36.9° above the horizontal. If the monitor's speed is a constant 2.10 cm/s, how much work is done on the monitor by (a) friction, (b) gravity, and (c) the normal force of the conveyor belt?

3 Work and Kinetic Energy

12. ● It takes 4.186 J of energy to raise the temperature of 1.0 g of water by 1.0°C. (a) How fast would a 2.0 g cricket have to jump to have that much kinetic energy? (b) How fast would a 4.0 g cricket have to jump to have the same amount of kinetic energy?

13. ● A bullet is fired into a large stationary absorber and comes to rest. Temperature measurements of the absorber show that the bullet lost 1960 J of kinetic energy, and high-speed photos of the bullet show that it was moving at 965 m/s just as it struck the absorber. What is the mass of the bullet?

14. ●● **Animal energy.** Adult cheetahs, the fastest of the great
BIO cats, have a mass of about 70 kg and have been clocked at up to 72 mph (32 m/s). (a) How many joules of kinetic energy does such a swift cheetah have? (b) By what factor would its kinetic energy change if its speed were doubled?

15. ●● A racing dog is initially running at 10.0 m/s, but is slowing down. (a) How fast is the dog moving when its kinetic energy has been reduced by half? (b) By what fraction has its kinetic energy been reduced when its speed has been reduced by half?

16. ●● If a running house cat has 10.0 J of kinetic energy at speed v, (a) At what speed (in terms of v) will she have 20.0 J of kinetic energy? (b) What would her kinetic energy be if she ran half as fast as the speed in part (a)?

17. ● A 0.145 kg baseball leaves a pitcher's hand at a speed of 32.0 m/s. If air drag is negligible, how much work has the pitcher done on the ball by throwing it?

18. ●●● A 1.50 kg book is sliding along a rough horizontal surface. At point *A* it is moving at 3.21 m/s, and at point *B* it has slowed to 1.25 m/s. (a) How much work was done on the book between *A* and *B*? (b) If −0.750 J of work is done on the book from *B* to *C*, how fast is it moving at point *C*? (c) How fast would it be moving at *C* if +0.750 J of work were done on it from *B* to *C*?

19. ●● **Stopping distance of a car.** The driver of an 1800 kg car (including passengers) traveling at 23.0 m/s slams on the

brakes, locking the wheels on the dry pavement. The coefficient of kinetic friction between rubber and dry concrete is typically 0.700. (a) Use the work–energy principle to calculate how far the car will travel before stopping. (b) How far would the car travel if it were going twice as fast? (c) What happened to the car's original kinetic energy?

20. • **Meteor crater.** About 50,000 years ago, a meteor crashed into the earth near present-day Flagstaff, Arizona. Recent (2005) measurements estimate that this meteor had a mass of about 1.4×10^8 kg (around 150,000 tons) and hit the ground at 12 km/s. (a) How much kinetic energy did this meteor deliver to the ground? (b) How does this energy compare to the energy produced in one day by a standard coal-fired power plant, which generates about 1 billion joules per second?

21. •• You throw a 20 N rock into the air from ground level and observe that, when it is 15.0 m high, it is traveling upward at 25.0 m/s. Use the work–energy principle to find (a) the rock's speed just as it left the ground and (b) the maximum height the rock will reach.

22. • A 0.420 kg soccer ball is initially moving at 2.00 m/s. A soccer player kicks the ball, exerting a constant 40.0 N force in the same direction as the ball's motion. Over what distance must her foot be in contact with the ball to increase the ball's speed to 6.00 m/s?

23. •• A 61 kg skier on level snow coasts 184 m to a stop from a speed of 12.0 m/s. (a) Use the work–energy principle to find the coefficient of kinetic friction between the skis and the snow. (b) Suppose a 75 kg skier with twice the starting speed coasted the same distance before stopping. Find the coefficient of kinetic friction between that skier's skis and the snow.

24. •• A block of ice with mass 2.00 kg slides 0.750 m down an inclined plane that slopes downward at an angle of 36.9° below the horizontal. If the block of ice starts from rest, what is its final speed? You can ignore friction.

4 Work Done by a Varying Force

25. • To stretch a certain spring by 2.5 cm from its equilibrium position requires 8.0 J of work. (a) What is the force constant of this spring? (b) What was the maximum force required to stretch it by that distance?

26. •• A spring is 17.0 cm long when it is lying on a table. One end is then attached to a hook and the other end is pulled by a force that increases to 25.0 N, causing the spring to stretch to a length of 19.2 cm. (a) What is the force constant of this spring? (b) How much work was required to stretch the spring from 17.0 cm to 19.2 cm? (c) How long will the spring be if the 25 N force is replaced by a 50 N force?

27. •• A spring of force constant 300.0 N/m and unstretched length 0.240 m is stretched by two forces, pulling in opposite directions at opposite ends of the spring, that increase to 15.0 N. How long will the spring now be, and how much work was required to stretch it that distance?

28. •• An unstretched spring has a force constant of 1200 N/m. How large a force and how much work are required to stretch the spring: (a) by 1.0 m from its unstretched length, and (b) by 1.0 m beyond the length reached in part (a)?

29. •• The graph in the accompanying figure shows the magnitude of the force exerted by a given spring as a function of the distance x the spring is stretched. How much work is needed to stretch this spring: (a) a distance of 5.0 cm, starting with it unstretched, and (b) from $x = 2.0$ cm to $x = 7.0$ cm?

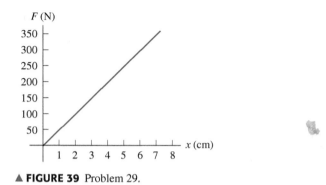

▲ **FIGURE 39** Problem 29.

5 Potential Energy

30. • A 575 N woman climbs a staircase that rises at 53° above
BIO the horizontal and is 4.75 m long. Her speed is a constant 45 cm/s. (a) Is the given weight a reasonable one for an adult woman? (b) How much has the gravitational potential energy increased by her climbing the stairs? (c) How much work has gravity done on her as she climbed the stairs?

31. • **How high can we jump?** The maximum height a typical
BIO human can jump from a crouched start is about 60 cm. By how much does the gravitational potential energy increase for a 72 kg person in such a jump? Where does this energy come from?

32. • A 72.0-kg swimmer jumps into the old swimming hole from a diving board 3.25 m above the water. Use energy conservation to find his speed just he hits the water (a) if he just holds his nose and drops in, (b) if he bravely jumps straight up (but just beyond the board!) at 2.50 m/s, and (c) if he manages to jump downward at 2.50 m/s.

33. •• A 2.50-kg mass is pushed against a horizontal spring of force constant 25.0 N/cm on a frictionless air table. The spring is attached to the tabletop, and the mass is not attached to the spring in any way. When the spring has been compressed enough to store 11.5 J of potential energy in it, the mass is suddenly released from rest. (a) Find the greatest speed the mass reaches. When does this occur? (b) What is the greatest acceleration of the mass, and when does it occur?

34. • A force of magnitude 800.0 N stretches a certain spring by 0.200 m from its equilibrium position. (a) What is the force constant of this spring? (b) How much elastic potential energy is stored in the spring when it is: (i) stretched 0.300 m from its equilibrium position and (ii) compressed by 0.300 m from its equilibrium position? (c) How much work was done in stretching the spring by the original 0.200 m?

35. • **Tendons.** Tendons are strong elastic fibers that attach mus-
BIO cles to bones. To a reasonable approximation, they obey Hooke's law. In laboratory tests on a particular tendon, it was found that, when a 250 g object was hung from it, the tendon stretched 1.23 cm. (a) Find the force constant of this tendon in N/m. (b) Because of its thickness, the maximum tension this

tendon can support without rupturing is 138 N. By how much can the tendon stretch without rupturing, and how much energy is stored in it at that point?

36. ••• A certain spring stores 10.0 J of potential energy when it is stretched by 2.00 cm from its equilibrium position. (a) How much potential energy would the spring store if it were stretched an additional 2.00 cm? (b) How much potential energy would it store if it were compressed by 2.00 cm from its equilibrium position? (c) How far from the equilibrium position would you have to stretch the string to store 20.0 J of potential energy? (d) What is the force constant of this spring?

37. • In designing a machine part, you need a spring that is 8.50 cm long when no forces act on it and that will store 15.0 J of energy when it is compressed by 1.20 cm from its equilibrium position. (a) What should be the force constant of this spring? (b) Can the spring store 850 J by compression?

38. •• **Leg presses.** As part of your daily workout, you lie on your back and push with your feet against a platform attached to two stiff springs arranged side by side so that they are parallel to each other. When you push the platform, you compress the springs. You do 80.0 J of work when you compress the springs 0.200 m from their uncompressed length. (a) What magnitude of force must you apply to hold the platform in this position? (b) How much *additional* work must you do to move the platform 0.200 m *farther*, and what maximum force must you apply?

39. •• **Food calories.** The *food calorie,* equal to 4186 J, is a
BIO measure of how much energy is released when food is metabolized by the body. A certain brand of fruit-and-cereal bar contains 140 food calories per bar. (a) If a 65 kg hiker eats one of these bars, how high a mountain must he climb to "work off" the calories, assuming that all the food energy goes only into increasing gravitational potential energy? (b) If, as is typical, only 20% of the food calories go into mechanical energy, what would be the answer to part (a)? *(Note: In this and all other problems, we are assuming that 100% of the food calories that are eaten are absorbed and used by the body. This is actually not true. A person's "metabolic efficiency" is the percentage of calories eaten that are actually used; the rest are eliminated by the body. Metabolic efficiency varies considerably from person to person.)*

40. •• **A good workout.** You overindulged on a delicious dessert,
BIO so you plan to work off the extra calories at the gym. To accomplish this, you decide to do a series of arm raises holding a 5.0 kg weight in one hand. The distance from your elbow to the weight is 35 cm, and in each arm raise you start with your arm horizontal and pivot it until it is vertical. Assume that the weight of your arm is small enough compared with the weight you are lifting that you can ignore it. As is typical, your muscles are 20% efficient in converting the food energy they use up into mechanical energy, with the rest going into heat. If your dessert contained 350 food calories, how many arm raises must you do to work off these calories? Is it realistic to do them all in one session?

41. •• **An exercise program.** A 75 kg person is put on an exer-
BIO cise program by a physical therapist, the goal being to burn up 500 food calories in each daily session. Recall that human muscles are about 20% efficient in converting the energy they use up into mechanical energy. The exercise program consists of a set of consecutive high jumps, each one 50 cm into the air (which is pretty good for a human) and lasting 2.0 s, on the average. How many jumps should the person do per session, and how much time should be set aside for each session? Do you think that this is a physically reasonable exercise session?

6 Conservation of Energy

42. • Tall Pacific Coast redwood trees (*Sequoia sempervirens*) can reach heights of about 100 m. If air drag is negligibly small, how fast is a sequoia cone moving when it reaches the ground if it dropped from the top of a 100 m tree?

43. • The total height of Yosemite Falls is 2425 ft. (a) How many more joules of gravitational potential energy are there for each kilogram of water at the top of this waterfall compared with each kilogram of water at the foot of the falls? (b) Find the kinetic energy and speed of each kilogram of water as it reaches the base of the waterfall, assuming that there are no losses due to friction with the air or rocks and that the mass of water had negligible vertical speed at the top. How fast (in m/s and mph) would a 70 kg person have to run to have that much kinetic energy? (c) How high would Yosemite Falls have to be so that each kilogram of water at the base had twice the kinetic energy you found in part (b); twice the speed you found in part (b)?

44. • **The speed of hailstones.** Although the altitude may vary considerably, hailstones sometimes originate around 500 m (about 1500 ft) above the ground. (a) Neglecting air drag, how fast will these hailstones be moving when they reach the ground, assuming that they started from rest? Express your answer in m/s and in mph. (b) From your own experience, are hailstones actually falling that fast when they reach the ground? Why not? What has happened to most of the initial potential energy?

45. •• Pebbles of weight w are launched from the edge of a vertical cliff of height h at speed v_0. How fast (in terms of the quantities just given) will these pebbles be moving when they reach the ground if they are launched (a) straight up, (b) straight down, (c) horizontally away from the cliff, and (d) at an angle θ above the horizontal? (e) How would the answers to the previous parts change if the pebbles weighed twice as much?

46. • **Volcanoes on Io.** Io, a satellite of Jupiter, is the most volcanically active moon or planet in the solar system. It has volcanoes that send plumes of matter over 500 km high (see the accompanying figure). Due to the satellite's small mass, the acceleration due to gravity on Io is only 1.81 m/s², and Io has no appreciable atmosphere. Assume that there is no variation in gravity over the distance traveled. (a) What must be the speed of material just as it leaves the volcano to reach an altitude of 500 km? (b) If the gravitational potential energy is zero at the surface, what is the potential energy for a 25 kg fragment at its maximum height on Io? How much would this gravitational potential energy be if it were at the same height above earth?

▲ **FIGURE 40** Problem 46.

47. •• **Human energy vs. insect energy.** For its size, the com-
BIO mon flea is one of the most accomplished jumpers in the animal world. A 2.0-mm-long, 0.50 mg critter can reach a height of 20 cm in a single leap. (a) Neglecting air drag, what is the take-off speed of such a flea? (b) Calculate the kinetic energy of this flea at takeoff and its kinetic energy per kilogram of mass. (c) If a 65 kg, 2.0-m-tall human could jump to the same height compared with his length as the flea jumps compared with its length, how high could he jump, and what takeoff speed would he need? (d) In fact, most humans can jump no more than 60 cm from a crouched start. What is the kinetic energy per kilogram of mass at takeoff for such a 65 kg person? (e) Where does the flea store the energy that allows it to make such a sudden leap?

48. •• A 25 kg child plays on a swing having support ropes that are 2.20 m long. A friend pulls her back until the ropes are 42° from the vertical and releases her from rest. (a) What is the potential energy for the child just as she is released, compared with the potential energy at the bottom of the swing? (b) How fast will she be moving at the bottom of the swing? (c) How much work does the tension in the ropes do as the child swings from the initial position to the bottom?

49. • **Tarzan and Jane.** Tarzan, in one tree, sights Jane in another tree. He grabs the end of a vine with length 20 m that makes an angle of 45° with the vertical, steps off his tree limb, and swings down and then up to Jane's open arms. When he arrives, his vine makes an angle of 30° with the vertical. Determine whether he gives her a tender embrace or knocks her off her limb by calculating Tarzan's speed just before he reaches Jane. You can ignore air resistance and the mass of the vine.

50. •• A slingshot obeying Hooke's law is used to launch pebbles vertically into the air. You observe that if you pull a pebble back 20.0 cm against the elastic band, the pebble goes 6.0 m high. (a) Assuming that air drag is negligible, how high will the pebble go if you pull it back 40.0 cm instead? (b) How far must you pull it back so it will reach 12.0 m? (c) If you pull a pebble that is twice as heavy back 20.0 cm, how high will it go?

51. •• When a piece of wood is pressed against a spring and compresses the spring by 5.0 cm, the wood gains a maximum kinetic energy K when it is released. How much kinetic energy (in terms of K) would the piece of wood gain if the spring were compressed 10.0 cm instead?

52. • A 1.5 kg box moves back and forth on a horizontal friction-less surface between two different springs, as shown in the accompanying figure. The box is initially pressed against the stronger spring, compressing it 4.0 cm, and then is released from rest. (a) By how much will the box compress the weaker spring? (b) What is the maximum speed the box will reach?

$k = 32$ N/cm   Box $k = 16$ N/cm

Frictionless surface

▲ **FIGURE 41** Problem 52.

53. •• A 12.0 N package of whole wheat flour is suddenly placed on the pan of a scale such as you find in grocery stores. The pan is supported from below by a vertical spring of force constant 325 N/m. If the pan has negligible weight, find the maximum distance the spring will be compressed if no energy is dissipated by friction.

54. •• A spring of negligible mass has force constant $k = 1600$ N/m. (a) How far must the spring be compressed for 3.20 J of potential energy to be stored in it? (b) You place the spring vertically with one end on the floor. You then drop a 1.20-kg book onto it from a height of 0.80 m above the top of the spring. Find the maximum distance the spring will be compressed.

7 Conservative and Nonconservative Forces

55. • A 1.50 kg brick is sliding along on a rough horizontal surface at 13.0 m/s. If the brick stops in 4.80 s, how much mechanical energy is lost, and what happens to this energy?

56. • A fun-loving 11.4 kg otter slides up a hill and then back down to the same place. If she starts up at 5.75 m/s and returns at 3.75 m/s, how much mechanical energy did she lose on the hill, and what happened to that energy?

57. • A 12.0 g plastic ball is dropped from a height of 2.50 m and is moving at 3.20 m/s just before it hits the floor. How much mechanical energy was lost during the ball's fall?

58. • You and three friends stand at the corners of a square whose sides are 8.0 m long in the middle of the gym floor, as shown in the accompanying figure. You take your physics book and push it from one person to the other. The book has a mass of 1.5 kg, and the coefficient of kinetic friction between the book and the floor is $\mu_k = 0.25$. (a) The book slides from you to Beth and then from Beth to Carlos, along the lines connecting these people. What is the work done by friction during this displacement? (b) You slide the book from you to Carlos along the diagonal of the square. What is the work done by friction during this displacement? (c) You slide the book to Kim who then slides it back to you. What is the total work done by friction during this motion of the book? (d) Is the friction force on the book conservative or nonconservative? Explain.

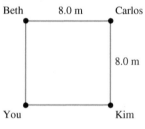

Beth   8.0 m   Carlos

8.0 m

You   Kim

▲ **FIGURE 42** Problem 58.

59. • While a roofer is working on a roof that slants at 36° above the horizontal, he accidentally nudges his 85.0 N toolbox, causing it to start sliding downward, starting from rest. If it starts 4.25 m from the lower edge of the roof, how fast will the toolbox be moving just as it reaches the edge of the roof if the kinetic friction force on it is 22.0 N?

60. •• A block with mass 0.50 kg is forced against a horizontal spring of negligible mass, compressing the spring a distance of 0.20 m, as shown in the accompanying figure. When released, the block moves on a horizontal tabletop for 1.00 m before coming to rest. The spring constant k is 100 N/m. What is the coefficient of kinetic friction μ_k between the block and the tabletop?

$k = 100$ N/m $m = 0.50$ kg

0.20 m

1.00 m

▲ **FIGURE 43** Problem 60.

61. •• A loaded 375 kg toboggan is traveling on smooth horizontal snow at 4.5 m/s when it suddenly comes to a rough region. The region is 7.0 m long and reduces the toboggan's speed by 1.5 m/s. (a) What average friction force did the rough region exert on the toboggan? (b) By what percent did the rough region reduce the toboggan's (i) kinetic energy and (ii) speed?

62. •• A 62.0 kg skier is moving at 6.50 m/s on a frictionless, horizontal snow-covered plateau when she encounters a rough patch 3.50 m long. The coefficient of kinetic friction between this patch and her skis is 0.300. After crossing the rough patch and returning to friction-free snow, she skis down an icy, frictionless hill 2.50 m high. (a) How fast is the skier moving when she gets to the bottom of the hill? (b) How much internal energy was generated in crossing the rough patch?

8 Power

63. • (a) How many joules of energy does a 100 watt lightbulb use every hour? (b) How fast would a 70 kg person have to run to have that amount of kinetic energy? Is it possible for a person to run that fast? (c) How high a tree would a 70 kg person have to climb to increase his gravitational potential energy relative to the ground by that amount? Are there any trees that tall?

64. • The engine of a motorboat delivers 30.0 kW to the propeller while the boat is moving at 15.0 m/s. What would be the tension in the towline if the boat were being towed at the same speed?

65. •• At 7.35 cents per kilowatt-hour, (a) what does it cost to operate a 10.0 hp motor for 8.00 hr? (b) What does it cost to leave a 75 W light burning 24 hours a day?

66. • A tandem (two-person) bicycle team must overcome a force of 165 N to maintain a speed of 9.00 m/s. Find the power required per rider, assuming that each contributes equally.

67. •• An elevator has mass 600 kg, not including passengers. The elevator is designed to ascend, at constant speed, a vertical distance of 20.0 m (five floors) in 16.0 s, and it is driven by a motor that can provide up to 40 hp to the elevator. What is the maximum number of passengers that can ride in the elevator? Assume that an average passenger has mass 65.0 kg.

68. •• U.S. power use. The total consumption of electrical energy in the United States is about 1.0×10^{19} joules per year. (a) Express this rate in watts and kilowatts. (b) If the U.S. population is about 310 million people, what is the average rate of electrical energy consumption per person?

69. •• Solar energy. The sun transfers energy to the earth by radiation at a rate of approximately 1.0 kW per square meter of surface. (a) If this energy could be collected and converted to electrical energy with 25% efficiency, how large an area (in square kilometers) would be required to collect the electrical energy used by the United States? (See the previous problem.) (b) If the solar collectors were arranged in a square array, what would be the length of its sides in kilometers and in miles? Does an array of these dimensions seem technologically feasible?

70. •• A 20.0 kg rock slides on a rough horizontal surface at 8.00 m/s and eventually stops due to friction. The coefficient of kinetic friction between the rock and the surface is 0.200. What average thermal power is produced as the rock stops?

71. •• Horsepower. In the English system of units, power is expressed as horsepower (hp) instead of watts, where 1.00 hp = 746 W. Horsepower is often used for motors and automobiles. (a) What should be the power rating in horsepower of a 100 W lightbulb? (b) How many watts does a 75 hp motor produce? (c) Electrical resistors are rated in watts to indicate how much power they can tolerate without burning up. If a resistor is rated at 2.00 W, what should be its rating in horsepower? (d) Our sun radiates 3.92×10^{26} J of energy each second. What is its horsepower rating? (e) How many kilowatt-hours of energy is produced when you run a 25 hp motor for 90 minutes?

72. •• BIO Maximum sustainable human power. The maximum sustainable mechanical power a human can produce is about $\frac{1}{3}$ hp. How many food calories can a human burn up in an hour by exercising at this rate? (Remember that only 20% of the food energy used goes into mechanical energy.)

73. •• BIO A typical flying insect applies an average force equal to twice its weight during each downward stroke while hovering. Take the mass of the insect to be 10 g, and assume the wings move an average downward distance of 1.0 cm during each stroke. Assuming 100 downward strokes per second, estimate the average power output of the insect.

74. •• When its 75-kW (100-hp) engine is generating full power, a small single-engine airplane with mass 700 kg gains altitude at a rate of 2.5 m/s (150 m/min, or 500 ft/min). What fraction of the engine power is being used to make the airplane climb? (The remainder is used to overcome the effects of air resistance and of inefficiencies in the propeller and engine.)

75. •• BIO The power of the human heart. The human heart is a powerful and extremely reliable pump. Each day it takes in and discharges about 7500 L of blood. Assume that the work done by the heart is equal to the work required to lift that amount of blood a height equal to that of the average American female, approximately 1.63 m. The density of blood is 1050 kg/m³. (a) How much work does the heart do in a day? (b) What is the heart's power output in watts? (c) In fact, the heart puts out more power than you found in part (b). Why? What other forms of energy does it give the blood?

76. •• At the site of a wind farm in North Dakota, the average wind speed is 9.3 m/s, and the average density of air is 1.2 kg/m³. (a) Calculate how much kinetic energy the wind contains, per cubic meter, at this location. (b) No wind turbine can capture all of the energy contained in the wind, the main reason being that capturing all the energy would require stopping the wind completely, meaning that air would stop flowing through the turbine. Suppose a particular turbine has blades with a radius of 41 m and is able to capture 35% of the available wind energy. What would be the power output of this turbine, under average wind conditions?

General Problems

77. • Bumper guards. You are asked to design spring bumpers for the walls of a parking garage. A freely rolling 1200 kg car moving at 0.65 m/s is to compress the spring no more than 7.0 cm before stopping. (a) What should be the force constant

of the spring, and what is the maximum amount of energy that gets stored in it? (b) If the springs that are actually delivered have the proper force constant but can become compressed by only 5.0 cm, what is the maximum speed of the given car for which they will provide adequate protection?

78. •• **Human terminal velocity.** By landing properly and on soft ground (and by being lucky!), humans have survived falls from airplanes when, for example, a parachute failed to open, with astonishingly little injury. Without a parachute, a typical human eventually reaches a terminal velocity of about 62 m/s. Suppose the fall is from an airplane 1000 m high. (a) How fast would a person be falling when he reached the ground if there were no air drag? (b) If a 70 kg person reaches the ground traveling at the terminal velocity of 62 m/s, how much mechanical energy was lost during the fall? What happened to that energy?

79. •• A wooden rod of negligible mass and length 80.0 cm is pivoted about a horizontal axis through its center. A white rat with mass 0.500 kg clings to one end of the stick, and a mouse with mass 0.200 kg clings to the other end. The system is released from rest with the rod horizontal. If the animals can manage to hold on, what are their speeds as the rod swings through a vertical position?

80. •• **Mountain climbing!** A 75.0 kg mountain climber is holding his 60.0 kg partner over a cliff when he suddenly steps on frictionless ice at the horizontal top of the cliff, as shown in the accompanying figure. The rope has negligible mass and is held horizontally by the climber. There is no appreciable friction at the icy edge of the cliff. Use energy methods to calculate the speed of the climbers after the lower one has descended 1.50 m starting from rest.

75.0 kg

60.0 kg

▲ **FIGURE 44** Problem 80.

81. •• **More mountain climbing!** What would be the speed of the climbers in the previous problem after they had moved 1.50 m if there were friction between the upper climber and the ice with a coefficient of kinetic friction of 0.250?

82. •• **Ski jump ramp.** You are designing a ski jump ramp for the next Winter Olympics. You need to calculate the vertical height h from the starting gate to the bottom of the ramp. The skiers push off hard with their ski poles at the start, just above the starting gate, so they typically have a speed of 2.0 m/s as they reach the gate. For safety, the skiers should have a speed of no more than 30.0 m/s when they reach the bottom of the ramp. You determine that for a 85.0-kg skier with good form, friction and air resistance will do total work of magnitude

4000 J on him during his run down the slope. What is the maximum height h for which the maximum safe speed will not be exceeded?

83. • **Rescue.** Your friend (mass 65.0 kg) is standing on the ice in the middle of a frozen pond. There is very little friction between her feet and the ice, so she is unable to walk. Fortunately, a light rope is tied around her waist and you stand on the bank holding the other end. You pull on the rope for 3.00 s and accelerate your friend from rest to a speed of 6.00 m/s while you remain at rest. What is the average power supplied by the force you applied?

84. •• On an essentially frictionless horizontal ice-skating rink, a skater moving at 3.0 m/s encounters a rough patch that reduces her speed by 45% due to a friction force that is 25% of her weight. Use the work–energy principle to find the length of the rough patch.

85. ••• **Pendulum.** A small 0.12 kg metal ball is tied to a very light (essentially massless) string 0.80 m long to form a pendulum that is then set swinging by releasing the ball from rest when the string makes a 45° angle with the vertical. Air drag and other forms of friction are negligible. What is the speed of the ball when the string passes through its vertical position, and what is the tension in the string at that instant?

86. •• A pump is required to lift 750 liters of water per minute from a well 14.0 m deep and eject it with a speed of 18.0 m/s. How much work per minute does the pump do?

87. •• A 350 kg roller coaster starts from rest at point A and slides down the frictionless loop-the-loop shown in the accompanying figure. (a) How fast is this roller coaster moving at point B? (b) How hard does it press against the track at point B?

25.0 m

3.00 m

B

4.00 m

12.0 m

▲ **FIGURE 45** Problem 87.

88. ••• **Automobile air-bag safety.** An automobile air bag cushions the force on the driver in a head-on collision by absorbing her energy before she hits the steering wheel. Such a bag can be modeled as an elastic force, similar to that produced by a spring. (a) Use energy conservation to show that the effective

▲ **FIGURE 46** Problem 88.

force constant k of the air bag is $k = mv_0^2/x_{max}^2$, where m is the mass of the driver, v_0 is the speed of the car (and driver) at the instant of the accident, and x_{max} is the maximum distance the bag gets compressed, which, in a severe accident, would be the distance from the driver's body to the steering wheel. (b) Show that the maximum force the air bag would exert on the driver is $F_{max} = mv_0^2/x_{max}$. (c) Now let's put in some realistic numbers. Experimental tests have shown that injury occurs when a force *density* greater than $5.0 \times 10^5 \, N/m^2$ acts on human tissue. (The *total* force is this force density times the area over which it acts.) As the accompanying figure shows, the force of the air bag acts mostly on the upper front half of the driver's body, over an area of about 2500 cm². (Check your own body to see if this is reasonable.) Use this value to calculate the total force on the driver's body at the threshold of injury. (d) Use your results to calculate the effective force constant k of the air bag and the maximum speed for which the bag will prevent injury to a 65 kg driver if she is 30 cm from the steering wheel at the instant of impact. Express the speed in m/s and mph. (e) How could you design a safer air bag for higher speed collisions? What things could you alter to do this? Would it be safe to make a stiffer air bag by inflating it more? Explain your reasoning.

89. •• In creating his definition of horsepower, James Watt, the
BIO inventor of the steam engine, calculated the power output of a horse operating a mill to grind grain or cut wood. The horse walked in a 24-ft diameter circle, making, according to Watt, 144 trips around the circle in an hour. (a) Using the currently accepted value of 746 watts for 1 horsepower, calculate the force (in pounds) with which Mr. Watt's horse must have been pulling. (b) Calculate the power output, in hp, of a 70-kg human being who climbs a 3.0-m-high set of stairs in 5.0 seconds.

90. •• All birds, independent of their size, must maintain a power
BIO output of 10–25 watts per kilogram of body mass in order to fly by flapping their wings. (a) The Andean giant hummingbird (*Patagona gigas*) has mass 70 g and flaps its wings 10 times per second while hovering. Estimate the amount of work done by such a hummingbird in each wingbeat. (b) A 70-kg athlete can maintain a power output of 1.4 kW for no more than a few seconds; the *steady* power output of a typical athlete is only 500 W or so. Is it possible for a human-powered aircraft to fly for extended periods by flapping its wings? Explain.

91. •• A 250 g object on a frictionless, horizontal lab table is pushed against a spring of force constant 35 N/cm and then released. Just before the object is released, the spring is compressed 12.0 cm. How fast is the object moving when it has gained half of the spring's original stored energy?

92. •• **Automobile accident analysis.** In an auto accident, a car hit a pedestrian and the driver then slammed on the brakes to stop the car. During the subsequent trial, the driver's lawyer claimed that the driver was obeying the posted 35 mph speed limit, but that the limit was too high to enable him to see and react to the pedestrian in time. You have been called as the state's expert witness. In your investigation of the accident site, you make the following measurements: The skid marks made while the brakes were applied were 280 ft long, and the tread on the tires produced a coefficient of kinetic friction of 0.30 with the road. (a) In your testimony in court, will you say that the driver was obeying the posted speed limit? You must be able to back up your answer with clear numerical reasoning during cross-examination. (b) If the driver's speeding ticket is $10 for each mile per hour he was driving above the posted speed limit, would he have to pay a ticket, and if so, how much would it be?

93. •• **Bungee jump.** A bungee cord is 30.0 m long and, when stretched a distance x, it exerts a restoring force of magnitude kx. Your father-in-law (mass 95.0 kg) stands on a platform 45.0 m above the ground, and one end of the cord is tied securely to his ankle and the other end to the platform. You have promised him that when he steps off the platform he will fall a maximum distance of only 41.0 m before the cord stops him. You had several bungee cords to select from, and you tested them by stretching them out, tying one end to a tree, and pulling on the other end with a force of 380.0 N. When you do this, what distance will the bungee cord that you should select have stretched?

94. •• **Riding a loop-the-loop.**
A car in an amusement park ride travels without friction along the track shown in the accompanying figure, starting from rest at point A. If the loop the car is currently on has a radius of 20.0 m, find the minimum height h so that the car will not fall off the track at the top of the circular part of the loop.

▲ **FIGURE 47** Problem 94.

95. •• A 2.0 kg piece of wood slides on the surface shown in the accompanying figure. All parts of the surface are frictionless, except for a 30-m-long rough segment at the bottom, where the coefficient of kinetic friction with the wood is 0.20. The wood starts from rest 4.0 m above the bottom. (a) Where will the wood eventually come to rest? (b) How much work is done by friction by the time the wood stops?

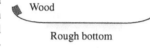
▲ **FIGURE 48** Problem 95.

96. •• A 68 kg skier approaches the foot of a hill with a speed of 15 m/s. The surface of this hill slopes up at 40.0° above the horizontal and has coefficients of static and kinetic friction of 0.75 and 0.25, respectively, with the skis. (a) Use energy conservation to find the maximum height above the foot of the hill that the skier will reach. (b) Will the skier remain at rest once she stops, or will she begin to slide down the hill? Prove your answer.

97. •• **Energy requirements of the body.** A 70 kg human uses
BIO energy at the rate of 80 J/s, on average, for just resting and sleeping. When the person is engaged in more strenuous activities, the rate can be much higher. (a) If the individual did nothing but rest, how many food calories per day would she or he have to eat to make up for those used up? (b) In what forms is energy used when a person is resting or sleeping? In other words, what happens to those 80 J/s? (*Hint: What kinds of energy, mechanical and otherwise, do our body components have?*) (c) If an average person rested and did other low-level activity for 16 hours (which consumes 80 J/s) and did light activity on the job for 8 hours (which consumes 200 J/s), how many calories would she or he have to consume per day to make up for the energy used up?

98. •• The aircraft carrier *USS George Washington* has mass 1.0×10^8 kg. When its engines are developing their full power of 260,000 hp, the *George Washington* travels at its top speed of 35 knots (65 km/h). If 70% of the power output of the engines is applied to pushing the ship through the water,

what is the magnitude of the force of water resistance that opposes the carrier's motion at this speed?

99. ●● Two paint buckets are connected by a lightweight rope passing over a pulley of negligible mass and friction. (a) As shown in the accompanying figure, the system is released from rest with the 12.0 kg bucket 2.00 m above the floor. Use energy conservation to find the speed with which this bucket strikes the floor. (b) Suppose the pulley had appreciable mass but no bearing friction. Would the bucket's speed be greater than, less than, or the same as you found in part (a)? Explain your reasoning in terms of energy.

▲ FIGURE 49
Problem 99.

12.0 kg

2.00 m

4.0 kg

100. ●●● A ball is thrown upward with an initial velocity of 15 m/s at an angle of 60.0° above the horizontal. Use energy conservation to find the ball's greatest height above the ground.

101. ●●● **Automotive power.** A truck engine transmits 28.0 kW (37.5 hp) to the driving wheels when the truck is traveling at a constant velocity of magnitude 60.0 km/h (37.7 mi/h) on a level road. (a) What is the resisting force acting on the truck? (b) Assume that 65% of the resisting force is due to rolling friction and the remainder is due to air resistance. If the force of rolling friction is independent of speed, and the force of air resistance is proportional to the square of the speed, what power will drive the truck at 30.0 km/h? At 120.0 km/h? Give your answers in kilowatts and in horsepower.

102. ●●● **Mass extinctions.** One of the greatest mass extinctions occurred about 65 million years ago, when, along with many other life-forms, the dinosaurs went extinct. Most geologists and paleontologists agree that this event was caused when a large asteroid hit the earth. Scientists estimate that this asteroid was about 10 km in diameter and that it would have been traveling at least as fast as 11 km/s. The density of asteroid material is about 3.5 g/cm³, on the average. (a) What would be the approximate mass of the asteroid, assuming it to be spherical? (b) How much kinetic energy would the asteroid have delivered to the earth? (c) In order to put the amount of energy you found in part (b) in perspective, consider the following: the total amount of energy used in one year by the human race is roughly 500 exajoules. If this rate of energy use remained constant, how many years would it take the human species to use an amount of energy equal to the amount delivered by this asteroid?

103. ●● **Avoiding mass extinctions.** It has been suggested that we can protect the earth from devastating asteroidal impacts such as the one discussed in the previous problem by using nuclear devices to alter the orbits of such asteroids around the sun so that they will miss our planet. If this is done very far from earth, it is necessary to move them only a few centimeters to spare the earth a mass extinction. How much energy would it take to move the asteroid that has been implicated in the dinosaur extinction by a few centimeters? (See the previous problem.) To make the calculation reasonable, assume that we need to exert a force on the asteroid that will accelerate it uniformly from rest through a distance of 5.0 cm in 0.50 s. The energy we must give to the asteroid is the added kinetic energy from this motion. To see if it is feasible to do this, how many 1.0 megaton bombs would it take to accomplish the task?

104. ●● The spring of a spring gun has force constant $k = 400$ N/m and negligible mass. The spring is compressed 6.00 cm, and a ball with mass 0.0300 kg is placed in the horizontal barrel against the compressed spring. The spring is then released, and the ball is propelled out the barrel of the gun. The barrel is 6.00 cm long, so the ball leaves the barrel at the same point that it loses contact with the spring. The gun is held so the barrel is horizontal. (a) Calculate the speed with which the ball leaves the barrel if you can ignore friction. (b) Calculate the speed of the ball as it leaves the barrel if a constant resisting force of 6.00 N acts on the ball as it moves along the barrel. (c) For the situation in part (b), at what position along the barrel does the ball have the greatest speed, and what is that speed? (In this case, the maximum speed does not occur at the end of the barrel.)

105. ●● A graph of the potential energy stored in a tendon as a
BIO function of the *square* of the distance x it has stretched from its equilibrium position is shown in the accompanying figure. (a) Does the tendon obey Hooke's law? Explain your reasoning. (b) What is the force constant of the tendon? (c) How far must the tendon be stretched from its equilibrium position to store 10.0 J of energy? (d) What force is necessary to hold the tendon in place in part (c)? (e) Sketch a clear graph of the potential energy stored in the tendon as a function of x.

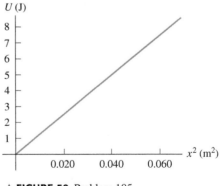

▲ **FIGURE 50** Problem 105.

106. •• A sled with rider having a combined mass of 125 kg travels over the perfectly smooth icy hill shown in the accompanying figure. How far does the sled land from the foot of the cliff?

22.5 m/s

11.0 m | Cliff

▲ **FIGURE 51** Problem 106.

ANSWERS TO SELECTED PROBLEMS

Conceptual Questions

1. The force one surface exerts on the other displaces the atoms of the surface from their equilibrium positions and imparts oscillatory motion to them. The energy associated with this motion is thermal energy.

5. The force of the rope on the object does work on the object. The force of the object on the rope does work on the rope. Thus, each force performs work on a different object; the work done on the rope is not part of the net work done on the object. The nonzero net work done on the object by the rope provides kinetic energy to the object.

7. In the absence of friction in the jack mechanism, the same work is done in both cases. When the jack is used, a smaller force is exerted over a larger distance to do the same amount of work as lifting the car directly.

9. The elastic potential energy of the compressed spring is converted into thermal energy, which is dispersed within the solution.

11. The kinetic energy comes from potential energy stored in your tensed muscles. When you jump, you push downward on the floor with a force greater than your weight. By Newton's third law, the floor pushes up on you with an upward force of the same magnitude. The work this force does on you increases your kinetic energy and lifts you into the air. You could not jump if you were floating in outer space, since there is nothing to exert a force on you.

13. The change in kinetic energy is proportional to the change in v^2. For 15 mph to 20 mph, the change in v^2 is 175 mph^2. For 10 mph to 15 mph, the change in v^2 is 125 mph^2. Thus, the change is greater for 15 mph to 20 mph.

15. Energy is transported from the sun to the earth by electromagnetic waves, such as visible light, that are radiated by the sun.

Part of this energy is converted to chemical energy by plants, using photosynthesis. This chemical energy is ingested when we eat the plants or eat an animal that has eaten the plants. Our bodies convert the chemical energy (food energy) into mechanical energy through the operation of our muscles.

Multiple-Choice Problems

1. B
3. A
5. C
7. A, D
9. A, D, E
11. B, D
13. C
15. C

Problems

1. 300 J
3. 5.22×10^4 J
5. (a) 3.60 J (b) -0.900 J
   (c) 0 (d) 0
   (e) 2.70 J
7. (a) 74 N (b) 330 J (c) -330 J
   (d) 0; 0 (e) 0
9. 2.62×10^9 J
11. (a) 324 J (b) -324 J (c) 0
13. 4.21 g
15. (a) 7.07 m/s (b) 3/4
17. 74.2 J
19. (a) 38.6 m (b) 154 m
    (c) converted to thermal energy
21. (a) 30.3 m/s (b) 46.9 m
23. (a) 0.0399 (b) 0.160
25. (a) 2.6×10^4 N/m
    (b) 650 N
27. 0.290 m, 0.375 J
29. (a) 6.2 J (b) 11.2 J
31. 420 J; from potential energy stored in his tensed muscles
33. (a) 3.03 m/s; as mass leaves spring
    (b) 95.9 m/s^2; just after mass is released
35. (a) 199 N/m (b) 69.3 cm, 47.8 J
37. (a) 2.08×10^5 N/m (b) no
39. (a) 920 (b) 180 m

41. 1.1×10^3 jumps; 37 min.; no
43. (a) 7.24×10^3 J (b) 7.24×10^3 J,
    120 m/s; 14 m/s, 32 mph (c) 4850 ft;
    9700 ft
45. (a)–(d) $\sqrt{v_0^2 + 2gh}$ (e) unchanged
47. (a) 2.0 m/s (b) 9.8×10^{-7} J, 2.0 J/kg
    (c) 200 m, 63 m/s (d) 5.9 J/kg (e) in its tensed legs
49. 7.9 m/s
51. $4K$
53. 7.38 cm
55. 127 J, converted to thermal energy
57. 0.233 J
59. 5.2 m/s
61. (a) 300 N (b) (i) 56% (ii) 33%
63. (a) 3.6×10^5 J (b) 100 m/s; no
    (c) 520 m; no
65. (a) \$4.39 (b) \$0.13
67. 28
69. (a) 1.3×10^3 km^2 (b) 36 km, 22 mi; yes
71. (a) 0.134 hp (b) 56 kW
    (c) 2.68×10^{-3} hp (d) 5.25×10^{23} hp
    (e) 28 kWh
73. 7.10×10^4 W
75. (a) 1.3×10^5 J (b) 1.5 W (c) kinetic energy, thermal energy
77. (a) 1.0×10^5 N/m, 250 J (b) 0.46 m/s
79. 1.83 m/s
81. 3.00 m/s
83. 390 W
85. 2.1 m/s, 1.9 N
87. (a) 16.0 m/s (b) 1.15×10^4 N
89. (a) 180 lb (b) 0.55 hp
91. 10 m/s
93. 0.602 m
95. (a) 20 m (b) -78 J
97. (a) 1.6×10^3 food calories/day
    (b) thermal energy
    (c) 2.48×10^3 food calories
99. (a) 4.43 m/s (b) less
101. (a) 1.68×10^3 N (b) 13.8 hp (c) 154 hp
103. 3.6×10^{13} J; 8.6×10^{-3} megaton bombs
105. (a) yes (b) 250 N/m (c) 28.3 cm
     (d) 70.8 N

Momentum

Steve Dunwell/Getty Images

When an 18-wheeler collides head-on with a compact car, why are the occupants of the car much more likely to be injured than those of the truck? How do you decide how to aim the cue ball in pool so as to knock the eight ball into the pocket? How can a rocket engine accelerate a space shuttle in outer space, where there's nothing to push against?

To answer these and similar questions, we need two new concepts—momentum and impulse—and a new conservation law: conservation of momentum. This law is every bit as important as conservation of energy, and its validity extends far beyond the bounds of classical mechanics, to include relativistic mechanics (the mechanics of the very fast) and quantum mechanics (the mechanics of the very small). Within classical mechanics, it enables us to analyze many situations that would be difficult to handle if we used Newton's laws directly. Among these situations are collision problems, in which two colliding objects exert large forces on each other for a short time.

The tugboat and the container ship have the same velocity, but if they accidentally collided with a dock, the container ship would do far more damage because of its greater mass. In this chapter we consider the combination of mass multiplied by velocity, which we call *momentum*.

1 Momentum

When a particle with mass m moves with velocity $\vec{v}$, we define its **momentum $\vec{p}$** as follows:

Definition of momentum

The momentum of a particle, denoted by $\vec{p}$, is the product of its mass m and its velocity $\vec{v}$:

$$\vec{p} = m\vec{v}. \qquad (1)$$

Unit: kg · m/s (This combination has no special name.)

From Chapter 8 of *College Physics*, Ninth Edition, Hugh D. Young. Copyright © 2012 by Pearson Education, Inc. Published by Pearson Addison-Wesley. All rights reserved.

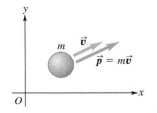

Momentum $\vec{p}$ is a vector quantity; a particle's momentum has the same direction as its velocity $\vec{v}$.

▲ **FIGURE 1** Momentum is a vector quantity.

Because velocity is a vector quantity, momentum is also a vector quantity. (See Figure 1.) Momentum has a magnitude (mv, mass times speed) and a direction (the same as that of the velocity vector). The momentum of a car driving north at 20 m/s is different from the momentum of the same car driving east at the same speed (even though both cars have the same kinetic energy). A fastball thrown by a major-league pitcher has greater momentum than the same ball thrown by a child, because the speed is greater. An 18-wheeler going 55 mi/h has greater momentum than a Saturn automobile going the same speed, because the truck's mass is greater.

Conceptual Analysis 1

Momentum and kinetic energy

Two objects have the same momentum but different masses. Which of the following statements about them is correct?

A. The one with less mass has more kinetic energy.
B. Both objects have the same kinetic energy.
C. The one with more mass has more kinetic energy.

SOLUTION Momentum is defined as $\vec{p} = m\vec{v}$, so if two objects have the same magnitude of momentum $p = mv$, the one with

the smaller mass m must have the greater speed v. However, kinetic energy depends on the *square* of speed: $K = \frac{1}{2}mv^2$. The kinetic energy can be expressed as

$$K = \tfrac{1}{2}mv^2 = \tfrac{1}{2}m\left(\frac{p}{m}\right)^2 = \frac{p^2}{2m}.$$

Solving for p, we get $p = \sqrt{2mK}$. Thus, if two objects have the same magnitude of momentum, p, the one with smaller mass m must have greater kinetic energy K. So choice A is right.

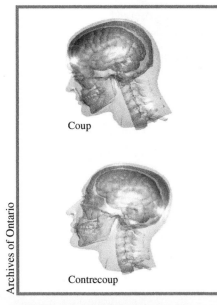

Coup

Contrecoup

▲ **BIO** Application **Contrecoup injury.** The large mass of the human brain makes us susceptible to a type of head trauma known as a contrecoup brain injury (*contrecoup* is French for "across from the blow"). A blow to the head accelerates both the skull and brain. The brain's large mass gives it considerable momentum. When the skull stops moving, the brain runs into it. Depending on how suddenly the skull slows down, this second, contrecoup blow to the brain can cause as much or more injury as the initial blow. Animals with less massive brains rarely suffer this type of injury.

We'll often express the momentum of a particle in terms of its components. It follows from Equation 1 that if the particle has velocity components v_x, v_y, and v_z, its components of momentum, p_x, p_y, and p_z, are given by

$$\begin{aligned} p_x &= mv_x \\ p_y &= mv_y \qquad \text{(components of momentum)} \\ p_z &= mv_z \end{aligned} \qquad (2)$$

These three component equations are equivalent to Equation 1. In most of the problems in this chapter, the velocities will lie in the x-y plane and $\vec{v}$ will have only x and y components, but all the component relations are easily generalized to three-dimensional situations in which three components of velocity are needed.

The importance of momentum can be traced to its close relation to Newton's second law, $\Sigma\vec{F} = m\vec{a}$. We assume for now that the mass m of the particle is constant. (Later we'll learn how to deal with systems in which the mass changes.) When m is constant, we can express Newton's second law for a particle in terms of momentum. First, the instantaneous acceleration $\vec{a}$ of the particle is defined as

$$\vec{a} = \lim_{\Delta t \to 0} \frac{\Delta\vec{v}}{\Delta t},$$

so Newton's second law can be written as

$$\Sigma\vec{F} = m\lim_{\Delta t \to 0} \frac{\Delta\vec{v}}{\Delta t}.$$

Now if m is constant, the right side of this expression is just the instantaneous rate change of momentum of the particle. To show this, we note that if m is constant, $m\,\Delta\vec{v}$ is the change of momentum during the interval Δt:

$$m\,\Delta\vec{v} = m(\vec{v}_2 - \vec{v}_1) = m\vec{v}_2 - m\vec{v}_1 = \vec{p}_2 - \vec{p}_1 = \Delta\vec{p},$$

so we obtain

Newton's second law in terms of momentum

The vector sum of forces acting on a particle equals the rate of change of momentum of the particle with respect to time:

$$\Sigma\vec{F} = \lim_{\Delta t \to 0} \frac{\Delta\vec{p}}{\Delta t}. \tag{3}$$

This, not $\Sigma\vec{F} = m\vec{a}$, is the modern equivalent of Newton's original statement of his second law. It is actually more general than our original form of the second law, because it includes the possibility of a change in momentum resulting from a change in mass as well as from a change in velocity. Note that both forms of the second law are valid only in inertial frames of reference.

Total Momentum

We define the *total momentum* of two or more particles as the vector sum of the momenta (plural of momentum) of the particles. Thus, if two particles A and B have momenta $\vec{p}_A$ and $\vec{p}_B$, their total momentum $\vec{P}$ is the vector sum

$$\vec{P} = \vec{p}_A + \vec{p}_B.$$

We can extend this definition directly to any number of particles.

Definition of total momentum

The total momentum $\vec{P}$ of any number of particles is equal to the vector sum of the momenta of the individual particles:

$$\vec{P} = \vec{p}_A + \vec{p}_B + \vec{p}_C + \cdots.$$
(total momentum of a system of particles) (4)

We'll often use Equation 4 in component form. If $p_{A,x}$, $p_{A,y}$, and $p_{A,z}$ are the components of momentum of particle A, $p_{B,x}$, $p_{B,y}$, and $p_{B,z}$ the components for particle B, and so on, then Equation 4 is equivalent to the component equations

$$\begin{aligned}
P_x &= p_{A,x} + p_{B,x} + \cdots, \\
P_y &= p_{A,y} + p_{B,y} + \cdots, \quad \text{(components of total momentum)} \quad (5) \\
P_z &= p_{A,z} + p_{B,z} + \cdots.
\end{aligned}$$

Momentum is sometimes called *linear momentum* to distinguish it from *angular momentum,* which plays an important role in rotational motion. We won't usually use the prefix *linear,* except where there is danger of confusion with angular momentum.

NOTE ▶ It's absolutely essential to remember that momentum is a vector quantity; Equations 1 through 5 are *vector* equations. (Equations 2 and 5 express a vector relationship in terms of components of the vectors.) We'll often add momentum vectors by the use of components, so everything that you've learned about components of vectors will be useful with momentum. ◄

EXAMPLE 1 Preliminary analysis of a collision

A small compact car with a mass of 1000 kg is traveling north on Morewood Avenue with a speed of 15 m/s. At the intersection of Morewood and Fifth Avenues, it collides with a truck with a mass of 2000 kg that is traveling east on Fifth Avenue at 10 m/s. Treating each vehicle as a particle, find the total momentum (magnitude and direction) just before the collision.

SOLUTION

SET UP Because momentum is a vector quantity, we need coordinate axes. We draw a sketch (Figure 2a), labeling the car A and the truck B.

SOLVE We need to find (1) the components of momentum of each vehicle, (2) the components of total momentum, and then (3) the magnitude and direction of the total momentum vector (as sketched in Figure 2b). The components of momentum of the two vehicles are

$$p_{A,x} = m_A v_{A,x} = (1000 \text{ kg})(0) = 0,$$
$$p_{A,y} = m_A v_{A,y} = (1000 \text{ kg})(15 \text{ m/s}) = 1.5 \times 10^4 \text{ kg} \cdot \text{m/s},$$
$$p_{B,x} = m_B v_{B,x} = (2000 \text{ kg})(10 \text{ m/s}) = 2.0 \times 10^4 \text{ kg} \cdot \text{m/s},$$
$$p_{B,y} = m_B v_{B,y} = (1000 \text{ kg})(0) = 0$$

There are no z components of velocity or momentum.

From Equations 5, the components of the total momentum $\vec{P}$ are

$$P_x = m_A v_{A,x} + m_B v_{B,x} = 0 + 2.0 \times 10^4 \text{ kg} \cdot \text{m/s}$$
$$= 2.0 \times 10^4 \text{ kg} \cdot \text{m/s},$$
$$P_y = m_A v_{A,y} + m_B v_{B,y} = 1.5 \times 10^4 \text{ kg} \cdot \text{m/s} + 0$$
$$= 1.5 \times 10^4 \text{ kg} \cdot \text{m/s}.$$

The total momentum $\vec{P}$ is a vector quantity with these components. Its magnitude is

$$P = \sqrt{(2.0 \times 10^4 \text{ kg} \cdot \text{m/s})^2 + (1.5 \times 10^4 \text{ kg} \cdot \text{m/s})^2}$$
$$= 2.5 \times 10^4 \text{ kg} \cdot \text{m/s}.$$

▲ FIGURE 2 Our sketches for this problem.

Its direction is given by the angle θ in Figure 2b, where

$$\tan\theta = \frac{1.5 \times 10^4 \text{ kg} \cdot \text{m/s}}{2.0 \times 10^4 \text{ kg} \cdot \text{m/s}} = \frac{3}{4}, \qquad \theta = 36.9°.$$

REFLECT It is essential to treat momentum as a vector. When we add the momenta of the two objects we must do vector addition, using the method of components. Each vehicle has momentum in only one coordinate direction so has only one nonzero component of momentum, but the total momentum of the system has both x and y components.

Practice Problem: If the car is moving at 15 m/s, how fast must the truck move for the total momentum vector to make a 45° angle with the $+x$ and $+y$ axes? *Answer:* 7.5 m/s.

2 Conservation of Momentum

The concept of momentum is particularly important in situations in which two or more objects interact. Let's consider first an idealized system consisting of two objects that interact with each other, but not with anything else—for example, two astronauts who touch each other as they float freely in the zero-gravity environment of outer space (Figure 3). Think of the astronauts as particles. Each particle exerts a force on the other; according to Newton's third law, the two forces are always equal in magnitude and opposite in direction. From Newton's second law, as reformulated in Equation 3, the vector sum of forces acting on each particle equals the rate of change of that particle's momentum. This means that, at any instant, the two rates of change of momentum are equal in magnitude and opposite in direction, so the rate of change of the *total* momentum is zero, and the total momentum is constant. We say that total momentum is *conserved.*

Let's focus our attention on a definite collection of particles that we'll call a **system.** For instance, the two astronauts in Figure 3 could be taken as a system. For any system, the various particles exert forces on each other. We'll call these **internal forces.** In addition, forces may be exerted on any part of the system by

The forces exerted by the astronauts on each other form an action–reaction pair.

▲ FIGURE 3 The internal forces the astronauts exert on each other don't change the total momentum of the two astronauts.

▶ **Application Strike!** A strike in bowling demonstrates conservation of momentum. The system consists of the ball and pins. Assuming that friction is negligible, the external forces acting on it—weight and normal forces—sum to zero, so the system can be regarded as isolated. Before the strike, the system's momentum is all in the moving ball (because the pins are stationary). Afterward, it is divided among the ball and the scattering pins—but the vector sum of the momenta of the ball and pins equals the momentum of the ball before impact.

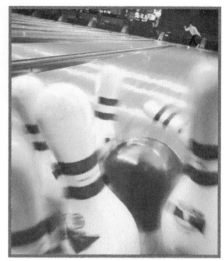

Jean Louis Batt/Getty Images

objects *outside* the system; we call these **external forces.** A system that is acted upon by *no* external forces is called an **isolated system.** We have defined the total momentum of the system, *P*, as the vector sum of the momenta of the individual particles:

$$\vec{P} = \vec{p}_A + \vec{p}_B + \vec{p}_C + \cdots. \qquad \text{(total momentum of a system)}$$

The essential point to be made is that **internal forces cannot change the total momentum of a system.**

Here's why: Suppose particle *A* exerts a force $\vec{F}_{A\,\text{on}\,B}$ on particle *B*. Then, from Newton's third law, particle *B* must simultaneously exert a force $\vec{F}_{B\,\text{on}\,A}$ on particle *A* that is equal in magnitude and opposite in direction: $\vec{F}_{A\,\text{on}\,B} = -\vec{F}_{B\,\text{on}\,A}$. Each force by itself would cause the total momentum of the system to change, according to Equation 3. But because the two forces are negatives of each other, the two rates of change of momentum are also negatives of each other, and the *total* rate of change of momentum from this interaction is zero. Similarly, the changes in momentum caused by *all* the internal forces cancel out in pairs, and the rate of change of the total momentum $\vec{P}$ with respect to time due to internal forces is always zero. Internal forces can change the momenta of individual particles, but not the total momentum of the system.

If the internal forces cannot change the total momentum, and if there are no external forces, then the total momentum cannot change. We conclude that **the total momentum of an isolated system is constant.** Furthermore, if there are external forces, but their vector sum is zero, the total momentum is again constant.

Conservation of momentum

The total momentum of a system is constant whenever the vector sum of the external forces on the system is zero. In particular, the total momentum of an isolated system is constant.

ActivPhysics 6.6: Saving an Astronaut
ActivPhysics 6.7: Explosion Problems

NOTE ▶ We have used Newton's second law to derive the principle of conservation of momentum, so we have to be careful to use this principle only in inertial frames of reference. ◀

In some ways, the principle of conservation of momentum is more general than the principle of conservation of mechanical energy. For example, it is valid *even when the internal forces are not conservative;* by contrast, mechanical energy is conserved *only when the internal forces are conservative.* In this chapter, we'll analyze some situations in which both momentum and mechanical energy are conserved and others in which only momentum is conserved. These two principles play a fundamental role in all areas of physics, and we'll encounter them throughout our study.

PROBLEM-SOLVING STRATEGY 1   **Conservation of momentum**

Momentum is a vector quantity; you *must* use vector addition to compute the total momentum of a system. Using components is usually the simplest method.

SET UP

1. Define the system you are analyzing. Choose a coordinate system, specifying the positive direction for each axis. Often, it is easiest to choose the x axis as having the direction of one of the initial velocities. Make sure that you are using an inertial frame of reference.
2. Treat each object as a particle. Sketch "before" and "after" diagrams, including your coordinate system. Add vectors on each diagram to represent all known velocities. Label the vectors with magnitudes, angles, components, or whatever information is given, and give each unknown magnitude, angle, or component an algebraic symbol. It's often helpful to use multiple subscripts on velocity and momentum symbols to ensure complete identification. For example, the initial value (i) of the x component of velocity of object A can be written as $v_{A,i,x}$.

SOLVE

3. Compute the x and y components of momentum of each particle, both before and after the interaction, using the relations $p_x = mv_x$ and $p_y = mv_y$. Some of the components will be expressed in terms of symbols representing unknown quantities. Even when all the velocities lie along a line (such as the x axis), the components of velocity and momentum along this line can be positive or negative, so be careful with signs!
4. Determine whether both the x and the y components of total momentum are conserved, and why or why not. If they are conserved, write a relation that equates the total *initial* x component of momentum to the total *final* x component of momentum. Write another equation for the y components. These two equations express conservation of momentum in component form. In some problems, only one component of momentum is conserved. If the sum of the x components of the external forces is zero, then the x component of total momentum is conserved, and so on.
5. Solve the equations you wrote in step 4 to determine whatever quantities the problem asks for. In some problems, you'll have to convert from the x and y components of a velocity to its magnitude and direction, and in others you'll need to make the opposite conversion from magnitude and direction to x and y components.

   Remember that the x and y components of velocity or momentum are *never* added together in the same equation.

REFLECT

6. As with all problem solving, especially when the results are expressed in symbols rather than numbers, try to think of particular cases in which you can guess what the results of your analysis should be. What happens when two masses are equal? When one mass is zero? Is the result what you would expect?

EXAMPLE 2   **Astronaut rescue**

An astronaut finds herself floating in space 100 m from her ship when her safety cable becomes unlatched. She and the ship are motionless relative to each other. The astronaut's mass (including space suit) is 100 kg; she has a 1.0 kg wrench and only a 20 minute air supply. Thinking back to her physics classes, she devises

Continued

a plan to use conservation of momentum to get back to the ship safely by throwing the wrench away from her. In what direction should she throw the wrench? What is the magnitude of her recoil velocity if she throws the wrench at 10 m/s? Will her recoil velocity be enough to get her back to the spacecraft before she runs out of air?

SOLUTION

SET UP We choose a system consisting of the astronaut plus the wrench. No external forces act on this system, so the total momentum is conserved. We draw diagrams showing the situation just before and just after she throws the wrench; we point the x axis to the right (Figure 4). We use the subscripts i and f (initial and final) to label the situations before and after the wrench is thrown, and we use subscripts A and W (astronaut and wrench) to identify the parts of the system.

SOLVE The astronaut needs to acquire a velocity *toward* the spaceship. Because the total momentum of herself and the wrench is zero, she should throw the wrench directly *away* from the ship.

All the vector quantities lie along the x axis, so we're concerned only with x components. We write an equation expressing the equality of the initial and final values of the total x component of momentum:

$$m_A(v_{A,i,x}) + m_W(v_{W,i,x}) = m_A(v_{A,f,x}) + m_W(v_{W,f,x})$$

In this case, the initial velocity of each object is zero, so the left side of the equation is zero. That is, $m_A(v_{A,f,x}) + m_W(v_{W,f,x}) = 0$. Solving for $v_{A,f,x}$, the astronaut's x component of velocity after she throws the wrench, we get

$$v_{A,f,x} = \frac{-m_W(v_{W,f,x})}{m_A} = \frac{-(1.0 \text{ kg})(10.0 \text{ m/s})}{(100 \text{ kg})} = -0.10 \text{ m/s}.$$

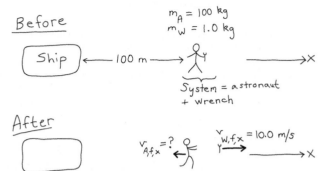

▲ **FIGURE 4** Our sketches for this problem.

The negative sign indicates that the astronaut is moving toward the ship, opposite to our chosen +x direction.

To find the total time required for the astronaut to travel 100 m (at constant velocity) to reach the ship, we use $x = vt$, or

$$t = \frac{100 \text{ m}}{0.10 \text{ m/s}} = 1.00 \times 10^3 \text{ s} = 16 \text{ min } 40 \text{ s}.$$

REFLECT With a 20 minute air supply, she makes it back to the ship safely, with 3 min 20 s, to spare.

Practice Problem: If the astronaut has only a 10 minute air supply left, how fast must she throw the wrench so that she makes it back to the spaceship in time? *Answer:* 17 m/s.

EXAMPLE 3   **Recoil of a rifle**

A marksman holds a 3.00 kg rifle loosely, allowing it to recoil freely when fired, and fires a bullet of mass 5.00 g horizontally with a speed $v_B = 300$ m/s. What is the recoil speed v_R of the rifle? What are the final kinetic energies of the bullet and the rifle?

SOLUTION

SET UP We consider an idealized model in which the horizontal forces the marksman exerts on the rifle are negligible. We also neglect the momentum of the expanding gases. Then we can consider the rifle and bullet as an isolated system. (The net vertical force is zero.) The total momentum $\vec{P}$ of the system is zero both before and after the marksman fires the rifle. We take the positive x axis to be the direction in which the rifle is aimed; Figure 5 shows our sketch.

SOLVE Before the bullet is fired, the x component of the total momentum is zero. After the bullet is fired, the x component of its momentum is $(5.00 \times 10^{-3} \text{ kg})(300 \text{ m/s})$ and that of the rifle is $(3.00 \text{ kg})v_{R,f,x}$. Conservation of the x component of total momentum, P_x, before and after the firing, gives us

$$P_{i,x} = P_{f,x} = 0 = (5.00 \times 10^{-3} \text{ kg})(300 \text{ m/s})$$
$$+ (3.00 \text{ kg})(v_{R,f,x}) \text{ (zero total momentum)},$$
$$v_{R,f,x} = -0.500 \text{ m/s}.$$

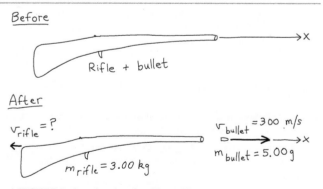

▲ **FIGURE 5** Our sketches for this problem.

The negative sign means that the recoil of the rifle is in the direction opposite that of the bullet. If the butt of a rifle were to hit your shoulder traveling at this speed, you would probably feel the "kick."

Continued

The final kinetic energy of the bullet is

$$K_{\text{bullet}} = \tfrac{1}{2}(5.00 \times 10^{-3}\,\text{kg})(300\,\text{m/s})^2 = 225\,\text{J},$$

and the final kinetic energy of the rifle is

$$K_{\text{rifle}} = \tfrac{1}{2}(3.00\,\text{kg})(0.500\,\text{m/s})^2 = 0.375\,\text{J}.$$

REFLECT The bullet acquires much greater kinetic energy than the rifle does because the bullet moves much farther than the rifle during the interaction, so the interaction force on the bullet does more work than the force on the rifle (even though the two forces are equal and opposite). In fact, the ratio of the two kinetic energies, 600 : 1, is equal to the inverse ratio of the masses. Note that because the bullet has much less mass than the rifle, it has much greater acceleration during the firing.

Practice Problem: The same rifle fires a bullet with mass 10.0 g with the same speed as before. For the same idealized model, find the ratio of the final kinetic energies of the bullet and rifle. *Answer:* 450 J/1.5 J, or a ratio of 300 : 1, independent of the muzzle velocity of the bullet.

EXAMPLE 4   **A head-on collision**

Two gliders move toward each other on a linear air track (Figure 6), which we assume is frictionless. Glider A has a mass of 0.50 kg, and glider B has a mass of 0.30 kg; both gliders move with an initial speed of 2.0 m/s. After they collide, glider B moves away with a final velocity whose x component is +2.0 m/s (Figure 6c). What is the final velocity of A?

SOLUTION

SET UP We take the x axis as lying along the air track, with the positive direction to the right. All the velocities and momenta have only x components. Our system consists of the two gliders. There are no external horizontal forces, so the x component of total momentum is the same before and after the collision.

SOLVE Let the final x component of velocity of A be $v_{A,f,x}$. Then we write an expression for the total x component of momentum before the collision (subscript i) and one for after the collision (subscript f):

$$P_{i,x} = (0.50\,\text{kg})(2.0\,\text{m/s}) + (0.30\,\text{kg})(-2.0\,\text{m/s}),$$
$$P_{f,x} = (0.50\,\text{kg})(v_{A,f,x}) + (0.30\,\text{kg})(+2.0\,\text{m/s}).$$

From conservation of the x component of momentum, these two quantities must be equal. When we solve the resulting equation for $v_{A,f,x}$, we get

$$v_{A,f,x} = -0.40\,\text{m/s}. \qquad \text{(final } x \text{ velocity of glider } A)$$

► **FIGURE 6**   (c) After collision

REFLECT The two initial velocities are equal in magnitude, but the two final velocities are not. Although the total momentum is the same before and after the collision, it is distributed differently after the collision than before.

Practice Problem: Suppose the initial x component of velocity of glider A is changed to 3.0 m/s, with all other values remaining the same as before. Find the velocity of glider A after the collision. *Answer:* 0.60 m/s.

EXAMPLE 5   **Collision in a horizontal plane**

Figure 7 shows two chunks of ice sliding on the surface of a frictionless frozen pond. Chunk A, with mass $m_A = 5.0\,\text{kg}$, moves with initial velocity $v_{A,i} = 2.0\,\text{m/s}$ parallel to the x axis. It collides with chunk B, which has mass $m_B = 3.0\,\text{kg}$ and is initially at rest. After the collision, the velocity of A is found to be $v_{A,f} = 1.0\,\text{m/s}$ in a direction at an angle $\alpha = 30°$ with the initial direction. What is the final velocity of B (magnitude and direction)?

SOLUTION

SET UP The velocities are not all along a single line, so we have to use both x and y components of momentum for each chunk of ice. There are no horizontal external forces, so the total horizontal momentum of the system is the same before and after the collision. Conservation of momentum requires that the sum of the x components before the collision must equal their sum after the collision, and similarly for the y components. We must

Continued

write a separate equation for each component. We draw in the coordinate axes as shown in Figure 7. We also express the final velocities in terms of their components.

SOLVE We start by writing expressions for the total x component of momentum before and after the collision. For the x components, we have

$$m_A(v_{A,i,x}) + m_B(v_{B,i,x})$$
$$= (5.0\,\text{kg})(2.0\,\text{m/s}) + (3.0\,\text{kg})(0), \quad (\text{before})$$
$$m_A(v_{A,f,x}) + m_B(v_{B,f,x})$$
$$= (5.0\,\text{kg})(1.0\,\text{m/s})(\cos 30°) + (3.0\,\text{kg})(v_{B,f,x}). \quad (\text{after})$$

Equating these two expressions and solving for $v_{B,f,x}$, we find that

$$v_{B,f,x} = 1.89\,\text{m/s}. \quad (x\text{ component of final velocity of }B)$$

Conservation of the y component of total momentum gives

$$m_A(v_{A,i,y}) + m_B(v_{B,i,y})$$
$$= (5.0\,\text{kg})(0) + (3.0\,\text{kg})(0), \quad (\text{before})$$
$$m_A(v_{A,f,y}) + m_B(v_{B,f,y})$$
$$= (5.0\,\text{kg})(1.0\,\text{m/s})(\sin 30°) + (3.0\,\text{kg})(v_{B,f,y}). \quad (\text{after})$$

Equating these two expressions and solving for $v_{B,f,y}$, we obtain

$$v_{B,f,y} = -0.83\,\text{m/s}. \quad (y\text{ component of final velocity of }B)$$

We now have the x and y components of the final velocity $\vec{v}_{B,f}$ of chunk B. The magnitude of $\vec{v}_{B,f}$ is

$$|\vec{v}_{B,f}| = \sqrt{(1.89\,\text{m/s})^2 + (-0.83\,\text{m/s})^2}$$
$$= 2.1\,\text{m/s}, \quad (\text{final }speed\text{ of }B)$$

▲ **FIGURE 7**

and the angle β of its direction from the positive x axis is

$$\beta = \tan^{-1}\frac{-0.83\,\text{m/s}}{1.89\,\text{m/s}} = -24°.$$

REFLECT It's essential to treat velocity and momentum as vector quantities, representing them in terms of components. You can then use these components to find the magnitudes and directions of unknown vector quantities.

Practice Problem: If chunk B has an initial velocity of magnitude 2.0 m/s in the $+y$ direction instead of being initially at rest, find its final velocity (magnitude and direction). *Answer:* 2.2 m/s, 32°.

Exploding projectile

A model rocket travels as a projectile in a parabolic path after its first stage burns out. At the top of its trajectory, where its velocity points horizontally to the right, a small explosion separates it into two sections with equal masses. One section falls straight down, with no horizontal motion. What is the direction of the motion of the other part just after the explosion?

A. Up and to the left
B. Straight up
C. Up and to the right

SOLUTION We consider the two rocket sections as a system. During the explosion, internal forces dominate, and the external forces of gravity and air drag can be neglected. Therefore, we can assume that, during the short time of the explosion, the total momentum is conserved. Figure 8 illustrates our reasoning. Before the explosion, the rocket's momentum points horizontally to the right. The *total* momentum of the system must be the same just after the explosion as just before. We're told that one section

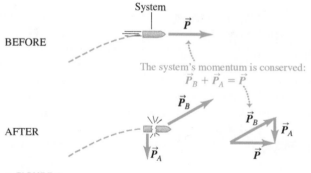

▲ **FIGURE 8**

moves straight down. Therefore, the other section must move up in order for the system as a whole to still have zero vertical momentum. This section must also move to the right, so that the system retains its original horizontal momentum. Thus, the correct choice is C.

3 Inelastic Collisions

In everyday speech, *collision* is likely to mean some sort of automotive disaster. We'll use it in that sense, but we'll also broaden the meaning to include any strong interaction between two objects that lasts a relatively short time. So we

Mastering**PHYSICS**

ActivPhysics 6.8: Skier and Cart

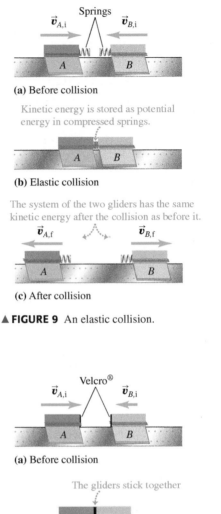

(a) Before collision

Kinetic energy is stored as potential energy in compressed springs.

(b) Elastic collision

The system of the two gliders has the same kinetic energy after the collision as before it.

(c) After collision

▲ **FIGURE 9** An elastic collision.

(a) Before collision

The gliders stick together

(b) Completely inelastic collision

The system of the two gliders has less kinetic energy after the collision than before it.

(c) After collision

▲ **FIGURE 10** A completely inelastic collision.

include not only car accidents, but also balls hitting each other on a billiard table, the slowing of neutrons in a nuclear reactor by encounters with nuclei, and the impact of a meteor on the Arizona desert.

If the interaction forces are much larger than any external forces, we can model the system as an *isolated* system, neglecting the external forces entirely. Two cars colliding at an icy intersection provide a good example. Even two cars colliding on dry pavement can be treated as an isolated system during the collision if, as happens all too often, the interaction forces between the cars are much larger than the external forces, such as friction forces of pavement against tires.

If the interaction forces between the objects are conservative, the total kinetic energy of the system is the same after the collision as before. Such a collision is called an **elastic collision.** A collision between two steel balls or two billiard balls is very nearly elastic, and collisions between subatomic particles are often, though not always, elastic. Figure 9 shows a model of an elastic collision. When the objects collide, the springs are momentarily compressed, and some of the original kinetic energy is converted to elastic potential energy. Then the objects bounce apart, the springs expand, and the potential energy is reconverted to kinetic energy.

A collision in which the total kinetic energy after the collision is *less* than that before the collision is called an **inelastic collision.** In one kind of inelastic collision, the colliding objects stick together and move as one object after the collision. In Figure 10, we've replaced the springs in Figure 9 with strips of Velcro®, causing the gliders to have a completely inelastic collision. A paintball striking a window shade, a bullet embedding itself in a block of wood, and two cars colliding and locking their fenders are additional examples of completely inelastic collisions.

Let's do a general analysis of a completely inelastic collision. Imagine two objects (*A* and *B*) that move along a straight line, which we'll designate as the *x* axis. Because they stick together after the collision, their final velocities must be equal, and the final total momentum is $\vec{P}_f = (m_A + m_B)\vec{v}_f$. We'll use $v_{f,x}$ to denote the *x* component of the common final velocity $\vec{v}_f$. We have

$$\vec{v}_{A,f} = \vec{v}_{B,f} = \vec{v}_f, \qquad v_{A,f,x} = v_{B,f,x} = v_{f,x}. \qquad \text{(equal final velocities)}$$

Conservation of momentum gives the relation

$$m_A(v_{A,i,x}) + m_B(v_{B,i,x}) = (m_A + m_B)(v_{f,x}). \qquad (6)$$

If we know the masses and initial velocities of the objects, we can compute the *x* component $v_{f,x}$ of the common final velocity $\vec{v}_f$.

Suppose, for example, that an object with mass m_A and initial velocity with component $v_{A,i,x}$ along the $+x$ axis collides inelastically with an object with mass m_B that is initially at rest ($v_{B,i,x} = 0$). From Equation 6, the common *x* component of velocity $v_{f,x}$ of the two objects after the collision is

$$v_{f,x} = \frac{m_A}{m_A + m_B}(v_{A,i,x}).$$

(common final velocity in completely inelastic collision) (7)

Let's verify that the total kinetic energy after this completely inelastic collision is less than before the collision. Using the above expression for $v_{f,x}$, we find that the kinetic energies K_i and K_f before and after the collision are, respectively,

$$K_i = \tfrac{1}{2}m_A(v_{A,i,x})^2,$$

$$K_f = \tfrac{1}{2}(m_A + m_B)(v_{f,x})^2 = \tfrac{1}{2}(m_A + m_B)\left(\frac{m_A}{m_A + m_B}\right)^2(v_{A,i,x})^2.$$

Dividing the second of these equations by the first, we find that the ratio of final to initial kinetic energy is

$$\frac{K_f}{K_i} = \frac{m_A}{m_A + m_B}. \tag{8}$$

Because $m_A + m_B$ is always greater than m_A, the right side of this equation is always less than 1. Therefore, as expected, the final kinetic energy of the system is less than the initial kinetic energy.

When two objects with equal mass have a completely inelastic collision, the final kinetic energy is one-half the initial value. Even when the initial velocity of m_B is not zero, it is not hard to verify that the kinetic energy after a completely inelastic collision is always less than before.

NOTE ▶ We don't recommend memorizing the preceding equations. We derived them only to prove that kinetic energy is always lost in a completely inelastic collision. ◀

▲ Application **Get outta my way!** Since momentum is the product of mass and velocity, even slow-moving objects can have substantial momentum if they are massive enough.

Quantitative Analysis 3   **Energy in an inelastic collision**

An iron block B with mass m_B slides with speed v_B across a frictionless horizontal plane (Figure 11). It collides with and sticks to a magnet M with mass m_M. The magnet is attached to a spring with spring constant k. We can find the speed V of the two blocks immediately after the collision by applying conservation of momentum and solving: $(m_B + m_M)V = m_B v_B$. The masses stop when the spring is compressed an amount x_{max}. Which of the following equations would you use to find x_{max}?

A. $\frac{1}{2}m_B V^2 = \frac{1}{2}k x_{max}^2$
B. $\frac{1}{2}m_B v_B^2 = \frac{1}{2}k x_{max}^2$
C. $\frac{1}{2}(m_M + m_B)V^2 = \frac{1}{2}k x_{max}^2$

SOLUTION Because the two masses stick together, mechanical energy is not conserved. Therefore, choice B, which equates the initial kinetic energy of the iron block and the final potential

energy of the compressed spring, can't be correct. However, once the masses have collided and stuck, mechanical energy is conserved while the masses compress the spring. Thus, the correct choice is C, which equates the kinetic energy of the blocks just after the collision with the final elastic potential energy of the spring. We have to find the speed V of the combined masses $(m_M + m_B)$ and then apply conservation of energy to the compression of the spring.

Iron block m_B — $\vec{v}_B$ → Magnet m_M — Spring with spring constant k ∿∿∿∿∿∿ → x

▲ **FIGURE 11**

EXAMPLE 6   Inelastic collision on an air track

We perform a collision experiment using the Velcro®-equipped gliders of Figure 10. As in Example 4, glider A has a mass of 0.50 kg and glider B has a mass of 0.30 kg; both move with initial speeds of 2.0 m/s. Find the final velocity of the joined gliders, and compare the initial and final kinetic energies.

SOLUTION

SET UP Figure 12 shows our sketches for this problem. As in Example 4, we point the x axis in the direction of motion. All the velocity and momentum vectors lie along the x axis.

SOLVE We need to write expressions for the total x component of momentum before and after the collision and equate them. From conservation of the x component of momentum, we have

$$(0.50 \text{ kg})(2.0 \text{ m/s}) + (0.30 \text{ kg})(-2.0 \text{ m/s})$$
$$= (0.50 \text{ kg} + 0.30 \text{ kg})(v_{f,x})$$
$$v_{f,x} = 0.50 \text{ m/s}.$$

Because $v_{f,x}$ is positive, the gliders move together to the right (the $+x$ direction) after the collision. Before the collision, the kinetic energy of glider A is

$$K_{A,i} = \tfrac{1}{2}m_A(v_{A,i,x})^2 = \tfrac{1}{2}(0.50 \text{ kg})(2.0 \text{ m/s})^2 = 1.0 \text{ J},$$

Before $\boxed{A}$ $\xrightarrow{v_{A,i,x} = 2.0 \text{ m/s}}$ $\xleftarrow{v_{B,i,x} = -2.0 \text{ m/s}}$ $\boxed{B}$ → x

$m_A = 0.50 \text{ kg}$ $m_B = 0.30 \text{ kg}$

After $\boxed{A|B}\xrightarrow{v_{f,x} = ?}$ → x

▲ **FIGURE 12** Our sketches for this problem.

and that of glider B is

$$K_{B,i} = \tfrac{1}{2}m_B(v_{B,i,x})^2 = \tfrac{1}{2}(0.30 \text{ kg})(-2.0 \text{ m/s})^2 = 0.60 \text{ J}.$$

Note that the initial kinetic energy of glider B is positive, even though the x components of its initial velocity, $v_{B,i,x}$, and momentum, $m_B(v_{B,i,x})$, are both negative. (Remember that

Continued

kinetic energy is a scalar, not a vector component, and that it can never be negative.)

The total kinetic energy before the collision is 1.6 J. The kinetic energy after the collision is

$$\tfrac{1}{2}(m_A + m_B)(v_{f,x})^2 = \tfrac{1}{2}(0.50 \text{ kg} + 0.30 \text{ kg})(0.50 \text{ m/s})^2$$
$$= 0.10 \text{ J}.$$

REFLECT The final kinetic energy is only $\tfrac{1}{16}$ of the original, and $\tfrac{15}{16}$ is "lost" in the collision. Of course, it isn't really lost; it is converted from mechanical energy to various other forms of energy. For instance, if there were a wad of chewing gum between the gliders, it would squash irreversibly on impact and become warmer. If the gliders coupled together like two freight cars, the energy would go into elastic waves that would eventually dissipate. If there were a spring between the gliders that compressed as they locked together, then the energy would be stored as potential energy in the spring. In all of these cases, the *total* energy of the system *is* conserved, even though *kinetic* energy is not. However, in an isolated system, momentum is *always* conserved, whether the collision is elastic or not.

Practice Problem: If glider A has twice the mass of glider B, determine the ratio of final to initial kinetic energy. *Answer:* $\tfrac{1}{9}$.

EXAMPLE 7 **The ballistic pendulum**

How fast is a speeding bullet? Figure 13 shows a simple form of ballistic pendulum, a system for measuring the speed of a bullet. The bullet, with mass m_B, is fired into a block of wood with mass m_W suspended like a pendulum. The bullet makes a completely inelastic collision with the block, becoming embedded in it. After the impact of the bullet, the block swings up to a maximum height h. Given values of h, m_B, and m_W, how can we find the initial speed v of the bullet? What becomes of its initial kinetic energy?

SOLUTION

SET UP We analyze this event in two stages: first, the embedding of the bullet in the block, and second, the subsequent swinging of the block on its strings. During the first stage, the bullet embeds itself in the block so quickly that the block doesn't have time to swing appreciably away from its initial position. So, during the impact, the supporting strings remain very nearly vertical, there is negligible external horizontal force acting on the system, and the horizontal component of momentum is conserved. In the second stage, after the collision, the block and bullet move as a unit. The only forces are the weight (a conservative force) and the string tensions (which do no work). As the pendulum swings upward and to the right, mechanical energy is conserved.

To keep the notation simple, we'll denote the x component of the bullet's velocity just before impact as v and the x component of the velocity of block plus bullet just after the impact as V.

SOLVE Figure 13 shows the situation just before impact, the situation just after impact, and the block (with the embedded bullet) at the highest point of its path. Conservation of momentum just before impact and just after gives us

$$m_B v = (m_B + m_W)V,$$
$$v = \frac{m_B + m_W}{m_B}V.$$

The kinetic energy of the system just after the collision is $K = \tfrac{1}{2}(m_B + m_W)V^2$. The pendulum comes to rest (for an instant) at a height h, where its kinetic energy $\tfrac{1}{2}(m_B + m_W)V^2$ has all become potential energy $(m_B + m_W)gh$; then it swings back down. Energy conservation gives

$$\tfrac{1}{2}(m_B + m_W)V^2 = (m_B + m_W)gh.$$

Assuming that h can be measured, we solve this equation for V:

$$V = \sqrt{2gh}. \quad \text{(velocity of block and bullet just after impact)}$$

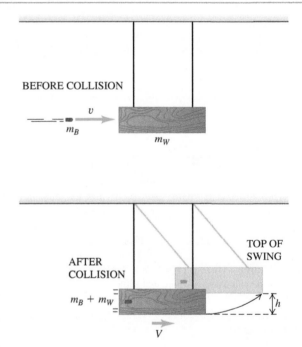

▲ **FIGURE 13** Using a ballistic pendulum to find a bullet's speed.

Now we substitute this result into the momentum equation to find v:

$$v = \frac{m_B + m_W}{m_B}\sqrt{2gh}. \quad \text{(speed of bullet just before impact)}$$

By measuring m_B, m_W, and h, we can compute the original velocity v of the bullet. For example, if $m_B = 5.00 \text{ g} = 0.00500 \text{ kg}$, $m_W = 2.00 \text{ kg}$, and $h = 3.00 \text{ cm} = 0.0300 \text{ m}$, then

$$v = \frac{2.00 \text{ kg} + 0.00500 \text{ kg}}{0.00500 \text{ kg}}\sqrt{2(9.80 \text{ m/s}^2)(0.0300 \text{ m})}$$
$$= 307 \text{ m/s}.$$

Continued

The x component V of velocity of the block just after impact is

$$V = \sqrt{2gh} = \sqrt{2(9.80 \text{ m/s}^2)(0.0300 \text{ m})}$$
$$= 0.767 \text{ m/s}.$$

Once we have the needed velocities, we can compute the kinetic energies just before and just after impact. The total kinetic energy just before impact is $K_i = \frac{1}{2}m_B v^2 = \frac{1}{2}(0.00500 \text{ kg}) \cdot (307 \text{ m/s})^2 = 236 \text{ J}$. We find that just after impact, it is $K_f = \frac{1}{2}(m_B + m_W)V^2 = \frac{1}{2}(2.005 \text{ kg}) \cdot (0.767 \text{ m/s})^2 = 0.590 \text{ J}$. Only a small fraction of the initial kinetic energy remains.

REFLECT When an object collides inelastically with a stationary object having much greater mass, nearly all of the first object's

kinetic energy is lost. In this problem, the wood splinters, and the bullet and wood become hotter as mechanical energy is converted to internal energy.

Practice Problem: Suppose the mass of the bullet, the mass of the block, and the height of the block's swing have the same values as above. If the bullet goes all the way through the block and emerges with half its initial velocity, what was its initial speed?

Answer: $v = \dfrac{2m_W}{m_B}\sqrt{2gh} = 615 \text{ m/s}.$

EXAMPLE 8 **Collision analysis, continued**

In Example 1, we considered the impending collision of a small car with a larger truck. It's now 2 seconds later, and the collision has occurred. Fortunately, all occupants were wearing seat belts, and there were no injuries; but the two vehicles became thoroughly tangled and moved away from the point of impact as one mass. The insurance adjuster has asked you to help find the velocity of the wreckage just after impact.

SOLUTION

SET UP Figure 14 shows our sketches. The "before" diagram is the same as the one for Example 1. We worked out the initial momentum components in that example. We suggest you review that calculation before proceeding. To find out what happens *after* the collision, we'll assume that we can treat the vehicles as an isolated system during the collision. This approach may seem implausible; the pavement certainly exerts substantial friction forces on the tires. But the interaction forces between the vehicles during the collision are much larger—so much larger, in fact, that they crumple the vehicles. So it's reasonable to neglect the friction forces and consider the two vehicles together as an isolated system during the impact.

SOLVE The total momentum $\vec{P}$ of the vehicles just after the collision is the same as we calculated in Example 1: $2.5 \times 10^4 \text{ kg} \cdot \text{m/s}$ in a direction $36.9°$ north from straight east. Assuming that no parts fall off the wreckage, the total mass of wreckage is $M = 3000 \text{ kg}$. Calling the final velocity $\vec{V}$, we have $\vec{P} = M\vec{V}$. The direction of the velocity $\vec{V}$ is the same as that of the momentum $\vec{P}$, and its magnitude is

$$V = \frac{P}{M} = \frac{2.5 \times 10^4 \text{ kg} \cdot \text{m/s}}{3000 \text{ kg}} = 8.3 \text{ m/s}. \quad \text{(final speed)}$$

This is an inelastic collision, so we expect the total kinetic energy to be less after the collision than before. When you make the calculations, you'll find that the initial kinetic energy is $2.1 \times 10^5 \text{ J}$ and the final kinetic energy is $1.0 \times 10^5 \text{ J}$. More than half of the initial kinetic energy is converted to other forms of energy.

REFLECT If you were tempted to find the final velocity by taking the vector sum of the initial velocities, go back two squares and ask yourself why you would expect that to work. Is there a law of conservation of velocities? *Absolutely not;* the conserved quantity is the total *momentum* of the system.

▲ **FIGURE 14** Our sketches for this problem.

Let's look again at the matter of neglecting the friction of tires against pavement and treating the two vehicles as an isolated system. Here are some numbers: The mass of the truck is 2000 kg, so its weight is about 20,000 N. If the coefficient of friction is 0.5, the friction force is somewhere around 10,000 N. That sounds like a large force. But suppose the truck runs into a brick wall while going 10 m/s. Its kinetic energy just before impact is $\frac{1}{2}(2000 \text{ kg})(10 \text{ m/s})^2 = 1.0 \times 10^5 \text{ J}$, so the force applied by the wall must do $-1.0 \times 10^5 \text{ J}$ of work on the truck to stop (and crumple) it. The truck may crumple 0.2 m or so; for the stopping force to do $-1.0 \times 10^5 \text{ J}$ of work in 0.2 m, the force must have a magnitude of $5.0 \times 10^5 \text{ N}$, or 50 times as great as the friction force. You'll see now why it's not so unreasonable to neglect the friction forces on both vehicles and assume that during the collision they form an isolated system.

Practice Problem: Suppose the vehicles are both moving at 10 m/s, the 2000 kg truck heading east and the 1000 kg car heading north. Find the velocity (magnitude and direction) of the wreckage. *Answer:* 7.5 m/s, 27° N of E.

▲ Application **Light sail.** All current space-ships use rockets of one sort or another. A disadvantage of a rocket is that the craft must carry its own fuel. One alternative is to use a light sail—an enormous sheet of reflective material. In 1873, James Clerk Maxwell showed that light reflected by a mirror applies a slight pressure to the mirror. Thus, in principle, light bouncing off a reflective sail could propel a spacecraft. The more perfectly reflective the sail, the greater its efficiency; for maximum momentum transfer we want the light to bounce off the sail rather than being absorbed.

MasteringPHYSICS

ActivPhysics 6.2: Collisions and Elasticity
ActivPhysics 6.3: Momentum Conservation and Collisions
ActivPhysics 6.4: Collision Problems
ActivPhysics 6.5: Car Collision: Two Dimensions
ActivPhysics 6.9: Pendulum Bashes Box
ActivPhysics 6.10: Pendulum Person—Projectile Bowling

4 Elastic Collisions

In Section 3, we defined an elastic collision in an isolated system to be a collision in which kinetic energy (as well as momentum) is conserved. Elastic collisions occur when the interaction forces between the objects are conservative. When two steel balls collide, they squash a little near the surface of contact, but then they spring back. Some of the kinetic energy is stored temporarily as elastic potential energy, but by the end of the collision it is reconverted to kinetic energy.

Let's look at an elastic collision between two objects A and B. We start with a head-on collision, in which all the velocities lie along the same line; we choose this line to be the x axis. Each momentum and velocity then has only an x component. (Later we'll consider collisions in two dimensions.) We'll simplify our notation, calling the x components of velocity before the collision $v_{A,i}$ and $v_{B,i}$ and those after the collision $v_{A,f}$ and $v_{B,f}$. From conservation of kinetic energy, we have

$$\tfrac{1}{2}m_A v_{A,i}^2 + \tfrac{1}{2}m_B v_{B,i}^2 = \tfrac{1}{2}m_A v_{A,f}^2 + \tfrac{1}{2}m_B v_{B,f}^2,$$

and conservation of momentum gives

$$m_A v_{A,i} + m_B v_{B,i} = m_A v_{A,f} + m_B v_{B,f}.$$

If the masses m_A and m_B and the initial velocities (i.e., x components) $v_{A,i}$ and $v_{B,i}$ are known, these two equations can be solved simultaneously to find the two final velocities $v_{A,f}$ and $v_{B,f}$.

The general solution is a little complicated, so we'll concentrate on the particular case in which object B is at rest before the collision. Think of it as a target for m_A to hit. Then the equations for conservation of kinetic energy and momentum are, respectively,

$$\tfrac{1}{2}m_A v_{A,i}^2 = \tfrac{1}{2}m_A v_{A,f}^2 + \tfrac{1}{2}m_B v_{B,f}^2 \tag{9}$$

and

$$m_A v_{A,i} = m_A v_{A,f} + m_B v_{B,f}. \tag{10}$$

These are a pair of simultaneous equations that can be solved for the two final velocities $v_{A,f}$ and $v_{B,f}$ in terms of the masses and the initial velocity $v_{A,i}$. This involves some fairly strenuous algebra; we'll omit the details and go straight to the beautifully simple final results. We find that

$$v_{A,f} = \frac{m_A - m_B}{m_A + m_B} v_{A,i}, \tag{11}$$

$$v_{B,f} = \frac{2m_A}{m_A + m_B} v_{A,i}. \tag{12}$$

Let's interpret these results by looking at several particular cases. Suppose object A is a Ping-Pong ball and B is a bowling ball (Figure 15a). We expect A to bounce back after the collision with a velocity nearly equal to its original value,

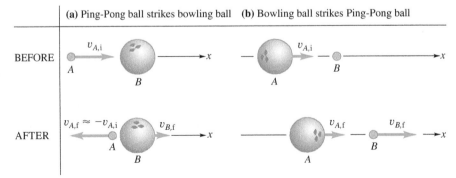

	(a) Ping-Pong ball strikes bowling ball	**(b)** Bowling ball strikes Ping-Pong ball
BEFORE	$v_{A,i}$	$v_{A,i}$
AFTER	$v_{A,f} \approx -v_{A,i}$ $v_{B,f}$	$v_{A,f}$ $v_{B,f}$

▶ **FIGURE 15** Collisions between a Ping-Pong ball and a bowling ball, one or the other of which is initially at rest.

but in the opposite direction, and we expect B's final velocity to be much smaller in magnitude. That's just what the equations predict: When m_A is much smaller than m_B, the fraction in the expression for $v_{A,f}$ in Equation 11 is approximately equal to -1, so $v_{A,f}$ is approximately equal to $-v_{A,i}$. Also, when m_A is much smaller than m_B, the fraction in Equation 12 is much smaller than 1, so $v_{B,f}$ (the final velocity of the bowling ball) is much less than $v_{A,i}$.

Figure 15b shows the opposite case, in which A is the bowling ball, B is the Ping-Pong ball, and m_A is much larger than m_B. What do you expect to happen in this case? Check your predictions against Equations 11 and 12.

Another interesting case occurs when the masses are equal, as in the case of the billiard balls in Figure 16. If $m_A = m_B$, then Equations 11 and 12 give $v_{A,f} = 0$ and $v_{B,f} = v_{A,i}$. That is, the object that was moving stops dead; it gives all of its momentum and kinetic energy to the object that was initially at rest. This behavior is familiar to all pool players and marble shooters.

Now comes a surprise bonus. From Equations 11 and 12, we can find the x component of the velocity of B relative to A after the collision (that is, $v_{B,f} - v_{A,f}$), by simply subtracting Equation 12 from Equation 11. The result is astonishingly simple:

$$v_{B,f} - v_{A,f} = v_{A,i}. \quad \text{(relative velocity before and after collision)} \quad (13)$$

Now, $v_{B,f} - v_{A,f}$ is the velocity of B relative to A *after* the collision, and $v_{A,i}$ is the negative of the velocity of B relative to A *before* the collision. Thus, **the relative velocity has the same magnitude, but opposite sign, before and after the collision.**

We have proved this result only for straight-line collisions in which one object is initially at rest, but it turns out that a similar *vector* relationship is a general property of *all* elastic collisions, even when both objects are moving initially and the velocities do not all lie along the same line. That is,

$$\vec{v}_{B,f} - \vec{v}_{A,f} = -(\vec{v}_{B,i} - \vec{v}_{A,i}).$$

This result provides an alternative and equivalent definition of an elastic collision: **In an elastic collision, the relative velocity of the two objects has the same magnitude before and after the collision, and the two relative velocities have opposite directions.** Whenever this condition is satisfied, the total kinetic energy is also conserved.

EXAMPLE 9 Elastic collision on an air track

Let's carry out another collision between the air-track gliders of Examples 4 and 6. This time, we equip the gliders with spring bumpers so that the collision will be elastic. As before, glider A has a mass of 0.50 kg, glider B has a mass of 0.30 kg, and each moves with an initial speed of 2.0 m/s as they approach each other. What are the velocities of A and B after the collision?

SOLUTION

SET UP We draw "before" and "after" sketches, using the same coordinate system as in Example 4 (Figure 17). The masses and initial velocities of the gliders are the same as in Examples 4 and 6, so the initial total kinetic energy (1.6 J) is also the same as in those examples.

SOLVE We can't use Equations 11 and 12 because in this instance neither object is at rest before the collision. But we can use conservation of momentum, along with the relative-velocity relation we've just discussed, to obtain two simultaneous equations for the two final velocities. Because we're dealing with a one-dimensional problem, we'll drop the x subscripts on the

When a moving object A has a 1-D elastic collision with an equal-mass, motionless object B...

...all of A's momentum and kinetic energy are transferred to B.

▲ FIGURE 16 An elastic collision between two objects of equal mass, one of which is initially at rest.

▲ FIGURE 17 Our sketches for this problem.

velocities, while keeping in mind that they are all x components of velocities.

Continued

From conservation of momentum,

$$m_A v_{A,i} + m_B v_{B,i} = m_A v_{A,f} + m_B v_{B,f},$$
$$(0.50 \text{ kg})(2.0 \text{ m/s}) + (0.30 \text{ kg})(-2.0 \text{ m/s})$$
$$= (0.50 \text{ kg})v_{A,f} + (0.30 \text{ kg})v_{B,f},$$
$$0.50 v_{A,f} + 0.30 v_{B,f} = 0.40 \text{ m/s}.$$

(In the last equation we've divided through by the unit "kg.") From the relative-velocity relation for an elastic collision,

$$v_{B,f} - v_{A,f} = -(v_{B,i} - v_{A,i})$$
$$= -(-2.0 \text{ m/s} - 2.0 \text{ m/s}) = 4.0 \text{ m/s}.$$

Solving these equations simultaneously, we obtain

$$v_{A,f} = -1.0 \text{ m/s}, \qquad v_{B,f} = 3.0 \text{ m/s}.$$
(final x components of velocity)

REFLECT Both gliders reverse their directions of motion; A moves to the left at 1.0 m/s and B moves to the right at 3.0 m/s. This result is different from the result of Example 4; but that collision was *not* an elastic one, so we shouldn't expect the results to be the same. In this case, the total kinetic energy after the collision is

$$K_f = \tfrac{1}{2}(0.50 \text{ kg})(-1.0 \text{ m/s})^2 + \tfrac{1}{2}(0.30 \text{ kg})(3.0 \text{ m/s})^2$$
$$= 1.6 \text{ J}.$$

This equals the total kinetic energy before the collision, as expected.

Practice Problem: Suppose we interchange the two gliders, making $m_A = 0.30$ kg and $m_B = 0.50$ kg. (We also turn them around, so the springs still meet.) If the initial speeds are the same as before, find the two final velocities. *Answers:* -3.0 m/s, 1.0 m/s.

EXAMPLE 10   Moderator in a nuclear reactor

High-speed neutrons are produced in a nuclear reactor during nuclear fission processes. Before a neutron can trigger additional fissions, it has to be slowed down by collisions with nuclei of a material called the *moderator.* In some reactors (including the one involved in the Chernobyl accident), the moderator consists of carbon in the form of graphite. The masses of nuclei and subatomic particles are measured in units called *atomic mass units,* abbreviated u, where $1 \text{ u} = 1.66 \times 10^{-27}$ kg. Suppose a neutron (mass 1.0 u) traveling at 2.6×10^7 m/s makes an elastic head-on collision with a carbon nucleus (mass 12 u) that is initially at rest. What are the velocities after the collision?

SOLUTION

SET UP Figure 18 shows our sketches. We use subscripts n and C to denote the neutron and carbon nucleus, respectively.

SOLVE Because we have a head-on elastic collision, all velocity and momentum vectors lie along the x axis, and we can use Equations 10 and 13, with $m_n = 1.0$ u, $m_C = 12$ u, and $v_{n,i} = 2.6 \times 10^7$ m/s. We'll get two simultaneous equations that we'll need to solve for $v_{n,f}$ and $v_{C,f}$.

First, conservation of the x component of momentum gives

$$m_n(v_{n,i}) + m_C(v_{C,i}) = m_n(v_{n,f}) + m_C(v_{C,f}),$$
$$(1.0 \text{ u})(2.6 \times 10^7 \text{ m/s}) + (12.0 \text{ u})(0)$$
$$= (1.0 \text{ u})v_{n,f} + (12.0 \text{ u})v_{C,f}.$$

Second, the relative-velocity relation yields

$$v_{n,i} - v_{C,i} = -(v_{n,f} - v_{C,f}),$$
$$2.6 \times 10^7 \text{ m/s} = v_{C,f} - v_{n,f}.$$

These are two simultaneous equations for $v_{n,f}$ and $v_{C,f}$. We'll let you do the algebra; the results are

$$v_{n,f} = -2.2 \times 10^7 \text{ m/s},$$
$$v_{C,f} = 0.40 \times 10^7 \text{ m/s}.$$
(final x velocities)

▲ **FIGURE 18** Our sketches for this problem.

REFLECT The neutron ends up with $\frac{11}{13}$ of its original speed, and the speed of the recoiling carbon nucleus is $\frac{2}{13}$ of the neutron's original speed. Kinetic energy is proportional to speed squared, so the neutron's final kinetic energy is $\left(\frac{11}{13}\right)^2$, or about 0.72 of its original value. If the neutron makes a second such collision, its kinetic energy is $(0.72)^2$, or about half its original value, and so on. After many such collisions, the neutron's kinetic energy is reduced to a small fraction (1/100 or less) of its initial value.

Practice Problem: If the neutron's kinetic energy is reduced to $\frac{9}{16}$ of its initial value in a single collision, what is the mass of the moderator nucleus? *Answer:* 7.0 u.

When an elastic collision between two objects isn't head-on, the velocities don't all lie along a single line. If they all lie in a plane, each final velocity has two unknown components, and there are four unknowns in all. Conservation of energy and conservation of the x and y components of momentum give only three equations. To determine the final velocities, we need additional information, such as the direction or magnitude of one of the final velocities.

EXAMPLE 11 **An off-center elastic collision on an air table**

Two pucks collide on a frictionless air-hockey table. The pucks have equal masses $m = 0.20$ kg. Puck A has an initial velocity of 4.0 m/s in the positive x direction and a final velocity of 2.0 m/s at an angle of 60° to the $+x$ axis. Puck B is initially at rest. Find the final velocity of puck B (magnitude and direction). Is the collision elastic?

SOLUTION

SET UP Figure 19 shows "before" and "after" diagrams. We take the x axis as the horizontal and the positive direction to the right.

SOLVE We need to write two equations, one for conservation of the x component of momentum and one for the y component. We denote the unknown components of the final velocity of B as $v_{B,f,x}$ and $v_{B,f,y}$. The x and y components of momentum of A after the collision are, respectively,

$$m_A(v_{A,f,x}) = (0.20 \text{ kg})(2.0 \text{ m/s}) \cos 60°$$

and

$$m_A(v_{A,f,y}) = (0.20 \text{ kg})(2.0 \text{ m/s}) \sin 60°.$$

The x and y components of momentum of B after the collision are, respectively,

$$m_B(v_{B,f,x}) = (0.20 \text{ kg})(v_{B,f,x})$$

and

$$m_B(v_{B,f,y}) = (0.20 \text{ kg})(v_{B,f,y}).$$

Conservation of the x component of total momentum gives

$$m_A(v_{A,i,x}) + m_B(v_{B,i,x}) = m_A(v_{A,f,x}) + m_B(v_{B,f,x}),$$
$$(0.20 \text{ kg})(4.0 \text{ m/s}) + 0 = (0.20 \text{ kg})(2.0 \text{ m/s}) \cos 60° + (0.20 \text{ kg})v_{B,f,x},$$

and

$$v_{B,f,x} = 3.0 \text{ m/s}. \quad \text{(final } x \text{ component of velocity of } B\text{)}$$

Conservation of the y component of total momentum gives the equations

$$m_A(v_{A,i,y}) + m_B(v_{B,i,y}) = m_A(v_{A,f,y}) + m_B(v_{B,f,y}),$$
$$0 = (0.20 \text{ kg})(2.0 \text{ m/s}) \sin 60° + (0.20 \text{ kg})v_{B,f,y},$$

and

$$v_{B,f,y} = -\sqrt{3} \text{ m/s} = -1.73 \text{ m/s}.$$
$$\text{(final } y \text{ component of velocity of } B\text{)}$$

The magnitude $v_{B,f}$ of the final velocity of B is

$$v_{B,f} = \sqrt{v_{B,f,x}^2 + v_{B,f,y}^2} = \sqrt{(3.0 \text{ m/s})^2 + (-\sqrt{3} \text{ m/s})^2}$$
$$= 2\sqrt{3} \text{ m/s} = 3.5 \text{ m/s}.$$

Its direction (an angle θ measured from the $+x$ axis) is

$$\theta = \tan^{-1} \frac{v_{B,f,y}}{v_{B,f,x}} = \tan^{-1}\left(\frac{-\sqrt{3} \text{ m/s}}{3.0 \text{ m/s}}\right) = -30°.$$

▲ FIGURE 19

Is kinetic energy conserved? The initial kinetic energy of A (equal to the initial *total* kinetic energy) is

$$K_{A,i} = K_i = \tfrac{1}{2}m_A(v_{A,i})^2 = \tfrac{1}{2}(0.20 \text{ kg})(4.0 \text{ m/s})^2 = 1.6 \text{ J}.$$

The final total kinetic energy of A and B together is

$$K_f = \tfrac{1}{2}m_A(v_{A,f})^2 + \tfrac{1}{2}m_B(v_{B,f})^2$$
$$= \tfrac{1}{2}(0.20 \text{ kg})(2.0 \text{ m/s})^2 + \tfrac{1}{2}(0.20 \text{ kg})(2\sqrt{3} \text{ m/s})^2$$
$$= 1.6 \text{ J}.$$

The total initial and final kinetic energies are equal, so the collision is elastic.

REFLECT We used a separate equation for conservation of each component of momentum. The x and y components of momentum are *never* added together in a conservation-of-momentum equation. Because the masses are equal, we could have simplified the calculations by dividing the factor m out of each momentum equation. The two final velocities are perpendicular. In fact, it can be shown that in *every* elastic collision between two objects with equal mass, when one object is initially at rest, the two final velocities are *always* perpendicular (except when the collision is head-on and one final velocity is zero). Every good billiards player is familiar with this fact.

Practice Problem: Suppose the final direction of puck A's velocity is at 30° to the $+x$ axis instead of 60°. Find the final velocity (magnitude and direction) of puck B. *Answers:* 2.5 m/s, $-24°$.

We've classified collisions according to energy considerations. A collision in which kinetic energy is conserved is called *elastic*. A collision in which the total kinetic energy decreases is called *inelastic*. There are also cases in which the final

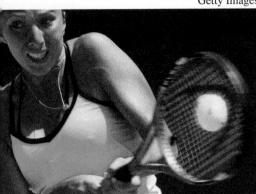

Getty Images

▲ **FIGURE 20** A racquet hitting a tennis ball. Typically, the ball is in contact with the racket for approximately 0.01 s. The ball flattens noticeably on both sides, and the frame of the racket vibrates during and after the impact.

ActivPhysics 6.1: Momentum and Energy Change

Stephen Dalton/Photo Researchers, Inc.

▲ **BIO Application Long legs for leaping.** Why are this frog's legs so long? Short legs could supply an equal magnitude of force. The answer hinges on the fact that muscles are limited in the force they can develop and the speed with which they can contract. The longer the frog's legs, the greater is the time interval during which the legs can deliver their force, and thus the greater is the total impulse delivered. Since impulse represents a change in momentum, longer legs result in a larger change in momentum, imparting a greater velocity to a frog of a given mass.

kinetic energy is *greater* than the initial kinetic energy. A recoiling rifle, discussed in Example 3, is an example.

NOTE ▶ We emphasize again that we can sometimes use conservation of momentum even when external forces act on the system. If the vector sum of the external forces is zero, momentum is conserved. Also, if the internal forces between colliding objects are much stronger than the net external force acting on the system, we may use an idealized model that neglects the external forces during the actual collision. ◀

5 Impulse

When a force acts on an object, the object's change in momentum depends on the force and on the time interval during which it acts. We've seen several examples of interactions in which large forces act during a short time of impact. A recoiling rifle, exploding projectiles, a tennis ball struck by a racket (Figure 20)—all are examples of such interactions. To analyze these events in detail, we'll find it useful to define a quantity called **impulse:**

Definition of impulse

When a constant force $\vec{F}$ acts on an object, the impulse of the force, denoted by $\vec{J}$, is the force multiplied by the time interval during which it acts:

$$\vec{J} = \vec{F}(t_f - t_i) = \vec{F}\,\Delta t. \tag{14}$$

Notice that impulse is a vector quantity; its direction is the same as that of the force $\vec{F}$.

Unit: Force times time $(\mathrm{N \cdot s})$. Because $1\,\mathrm{N} = 1\,\mathrm{kg \cdot m/s^2}$, an alternative set of units for impulse is $\mathrm{kg \cdot m/s}$; thus, the units of impulse are the same as those of momentum.

To see what impulse is good for, let's go back to Newton's second law, as we restated it in terms of momentum in Equation 4, namely,

$$\vec{F} = \lim_{\Delta t \to 0} \frac{\Delta \vec{p}}{\Delta t},$$

where $\vec{F}$ represents the vector sum (resultant) of forces acting on an object. If $\vec{F}$ doesn't vary with time, we can simplify this equation to

$$\vec{F} = \frac{\Delta \vec{p}}{\Delta t}, \quad \text{or} \quad \Delta \vec{p} = \vec{F}\,\Delta t.$$

Combining this result with Equation 14, we get the following relation, called the **impulse–momentum theorem:**

Relation of impulse to change in momentum:
The impulse–momentum theorem

When a constant force $\vec{F}$ acts on an object during a time interval $\Delta t = t_f - t_i$, the change in the object's momentum is equal to the impulse of the force acting on the object, or

$$\Delta \vec{p} = \vec{F}\,\Delta t = \vec{F}(t_f - t_i) = \vec{J}. \tag{15}$$

Unit: mass times velocity $(\mathrm{kg \cdot m/s})$

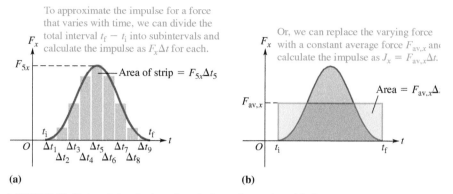

To approximate the impulse for a force that varies with time, we can divide the total interval $t_f - t_i$ into subintervals and calculate the impulse as $F_x \Delta t$ for each.

Area of strip $= F_{5x} \Delta t_5$

Or, we can replace the varying force with a constant average force $F_{av,x}$ and calculate the impulse as $J_x = F_{av,x} \Delta t$.

Area $= F_{av,x} \Delta$

(a)

(b)

▲ FIGURE 21 Determining the impulse of a force that varies with time.

As noted, impulse and momentum are both vector quantities, and Equations 14 and 15 are vector equations. In specific problems, it's often easiest to use these equations in component form:

$$J_x = F_x \Delta t = p_{f,x} - p_{i,x} = mv_{f,x} - mv_{i,x},$$
$$J_y = F_y \Delta t = p_{f,y} - p_{i,y} = mv_{f,y} - mv_{i,y}.$$

(16)

Now, what if the force isn't constant? Suppose, for example, that the x component of force varies, as shown in Figure 21. Then we can divide the total time interval $t_f - t_i$ into small subintervals, as in Figure 21a, apply Equation 15 to each, and add all the $\vec{F} \Delta t$ quantities. Thus, the impulse–momentum relation $\vec{J} = \vec{p}_f - \vec{p}_i$ is valid even when the force $\vec{F}$ varies with time. Figure 21a also shows that the impulse of the force is the area under the graph of force versus time.

As shown in Figure 21b, we can also define an average force $\vec{F}_{av}$ such that even when $\vec{F}$ isn't constant, its impulse $\vec{J}$ is given by

$$\vec{J} = \vec{F}_{av}(t_f - t_i).$$

(17)

Conceptual Analysis 4

Soften the blow

A baseball player catching a fastball lets his hand move backward (in the direction of the ball's motion) during the catch. This maneuver reduces the force of impact on his hand principally because:

A. the speed of impact is lessened.
B. the time of impact is increased.
C. the impulse is reduced.

SOLUTION Whether the hand moves or not, $\Delta \vec{p}$, and therefore the impulse $\vec{J}$, is roughly the same, because the speed of the ball is much larger than any motion of the hand. However, for the same impulse, the relation $\vec{J} = \vec{F}_{av} \Delta t$ shows that if we increase the time interval Δt of the interaction, we decrease the average force. The correct answer is B.

EXAMPLE 12 **A ball hits a wall**

Suppose you throw a ball with mass 0.40 kg against a brick wall (Figure 22). It hits the wall moving horizontally to the left at 30 m/s and rebounds horizontally to the right at 20 m/s. Find the impulse of the force exerted on the ball by the wall. If the ball is in contact with the wall for 0.010 s, find the average force on the ball during the impact.

▲ FIGURE 22 Impulse imparted to a wall by a ball that hits the wall and rebounds.

Continued

SOLUTION

SET UP We take the x axis as horizontal and the positive direction to the right.

SOLVE We need to find the x component of momentum just before and just after impact, find the *change* in momentum, and then equate this change to the impulse. Then we divide by the time interval to find the average force on the ball.

The initial x component of momentum of the ball is

$$p_{i,x} = mv_{i,x} = (0.40\ \text{kg})(-30\ \text{m/s}) = -12\ \text{kg} \cdot \text{m/s}.$$

The final x component of momentum is

$$p_{f,x} = mv_{f,x} = +(0.40\ \text{kg})(20\ \text{m/s}) = 8.0\ \text{kg} \cdot \text{m/s}.$$

The change in the x component of momentum is

$$\Delta p_x = p_{f,x} - p_{i,x} = mv_{f,x} - mv_{i,x}$$
$$= 8.0\ \text{kg} \cdot \text{m/s} - (-12\ \text{kg} \cdot \text{m/s}) = 20\ \text{kg} \cdot \text{m/s}.$$

(Note the signs carefully. The initial x component of momentum is negative, and we are subtracting it from the final value to find the change Δp_x.)

According to Equation 17, the preceding result equals the x component of impulse of the force exerted on the ball by the wall, so $J_x = 20\ \text{kg} \cdot \text{m/s} = 20\ \text{N} \cdot \text{s}$.

If the force acts for 0.010 s, then, from $J_x = F_{av,x}\,\Delta t$,

$$F_{av,x} = \frac{J_x}{\Delta t} = \frac{20\ \text{N} \cdot \text{s}}{0.010\ \text{s}} = 2000\ \text{N}.$$

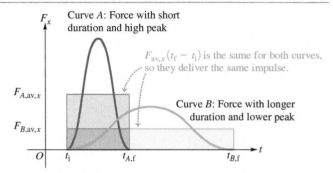

▲ **FIGURE 23** Forces that differ in duration and peak magnitude may deliver the same impulse.

REFLECT The force exerted by the wall on the ball isn't constant; its variation with time may be similar to a varying force described by one of the curves in Figure 23. The force is zero before impact, rises to a maximum, and then decreases to zero when the ball loses contact with the wall. If the ball is relatively rigid, like a baseball or a golf ball, the time of collision is small and the maximum force is large, as in curve A of the figure. If the ball is softer, like a tennis ball, the collision time is larger and the maximum force is less, as in curve B. Either way, the area under the curve represents the same impulse: $J_x = F_{av,x}\,\Delta t$.

Practice Problem: Suppose you have a pitching machine that throws five balls per second, with the same mass and initial and final velocities as given in this example. Find the average force exerted on the wall by this stream of balls. *Answer:* 100 N.

EXAMPLE 13 **Kicking a soccer ball**

Let's consider the soccer ball in Figure 24a. The ball has mass 0.40 kg. Initially it moves horizontally to the left at 20 m/s, but then it is kicked and given a velocity with magnitude 30 m/s and direction 45° upward and to the right. Find the impulse of the force and the average force on the ball, assuming a collision time $\Delta t = 0.010$ s.

SOLUTION

SET UP The velocities aren't along the same line, so we must treat momentum and impulse as vector quantities, using their x and y components. As shown in Figure 24a, we point the x axis to

the right and the y axis upward. We find the following initial and final velocity components:

$$v_{i,x} = -20\ \text{m/s}, \qquad v_{i,y} = 0,$$
$$v_{f,x} = v_{f,y} = \cos 45°(v_f) = (0.707)(30\ \text{m/s}) = 21\ \text{m/s}.$$

(a) Before-and-after diagram

(b) Average force on the ball

▲ **FIGURE 24**

Continued

SOLVE The x component of the impulse is equal to the x component of the change in momentum, and the same is true for the y components:

$$J_x = m(v_{f,x} - v_{i,x}) = (0.40\text{ kg})[21\text{ m/s} - (-20\text{ m/s})]$$
$$= 16.4\text{ kg} \cdot \text{m/s},$$
$$J_y = m(v_{f,y} - v_{i,y}) = (0.40\text{ kg})(21\text{ m/s} - 0) = 8.4\text{ kg} \cdot \text{m/s}.$$

The components of average force on the ball (Figure 24b) are

$$F_{\text{av},x} = \frac{J_x}{\Delta t} = 1640\text{ N}, \qquad F_{\text{av},y} = \frac{J_y}{\Delta t} = 840\text{ N}.$$

The magnitude and direction of the average force are, respectively,

$$F_{\text{av}} = \sqrt{(1640\text{ N})^2 + (840\text{ N})^2} = 1.8 \times 10^3\text{ N},$$
$$\theta = \tan^{-1}\frac{840\text{ N}}{1640\text{ N}} = 27°,$$

where θ is measured counterclockwise from the $+x$ axis.

REFLECT The direction of the ball's final velocity is not the same as that of the average force acting on it. Indeed, there's no reason it should be. The average magnitude of force on the ball is about 400 lb; that's roughly three times as much force as though you just stood on the ball!

Practice Problem: Suppose the ball is moving at 30° downward from the horizontal before it is kicked. If all the numerical values are the same as before, find the magnitude and direction of the average force on the ball. *Answer:* 2.0×10^3 N, 39°.

NOTE ▶ The relation between impulse and change in momentum, $\Delta \vec{p} = \vec{F}\,\Delta t = \vec{J}$ (Equation 15), has a superficial resemblance to the work–kinetic energy theorem, namely, $W_{\text{total}} = K_f - K_i$. However, there are important differences. First, impulse is a product of a force and a *time* interval, while work is a product of a force and a *distance* and depends on the angle between the force and displacement vectors. Second, impulse and momentum are vector quantities, and work and kinetic energy are scalars. Even in straight-line motion, in which only one component of a vector is involved, force, velocity, and momentum may have components along this line that are either positive or negative. ◀

6 Center of Mass

We can restate the principle of conservation of momentum in a useful way with the help of the concept of **center of mass,** which we define as follows:

Definition of center of mass

Suppose we have several particles A, B, etc., with masses m_A, m_B, ... Let the coordinates of A be (x_A, y_A), let those of B be (x_B, y_B), and so on. We define the center of mass of the system as the point having coordinates $(x_{\text{cm}}, y_{\text{cm}})$ given by

$$x_{\text{cm}} = \frac{m_A x_A + m_B x_B + m_C x_C + \cdots}{m_A + m_B + m_C + \cdots},$$
$$y_{\text{cm}} = \frac{m_A y_A + m_B y_B + m_C y_C + \cdots}{m_A + m_B + m_C + \cdots}. \qquad (18)$$

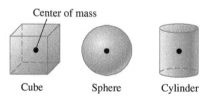
Center of mass

Cube   Sphere   Cylinder

If a homogeneous object has a geometric center, that is where the center of mass is located.

In statistical language, the center of mass is a *mass-weighted average* position of the particles.

For a solid object, which we often model as having a continuous distribution of matter, locating the center of mass often frequently requires calculus. However, symmetry considerations can be helpful. For example, whenever a homogeneous solid object has a geometric center, such as a billiard ball, an ice cube, or a can of frozen orange juice, the center of mass is at the geometric center (Figure 25). Also, whenever an object has an axis of symmetry, such as a wheel or a pulley, the center of mass always lies on that axis. Note, however, that the center of mass isn't always within the object. For example, the center of mass of a doughnut is right in the middle of the hole.

Axis of symmetry

Disk   Donut

If an object has an axis of symmetry, the center of mass lies along it. As in the case of the donut, the center of mass may not be within the object.

▲ **FIGURE 25** Location of the center of mass for some symmetric objects.

When the particles in a system move, the center of mass may also move. Equations 18 give the coordinates (x_{cm}, y_{cm}) of the center of mass in terms of the coordinates of the particles. The rates of change of these quantities (the components of the velocity of the center of mass) are related to the components of the velocity of the particles in the same way. Therefore, we immediately find the following relation:

Velocity of center of mass

The velocity $\vec{v}_{cm}$ of the center of mass of a collection of particles is the mass-weighted average of the velocities of the individual particles:

$$\vec{v}_{cm} = \frac{m_A \vec{v}_A + m_B \vec{v}_B + m_C \vec{v}_C + \cdots}{m_A + m_B + m_C + \cdots}. \tag{19}$$

In terms of components,

$$v_{cm,x} = \frac{m_A v_{A,x} + m_B v_{B,x} + m_C v_{C,x} + \cdots}{m_A + m_B + m_C + \cdots},$$

$$v_{cm,y} = \frac{m_A v_{A,y} + m_B v_{B,y} + m_C v_{C,y} + \cdots}{m_A + m_B + m_C + \cdots}. \tag{20}$$

We denote the total mass $m_A + m_B + \cdots$ by M; we can then rewrite Equation 19 as

$$M\vec{v}_{cm} = m_A \vec{v}_A + m_B \vec{v}_B + m_C \vec{v}_C + \cdots.$$

The right side is the total momentum of the system, so we have $\vec{P} = M\vec{v}_{cm}$.

Total momentum $\vec{P}$ in terms of center of mass

For a system of particles, the total momentum $\vec{P}$ is the total mass $M = m_A + m_B + \cdots$ times the velocity $\vec{v}_{cm}$ of the center of mass:

$$M\vec{v}_{cm} = m_A \vec{v}_A + m_B \vec{v}_B + m_C \vec{v}_C + \cdots = \vec{P} \tag{21}$$

It follows that, for an *isolated* system, in which the total momentum is constant, the velocity of the center of mass is also constant.

EXAMPLE 14 **Quarreling pets**

A 2.0 kg cat and a 3.0 kg dog are moving toward each other along the x axis, heading for a fight. At a particular instant, the cat is 1.0 m to the right of the origin and is moving in the $+x$ direction with speed 3.0 m/s, and the dog is 2.0 m to the right of the origin, moving in the $-x$ direction with speed 1.0 m/s. Find the position and velocity of the center of mass of the two-pet system, and also find the total momentum of the system.

SOLUTION

SET UP Figure 26 shows our sketch. We represent the pets' motion as x components of velocity, being careful with signs.

SOLVE To find the center of mass of the two-pet system, we use Equation 18:

$$x_{cm} = \frac{m_{cat}(x_{cat}) + m_{dog}(x_{dog})}{m_{cat} + m_{dog}}$$

$$= \frac{(2.0\ \text{kg})(1.0\ \text{m}) + (3.0\ \text{kg})(2.0\ \text{m})}{2.0\ \text{kg} + 3.0\ \text{kg}} = 1.6\ \text{m}.$$

▲ **FIGURE 26** Our sketch for this problem.

Continued

To find the velocity of the center of mass, we use Equation 20:

$$v_{cm,x} = \frac{m_{cat}v_{cat,x} + m_{dog}v_{dog,x}}{m_{cat} + m_{dog}}$$

$$= \frac{(2.0\text{ kg})(3.0\text{ m/s}) + (3.0\text{ kg})(-1.0\text{ m/s})}{2.0\text{ kg} + 3.0\text{ kg}}$$

$$= 0.60\text{ m/s}.$$

The total x component of momentum is the sum of the x components of momenta of the two animals:

$$P_x = m_{cat}(v_{cat,x}) + m_{dog}(v_{dog,x})$$

$$= (2.0\text{ kg})(3.0\text{ m/s}) + (3.0\text{ kg})(-1.0\text{ m/s})$$

$$= 3.0\text{ kg} \cdot \text{m/s}.$$

Alternatively, the total momentum is the total mass M, times the velocity of the center of mass:

$$P_x = Mv_{cm,x} = (5.0\text{ kg})(0.60\text{ m/s}) = 3.0\text{ kg} \cdot \text{m/s}.$$

REFLECT As always, remember that an object moving in the $-x$ direction has a negative x component of velocity. The total momentum of the system is equal to the momentum of a single particle with mass equal to the total mass of the system and with velocity equal to the velocity of the center of mass of the system.

Practice Problem: At the instant described, the cat decides to avoid combat. It quickly turns around and runs in the $-x$ direction with speed 2.0 m/s. Find the position and velocity of the center of mass, and the total momentum of the system, at this instant. *Answers:* $x_{cm} = 1.6$ m, $v_{cm} = -1.4$ m/s, $P_x = -7.0$ kg $\cdot$ m/s.

7 Motion of the Center of Mass

In Section 6, we defined the center of mass of a system of particles as an average position of the particles, weighted according to their masses. We found that the total momentum of the system is related simply to the total mass and the velocity of the center of mass. Now our final step is to look at the relationship between the acceleration of the center of mass and the forces acting on the system. Again we'll find a simple and elegant relation.

Equations 20 and 21 give the velocity of the center of mass in terms of the velocities of the individual particles. Proceeding one additional step, we take the rate of change of each term in these equations to show that the accelerations are related in the same way. Let $\vec{a}_{cm}$ be the acceleration of the center of mass (the rate of change of $\vec{v}_{cm}$ with respect to time); then

$$M\vec{a}_{cm} = m_A\vec{a}_A + m_B\vec{a}_B + m_C\vec{a}_C + \cdots \tag{22}$$

Now, $m_A\vec{a}_A$ is equal to the vector sum of forces on particle A, and so on, so the right side of Equation 22 is equal to the vector sum $\Sigma\vec{F}$ of *all* the forces acting on *all* the particles. Just as we did in Section 2, we may classify each force as *internal* or *external*. The sum of forces on all the particles is then

$$\Sigma\vec{F} = \Sigma\vec{F}_{ext} + \Sigma\vec{F}_{int} = M\vec{a}_{cm}.$$

Because of Newton's third law, the internal forces all cancel in pairs, and $\Sigma\vec{F}_{int} = 0$. Only the sum of the external forces is left, and we have the following result:

Acceleration of center of mass
When an object or a collection of particles is acted on by external forces, the center of mass moves just as though all the mass were concentrated at that point and were acted on by a resultant force equal to the sum of the external forces on the system. Stated symbolically, this relationship is

$$\Sigma\vec{F}_{ext} = M\vec{a}_{cm}. \tag{23}$$

Let's look at some applications of this result. Suppose the center of mass of an adjustable wrench lies partway down the handle. Figure 27 shows what happens when we send the wrench spinning across a smooth tabletop. The overall motion appears complicated, but the center of mass (marked by a white dot) follows a straight line, as though all the mass were concentrated at that point. As

John Slater/Corbis

▲ Application **Please don't sneeze!** To the physics students in the audience, these acrobats are demonstrating the concept of the center of mass of a system. Individually, each of them has his or her own separate mass. However, while moving together, they can be considered as one large mass centered at the mass-weighted average position of all the acrobats. As long as this center of mass is positioned directly above the bicycle, they can keep up their precarious balancing act.

▲ **FIGURE 27** The center of mass of this wrench is marked with a white dot. The total external force acting on the wrench is small. As the wrench spins on a smooth horizontal surface, the center of mass moves in a straight line.

another example, suppose an explosive shell traveling in a parabolic trajectory (neglecting air resistance) explodes in flight, splitting into two fragments with equal mass (Figure 28a). The fragments follow new parabolic paths, but the center of mass of the shell continues on the original parabolic trajectory, just as though all the mass were still concentrated at that point. Exploding fireworks are a spectacular example of this principle (Figure 28b).

The property of the center of mass we've just discussed will be important when we analyze the motion of extended rigid objects. The center of mass also plays an important role in the motion of astronomical objects. The earth and the moon revolve in orbits centered on their center of mass, as do the two stars in a binary system.

Finally, we note again that, for an isolated system, $\sum \vec{F}_{ext} = 0$. In this case, Equation 23 shows that the acceleration $\vec{a}_{cm}$ of the center of mass is zero, so its velocity $\vec{v}_{cm}$ is constant, and from Equation 21, the total momentum $\vec{P}$ is also constant. This conclusion reaffirms our statement in Section 2 that the total momentum of an isolated system is constant.

8 Rocket Propulsion

Momentum considerations are particularly useful when we have to analyze a system in which the masses of parts of the system change with time. In such cases, we can't use Newton's second law ($\sum \vec{F} = m\vec{a}$) directly, because m changes. Rocket propulsion offers a typical and interesting example of this kind of analysis. A rocket is propelled forward by the rearward ejection of burned fuel that initially was in the rocket. The forward force on the rocket is the reaction to the backward force on the ejected material. The total mass of the system is constant, but the mass of the rocket itself decreases as material is ejected. As a simple example, we consider a rocket fired in outer space, where there is no gravitational field and no air resistance (so that the system is isolated). We choose our x axis to be along the rocket's direction of motion.

NOTE ▶ Be especially careful with signs in this discussion. Negative signs may appear where you don't expect them; be sure you understand why they have to be where they are. ◀

Figure 29 shows the rocket at a time t after firing, when its mass is m and the x component of its velocity relative to our coordinate system is v. The x component of the total momentum P at this instant is $P = mv$. In a short time interval

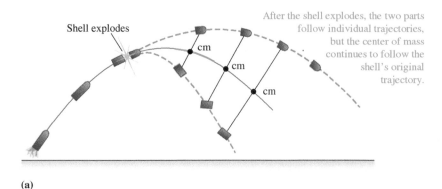

Shell explodes

cm

cm

cm

After the shell explodes, the two parts follow individual trajectories, but the center of mass continues to follow the shell's original trajectory.

(a)

(b)

▲ **FIGURE 28** (a) A projectile explodes in flight. If air resistance can be ignored, the fragments follow individual parabolic trajectories, but the center of mass continues on the same trajectory the projectile was following before it exploded. (b) A firework represents an exploding projectile.

At time t, the rocket has mass m and x component of velocity v.

At time $t + \Delta t$, the rocket has mass $m + \Delta m$ (where Δm is inherently *negative*) and x component of velocity $v + \Delta v$. The burned fuel has x component of velocity $v' = v - v_{ex}$ and mass $-\Delta m$. (The minus sign is needed to make $-\Delta m$ *positive*, because Δm is negative.)

(a)   **(b)**

▲ **FIGURE 29** A rocket moving in gravity-free outer space.

Δt, the mass of the rocket changes by an amount Δm. This is an inherently negative quantity, because the rocket's mass m *decreases* with time as fuel is burned. During Δt, a positive mass $(-\Delta m)$ of burned fuel is ejected from the rocket. Let v_{ex} be the exhaust speed of this material relative to the rocket. Then the x component of the velocity v' of the fuel relative to our coordinate system is

$$v' = v - v_{ex},$$

and the x component of momentum of the mass $-\Delta m$ is

$$(-\Delta m)v' = (-\Delta m)(v - v_{ex}).$$

At the end of the time interval Δt, the mass of the rocket (including the unburned fuel) has decreased to $m + \Delta m$, and the rocket's velocity has increased to $v + \Delta v$ (Figure 29). (Remember that Δm is negative.) The rocket's momentum at this time is

$$(m + \Delta m)(v + \Delta v).$$

Thus, the total x component of the momentum of the rocket plus the ejected fuel at time $t + \Delta t$ is

$$P = (m + \Delta m)(v + \Delta v) + (-\Delta m)(v - v_{ex}).$$

According to our initial assumption, the rocket and fuel are an isolated system. Hence, momentum is conserved; the total momentum P of the system must be the same at time t and at time $t + \Delta t$:

$$mv = (m + \Delta m)(v + \Delta v) + (-\Delta m)(v - v_{ex}).$$

This equation can be simplified to

$$m \, \Delta v = -\Delta m v_{ex} - \Delta m \, \Delta v.$$

We can neglect the term $\Delta m \, \Delta v$ because it is a product of two small quantities and thus is much smaller than the other terms. Dropping that term, dividing by Δt, and rearranging terms, we find that

$$m\frac{\Delta v}{\Delta t} = -v_{ex}\frac{\Delta m}{\Delta t}. \tag{24}$$

Because $\Delta v/\Delta t$ is the x component of acceleration of the rocket, the left side of this equation (mass times acceleration) equals the x component of the resultant force F, or *thrust,* on the rocket, so

$$F = -v_{ex}\frac{\Delta m}{\Delta t}. \qquad \text{(thrust of rocket)} \tag{25}$$

▲ **BIO Application A jet-propelled . . . jellyfish?** These jellyfish move by using the same physical principles of propulsion that we see in interplanetary rockets. By forcing water out of their bells in one direction, they are able to move in the opposite direction.

The thrust is proportional both to the relative speed v_{ex} of the ejected fuel and to the (positive) mass of fuel ejected per unit time, $-\Delta m/\Delta t$. (Remember that $\Delta m/\Delta t$ is negative because it is the rate of change of the rocket's mass.)

The x component of acceleration a of the rocket is

$$a = \frac{\Delta v}{\Delta t} = -\frac{v_{ex}}{m}\frac{\Delta m}{\Delta t}. \qquad \text{(acceleration of rocket)} \qquad (26)$$

The rocket's mass m decreases continuously while the fuel is being consumed. If v_{ex} and $\Delta m/\Delta t$ are constant, the acceleration increases until all the fuel is gone.

EXAMPLE 15   Launch of a rocket

A rocket floats next to an interplanetary space station far from any planet. It ignites its engine. In the first second of its flight, it ejects $\frac{1}{60}$ of its mass with a relative velocity magnitude of 2400 m/s. Find its acceleration.

SOLUTION

SET UP AND SOLVE We are given that $\Delta m = -m/60$ and $\Delta t = 1.0$ s. We use the same coordinate system as in Figure 29, with the $+x$ axis to the right.

The acceleration is given by Equation 26:

$$a = -\frac{v_{ex}}{m}\frac{\Delta m}{\Delta t}$$

$$= -\frac{2400 \text{ m/s}}{m}\left(\frac{-m/60}{1.0 \text{ s}}\right) = 40 \text{ m/s}^2.$$

REFLECT At the start of the flight, when the velocity of the rocket is zero, the ejected exhaust is moving to the left, relative to our coordinate system, at 2400 m/s. At the end of the first sec-ond, the rocket is moving at 40 m/s. The speed of the exhaust rel-ative to our system is 2360 m/s. We could now compute the acceleration at $t = 1.0$ s (using the decreased rocket mass), find the velocity at $t = 2.0$ s, and so on, stepping through the calcula-tion one second at a time until all the fuel is used up. As the mass decreases, the acceleration in successive 1 s intervals increases.

Detailed calculation shows that, after about 22 s, the rocket's velocity in our coordinate system passes 2400 m/s. The exhaust ejected after this time therefore moves *forward*, not backward, in our system. The final velocity acquired by the rocket can be greater in magnitude (and is often *much* greater) than the relative speed v_{ex}.

Practice Problem: Find the rocket's velocities 2.0 s and 3.0 s after launch. *Answers:* 81 m/s, 122 m/s.

In the early days of rocket propulsion, people who didn't understand conser-vation of momentum thought that a rocket couldn't function in outer space because it wouldn't have anything to "push against." On the contrary, rockets work *best* in outer space! Figure 30 shows a dramatic example of rocket propul-sion. The rocket is *not* "pushing against the ground" to get into the air.

NASA

▲ **FIGURE 30** Launch of the Titan 4B Cen-taur, a dramatic example of rocket propulsion.

CHAPTER SUMMARY

Momentum

(Section 1) The momentum $\vec{p}$ of a particle with mass m moving with velocity $\vec{v}$ is defined as the vector quantity $\vec{p} = m\vec{v}$ (Equation 1). Newton's second law can be restated as follows: The rate of change of momentum of a particle equals the vector sum of the forces acting on it:

$$\sum \vec{F} = \lim_{\Delta t \to 0} \frac{\Delta \vec{p}}{\Delta t}. \qquad (3)$$

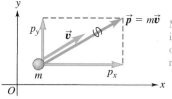

Momentum is a vector quantity; it has the same direction as the object's velocity and can be represented by components.

The total momentum $\vec{P}$ of a system of particles is the vector sum of the momenta of the individual particles:

$$\vec{P} = \vec{p}_A + \vec{p}_B + \cdots = m_A\vec{v}_A + m_B\vec{v}_B + \cdots. \qquad (4, 5)$$

Conservation of Momentum

(Section 2) An internal force is a force exerted by one part of a system on another part of the same system; an external force is a force exerted on part or all of a system by something outside the system. An isolated system is a system that experiences either no external forces or external forces whose vector sum is zero. The total momentum of an isolated system is constant: $\vec{P}_i = \vec{P}_f$. Each component of momentum is conserved separately.

Isolated system: astronaut (A) + wrench (W)

When the astronaut throws the wrench, the total momentum $\vec{P}$ of the system is conserved, although the individual momenta $\vec{p}_A$ and $\vec{p}_W$ are not.

Collisions

(Sections 3 and 4) Collisions can be classified according to energy relations and final velocities. In an elastic collision between two objects, kinetic energy is conserved and the initial and final relative velocities have the same magnitude. In an inelastic two-object collision, the final kinetic energy is less than the initial kinetic energy; if the two objects have the same final velocity (for instance, if they stick together), the collision is completely inelastic.

Elastic:
K conserved

Inelastic:
Some K lost

Completely inelastic:
Objects have same $\vec{v}_f$

Impulse

(Section 5) The impulse $\vec{J}$ of a constant force $\vec{F}$ acting over a time interval Δt from t_i to t_f is the vector quantity $\vec{J} = \vec{F}(t_f - t_i) = \vec{F}\,\Delta t$ (Equation 14). The change in momentum of a particle during any time interval equals the impulse of the total force acting on the particle: $\Delta \vec{p} = \vec{F}\,\Delta t = \vec{F}(t_f - t_i) = \vec{J}$ (Equation 15).

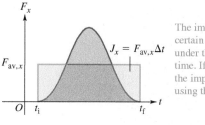

The impulse $\vec{J}$ of a force over a certain time interval is the area under the graph of force versus time. If the force varies with time, the impulse may be calculated by using the average force.

Center of Mass

(Sections 6 and 7) The coordinates x_{cm} and y_{cm} of the center of mass of a system of particles are defined as

$$x_{cm} = \frac{m_A x_A + m_B x_B + m_C x_C + \cdots}{m_A + m_B + m_C + \cdots},$$
$$y_{cm} = \frac{m_A y_A + m_B y_B + m_C y_C + \cdots}{m_A + m_B + m_C + \cdots}. \qquad (18)$$

The total momentum $\vec{P}$ of the system equals the total mass M, multiplied by the velocity $\vec{v}_{cm}$ of the center of mass:

$$M\vec{v}_{cm} = m_A\vec{v}_A + m_B\vec{v}_B + m_C\vec{v}_C + \cdots = \vec{P} \qquad (21)$$

The center of mass of a system moves as though all the mass were concentrated at the center of mass: $\sum \vec{F}_{ext} = M\vec{a}_{cm}$ (Equation 23).

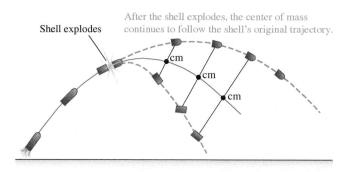

Shell explodes

After the shell explodes, the center of mass continues to follow the shell's original trajectory.

Continued

Rocket Propulsion

(Section 8) In rocket propulsion, the mass of the rocket changes as the fuel is burned. Analysis of the momentum relations must include the momentum carried away by the fuel, as well as the momentum of the rocket itself.

Momentum: Problem Set

For instructor-assigned homework, go to www.masteringphysics.com

Conceptual Questions

1. The objects shown in Figure 31 move together. Identify internal and external forces for each of the following systems: (a) The system consists of only block A. (b) The system consists of only block B. (c) The system consists of both blocks A and B.

Frictionless horizontal table

▲ **FIGURE 31** Question 1.

2. Gliders A and B are headed directly toward each other on an air track and collide head-on. Identify the internal and external forces on each glider during the collision. What are the internal and external forces if the system consists of *both* gliders?

3. Example 3, as well as some of the problems in this chapter, describe how, when an object explodes into two fragments, the lighter one gets more kinetic energy than the heavier one. How can this be so, since both fragments are acted upon by the same force for the same amount of time during the explosion? (*Hint:* Does the force act over the same *distance* on each fragment?)

4. Is the momentum of a satellite in a circular orbit conserved? What about its kinetic energy? Explain your reasoning.

5. Golfers, tennis players, and baseball batters are told to "follow through" with their swing. Why? What does a follow-through enable them to do?

6. When a catcher in a baseball game catches a fast ball, he does not hold his arms rigid, but relaxes them so that the mitt moves several inches while the ball is being caught. Why is this important?

7. A woman stands in the middle of a perfectly smooth, frictionless, frozen lake. She can set herself in motion by throwing things, but suppose she has nothing to throw. Can she propel herself to shore *without* throwing anything? Explain.

8. When rockets were first suggested, some people scoffed that they would not work in space because there is nothing out there for them to push against. So why *do* they work in space, since there really is nothing out there for them to push against?

9. (a) If the momentum of a *single* object is equal to zero, must its kinetic energy also be zero? (b) If the momentum of a *pair* of objects is equal to zero, must the kinetic energy of those objects also be zero? (c) If the kinetic energy of a pair of objects is equal to zero, must the momentum of those objects also be zero? Explain your reasoning in each case.

10. (a) When a large car collides with a small car, which one undergoes the greater change in momentum, the large one or the small one? Or is it the same for both? (b) In light of your answer to part (a), why are the occupants of the small car more likely to be hurt than those of the large car, assuming that both cars are equally sturdy?

11. When rain falls from the sky, what becomes of the momentum of the raindrops as they hit the ground? Is your answer also valid for Newton's famous apple?

12. An egg is released from the roof of a building and falls to the ground. As the egg falls, what happens to the momentum of the system of the egg plus the earth?

13. A machine gun is fired at a steel plate. Is the impulse imparted to the plate from the impact of the bullets greater if the bullets bounce off or if they are squashed and stick to the plate?

14. In a zero-gravity environment, can a rocket-propelled spaceship ever attain a speed greater than the relative speed with which the burnt fuel is exhausted? Explain.

15. At the highest point in its parabolic trajectory, a shell explodes into two fragments. Is it possible for *both* fragments to fall straight down after the explosion? Why or why not?

16. If the movie "supergorilla" King Kong beats his chest on a frozen frictionless lake, will he go backward? Why?

Multiple-Choice Problems

1. A small car collides head-on with a large SUV. Which of the following statements concerning this collision are correct? (There may be more than one correct choice.)
   A. Both vehicles are acted upon by the same magnitude of average force during the collision.
   B. The small car is acted upon by a greater magnitude of average force than the SUV.
   C. The small car undergoes a greater change in momentum than the SUV.
   D. Both vehicles undergo the same change in magnitude of momentum.

2. A ball of mass 0.18 kg moving with speed 11.3 m/s collides head-on with an identical stationary ball. (Notice that we do not know the type of collision.) Which of the following quantities can be calculated from this information alone?
   A. The force each ball exerts on the other.
   B. The velocity of each ball after the collision.
   C. Total kinetic energy of both balls after the collision.
   D. Total momentum of both balls after the collision.

3. A proton with a speed of 50,000 km/s makes an *elastic* head-on collision with a stationary carbon nucleus. We can look up the masses of both particles. Which of the following quantities can be calculated from only the known information? (There may be more than one correct choice.)

A. The velocity of the proton and carbon nucleus after the collision.

B. The kinetic energy of each of the particles after the collision.

C. The momentum of each of the particles after the collision.

4. In which of the following collisions would you expect the kinetic energy to be conserved? (There may be more than one correct choice.)

A. A bullet passes through a block of wood.

B. Two bull elk charge each other and lock horns.

C. Two asteroids collide by a glancing blow, but do not actually hit each other, and their only interaction is through gravity.

D. Two cars with springlike bumpers collide at fairly low speeds.

5. A rifle of mass M is initially at rest, but is free to recoil. It fires a bullet of mass m with a velocity $+v$ relative to the ground. After the rifle is fired, its velocity relative to the ground is

A. $-\sqrt{m/M}v$.   B. $-mv/(m + M)$.

C. $-mv/M$.   D. $-v$.

6. Two carts, one twice as heavy as the other, are at rest on a horizontal frictionless track. A person pushes each cart with the same force for 5 s. If the kinetic energy of the *lighter* cart after the push is K, the kinetic energy of the heavier cart is

A. $\frac{1}{4}K$.   B. $\frac{1}{2}K$.   C. K.

D. $2K$.   E. $4K$.

7. A 70-kg wide receiver running west at 8 m/s collides head-on with, and is seized by, a 140-kg lineman lumbering eastward at 4 m/s. In this collision, the greater change in kinetic energy is experienced by

A. the wide receiver.   B. the lineman

C. neither; they experience the same change in kinetic energy.

8. Two masses, M and $5M$, are at rest on a horizontal frictionless table with a compressed spring of negligible mass between them. When the spring is released (there may be more than one correct choice),

A. the two masses receive equal magnitudes of momentum.

B. the two masses receive equal amounts of kinetic energy from the spring.

C. the heavier mass gains more kinetic energy than the lighter mass.

D. the lighter mass gains more kinetic energy than the heavier mass.

9. Cart A, of mass 1 kg, approaches and collides with cart B, which has a mass of 4 kg and is initially at rest. (See Figure 32.) When the springs have reached their maximum compression,

A. cart A has come to rest relative to the ground.

B. both carts have the same velocity.

C. both carts have the same momentum.

D. all the initial kinetic energy of cart A has been converted to elastic potential energy.

10. A glider airplane is coasting horizontally when a very heavy object suddenly falls out of it. As a result of dropping this object, the glider's speed will

A. increase.

B. decrease.

C. remain the same as it was.

11. Which of the following statements is true for an *inelastic* collision? (There may be more than one correct choice.)

A. Both momentum and kinetic energy are conserved.

B. Momentum is conserved, but kinetic energy is not conserved.

C. Kinetic energy is conserved, but momentum is not conserved.

D. The amount of momentum lost by one object is the same as the amount gained by the other object.

E. The amount of kinetic energy lost by one object is the same as the amount gained by the other object.

12. Which of the following statements is true for an *elastic* collision? (There may be more than one correct choice.)

A. Both momentum and kinetic energy are conserved.

B. Momentum is conserved, but kinetic energy is not conserved.

C. Kinetic energy is conserved, but momentum is not conserved.

D. The amount of momentum lost by one object is the same as the amount gained by the other object.

E. The amount of kinetic energy lost by one object is the same as the amount gained by the other object.

13. Two lumps of clay having equal masses and speeds, but traveling in opposite directions on a frictionless horizontal surface, collide and stick together. Which of the following statements about this system of lumps must be true? (There may be more than one correct choice.)

A. The momentum of the system is conserved during the collision.

B. The kinetic energy of the system is conserved during the collision.

C. The two masses lose all their kinetic energy during the collision.

D. The velocity of the center of mass of the system is the same after the collision as it was before the collision.

14. A heavy rifle initially at rest fires a light bullet. Which of the following statements about these objects is true? (There may be more than one correct choice.)

A. The bullet and rifle both gain the same magnitude of momentum.

B. The bullet and rifle are both acted upon by the same average force during the firing.

C. The bullet and rifle both have the same acceleration during the firing.

D. The bullet and the rifle gain the same amount of kinetic energy.

15. You drop an egg from rest with no air resistance. As it falls,

A. only its momentum is conserved.

B. only its kinetic energy is conserved.

C. both its momentum and its mechanical energy are conserved.

D. its mechanical energy is conserved, but its momentum is not conserved.

▲ **FIGURE 32** Multiple-choice problem 9.

Problems

1 Momentum

1. • For each case in Figure 33, the system consists of the masses shown with the indicated velocities. Find the net momentum of each system.

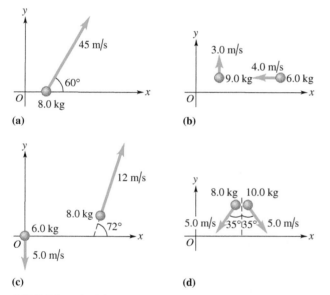

▲ **FIGURE 33** Problem 1.

2. • For each case in Figure 34, the system consists of the masses shown with the indicated velocities. Find the x and y components of the net momentum of each system.

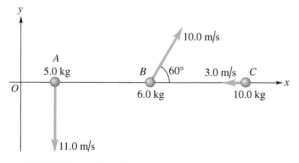

▲ **FIGURE 34** Problem 2.

3. • Three objects A, B, and C are moving as shown in Figure 35. Find the x and y components of the net momentum of the particles if we define the system to consist of (a) A and C, (b) B and C, (c) all three objects.

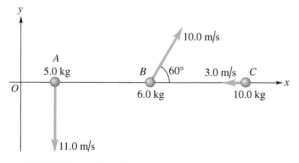

▲ **FIGURE 35** Problem 3.

4. • A 1200 kg car is moving on the freeway at 65 mph. (a) Find the magnitude of its momentum and its kinetic energy in SI units. (b) If a 2400 kg SUV has the same speed as the 1200 kg car, how much momentum and kinetic energy does it have?

5. • The speed of the fastest-pitched baseball was 45 m/s, and the ball's mass was 145 g. (a) What was the magnitude of the momentum of this ball, and how many joules of kinetic energy did it have? (b) How fast would a 57 gram ball have to travel to have the same amount of (i) kinetic energy, and (ii) momentum?

6. •• **Some useful relationships.** The following relationships between the momentum and kinetic energy of an object can be very useful for calculations: If an object of mass m has momentum of magnitude p and kinetic energy K, show that (a) $K = (p^2/2m)$, and (b) $p = \sqrt{2mK}$. (c) Find the momentum of a 1.15 kg ball that has 15.0 J of kinetic energy. (d) Find the kinetic energy of a 3.50 kg cat that has 0.220 kg · m/s of momentum.

7. •• The magnitude of the momentum of a cat is p. What would be the magnitude of the momentum (in terms of p) of a dog having three times the mass of the cat if it had (a) the same speed as the cat, and (b) the same kinetic energy as the cat?

2 Conservation of Momentum

8. • Two figure skaters, one weighing 625 N and the other 725 N, push off against each other on frictionless ice. (a) If the heavier skater travels at 1.50 m/s, how fast will the lighter one travel? (b) How much kinetic energy is "created" during the skaters' maneuver, and where does this energy come from?

9. • **Recoil speed of the earth.** In principle, any time someone jumps up, the earth moves in the opposite direction. To see why we are unaware of this motion, calculate the recoil speed of the earth when a 75 kg person jumps upward at a speed of 2.0 m/s.

10. • On a frictionless air track, a 0.150 kg glider moving at 1.20 m/s to the right collides with and sticks to a stationary 0.250 kg glider. (a) What is the net momentum of this two-glider system before the collision? (b) What must be the net momentum of this system after the collision? Why? (c) Use your answers in parts (a) and (b) to find the speed of the gliders after the collision. (d) Is kinetic energy conserved during the collision?

11. • **Baseball.** A regulation 145 g baseball can be hit at speeds of 100 mph. If a line drive is hit essentially horizontally at this speed and is caught by a 65 kg player who has leapt directly upward into the air, what horizontal speed (in cm/s) does he acquire by catching the ball?

12. • You are standing on a sheet of ice that covers the football stadium parking lot in Buffalo; there is negligible friction between your feet and the ice. A friend throws you a 0.400 kg ball that is traveling horizontally at 10.0 m/s. Your mass is 70.0 kg. (a) If you catch the ball, with what speed do you and the ball move afterwards? (b) If the ball hits you and bounces off your chest, so that afterwards it is moving horizontally at 8.00 m/s in the opposite direction, what is your speed after the collision?

13. •• On a frictionless, horizontal air table, puck A (with mass 0.250 kg) is moving to the right toward puck B (with mass 0.350 kg), which is initially at rest. After the collision, puck A has a velocity of 0.120 m/s to the left, and puck B has a velocity of 0.650 m/s to the right. (a) What was the speed of puck A

before the collision? (b) Calculate the change in the total kinetic energy of the system that occurs during the collision.

14. ●● Block A in Figure 36 has mass 1.00 kg, and block B has mass 3.00 kg. The blocks are forced together, compressing a spring S between them; then the system is released from rest on a level, frictionless surface. The spring, which has negligible mass, is not fastened to either block and drops to the surface after it has expanded. Block B acquires a speed of 1.20 m/s. (a) What is the final speed of block A? (b) How much potential energy was stored in the compressed spring?

$m_A = 1.00$ kg $m_B = 3.00$ kg
S

▲ **FIGURE 36** Problem 14.

15. ●● Two ice skaters, Daniel (mass 65.0 kg) and Rebecca (mass 45.0 kg), are practicing. Daniel stops to tie his shoelace and, while at rest, is struck by Rebecca, who is moving at 13.0 m/s before she collides with him. After the collision, Rebecca has a velocity of magnitude 8.00 m/s at an angle of 53.1° from her initial direction. Both skaters move on the frictionless, horizontal surface of the rink. (a) What are the magnitude and direction of Daniel's velocity after the collision? (b) What is the change in total kinetic energy of the two skaters as a result of the collision?

16. ●● You (mass 55 kg) are riding your frictionless skateboard (mass 5.0 kg) in a straight line at a speed of 4.5 m/s when a friend standing on a balcony above you drops a 2.5 kg sack of flour straight down into your arms. (a) What is your new speed, while holding the flour sack? (b) Since the sack was dropped vertically, how can it affect your *horizontal* motion? Explain. (c) Suppose you now try to rid yourself of the extra weight by throwing the flour sack straight up. What will be your speed while the sack is in the air? Explain.

17. ●● A 4.25 g bullet traveling horizontally with a velocity of magnitude 375 m/s is fired into a wooden block with mass 1.12 kg, initially at rest on a level frictionless surface. The bullet passes *through* the block and emerges with its speed reduced to 122 m/s. How fast is the block moving just after the bullet emerges from it?

18. ●● A ball with a mass of 0.600 kg is initially at rest. It is struck by a second ball having a mass of 0.400 kg, initially moving with a velocity of 0.250 m/s toward the right along the x axis. After the collision, the 0.400 kg ball has a velocity of 0.200 m/s at an angle of 36.9° above the x axis in the first quadrant. Both balls move on a frictionless, horizontal surface. (a) What are the magnitude and direction of the velocity of the 0.600 kg ball after the collision? (b) What is the change in the total kinetic energy of the two balls as a result of the collision?

19. ●● **Combining conservation laws.** A 5.00 kg chunk of ice is sliding at 12.0 m/s on the floor of an ice-covered valley when it collides with and sticks to another 5.00 kg chunk of ice that is initially at rest. (See Figure 37.) Since the valley is icy, there is no friction. After the collision, how high above the valley floor will the combined chunks go? (*Hint:* Break this problem into two parts—the collision and the behavior after the collision—and apply the appropriate conservation law to each part.)

5.0 kg 12.0 m/s   5.0 kg

▲ **FIGURE 37** Problem 19.

20. ●● **Combining conservation laws.** A 15.0 kg block is attached to a very light horizontal spring of force constant 500.0 N/m and is resting on a frictionless horizontal table. (See Figure 38.) Suddenly it is struck by a 3.00 kg stone traveling horizontally at 8.00 m/s to the right, whereupon the stone rebounds at 2.00 m/s horizontally to the left. Find the maximum distance that the block will compress the spring after the collision. (*Hint:* Break this problem into two parts—the collision and the behavior after the collision—and apply the appropriate conservation law to each part.)

15.0 kg
3.00 kg 8.00 m/s

▲ **FIGURE 38** Problem 20.

3 Inelastic Collisions

21. ● Three identical boxcars are coupled together and are moving at a constant speed of 20.0 m/s on a level track. They collide with another identical boxcar that is initially at rest and couple to it, so that the four cars roll on as a unit. Friction is small enough to be neglected. (a) What is the speed of the four cars? (b) What percentage of the kinetic energy of the boxcars is dissipated in the collision? What happened to this energy?

22. ● On a highly polished, essentially frictionless lunch counter, a 0.500 kg submarine sandwich moving 3.00 m/s to the left collides with a 0.250 kg grilled cheese sandwich moving 1.20 m/s to the right. (a) If the two sandwiches stick together, what is their final velocity? (b) How much mechanical energy dissipates in the collision? Where did this energy go?

23. ●● An astronaut in space cannot use a scale or balance to weigh objects because there is no gravity. But she does have devices to measure distance and time accurately. She knows her own mass is 78.4 kg, but she is unsure of the mass of a large gas canister in the airless rocket. When this canister is approaching her at 3.50 m/s, she pushes against it, which slows it down to 1.20 m/s (but does not reverse it) and gives her a speed of 2.40 m/s. (a) What is the mass of this canister? (b) How much kinetic energy is "lost" in this collision, and what happens to that energy?

24. ●● On a very muddy football field, a 110-kg linebacker tackles an 85-kg halfback. Immediately before the collision, the linebacker is slipping with a velocity of 8.8 m/s north and the halfback is sliding with a velocity of 7.2 m/s east. What is the velocity (magnitude and direction) at which the two players move together immediately after the collision?

25. ●● A 5.00 g bullet is fired horizontally into a 1.20 kg wooden block resting on a horizontal surface. The coefficient of kinetic friction between block and surface is 0.20. The bullet remains embedded in the block, which is observed to slide 0.230 m along the surface before stopping. What was the initial speed of the bullet?

26. •• You and your friends are doing physics experiments on a frozen pond that serves as a frictionless, horizontal surface. Sam, with mass 80.0 kg, is given a push and slides eastward. Abigail, with mass 50.0 kg, is sent sliding northward. They collide, and after the collision Sam is moving at 37.0° north of east with a speed of 6.00 m/s and Abigail is moving at 23.0° south of east with a speed of 9.00 m/s. (a) What was the speed of each person before the collision? (b) By how much did the total kinetic energy of the two people decrease during the collision?

27. •• A hungry 11.5 kg predator fish is coasting from west to east at 75.0 cm/s when it suddenly swallows a 1.25 kg fish swimming from north to south at 3.60 m/s. Find the magnitude and direction of the velocity of the large fish just after it snapped up this meal. Neglect any effects due to the drag of the water.

28. •• **Bird defense.** To protect their young in the nest, peregrine
BIO falcons will fly into birds of prey (such as ravens) at high speed. In one such episode, a 600 gram falcon flying at 20.0 m/s ran into a 1.5 kg raven flying at 9.0 m/s. The falcon hit the raven at right angles to its original path and bounced back with a speed of 5.0 m/s. (These figures were estimated by one of the authors (WRA) as he watched this attack occur in northern New Mexico.) By what angle did the falcon change the raven's direction of motion?

29. •• **Accident analysis.** Two cars collide at an intersection. Car A, with a mass of 2000 kg, is going from west to east, while car B, of mass 1500 kg, is going from north to south at 15 m/s. As a result of this collision, the two cars become enmeshed and move as one afterwards. In your role as an expert witness, you inspect the scene and determine that, after the collision, the enmeshed cars moved at an angle of 65° south of east from the point of impact. (a) How fast were the enmeshed cars moving just after the collision? (b) How fast was car A going just before the collision?

30. •• A hockey puck B rests on frictionless, level ice and is struck by a second puck A, which was originally traveling at 40.0 m/s and which is deflected 30.0° from its original direction. (See Figure 39.) Puck B acquires a velocity at a 45.0° angle to the original direction of A. The pucks have the same mass. (a) Compute the speed of each puck after the collision. (b) What fraction of the original kinetic energy of puck A dissipates during the collision?

▲ **FIGURE 39** Problem 30.

4 Elastic Collisions

31. • A 0.300 kg glider is moving to the right on a frictionless, horizontal air track with a speed of 0.80 m/s when it makes a head-on collision with a stationary 0.150 kg glider. (a) Find the magnitude and direction of the final velocity of each glider if the collision is elastic. (b) Find the final kinetic energy of each glider.

32. • On a cold winter day, a penny (mass 2.50 g) and a nickel (mass 5.00 g) are lying on the smooth (frictionless) surface of a frozen lake. With your finger, you flick the penny toward the

nickel with a speed of 2.20 m/s. The coins collide elastically; calculate both their final velocities (speed and direction).

33. •• **Nuclear collisions.** Collisions between atomic and subatomic particles are often perfectly elastic. In one such collision, a proton traveling to the right at 258 km/s collides head-on and elastically with a stationary alpha particle (a helium nucleus, having mass 6.65×10^{-27} kg). Consult Appendix E as needed. (a) Find the magnitude and direction of the velocity of each particle after the collision. (b) How much kinetic energy does the proton lose during the collision? (c) How can the collision be elastic if the proton loses kinetic energy?

34. •• On an air track, a 400.0 g glider moving to the right at 2.00 m/s collides elastically with a 500.0 g glider moving in the opposite direction at 3.00 m/s. Find the velocity of each glider after the collision.

35. •• Blocks A (mass 2.00 kg) and B (mass 10.00 kg) move on a frictionless, horizontal surface. Initially, block B is at rest and block A is moving toward it at 2.00 m/s. The blocks are equipped with ideal spring bumpers, as in Example 9. The collision is head-on, so all motion before and after the collision is along a straight line. (a) Find the maximum energy stored in the spring bumpers and the velocity of each block at that time. (b) Find the velocity of each block after they have moved apart.

36. •• Two identical objects traveling in opposite directions with the same speed V make a head-on collision. Find the speed of each object after the collision if (a) they stick together and (b) if the collision is perfectly elastic.

5 Impulse

37. • A catcher catches a 145 g baseball traveling horizontally at 36.0 m/s. (a) How large an impulse does the ball give to the catcher? (b) If the ball takes 20 ms to stop once it is in contact with the catcher's glove, what average force did the ball exert on the catcher?

38. • A block of ice with a mass of 2.50 kg is moving on a frictionless, horizontal surface. At $t = 0$, the block is moving to the right with a velocity of magnitude 8.00 m/s. Calculate the magnitude and direction of the velocity of the block after each of the following forces has been applied for 5.00 s: (a) a force of 5.00 N directed to the right; (b) a force of 7.00 N directed to the left.

39. •• **Biomechanics.** The mass of a regulation tennis ball is
BIO 57 g (although it can vary slightly), and tests have shown that the ball is in contact with the tennis racket for 30 ms. (This number can also vary, depending on the racket and swing.) We shall assume a 30.0 ms contact time throughout this problem. The fastest-known served tennis ball was served by "Big Bill" Tilden in 1931, and its speed was measured to be 73.14 m/s. (a) What impulse and what force did Big Bill exert on the tennis ball in his record serve? (b) If Big Bill's opponent returned his serve with a speed of 55 m/s, what force and what impulse did he exert on the ball, assuming only horizontal motion?

40. •• To warm up for a match, a tennis player hits the 57.0 g ball vertically with her racket. If the ball is stationary just before it is hit and goes 5.50 m high, what impulse did she impart to it?

41. •• A 150 gram baseball is hit toward the left by a bat. The magnitude of the force the bat exerts on the ball as a function of time is shown in Figure 40. (a) Find the magnitude and direction of the impulse that the bat imparts to the ball. (b) Find the magnitude and direction of the ball's velocity just

after it is hit by the bat if the ball is initially (i) at rest, and (ii) moving to the right at 30.0 m/s.

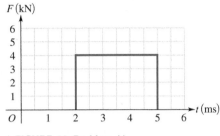

▲ **FIGURE 40** Problem 41.

42. •• Your little sister (mass 25.0 kg) is sitting in her little red wagon (mass 8.50 kg) at rest. You begin pulling her forward and continue accelerating her with a constant force for 2.35 s, at the end of which time she's moving at a speed of 1.80 m/s. (a) Calculate the impulse you imparted to the wagon and its passenger. (b) With what force did you pull on the wagon?

43. •• **Bone fracture.** Experimental tests have shown that bone
BIO will rupture if it is subjected to a force density of $1.0 \times 10^8 \text{ N/m}^2$. Suppose a 70.0 kg person carelessly roller-skates into an overhead metal beam that hits his forehead and completely stops his forward motion. If the area of contact with the person's forehead is 1.5 cm^2, what is the greatest speed with which he can hit the wall without breaking any bone if his head is in contact with the beam for 10.0 ms?

44. •• A bat strikes a 0.145 kg baseball. Just before impact, the ball is traveling horizontally to the right at 50.0 m/s, and it leaves the bat traveling to the left at an angle of 30° above horizontal with a speed of 65.0 m/s. (a) What are the horizontal and vertical components of the impulse the bat imparts to the ball? (b) If the ball and bat are in contact for 1.75 ms, find the horizontal and vertical components of the average force on the ball.

7 Motion of the Center of Mass

45. • Calculate the location of the center of mass of the earth-moon system (that is, find the distance of the center of mass from the earth's center). And assume the orbital radius of the moon is equal to the distance between the centers of the earth and the moon. What can you say about the position of the center of mass with respect to the earth's surface?

46. • Two small-sized objects are placed on a uniform 9.00 kg plastic beam 3.00 m long, as shown in Figure 41. Find the location of the center of mass of this system by setting $x = 0$ at (a) the left end of the beam and (b) the right end of the beam. (c) Do you get the same result both ways?

▲ **FIGURE 41** Problem 46.

47. •• **Detecting planets around other stars.** Roughly 500 planets have so far been detected beyond our solar system. This is accomplished by looking for the effect the planet has on the star. The star is not truly stationary; instead, it and its planets orbit around the center of mass of the system. Astronomers can measure this wobble in the position of a star. (a) For a star with the mass and size of our sun and having a planet with five times the mass of Jupiter, where would the center of mass of this system be located, relative to the center of the star, if the distance from the star to the planet was the same as the distance from Jupiter to our sun? (b) If the planet had earth's mass, where would the center of mass of the system be located if the planet was just as far from the star as the earth is from the sun? (c) In view of your results in parts (a) and (b), why is it much easier to detect stars having large planets rather than small ones?

48. • Three odd-shaped blocks of chocolate have the following masses and center-of-mass coordinates: (1) 0.300 kg, $(0.200 \text{ m}, 0.300 \text{ m})$; (2) 0.400 kg, $(0.100 \text{ m}, -0.400 \text{ m})$; (3) 0.200 kg, $(-0.300 \text{ m}, 0.600 \text{ m})$. Find the coordinates of the center of mass of the system of three chocolate blocks.

49. •• A machine part consists of a thin, uniform 4.00-kg bar that is 1.50 m long, hinged perpendicular to a similar vertical bar of mass 3.00 kg and length 1.80 m. The longer bar has a small but dense 2.00-kg ball at one end (Fig. 42). By what distance will the center of mass of this part move horizontally and vertically if the vertical bar is pivoted counterclockwise through 90° to make the entire part horizontal?

▲ **FIGURE 42** Problem 49.

50. •• **Changing your center of mass.** To keep the calculations
BIO fairly simple, but still reasonable, we shall model a human leg that is 92.0 cm long (measured from the hip joint) by assuming that the upper leg and the lower leg (which includes the foot) have equal lengths and that each of them is uniform. For a 70.0 kg person, the mass of the upper leg would be 8.60 kg, while that of the lower leg (including the foot) would be 5.25 kg. Find the location of the center of mass of this leg, relative to the hip joint, if it is (a) stretched out horizontally and (b) bent at the knee to form a right angle with the upper leg remaining horizontal.

51. • A 1200 kg station wagon is moving along a straight highway at 12.0 m/s. Another car, with mass 1800 kg and speed 20.0 m/s, has its center of mass 40.0 m ahead of the center of mass of the station wagon. (See Figure 43.) (a) Find the position of the center of mass of the system consisting of the two automobiles. (b) Find the magnitude of the total momentum of the system from the given data. (c) Find the speed of the center of mass of the system. (d) Find the total momentum of the system, using the speed of the center of mass. Compare your result with that of part (b).

▲ **FIGURE 43** Problem 51.

52. •• **Walking in a boat.** A 45.0 kg woman stands up in a 60.0 kg canoe of length 5.00 m. She walks from a point 1.00 m from one

end to a point 1.00 m from the other end. (See Figure 44.) If the resistance of the water is negligible, how far does the canoe move during this process?

Start   Finish

← 1.00 m → ← 3.00 m → ← 1.00 m →

▲ **FIGURE 44** Problem 52.

8 Rocket Propulsion

53. • A small rocket burns 0.0500 kg of fuel per second, ejecting it as a gas with a velocity of magnitude 1600 m/s relative to the rocket. (a) What is the thrust of the rocket? (b) Would the rocket operate in outer space, where there is no atmosphere? If so, how would you steer it? Could you brake it?

54. • A rocket is fired in deep space, where gravity is negligible. If the rocket has an initial mass of 6000 kg and ejects gas at a relative velocity of magnitude 2000 m/s, how much gas must it eject in the first second to have an initial acceleration of 25.0 m/s^2.

55. • A rocket is fired in deep space, where gravity is negligible. In the first second, it ejects 1/160 of its mass as exhaust gas and has an acceleration of 15.0 m/s^2. What is the speed of the exhaust gas relative to the rocket?

56. •• In outer space, where gravity is negligible, a 75,000 kg rocket (including 50,000 kg of fuel) expels this fuel at a steady rate of 135 kg/s with a speed of 1200 m/s relative to the rocket. (a) Find the thrust of the rocket. (b) What are the initial acceleration and the maximum acceleration of the rocket? (c) After the fuel runs out, what happens to this rocket's acceleration? Does it (i) remain the same as it was just as the fuel ran out, (ii) suddenly become zero, or (iii) gradually drop to zero? Explain your reasoning. (d) After the fuel runs out, what happens to the rocket's speed? Does it (i) remain the same as it was just as the fuel ran out, (ii) suddenly become zero, or (iii) gradually drop to zero? Explain your reasoning.

57. •• A 70-kg astronaut floating in space in a 110-kg MMU (manned maneuvering unit) experiences an acceleration of 0.029 m/s^2 when he fires one of the MMU's thrusters. (a) If the speed of the escaping N$_2$ gas relative to the astronaut is 490 m/s, how much gas is used by the thruster in 5.0 s? (b) What is the thrust of the thruster?

General Problems

58. •• In 1.00 second an automatic paintball gun can fire 15 balls, each with a mass of 0.113 g, at a muzzle velocity of 88.5 m/s. Calculate the average recoil force experienced by the player who's holding the gun.

59. •• In a volcanic eruption, a 2400-kg boulder is thrown vertically upward into the air. At its highest point, it suddenly explodes (due to trapped gases) into two fragments, one being three times the mass of the other. The lighter fragment starts out with only horizontal velocity and lands 274 m directly north of the point of the explosion. Where will the other fragment land? Neglect any air resistance.

60. •• A 5.00 kg ornament is hanging by a 1.50 m wire when it is suddenly hit by a 3.00 kg missile traveling horizontally at 12.0 m/s. The missile embeds itself in the ornament during the collision. What is the tension in the wire immediately after the collision?

61. •• A stone with a mass of 0.100 kg rests on a frictionless, horizontal surface. A bullet of mass 2.50 g traveling horizontally at 500 m/s strikes the stone and rebounds horizontally at right angles to its original direction with a speed of 300 m/s. (a) Compute the magnitude and direction of the velocity of the stone after it is struck. (b) Is the collision perfectly elastic?

62. •• A steel ball with a mass of 40.0 g is dropped from a height of 2.00 m onto a horizontal steel slab. The ball rebounds to a height of 1.60 m. (a) Calculate the impulse delivered to the ball during the impact. (b) If the ball is in contact with the slab for 2.00 ms, find the average force on the ball during the impact.

63. •• A movie stuntman (mass 80.0 kg) stands on a window ledge 5.0 m above the floor (Fig. 45). Grabbing a rope attached to a chandelier, he swings down to grapple with the movie's villain (mass 70.0 kg), who is standing directly under the chandelier. (Assume that the stuntman's center of mass moves downward 5.0 m. He releases the rope just as he reaches the villain.) (a) With what speed do the entwined foes start to slide across the floor? (b) If the coefficient of kinetic friction of their bodies with the floor is $\mu_k = 0.250$, how far do they slide?

5.0 m   m = 80.0 kg

m = 70.0 kg

▲ **FIGURE 45** Problem 63.

64. •• **Tennis, anyone?** Tennis players sometimes leap into the air to return a volley. (a) If a 57 g tennis ball is traveling horizontally at 72 m/s (which does occur), and a 61 kg tennis player leaps vertically upward and hits the ball, causing it to travel at 45 m/s in the reverse direction, how fast will her center of mass be moving horizontally just after hitting the ball? (b) If, as is reasonable, her racket is in contact with the ball for 30.0 ms, what force does her racket exert on the ball? What force does the ball exert on the racket?

65. •• Two identical masses are released from rest in a smooth hemispherical bowl of radius R, from the positions shown in Fig. 46. You can ignore friction between the masses and the surface of the bowl. If they stick together when they collide, how high above the bottom of the bowl will the masses go after colliding?

▲ **FIGURE 46** Problem 65.

66. •• Two identical 1.50 kg masses are pressed against opposite ends of a light spring of force constant 1.75 N/cm, compressing the spring by 20.0 cm from its normal length. Find the speed of each mass when it has moved free of the spring on a frictionless horizontal lab table.

67. •• A rifle bullet with mass 8.00 g strikes and embeds itself in a block with a mass of 0.992 kg that rests on a frictionless, horizontal surface and is attached to a coil spring. (See Figure 47.) The impact compresses the spring 15.0 cm. Calibration of the spring shows that a force of 0.750 N is required to compress the spring 0.250 cm. (a) Find the magnitude of the block's velocity just after impact. (b) What was the initial speed of the bullet?

▲ **FIGURE 47** Problem 67.

68. •• A 5.00 g bullet traveling horizontally at 450 m/s is shot *through* a 1.00 kg wood block suspended on a string 2.00 m long. If the center of mass of the block rises a distance of 0.450 cm, find the speed of the bullet as it emerges from the block.

69. •• Jonathan and Jane are sitting in a sleigh that is at rest on frictionless ice. Jonathan's weight is 800 N, Jane's weight is 600 N, and that of the sleigh is 1000 N. They see a poisonous spider on the floor of the sleigh and immediately jump off. Jonathan jumps to the left with a velocity (relative to the ice) of 5.00 m/s at 30.0° above the horizontal, and Jane jumps to the right at 7.00 m/s at 36.9° above the horizontal (relative to the ice). Calculate the sleigh's horizontal velocity (magnitude and direction) after they jump out.

70. •• **Animal propulsion.** Squids and octopuses propel themBIO selves by expelling water. They do this by taking the water into a cavity and then suddenly contracting the cavity, forcing the water to shoot out of an opening. A 6.50 kg squid (including the water in its cavity) that is at rest suddenly sees a dangerous predator. (a) If this squid has 1.75 kg of water in its cavity, at what speed must it expel the water to suddenly achieve a speed of 2.50 m/s to escape the predator? Neglect any drag effects of the surrounding water. (b) How much kinetic energy does the squid create for this escape maneuver?

71. •• The objects in Figure 48 are constructed of uniform wire bent into the shapes shown. Find the position of the center of mass of each one.

▲ **FIGURE 48** Problem 71.

72. •• **Origin of the moon.** Astronomers believe that our moon originated when a Mars-sized body collided with the earth over 4.5 billion years ago, knocking off matter that condensed to form the moon. To get some idea of how such a collision would affect the earth, assume that the collision occurred head-on (with the two bodies traveling in opposite directions), that the Mars-sized body merged completely with the earth and was originally the same mass as Mars, and that the earth's orbital speed was the same as it is now. Assume further that the speed of the colliding body was equal to the earth's escape velocity of 11 km/s (although it could have been greater). (a) By how much (in m/s) did such a collision change the earth's speed? Consult Appendix E. (b) How much thermal energy would such a collision create? (c) To how many megaton bombs is the energy in part (b) equivalent? (One ton of TNT releases 4.184×10^9 J of energy.)

73. •• **Changing mass.** A railroad hopper car filled with sand is rolling with an initial speed of 15.0 m/s on straight, horizontal tracks. You can ignore frictional forces on the railroad car. The total mass of the car plus sand is 85,000 kg. The hopper door is not fully closed so sand leaks out the bottom. After 20 min, 13,000 kg of sand has leaked out. Then what is the speed of the railroad car? (Compare your analysis with that used to solve Problem 16.)

74. •• **Forensic science.** Forensic scientists can measure the muzzle velocity of a gun by firing a bullet horizontally into a large hanging block that absorbs the bullet and swings upward. (See Figure 49.) The measured maximum angle of swing can be used to calculate the speed of the bullet. In one such test, a rifle fired a 4.20 g bullet into a 2.50 kg block hanging by a thin wire 75.0 cm long, causing the block to swing upward to a maximum angle of 34.7° from the vertical. What was the original speed of this bullet?

▲ **FIGURE 49** Problem 74.

75. •• A 20.0-kg lead sphere is hanging from a hook by a thin wire 3.50 m long, and is free to swing in a complete circle. Suddenly it is struck horizontally by a 5.00-kg steel dart that embeds itself in the lead sphere. What must be the minimum initial speed of the dart so that the combination makes a complete circular loop after the collision?

76. •• A blue puck with mass 0.0400 kg, sliding with a velocity of magnitude 0.200 m/s on a frictionless, horizontal air table, makes a perfectly elastic, head-on collision with a red puck with mass m, initially at rest. After the collision, the velocity of the blue puck is 0.050 m/s in the same direction as its initial velocity. Find (a) the velocity (magnitude and direction) of the red puck after the collision; and (b) the mass m of the red puck.

77. •• **The structure of the atom.** During 1910–1911, Sir Ernest Rutherford performed a series of experiments to determine the structure of the atom. He aimed a beam of alpha particles (helium nuclei, of mass 6.65×10^{-27} kg) at an extremely thin sheet of gold foil. Most of the alphas went right through with little deflection, but a small percentage bounced directly back. These results told him that the atom must be mostly empty space with an extremely small nucleus. The alpha particles that bounced back must have made a head-on collision with this nucleus. A typical speed for the alpha particles before the collision was 1.25×10^7 m/s, and the gold atom has a mass of 3.27×10^{-25} kg. Assuming (quite reasonably) elastic

collisions, what would be the speed after the collision of a gold atom if an alpha particle makes a direct hit on the nucleus?

78. •• **Rocket failure!** Just as it has reached an upward speed of 5.0 m/s during a vertical launch, a rocket explodes into two pieces. Photographs of the explosion reveal that the lower piece, with a mass one-fourth that of the upper piece, was moving downward at 3.0 m/s the instant after the explosion. (a) Find the speed of the upper piece just after the explosion. (b) How high does the upper piece go above the point where the explosion occurred?

79. •• In a common physics demonstration, two identical carts having rigid metal surfaces and equal speeds collide with each other. Each cart has a piece of Velcro® at one end and a spring at the other end. For each collision shown in the figure, find the magnitude and direction of the velocity of each cart after the collision. Are both collisions elastic? What causes one of them to be inelastic, and what happens to the "lost" kinetic energy?

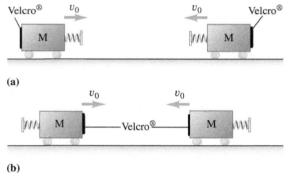

(a)

(b)

▲ **FIGURE 50** Problem 79.

80. •• A 7.0 kg shell at rest explodes into two fragments, one with a mass of 2.0 kg and the other with a mass of 5.0 kg. If the heavier fragment gains 100 J of kinetic energy from the explosion, how much kinetic energy does the lighter one gain?

81. •• **Radioactive beta decay.** *Beta decay* is a radioactive decay in which a neutron in the nucleus of an atom breaks apart (decays) to form a proton, an electron, and an antineutrino. The electron is also known as a *beta particle*. The proton remains in the nucleus, while the electron and antineutrino shoot out. Before the existence of the antineutrino was suspected, it was assumed that only the electron was emitted. Assuming (incorrectly) that there is no antineutrino, and that the neutron is initially at rest inside the nucleus, find (a) the ratio of the speed of the electron to the speed of the proton just after the decay and (b) the ratio of the kinetic energy of the electron to that of the proton just after the decay. (c) Use the results from parts (a) and (b) to explain why it is the electron, and not the proton, that shoots out of the nucleus. (*Note:* Electrons actually emerge with a range of speeds; this observation provided the first experimental evidence that an additional particle (the antineutrino) must also be emitted.)

82. •• A 15.0 g acorn falls from rest from the top of a 35.0-m-high oak tree. When it is halfway to the ground, a 135 g bird gliding horizontally at 75.0 cm/s scoops it up with its beak. Find (a) the horizontal and vertical components of the bird's velocity, and (b) the speed of the bird and the angle its velocity makes with the vertical, just after the bird scoops up the acorn.

83. •• **Accident analysis.** A 1500 kg sedan goes through a wide intersection traveling from north to south when it is hit by a 2200 kg SUV traveling from east to west. The two cars become enmeshed due to the impact and slide as one thereafter. On-the-scene measurements show that the coefficient of kinetic friction between the tires of these cars and the pavement is 0.75, and the cars slide to a halt at a point 5.39 m west and 6.43 m south of the impact point. How fast was each car traveling just before the collision?

Passage Problems

BIO Momentum and the squirting squid. An interesting use of "rocket power" is that used by cephalopods such as octopi and squids. These animals take in seawater and then squirt it out at high speed. A 2.5-kg squid can expel 0.25 kg of seawater (in a short burst of 0.20 s) with a speed of 600 cm/s.

84. What is the momentum of one squirt of water?
  A. 1.2 kg · m/s in the direction of the squirt
  B. 1.5 kg · m/s in the direction of the squirt
  C. 12 kg · m/s in the direction of the squirt
  D. 15 kg · m/s in the direction of the squirt

85. How much momentum does this give the squid?
  A. 1.2 kg · m/s in the direction of the squirt
  B. 1.5 kg · m/s in the direction of the squirt
  C. 15 kg · m/s in the direction of the squirt
  D. 1.2 kg · m/s in the direction opposite to the squirt
  E. 1.5 kg · m/s in the direction opposite to the squirt
  F. 15 kg · m/s in the direction opposite to the squirt

86. What would be the speed of the squid immediately after one squirt?
  A. 10 cm/s
  B. 20 cm/s
  C. 40 cm/s
  D. 60 cm/s
  E. 120 cm/s

87. After three quick squirts (in the same direction) what is the speed of the squid? Ignore the drag on the squid from the ocean water.
  A. 60 cm/s
  B. 120 cm/s
  C. 180 cm/s
  D. 200 cm/s
  E. 240 cm/s

ANSWERS TO SELECTED PROBLEMS

Conceptual Questions

1. The free-body diagrams are given in the figure below. n_{BA} is the normal force that B exerts on A, n_{AB} is the normal force that A exerts on B, and n is the normal force that the table exerts on B. f_{BA} is the friction force that B exerts on A, f_{AB} is the friction force that A exerts on B, and f is the friction force that the table exerts on B. (a) For block A, n_{BA}, f_{BA}, and w_A are all external forces. (b) For block B, n, n_{AB}, f_{AB}, f, P, and w_B are all external forces. (c) P, f, n, w_A, and w_B are external forces; n_{BA}, n_{AB}, f_{BA}, and f_{AB} are internal forces.

3. Since the same force gives the lighter fragment a greater acceleration, the lighter fragment gains more velocity in the same time.

5. The follow-through increases the time the force acts and therefore increases the impulse applied to the ball. This in turn increases the final momentum and speed of the struck object.

9. (a) Yes. $K = p^2/2m$, so if $p = 0$, then $K = 0$. (b) No. The system can have zero total momentum because the objects have equal nonzero momenta in opposite directions. But the kinetic energy of each object does not depend on the direction of the object's velocity and thus is never negative. Therefore, the kinetic energies do not add to zero. (c) Yes. The only way the total kinetic energy can be zero is for each object to be at rest.

11. If a drop is considered to be the system, the system is not isolated. The drop gains momentum as it falls, because of the external force of gravity. When the drop strikes the ground, the momentum of the drop is removed by the net upward impulse due to the force exerted by the ground. If the drop and earth are considered to be an isolated system, the total momentum is zero before the drop starts to fall; remains zero as the drop falls, because the earth moves toward the drop; and is zero after the drop lands and both drop and earth come to rest.

13. Since the change in momentum is greater when the bullets bounce off, the impulse applied by the plate is greater in that case. By Newton's third law, the impulse applied to the plate is also greater.

15. No. The horizontal component of momentum must be conserved. It is nonzero just before the explosion, so it cannot be zero immediately after the explosion.

Multiple-Choice Problems

1. A, D
3. A, B, C
5. C
7. A
9. B
11. B, D
13. A, C, D
15. D

Problems

1. (a) 44 kg · m/s (b) 0 (c) −12 kg · m/s (d) −2 kg · m/s
3. (a) −30 kg · m/s; −55 kg · m/s (b) 0; 52 kg · m/s (c) 0; −3 kg · m/s
5. (a) 6.5 kg · m/s; 150 J (b) (i) 73 m/s (ii) 110 m/s
7. (a) $3p$ (b) $\sqrt{3}p$
9. 2.5×10^{-23} m/s
11. 9.9 cm/s
13. (a) 0.790 m/s (b) −0.0023 J
15. (a) 7.20 m/s at 38.0° (b) −680 J
17. 0.960 m/s
19. 1.8 m
21. (a) 15.0 m/s (b) 25.0%; converted to other forms
23. (a) 81.8 kg (b) 216 J
25. 229 m/s

27. 0.763 m/s at 27.6° south of east
29. (a) 7.1 m/s (b) 5.2 m/s
31. (a) 0.300 kg: 0.27 m/s to the right; 0.150 kg: 1.07 m/s to the right (b) 0.300 kg: 0.011 J; 0.150 kg: 0.086 J
33. (a) proton: 154 km/s to the left; alpha particle: 104 km/s to the right (b) 3.58×10^{-17} J (c) total kinetic energy of the system is conserved
35. (a) 0.333 m/s, 3.33 J (b) −1.33 m/s (A), +0.67 m/s (B)
37. (a) 5.22 kg · m/s (b) 261 N
39. (a) 4.2 kg · m/s; 140 N (b) −7.3 kg · m/s; −240 N
41. (a) 120.0 N/s, to the left (b) (i) 80 m/s, to the left (ii) 50 m/s, to the left
43. 2.1 m/s
45. 4670 km
47. (a) 3.70×10^9 m (b) 4.48×10^5 m (c) star moves in orbit of larger radius
49. (a) 0.700 m upward and 0.700 m to the right
51. (a) 16.0 m behind leading car (b) 5.04×10^4 kg · m/s (c) 16.8 m/s (d) 5.04×10^4 kg · m/s; same
53. (a) 80.0 N (b) Yes. Eject gas in the appropriate direction.
55. 2.4 km/s
57. (a) 53 g (b) 5.19 N
59. 91.3 m south
61. (a) 14.6 m/s, at 31.0° from the original direction of the bullet (b) no; $\Delta K = -189$ J
63. (a) 5.28 m/s (b) 5.7 m
65. $R/4$
67. (a) 2.60 m/s (b) 325 m/s
69. 0.105 m/s
73. 0.400 m/s
75. 65.5 m/s
77. 4.98×10^5 m/s
79. (a) A: v_0 to the left; B: v_0 to the right; elastic (b) both carts are at rest; inelastic
81. 250 J
83. $v_{suv} = 12$ m/s
    $v_{sedan} = 21$ m/s

Passage Problems

85. E
87. C

Rotational Motion

EFE/Javier Lizón/NewsCom

Previously, we would have considered these cyclists as so many particles in motion up the road. However, while each bicycle moves along the road, its wheels move in circles. In this chapter we start to look at objects that cannot be treated as particles. In particular, we will look at the motion of objects that *rotate*.

What do a Ferris wheel, a circular saw blade, and a ceiling fan have in common? None of these objects can be represented adequately as a moving *point;* each is a rigid object that *rotates* about an axis that is stationary in some inertial frame of reference. Rotation occurs on all size scales, from the motion of electrons in atoms to the motion of hurricanes, to the motions of entire galaxies.

In this chapter, we'll consider the motion of objects that have a definite and unchanging size and shape; we'll neglect any stretching, twisting, and squeezing caused by the forces acting on the object. We call this idealized model a **rigid body.** (We could call it a rigid *object,* but physicists usually call it a rigid body.) We'll begin with kinematic language for describing rotational motion. Next, we'll look at the kinetic energy of rotation—the key to applying energy methods to rotational motion. Then we develop principles of rotational dynamics, analogous to Newton's laws for particles, to relate the forces on an object to its rotational motion.

1 Angular Velocity and Angular Acceleration

Let's think first about a rigid body that rotates about a stationary axis. (We'll also use the term *fixed axis.*) Both terms refer to an axis that is at rest in some inertial frame of reference and doesn't change direction relative to that frame. The body might be the shaft of a motor, a chunk of roast beef on a barbecue skewer, or a merry-go-round. Figure 1 shows a rigid body rotating about a stationary axis passing through point O (which may be the origin of a coordinate system) and perpendicular to the plane of the diagram. Line OP is fixed in the body and

Generic rigid body rotating counterclockwise around an axis at the origin

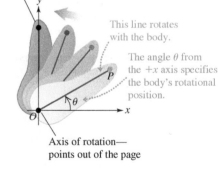

This line rotates with the body.

The angle θ from the +x axis specifies the body's rotational position.

Axis of rotation— points out of the page

▲ **FIGURE 1** A rigid body rotating about an axis pointing out of the paper.

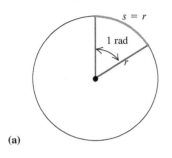

One radian is the angle at which the arc s has the same length as the radius r.

(a)

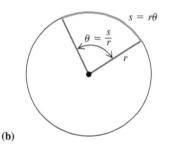

An angle θ in radians is the ratio of the arc length s to the radius r.

$$s = r\theta$$

$$\theta = \frac{s}{r}$$

(b)

▲ **FIGURE 2** An angle θ in radians is defined as the ratio of the arc length s to the radius r.

Angular displacement $\Delta\theta$ of a rotating rigid body over a time interval Δt:

$$\Delta\theta = \theta_2 - \theta_1$$

At t_2

$\Delta\theta$

At t_1

θ_2

P

θ_1

(a)

(b)

▲ **FIGURE 3** (a) Angular displacement $\Delta\theta$ of a rotating body. (b) Every part of a rigid body has the same angular velocity.

rotates with it. The angle θ that this line makes with the $+x$ axis describes the rotational position of the body and serves as a *coordinate* for the body's rotational position. Thus, θ is analogous to x, which we used as the coordinate to specify position in our treatment of straight-line motion of a particle.

We usually measure the angle θ in **radians.** As is shown in Figure 2a, 1 radian (denoted 1 rad) is defined as the angle subtended at the center of a circle by an arc with a length equal to the radius of the circle. In Figure 2b, an angle θ is subtended by an arc of length s on a circle of radius r; θ (in radians) is equal to s divided by r:

$$\theta = \frac{s}{r}, \qquad \text{or} \qquad s = r\theta. \tag{1}$$

An angle measured in radians is the quotient of two lengths, so it is a pure number, without dimensions. If $s = 1.5$ m and $r = 1.0$ m, then $\theta = 1.5$, but we'll often write this as 1.5 rad to distinguish it from an angle measured in degrees or revolutions.

The circumference of a circle is 2π times the radius, so there are 2π (about 6.283) radians in one complete revolution ($360°$). Therefore,

$$1 \text{ rad} = \frac{360°}{2\pi} = 57.3°.$$

Similarly, $180° = \pi$ rad, $90° = \pi/2$ rad, and so on.

We'll often encounter angles greater than $360°$; for a body in constant rotation, the angle θ may increase or decrease continuously.

Angular Velocity

Just as we described straight-line motion in terms of the rate of change of the coordinate x, we can describe rotational motion of a rigid body in terms of the rate of change of θ. In Figure 3a, a reference line OP in a rotating body makes an angle θ_1 with the $+x$ axis at time t_1. At a later time t_2, the angle has changed to θ_2. We define the **average angular velocity** ω_{av} of the body as follows:

Definition of average angular velocity

When a rigid body rotates through an angular displacement $\Delta\theta = \theta_2 - \theta_1$ in a time interval $\Delta t = t_2 - t_1$, the average angular velocity ω_{av} is defined as the ratio of the angular displacement to the time interval:

$$\omega_{av} = \frac{\theta_2 - \theta_1}{t_2 - t_1} = \frac{\Delta\theta}{\Delta t}. \tag{2}$$

Unit: rad/s

We can then define the **instantaneous angular velocity** ω as the limit of ω_{av} as Δt approaches zero:

$$\omega = \lim_{\Delta t \to 0} \frac{\Delta\theta}{\Delta t}. \tag{3}$$

Because the body is rigid, all lines in it rotate through the same angle in the same time (Figure 3b). Thus, **at any given instant, every part of a rigid body has the same angular velocity.** If the angle θ is measured in radians, the unit of angular velocity is 1 radian per second (1 rad/s). Other units, such as the revolution per minute (rev/min or rpm), are often used. Two useful conversions are

$$1 \text{ rev/s} = 2\pi \text{ rad/s} \quad \text{and} \quad 1 \text{ rev/min} = 1 \text{ rpm} = \frac{2\pi}{60} \text{ rad/s}. \quad (4)$$

Conceptual Analysis 1

Merry-go-round

A boy and a girl ride a turning merry-go-round. The boy is at the outer edge; the girl is near the axis of rotation. How do their angular velocities compare?

A. The boy has the greater angular velocity.
B. The girl has the greater angular velocity.
C. Both children have the same angular velocity.

SOLUTION An object's *angular* velocity, as opposed to its (straight-line) velocity, is determined by the change in angle of a line drawn from the axis of rotation to the object during any given unit of time (Figure 4). Both children have fixed positions

▶ **FIGURE 4**

on the same rotating object; they rotate through the same angle $\Delta\theta$ in the same time interval Δt. Their angular velocity is the same as that of the merry-go-round. Answer C is correct.

Angular Acceleration

When the angular velocity of a rigid body changes, the body has an angular acceleration. If ω_1 and ω_2 are the instantaneous angular velocities at times t_1 and t_2, respectively (Figure 5), we define the **average angular acceleration** α_{av} as follows:

Definition of average angular acceleration
The average angular acceleration α_{av} of a rotating rigid body is the change in angular velocity, $\Delta\omega$, divided by the time interval Δt:

$$\alpha_{av} = \frac{\omega_2 - \omega_1}{t_2 - t_1} = \frac{\Delta\omega}{\Delta t}. \quad (5)$$

Unit: rad/s^2

The average angular acceleration is the change in angular velocity divided by the time interval:

$$\alpha_{av} = \frac{\omega_2 - \omega_1}{t_2 - t_1} = \frac{\Delta\omega}{\Delta t}$$

At t_1 At t_2

▲ **FIGURE 5** The meaning of angular acceleration.

The **instantaneous angular acceleration** α is the limit of α_{av} as $\Delta t \to 0$:

$$\alpha = \lim_{\Delta t \to 0} \frac{\Delta\omega}{\Delta t}. \quad (6)$$

▶ Application **A boring tool?** The old-fashioned hand drill uses the principle of relative angular velocity to allow a carpenter to bore holes in very hard woods. Each part of the large wheel connected to the drill's handle has the same angular velocity. However, the large size of this wheel accommodates a large number of gear teeth compared with the few teeth that fit on the small wheel turning the drill bit. When these wheels are coupled together, a relatively small angular velocity of the handle can cause a much greater angular velocity of the drill bit, allowing it to penetrate dense woods with speed and precision.

Image Source/Getty Images/Royalty Free

EXAMPLE 1 Rotation of a compact disc

A compact disc (CD) rotates at high speed while a laser reads data encoded in a spiral pattern. The disc has radius $R = 6.0$ cm $= 0.060$ m; when data are being read, it spins at 7200 rev/min. What is the CD's angular velocity ω in radians per second? How much time is required for it to rotate through $90°$? If it starts from rest and reaches full speed in 4.0 s, what is its average angular acceleration?

SOLUTION

SET UP We make a sketch, showing the data (Figure 6). We need to be careful to use consistent units; we'll choose radians, meters, and seconds.

SOLVE To convert the disc's angular velocity ω to radians per second, we multiply by $(1 \text{ min}/60 \text{ s})$ and by $(2\pi \text{ rad}/1 \text{ rev})$:

$$\omega = \frac{7200 \text{ rev}}{1 \text{ min}} = \frac{7200 \text{ rev}}{1 \text{ min}} \left(\frac{1 \text{ min}}{60 \text{ s}}\right)\left(\frac{2\pi \text{ rad}}{1 \text{ rev}}\right) = 754 \text{ rad/s}.$$

From the definition of angular velocity $(\omega = \Delta\theta/\Delta t)$, we find the time Δt for the disc to turn through $90°$ $(\pi/2 \text{ rad})$:

$$\Delta t = \frac{\Delta\theta}{\omega} = \frac{\pi/2 \text{ rad}}{754 \text{ rad/s}} = 0.0021 \text{ s} = 2.1 \text{ ms}.$$

From the definition of angular acceleration $(\alpha_{av} = \Delta\omega/\Delta t)$, if the disc reaches a final angular velocity of 754 rad/s in 4.0 s (starting from rest), the average angular acceleration is

$$\alpha_{av} = \frac{\Delta\omega}{\Delta t} = \frac{754 \text{ rad/s}}{4.0 \text{ s}} = 189 \text{ rad/s}^2.$$

REFLECT A typical circular (table or radial-arm) saw found in woodworking shops runs at 3600 rev/min and reaches full

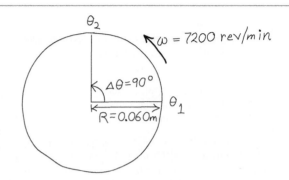

▲ **FIGURE 6** Our sketch for this problem.

speed about 1 s after it is turned on. The radius of a typical blade is 12 cm. Note, however, that the radius is not needed for the angular acceleration calculation. The angular acceleration is about twice that for the CD.

Practice Problem: An old-fashioned vinyl record is designed to turn at 33 rev/min. Find the angular velocity and period (the time for one revolution) of this record. *Answers:* $\omega = 3.5 \text{ rad/s}$, $T = 1.8 \text{ s}$.

You've probably noticed that we're using Greek letters for angular kinematic quantities: θ for angular position, ω for angular velocity, and α for angular acceleration. These are analogous to x for position, v_x for the x component of velocity, and a_x for the x component of acceleration, respectively, in straight-line motion. In each case, velocity is the rate of change of position, and acceleration is the rate of change of velocity.

We've used the word *velocity* rather loosely in our discussion of angular quantities; we haven't said anything about vector aspects of these quantities. But in the preceding discussion, the angular quantities *do* have algebraic signs. When an object rotates about an axis that is perpendicular to the plane of the drawing, it's customary to take the counterclockwise sense of rotation as positive and the clockwise sense as negative (Figure 7). For example, if the compact disk in Example 1 were to reverse its sense of rotation from 800 rad/s counterclockwise (positive) to 600 rad/s clockwise (negative) in 4.0 s, the average angular acceleration would be

$$\alpha_{av} = \frac{\omega_2 - \omega_1}{t_2 - t_1} = \frac{(-600 \text{ rad/s}) - (800 \text{ rad/s})}{4.0 \text{ s}} = -350 \text{ rad/s}^2.$$

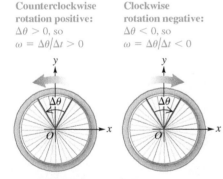

Counterclockwise rotation positive:
$\Delta\theta > 0$, so
$\omega = \Delta\theta/\Delta t > 0$

Clockwise rotation negative:
$\Delta\theta < 0$, so
$\omega = \Delta\theta/\Delta t < 0$

▲ **FIGURE 7** The convention for the sign of angular velocity.

MasteringPHYSICS

ActivPhysics 7.7: Rotational Kinematics

2 Rotation with Constant Angular Acceleration

Analyzing straight-line motion is particularly simple when the acceleration is constant. This is also true of rotational motion: When the angular acceleration is constant, we can derive equations for angular velocity and angular position using exactly the same procedure that we used for straight line motion with constant acceleration.

Let's proceed to derive relationships among the various angular quantities, assuming a constant angular acceleration α. We define θ_0 to be the angular position at time $t = 0$, θ the angular position at any later time t, ω_0 the angular velocity at time $t = 0$, and ω the angular velocity at any later time t. The angular acceleration α is constant and equal to the average value for any interval. Using Equation 5 with the interval from 0 to t, we find that

$$\alpha = \frac{\omega - \omega_0}{t - 0}, \qquad \text{or}$$
$$\omega = \omega_0 + \alpha t. \qquad \text{(angular velocity as function of time)} \qquad (7)$$

The product αt is the total change in ω between $t = 0$ and the later time t; the angular velocity ω at time t is the sum of the initial value ω_0 and this total change.

With constant angular acceleration, the angular velocity changes at a uniform rate, so its average value ω_{av} between 0 and t is the average of the initial and final values:

$$\omega_{\text{av}} = \frac{\omega_0 + \omega}{2}. \qquad (8)$$

We also know that ω_{av} is the total angular displacement $(\theta - \theta_0)$ divided by the time interval $(t - 0)$:

$$\omega_{\text{av}} = \frac{\theta - \theta_0}{t - 0}. \qquad (9)$$

When we equate Equations 8 and 9 and multiply the result by t, we get

$$\theta - \theta_0 = \tfrac{1}{2}(\omega_0 + \omega)t. \qquad (10)$$

Note that this relation doesn't contain the angular acceleration α.

To obtain a relation between θ and t that doesn't contain ω, we substitute Equation 7 into Equation 10:

$$\theta - \theta_0 = \tfrac{1}{2}(\omega_0 + \omega_0 + \alpha t)t,$$
$$\theta = \theta_0 + \omega_0 t + \tfrac{1}{2}\alpha t^2. \qquad (11)$$
$$\text{(angular position with constant angular acceleration)}$$

That is, if at the initial time $t = 0$, the body is at angular position θ_0 and has angular velocity ω_0, then its angular position θ at any later time t is the sum of three terms: its initial angular position θ_0, plus the rotation $\omega_0 t$ it would have if the angular velocity were constant, plus an additional rotation $\tfrac{1}{2}\alpha t^2$ caused by the changing angular velocity.

We can combine Equations 7 and 11 to obtain a relation between θ and ω that doesn't contain t. We invite you to work out the details. In fact, because of the perfect analogy between straight-line and rotational quantities, we can simply replace each straight-line quantity by its rotational analog; we get

$$\omega^2 = \omega_0^2 + 2\alpha(\theta - \theta_0). \qquad (12)$$
$$\text{(angular velocity in terms of angular displacement)}$$

Keep in mind that all of these results are valid *only* when the angular acceleration α is constant; be careful not to try to apply them to problems in which α is

TABLE 1 Comparison of linear and angular motion with constant acceleration

Straight-line motion with constant linear acceleration	Fixed-axis rotation with constant angular acceleration	
$a = \text{constant}$	$\alpha = \text{constant}$	
$v = v_0 + at$	$\omega = \omega_0 + \alpha t$	(7)
$x = x_0 + v_0 t + \frac{1}{2}at^2$	$\theta = \theta_0 + \omega_0 t + \frac{1}{2}\alpha t^2$	(11)
$v^2 = v_0^2 + 2a(x - x_0)$	$\omega^2 = \omega_0^2 + 2\alpha(\theta - \theta_0)$	(12)
$x - x_0 = \frac{1}{2}(v + v_0)t$	$\theta - \theta_0 = \frac{1}{2}(\omega + \omega_0)t$	(10)

not constant. Table 1 compares Equations 7, 10, 11, and 12, for fixed-axis rotation with constant angular acceleration, to the analogous equations for straight-line motion with constant acceleration.

EXAMPLE 2   Rotation of a bicycle wheel

The angular velocity of the rear wheel of a stationary exercise bike is 4.00 rad/s at time $t = 0$, and its angular acceleration is constant and equal to 2.00 rad/s². A particular spoke coincides with the $+x$ axis at time $t = 0$ (Figure 8). What angle does this spoke make with the $+x$ axis at time $t = 3.00$ s? What is the wheel's angular velocity at this time?

At $t = 0$:
$\alpha = 2.00$ rad/s²
$\omega_0 = 4.00$ rad/s
$\theta_0 = 0$ for chosen spoke

▲ FIGURE 8

SOLUTION

SET UP We take $\theta = 0$ at the position where the chosen spoke is horizontal, and we take the counterclockwise sense of rotation to be positive. The initial conditions are $\theta_0 = 0$, $\omega_0 = 4.00$ rad/s, and $\alpha = 2.00$ rad/s².

SOLVE We can use Equations 11 and 7 to find θ and ω at any time. The angle θ is given as a function of time by Equation 11:

$$\theta = \theta_0 + \omega_0 t + \frac{1}{2}\alpha t^2$$
$$= 0 + (4.00 \text{ rad/s})(3.00 \text{ s}) + \frac{1}{2}(2.00 \text{ rad/s}^2)(3.00 \text{ s})^2$$
$$= 21.0 \text{ rad} = 21.0 \text{ rad}\left(\frac{1 \text{ rev}}{2\pi \text{ rad}}\right) = 3.34 \text{ rev}.$$

The wheel has turned through three complete revolutions plus an additional 0.34 rev, or $(0.34 \text{ rev})(2\pi \text{ rad/rev}) = 2.14 \text{ rad} = 123°$. Thus, the chosen spoke is at an angle of 123° with the $+x$ axis.

The wheel's angular velocity ω is given as a function of time by Equation 7, $\omega = \omega_0 + \alpha t$. At time $t = 3.0$ s,

$$\omega = 4.00 \text{ rad/s} + (2.00 \text{ rad/s}^2)(3.00 \text{ s}) = 10.0 \text{ rad/s}.$$

Alternatively, from Equation 12, we get

$$\omega^2 = \omega_0^2 + 2\alpha(\theta - \theta_0)$$
$$= (4.00 \text{ rad/s})^2 + 2(2.00 \text{ rad/s}^2)(21.0 \text{ rad}) = 100 \text{ rad}^2/\text{s}^2,$$
$$\omega = 10.0 \text{ rad/s} = 1.59 \text{ rev/s}.$$

REFLECT Note the step-by-step similarity between these equations and the kinematic relations for straight-line motion.

Practice Problem: Suppose we double the angular acceleration. What would be the new values for θ and ω? *Answers:* $\theta = 30.0$ rad, $\omega = 16.0$ rad/s.

MasteringPHYSICS

PhET: Ladybug Revolution

3 Relationship between Linear and Angular Quantities

In order to develop the principles of dynamics for rigid bodies, we need to be able to find the velocity and acceleration of a particular point in a rotating rigid body. For example, to find the kinetic energy of a rotating object, we have to start from $K = \frac{1}{2}mv^2$ for a particle. That requires knowing v for a particle in a rigid body. We'll need to be able to find the acceleration of a point in a rigid body in order to work out general relations between force and motion for rotation, starting from $\Sigma \vec{F} = m\vec{a}$.

So it's worthwhile to develop general relations between the angular velocity and acceleration of a rigid body rotating about a fixed axis, on the one hand, and the velocity and acceleration of a specific point in the body, on the other. We'll sometimes use the terms *linear velocity* and *linear acceleration* to make sure we distinguish clearly between these and the *angular* quantities introduced in this chapter.

When a rigid body rotates about a fixed axis, every particle in the body moves in a circular path that is centered on the axis and lies in a plane perpendicular to the axis. The speed of a particle is directly proportional to the body's angular velocity; the faster the body rotates, the greater is the speed of each particle. In Figure 9, point P is a constant distance r away from the axis of rotation, and it moves in a circle of radius r. At any time, the angle θ (in radians) and the arc length s are related by the formula

$$s = r\theta.$$

When the angle θ increases by a small amount $\Delta\theta$ during a time interval Δt, the particle moves through an arc length $\Delta s = r\,\Delta\theta$. Thus the average speed of the particle is given by

$$v_{\text{av}} = \frac{\Delta s}{\Delta t} = r\frac{\Delta\theta}{\Delta t} = r\omega_{\text{av}}.$$

In the limit as $\Delta t \to 0$, this equation becomes

$$v = r\omega. \tag{13}$$

We'll continue to use the term *speed* to mean the magnitude of a particle's linear velocity; the *direction* of the particle's linear velocity is tangent to its circular path at each point.

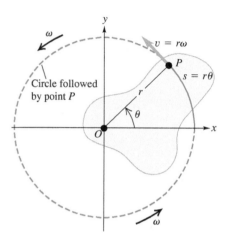

▲ **FIGURE 9** The distance s traversed by a point P on a rigid body equals $r\theta$ if θ is measured in radians.

Quantitative Analysis 2

Rotating disk

A disk rotates about an axis perpendicular to its plane. Point B on the disk is three times farther from the axis than point A. If the speed of point B is v, what is the speed of point A?

A. $3v$ B. $\frac{1}{3}v$ C. v

SOLUTION Speed in this case means, the magnitude of *linear* velocity, not the magnitude of *angular* velocity. Because the disk is a rigid object, all points on the disk rotate with the same angular velocity ω. The speed of a point is directly proportional to its distance r from the axis of rotation: $v = r\omega$. Because point A is one-third the distance from the axis as point B, its speed is $v/3$ (choice B).

We can represent the acceleration $\vec{a}$ of a particle in terms of its radial and tangential components (Figure 10). By definition, the radial component a_{rad} at each point is along a radial line from the particle to the center of its circular path. The tangential component a_{tan} is tangent to the path at each point (and thus parallel or antiparallel to the velocity at each point). Because the particles in a rotating rigid body move in circular paths, every particle *must* have a radial component of acceleration. When the body undergoes angular acceleration, every particle must also have a tangential component of acceleration.

To find the **tangential component of acceleration,** a_{tan}, we note that if the angular velocity ω changes by an amount $\Delta\omega$, the particle's speed changes by an amount Δv given by

$$\Delta v = r\,\Delta\omega.$$

SSPL/The Image Works

◀ **Application** **Not so fast.** This is a velocipede, one of the earliest bicycles produced. When invented in the 1800s, it was more of a curiosity than a practical means of transportation. Because the pedals attach directly to the front wheel, the wheel turns only once for each revolution of the pedals. Therefore, the only way to achieve a reasonable forward speed at a feasible rate of pedaling is to use a huge front wheel. These bicycles are difficult to mount and quite dangerous. Bicycles did not become widely used for transportation until the development of the chain-and-sprocket mechanism, which allowed each turn of the pedals to rotate a smaller wheel more than once.

Radial and tangential acceleration components:
• a_{rad} is point P's centripetal acceleration.
• a_{tan} means that P's rotation is speeding up (the body has angular acceleration).

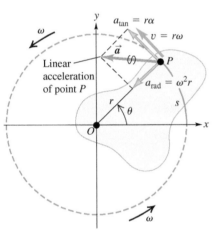

▲ **FIGURE 10** The components of acceleration for a point P on a rigid body whose angular rotation is speeding up.

This corresponds to a component of acceleration a_{tan} tangent to the particle's circular path. If these changes take place in a small time interval Δt, then

$$(a_{tan})_{av} = \frac{\Delta v}{\Delta t} = r\frac{\Delta \omega}{\Delta t},$$

and in the limit as $\Delta t \rightarrow 0$,

$$a_{tan} = r\alpha, \tag{14}$$

where a_{tan} is the **tangential component of instantaneous acceleration.** This component is parallel to the instantaneous velocity at each point; it acts to change the *magnitude* of velocity of the particle (i.e., its speed). It is equal to the rate of change of speed. This component of a particle's acceleration is always tangent to the circular path of the particle.

The **radial component of acceleration,** a_{rad}, of the particle is associated with change in *direction* of the particle's velocity. We worked out the relation $a_{rad} = v^2/r$ for a particle moving in a circle with radius r. We can express this in terms of ω by using Equation 13:

$$a_{rad} = \frac{v^2}{r} = \omega^2 r. \tag{15}$$

This is true at each instant, even when ω and v are not constant.

The vector sum of the radial and tangential components of acceleration of a particle in a rotating body is the linear acceleration $\vec{a}$ (Figure 10). We use the modifier *linear* to emphasize that $\vec{a}$ is the rate of change of velocity $\vec{v}$, *not* the rate of change of angular velocity. The radial and tangential components are always perpendicular, so the magnitude of $\vec{a}$ is given by

$$|\vec{a}| = a = \sqrt{a_{rad}^2 + a_{tan}^2}.$$

NOTE ▶ Remember that Equation 1 $(s = r\theta)$ is valid *only* when θ is measured in radians. The same is true of any equation derived from that relation, including Equations 13, 14, and 15. When you use these equations, you *must* express the angular quantities in radians, not revolutions or degrees. ◀

Conceptual Analysis 3

Angular and centripetal acceleration

A disk spins with increasing angular velocity. Point B on the disk is twice as far from the axis of rotation as point A is. Which of the following statements is or are correct?

A. The angular acceleration of A is greater than that of B.
B. The radial acceleration of A is greater than that of B.
C. A and B have the same angular acceleration.
D. A and B have the same radial acceleration.

SOLUTION The disk's angular velocity is increasing, so the disk has an angular acceleration. All points on the disk rotate through the same angle in a given time interval and thus have the same angular velocity and angular acceleration. Therefore, choice A is incorrect and C is correct. The radial acceleration of each point is $a_{rad} = \omega^2 r$. Point B is farther from the axis than point A is, so its radial acceleration is greater than that of A, and answers B and D are incorrect. The only correct choice is C.

EXAMPLE 3   Throwing a discus

A discus thrower turns with angular acceleration $\alpha = 50 \text{ rad/s}^2$, moving the discus in a circle of radius 0.80 m (Figure 11). Find the radial and tangential components of acceleration of the discus (modeled as a point) and the magnitude of its acceleration at the instant when the angular velocity is 10 rad/s.

▲ FIGURE 11

SOLUTION

SET UP As shown in Figure 12, we model the thrower's arm as a rigid body, so r is constant. (This may not be completely realistic.) We model the discus as a particle moving in a circular path.

SOLVE The components of acceleration are given by Equations 14 and 15:

$$a_{rad} = \omega^2 r = (10 \text{ rad/s})^2 (0.80 \text{ m}) = 80 \text{ m/s}^2,$$
$$a_{tan} = r\alpha = (0.80 \text{ m})(50 \text{ rad/s}^2) = 40 \text{ m/s}^2.$$

The magnitude of the acceleration vector is

$$a = \sqrt{a_{rad}^2 + a_{tan}^2} = 89 \text{ m/s}^2.$$

REFLECT The magnitude of the acceleration is about nine times the acceleration due to gravity; the corresponding force supplied by the thrower's arm must be about nine times the weight of the discus. Note that we have dropped the unit *radian* from our final results; we can do this because a radian is a dimensionless quantity.

▲ FIGURE 12 Our sketch for this problem.

Practice Problem: What is the direction of the acceleration vector of the discus if the angular acceleration is 25 rad/s²? *Answer:* 14° from a radial line toward the center of the circle.

EXAMPLE 4   Designing a propeller

You are asked to design an airplane propeller to turn at 1500 rev/min. The forward airspeed of the plane is to be 90 m/s, and the speed of the tips of the propeller blades through the air must not exceed 300 m/s, the speed of sound in very cold air (Figure 13). Determine the maximum radius of the propeller.

▲ FIGURE 13

SOLUTION

SET UP Figure 14 shows how we sketch this problem. The velocity of each propeller tip is the vector sum of the velocity $\vec{v}_{plane}$ of the plane through the air (magnitude 90 m/s) and the tangential velocity $\vec{v}_{tan}$ of the tip relative to the plane (magnitude $v_{tan} = r\omega$, where r is to be determined).

SOLVE First we convert the angular velocity ω to rad/s:

$$\omega = 1500 \text{ rpm} = \left(\frac{1500 \text{ rev}}{1 \text{ min}}\right)\left(\frac{2\pi \text{ rad}}{1 \text{ rev}}\right)\left(\frac{1 \text{ min}}{60 \text{ s}}\right) = 157 \text{ rad/s}.$$

The tangential velocity $v_{tan} = r\omega$ of the propeller tip is perpendicular to the forward velocity v_{plane} of the plane through the air

Continued

(Figure 14). The magnitude of the vector sum of these velocities is

$$v_{tip} = \sqrt{v_{plane}^2 + v_{tan}^2} = \sqrt{v_{plane}^2 + (r\omega)^2}$$
$$= \sqrt{(90 \text{ m/s})^2 + (157 \text{ rad/s})^2 r^2}.$$

To find the desired propeller radius (at which $v_{tip} = 300$ m/s), we solve this equation for r:

$$(90 \text{ m/s})^2 + (157 \text{ rad/s})^2 r^2 = (300 \text{ m/s})^2,$$
$$r = \frac{1}{157 \text{ rad/s}} \sqrt{(300 \text{ m/s})^2 - (90 \text{ m/s})^2}$$
$$= 1.82 \text{ m}.$$

REFLECT If the radius r is greater than 1.82 m, the airspeed at the propeller tips is greater than 300 m/s, meaning that it is supersonic in cold air.

We can find the radial acceleration of a propeller tip with our calculated radius, using Equation 15:

$$a_{rad} = \omega^2 r$$
$$= (157 \text{ rad/s})^2 (1.82 \text{ m}) = 4.49 \times 10^4 \text{ m/s}^2.$$

From $\Sigma \vec{F} = m\vec{a}$, the propeller must provide a centripetal force of magnitude 4.49×10^4 N (about 10,000 pounds) for each

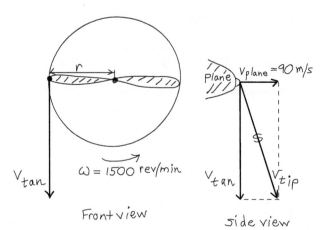

▲ **FIGURE 14** Our sketches for this problem.

kilogram of tip! The propeller has to be made out of tough material.

Practice Problem: If the plane's forward airspeed is 180 m/s and $\omega = 3000$ rev/min, what is the maximum propeller radius? *Answer:* 0.764 m.

EXAMPLE 5   Bicycle gears

How are the angular speeds of the two bicycle sprockets in Figure 15 related to their respective numbers of teeth, N_A and N_B?

SOLUTION

SET UP AND SOLVE The chain does not slip or stretch; therefore, it moves at the same tangential speed v on both sprockets. We use the relation $v = r\omega$ for each sprocket and equate the two tangential speeds:

$$v = r_A \omega_A = r_B \omega_B, \quad \text{or} \quad \frac{\omega_B}{\omega_A} = \frac{r_A}{r_B}.$$

The angular speed of each sprocket is inversely proportional to its radius.

This relationship holds as well for pulleys connected by a belt, provided that the belt doesn't slip. Also, for chain sprockets, the spacing of the teeth must be the same on both sprockets for the chain to mesh properly with both. Let N_A and N_B be the numbers of teeth on the two sprockets; then

$$\frac{2\pi r_A}{N_A} = \frac{2\pi r_B}{N_B}, \quad \text{or} \quad \frac{r_A}{r_B} = \frac{N_A}{N_B}.$$

Combining this equation with the previous one, we get

$$\frac{\omega_B}{\omega_A} = \frac{N_A}{N_B}.$$

REFLECT The angular speed of each sprocket is inversely proportional to its number of teeth. On an 18-speed bike, you get the highest angular speed ω_B of the rear wheel for a given pedaling

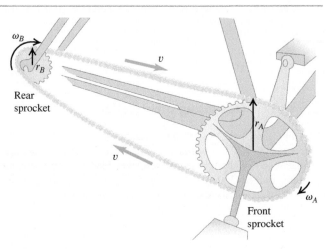

▲ **FIGURE 15**

rate ω_A using the larger-radius front sprocket and the smallest-radius rear sprocket, giving the maximum front-to-back-teeth ratio N_A/N_B.

Practice Problem: If the front sprocket has four times as many teeth as the rear sprocket and the rear wheel radius is 0.33 m, how fast is the bike moving when the pedaling rate is $\omega_A = 0.80$ rev/s? *Answer:* 6.6 m/s.

4 Kinetic Energy of Rotation and Moment of Inertia

A rotating rigid body consists of mass in motion, so it has kinetic energy. We can express this kinetic energy in terms of the body's angular velocity and a new quantity called moment of inertia, that we'll define shortly. To develop this relationship, we think of the body as made up of a lot of particles, with masses m_A, m_B, m_C, . . . , at distances r_A, r_B, r_C, . . . , from the axis of rotation. The particles don't necessarily all lie in the same plane, so we specify that each r is the perpendicular distance from the particle to the axis.

When a rigid body rotates about a fixed axis, the speed v of a typical particle is given by Equation 13, $v = r\omega$, where ω is the body's angular velocity in radians per second. Particle A has a perpendicular distance r_A from the axis of rotation and has a speed v_A given by $v_A = r_A\omega$. Different particles have different values of r and v, but ω is the same for all. (Otherwise the body wouldn't be rigid.) The kinetic energy K_A of particle A can be expressed as

$$K_A = \tfrac{1}{2}m_A v_A^2 = \tfrac{1}{2}m_A\left(r_A^2\omega^2\right).$$

The total kinetic energy K of the body is the sum of the kinetic energies of all its particles:

$$
\begin{aligned}
K &= \tfrac{1}{2}m_A v_A^2 + \tfrac{1}{2}m_B v_B^2 + \tfrac{1}{2}m_C v_C^2 + \cdots \\
&= \tfrac{1}{2}m_A\left(r_A^2\omega^2\right) + \tfrac{1}{2}m_B\left(r_B^2\omega^2\right) + \tfrac{1}{2}m_C\left(r_C^2\omega^2\right) + \cdots \\
&= \tfrac{1}{2}\left(m_A r_A^2 + m_B r_B^2 + m_C r_C^2 + \cdots\right)\omega^2.
\end{aligned}
$$

The quantity in parentheses in the last line, obtained by multiplying the mass of each particle by the square of its distance from the axis of rotation and adding all the products together, is called the **moment of inertia** of the body, denoted by I:

Definition of moment of inertia

A body's moment of inertia, I, describes how its mass is distributed in relation to an axis of rotation:

$$I = m_A r_A^2 + m_B r_B^2 + m_C r_C^2 + \cdots. \tag{16}$$

Unit: $kg \cdot m^2$

In terms of moment of inertia I, the kinetic energy K of a rotating rigid body is

$$K = \tfrac{1}{2}I\omega^2. \tag{17}$$

This is analogous to the expression $K = \tfrac{1}{2}mv^2$ for the kinetic energy of a particle; thus moment of inertia is analogous to mass, and angular velocity ω is analogous to speed v. This kinetic energy is not a new form of energy; it's the same physical quantity that we expressed as $\tfrac{1}{2}mv^2$ for a single particle. But Equation 17 is much easier to use when we have to find the kinetic energy of a rotating body.

▶ **Application** **Faster, not heavier.** One way to store energy is in a rotating disk, called a flywheel. Traditional flywheels, like the one shown here, are massive, carefully machined steel disks. The danger of such flywheels is that if the disk breaks, the parts fly off like cannonballs. As we've learned, however, the flywheel's kinetic energy is proportional to the *square* of its angular velocity: $K = \tfrac{1}{2}I\omega^2$. Therefore, a flywheel's angular velocity is more important than its mass (or moment of inertia) for storing energy. Engineers are now developing lightweight composite flywheels that rotate at very high speed. These flywheels break by unraveling, not by fragmenting into projectiles, so they pose less danger than traditional flywheels. Future generations of hybrid autos may use such flywheels in place of batteries to store energy.

MasteringPHYSICS

ActivPhysics 7.7: Rotational Kinematics

f8 Imaging/Hulton Archive/Getty Images

NOTE ► As in our previous discussion, ω *must* be measured in radians per second, not revolutions or degrees per second. ◄

EXAMPLE 6 **An abstract sculpture**

An artist is designing a part for a kinetic sculpture. The part consists of three massive disks connected by light supporting rods (Figure 16) that can be considered massless. Find the moment of inertia about an axis passing through disks B and C and the moment of inertia about an axis that passes through disk A and is perpendicular to the plane of that disk. If the object rotates about the axis through disk A with angular velocity 4.0 rad/s, find its kinetic energy.

▲ FIGURE 16

SOLUTION

SET UP For each calculation, we need to find the perpendicular distance from each disk to the axis of rotation. We'll model each disk as a point. For the axis passing through disks B and C, their distance from that axis is zero. Similarly, the distance of disk A from the axis passing through it is zero.

SOLVE The moment of inertia is defined as $I = m_A r_A^2 + m_B r_B^2 + m_C r_C^2$, where each r is measured from the chosen axis of rotation. For axis BC, disks B and C both lie *on* the axis $(r_B = r_C = 0)$, so neither contributes to the moment of inertia. Only disk A contributes; $m_A = 0.30$ kg, $r_A = 0.40$ m, and we find that

$$I_{BC} = m_A r_A^2 = (0.30 \text{ kg})(0.40 \text{ m})^2 = 0.048 \text{ kg} \cdot \text{m}^2.$$

For the axis through point A perpendicular to the plane of the diagram, disk A lies on the axis, so $r_A = 0$. The masses are the same as before, but now

$$r_B = 0.50 \text{ m} \qquad \text{and} \qquad r_C = 0.40 \text{ m}.$$

The moment of inertia for this axis is

$$\begin{aligned} I_A &= m_B r_B^2 + m_C r_C^2 \\ &= (0.10 \text{ kg})(0.50 \text{ m})^2 + (0.20 \text{ kg})(0.40 \text{ m})^2 \\ &= 0.057 \text{ kg} \cdot \text{m}^2. \end{aligned}$$

If the object rotates about this axis with angular velocity $\omega = 4.0$ rad/s, its kinetic energy is

$$K = \tfrac{1}{2} I_A \omega^2 = \tfrac{1}{2}(0.057 \text{ kg} \cdot \text{m}^2)(4.0 \text{ rad/s})^2 = 0.46 \text{ J}.$$

REFLECT The moment of inertia of an object depends on the location of the axis. We can't just say, "The moment of inertia of this body is 0.048 kg · m²." We have to say, "The moment of inertia of this object *with respect to axis BC* is 0.048 kg · m²." Note that whenever a particle lies on the axis of rotation, $r = 0$, so that particle does not contribute to the moment of inertia.

Practice Problem: Find the moment of inertia and the corresponding rotational kinetic energy if the sculpture rotates with angular velocity $\omega = 4.0$ rad/s about an axis through point B, perpendicular to the plane of the diagram. *Answers:* 0.093 kg · m², 0.74 J.

In Example 6, we represented the body as several point masses and we evaluated the sum in Equation 16 directly. When the body is a continuous distribution of matter, such as a solid cylinder or plate, we need methods of integral calculus to evaluate the sum. Table 2 gives moments of inertia for several familiar shapes in terms of the masses and dimensions. In the formulas in the table, note that dimensions measured parallel to the axis of rotation never appear in the expressions. For example, two solid cylinders with the same mass and radius have equal moments of inertia about their axes, even if their lengths are different.

NOTE ► You may be tempted to try to compute the moment of inertia of a body by assuming that all of its mass is concentrated at the center of mass and then multiplying the total mass by the square of the distance from the center of mass to the axis. Resist that temptation; it doesn't work! For example, when a uniform thin rod with length L and mass M rotates about an axis through one end and perpendicular to the rod, the moment of inertia is $I = ML^2/3$. (Table 2b). If we took the mass as concentrated at the center of the rod, a distance $L/2$ from the axis, we would obtain the *incorrect* result $I = M(L/2)^2 = ML^2/4$. ◄

TABLE 2   Moments of inertia for various bodies

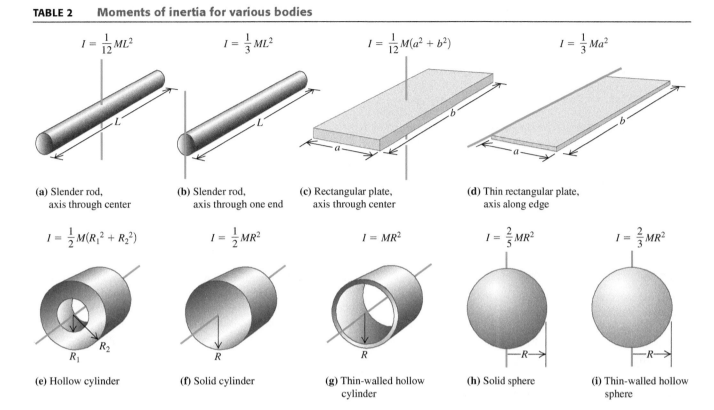

(a) Slender rod, axis through center
$$I = \frac{1}{12}ML^2$$

(b) Slender rod, axis through one end
$$I = \frac{1}{3}ML^2$$

(c) Rectangular plate, axis through center
$$I = \frac{1}{12}M(a^2 + b^2)$$

(d) Thin rectangular plate, axis along edge
$$I = \frac{1}{3}Ma^2$$

(e) Hollow cylinder
$$I = \frac{1}{2}M(R_1^2 + R_2^2)$$

(f) Solid cylinder
$$I = \frac{1}{2}MR^2$$

(g) Thin-walled hollow cylinder
$$I = MR^2$$

(h) Solid sphere
$$I = \frac{2}{5}MR^2$$

(i) Thin-walled hollow sphere
$$I = \frac{2}{3}MR^2$$

Now that we know how to calculate the kinetic energy of a rotating rigid body, we can apply our energy principles to rotational motion. Here are some points of strategy and some examples.

PROBLEM-SOLVING STRATEGY 1   Rotational energy

The idea is that the kinetic energy K is expressed in terms of the moment of inertia I and angular velocity ω of the body instead of its mass m and speed v. You can use work–energy relations and conservation of energy to find relations involving the position and motion of a rotating body.

The kinematic relations of Section 3, particularly Equations 13 and 14, are often useful, especially when a rotating cylindrical body functions as any sort of pulley. Examples 7 and 8 illustrate this point; in both, the angular velocity ω and the tangential component of velocity v_{tan} at the surface of the cylinder are related by $v_{\text{tan}} = r\omega$.

EXAMPLE 7   A cable unwinding from a winch

A light, flexible, nonstretching cable is wrapped several times around a winch drum—a solid cylinder with mass 50 kg and diameter 0.12 m that rotates about a stationary horizontal axis that turns in frictionless bearings (Figure 17). The free end of the cable is pulled with a constant force of magnitude 9.0 N for a distance of 2.0 m. It unwinds without slipping, turning the cylinder as it does so. If the cylinder is initially at rest, find its final angular velocity ω and the final speed v of the cable.

▲ FIGURE 17

Continued

SOLUTION

SET UP Figure 18 shows how we sketch this problem.

SOLVE No energy is lost in friction, so the final kinetic energy $K = \frac{1}{2}I\omega^2$ of the cylinder is equal to the work $W = Fs$ done by the force (of magnitude F, pulling through a distance s parallel to the force) acting on the cylinder. We need to use the mass and diameter of the cylinder to determine its moment of inertia, from Table 2. The work done on the cylinder by the force is

$$W = Fs = (9.0\,\text{N})(2.0\,\text{m}) = 18\,\text{J}.$$

From Table 2f, the moment of inertia for a solid cylinder is

$$I = \tfrac{1}{2}MR^2 = \tfrac{1}{2}(50\,\text{kg})(0.060\,\text{m})^2 = 0.090\,\text{kg}\cdot\text{m}^2.$$

The work–energy theorem $(W = \Delta K)$ then gives

$$18\,\text{J} = \tfrac{1}{2}(0.090\,\text{kg}\cdot\text{m}^2)\omega^2,$$
$$\omega = 20\,\text{rad/s}.$$

The final speed of the cable is equal to the final tangential speed v_{tan} of the cylinder, given by Equation 13:

$$v_{\text{tan}} = R\omega = (0.060\,\text{m})(20\,\text{rad/s}) = 1.2\,\text{m/s}.$$

▲ **FIGURE 18** Our sketch for this problem.

REFLECT The speed of the cable at each instant equals the tangential component of velocity of the cylinder because there is no slipping between cable and cylinder; if there were slipping, the winch wouldn't work.

Practice Problem: Suppose we replace the solid cylinder with a thin-walled cylinder having the same mass and radius. (a) How does the final speed of the cable differ from our result for the solid cylinder? (b) Does this mean that energy is not conserved? *Answers:* (a) $v_{\text{tan}} = 0.85\,\text{m/s}$; (b) no; kinetic energy is the same.

EXAMPLE 8 **Conservation of energy in a well**

In an old-fashioned well, a bucket is suspended over the well shaft by a winch and rope (Figure 19). The winch includes a solid cylinder with mass M and radius R and rotates without friction about a horizontal axis. The bucket (mass m) must descend a height h to reach the water; it is suspended by a rope of negligible mass that wraps around the winch. If the winch handle falls off, releasing the bucket to fall to the water, rotating the cylinder as it falls, find the speed v of the bucket and the angular velocity ω of the cylinder just before the bucket hits the water.

▶ **FIGURE 19**

SOLUTION

SET UP This problem is similar to Example 7, but it isn't identical, because both the rotating cylinder and the falling bucket have kinetic energy. Figure 20 shows our sketches. Since we will use conservation of energy, we draw before and after diagrams. We take the potential energy of the bucket–earth system as zero $(U = 0)$ when the bucket is at the water level. Then the bucket's initial potential energy is $U_i = mgh$ and the final value U_f is zero. The initial kinetic energy K_i is also zero. Just before impact, the bucket (mass m) has kinetic energy $\frac{1}{2}mv^2$ and the rotating cylin-

der has kinetic energy $\frac{1}{2}I\omega^2$. The speed v of the dropping bucket at any time is proportional to the angular velocity ω of the cylinder at that time: $v = r\omega$ (assuming that the rope unwinds without slipping). There are no nonconservative forces, so the initial and final total energies are equal.

SOLVE Conservation of energy tells us that $K_i + U_i = K_f + U_f$. (The cable does no net work; at the bucket end the force and displacement are in the same direction, and at the winch end they are in opposite directions. So the *total* work done by the two ends of the cable is zero.)

Continued

Just before the bucket hits the water, both it and the cylinder have kinetic energy. The total kinetic energy K_f at that time is

$$K_f = \tfrac{1}{2}mv^2 + \tfrac{1}{2}I\omega^2.$$

From Table 2, we find that the moment of inertia of the cylinder is $I = \tfrac{1}{2}MR^2$. Also, v and ω are related by $v = R\omega$, because the speed of mass m must equal the tangential speed of the outer surface of the cylinder. Using these relations and equating the initial and final total energies, we find that

$$K_i + U_i = K_f + U_f,$$

$$0 + mgh = \tfrac{1}{2}mv^2 + \tfrac{1}{2}\left(\tfrac{1}{2}MR^2\right)\left(\frac{v}{R}\right)^2 = \tfrac{1}{2}\left(m + \tfrac{1}{2}M\right)v^2,$$

$$v = \sqrt{\frac{2gh}{1 + M/2m}}.$$

The final angular velocity ω is obtained from $\omega = v/R$.

REFLECT We can check some particular cases. When M is much larger than m (i.e., a very heavy cylinder and a tiny bucket), v is very small, as we would expect. When M is much *smaller* than m (i.e., a very light cylinder and a heavy bucket), there isn't much to hold the bucket back, and its final speed is nearly equal to the speed of a body in free fall with initial height h, namely, $\sqrt{2gh}$. Does it surprise you that v doesn't depend on the radius of the cylinder?

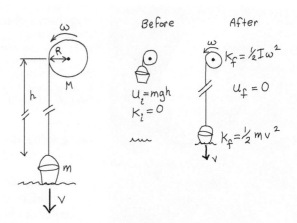

▲ **FIGURE 20** Our sketches for this problem.

Practice Problem: If the winch has the form of a thin cylindrical shell with mass M and radius R, derive expressions for the speed of the bucket and the angular velocity of the cylinder just before the bucket hits the water. *Answer:*

$$v = \sqrt{\frac{2gh}{1 + M/m}}.$$

Potential Energy of a Rigid Body

Later we'll need to know how to calculate the potential energy of a rigid body. In a uniform gravitational field, the gravitational potential energy is the same as though all the mass were concentrated at the center of mass of the body. Suppose we take the y axis vertically upward and define the potential energy to be zero at $y = 0$. Then, for an object with total mass M, the potential energy U is simply

$$U = Mgy_{cm}, \tag{18}$$

where y_{cm} is the vertical coordinate of the center of mass. As always, we need to define the origin of coordinates, where $y_{cm} = 0$ and $U = 0$.

To prove the equations, we again represent the body as a collection of mass elements $m_A, m_B, m_C, \cdots$. The weight of element m_A is $m_A g$, its potential energy is $m_A g y_A$, and the *total* potential energy is

$$U = m_A g y_A + m_B g y_B + m_C g y_C + \cdots.$$

But from the equations, which define the coordinates of the center of mass,

$$m_A y_A + m_B y_B + m_C y_C + \cdots = (m_A + m_B + m_C + \cdots)y_{cm} = My_{cm},$$

where $M = m_A + m_B + m_C + \cdots$ is the total mass. Combining this with the earlier expression for U, we obtain

$$U = Mgy_{cm},$$

in agreement with Equation 18.

ActivPhysics 7.12: Woman and Flywheel Elevator—Dynamics Approach
ActivPhysics 7.13: Rotoride—Energy Approach

5 Rotation about a Moving Axis

In the examples of rigid-body motion we've talked about so far, the axis of rotation has been stationary. Now let's consider some situations in which the axis moves. Familiar examples include a ball rolling down a hill or a yo-yo dropping

JPL/NASA

◀ **Application Spinning through space.** The moon rotates around its axis while orbiting the earth. Thus, it is an example of a body that rotates about a moving axis; its kinetic energy is the sum of its rotational energy and the translational energy of motion of its center of mass. But the earth also rotates on its axis, and the earth–moon system rotates while orbiting the sun, which itself moves as part of the Milky Way galaxy, which rotates while moving through space. Although these systems are not rigid bodies, in each case their kinetic energy has both rotational and translational terms.

This simple baton toss can be represented as a combination of **rotation** and **translation:**

Rotation about the center of mass, plus

Translation of the center of mass

▲ **FIGURE 21** The motion of a rigid body can always be represented as a combination of rotation about the center of mass and translation of the center of mass.

as the string unwinds. We can apply energy considerations to such problems, but we need two additional principles:

1. **Every possible motion of a rigid body can be represented as a combination of motion of the center of mass and rotation about an axis through the center of mass.**
2. **The total kinetic energy can always be represented as the sum of a part associated with motion of the center of mass, treated as a point, plus a part associated with rotation about an axis through the center of mass.**

Figure 21 illustrates the first of these principles. We'll often use the terms *translational* and *rotational* motion to refer to motion of the center of mass and rotational motion, respectively.

Suppose the rigid body has mass M and moment of inertia I_{cm} about the axis through the center of mass. If the center of mass has translational motion with velocity of magnitude v_{cm}, and the object rotates with angular velocity ω about this axis, the total kinetic energy K_{total} is given by

$$K_{total} = \tfrac{1}{2}Mv_{cm}^2 + \tfrac{1}{2}I_{cm}\omega^2. \tag{19}$$

We'll omit detailed derivation of this relationship and simply remark that it looks reasonable and that it can be proved rigorously. We'll often refer to the two terms in Equation 19 as *translational kinetic energy* ($K_{trans} = \tfrac{1}{2}Mv_{cm}^2$, associated with motion of the center of mass) and *rotational kinetic energy* ($K_{rot} = \tfrac{1}{2}I_{cm}\omega^2$, associated with rotation about an axis through the center of mass). With the help of Equation 19, we can apply conservation of energy to many problems involving rigid bodies whose axis of rotation moves. We'll continue to assume, however, that the *direction* of the axis of rotation doesn't change.

NOTE ▶ When applying Equation 19, we *must* use the moment of inertia about the axis through the center of mass; otherwise this relationship isn't applicable.

Conceptual Analysis 4

Racing canned food

A can of dog food (with fairly solid contents) and a can of chicken broth are released simultaneously to roll down an inclined plane. The two cans have the same diameter and the same mass. Which can (if either) reaches the bottom of the plane first?

A. The dog food.
B. The chicken broth.
C. They arrive simultaneously.

SOLUTION Because the equal masses roll down from the same height, the decrease in gravitational potential energy U_{grav} is the same for both cans. This energy is converted to kinetic energy;

some of it becomes *translational* kinetic energy K_{trans} (energy of motion of the center of mass), and some becomes *rotational* kinetic energy K_{rot}. Conservation of energy gives $U_{grav,i} = K_{trans,f} + K_{rot,f}$. Because both cans have the same $U_{grav,i}$, the can with the smaller $K_{rot,f}$ will have the larger $K_{trans,f}$, and therefore the larger value of $\tfrac{1}{2}mv^2$ and of v. The can with the larger v wins the race. Both cans have the same mass, but much of the fluid chicken broth does not rotate—mostly just the can rotates—and this results in a smaller K_{rot} for the chicken broth, a larger K_{trans}, and therefore a larger v. Choice B is correct; the chicken broth wins the race to the bottom of the slope. (We've neglected the fact that some mechanical energy may be dissipated by the internal motion of the viscous chicken broth.)

EXAMPLE 9   A primitive yo-yo

Figure 22 shows a primitive (and not very practical) yo-yo in the form of a solid disk with radius R and total mass M. It is released from rest, the supporting hand is stationary, and the string unwinds without slipping. Find an expression for the speed v_{cm} of the center of mass of the solid cylinder after it has dropped a distance h.

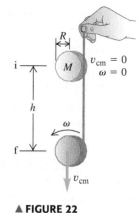

▲ FIGURE 22

SOLUTION

SET UP We take the potential energy to be zero at a distance h below the starting point. Then the initial and final potential energies are $U_i = Mgh$ and $U_f = 0$. The initial kinetic energy K_i is zero, and the final kinetic energy K_f is given by Equation 19:

$$K_f = \tfrac{1}{2}Mv_{cm}^2 + \tfrac{1}{2}I_{cm}\omega^2.$$

There are no nonconservative forces, so the total energy is conserved:

$$K_i + U_i = K_f + U_f.$$

SOLVE From conservation of energy,

$$0 + Mgh = \tfrac{1}{2}Mv_{cm}^2 + \tfrac{1}{2}I_{cm}\omega^2.$$

Both v_{cm} and ω are unknown; but if we assume that the string unwinds without slipping, these two quantities are *proportional*. When the cylinder has rotated through one complete revolution $(2\pi$ radians$)$, the string has unwound a distance equal to the circumference of the cylinder $(2\pi R)$. Thus the distance traveled during any time interval Δt is R times the *angular* displace-

ment during that interval. It follows that $v_{cm} = R\omega$. Also, from Table 2, $I_{cm} = \tfrac{1}{2}MR^2$, so conservation of energy gives

$$Mgh = \tfrac{1}{2}Mv_{cm}^2 + \tfrac{1}{2}\left(\tfrac{1}{2}MR^2\right)\left(\frac{v_{cm}}{R}\right)^2 = \tfrac{3}{4}Mv_{cm}^2$$

and

$$v_{cm} = \sqrt{\tfrac{4}{3}gh}.$$

REFLECT If the object had fallen freely from a height h, its final speed would be $v_{cm} = \sqrt{2gh}$. The actual speed is less than this, because the same total energy has to be shared by the translational (center-of-mass) motion and the rotational motion. Note that both the mass and radius of the object cancel out, so the results would be the same for a long, skinny solid cylinder and a thin solid disk (but not for a cylindrical shell or a doughnut-shaped disk).

Practice Problem: Carry out the same analysis for a thin-walled cylinder. *Answer:* $v_{cm} = \sqrt{gh}$.

EXAMPLE 10   Race of the rolling objects

In a lecture demonstration, an instructor "races" various round objects by releasing them from rest at the top of an inclined plane and then rolling them down the plane (Figure 23). The students guess (and sometimes bet on) which object will win. Suppose a thin-walled hollow cylinder (Table 2g) and a solid cylinder (Table 2f) race. Which one would you bet on to win the race?

▲ FIGURE 23

SOLUTION

SET UP We use conservation of energy, ignoring rolling friction and air drag. If the objects roll without slipping, then no work is done by friction and the total energy is conserved. Each object starts from rest at the top of an incline with height h, so $K_i = 0$, $U_i = mgh$, and $U_f = 0$ for each. From Equation 19,

$$K_f = \tfrac{1}{2}mv_{cm}^2 + \tfrac{1}{2}I_{cm}\omega^2.$$

Both v_{cm} and ω are unknown; but if we assume that the objects roll without slipping, these two quantities are *proportional*. When an object with radius R has rotated through one complete revolution $(2\pi$ radians$)$, it has rolled a distance equal to its circumference $(2\pi R)$. Thus the distance traveled during any time interval Δt is R times the *angular* displacement during that interval, and it follows that $v_{cm} = R\omega$. (The geometry of this situation is identical to that in Example 9, in which the speed of the center-of-mass of the yo-yo is proportional to its angular velocity.)

Continued

SOLVE For the thin-walled cylindrical shell, Table 2g gives $I_{shell} = MR^2$. Conservation of energy then results in

$$0 + Mgh = \tfrac{1}{2}Mv_{cm}^2 + \tfrac{1}{2}I_{shell}\omega^2 = \tfrac{1}{2}Mv_{cm}^2 + \tfrac{1}{2}(MR^2)(v_{cm}/R)^2$$
$$= \tfrac{1}{2}Mv_{cm}^2 + \tfrac{1}{2}Mv_{cm}^2 = Mv_{cm}^2,$$
$$v_{cm} = \sqrt{gh}.$$

For the solid cylinder, Table 2f gives $I_{solid} = \tfrac{1}{2}MR^2$, and the corresponding equations are

$$0 + Mgh = \tfrac{1}{2}Mv_{cm}^2 + \tfrac{1}{2}I_{solid}\omega^2 = \tfrac{1}{2}Mv_{cm}^2 + \tfrac{1}{2}(\tfrac{1}{2}MR^2)(v_{cm}/R)^2$$
$$= \tfrac{1}{2}Mv_{cm}^2 + \tfrac{1}{4}Mv_{cm}^2 = \tfrac{3}{4}Mv_{cm}^2,$$
$$v_{cm} = \sqrt{\tfrac{4}{3}gh}.$$

We see that the solid cylinder's speed at the bottom of the hill is greater than that of the hollow cylinder by a factor of $\sqrt{\tfrac{4}{3}}$, so the solid cylinder wins the race.

We can generalize this result in an elegant way. We note that the moments of inertia of all the round objects in Table 2 (about axes through their centers of mass) can be expressed as $I_{cm} = \beta MR^2$, where β is a pure number between 0 and 1 that depends on the shape of the body. For a thin-walled hollow cylinder, $\beta = 1$; for a solid cylinder, $\beta = \tfrac{1}{2}$; and so on. From conservation of energy,

$$0 + Mgh = \tfrac{1}{2}Mv_{cm}^2 + \tfrac{1}{2}I\omega^2 = \tfrac{1}{2}Mv_{cm}^2 + \tfrac{1}{2}(\beta MR^2)(v_{cm}/R)^2$$
$$= \tfrac{1}{2}(1 + \beta)Mv_{cm}^2,$$
$$v_{cm} = \sqrt{\frac{2gh}{1 + \beta}}.$$

REFLECT This is a fairly amazing result; the final speed of the center of mass doesn't depend on either the mass M of the body or its radius R. All uniform solid cylinders have the same speed at the bottom, even if their masses and radii are different, because they have the same β. All solid spheres have the same speed, and so on. The smaller the value of β, the faster the body is moving at the bottom (and at any point on the way down). Small-β bodies always beat large-β bodies because they have less kinetic energy tied up in rotation and have more available for translation. For the hollow cylinder $(\beta = 1)$, the translational and rotational energies at any point are equal, but for the solid cylinder $(\beta = \tfrac{1}{2})$, the rotational energy at any point is half the translational energy. Reading the values of β from Table 2, we see that the order of finish is as follows: any solid sphere, any solid cylinder, any thin spherical shell, and any thin cylindrical shell.

Practice Problem: (a) Find the ratio of the final speeds for a solid sphere and a solid cylinder. (b) Why aren't the expressions for moments of inertia of these two objects the same? *Answers:* (a) 1.035; (b) the sphere has a greater fraction of its mass close to the axis than the cylinder has.

CHAPTER SUMMARY

Angular Velocity and Angular Acceleration

(Section 1) When a rigid body rotates about a stationary axis, its position is described by an angular coordinate θ. When an object turns through an angle $\Delta\theta$ in a time interval Δt, the average angular velocity ω_{av} is defined as $\omega_{av} = \Delta\theta/\Delta t$ (Equation 2). The instantaneous angular velocity ω is

$$\omega = \lim_{\Delta t \to 0} \frac{\Delta\theta}{\Delta t}. \tag{3}$$

If the angular velocity changes by an amount $\Delta\omega$ in a time interval Δt, the average angular acceleration α_{av} is defined as $\alpha_{av} = \Delta\omega/\Delta t$ (Equation 5), and the instantaneous angular velocity α is

$$\alpha = \lim_{\Delta t \to 0} \frac{\Delta\omega}{\Delta t}. \tag{6}$$

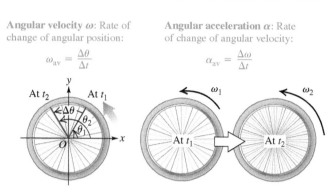

Angular velocity ω: Rate of change of angular position:

$$\omega_{av} = \frac{\Delta\theta}{\Delta t}$$

Angular acceleration α: Rate of change of angular velocity:

$$\alpha_{av} = \frac{\Delta\omega}{\Delta t}$$

Rotation with Constant Angular Acceleration

(Section 2) When a body rotates with constant angular acceleration, the angular position, velocity, and acceleration are related by the equations: $\omega = \omega_0 + \alpha t$ (Equation 7), $\theta - \theta_0 = \frac{1}{2}(\omega_0 + \omega)t$ (Equation 10), $\theta = \theta_0 + \omega_0 t + \frac{1}{2}\alpha t^2$ (Equation 11), and $\omega^2 = \omega_0^2 + 2\alpha(\theta - \theta_0)$ (Equation 12), where θ_0 and ω_0 are the initial values of the angular position and angular velocity, respectively, of the body.

Relationship between Linear and Angular Quantities

(Section 3) A particle in a rotating rigid body at a distance r from the axis of rotation has a tangential speed v given by $v = r\omega$ (Equation 13). The particle's acceleration $\vec{a}$ has a tangential component $a_{tan} = r\alpha$ (Equation 14) and a radial component

$$a_{rad} = \frac{v^2}{r} = \omega^2 r. \tag{15}$$

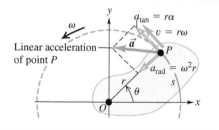

Linear acceleration of point P

$$a_{tan} = r\alpha$$
$$v = r\omega$$
$$a_{rad} = \omega^2 r$$

Kinetic Energy of Rotation and Moment of Inertia

(Section 4) The moment of inertia I of a body with respect to a given axis is defined as $I = m_A r_A^2 + m_B r_B^2 + m_C r_C^2 + \cdots$ (Equation 16) where r_A is the distance of mass element m_A from the axis of rotation, and so on. The kinetic energy of a rigid body rotating about a stationary axis is given by $K = \frac{1}{2}I\omega^2$ (Equation 17). In a uniform gravitational field, the gravitational potential energy of a rigid body with center of mass at a distance y_{cm} above the reference level (where $U = 0$) is $U = Mgy_{cm}$ (Equation 18).

Rotation about a Moving Axis

(Section 5) When a rigid body undergoes both motion of its center of mass and rotation about an axis through the center of mass, the total kinetic energy is given by

$$K_{total} = \frac{1}{2}Mv_{cm}^2 + \frac{1}{2}I_{cm}\omega^2. \tag{19}$$

$$K_{total} = \frac{1}{2}Mv_{cm}^2 + \frac{1}{2}I_{cm}\omega^2$$

Rotational Motion: Problem Set

For instructor-assigned homework, go to www.masteringphysics.com

Conceptual Questions

1. What is the difference between the tangential acceleration and the radial acceleration of a point on a rotating object?
2. A flywheel rotates with constant angular velocity. Does a point on its rim have tangential acceleration? radial acceleration? Are these accelerations constant in magnitude? in direction?
3. A flywheel rotates with constant angular acceleration. Does a point on its rim have tangential acceleration? radial acceleration? Are these accelerations constant in magnitude? in direction?
4. How might you experimentally determine a moment of inertia of an *irregularly* shaped body by using materials from a typical introductory physics laboratory (such as pulleys, turntables, timers, etc.)?
5. A uniform ring of mass M and radius R and a point mass M a distance R from the axis of the ring both rotate about that axis, which is perpendicular to the ring at its center. Both objects have the same formula for their moment of inertia, $I = MR^2$, about this axis. (a) Is there a good physical reason that they have the same formula? (b) If the ring were replaced by a solid uniform disk of mass M and radius R, would the disk and point mass then have the same moment-of-inertia formula? Why or why not?
6. What is the purpose of the spin cycle of a washing machine? Explain in terms of acceleration components.
7. According to experienced riders, you make a bike less tiring to ride if you reduce its weight in the wheels rather than in the frame. Why is this so?
8. A solid ball, a solid cylinder, and a hollow cylinder roll down a slope. Which one reaches the bottom first? last? Does it matter whether the radii are the same? What about the masses?
9. Experienced cooks can tell whether an egg is raw or hard boiled by rolling it down a slope (and taking care to catch it at the bottom). How is this possible? Which type of egg should reach the bottom of the slope first?
10. Part of the kinetic energy of a moving automobile is in the rotational motion of its wheels. When the brakes are applied hard on an icy street, the wheels lock and the car starts to slide. What becomes of the rotational kinetic energy?
11. Can you think of a body that has the same moment of inertia for all possible axes? If so, give an example, and if not, explain why this is not possible. Can you think of a body that has the same moment of inertia for all axes passing through a certain point? If so, give an example and indicate where the point is located.
12. A client has come to you with two metal balls of the same size and mass. He thinks that one might be solid and the other might be hollow inside. By rolling both balls down a slope, how could you tell which one is hollow and which is solid?
13. In what ways does a jogger's body have *rotational* kinetic energy?
14. As a car of mass M travels with speed V, its kinetic energy is $\frac{1}{2}MV^2$. But this is not the whole story. What additional contributions are there to this car's kinetic energy from *internal* motion, both translational and rotational?
15. If a ball rolls down an *irregularly* shaped hill without slipping, it is very easy to find its speed at the bottom by using conservation of energy. Why could we not just as easily use Newton's second law to find the speed?

Multiple-Choice Problems

1. When a wheel turns through one complete rotation, the angle (in *radians*) that it has turned through is closest to
   A. 57.   B. 6.   C. 360.
2. Two points are on a disk that rotates about an axis perpendicular to the plane of the disk at its center. Point B is 3 times as far from the axis as point A. If the linear speed of point B is V, then the linear speed of point A is
   A. $9V$.   B. $3V$.   C. V.
   D. $\dfrac{V}{3}$.   E. $\dfrac{V}{9}$.
3. A bicycle wheel rotating at a rate of 12 rad/s begins to accelerate at a rate of 2 rad/s^2. After 5 seconds the rate of rotation will be
   A. 2 rad/s   B. 10 rad/s   C. 17 rad/s   D. 22 rad/s
4. You are designing a flywheel to store large amounts of kinetic energy. Which one of the following uniform shapes will be the *most* effective for storing the greatest amount of kinetic energy if all the objects have the same mass and same angular velocity?
   A. A solid sphere of diameter D rotating about a diameter.
   B. A solid cylinder of diameter D rotating about an axis perpendicular to each face through its center.
   C. A thin-walled hollow cylinder of diameter D rotating about an axis perpendicular to the plane of the circular face at its center.
   D. A solid thin bar of length D rotating about an axis perpendicular to it at its center.

5. Four uniform objects having the same mass and diameter are released simultaneously from rest at the same distance above the bottom of a hill and roll down without slipping. The objects are a solid sphere, a solid cylinder, a hollow cylinder, and a thin-walled hollow cylinder, as illustrated in Table 1 at the end of this problem set. Which of these objects will be the first one to reach the bottom of the hill?
   A. The solid sphere
   B. The solid cylinder
   C. The hollow cylinder
   D. The thin-walled hollow cylinder

6. Which of the objects in question 5 will be the last one to reach the bottom of the hill?
   A. The solid sphere
   B. The solid cylinder
   C. The hollow cylinder
   D. The thin-walled hollow cylinder

7. For the objects in question 5, which of the following statements are correct? (There may be more than one correct choice.)
   A. All these objects have the same forward speed at the bottom of the hill.
   B. All these objects have the same kinetic energy at the bottom of the hill.
   C. All these objects have the same rotational kinetic energy at the bottom of the hill.
   D. All these objects have the same angular velocity at the bottom of the hill.

8. Two uniform solid spheres of the same size, but different mass, are released from rest simultaneously at the same height on a hill and roll to the bottom without slipping. Which of the following statements about these spheres are true? (There may be more than one correct choice.)
   A. Both spheres reach the bottom at the same time.
   B. The heavier sphere reaches the bottom ahead of the lighter one.
   C. Both spheres arrive at the bottom with the same forward speed.
   D. Both spheres arrive at the bottom with the same total kinetic energy.

9. A disk starts from rest and has a constant angular acceleration. If it takes time T to make its first revolution, in time $2T$ (starting from rest) the disk will make
   A. $\sqrt{2}$ revolutions.
   B. 2 revolutions.
   C. 4 revolutions.
   D. 8 revolutions.

10. Two unequal masses m and $2m$ are attached to a thin bar of negligible mass that rotates about an axis perpendicular to the bar. When m is a distance $2d$ from the axis and $2m$ is a distance d from the axis, the moment of inertia of this combination is I. If the masses are now interchanged, the moment of inertia will be
   A. $\frac{2}{3}I$.   B. I.   C. $\frac{3}{2}I$.
   D. $2I$.   E. $4I$.

11. A thin uniform bar has a moment of inertia I about an axis perpendicular to it through its center. If both the mass and length of this bar are doubled, its moment of inertia about the same axis will be
   A. $2I$.   B. $4I$.
   C. $8I$.   D. $16I$.

12. Two small objects of equal weight are attached to the ends of a thin weightless bar that spins about an axis perpendicular to the bar at its center. Each mass is a distance d from the axis of rotation. The system spins at a rate so that its kinetic energy is K. If both masses are now moved closer in so that each is $d/2$ from the rotation axis, while the angular velocity does not change, the kinetic energy of the system will be
   A. $\frac{1}{4}K$.   B. $\frac{1}{2}K$.
   C. $2K$.   D. $4K$.

13. A disk starts from rest and rotates with constant angular acceleration. If the angular velocity is ω at the end of the first two revolutions, then at the end of the first eight revolutions it will be
   A. $\sqrt{2}\omega$.   B. 2ω.
   C. 4ω.   D. 16ω.

14. Two identical merry-go-rounds are rotating at the same speed. One is crowded with riding children; the other is nearly empty. If both merry-go-rounds cut off their motors at the same time and coast to a stop, slowed only by friction (which you can assume is the same for both merry-go-rounds), which will take longer to stop?
   A. The crowded merry-go-round
   B. The empty merry-go-round
   C. The same time for both.

15. A solid sphere and a hollow sphere, both uniform and having the same mass and radius, are released from rest at the same height on a ramp. If they roll down the ramp without slipping, which one will have the greater forward velocity at the bottom of the ramp?
   A. The solid sphere
   B. The hollow sphere
   C. Both will have the same forward velocity.

16. A uniform ball rolls without slipping toward a hill with a forward speed V. In which case will this ball go farther up the hill?
   A. There is enough friction on the hill to prevent slipping of the ball.
   B. The hill is frictionless.
   C. The ball will reach the same height in both cases, since it has the same initial kinetic energy in each case.

Problems

1 Angular Velocity and Angular Acceleration

1. ● A flexible straight wire 75.0 cm long is bent into the arc of a circle of radius 2.50 m. What angle (in radians and degrees) will this arc subtend at the center of the circle?

2. ● (a) What angle in radians is subtended by an arc 1.50 m in length on the circumference of a circle of radius 2.50 m? What is this angle in degrees? (b) An arc 14.0 cm in length on the circumference of a circle subtends an angle of 128°. What is the radius of the circle? (c) The angle between two radii of a circle with radius 1.50 m is 0.700 rad. What length of arc is intercepted on the circumference of the circle by the two radii?

3. ● (a) Calculate the angular velocity (in rad/s) of the second, minute, and hour hands on a wall clock. (b) What is the period of each of these hands?

4. ● The once-popular LP (long-play) records were 12 in. in diameter and turned at a constant $33\frac{1}{3}$ rpm. Find (a) the angular speed of the LP in rad/s and (b) its period in seconds.

5. • If a wheel 212 cm in diameter takes 2.25 s for each revolution, find its (a) period and (b) angular speed in rad/s.

6. • Find the angular velocity, in rad/s, of (a) the earth due to its daily spin on its axis, (b) the earth due to its yearly motion around the sun, and (c) our moon due to its monthly motion around the earth. Consult Appendix E as needed.

7. • A laser beam aimed from the earth is swept across the face of the moon. (a) If the beam is rotated at an angular velocity of 1.50×10^{-3} rad/s, at what speed does the laser light move across the moon's surface? (b) If the diameter of the laser spot on the moon is 6.00 km, what is the angle of divergence of the laser beam?

8. • **Communications satellites.** Communications satellites are placed in orbits so that they always remain above the same point of the earth's surface. (a) What must be the period of such a satellite? (b) What is its angular velocity in rad/s?

9. • An airplane propeller is rotating at 1900 rpm. (a) Compute the propeller's angular velocity in rad/s. (b) How many seconds does it take for the propeller to turn through 35°? (c) If the propeller were turning at 18 rad/s, at how many rpm would it be turning? (d) What is the period (in seconds) of this propeller?

10. •• A wall clock on Planet X has two hands that are aligned at midnight and turn in the same direction at uniform rates, one at 0.0425 rad/s and the other at 0.0163 rad/s. At how many seconds after midnight are these hands (a) first aligned and (b) next aligned?

2 Rotation with Constant Angular Acceleration

11. • A turntable that spins at a constant 78.0 rpm takes 3.50 s to reach this angular speed after it is turned on. Find (a) its angular acceleration (in rad/s²), assuming it to be constant, and (b) the number of degrees it turns through while speeding up.

12. • When the power is turned off on a turntable spinning at 78.0 rpm, you find that it takes 10.5 revolutions for it to stop while slowing down at a uniform rate. (a) What is the angular acceleration (in rad/s²) of this turntable? (b) How long does it take to stop after the power is turned off?

13. • **DVDs.** The angular speed of digital video discs (DVDs) varies with whether the inner or outer part of the disc is being read. (CDs function in the same way.) Over a 133 min playing time, the angular speed varies from 570 rpm to 1600 rpm. Assuming it to be constant, what is the angular acceleration (in rad/s²) of such a DVD?

14. • A circular saw blade 0.200 m in diameter starts from rest. In 6.00 s, it reaches an angular velocity of 140 rad/s with constant angular acceleration. Find the angular acceleration and the angle through which the blade has turned in this time.

15. • A wheel turns with a constant angular acceleration of 0.640 rad/s². (a) How much time does it take to reach an angular velocity of 8.00 rad/s, starting from rest? (b) Through how many revolutions does the wheel turn in this interval?

16. • An electric fan is turned off, and its angular velocity decreases uniformly from 500.0 rev/min to 200.0 rev/min in 4.00 s. (a) Find the angular acceleration in rev/s² and the number of revolutions made by the motor in the 4.00 s interval. (b) How many more seconds are required for the fan to come to rest if the angular acceleration remains constant at the value calculated in part (a)?

17. •• A flywheel in a motor is spinning at 500.0 rpm when a power failure suddenly occurs. The flywheel has mass 40.0 kg and diameter 75.0 cm. The power is off for 30.0 s, and during this time the flywheel slows down uniformly due to friction in its axle bearings. During the time the power is off, the flywheel makes 200.0 complete revolutions. (a) At what rate is the flywheel spinning when the power comes back on? (b) How long after the beginning of the power failure would it have taken the flywheel to stop if the power had not come back on, and how many revolutions would the wheel have made during this time?

18. •• A flywheel having constant angular acceleration requires 4.00 s to rotate through 162 rad. Its angular velocity at the end of this time is 108 rad/s. Find (a) the angular velocity at the beginning of the 4.00 s interval; (b) the angular acceleration of the flywheel.

19. •• Emilie's potter's wheel rotates with a constant 2.25 rad/s² angular acceleration. After 4.00 s, the wheel has rotated through an angle of 60.0 rad. What was the angular velocity of the wheel at the beginning of the 4.00 s interval?

20. •• Derive Eq. 12 by combining Eqs. 7 and 11 to eliminate t.

3 Relationship between Linear and Angular Quantities

21. • A car is traveling at a speed of 63 mi/h on a freeway. If its tires have diameter 24.0 in and are rolling without sliding or slipping, what is their angular velocity?

22. • (a) A cylinder 0.150 m in diameter rotates in a lathe at 620 rpm. What is the tangential speed of the surface of the cylinder? (b) The proper tangential speed for machining cast iron is about 0.600 m/s. At how many revolutions per minute should a piece of stock 0.0800 m in diameter be rotated in a lathe to produce this tangential speed?

23. • A wheel rotates with a constant angular velocity of 6.00 rad/s. (a) Compute the radial acceleration of a point 0.500 m from the axis, using the relation $a_{rad} = \omega^2 r$. (b) Find the tangential speed of the point, and compute its radial acceleration from the relation $a_{rad} = v^2/r$.

24. • **Ultracentrifuge.** Find the required angular speed (in rpm) of an ultracentrifuge for the radial acceleration of a point 2.50 cm from the axis to equal 400,000g.

25. •• **Exercise!** An exercise bike that you pedal in place has a bicycle chain connecting the wheel you pedal to the large wheel in front, as shown in Figure 24. For the wheel *diameters* shown, how many rpm must you produce to turn the large wheel at 75 rpm?

▲ **FIGURE 24** Problem 25.

26. •• A flywheel with a radius of 0.300 m starts from rest and accelerates with a constant angular acceleration of 0.600 rad/s². Compute the magnitude of the tangential acceleration, the radial acceleration, and the resultant acceleration of a point on its rim (a) at the start, (b) after it has turned through 60.0°, and (c) after it has turned through 120.0°.

27. • **Electric drill.** According to the shop manual, when drilling a 12.7-mm-diameter hole in wood, plastic, or aluminum, a drill should have a speed of 1250 rev/min. For a 12.7-mm-diameter drill bit turning at a constant 1250 rev/min, find (a) the maximum linear speed of any part of the bit and (b) the maximum radial acceleration of any part of the bit.

28. •• **Dental hygiene.** Electric toothbrushes
BIO can be effective in removing dental plaque. One model consists of a head 1.1 cm in diameter that rotates back and forth through a 70.0° angle 7600 times per minute. The rim of the head contains a thin row of bristles. (See Figure 25.) (a) What is the average angular speed in each direction of the rotating head, in rad/s? (b) What is the average linear speed in each direction of the bristles

▲ **FIGURE 25** Problem 28.

against the teeth? (c) Using your own observations, what is the approximate speed of the bristles against your teeth when you brush by hand with an *ordinary* toothbrush?

29. •• The spin cycles of a washing machine have two angular speeds, 423 rev/min and 640 rev/min. The internal diameter of the drum is 0.470 m. (a) What is the ratio of the maximum radial force on the laundry for the higher angular speed to that for the lower speed? (b) What is the ratio of the maximum tangential speed of the laundry for the higher angular speed to that for the lower speed? (c) Find the laundry's maximum tangential speed and the maximum radial acceleration, in terms of g.

4 Kinetic Energy of Rotation and Moment of Inertia

30. • A twirler's baton is made of a slender metal cylinder of mass M and length L. Each end has a rubber cap of mass m, and you can accurately treat each cap as a particle in this problem. Find the total moment of inertia of the baton about the usual twirling axis (perpendicular to the baton through its center).

31. •• A thin uniform bar has two small balls glued to its ends. The bar is 2.00 m long and has mass 4.00 kg, while the balls each have mass 0.500 kg and can be treated as point masses. Find the moment of inertia of this combination about each of the following axes: (a) an axis perpendicular to the bar through its center; (b) an axis perpendicular to the bar through one of the balls; (c) an axis parallel to the bar through both balls.

32. • Use the formulas of Table 1 to find the moment of inertia about each of the following axes for a rod that is 0.300 cm in diameter and 1.50 m long, with a mass of 0.0420 kg: (a) about an axis perpendicular to the rod and passing through its center; (b) about an axis perpendicular to the rod and passing through one end; and (c) about an axis along the length of the rod.

33. •• Four small 0.200 kg spheres, each of which you can regard as a point mass, are arranged in a square 0.400 m on a side and

connected by light rods. (See Figure 26.) Find the moment of inertia of the system about an axis (a) through the center of the square, perpendicular to its plane at point O; (b) along the line AB; and (c) along the line CD.

▲ **FIGURE 26** Problem 33.

34. •• **Compound objects.** Moment of inertia is a scalar. Therefore, if several objects are connected together, the moment of inertia of this compound object is simply the scalar (algebraic) sum of the moments of inertia of each of the component objects. Use this principle to answer each of the following questions about the moment of inertia of compound objects: (a) A thin uniform 2.50 kg bar 1.50 m long has a small 1.25 kg mass glued to each end. What is the moment of inertia of this object about an axis perpendicular to the bar through its center? (b) What is the moment of inertia of the object in part (a) about an axis perpendicular to the bar at one end? (c) A 725 g metal wire is bent into the shape of a hoop 60.0 cm in diameter. Six wire spokes, each of mass 112 g, are added from the center of the hoop to the rim. What is the moment of inertia of this object about an axis perpendicular to it through its center?

35. •• **Energy from the Moon?** Suppose that sometime in the future we decide to tap the moon's rotational energy for use on earth. You may need to know that the moon spins on its axis once every 27.3 days. Assume that the moon is uniform throughout. (a) How much total energy could we get from the moon's rotation? (b) The world presently uses about 5.0 × 10²⁰ J of energy per year. If in the future the world uses five times as much energy yearly, for how many years would the moon's rotation provide us energy? In light of your answer, does this seem like a cost-effective energy source in which to invest?

36. •• A wagon wheel is constructed as shown in Figure 27. The radius of the wheel is 0.300 m, and the rim has a mass of 1.40 kg. Each of the wheel's eight spokes, which come out from the center and are 0.300 m long, has a mass of 0.280 kg. What is the moment of inertia of the wheel about an axis through its center and perpendicular to the plane of the wheel?

▲ **FIGURE 27** Problem 36.

37. •• You need to design an industrial turntable that is 60.0 cm in diameter and has a kinetic energy of 0.250 J when turning at 45.0 rpm (rev/min). (a) What must

be the moment of inertia of the turntable about the rotation axis? (b) If your workshop makes this turntable in the shape of a uniform solid disk, what must be its mass?

38. ● A grinding wheel in the shape of a solid disk is 0.200 m in diameter and has a mass of 3.00 kg. The wheel is rotating at 2200 rpm about an axis through its center. (a) What is its kinetic energy? (b) How far would it have to drop in free fall to acquire the same amount of kinetic energy?

39. ●● The flywheel of a gasoline engine is required to give up 500 J of kinetic energy while its angular velocity decreases from 650 rev/min to 520 rev/min. What moment of inertia is required?

40. ●● An airplane propeller is 2.08 m in length (from tip to tip) with mass 117 kg and is rotating at 2400 rpm (rev/min) about an axis through its center. You can model the propeller as a slender rod. (a) What is its rotational kinetic energy? (b) Suppose that, due to weight constraints, you had to reduce the propeller's mass to 75.0% of its original mass, but you still needed to keep the same size and kinetic energy. What would its angular speed have to be, in rpm?

41. ●● **Storing energy in flywheels.** It has been suggested that we should use our power plants to generate energy in the off-hours (such as late at night) and store it for use during the day. One idea put forward is to store the energy in large flywheels. Suppose we want to build such a flywheel in the shape of a hollow cylinder of inner radius 0.500 m and outer radius 1.50 m, using concrete of density $2.20 \times 10^3 \text{ kg/m}^3$. (a) If, for stability, such a heavy flywheel is limited to 1.75 second for each revolution and has negligible friction at its axle, what must be its length to store 2.5 MJ of energy in its rotational motion? (b) Suppose that by strengthening the frame you could safely double the flywheel's rate of spin. What length of flywheel would you need in that case? (Solve this part *without* reworking the entire problem!)

42. ●● A light string is wrapped around the outer rim of a solid uniform cylinder of diameter 75.0 cm that can rotate without friction about an axle through its center. A 3.00 kg stone is tied to the free end of the string, as shown in Figure 28. When the system is released from rest, you determine that the stone reaches a speed of 3.50 m/s after having fallen 2.50 m. What is the mass of the cylinder?

▲ **FIGURE 28** Problem 42.

43. ●● A solid uniform 3.25 kg cylinder, 65.0 cm in diameter and 12.4 cm long, is connected to a 1.50 kg weight over two massless frictionless pulleys as shown in Figure 29. The cylinder is free to rotate about an axle through its center perpendicular to its circular faces, and the system is released from rest. (a) How far must the 1.50 kg weight fall before it reaches a speed of 2.50 m/s? (b) How fast is the cylinder turning at this instant?

3.25 kg

1.50 kg

▲ **FIGURE 29** Problem 43.

44. ●● A compound disk of outside diameter 140.0 cm is made up of a uniform solid disk of radius 50.0 cm and area density 3.00 g/cm² surrounded by a concentric ring of inner radius 50.0 cm, outer radius 70.0 cm, and area density 2.00 g/cm². Find the moment of inertia of this object about an axis perpendicular to the plane of the object and passing through its center.

5 Rotation about a Moving Axis

45. ● **Gymnastics.** We can roughly model a gymnastic tumbler
BIO as a uniform solid cylinder of mass 75 kg and diameter 1.0 m. If this tumbler rolls forward at 0.50 rev/s, (a) how much total kinetic energy does he have and (b) what percent of his total kinetic energy is rotational?

46. ●● A bicycle racer is going downhill at 11.0 m/s when, to his horror, one of his 2.25 kg wheels comes off when he is 75.0 m above the foot of the hill. We can model the wheel as a thin-walled cylinder 85.0 cm in diameter and neglect the small mass of the spokes. (a) How fast is the wheel moving when it reaches the foot of the hill if it rolled without slipping all the way down? (b) How much total kinetic energy does the wheel have when it reaches the bottom of the hill?

47. ● A 2.20-kg hoop 1.20 m in diameter is rolling to the right without slipping on a horizontal floor at a steady 3.00 rad/s. (a) How fast is its center moving? (b) What is the total kinetic energy of the hoop?

48. ●● A solid uniform sphere and a uniform spherical shell, both having the same mass and radius, roll without slipping down a hill that rises at an angle θ above the horizontal. Both spheres start from rest at the same vertical height h. (a) How fast is each sphere moving when it reaches the bottom of the hill? (b) Which sphere will reach the bottom first, the hollow one or the solid one?

49. ●● A size-5 soccer ball of diameter 22.6 cm and mass 426 g rolls up a hill without slipping, reaching a maximum height of 5.00 m above the base of the hill. We can model this ball as a thin-walled hollow sphere. (a) At what rate was it rotating at

the base of the hill? (b) How much rotational kinetic energy did it then have?

50. •• A solid uniform marble and a block of ice, each with the same mass, start from rest at the same height H above the bottom of a hill and move down it. The marble rolls without slipping, but the ice slides without friction. (a) Find the speed of each of these objects when it reaches the bottom of the hill. (b) Which object is moving faster at the bottom, the ice or the marble? (c) Which object has more kinetic energy at the bottom, the ice or the marble?

51. •• What fraction of the total kinetic energy is rotational for the following objects rolling without slipping on a horizontal surface? (a) a uniform solid cylinder; (b) a uniform sphere; (c) a thin-walled, hollow sphere; (d) a hollow cylinder with outer radius R and inner radius $R/2$.

52. •• A string is wrapped several times around the rim of a small hoop with a radius of 0.0800 m and a mass of 0.180 kg. If the free end of the string is held in place and the hoop is released from rest (see Figure 30), calculate the angular speed of the rotating hoop after it has descended 0.750 m.

0.0800 m

▲ **FIGURE 30** Problem 52.

53. •• An apparatus for launching a small boat consists of a 150.0 kg cart that rides down a set of tracks on four solid steel wheels, each with radius 20.0 cm and mass 45.0 kg. The tracks slope at an angle of 7.50° to the horizontal, and the boat's mass is 750.0 kg. If the boat is released from rest a distance of 16.0 m from the water (measured along the slope), how fast will it be moving when it reaches the water? Assume the wheels roll without slipping, and that there is no energy loss due to friction.

54. •• A uniform marble rolls down a symmetric bowl, starting from rest at the top of the left side. The top of each side is a distance h above the bottom of the bowl. The left half of the bowl is rough enough to cause the marble to roll without slipping, but the right half has no friction because it is coated with oil. (a) How far up the smooth side will the marble go, measured vertically from the bottom? (b) How high would the marble go if both sides were as rough as the left side? (c) How do you account for the fact that the marble goes *higher* with friction on the right side than without friction?

General Problems

55. •• A 7300 N elevator is to be given an acceleration of $0.150g$ by connecting it to a cable of negligible weight wrapped around a turning cylindrical shaft. If the shaft's diameter can be no larger than 16.0 cm due to space limitations, what must be its minimum angular acceleration to provide the required acceleration of the elevator?

56. •• A 392-N wheel comes off a moving truck and rolls without slipping along a highway. At the bottom of a hill it is rotating at 25.0 rad/s. The radius of the wheel is 0.600 m, and its moment of inertia about its rotation axis is $0.800 MR^2$. Friction does work on the wheel as it rolls up the hill to a stop, a height h above the bottom of the hill; this work has absolute value 3500 J. Calculate h.

57. •• **Odometer.** The odometer (mileage gauge) of a car tells you the number of miles you have driven, but it doesn't count the miles directly. Instead, it counts the number of revolutions of your car's wheels and converts this quantity to mileage, assuming a standard size tire and that your tires do not slip on the pavement. (a) A typical midsize car has tires 24 inches in diameter. How many revolutions of the wheels must the odometer count in order to show a mileage of 0.10 mile? (b) What will the odometer read when the tires have made 5,000 revolutions? (c) Suppose you put oversize 28-inch-diameter tires on your car. How many miles will you really have driven when your odometer reads 500 miles?

58. •• **Speedometer.** Your car's speedometer works in much the same way as its odometer (see the previous problem), except that it converts the angular speed of the wheels to a linear speed of the car, assuming standard-size tires and no slipping on the pavement. (a) If your car has standard 24-inch-diameter tires, how fast are your wheels turning when you are driving at a freeway speed of 55 mph? (b) How fast are you going when your wheels are turning at 500 rpm? (c) If you put on undersize 20-inch-diameter tires, what will the speedometer read when you are actually traveling at 50 mph?

59. •• When a toy car is rapidly scooted across the floor, it stores energy in a flywheel. The car has mass 0.180 kg, and its flywheel has moment of inertia 4.00×10^{-5} kg·m². The car is 15.0 cm long. An advertisement claims that the car can travel at a scale speed of up to 700 km/h (440 mi/h). The scale speed is the speed of the toy car multiplied by the ratio of the length of an actual car to the length of the toy. Assume a length of 3.0 m for a real car. (a) For a scale speed of 700 km/h, what is the actual translational speed of the car? (b) If all the kinetic energy that is initially in the flywheel is converted to the translational kinetic energy of the toy, how much energy is originally stored in the flywheel? (c) What initial angular velocity of the flywheel was needed to store the amount of energy calculated in part (b)?

60. •• A passenger bus in Zurich, Switzerland, derived its motive power from the energy stored in a large flywheel. Whenever the bus was stopped at a station, the wheel was brought up to speed with the use of an electric motor that could then be attached to the electric power lines. The flywheel was a solid cylinder with a mass of 1000 kg and a diameter of 1.80 m; its top angular speed was 3000 rev/min. At this angular speed, what was the kinetic energy of the flywheel?

61. •• **Kinetic energy of the earth.** Assuming that the earth is of uniform density inside, find the kinetic energy of the earth (a) due to its yearly motion around the sun and (b) due to its daily spin on its axis. (c) What percent of the earth's total kinetic energy is contained in its axial spin motion?

62. •• **Compact discs.** When a compact disc (CD) is playing, the angular speed of the turntable is adjusted so that the laser beam,

which reads the digital information encoded in the surface of the disc, maintains a constant *tangential* speed. The laser begins tracking at the inside of the disc and spirals outward as the disc plays, while the angular speed of the disc varies between 500 rpm and 200 rpm. A certain CD (see Figure 31) plays for 74 minutes and has a playing area

Playing area

12.1 cm

▲ **FIGURE 31** Problem 62.

of outer diameter 12.1 cm (which is also essentially the outside diameter of the disc). (a) What is the tangential speed of the laser beam? (b) What is the diameter of the inside of the playing area of this CD? (c) What is the angular acceleration of the CD while it is playing, assuming it to be constant?

63. •• A vacuum cleaner belt is looped over a shaft of radius 0.45 cm and a wheel of radius 2.00 cm. The motor turns the shaft at 60.0 rev/s and the moving belt turns the wheel, which in turn is connected by another shaft to the roller that beats the dirt out of the rug being vacuumed (see Figure 32). Assume that the belt doesn't slip on either the shaft or the wheel. (a) What is the speed of a point on the belt? (b) What is the angular velocity of the wheel, in rad/s?

Motor shaft

60.0 rev/s

Roller shaft

▲ **FIGURE 32** Problem 63.

64. •• A basketball (which can be closely modeled as a hollow spherical shell) rolls down a mountainside into a valley and then up the opposite side, starting from rest at a height H_0 above the bottom. In Figure 33, the rough part of the terrain prevents slipping while the smooth part has no friction. (a) How high, in terms of H_0, will it go up the other side? (b) Why doesn't the ball return to height H_0? Has it lost any of its original potential energy?

Rough

Smooth

H_0

▲ **FIGURE 33** Problem 64.

65. •• **Human rotational energy.** A dancer is spinning at 72 rpm
BIO about an axis through her center with her arms outstretched, as shown in Figure 34. From biomedical measurements, the typical distribution of mass in a human body is as follows:

Head: 7.0%
Arms: 13% (for both)
Trunk and legs: 80.0%

Suppose you are this dancer. Using this information plus length measurements on your own body, calculate (a) your moment of inertia about your spin axis and (b) your rotational kinetic energy. Use the figures in Table 1 to model reasonable approximations for the pertinent parts of your body.

66. •• A solid uniform spherical boulder rolls down the hill as shown in Figure 35, starting from rest when it is 50.0 m above the bottom. The upper half of the hill ▲ **FIGURE 34** Problem 65. is free of ice, so the boulder rolls without slipping. But the lower half is covered with perfectly smooth ice. How fast is the boulder moving when it reaches the bottom of the hill?

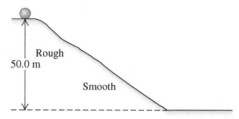

Rough
50.0 m

Smooth

▲ **FIGURE 35** Problem 66.

67. •• A thin uniform rod 50.0 cm long with mass 0.320 kg is bent at its center into a V shape, with a 70.0° angle at its vertex. Find the moment of inertia of this V-shaped object about an axis perpendicular to the plane of the V at its vertex.

68. •• In redesigning a piece of equipment, you need to replace a solid spherical part of mass M with a hollow spherical shell of the same size. If both parts must spin at the same rate about an axis through their center, and the new part must have the same kinetic energy as the old one, what must be the mass of the new part in terms of M?

69. •• A solid uniform spherical stone starts moving from rest at the top of a hill. At the bottom of the hill the ground curves upward, launching the stone vertically a distance H below its start. How high will the stone go (a) if there is no friction on the hill and (b) if there is enough friction on the hill for the stone to roll without slipping? (c) Why do you get two different answers even though the stone starts with the same gravitational potential energy in both cases?

70. •• A solid, uniform ball rolls without slipping up a hill, as shown in Figure 36. At the top of the hill, it is moving horizontally; then it goes over the vertical cliff. (a) How far from the foot of the cliff does the ball land, and how fast is it moving just before it lands? (b) Notice that when the ball lands, it has a larger translational speed than it had at the bottom of the hill. Does this mean that the ball somehow *gained* energy by going up the hill? Explain!

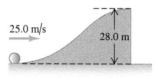

25.0 m/s

28.0 m

▲ **FIGURE 36** Problem 70.

71. •• **The kinetic energy of walking.** If a person of mass M
BIO simply moved forward with speed V, his kinetic energy
would be $\frac{1}{2}MV^2$. However, in addition to possessing a forward motion, various parts of his body (such as the arms and
legs) undergo rotation. Therefore, his total kinetic energy is
the sum of the energy from his forward motion plus the rotational kinetic energy of his arms and legs. The purpose of this
problem is to see how much this rotational motion contributes
to the person's kinetic energy. Biomedical measurements
show that the arms and hands together typically make up
13% of a person's mass, while the legs and feet together
account for 37%. For a rough (but reasonable) calculation, we
can model the arms and legs as thin uniform bars pivoting
about the shoulder and hip, respectively. In a brisk walk, the
arms and legs each move through an angle of about $\pm 30°$ (a
total of 60°) from the vertical in approximately 1 second. We
shall assume that they are held straight, rather than being
bent, which is not quite true. Let us consider a 75 kg person
walking at 5.0 km/h, having arms 70 cm long and legs 90 cm
long. (a) What is the average angular velocity of his arms and
legs? (b) Using the average angular velocity from part (a),
calculate the amount of rotational kinetic energy in this person's arms and legs as he walks. (c) What is the total kinetic
energy due to both his forward motion and his rotation?
(d) What percentage of his kinetic energy is due to the rotation of his legs and arms?

72. •• **The kinetic energy of running.** Using the previous prob-
BIO lem as a guide, apply it to a person running at 12 km/h, with
his arms and legs each swinging through $\pm 30°$ in $\frac{1}{2}$ s. As
before, assume that the arms and legs are kept straight.

73. •• The pulley in Fig. 37 has radius R and a moment of inertia
I. The rope does not slip over the pulley, and the pulley spins
on a frictionless axle. The coefficient of kinetic friction
between block A and the tabletop is μ_k The system is released
from rest, and block B descends. Block A has mass m_A and
block B has mass m_B Use energy methods to calculate the
speed of block B as a function of the distance d that it has
descended.

▲ **FIGURE 37** Problem 73.

Passage Problems

BIO The spinning wheel. When we first observe a wheel it is spinning *clockwise* at 30 rad/s, but when we observe it 10 seconds later
it is spinning *counterclockwise* at 30 rad/s. (See Figure 38.)
Assume that the wheel's angular acceleration is constant during
the 10-second interval and that our point of view does not change.

▲ **FIGURE 38** Problems 74–77.

74. What is the wheel's average angular velocity during the 10-s
interval?
   A. 0 rad/s
   B. 15 rad/s
   C. 30 rad/s
   D. 60 rad/s

75. What is the wheel's angular acceleration during the 10-s interval?
   A. 0 rad/s²
   B. 1.5 rad/s²
   C. 3 rad/s²
   D. 6 rad/s²
   E. 60 rad/s²

76. What is the wheel's angular displacement over the 10-s interval?
   A. 0 rad
   B. 300 rad
   C. 600 rad
   D. 1500 rad

77. Assuming that the wheel continues with the same constant
angular acceleration, what would its angular displacement be
over the next 10-s interval (i.e., between 10 s and 20 s)?
   A. 0 rad
   B. 300 rad
   C. 450 rad
   D. 600 rad

TABLE 1   Moments of inertia for various bodies

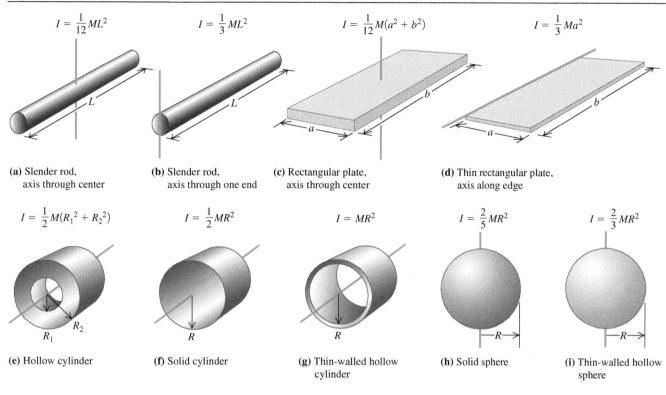

$I = \frac{1}{12}ML^2$

(a) Slender rod,
axis through center

$I = \frac{1}{3}ML^2$

(b) Slender rod,
axis through one end

$I = \frac{1}{12}M(a^2 + b^2)$

(c) Rectangular plate,
axis through center

$I = \frac{1}{3}Ma^2$

(d) Thin rectangular plate,
axis along edge

$I = \frac{1}{2}M(R_1^2 + R_2^2)$

(e) Hollow cylinder

$I = \frac{1}{2}MR^2$

(f) Solid cylinder

$I = MR^2$

(g) Thin-walled hollow
cylinder

$I = \frac{2}{5}MR^2$

(h) Solid sphere

$I = \frac{2}{3}MR^2$

(i) Thin-walled hollow
sphere

ANSWERS TO SELECTED PROBLEMS

Conceptual Questions

1. The tangential acceleration is parallel to the instantaneous velocity at each point and is equal to the rate of change of the speed of the point. The radial acceleration is associated with the rate of change of the direction of the point's velocity.

3. Yes, the point has both tangential and radial acceleration. The tangential acceleration has a constant magnitude $r\alpha$. It is tangential to the circular path and changes direction as the flywheel rotates. The radial acceleration is $r\omega^2$ and is not constant in magnitude, since α changes ω. The radial acceleration is directly radially inward and changes direction as the flywheel rotates.

5. (a) Yes, the ring is a collection of point masses, all the same distance R from the axis. (b) No, the point mass has $I = MR^2$, and the solid uniform disk has $I = \frac{1}{2}MR^2$. The mass of the disk is spread between the axis and a distance R from the axis, so I for the disk is less than MR^2.

7. Some of the energy supplied to the bike goes into rotational kinetic energy of the wheels, rather than translational kinetic energy of the bike. The amount of translational kinetic energy lost to rotation of

the wheels increases as the mass of the wheels increases.

9. When the raw egg rolls, only the liquid near the shell rotates, whereas all the contents of the hard-boiled egg rotate. The raw egg therefore has a smaller moment of inertia and will reach the bottom of the slope first.

13. His legs and arms move in circular arcs relative to his hips and shoulders, respectively.

15. The acceleration depends on the slope of the hill. If the slope changes along the path, then the translational acceleration of the ball changes and constant-acceleration equations cannot be used.

Multiple-Choice Problems

1. B
3. D
5. A
7. B
9. C
11. C
13. B
15. A

Problems

1. 17.2°
3. (a) 0.105 rad/s; 1.75×10^{-3} rad/s; 1.45×10^{-4} rad/s (b) 1 min; 1 hr; 12 hr

5. (a) 2.25 s (b) 2.79 rad/s
7. (a) 5.76×10^5 m/s (b) 1.56×10^{-5} rad
9. (a) 200 rad/s (b) 3.1×10^{-3} s (c) 170 rpm (d) 0.032 s
11. (a) 2.33 rad/s² (b) 818°
13. 0.0135 rad/s²
15. (a) 12.5 s (b) 7.96 rev
17. (a) 300 rpm (b) 75.0 s; 312 rev
19. 10.5 rad/s
21. 92 rad/s
23. (a) 18.0 m/s² (b) 3.00 m/s, 18.0 m/s²
25. 28 rpm
27. (a) 0.831 m/s (b) 109 m/s²
29. (a) 2.29 (b) 1.51 (c) 15.7 m/s, 108g
31. (a) 2.33 kg · m² (b) 7.33 kg · m² (c) 0
33. (a) 0.0640 kg · m² (b) 0.0320 kg · m² (c) 0.0320 kg · m²
35. (a) 3.16×10^{23} J (b) 126 years
37. (a) 0.0225 kg · m² (b) 0.500 kg
39. 0.600 kg · m²
41. (a) 2.25 m (b) 5.63 m
43. (a) 0.664 m (b) 7.69 rad/s
45. (a) 140 J (b) 33%
47. (a) 1.80 m/s (b) 7.18 J
49. (a) 67.9 rad/s (b) 8.35 J
51. (a) 1/3 (b) 2/7 (c) 2/5 (d) 5/13
53. 6.15 m/s
55. 18.4 rad/s²
57. (a) 84.0 rev (b) 5.95 mi (c) 583 mi
59. (a) 9.72 m/s (b) 8.50 J (c) 652 rad/s

61. (a) 2.66×10^{33} J (b) 2.57×10^{29} J
    (c) 9.66×10^{-3}%
63. (a) 1.70 m/s (b) 84.8 rad/s
65. (a) 3.3 kg $\cdot$ m^2 (b) 93 J
67. 6.67×10^{-3} kg $\cdot$ m^2

69. (a) H (b) $5H/7$ (c) in (b), stone ends up
    with rotational kinetic energy
71. (a) 1.05 rad/s (b) 5.0 J (c) 78.5 J
    (d) 6.4%
73. (a) 23.0 m

Passage Problems

75. D
77. D

Dynamics of
Rotational Motion

From Chapter 10 of *College Physics*, Ninth Edition, Hugh D. Young. Copyright © 2012 by Pearson Education, Inc.
Published by Pearson Addison-Wesley. All rights reserved.

Dynamics of Rotational Motion

NASA

This disk galaxy exemplifies conservation of *angular momentum*— the rotational analog of linear momentum. As this air moves inward, its angular velocity increases . . . as you see.

W hen you use a wrench to loosen lug nuts when you change a flat tire, the whole wheel starts to turn unless you find a way to hold it still. What is it about the force you apply to the handle of the wrench that makes the wheel turn? More generally, what is it that gives a rotating body an *angular* acceleration? A force is a push or a pull, but to produce rotational motion, we need a twisting or turning action.

In this chapter we'll define a physical quantity, *torque*, that describes the twisting or turning effort of a force. We'll incorporate this quantity into a fundamental dynamic relationship for rotational motion. We also need to look at work and power in rotational motion to understand such problems as how energy is transmitted by a rotating shaft (e.g., a drive shaft or an axle in a car or the shaft of a rotating turbine in a jet engine). Next, we'll develop a new conservation principle, *conservation of angular momentum*, that is useful in analyzing rotational motion, but that has much broader significance as well. We'll explore the relevance of torque for problems involving *equilibrium* of a rigid body. Then we'll conclude this chapter by studying briefly how gyroscopes work. Rotational motion can have some interesting surprises, as you may know if you've ever played with a toy gyroscope.

1 Torque

What is it about a force that determines how effective it is in causing or changing a rotational motion? The magnitude and direction of the force certainly play a role, but the point at which the force is applied is also important. When you try to swing a heavy door open, it's a lot easier if you push near the knob than if you push close to the hinges. The farther from the axis of rotation you push, the more effective the push is. In Figure 1, a wrench is being used to loosen a tight bolt. Note that force $\vec{F}_b$, applied at the end of the handle, is more effective than force $\vec{F}_a$, applied

ActivPhysics 7.1: Calculating Torques

near the bolt, even though the two forces have equal magnitude. Force $\vec{F}_c$, directed along the length of the handle, does no good at all.

The quantitative measure of the tendency of a force to cause or change a body's rotational motion is called **torque.** Figure 2 shows a body that can rotate about an axis that passes through point O and is perpendicular to the plane of the figure. The body is acted on by a force $\vec{F}_1$ in the plane of the figure. The tendency of $\vec{F}_1$ to cause a rotation about point O depends on the magnitude F_1 of the force. It also depends on the perpendicular distance l_1 between the line of action of the force (i.e., the line along which the force vector lies) and O. The distance l_1 plays the role of the wrench handle, and we call it the **moment arm** (or *lever arm*) of force $\vec{F}_1$ about O. The twisting effort is proportional to both F_1 and l_1. We define the **torque,** or **moment,** of the force $\vec{F}_1$ with respect to point O as the product $F_1 l_1$. We use the Greek letter τ ("tau") to denote torque:

Definition of torque

Torque is a quantitative measure of the tendency of a force to cause or change rotational motion around a chosen axis. Torque is the product of the magnitude of the force and the moment arm, which is the perpendicular distance between the axis and the line of action of the force:

$$\tau = Fl \qquad (1)$$

Unit: newton-meter (N · m)

> **NOTE** ▶ The SI unit of torque is the newton-meter. In our discussion of work and energy, we called this combination the *joule*. But torque is *not* work or energy, and torque should be expressed in newton-meters, not joules. ◀

Figure 3 shows two additional forces acting on the body shown in Figure 2. The moment arm of $\vec{F}_2$ is the perpendicular distance l_2, just as the moment arm of $\vec{F}_1$ is the perpendicular distance l_1. Force $\vec{F}_3$ has a line of action that passes *through* the reference point O, so the moment arm for $\vec{F}_3$ is zero, and its torque with respect to point O is zero. Note that torque is always defined with reference to a specific point that could serve as an axis of rotation. Often (but not always), we take this point as the origin of our coordinate system. If we change the position of that point, the torque of each force usually also changes.

Force $\vec{F}_1$ in Figure 3 tends to cause *counterclockwise* rotation about O, and $\vec{F}_2$ tends to cause *clockwise* rotation. To distinguish between these two possibilities, we'll use the convention that **counterclockwise torques are positive and clockwise torques are negative.** With this convention, the torque τ_1 of $\vec{F}_1$ about O is

$$\tau_1 = +F_1 l_1$$

and the torque τ_2 of $\vec{F}_2$ is

$$\tau_2 = -F_2 l_2.$$

Note that this choice of signs is consistent with our choice for angular position, velocity, and acceleration. Thus, we'll sometimes refer to counterclockwise rotation as the **positive sense of rotation.**

Figure 4 shows a force $\vec{F}$ applied at a point P. The vector $\vec{r}$ represents the position of P with respect to the chosen axis through O. There are several alternative ways to calculate the torque of this force. We can find the moment arm l and use $\tau = Fl$. Or we can determine the angle ϕ between the directions of vectors $\vec{F}$ and $\vec{r}$; the moment arm is $r\sin\phi$, so $\tau = rF\sin\phi$. Finally, we can represent $\vec{F}$ in

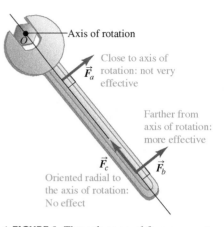

▲ **FIGURE 1** These three equal forces are *not* equally effective at loosening the nut.

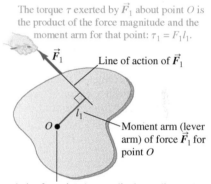

▲ **FIGURE 2** The torque of a force about a point is the product of the magnitude of the force and the moment arm.

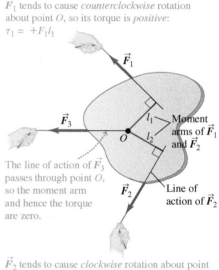

▲ **FIGURE 3** The sign of a torque depends on whether it tends to cause clockwise or counterclockwise rotation about the chosen point. A force whose line of action passes through the chosen point has no torque.

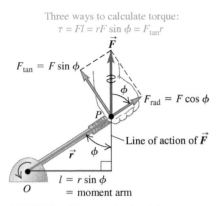

Three ways to calculate torque:
$$\tau = Fl = rF \sin\phi = F_{\text{tan}}r$$

$F_{\text{tan}} = F \sin\phi$

$F_{\text{rad}} = F \cos\phi$

Line of action of $\vec{F}$

$l = r \sin\phi$ = moment arm

▲ **FIGURE 4** The magnitude of the torque caused by a force $\vec{F}$ depends only on the tangential component of the force: $\tau = rF \sin\phi$.

terms of a radial component F_{rad} along the direction of $\vec{r}$ (the radial line from O to P) and a tangential component F_{tan} at right angles, perpendicular to $\vec{r}$. (We call F_{tan} a tangential component because when the object rotates, the point P at which the force acts moves in a circle, and this component is tangent to that circle.) Then $F_{\text{tan}} = F \sin\phi$, and

$$\tau = F_{\text{tan}}r = r(F \sin\phi) = Fl. \qquad (2)$$

The component F_{rad} has no torque with respect to O, because its moment arm with respect to that point is zero.

NOTE ▶ Equations 1 and 2 give the *magnitude* of torque. When we use the sign conventions we've described (counterclockwise positive, clockwise negative), we have to be sure to attach the correct sign to each torque. ◀

EXAMPLE 1   A weekend plumber

An amateur plumber, unable to loosen a pipe fitting, slips a piece of scrap pipe (a "cheater") over the handle of his wrench. He then applies his full weight of 900 N to the end of the cheater by standing on it. The distance from the center of the fitting to the point where the weight acts is 0.80 m, and the wrench handle and cheater make an angle of 19° with the horizontal (Figure 5a). Find the magnitude and direction of the torque of his weight about the center of the pipe fitting.

SOLUTION

SET UP Figure 5b diagrams the position of the force exerted by the plumber in relation to the axis of rotation at point O.

SOLVE We have a choice of several methods for solving this problem. From Figure 5b, the angle ϕ between the vectors $\vec{r}$ and $\vec{F}$ is 109°, and the moment arm l is

$$l = (0.80\text{ m})(\sin 109°) = (0.80\text{ m})(\sin 71°)$$
$$= 0.76\text{ m}.$$

We can find the magnitude of the torque from either Equation 1 or Equation 2. From Equation 1,

$$\tau = Fl = (900\text{ N})(0.76\text{ m}) = 680\text{ N} \cdot \text{m}.$$

Or, from Equation 2,

$$\tau = rF \sin\phi = (0.80\text{ m})(900\text{ N})(\sin 109°) = 680\text{ N} \cdot \text{m}.$$

ALTERNATIVE SOLUTION Alternatively, we can start with the components of $\vec{F}$. From Figure 6b, we see that the component of force $\vec{F}$ perpendicular to $\vec{r}$ (which we call F_{tan}, as explained earlier) is

$$F_{\text{tan}} = F(\cos 19°) = (900\text{ N})(\cos 19°) = 850\text{ N}.$$

Then the torque is

$$\tau = F_{\text{tan}}r = (850\text{ N})(0.80\text{ m}) = 680\text{ N} \cdot \text{m}.$$

REFLECT The force tends to produce a counterclockwise rotation about O, so with the convention described above, this torque is $+680\text{ N} \cdot \text{m}$, *not* $-680\text{ N} \cdot \text{m}$. Also, please don't try to use this plumbing technique at home; you're very likely to break a pipe.

Practice Problem: If the pipe fitting under consideration can withstand a maximum torque of $1000\text{ N} \cdot \text{m}$ without breaking, what is the maximum moment arm at which our amateur plumber can safely apply his full weight? *Answer:* 1.12 m.

0.80 m

$F = 900$ N

19°

(a) Diagram of situation

Point at which force acts ⋯ Line of action of force

Position vector from point O to the point at which the force acts

Angle ϕ between line of action of force and radial direction $\phi = 109°$ 71° $r = 0.80$ m

F_{tan} 19°   Point where axis of rotation intersects plane of diagram

$F = 900$ N ℓ O

Moment arm (perpendicular distance from axis of rotation to line of action of force)

(b) Free-body diagram

▲ **FIGURE 5**

▶ Application **Don't fall for it.** To stay balanced while walking the tightrope, this acrobat must keep her center of mass directly above the rope. If the center of mass shifts to one side, gravity will exert a torque on the acrobat, tending to cause a rotation about the rope—a fall. To stay balanced, the acrobat must create a countertorque having equal magnitude and opposite sign. That is why tightrope walkers carry a long pole. Because the torque due to a force is the product of the magnitude of the force and the moment arm, the gravitational forces on the ends of the pole exert significant torques. Thus, the acrobat controls the net torque acting on her center of gravity by manipulating the pole. Also, the acrobat holds the pole low, moving her center of gravity closer to the rope.

David Cumming/Corbis

Often, one of the important forces acting on a body is its weight. This force is not concentrated at a single point, but is distributed over the entire body. Nevertheless, it turns out that **in a uniform gravitational field, the total torque on a body due to its weight is the same as though all the weight were concentrated at the *center of mass* of the body.** We'll derive this relationship later in this chapter and use it for several problems.

2 Torque and Angular Acceleration

We're now ready to develop the fundamental dynamical relation for rotational motion of a rigid body. We'll show that the angular acceleration of a rotating body is directly proportional to the sum of the torques with respect to the axis of rotation. The proportionality factor is the moment of inertia.

To develop this relationship, we again imagine a body as being made up of a large number of particles. Figure 6 shows a particular particle, labeled A, that has mass m_A and is located a perpendicular distance r_A from the axis of rotation of the body. The *total force* $\vec{F}_A$ acting on this particle has a component $F_{A,\mathrm{rad}}$ along the radial direction and a component $F_{A,\tan}$ tangent to the circle of radius r_A in which the particle moves as the body rotates. (The force $\vec{F}_A$ may also have a component parallel to the axis of rotation, but this component has no torque with respect to the axis and therefore can be ignored in the analysis that follows.) Newton's second law for the tangential components is

$$F_{A,\tan} = m_A a_{A,\tan}. \tag{3}$$

We can express $a_{A,\tan}$ in terms of the angular acceleration α, using $a_{A,\tan} = r_A \alpha$. Using this relation and multiplying both sides of Equation 3 by r_A we obtain

$$F_{A,\tan} r_A = m_A r_A (r_A \alpha) = (m_A r_A^2)\alpha. \tag{4}$$

Now, $F_{A,\tan} r_A$ is just the torque τ_A of the force F_A with respect to the axis through point O. Also, $m_A r_A^2$ is the moment of inertia of particle A about this axis. The component $F_{A,\mathrm{rad}}$ acts along a line passing through the axis of rotation and so has no torque with respect to the axis. Hence, we can rewrite Equation 4 as

$$\tau_A = I_A \alpha = (m_A r_A^2)\alpha.$$

We can write an equation like this for every particle in the body and then add all the equations together:

$$\tau_A + \tau_B + \tau_C + \cdots = (m_A r_A^2 + m_B r_B^2 + m_C r_C^2 + \cdots)\alpha$$

The left side of this equation is the sum of *all* the torques acting on *all* the particles. We'll call this sum simply $\Sigma\tau$. The right side of the equation is the total moment of inertia, namely,

$$I = m_A r_A^2 + m_B r_B^2 + m_C r_C^2 + \cdots,$$

multiplied by the angular acceleration α, which is the same for every particle in the body. Thus, for the entire body, we have the following relationship:

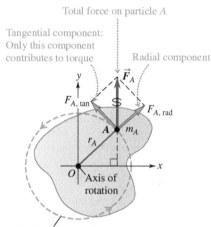

Total force on particle A

Tangential component: Only this component contributes to torque

Radial component

Path of particle A as body rotates

▲ **FIGURE 6** The components of the net force acting on one of the particles of a rigid body.

ActivPhysics 7.8: Rotoride—Dynamics Approach
ActivPhysics 7.9: Falling Ladder
ActivPhysics 7.10: Woman and Flywheel Elevator—Dynamics Approach

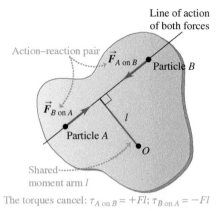

The torques cancel: $\tau_{A\,on\,B} = +Fl$; $\tau_{B\,on\,A} = -Fl$

▲ **FIGURE 7** Why internal forces do not contribute to net torque.

Relation of torque to angular acceleration

The net torque (about a chosen axis) of all the forces acting on a rigid body equals the body's moment of inertia (about that axis), multiplied by its angular acceleration:

$$\Sigma\tau = I\alpha. \qquad (5)$$

This equation is the rotational analog of Newton's second law, $\Sigma\vec{F} = m\vec{a}$. It is the dynamic relationship we need to relate the rotational motion of a rigid body to the forces acting on it.

Now let's think a little more about the forces. The force $\vec{F}$ on each particle is the vector sum of the external and internal forces acting on it. The internal forces that any pair of particles exert on each other are an action–reaction pair. According to Newton's third law, they have equal magnitude and opposite direction (Figure 7). Assuming that they act along the line joining the two particles, their *moment arms* with respect to any axis are also equal, so the *torques* for each such pair add to zero. Indeed, **the torques due to all the internal forces add to zero,** so the sum of the torques on a body includes only the torques of the *external* forces acting on the body.

 Net torque on a pulley

Figure 8 shows two blocks with equal mass suspended by a cord over a pulley whose mass is half the mass of each block. Block *B* is given an initial push downward, after which it moves downward with constant velocity. There is no friction in the pulley axle, and the cord's weight can be ignored. While *B* is moving down,

A. the left cord pulls on the pulley with greater force than the right cord.
B. the left and right cords pull with equal force on the pulley.
C. the right cord pulls with greater force on the pulley than the left cord.

SOLUTION After the initial push, each block moves with constant velocity and so is in equilibrium. The tension in each side of the cord is equal to the weight of one block, so the tensions on the two sides of the cord are equal. The torques applied to the pulley

▲ **FIGURE 8**

by the two sides of the cord are equal in magnitude but opposite in sign. Therefore, the net torque on the pulley is zero, and its angular acceleration is zero. The two blocks move with constant velocity, and the pulley turns with constant angular velocity. If either answer A or answer C were correct, the pulley would have a nonzero angular acceleration. Answer B is correct.

 Rotating masses

Two heavy masses are mounted on a light rod that can be rotated by a string wrapped around a central cylinder of negligible mass, forming a winch (Figure 9). A force *F* is applied to the string to turn the system. With respect to the variables given in the figure, the equation for the angular acceleration α is

A. $rF/2mR^2$.
B. $RF/2mr^2$.
C. $rF/3mR^2$.
D. $RF/3mr^2$.

SOLUTION From Equation 5, $\alpha = (\Sigma\tau)/I$. The only torque with respect to the axis of rotation is supplied by the string force

(magnitude F), which is always tangent to the surface of the small cylinder. The moment arm of the force is the radius r of the cylinder, so the torque is $\tau = rF$. The moment of inertia I is the sum of the mR^2 terms for each mass. Because both m and $2m$ are at distance R from the axis of rotation, the total moment of inertia is $3mR^2$. Combining the results for torque and moment of inertia, we get $rF/3mR^2$ (answer C).

▲ **FIGURE 9**

PROBLEM-SOLVING STRATEGY 1 Rotational dynamics (MP)

Our strategy for solving problems in rotational dynamics is below.

SET UP

1. Sketch the situation and select a body or bodies to analyze. You will apply $\sum \vec{F} = m\vec{a}$ or $\sum \tau = I\alpha$, or sometimes both, to each object.
2. Draw a free-body diagram for each body. Because we're now dealing with extended bodies rather than objects that can be treated as particles, your diagram must show the shape of the body accurately, with all dimensions and angles that you'll need for calculations of torque. A body may have translational motion, rotational motion, or both. As always, include all the forces that act on each body (and no others), including the body's weight (taken to act at the center of mass).
3. Choose coordinate axes for each body. Remember that, by convention, the positive sense of rotation is counterclockwise; this is the positive sense for angular position, angular velocity, angular acceleration, and torque.
4. If more than one object is involved, carry out the preceding steps for each object. There may be geometrical relations between the motions of two or more objects or between the translational and rotational motions of the same object. Express these in algebraic form, usually as relations between two linear accelerations or between a linear acceleration and an angular acceleration.

SOLVE

5. Write a separate equation of motion ($\sum \vec{F} = m\vec{a}$ or $\sum \tau = I\alpha$, or both) for each body, including separate equations for the x and y components of forces if necessary. Then solve the equations to find the unknown quantities. This may involve solving a set of simultaneous equations.

REFLECT

6. Check particular cases or extreme values of quantities when possible, and compare the results for these particular cases or values with your intuitive expectations. Ask yourself whether the result makes sense.

EXAMPLE 2 Unwinding a winch (again)

A cable is wrapped several times around a uniform solid cylinder with diameter 0.12 m and mass 50 kg that can rotate freely about its axis. The cable is pulled by a force with magnitude 9.0 N. Assuming that the cable unwinds without stretching or slipping, find the magnitude of its acceleration.

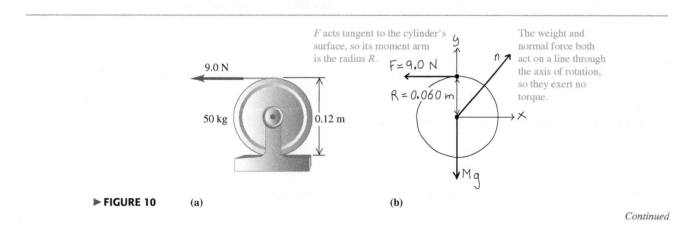

► FIGURE 10 (a) (b)

Continued

SOLUTION

SET UP We draw a free-body diagram for the cylinder (Figure 10b). Because the force acts tangent to the outside of the cylinder, its moment arm relative to the axis of rotation is the cylinder's radius.

SOLVE The torque is $\tau = Fl = (9.0\,\text{N})(0.060\,\text{m}) = 0.54\,\text{N} \cdot \text{m}$. The moment of inertia is

$$I = \tfrac{1}{2}MR^2 = \tfrac{1}{2}(50\,\text{kg})(0.060\,\text{m})^2 = 0.090\,\text{kg} \cdot \text{m}^2.$$

The angular acceleration α is given by Equation 5:

$$\alpha = \frac{\tau}{I} = \frac{0.54\,\text{N} \cdot \text{m}}{0.090\,\text{kg} \cdot \text{m}^2} = 6.0\,\text{rad/s}^2.$$

The magnitude a of the acceleration of the cable is given by the equation below:

$$a = R\alpha = (0.060\,\text{m})(6.0\,\text{rad/s}^2)$$
$$= 0.36\,\text{m/s}^2.$$

REFLECT In the equation $\alpha = \tau/I$, check the units to make sure they are consistent.

Practice Problem: Use the preceding results to determine the speed of the cable after it has been pulled 2.0 m. *Answer:* 1.2 m/s.

EXAMPLE 3   Dynamics of a bucket in a well

Find the acceleration of the bucket (mass m) and the angular acceleration of the winch cylinder.

SOLUTION

SET UP We start by sketching the situation, (Figure 11a). As before, the winch cylinder has mass M and radius R; the bucket has mass m and falls a distance h. We must treat the two objects separately, so we draw a free-body diagram for each (Figure 11b). We take the positive direction of the y coordinate for the bucket to be downward; the positive sense of rotation for the winch is counterclockwise. We assume that the rope is massless and that it unwinds without slipping.

SOLVE Newton's second law applied to the bucket (mass m) gives

$$\Sigma F_y = mg - T = ma_y.$$

The forces on the cylinder are its weight Mg, the upward normal force n exerted by the axle, and the rope tension T. The first two forces act along lines through the axis of rotation and thus have no torque with respect to that axis. The moment arm of the force T on the cylinder is R, and the torque is $\tau = TR$. Applying Equation 5 and the expression for the moment of inertia of a solid cylinder to the winch cylinder, we find that

$$\Sigma\tau = I\alpha \quad \text{and} \quad TR = \tfrac{1}{2}MR^2\alpha.$$

As in Example 2, the angular acceleration α of the cylinder is proportional to the magnitude of acceleration a_y of the unwinding rope: $a_y = R\alpha$. We use this equation to replace $(R\alpha)$ with a_y in the cylinder equation, and then we divide by R. The result is

$$T = \tfrac{1}{2}Ma_y.$$

Now we substitute this expression for T into the equation of motion for the bucket (mass m):

$$mg - \tfrac{1}{2}Ma_y = ma_y.$$

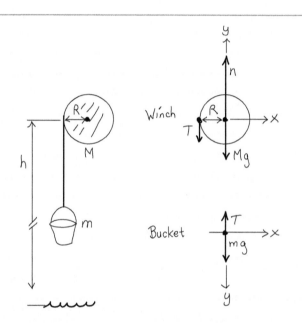

(a) Diagram of situation   (b) Free-body diagrams

▲ **FIGURE 11** Our sketches for this problem.

When we solve this equation for a_y, we get

$$a_y = \frac{g}{1 + M/2m}.$$

Combining this result with the kinematic equation $a_y = R\alpha$, we obtain the angular acceleration α:

$$\alpha = \frac{g/R}{1 + M/2m}.$$

Continued

Finally, we can substitute the equation for a_y back into the equation $\Sigma\vec{F} = m\vec{a}$ for m to get an expression for the tension T in the rope:

$$T = mg - ma_y = mg - m\frac{g}{1 + M/2m} \quad \text{and} \quad T = \frac{mg}{1 + 2m/M}.$$

REFLECT First, note that the tension in the rope is *less than* the weight mg of the bucket; if the two forces were equal (in magnitude), the bucket wouldn't accelerate downward.

We can check two particular cases. When M is much larger than m (a massive winch and a little bucket), the ratio m/M is much smaller than unity. Then the tension is nearly equal to mg, and the acceleration a_y is correspondingly much *less* than g. When M is zero, $T = 0$ and $a = g$; the bucket then falls freely. If it starts from rest at a height h above the water, its speed v when it strikes the water is given by $v^2 = 2a_y h$; thus,

$$v = \sqrt{2a_y h} = \sqrt{\frac{2gh}{1 + M/2m}}.$$

Note that there we couldn't find the tension in the rope or the accelerations of the winch cylinder and bucket using energy considerations.

Practice Problem: (a) What is the relation between m and M if the bucket's acceleration is half the acceleration of free fall? (b) In this case, what is the rope tension T? *Answer:* (a) $m = M/2$; (b) $T = mg/2 = Mg/4$.

NOTE ▶ In problems such as Example 3, in which an object is suspended by a rope, you may be tempted to assume at the start that the tension in the rope is equal to the object's weight. If the object is in equilibrium, this may be true, but when the object accelerates, the tension is usually *not* equal to the object's weight. Be careful! ◀

Rotation about a Moving Axis

Previously, we discussed the kinetic energy of a rigid body rotating about a moving axis. We can extend our analysis of the dynamics of rotational motion to some cases in which the axis of rotation moves. In these cases, the body has both translational and rotational motion. Every possible motion of a rigid body can be represented as a combination of translational motion of the center of mass and rotation about an axis through the center of mass. A rolling wheel or ball and a yo-yo unwinding at the end of a string are familiar examples of such motion.

The key to this more general analysis, which we won't derive in detail, is that Equation 5 ($\Sigma\tau = I\alpha$) is valid *even when the axis of rotation moves* if the following two conditions are met: (1) The axis must be an axis of symmetry and must pass through the center of mass of the body; (2) the axis must not change direction. Note that the moving axis is not necessarily at rest in an inertial frame of reference. The moment of inertia must be computed with respect to the moving axis through the center of mass; to emphasize this point, we'll denote it as I_{cm}.

MasteringPHYSICS

ActivPhysics 7.11: Race Between a Block and a Disk

PROBLEM-SOLVING STRATEGY 2 **Rotation about a moving axis** (MP)

The problem-solving strategy outlined in Section 2 is equally useful here. There is one new wrinkle: When a rigid body undergoes translational and rotational motion at the same time, we need two separate equations of motion *for the same body*. (The situation is reminiscent of our analysis of projectile motion, where we used separate equations for the x and y coordinates of a projectile.)

For a rigid body, one of the equations of motion is based on $\Sigma\vec{F} = m\vec{a}$ for the translational motion of the center of mass of the body. For a body with total mass M, the acceleration $\vec{a}_{cm}$ of the center of mass is the same as that of a point mass M acted on by all the forces that act on the actual body. The other equation of motion is based on $\Sigma\tau = I_{cm}\alpha$ for the rotational motion of the body about the axis through the center of mass with moment of inertia I_{cm}. In addition, there is often a geometric relation between the linear and angular accelerations, such as when a wheel rolls without slipping or a string rotates a pulley while passing over it.

EXAMPLE 4 **Dynamics of a primitive yo-yo**

Let's consider again the yo-yo. As shown in Figure 12a, the yo-yo consists of a solid disk with radius R and mass M. In our previous analysis, we used energy considerations to find the yo-yo's speed after it had dropped a certain distance. Now let's find the acceleration of the yo-yo and the tension in the string (which we can't do by using energy considerations alone).

SOLUTION

SET UP We start with a free-body diagram, including a coordinate system (Figure 12b). If the string unwinds without slipping, the linear displacement of the center of mass of the cylindrical yo-yo in any time interval equals R times its angular displacement. This gives us the kinematic relations $v_{cm,y} = R\omega$ and $a_{cm,y} = R\alpha$. (If this scenario isn't obvious, imagine moving along with the center of mass of the cylinder and watching the string unwind. From that point of view, the kinematic situation is just the same as in Examples 2 and 3.)

SOLVE The equation for the translational motion of the center of mass is

$$\Sigma F_y = Mg - T = Ma_{cm,y}.$$

The moment of inertia for an axis through the center of mass is $I_{cm} = \frac{1}{2}MR^2$, and the equation for rotational motion about the axis through the center of mass is

$$\Sigma\tau = TR = I_{cm}\alpha = \frac{1}{2}MR^2\alpha.$$

We can now combine this equation with the relation $a_{cm,y} = R\alpha$ to eliminate α, obtaining $TR = \frac{1}{2}MRa_{cm,y}$, or $T = \frac{1}{2}Ma_{cm,y}$. Finally, we combine this result with the equation for the center-of-mass motion ($\Sigma F_y = Mg - T = Ma_{cm,y}$) to obtain expressions for T and $a_{cm,y}$. The results are amazingly simple:

$$a_{cm,y} = \tfrac{2}{3}g, \qquad T = \tfrac{1}{3}Mg.$$

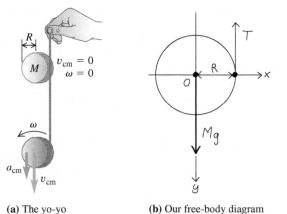

(a) The yo-yo   **(b)** Our free-body diagram

▲ **FIGURE 12**

REFLECT The acceleration and tension are both proportional to g, as we should expect. The acceleration is independent of M and R, and the mass cancels out of the dynamic equations. For a yo-yo in the form of a solid disk, the acceleration is exactly two-thirds the acceleration of free fall.

Practice Problem: If the solid cylinder is replaced by a thin cylindrical shell with the same mass and radius as before, find $a_{cm,y}$ and T. *Answer:* $a_{cm,y} = g/2$, $T = Mg/2$.

EXAMPLE 5 **A rolling bowling ball**

A bowling ball rolls without slipping down the return ramp at the side of the alley (Figure 13a). The ramp is inclined at an angle β to the horizontal. What is the ball's acceleration? What is the friction force acting on the ball? Treat the ball as a uniform solid sphere, ignoring the finger holes.

SOLUTION

SET UP Again, let's start with a free-body diagram, with the positive coordinate directions indicated (Figure 13b). The moment of inertia of a solid sphere about an axis through its center of mass is $I_{cm} = \frac{2}{5}MR^2$. Because the ball rolls without slipping, the acceleration $a_{cm,x}$ of the center of mass is proportional to the ball's angular acceleration α ($a_{cm,x} = R\alpha$). We've represented the forces in terms of their components; it's most convenient to take the axes as parallel and perpendicular to the sloping ramp. The contact force of the ramp on the ball is represented in terms of its normal (n) and frictional (f_s) components. Note that f_s is a *static* friction force, because the ball doesn't slip on the ramp.

SOLVE The equations of motion for translational motion and for rotation about the axis through the center of mass are:

Translation: $\Sigma F_x = Mg\sin\beta - f_s = Ma_{cm,x}$,
Rotation: $\Sigma\tau = f_sR = I_{cm}\alpha = \left(\frac{2}{5}MR^2\right)\alpha$.

We eliminate α from the second equation by using the kinematic relation $a_{cm} = R\alpha$. Then we express I_{cm} in terms of M and R and divide through by R:

$$f_sR = I_{cm}\alpha = \left(\tfrac{2}{5}MR^2\right)\left(\frac{a_{cm,x}}{R}\right) \quad \text{and} \quad f_s = \tfrac{2}{5}Ma_{cm,x}.$$

Next, we insert this expression for f_s into the first equation above and solve for $a_{cm,x}$:

$$Mg\sin\beta - \tfrac{2}{5}Ma_{cm,x} = Ma_{cm,x},$$
$$a_{cm,x} = \tfrac{5}{7}g\sin\beta.$$

Finally, we substitute the right-hand side of this result back into the expression for f_s to obtain

$$f_s = \tfrac{2}{7}Mg\sin\beta.$$

Continued

REFLECT The acceleration is $\frac{5}{7}$ as large as it would be if the ball could *slide* without friction down the slope. That is why the friction force f_s is a *static* friction force; it is needed to prevent slipping and to give the ball its angular acceleration. We can derive an expression for the minimum coefficient of static friction μ_s needed to prevent slipping. The magnitude of the normal force is $n = Mg\cos\beta$. To prevent slipping, the coefficient of friction must be at least as great as

$$\mu_s = \frac{\frac{2}{7}Mg\sin\beta}{Mg\cos\beta} = \frac{2}{7}\tan\beta.$$

If the plane is tilted only a little, β and $\tan\beta$ are small, and only a small value of μ_s is needed to prevent slipping. But as the angle increases, the required value of μ_s also increases, as we would expect intuitively.

Finally, suppose μ_s is *not* large enough to prevent slipping. Then we have a whole new ball game, so to speak. Our basic dynamic equations are still valid, but now the ball slides and rotates at the same time. There is no longer a definite relation between $a_{cm,x}$ and α, and the friction force is now a *kinetic* friction force, given by $f_k = \mu_k n = \mu_k Mg\cos\beta$. The acceleration of the center of mass is then

$$a_{cm,x} = g(\sin\beta - \mu_k\cos\beta).$$

Practice Problem: Suppose we replace the bowling ball with a solid cylinder. Then the minimum coefficient of static friction needed to prevent slipping is $\mu_s = k\tan\beta$, where k is a dimensionless constant (equal to $\frac{2}{7}$ for the bowling ball). Determine the value of k for the cylinder. *Answer:* $k = \frac{1}{3}$.

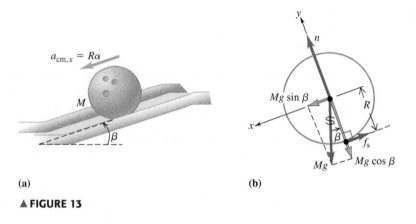

(a)

(b)

▲ **FIGURE 13**

3 Work and Power in Rotational Motion

When you pedal a bicycle, you apply forces to a rotating body and do work on it. Similar things happen in many real-life situations, such as a rotating motor shaft driving a power tool or a car engine propelling the vehicle. We can express this work in terms of torque and angular displacement.

Suppose a tangential force with constant magnitude F_{tan} acts at the rim of a merry-go-round platform with radius R (Figure 14) while the platform rotates through an angle $\Delta\theta$ about a fixed axis during a small time interval Δt. The displacement of the point at which the force acts is Δs. By definition, the work ΔW done by the force F_{tan} is $\Delta W = F_{tan}\Delta s$. If θ is measured in radians, $\Delta s = R\Delta\theta$, and it follows that

$$\Delta W = F_{tan}R\,\Delta\theta.$$

Now, $F_{tan}R$ is the *torque* τ due to the force F_{tan}, so

$$\Delta W = \tau\,\Delta\theta. \qquad (6)$$

If the torque is *constant* while the angle changes by a finite amount $\Delta\theta = \theta_2 - \theta_1$, then the work done on the body by the torque is as follows:

▲ **BIO Application Sensing angular acceleration.** How do we detect angular movement so that we can perform complex activities such as tumbling and diving? The mammalian inner ear has three semicircular canals filled with a viscous fluid. The canals are oriented such that they represent each of the three spatial axes. In response to angular acceleration, the canals and the sensory cells they contain rotate relative to the internal fluid, and this motion is detected by the cells and converted to electrical signals that are sent to the brain. Long before humans understood them, physical laws shaped evolution's design of life.

When Watson and Crick proposed the famous DNA double helix as the repository of genetic information, some scientists argued that an insurmountable amount of work would be required to unwind the helix during its replication, a necessary step in duplicating genes during cell division. The very long DNA molecule must rotate as it unwinds, and the friction between the rotating DNA and the fluid requires a continuous application of torque. Some thought that the torque required might be beyond the ability of biological molecular mechanisms to supply. A straightforward physics calculation showed that the energy required to overcome resistance to rotation was insignificant. The molecular motor responsible for unwinding DNA is called helicase (in yellow), which uses the energy stored in ATP to do its work, as is typical with molecular motors.

Chris Pelkie and Daniel Ripoll

Work done by a constant torque

The work done on a body by a constant torque equals the product of the torque and the angular displacement of the body:

$$W = \tau(\theta_2 - \theta_1) = \tau \, \Delta\theta. \qquad (7)$$

This equation is the rotational analog, $W = F_\parallel s$, for the work done by a constant force with component $F_\parallel$ in the direction of displacement.

Unit: If τ is expressed in newton-meters $(\mathrm{N \cdot m})$ and θ in radians, the work is in joules.

The force in Figure 14b has no radial component. If there were such a component, it would do no work, because the displacement of the point of application has no radial component. A radial component of force would also make no contribution to the torque about the axis of rotation, so Equations 6 and 7 are correct for any force, even if it does have a radial component. The same argument applies to an *axial* component of force—that is, a component parallel to the axis of rotation.

What about the *power* associated with work done by a torque acting on a rotating body? When we divide both sides of Equation 7 by the time interval Δt during which the angular displacement occurs, we find that

$$\frac{\Delta W}{\Delta t} = \tau \frac{\Delta\theta}{\Delta t}.$$

But $\Delta W / \Delta t$ is the rate of doing work, or *power P*, and $\Delta\theta / \Delta t$ is the body's angular velocity ω, so we obtain the following relation for power in rotational motion:

$$P = \tau\omega. \qquad (8)$$

When a torque τ (with respect to the axis of rotation) acts on a body that rotates with angular velocity ω, its power (rate of doing work) is the product of torque and angular velocity. This is the analog of the relation $P = Fv$ for particle motion.

NOTE ► In the relations just derived, angular displacements *must* be expressed in radians and angular velocities in radians per second. ◄

Child applies tangential force

$\vec{F}_{\text{tan}}$

(a)

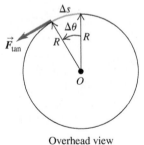

Δs

$\vec{F}_{\text{tan}}$

$\Delta\theta$

R R

O

Overhead view of merry-go-round

(b)

▲ **FIGURE 14** The work done by a tangential force acting on a body.

EXAMPLE 6   **Power of an electric motor**

An electric motor exerts a constant torque of $\tau = 10 \, \mathrm{N \cdot m}$ on a grindstone mounted on its shaft; the moment of inertia of the grindstone is $I = 2.0 \, \mathrm{kg \cdot m^2}$. If the system starts from rest, find the work done by the motor in 8.0 s and the kinetic energy at the end of this time. What was the average power delivered by the motor?

Continued

SOLUTION

SET UP AND SOLVE We want to use Equation 7 ($W = \tau \, \Delta\theta$) to find the total work done and then divide that by the time interval $\Delta t = 8.0$ s to find the average power (work per unit time). But first we need to find the total angle $\Delta\theta$ (in radians) through which the grindstone turns. The angular acceleration α is constant, so we can use $\tau = I\alpha$ to find α and then apply the formulas for constant angular acceleration.

The angular acceleration is

$$\alpha = \frac{\tau}{I} = \frac{10 \, \text{N} \cdot \text{m}}{2.0 \, \text{kg} \cdot \text{m}^2} = 5.0 \, \text{rad/s}^2.$$

For constant angular acceleration,

$$\theta = \theta_0 + \omega_0 t + \tfrac{1}{2}\alpha t^2 = 0 + 0 + \tfrac{1}{2}(5.0 \, \text{rad/s}^2)(8 \, \text{s})^2 = 160 \, \text{rad}.$$

The total work is

$$W = \tau \, \Delta\theta = (10 \, \text{N} \cdot \text{m})(160 \, \text{rad}) = 1600 \, \text{J}.$$

Finally, the average power is the total work divided by the time interval:

$$P_{av} = \frac{W}{\Delta t} = \frac{1600 \, \text{J}}{8.0 \, \text{s}} = 200 \, \text{J/s} = 200 \, \text{W}.$$

REFLECT We can check the energy relations. The angular velocity of the grindstone after 8.0 s is

$$\omega = \alpha t = (5.0 \, \text{rad/s}^2)(8.0 \, \text{s}) = 40 \, \text{rad/s}.$$

The grindstone's kinetic energy at this time is

$$K = \tfrac{1}{2}I\omega^2 = \tfrac{1}{2}(2.0 \, \text{kg} \cdot \text{m}^2)(40 \, \text{rad/s})^2 = 1600 \, \text{J}.$$

This amount equals the total work done, as of course it must. Note that the power is *not* constant during this process. The torque is constant, but as the angular velocity increases, so does the rate of doing work. The instantaneous power, $\tau\omega$, increases linearly with time, from zero, when $\omega = 0$, to 400 W, with an average value of 200 W.

Practice Problem: In this problem, suppose we use a larger motor that applies a constant torque of $20 \, \text{N} \cdot \text{m}$. Find the total work done in 8.0 s and the average power during this period. *Answer:* 6400 J, 800 W.

4 Angular Momentum

An Olympic ice skater with outstretched arms sets herself spinning about a vertical axis. When she pulls her arms in to her sides, she spins faster. When an Olympic diver goes off the high board in a "layout" position and then pulls his knees in toward his chest into a "tuck" position, he spins faster, even though there is no appreciable external torque acting on him. Both of these familiar phenomena, and many others (Figure 15), can be understood on the basis of a quantity called *angular momentum*, which we'll introduce in this section.

Every rotational quantity that we've seen so far in this chapter and the previous one is the analog of some quantity related to the motion of a particle. Angular momentum is the analog of the linear momentum ($\vec{p} = m\vec{v}$) of a particle. We define angular momentum as follows:

Definition of angular momentum
When a rigid body with moment of inertia I (with respect to a specified symmetry axis) rotates with angular velocity ω about that axis, the **angular momentum** of the body with respect to the axis is the product of the moment of inertia I about the axis and the angular velocity ω. We denote angular momentum by L:

$$L = I\omega. \tag{9}$$

The sign of angular momentum depends on the sign of ω; thus, according to our usual convention, it is positive for counterclockwise rotation and negative for clockwise rotation.

Unit: $\text{kg} \cdot \text{m}^2/\text{s}$

Mark Dadswell/Getty Images

▲ **FIGURE 15** As this diver goes into a tuck, her rotation speeds up, because angular momentum is conserved.

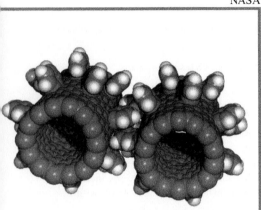

NASA

▲ Application **Gearing down.**
Nanoengineering involves the construction of submicroscopic machines, often built through the manipulation of individual atoms. Engineers have recently made tiny gears from carbon "nanotubes" with interlocking teeth made of organic molecules precisely placed on the tube surfaces. The operation of these gears is based on the same physical principles of torque and angular momentum as are applied to their macroscopic counterparts. To turn the gears, a laser shines tangentially onto the atoms at the end of the cylinder, creating a torque. This torque can cause a gear to rotate up to several thousand times per nanosecond.

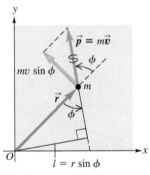

▲ **FIGURE 16** A particle with mass m rotating in the x-y plane. The angular momentum of the particle has magnitude $L = mvl$.

The basic dynamic principle for rotational motion (Equation 5, $\sum \tau = I\alpha$) can be restated in terms of angular momentum. If the axis doesn't move within the rotating object, then I is constant. In that case,

$$I\alpha = I\frac{\Delta\omega}{\Delta t} = \frac{\Delta(I\omega)}{\Delta t} = \frac{\Delta L}{\Delta t},$$

and Equation 5 can be rewritten as follows:

Torque and rate of change of angular momentum
The rate of change of angular momentum of a rigid body with respect to any axis equals the sum of the torques of the forces acting on it with respect to that axis:

$$\sum \tau = \frac{\Delta L}{\Delta t}. \tag{10}$$

We'll use this result soon when we discuss a conservation principle for angular momentum.

We can also define angular momentum for a single particle. In Figure 16, a particle moves in the x-y plane; its radial and tangential components of velocity are shown. The instantaneous velocity and linear momentum of the particle lie along a line at a perpendicular distance l from the axis through point O. We define the angular momentum of this particle as

$$L = mvl. \tag{11}$$

In the figure, the directions of $\vec{v}$ and $\vec{p}$ correspond to a counterclockwise (positive) sense of rotation. The distance l serves as a moment arm for the velocity, analogous to the moment arm (or lever arm) of a force in the definition of torque.

Equation 11 is consistent with our original definition of angular momentum of a rigid body. Suppose the object consists of a collection of particles with masses $m_A, m_B, m_C, \ldots$ at distances $r_A, r_B, r_C, \ldots$ from the axis through O. For each particle, the angle ϕ in Figure 16 is $90°$, so the moment arm l for particle A is its distance r_A from the axis of rotation. When the object rotates with angular velocity ω, the magnitude v_A of the velocity of particle A is $v_A = \omega r_A$, and the angular momentum L_A of this particle is

$$L_A = m_A v_A r_A = m_A(\omega r_A) r_A = m_A r_A^2 \omega.$$

If the object is rigid, *all* the particles must have the same angular velocity ω; the total angular momentum of all the particles is then

$$L = (m_A r_A^2 + m_B r_B^2 + m_C r_C^2 + \cdots)\omega = I\omega,$$

in agreement with our previous definition of the angular momentum of a rigid body.

NOTE ▶ As with all angular quantities, angular momentum is defined with reference to a particular axis of rotation. It is essential to specify this axis and use it consistently when applying the principles we've just discussed. ◀

Equation 10 will be particularly useful when we develop the principle of conservation of angular momentum in the next section. We've discussed changes in angular momentum that occur when the angular velocity ω of a body changes, but there are also cases in which ω is constant and I changes because of a change of shape or rearrangement of component parts of a body. In cases where I isn't constant, Equation 5 ($\sum \tau = I\alpha$) isn't valid. But the angular momentum is still given at each instant by $L = I\omega$, and the rate of change of angular momentum is still given by Equation 10. The next section includes some examples in which we have to take this more general view.

We've discussed angular momentum in the context of macroscopic bodies, but it is vitally important in physics at all scales, from nuclear to galactic. Angular momentum plays an essential role in classifying the quantum states of nuclei, atoms, and molecules and in describing their interactions. Angular momentum considerations are also an important tool in analyzing the motions of stars, galaxies, and nebulae. Along with mass, energy, and momentum, angular momentum is one of the unifying threads woven through the entire fabric of physical science.

EXAMPLE 7   A kinetic sculpture

A part of a mobile suspended from the ceiling of an airport terminal building consists of two metal spheres, each with mass 2.0 kg, connected by a uniform metal rod with mass 3.0 kg and length $s = 4.0$ m. The assembly is suspended at its midpoint by a wire and rotates in a horizontal plane, making 3.0 revolutions per minute. Find the angular momentum and kinetic energy of the assembly.

SOLUTION

SET UP Figure 17 shows our sketch. We draw the assembly as viewed from above (or below), in its plane of rotation.

SOLVE First, we need to find the moment of inertia of the assembly about an axis through its midpoint; we'll assume that each sphere can be treated as a point. Then the angular momentum L is given by $L = I\omega$, and the kinetic energy is $K = \frac{1}{2}I\omega^2$.

The moment of inertia of each sphere (treated as a point) is

$$I_{sphere} = m\left(\frac{s}{2}\right)^2 = (2.0 \text{ kg})(2.0 \text{ m})^2 = 8.0 \text{ kg} \cdot \text{m}^2.$$

From Table 9.2, the moment of inertia of a rod about an axis through its midpoint and perpendicular to its length is

$$I_{rod} = \frac{1}{12}Ms^2 = \frac{1}{12}(3.0 \text{ kg})(4.0 \text{ m})^2 = 4.0 \text{ kg} \cdot \text{m}^2.$$

So the total moment of inertia of the assembly is

$$I_{total} = 2(8.0 \text{ kg} \cdot \text{m}^2) + 4.0 \text{ kg} \cdot \text{m}^2 = 20 \text{ kg} \cdot \text{m}^2.$$

The angular velocity is given in revolutions per minute; we must convert it to radians per second:

$$\omega = 3.0 \text{ rev/min} = \left(\frac{3.0 \text{ rev}}{1 \text{ min}}\right)\left(\frac{1 \text{ min}}{60 \text{ s}}\right)\left(\frac{2\pi \text{ rad}}{1 \text{ rev}}\right) = 0.31 \text{ rad/s}.$$

▲ **FIGURE 17**

Now we can calculate the angular momentum of the assembly:

$$L = I\omega = (20 \text{ kg} \cdot \text{m}^2)(0.31 \text{ rad/s}) = 6.2 \text{ kg} \cdot \text{m}^2/\text{s}.$$

The kinetic energy is

$$K = \frac{1}{2}I\omega^2 = \frac{1}{2}(20 \text{ kg} \cdot \text{m}^2)(0.31 \text{ rad/s})^2$$
$$= 0.96 \text{ kg} \cdot \text{m}^2/\text{s}^2 = 0.96 \text{ J}.$$

REFLECT The mass of the rod is comparable to that of the spheres, but it contributes less to the total moment of inertia because most of its mass is closer to the axis of rotation than are the masses of the spheres.

Practice Problem: How long would an equal-mass rod have to be in order for its contribution to the total moment of inertia to equal that of the two spheres together? *Answer:* 8.0 m.

5 Conservation of Angular Momentum

We've seen that angular momentum can be used in an alternative statement of the basic dynamic principle for rotational motion. Angular momentum also forms the basis for a very important conservation principle: the principle of **conservation of angular momentum.** Like conservation of energy and conservation of linear momentum, this principle appears to be a universal conservation law, valid at all scales, from atomic and nuclear systems to the motions of galaxies.

The principle is based on the concept of an **isolated system**. We generalize this term to mean a system in which the total external force is zero *and* the total external torque is zero. Then our new conservation principle states simply that **the total angular momentum of an isolated system is constant.**

MasteringPHYSICS

PhET: Torque
ActivPhysics 7.14: Ball Hits Bat

◀ **Application** **The day the day got shorter.** The earthquake that caused the devastating tsunami of December 26, 2004, represented a rupture along a 1200 km stretch of the fault where the India plate of the earth's crust dives under the Burma plate, allowing the India plate to move downward by about 15 m. This downward shift of mass reduced our planet's moment of inertia slightly. Its angular momentum about its axis of rotation is very nearly constant; to conserve this angular momentum, the speed of rotation increased, shortening the length of the day. Scientists estimated that the quake shortened the length of the day by 2.7 microseconds.

The proof of this principle follows directly from Equation 10 ($\Sigma\tau = \Delta L/\Delta t$). When a system has several parts, the internal forces that the parts exert on each other cause changes in the angular momenta of the parts, but the *total* angular momentum of the system doesn't change. Here's an example: When two bodies A and B interact with each other but not with anything else, A and B together form an *isolated system*. Suppose body A exerts a force $\vec{F}_{A\text{ on }B}$ on body B; the corresponding torque (with respect to whatever axis we choose) is $\tau_{A\text{ on }B}$. According to Equation 10, this torque is equal to the rate of change of angular momentum of B:

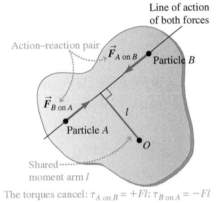

$$\tau_{A\text{ on }B} = \frac{\Delta L_B}{\Delta t}.$$

At the same time, body B exerts a force $\vec{F}_{B\text{ on }A}$ on body A, with a corresponding torque $\tau_{B\text{ on }A}$, and

$$\tau_{B\text{ on }A} = \frac{\Delta L_A}{\Delta t}.$$

From Newton's third law, $\vec{F}_{B\text{ on }A} = -\vec{F}_{A\text{ on }B}$. Furthermore, if the forces act along the same line, their moment arms with respect to the chosen axis are equal. Figure 7 demonstrated this point; we repeat it here as Figure 18. Thus, the torques of these two forces are equal and opposite, and $\tau_{B\text{ on }A} = -\tau_{A\text{ on }B}$. So when we add the preceding two equations, we find that

$$\frac{\Delta L_A}{\Delta t} + \frac{\Delta L_B}{\Delta t} = 0,$$

▲ **FIGURE 18** Why internal forces cannot change the total angular momentum of a system.

or, because $L_A + L_B$ is the *total* angular momentum L of the system,

$$\frac{\Delta L}{\Delta t} = 0. \tag{12}$$

That is, the total angular momentum of the system is constant; we also say that it is *conserved*. The torques of the internal forces can transfer angular momentum from one interacting object to another, but they can't change the *total* angular momentum of the system.

Conservation of angular momentum

When the sum of the torques of all the external forces acting on a system is zero, the total angular momentum of the system is constant (conserved).

An ice skater performing a pirouette on the toe of one skate takes advantage of this principle. Figure 19 shows the skater at the start of her pirouette, with her arms extended and with a counterclockwise angular momentum. As she pulls in her arms, she reduces her moment of inertia I. Because her angular momentum $L = I\omega$ must remain constant as I decreases, her angular velocity ω increases; she spins faster. That is,

▲ **FIGURE 19** As this skater reduces her moment of inertia by pulling in her arms, she spins faster, conserving angular momentum.

$$I_i\omega_i = I_f\omega_f. \tag{13}$$

A diver going into a tuck uses the same principle. Only by reducing his moment of inertia is he able to rotate multiple times before hitting the water. Notice that the skater and the diver can both be treated as isolated systems. The net external forces and torques on the skater are slight. Gravity has a major effect on the diver's translational motion, but once he is in the air it exerts no net torque on him. Thus, in terms of angular momentum, he is isolated.

EXAMPLE 8 **Two rotating disks interacting**

Figure 20 shows two disks, one an engine flywheel, the other a clutch plate attached to a transmission shaft. Their moments of inertia are I_A and I_B; initially, they are rotating with constant angular velocities ω_A and ω_B, respectively. We then push the disks together with forces acting along the axis, so as not to apply any torque on either disk. The disks rub against each other and eventually reach a common final angular velocity ω_f. Derive an expression for ω_f.

► **FIGURE 20**

SOLUTION

SET UP The two disks are an isolated system. The only torque acting on either disk is the torque applied by the other disk; there are no external torques. Thus the total angular momentum of the system is the same before and after they are pushed together. At the end, they rotate together as one body with total moment of inertia $I_f = I_A + I_B$ and angular velocity ω_f.

SOLVE Conservation of angular momentum gives

$$I_A\omega_A + I_B\omega_B = (I_A + I_B)\omega_f,$$
$$\omega_f = \frac{I_A\omega_A + I_B\omega_B}{I_A + I_B}.$$

REFLECT This is the analog of a completely inelastic collision of two particles. The final kinetic energy is always less than the initial value. This can be proved in general, using the above expression for ω_f.

Practice Problem: Suppose $I_B = 2I_A$. How must ω_A and ω_B be related if the entire system comes to rest after the interaction? *Answer:* $\omega_A = -2\omega_B$.

Quantitative Analysis 3 **Mass on a string: I**

In Figure 21, a block slides in a circular path on a horizontal frictionless plane under the action of a string that passes through a hole in the plane and is held vertically underneath it. By pulling on the lower end of the string, we reduce the radius to half of its original value. If the initial speed of the block is v_i, then the speed of the block after the string is shortened is

A. $\frac{1}{2}v_i$.　B. $2v_i$.　C. $4v_i$.

SOLUTION From Equation 11 the angular momentum of the block about a vertical axis through the hole is mvr. The force from the string pulls directly toward the axis. Therefore, it exerts no torque with respect to this axis, and it cannot change the block's angular momentum. Thus the angular momentum mvr of

▲ **FIGURE 21**

the block must be constant. If r is reduced by half, then v must double to keep the angular momentum constant (answer B).

Quantitative Analysis 4

Mass on a string: II

Let's consider again the whirling block shown in Figure 21. By letting additional string pass through the hole in the plane, we increase the radius to twice its original value. If the initial tension in the string is T, then the tension in the string after the radius is increased is

A. $\frac{1}{2}T$.
B. $\frac{1}{4}T$.
C. $\frac{1}{8}T$.

SOLUTION From Quantitative Analysis 3, we see that in this situation the angular momentum of the block doesn't change: if r is doubled, then v must decrease by half. The tension T provides the needed centripetal force, according to the relationship $T = mv^2/r$. In the situation presented here, r doubles and v is reduced to half its original value. Thus, in the expression for T, the denominator doubles and the numerator is reduced to one-fourth its initial value, for an overall reduction of T to one-eighth of its initial value (answer C).

EXAMPLE 9 **Anyone can be a ballerina**

An acrobatic physics professor stands at the center of a turntable, holding his arms extended horizontally, with a 5.0 kg dumbbell in each hand (Figure 22). He is set rotating about a vertical axis, making one revolution in 2.0 s. His moment of inertia (without the dumbbells) is 3.0 kg · m² when his arms are outstretched, and drops to 2.2 kg · m² when his arms are pulled in close to his chest. The dumbbells are 1.0 m from the axis initially and 0.20 m from it at the end. Find the professor's new angular velocity if he pulls the dumbbells close to his chest, and compare the final total kinetic energy with the initial value.

▶ **FIGURE 22**   BEFORE   AFTER

SOLUTION

SET UP If we neglect friction in the turntable, there are no external torques with respect to the vertical axis, and the angular momentum about this axis is constant. That is,

$$I_i\omega_i = I_f\omega_f,$$

where I_i and ω_i are the initial total moment of inertia and angular velocity, respectively, and I_f and ω_f are the final values.

SOLVE In each case, $I = I_{prof} + I_{dumb}$; thus,

$$I_i = 3.0\,\text{kg} \cdot \text{m}^2 + 2(5.0\,\text{kg})(1.0\,\text{m})^2 = 13\,\text{kg} \cdot \text{m}^2$$
$$I_f = 2.2\,\text{kg} \cdot \text{m}^2 + 2(5.0\,\text{kg})(0.20\,\text{m})^2 = 2.6\,\text{kg} \cdot \text{m}^2$$
$$\omega_i = 2\pi\frac{1\,\text{rev}}{2.0\,\text{s}} = \pi\,\text{rad/s}.$$

From conservation of angular momentum,

$$(13\,\text{kg} \cdot \text{m}^2)(\pi\,\text{rad/s}) = (2.6\,\text{kg} \cdot \text{m}^2)\omega_f,$$
$$\omega_f = 5.0\pi\,\text{rad/s} = 2.5\,\text{rev/s}.$$

That is, the angular velocity increases by a factor of five.

The initial kinetic energy is

$$K_i = \tfrac{1}{2}I_i\omega_i^2 = \tfrac{1}{2}(13\,\text{kg} \cdot \text{m}^2)(\pi\,\text{rad/s})^2$$
$$= 64\,\text{J}.$$

The final kinetic energy is

$$K_f = \tfrac{1}{2}I_f\omega_f^2 = \tfrac{1}{2}(2.6\,\text{kg} \cdot \text{m}^2)(5.0\pi\,\text{rad/s})^2$$
$$= 320\,\text{J}.$$

REFLECT Where did the "extra" 256 J of kinetic energy come from?

Practice Problem: Suppose the professor drops the dumbbells and then pulls his arms close to his chest. What is his final angular velocity? *Answer:* 0.68 rev/s.

EXAMPLE 10 **Angular momentum in a crime bust**

A uniform door 1.0 m wide with a mass of 15 kg is hinged at one side so that it can rotate without friction about a vertical axis. The door is unlatched. A police detective fires a bullet with a mass of 10 g and a speed of 400 m/s into the exact center of the door in a direction perpendicular to the plane of the door. Find the angular velocity of the door just after the bullet embeds itself in it. Is kinetic energy conserved?

Continued

SOLUTION

SET UP We consider the door and bullet together as a system. We denote the mass of the bullet as m, the mass of the door as M, and the door's width as s. Figure 23 shows our sketch. There is no external torque about the axis defined by the hinges, so angular momentum about this axis is conserved. We find the initial angular momentum of the bullet from Equation 11 ($L = mvl$). This quantity is equal to the final total angular momentum $I_{total}\omega_f$, where $I_{total} = I_{door} + I_{bullet}$.

SOLVE We compute all moments of inertia and angular momenta with respect to the axis defined by the door's hinges. The initial angular momentum of the bullet is

$$L_{bullet} = m_{bullet}v_{bullet}l = (0.010\ kg)(400\ m/s)(0.50\ m)$$
$$= 2.0\ kg \cdot m^2/s.$$

The moment of inertia of the door is

$$I_{door} = \frac{Ms^2}{3} = \frac{(15\ kg)(1.0\ m)^2}{3} = 5.0\ kg \cdot m^2.$$

The moment of inertia of the bullet (with respect to the axis along the hinges) is

$$I_{bullet} = ml^2 = (0.010\ kg)(0.50\ m)^2 = 0.0025\ kg \cdot m^2.$$

Conservation of angular momentum requires that $m_{bullet}v_{bullet}l = I_{total}\omega_f$, so we can solve for the final angular velocity ω_f:

$$2.0\ kg \cdot m^2/s = (5.0\ kg \cdot m^2 + 0.0025\ kg \cdot m^2)\omega_f,$$
$$\omega_f = 0.40\ rad/s.$$

The initial kinetic energy of the bullet is

$$K_i = \tfrac{1}{2}mv^2 = \tfrac{1}{2}(0.010\ kg)(400\ m/s)^2$$
$$= 800\ J.$$

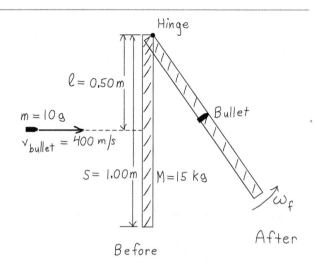

▲ **FIGURE 23**

The final total kinetic energy of the door and bullet is

$$K_f = \tfrac{1}{2}I\omega^2 = \tfrac{1}{2}(5.0025\ kg \cdot m^2)(0.40\ rad/s)^2$$
$$= 0.40\ J.$$

REFLECT Kinetic energy is *not* conserved. The final kinetic energy is only $\frac{1}{2000}$ of the initial value. The collision of bullet and door is inelastic because nonconservative forces act during the impact. Thus, we do not expect kinetic energy to be conserved.

Practice Problem: Suppose the bullet goes through the door and emerges with a speed of 100 m/s. Find the final angular velocity of the door just after the bullet goes through it. *Answer:* 0.30 rad/s.

6 Equilibrium of a Rigid Body

Here's an experiment to try: Face a wall, with your toes just touching the wall. Now try standing on tiptoe. What happens? You start falling over backward. Why? There is a net torque on you, and you are no longer in equilibrium. The need to consider torque occurs with a suspension bridge, a ladder leaning against a wall, or a crane hoisting a bucket full of concrete.

A body that can be modeled as a particle is in equilibrium whenever the vector sum of the forces acting on it is zero. But for the problems that we've just described, that condition isn't enough. Many bodies can't be adequately modeled as particles. The vector sum of the forces on such a body must still be zero, but an additional requirement must be satisfied to ensure that the body has no tendency to *rotate*. This requirement is based on the principles of rotational dynamics developed in this chapter. For a rigid body in equilibrium, the sum of the *torques* about any axis must be zero. We can compute the torque due to the weight of a body using the concept of center of mass and the related concept of center of gravity, which we'll introduce in this section.

Conditions for Equilibrium

A particle acted on by several forces is in equilibrium (in an inertial frame of reference) if the vector sum of the forces acting on the particle is zero ($\sum \vec{F} = 0$). This is often called the **first condition for equilibrium.** In terms of x and y components,

$$\sum F_x = 0, \qquad \sum F_y = 0. \tag{14}$$

For a rigid body, there is a **second condition for equilibrium** that must be met if the body is not to rotate:

Second condition for equilibrium

The sum of the torques due to all forces acting on the body, with respect to any specified axis, must be zero:

$$\sum \tau = 0. \qquad \text{(about any axis)} \tag{15}$$

The second condition for equilibrium is based on the dynamics of rotational motion in exactly the same way that the first condition is based on Newton's first law. A rigid body at rest has zero angular momentum ($L = 0$). For it to *remain* at rest, the *rate of change* of angular momentum $\Delta L/\Delta t$ must also be zero. From Equation 10, this means that the sum of the torques ($\sum \tau$) of all the forces acting on the object must be zero. Furthermore, because every point in the body is at rest in an inertial frame, any axis can be used as a reference line. Therefore, the sum of the torques about *any* axis must be zero. The object doesn't actually have to be pivoted about an axis through the chosen point. If a rigid body is in equilibrium, it can't have any tendency to begin to rotate about *any* axis. Thus, the sum of the torques must be zero, *no matter what axis is chosen.* (But don't compute some of the torques with respect to one axis and others with respect to a different axis; choose one axis and use it consistently.)

Although the choice of axis is arbitrary, once we choose it we must use the same axis to calculate all of the torques. An important element of the strategy for problems involving torques is to pick the axis or axes so as to simplify the calculations as much as possible.

Torque Due to Gravitational Force

In most equilibrium problems, one of the forces acting on the object is its weight. We need to be able to calculate the torque of this force. The weight doesn't act at a single point; rather, it is distributed over the entire body. But when the acceleration due to gravity is the same at every point in the body, we can always calculate the torque due to the body's weight by assuming that the entire force of gravity is concentrated at the center of mass of the object. We stated this principle, without detailed proof, in Section 1. Because of it, the center of mass of an object is sometimes called its *center of gravity* (cg). Note, however, that the center of mass is defined independently of any gravitational effect.

We can often use symmetry considerations to locate the center of gravity of a body. **The center of gravity of a homogeneous sphere, cube, circular disk, or rectangular plate is at its geometric center. The center of gravity of a right circular cylinder or cone is on the axis of symmetry, and so on.**

The center of gravity has several other important properties. First, when a body is in equilibrium in a gravitational field, supported or suspended at a single point, the center of gravity is always at or directly above or below the point of suspension. If it were anywhere else, the weight would have a torque with respect to that point, and the body could not be in rotational equilibrium.

This fact can be used to determine experimentally the location of the center of gravity of an irregular body (Figure 24). Try the following experiment: Cut an

Where do you place the string so that this cutout will hang horizontally?

1) Hold the cutout by any point on its edge and allow it to hang freely. A vertical line drawn from your hand passes through the center of gravity.

2) Repeat the process, holding the cutout at a different point. The spot where your two lines cross is the center of gravity.

Center of gravity

When suspended from the center of gravity, the cutout hangs level.

▲ **FIGURE 24** How to find the center of gravity of a flat object.

irregular shape out of cardboard, and then grasp it gently between your thumb and forefinger. The body rotates until its center of gravity is directly below the point you're grasping. Draw a vertical line through this point; the center of gravity must lie along this line. Repeat this procedure for a different suspension point; the intersection of the two lines must be the center of gravity. Pick a third point; the three lines must intersect at a single point. Once you've located the intersection point, poke a small hole in the body at that point and insert a pointed pen or pencil to confirm that the body balances there.

A force applied to a rigid body at its center of gravity doesn't tend to cause the body to rotate about an axis through that point. A force applied at any other point can cause both rotational and translational motion. We used this fact implicitly in the examples of Section 2.

▲ Application **An accident waiting to happen?** If these plates were not spinning rapidly, it would be nearly impossible to balance them on the ends of their sticks. When they are spinning, each stick exerts frictional forces on the underside of its plate; these forces tend to move the point of contact of the stick toward the center of the plate. Once centered, each spinning plate behaves like a gyroscope flywheel with its axis vertical and its center of mass directly above the point of support. Although the plates aren't in equilibrium (because they are slowing down), they can maintain their spinning motion for a considerable time.

PROBLEM-SOLVING STRATEGY 3 Equilibrium of a rigid body

The principles of rigid-body equilibrium are few and simple: The vector sum of the forces on the object must be zero, and the sum of the torques about any axis must be zero. The more challenging part is applying these principles to specific problems. Careful and systematic problem-solving methods always pay off. The following strategy is similar to the suggestions for equilibrium of a particle.

SET UP

1. Sketch the physical situation, including dimensions.
2. Choose some appropriate body as the body in equilibrium and draw a free-body diagram, showing the forces acting *on* this body and no others. Follow all the rules and sign conventions we've discussed previously. *Do not* include forces exerted *by* this body on other bodies. Be careful to show correctly the point at which each force acts; this is crucial for correct torque calculations.
3. Draw coordinate axes, and represent the forces in terms of their components with respect to these axes.

SOLVE

4. Write equations expressing the equilibrium conditions. Remember that $\sum F_x = 0$, $\sum F_y = 0$, and $\sum \tau = 0$ are always separate equations; *never* add x and y components in a single equation.
5. In choosing an axis of rotation for computing torques, note that if a force has a line of action that goes *through* a particular rotation axis, the torque of the force with respect to that axis is zero. You can often eliminate unknown forces or components from the torque equation by a clever choice of axis. Also remember that when a force is represented in terms of its components, you can compute the torque of that force by finding the torque of each component separately, each with its appropriate moment arm and sign, and adding the results. This approach is often easier than determining the moment arm of the original force.

REFLECT

6. You always need as many equations as you have unknowns. Depending on the number of unknowns, you may need to compute torques with respect to two or more rotation axes to obtain enough equations. There often are several equally good sets of force and torque equations for a particular problem; there is usually no single "right" combination of equations. When you have as many independent equations as unknowns, you can solve the equations simultaneously. We'll illustrate this point in some of the examples that follow by using various sets of equations.

EXAMPLE 11 Playing on a seesaw

You and a friend play on a seesaw. Your mass is 90 kg, and your friend's mass is 60 kg. The seesaw board is 3.0 m long and has negligible mass. Where should the pivot be placed so that the seesaw will balance when you sit on the left end and your friend sits on the right end?

SOLUTION

SET UP Figure 25 shows our sketches. First we sketch the physical situation, and then we make a free-body diagram, placing the pivot at a distance x from the left end. Note that each weight is the corresponding mass multiplied by g, so g will divide out of the final result. Remember that counterclockwise torques are positive and clockwise torques are negative. For the seesaw to be in equilibrium, the sum of the torques about any axis must be zero. We choose to take torques about the pivot axis; then the normal force acting at the pivot doesn't enter into the analysis. The moment arms are x for you and $(3.0 \text{ m} - x)$ for your friend.

SOLVE Your torque is $\tau_{\text{you}} = +(90 \text{ kg})gx$. Your friend is $3.0 \text{ m} - x$ from the pivot, and the corresponding torque is $\tau_{\text{friend}} = -(60 \text{ kg})g(3.0 \text{ m} - x)$. For equilibrium, the sum of these torques must be zero:

$$\tau_{\text{you}} + \tau_{\text{friend}} = 0$$
$$+(90 \text{ kg})gx - (60 \text{ kg})g(3.0 \text{ m} - x) = 0.$$

We divide through by g and solve for x, obtaining $x = 1.2 \text{ m}$.

REFLECT If we put the pivot at the center of the board ($x = 1.5 \text{ m}$), we would have equal moment arms but unequal weights, so it's clear that the pivot must be to the *left* of center.

(a) Sketch of physical situation

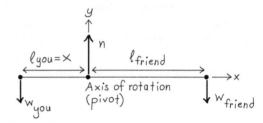

(b) Free-body diagram

▲ **FIGURE 25**

Practice Problem: If the board has a mass of 20 kg, where should the pivot be placed for balance? *Answer:* 1.24 m from the left end.

EXAMPLE 12 A heroic rescue

Sir Lancelot is trying to rescue the Lady Elayne from the Black Castle by climbing a uniform ladder that is 5.0 m long and weighs 180 N. Lancelot, who weighs 800 N, stops a third of the way up the ladder (Figure 26a). The bottom of the ladder rests on a horizontal stone ledge and leans across the castle's moat in equilibrium against a vertical wall that is frictionless because of a thick layer of moss. The ladder makes an angle of 53° with the horizontal, conveniently forming a 3–4–5 right triangle. **(a)** Find the normal and friction forces on the ladder at its base. **(b)** Find the minimum coefficient of static friction needed to prevent slipping. **(c)** Find the magnitude and direction of the contact force on the ladder at the base.

SOLUTION

SET UP Figure 26b shows a free-body diagram for the ladder. Since it is described as "uniform," we can assume that its center of gravity is at its center, halfway between the base and the wall. Lancelot's weight pushes down on the ladder at a point one-third of the way from the base toward the wall. The contact force n_1 at the top of the ladder is horizontal and to the left, because the wall is frictionless. The components of the contact force at the base are the upward normal force n_2 and the friction force f_s, which must point to the right to prevent slipping.

SOLVE Part (a) The first condition for equilibrium, in component form, gives

$$\Sigma F_x = f_s + (-n_1) = 0,$$
$$\Sigma F_y = n_2 + (-800 \text{ N}) + (-180 \text{ N}) = 0.$$

These are two equations for the three unknowns n_1, n_2, and f_s. The first equation tells us that the two horizontal forces must be equal and opposite, and the second equation gives $n_2 = 980 \text{ N}$. That is, the ledge pushes up with a force of 980 N to balance the total (downward) weight $(800 \text{ N} + 180 \text{ N})$.

Continued

We don't yet have enough equations, but now we can use the second condition for equilibrium. We can take torques about any point we choose. The smart choice is the point that will give us the fewest terms and fewest unknowns in the torque equation. With this thought in mind, we choose point B, at the base of the ladder. The two forces n_2 and f_s have no torque about that point. From Figure 26b, we see that the moment arm for the ladder's weight is 1.5 m, the moment arm for Lancelot's weight is 1.0 m, and the moment arm for n is 4.0 m. The torque equation for point B is thus

$$\Sigma\tau_B = n_1(4.0\text{ m}) - (180\text{ N})(1.5\text{ m})$$
$$- (800\text{ N})(1.0\text{ m}) + n_2(0) + f_s(0) = 0.$$

Solving for n_1, we get

$$n_1 = 268\text{ N}.$$

Now we substitute this result back into the equation $\Sigma F_x = 0$ to get

$$f_s = 268\text{ N}.$$

Part (b) The static friction force f_s cannot exceed $\mu_s n_2$, so the *minimum* coefficient of static friction to prevent slipping is

$$(\mu_s)_{min} = \frac{f_s}{n_2} = \frac{268\text{ N}}{980\text{ N}} = 0.27.$$

Part (c) The components of the contact force at the base are the static friction force $f_s = 286$ N and the normal force $n_2 = 980$ N; the magnitude of $\vec{F}_B$ is

$$F_B = \sqrt{(268\text{ N})^2 + (980\text{ N})^2} = 1020\text{ N},$$

and its direction (Figure 26c) is

$$\theta = \tan^{-1}\frac{980\text{ N}}{268\text{ N}} = 75°.$$

REFLECT First, the contact force $\vec{F}_B$ at an angle of 75° is *not* directed along the length of the ladder, which is at an angle of 53° If it were, the sum of torques with respect to the point where Lancelot stands couldn't be zero.

Second, as Lancelot climbs higher on the ladder, the moment arm and torque of his weight about B increase, thereby increasing the values of n_1, f_s, and $(\mu_s)_{min}$. At the top, his moment arm would be nearly 3 m, giving a minimum coefficient of static friction of nearly 0.7. An aluminum ladder on a wood floor wouldn't have a value of μ_s this large, so present-day aluminum ladders are usually equipped with nonslip rubber feet.

Third, a larger ladder angle (i.e., a more upright ladder) would decrease the moment arms of the weights of the ladder and Lancelot with respect to B and would increase the moment arm of n_1, all of which would decrease the required friction force. Some manufacturers recommend that their ladders be used at an angle of 75°. (Why not 90°?)

Practice Problem: Carry out an alternative procedure for obtaining the results asked for in Parts (a), (b), and (c) by taking torques about an axis at the top of the ladder; check to see that your results agree with the previous ones.

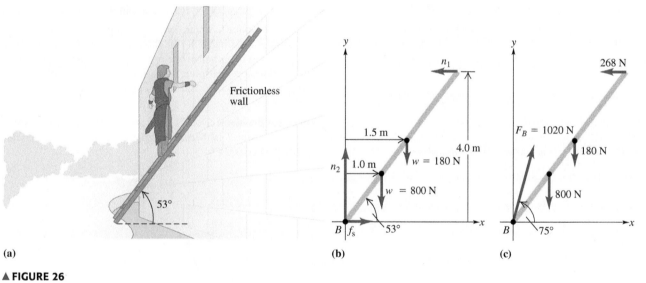

(a)

(b)

(c)

▲ **FIGURE 26**

EXAMPLE 13 **Equilibrium and pumping iron**

Figure 27a shows a human arm lifting a dumbbell. The forearm is in equilibrium under the action of the weight w of the dumbbell, the tension T in the tendon connected to the biceps muscle at point A, and the forces exerted on the forearm by the upper arm at the elbow joint. For clarity, the tendon force has been displaced away from the elbow farther than its actual position. The weight w and the angle θ are given. Find the tension T in the tendon and the two components of force (E_x and E_y) at the elbow (three unknown quantities in all). Neglect the weight of the forearm itself. Evaluate your results for $w = 50$ N, $d = 0.10$ m, $l = 0.50$ m, and $\theta = 80°$.

Continued

SOLUTION

SET UP As the body in equilibrium, we choose the forearm plus dumbbell (the colored elements in Figure 27a). Figure 27b shows our free-body diagram. We apply a coordinate system and draw the three forces on the forearm, representing the tension force and the forces on the elbow in terms of components along the x and y directions. Note that we don't yet know the sign of the elbow force component E_y (although we drew it as positive for convenience); it could come out either way. Study this free-body diagram; be sure you understand how these forces allow you to lift things.

SOLVE First we use the components T_x and T_y of the tension force, along with the given angle θ, to represent the unknown magnitude:

$$T_x = T\cos\theta \qquad T_y = T\sin\theta.$$

Next we note that if we take torques about the elbow joint (point E), the resulting torque equation does not contain E_x, E_y, or T_x because the lines of action of all these forces pass through this point. The torque equation is then simply

$$\Sigma\tau_E = lw - dT_y = 0.$$

From this equation, we find that

$$T_y = \frac{lw}{d} \qquad \text{and} \qquad T = \frac{lw}{d\sin\theta}.$$

To find E_x and E_y, we could now use the first condition for equilibrium: $\Sigma F_x = 0$ and $\Sigma F_y = 0$. Instead, for added practice in using torques, we take torques about the point A where the tendon is attached:

$$(l - d)w + dE_y = 0 \qquad \text{and} \qquad E_y = -\frac{(l - d)w}{d}.$$

The negative sign shows that our initial guess for the direction of E_y was wrong; it is actually vertically *downward*.

Finally, we take torques about point B in the figure and remember to use the shortest perpendicular distance to the vector $\vec{w}$ to simplify our calculations.

$$\Sigma\tau_B = lw - hE_x = 0 \qquad \text{and} \qquad E_x = \frac{lw}{h}.$$

Evaluating our expressions for $w = 50\,\text{N}$, $d = 0.10\,\text{m}$, $l = 0.50\,\text{m}$, and $\theta = 80°$, we get $\tan\theta = h/d$, and we find $h = d\tan\theta = (0.10\,\text{m})(5.67) = 0.57\,\text{m}$. We then have

$$T = \frac{(0.50\,\text{m})(50\,\text{N})}{(0.10\,\text{m})(0.98)} = 250\,\text{N},$$

$$E_y = -\frac{(0.50\,\text{m} - 0.10\,\text{m})(50\,\text{N})}{0.10\,\text{m}} = -200\,\text{N},$$

$$E_x = \frac{(0.50\,\text{m})(50\,\text{N})}{0.57\,\text{m}} = 44\,\text{N}.$$

The magnitude of the force at the elbow is

$$E = \sqrt{E_x^2 + E_y^2} = 200\,\text{N}.$$

As we mentioned earlier, we have not explicitly used the first condition for equilibrium, that the vector sum of the forces be zero. To check our answer, we can compute ΣF_x and ΣF_y to verify that they really *are* zero. Such checks help verify internal consistency. Checking, we obtain

$$\Sigma F_x = E_x - T_x = 44\,\text{N} - (250\,\text{N})\cos 80° = 0,$$
$$\Sigma F_y = E_y + T_y - w$$
$$= -200\,\text{N} + (250\,\text{N})\sin 80° - 50\,\text{N} = 0.$$

REFLECT Notice how much we have simplified these calculations by using a little ingenuity in choosing the point for calculating torques so as to eliminate one or more of the unknown quantities. In the last step, the force T has no torque about point B; thus, when the torques of T_x and T_y are computed separately, they must add to zero.

Practice Problem: Double the weight of the dumbbell. What is the new tension T in the tendon connected to the biceps muscle at point B? *Answer: $T = 510\,\text{N}$.*

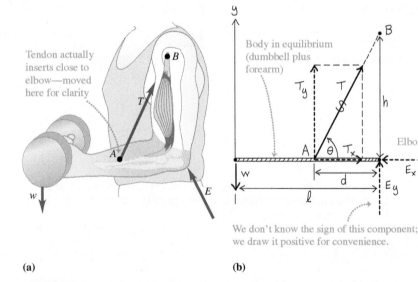

(a)

(b)

▲ **FIGURE 27**

7 Vector Nature of Angular Quantities

Rotational quantities associated with an axis of rotation, such as angular velocity, angular momentum, and torque, can be represented as *vector* quantities. For a body rotating about a fixed axis that is an axis of symmetry, the directions of these vector quantities are along the axis of rotation, in a direction given by the **right-hand rule,** illustrated in Figure 28. If you curl the fingers of your *right* hand in the direction the object rotates, then your thumb points in the direction of the vector angular velocity $\vec{\omega}$ and angular momentum $\vec{L}$. In the case of a torque, you curl the fingers of your right hand in the direction the torque would turn the body if acting on its own; then your thumb points in the torque's direction.

So far, we've dealt with rotating bodies whose axis of rotation, whether stationary or moving, has a fixed direction that is perpendicular to the planes in which the particles of the body revolve. (We've oriented our coordinate systems so that the particles of the body move parallel to the *x-y* plane and the axis of rotation is perpendicular to that plane.) When the axis of rotation can change direction, the situation becomes much richer in the variety of physical phenomena (some quite unexpected) that can occur. For example, if you try to balance a stationary top on its point, it falls over; but when it's spinning, it balances easily. Why? And why are bicycles "tippy" when moving slowly but stable when moving fast? General answers to questions such as these are quite complex, but we can go a little way into understanding this behavior.

For a symmetric body turning about its axis of symmetry, the magnitude of the angular momentum is $L = I\omega$ (Equation 9). The corresponding relationship between *vector* angular momentum and *vector* angular velocity is

$$\vec{L} = I\vec{\omega}, \tag{16}$$

where I is the moment of inertia about the axis of rotation. Thus, for rotation about an axis of symmetry, the angular velocity and angular momentum vectors have the same direction. Furthermore, we can define a vector torque that is related to the rate of change of vector angular momentum with respect to time by a vector equation analogous to Equation 10:

$$\sum\vec{\tau} = \frac{\Delta\vec{L}}{\Delta t}, \quad \text{or} \quad \Delta\vec{L} = \sum\vec{\tau}\,\Delta t. \tag{17}$$

In the problems we've worked out so far, $\sum\vec{\tau}$ and $\vec{L}$ have always had the same direction, so only one component of each vector quantity is different from zero. But Equation 17 is valid even when $\sum\vec{\tau}$ and $\vec{L}$ have different directions. Then the *direction* of the axis of rotation may change, as with a spinning top, and we have to consider the vector nature of the various angular quantities carefully.

An example of a three-dimensional application of Equation 17 is the gyroscope. Figure 29 shows a typical toy gyroscope. We set the flywheel spinning by wrapping a string around its shaft and pulling. When the shaft is supported at only one end, as shown in the figure, one possible motion is a steady circular motion of the axis in a horizontal plane, combined with the spinning motion of the flywheel about the axis. This phenomenon is quite unexpected when you see it for the first time; intuition suggests that the free end of the axis should simply drop if it isn't supported. Indeed, if the flywheel isn't spinning, that *is* what happens. The vector nature of angular momentum is the key to understanding the horizontal motion of the axis when the wheel is spinning.

Suppose we take a stationary gyroscope and lift the flywheel until its axis is horizontal, as shown in Figure 30. Then when we let it go, two forces act on the flywheel: its weight $\vec{w}$, acting downward at the center of mass, and the normal force $\vec{n}$ at the pivot point O. The weight has a moment arm r; the resulting torque, whose direction is given by the right-hand rule, causes the free end of the flywheel

You must use your right hand!

Right-hand screws are threaded so that they move in the direction of the torque applied to them.

▲ **FIGURE 28** The right-hand rule for angular quantities.

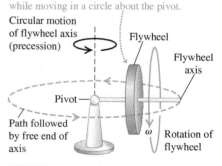

▲ **FIGURE 29** A typical toy gyroscope.

When the flywheel is not rotating, its weight creates a torque around the pivot, causing it to fall along a circular path until its axis rests on the table surface.

In falling, the flywheel rotates about the pivot and thus has an angular momentum $\vec{L}$. The *direction* of $\vec{L}$ stays constant.

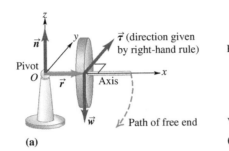

Pivot O Axis   Path of free end

(a)

Pivot O Flywheel

View from above as flywheel falls

(b)

▲ **FIGURE 30** What happens when we lift and release a gyroscope that is not rotating.

▲ **Application The reason for rifling.** This photo looks out through the barrel of one of the guns that protected the Maginot line in France. The spiral ridges, called *rifling,* exert a torque on the shell as it is fired, so that the shell is spinning as it emerges from the gun. This spin stabilizes the bullet by giving it an angular momentum that points in the direction of the bullet's motion. Whereas a non-spinning bullet would be inclined to tumble, a spinning bullet flies straight. (In fact, when liquid-fueled rockets were developed, they had to be equipped with complex active stabilization systems precisely because they could not be spun.) Rifles are named after the fact that their barrels are rifled.

When the flywheel is rotating, the system starts with an angular momentum $\vec{L}_i$ parallel to the flywheel's axis of rotation.

Rotation of flywheel

$\vec{\tau}$ Torque due to weight force (as in Figure 30)

$\vec{L}_i$

Initial angular momentum due to rotation of flywheel

ω

(a)

Now the effect of the torque is to cause the angular momentum to precess around the pivot. The gyroscope circles around its pivot without falling.

$\vec{L}_f$ $\Delta\vec{L}$ $\Delta\vec{L}$ $\Delta\vec{L}$ $\Delta\vec{L}$ $\Delta\vec{L}$

$\vec{L}_i$

View from above

(b)

▲ **FIGURE 31** What happens when we set a gyroscope rotating before releasing it.

axis to fall along a path forming a circle in a vertical plane, centered on the pivot, until it hits the table. In doing so, the torque gives the flywheel angular momentum according to Equation 17: $\Delta\vec{L} = \sum\vec{\tau}\,\Delta t$. Because the axis of rotation is stationary, the directions of both the torque and the angular momentum are constant. Indeed, if we divide the motion into time intervals Δt (Figure 30b), we see that the successive $\Delta\vec{L}$'s are all parallel. These $\Delta\vec{L}$'s add to give a horizontal angular momentum that is constant in *direction* but continuously increases in *magnitude*.

Now let's start over; this time we lift the flywheel and start it rotating before we let it go (Figure 31). Now the initial angular momentum $\vec{L}$ of the flywheel (before we let it go) is *along* the flywheel's axis of rotation. Once we let go, the flywheel is acted upon by a torque due to the weight and normal forces, as before. Again, we divide the motion into time intervals Δt (Figure 31b). Each $\Delta\vec{L}$ is perpendicular to the flywheel's axis. This causes the *direction* of $\vec{L}$ to change, but not its *magnitude*. The center of mass of the flywheel moves in a horizontal circle. The normal force magnitude n is then equal to the flywheel's weight w, and the corresponding torque is $\tau = rw$. (The situation is analogous to a particle moving in uniform circular motion, where the centripetal force causes changes $\Delta\vec{p}$ in linear momentum that are always perpendicular to the linear momentum $\vec{p}$ that already exists, changing the direction of $\vec{p}$, but not its magnitude.)

In Figure 31a, at the instant shown, the gyroscope has a definite nonzero angular momentum described by the vector $\vec{L}_i$. The *change* $\Delta\vec{L}$ in angular momentum in a short time interval Δt following this instant is given by Equation 17:

$$\Delta\vec{L} = \vec{\tau}\,\Delta t.$$

The direction of $\Delta\vec{L}$ is the same as that of $\vec{\tau}$. After a time Δt, the angular momentum is $\vec{L}_i + \Delta\vec{L}$. As the vector diagram shows, this means that the gyroscope axis has turned through a small angle $\Delta\phi$ given by $\Delta\phi = |\Delta\vec{L}|/|\vec{L}|$. We see that such a motion of the axis, called **precession,** is required by the torque–angular momentum relationship.

The rate at which the axis moves, $\Delta\phi/\Delta t$, is called the *precession angular velocity*. Denoting this quantity by Ω, we find that

$$\Omega = \frac{\Delta\phi}{\Delta t} = \frac{|\Delta\vec{L}|/|\vec{L}|}{\Delta t} = \frac{\tau}{L} = \frac{wr}{I\omega}. \tag{18}$$

Thus, the precession angular velocity is *inversely* proportional to the angular velocity of spin about the axis. A rapidly spinning gyroscope precesses slowly; as the flywheel slows down, the precession angular velocity *increases*.

EXAMPLE 14 **A laboratory gyroscope**

Figure 32 shows a top view of a gyro-scope wheel in the form of a solid cylin-der, driven by an electric motor. The pivot is at O, and the mass of the axle and motor are negligible. Is the precession clockwise or counterclockwise, as seen from above? If the gyroscope takes 4.0 s for one revolution of precession, what is the wheel's angular velocity?

(a) Top view of spinning cylindrical gyroscope wheel

(b) Vector diagram

▲ **FIGURE 32**

SOLUTION

SET UP The right-hand rule shows that $\vec{\omega}$ and $\vec{L}$ are to the left (Figure 32b). The weight $\vec{w}$ points into the page, the torque $\vec{\tau}$ is toward the top of the page, with magnitude rw (where r is the dis-tance from the pivot point O to the center of mass of the cylin-der), and $\Delta\vec{L}/\Delta t$ is also toward the top of the page. Adding a small $\Delta\vec{L}$ to the $\vec{L}$ that we have at the start changes the direction of $\vec{L}$ as shown, so the precession is clockwise as seen from above.

Be careful not to mix up ω and Ω. The precession angular velocity Ω is given as $\Omega = (1\ \text{rev})/(4.0\ \text{s}) = (2\pi\ \text{rad})/(4.0\ \text{s}) = \pi/2\ \text{rad/s}$. The weight is equal to mg, and the moment of inertia of a solid cylinder with radius R is $I = \frac{1}{2}mR^2$.

SOLVE As shown in the "Set Up" discussion, the precession is clockwise as seen from above. Solving Equation 18 for ω, we find that

$$\omega = \frac{wr}{I\Omega} = \frac{mgr}{(mR^2/2)\Omega}$$
$$= \frac{2(9.8\ \text{m/s}^2)(2.0 \times 10^{-2}\ \text{m})}{(3.0 \times 10^{-2}\ \text{m})^2(\pi/2\ \text{rad/s})} = 280\ \text{rad/s} = 2700\ \text{rev/min}.$$

REFLECT The mass of the flywheel divides out and does not appear in the final result. If we double the mass, the torque caus-ing the precession doubles, but the moment of inertia also dou-bles, and the two effects cancel.

As the gyroscope precesses, the center of mass moves in a circle with radius r in a horizontal plane. Its vertical component of acceleration is zero, so the pivot must exert an upward normal force $\vec{n}$ just equal in magnitude to the weight. The circular motion of the center of mass with angular velocity Ω requires a force $\vec{F}$ directed toward the center of the circle, with magnitude $F = m\Omega^2 r$. This force must also be supplied by the pivot.

The preceding analysis of the gyroscope gives us a glimpse into the rich-ness of the dynamics of rotational motion, which can involve some complex phenomena.

CHAPTER SUMMARY

Torque

(Section 1) When a force F acts on a body, the torque τ of that force with respect to a point O is given by $\tau = Fl = rF\sin\phi$ (Equations 1 and 2). We use the sign convention that a torque tending to cause counterclockwise rotation is positive, while one tending to cause clockwise rotation is negative.

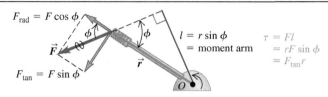

$F_{\text{rad}} = F\cos\phi$

$F_{\text{tan}} = F\sin\phi$

$l = r\sin\phi$
$= $ moment arm

$\tau = Fl$
$= rF\sin\phi$
$= F_{\text{tan}}r$

Torque and Angular Acceleration

(Section 2) The angular acceleration α of a rigid body rotating about a stationary axis is related to the total torque $\Sigma\tau$ and the moment of inertia I of the body by $\Sigma\tau = I\alpha$ (Equation 5). This relation is also valid for a body with a moving axis of rotation, provided that the rotation axis is an axis of symmetry that passes through the center of mass and does not change direction.

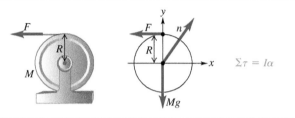

$\Sigma\tau = I\alpha$

Work and Power

(Section 3) When a constant torque τ acts on a rigid body that undergoes an angular displacement $\Delta\theta$ from θ_1 to θ_2, the work W done by the torque is $W = \tau(\theta_2 - \theta_1) = \tau\,\Delta\theta$ (Equation 7). When the object rotates with angular velocity ω, the power P (rate at which the torque does work) is $P = \tau\omega$ (Equation 8).

Angular Momentum

(Section 4) The angular momentum L, with respect to an axis through a point O, of a particle with mass m and velocity $\vec{v}$ is $L = mvl$ (Equation 11). When a rigid body with moment of inertia I rotates with angular velocity ω about a stationary axis, the angular momentum with respect to that axis is $L = I\omega$ (Equation 9).

In terms of torque τ and angular momentum L, the basic dynamic relation for rotational motion can be restated as

$$\Sigma\tau = \frac{\Delta L}{\Delta t}. \tag{10}$$

$\vec{p} = m\vec{v}$

$mv\sin\phi$

$L = mvr\sin\phi = mvl$

$l = r\sin\phi$

Conservation of Angular Momentum

(Section 5) If a system consists of bodies that interact with each other but not with anything else, or if the total torque associated with the external forces is zero, then the total angular momentum of the system is constant (conserved): $\vec{L}_i = \vec{L}_f$.

Equilibrium of a Rigid Body

(Section 6) The two conditions for equilibrium of a rigid body are $\Sigma\vec{F} = 0$ (Equation 14) and $\Sigma\tau = 0$ (Equation 15). The former ensures that the center of mass of the body has no linear acceleration a, and the latter ensures that it has no angular acceleration α about any axis.

Continued

Vector Nature of Angular Quantities

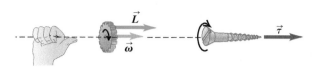

(Section 7) Vector angular velocity $\vec{\omega}$ is a vector quantity whose direction is that of the axis of rotation and whose magnitude is the (scalar) angular velocity. The sense of the vector $\vec{\omega}$ is given by the right-hand rule. When a body rotates about an axis of symmetry, the vector angular momentum $\vec{L}$ is given by $\vec{L} = I\vec{\omega}$.

In terms of vector torque $\vec{\tau}$ and angular momentum $\vec{L}$, the basic dynamic relation for rotational motion can be restated as

$$\sum \vec{\tau} = \frac{\Delta \vec{L}}{\Delta t}. \qquad (17)$$

Dynamics of Rotational Motion: Problem Set

MP For instructor-assigned homework, go to www.masteringphysics.com

Conceptual Questions

1. When tightening a bolt, mechanics sometimes extend the length of a wrench handle by slipping a section of pipe over the handle. Why could this procedure easily damage the bolt?
2. Must there necessarily be matter at the center of mass of an object? Illustrate your answer with several common examples.
3. Two identical uniform 12 inch bricks are placed one atop the other and pushed past the edge of a table. (See Figure 33.) What is the greatest that x can be?

4. A uniform 10 cm × 20 cm box is placed on a ramp that rises at an angle θ above the horizontal. (See Figure 34.) Assuming that there is enough friction to ▲ **FIGURE 33** Question 3. prevent this box from sliding, what is the largest that θ can be without tipping it over?
5. (a) Can you change the location of your body's center of mass? How? (b) Can you change your body's moment of inertia? How?
6. Serious bicyclists say that if you reduce the weight of a bike, it is more effective if you do so in the wheels rather than in the frame. Why would reducing weight in the wheels make it easier on the bicyclist than reducing the same amount in the frame?

▲ **FIGURE 34** Question 4.

7. When a tall, heavy object, such as a refrigerator, is pushed across a rough floor, what things determine whether it slides or tips?
8. (a) If the forces on an object balance, do the torques necessarily balance? (b) If the torques on an object balance, do the forces necessarily balance? Illustrate your answers with clear examples.

9. Why is a tapered water glass with a narrow base easier to tip over than one with straight sides? Does it matter whether the glass is full or empty?
10. True or false? In picking an axis about which to compute torques in rotational equilibrium, it is nearly always best to choose an axis through the center of mass of the object. Explain your reasoning.
11. People sometimes prop open a door by wedging an object in the space between the vertical hinged side of the door and the frame. Explain why this often results in the hinge screws being ripped out.
12. **Global warming.** As the earth's climate continues to warm, ice near the poles will melt and be added to the oceans. What effect will this have on the length of the day? (*Hint:* Consult a map to see where the oceans lie.)
13. In terms of torques, discuss the action of a claw hammer in pulling out nails.
14. You make two versions of the same object out of the same material having uniform density. For one version all the dimensions are exactly twice as great as for the other one. If the same torque acts on both versions, giving the smaller version angular acceleration α, what will be the angular acceleration of the larger version in terms of α?
15. If two spinning objects have the same angular momentum, will they necessarily have the same rotational kinetic energy? If they have the same rotational kinetic energy, will they necessarily have the same angular momentum?

Multiple-Choice Problems

1. You are designing a wheel that must have a fixed mass and diameter, but that can have its mass distributed in various uniform ways. If the torque you exert on it is also fixed, which of the wheels shown will have the *smallest* angular acceleration about an axis perpendicular to it at its center?

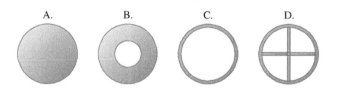

A.   B.   C.   D.

2. Two equal masses m are connected by a very light string over a frictionless pulley of mass $m/2$. (See Figure 35.) The system has been given a push to get it moving as shown, but that push is no longer acting. In which segment of the string is the tension greater?

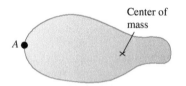

A. The tension in A is greater.
B. The tension in B is greater.
C. The two tensions are the same.

▲ **FIGURE 35** Multiple-choice problem 2.

3. The irregular object shown in Figure 36 is dropped from rest on the moon, where there is no air. Its center of mass is as shown in the figure. What will it do after it is dropped?
A. It will start rotating clockwise about its center of mass.
B. It will start rotating counterclockwise about its center of mass.
C. It will rotate until point A is directly below its center of mass, and then it will stop turning.
D. It will rotate until point A is directly above its center of mass, and then it will stop turning.
E. It will not rotate.

▲ **FIGURE 36** Multiple-choice problem 3.

4. A student is sitting on a frictionless rotating stool with her arms outstretched holding equal heavy weights in each hand. If she suddenly lets go of the weights, her angular speed will
A. increase
B. stay the same
C. decrease.

5. If the torques on an object balance, then it follows that this object (there could be more than one correct choice)
A. cannot be rotating.
B. cannot have any angular acceleration.
C. cannot be moving.
D. cannot be accelerating.

6. If the forces on an object balance, then it follows that this object (there could be more than one correct choice)
A. cannot be rotating.
B. cannot have any angular acceleration.
C. cannot be moving.
D. cannot be accelerating.

7. A solid uniform ball and a solid uniform cylinder with the same mass and diameter are released from rest and roll without slipping down a hill. Which one will have a *greater linear* acceleration on the hill?
A. the sphere.
B. the cylinder.
C. They will both have the same acceleration.

8. A uniform beam is suspended horizontally as shown in Figure 37. It is attached to the wall by a small hinge. The force that the hinge exerts *on the beam* has components
A. upward and to the right.
B. upward and to the left.
C. downward and to the right.
D. downward and to the left.

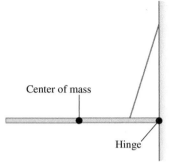

▲ **FIGURE 37** Multiple-choice problem 8.

9. Two identical cars are traveling in the same lane 100 m apart on a freeway. The lead car is moving at 88 km/h and the trailing car is moving at 82 km/h. From the point of view of a stationary observer by the road, what is happening to the center of mass of the system consisting of the two cars?
A. It is moving backward at 3 km/h.
B. It is moving forward at 3 km/h.
C. It is moving backward at 85 km/h.
D. It is moving forward at 85 km/h.

10. A person pushes vertically downward with force P on a lever of length L that is inclined at an angle θ above the horizontal as shown in Figure 38. The torque that the person's push produces about point A is
A. $PL \sin\theta$.
B. $PL \cos\theta$.
C. PL.

▲ **FIGURE 38** Multiple-choice problem 10.

11. String is wrapped around the outer rim of a solid uniform cylinder that is free to rotate about a frictionless axle through its center. When the string is pulled with a force P tangent to the rim, it gives the cylinder an angular acceleration α. If the cylinder had *twice* the radius, but everything else was the same, the angular acceleration would be
A. 4α.　　　　B. 2α.
C. $\alpha/2$.　　　　D. $\alpha/4$.

12. A weight W swings from a hook in the ceiling by a light string of length L, as shown in Figure 39. T is the tension in the string. When the string makes an angle θ with the vertical, the *net* torque about the hook is
A. WL.
B. $(W - T)L$.
C. TL.
D. $WL \sin\theta$.
E. $WL \cos\theta$.

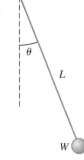

13. A ball of mass 0.20 kg is whirled in a horizontal circle at the end of a light string 75 cm long at a speed of 3.0 m/s. If the string is lengthened to 1.5 m while the ball is being twirled, then the speed of the ball will now be
A. 12 m/s.　　B. 6.0 m/s.　　C. 1.5 m/s.　　D. 0.75 m/s.

▲ **FIGURE 39** Multiple-choice problem 12.

14. A heavy solid disk rotating freely and slowed only by friction applied at its outer edge takes 100 seconds to come to a stop. If the disk had twice the radius and twice the mass, but the frictional force remained the same, the time it would it take the wheel to come to a stop from the same initial rotational speed is
   A. 25 s   B. 100 s   C. 400 s   D. 800 s

15. A uniform metal meterstick is balanced as shown in Figure 40 with a 1.0 kg rock attached to the left end of the stick. (Pay attention to the scale of the diagram.) What is the mass of the meterstick?
   A. 0.60 kg.   B. 1.0 kg.   C. 2.0 kg.   D. 3.0 kg.

▲ **FIGURE 40** Multiple-choice problem 15.

Problems

1 Torque

1. • Calculate the torque (magnitude and direction) about point O due to the force $\vec{F}$ in each of the situations sketched in Figure 41. In each case, the force $\vec{F}$ and the rod both lie in the plane of the page, the rod has length 4.00 m, and the force has magnitude 10.0 N.

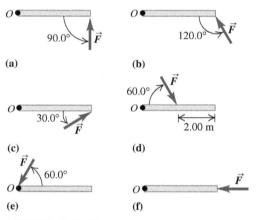

▲ **FIGURE 41** Problem 1.

2. • Calculate the net torque about point O for the two forces applied as in Figure 42. The rod and both forces are in the plane of the page.

▲ **FIGURE 42** Problem 2.

3. •• Three forces are applied to a wheel of radius 0.350 m, as shown in Fig. 43. One force is perpendicular to the rim, one is tangent to it, and the other one makes a 40.0° angle with the radius. What is the net torque on the wheel due to these three forces for an axis perpendicular to the wheel and passing through its center?

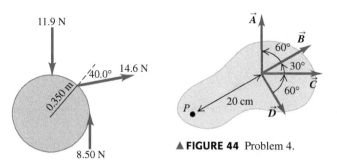

▲ **FIGURE 43** Problem 3.

▲ **FIGURE 44** Problem 4.

4. • In Figure 44, forces $\vec{A}$, $\vec{B}$, $\vec{C}$, and $\vec{D}$, each have magnitude 50 N and act at the same point on the object. (a) What torque (magnitude and direction) does each of these forces exert on the object about point P? (b) What is the total torque about point P?

5. •• A square metal plate 0.180 m on each side is pivoted about an axis through point O at its center and perpendicular to the plate. (See Figure 45.) Calculate the net torque about this axis due to the three forces shown in the figure if the magnitudes of the forces are $F_1 = 18.0$ N, $F_2 = 26.0$ N, and $F_3 = 14.0$ N. The plate and all forces are in the plane of the page.

▲ **FIGURE 45** Problem 5.

2 Torque and Angular Acceleration

6. • A cord is wrapped around the rim of a wheel 0.250 m in radius, and a steady pull of 40.0 N is exerted on the cord. The wheel is mounted on frictionless bearings on a horizontal shaft through its center. The moment of inertia of the wheel about this shaft is 5.00 kg · m². Compute the angular acceleration of the wheel.

7. • A certain type of propeller blade can be modeled as a thin uniform bar 2.50 m long and of mass 24.0 kg that is free to rotate about a frictionless axle perpendicular to the bar at its midpoint. If a technician strikes this blade with a mallet 1.15 m from the center with a 35.0 N force perpendicular to the blade, find the maximum angular acceleration the blade could achieve.

8. •• A 750 gram grinding wheel 25.0 cm in diameter is in the shape of a uniform solid disk. (We can ignore the small hole at the center.) When it is in use, it turns at a constant 220 rpm about an axle perpendicular to its face through its center. When the power switch is turned off, you observe that the wheel stops in 45.0 s with constant angular acceleration due to friction at the axle. What torque does friction exert while this wheel is slowing down?

9. •• A grindstone in the shape of a solid disk with diameter 0.520 m and a mass of 50.0 kg is rotating at 850 rev/min. You press an ax against the rim with a normal force of 160 N (see Figure 46), and the grindstone comes to rest in 7.50 s. Find the coefficient of kinetic friction between the ax and the grindstone. There is negligible friction in the bearings.

349

▲ FIGURE 46 Problem 9.

10. •• A solid, uniform cylinder with mass 8.25 kg and diameter 15.0 cm is spinning at 220 rpm on a thin, frictionless axle that passes along the cylinder axis. You design a simple friction brake to stop the cylinder by pressing the brake against the outer rim with a normal force. The coefficient of kinetic friction between the brake and rim is 0.333. What must the applied normal force be to bring the cylinder to rest after it has turned through 5.25 revolutions?

11. •• A 2.00 kg stone is tied to a thin, light wire wrapped around the outer edge of the uniform 10.0 kg cylindrical pulley shown in Figure 47. The inner diameter of the pulley is 60.0 cm, while the outer diameter is 1.00 m. The system is released from rest, and there is no friction at the axle of the pulley. Find (a) the acceleration of the stone, (b) the tension in the wire, and (c) the angular acceleration of the pulley.

▲ FIGURE 47 Problem 11.

12. •• A light rope is wrapped several times around a large wheel with a radius of 0.400 m. The wheel rotates in frictionless bearings about a stationary horizontal axis, as shown in Figure 48. The free end of the rope is tied to a suitcase with a mass of 15.0 kg. The suitcase is released from rest at a height of 4.00 m above the ground. The suitcase has a speed of 3.50 m/s when it reaches the ground. Calculate (a) the angular velocity of the wheel when the suitcase reaches the ground and (b) the moment of inertia of the wheel.

13. •• A 22,500 N elevator is to be accelerated upward by connecting it to a counterweight using a light (but strong!)

▲ FIGURE 48 Problem 12.

cable passing over a solid uniform disk-shaped pulley. There is no appreciable friction at the axle of the pulley, but its mass is 875 kg and it is 1.50 m in diameter. (a) How heavy should the counterweight be so that it will accelerate the elevator upward through 6.75 m in the first 3.00 s, starting from rest? (b) Under these conditions, what is the tension in the cable on each side of the pulley?

14. •• A thin, light string is wrapped around the rim of a 4.00 kg solid uniform disk that is 30.0 cm in diameter. A person pulls on the string with a constant force of 100.0 N tangent to the disk, as shown in Figure 49. *The disk is not attached to anything and is free to move and turn.* (a) Find the angular acceleration of the disk about its center of mass and the linear acceleration of its center of mass. (b) If the disk is replaced by a hollow thin-walled cylinder of the same mass and diameter, what will be the accelerations in part (a)?

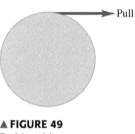

▲ FIGURE 49 Problem 14.

15. •• A uniform, 8.40-kg, spherical shell 50.0 cm in diameter has four small 2.00-kg masses attached to its outer surface and equally spaced around it. This combination is spinning about an axis running through the center of the sphere and two of the small masses (Fig. 50). What friction torque is needed to reduce its angular speed from 75.0 rpm to 50.0 rpm in 30.0 s?

▲ FIGURE 50 Problem 15.

16. •• A hollow spherical shell with mass 2.00 kg rolls without slipping down a 38.0° slope. (a) Find the acceleration of the shell and the friction force on it. Is the friction kinetic or static friction? Why? (b) How would your answers to part (a) change if the mass were doubled to 4.00 kg?

17. •• A solid disk of radius 8.50 cm and mass 1.25 kg, which is rolling at a speed of 2.50 m/s, begins rolling without slipping up a 10.0° slope. How long will it take for the disk to come to a stop?

3 Work and Power in Rotational Motion

18. • What is the power output in horsepower of an electric motor turning at 4800 rev/min and developing a torque of 4.30 N·m?

19. • A playground merry-go-round has a radius of 4.40 m and a moment of inertia of 245 kg·m² and turns with negligible friction about a vertical axle through its center. (a) A child applies a 25.0 N force tangentially to the edge of the merry-go-round for 20.0 s. If the merry-go-round is initially at rest, what is its angular velocity after this 20.0 s interval? (b) How much work did the child do on the merry-go-round? (c) What is the average power supplied by the child?

20. • The flywheel of a motor has a mass of 300.0 kg and a moment of inertia of 580 kg · m². The motor develops a constant torque of 2000.0 N · m, and the flywheel starts from rest. (a) What is the angular acceleration of the flywheel? (b) What is its angular velocity after it makes 4.00 revolutions? (c) How much work is done by the motor during the first 4.00 revolutions?

21. •• (a) Compute the torque developed by an industrial motor whose output is 150 kW at an angular speed of 4000.0 rev/min. (b) A drum with negligible mass and 0.400 m in diameter is attached to the motor shaft, and the power output of the motor is used to raise a weight hanging from a rope wrapped around the drum. How heavy a weight can the motor lift at constant speed? (c) At what constant speed will the weight rise?

4 Angular Momentum

22. • Calculate the angular momentum and kinetic energy of a solid uniform sphere with a radius of 0.120 m and a mass of 14.0 kg if it is rotating at 6.00 rad/s about an axis through its center.

23. •• (a) Calculate the magnitude of the angular momentum of the earth in a circular orbit around the sun. Is it reasonable to model it as a particle? (b) Calculate the magnitude of the angular momentum of the earth due to its rotation around an axis through the north and south poles, modeling it as a uniform sphere.

24. • A small 0.300 kg bird is flying horizontally at 3.50 m/s toward a 0.750 kg thin bar hanging vertically from a hook at its upper end, as shown in Figure 51. (a) When the bird is far from the bar, what are the magnitude and direction (clockwise or counterclockwise) of its angular momentum about a horizontal axis perpendicular to the plane of the figure and passing through (i) point A, (ii) point B, and (iii) point C? (b) Repeat part (a) when the bird is just ready to hit the bar, but is still flying horizontally.

▲ FIGURE 51 Problem 24.

25. • A small 4.0 kg brick is released from rest 2.5 m above a horizontal seesaw on a fulcrum at its center, as shown in Figure 52. Find the angular momentum of this brick about a horizontal axis through the fulcrum and perpendicular to the plane of the figure (a) the instant the brick is released and (b) the instant before it strikes the seesaw.

▲ FIGURE 52 Problem 25.

26. • A woman with mass 50.0 kg is standing on the rim of a large disk that is rotating at 0.50 rev/s about an axis perpendicular to it through its center. The disk has a mass of 110 kg and a radius of 4.0 m. Calculate the magnitude of the total angular momentum of the woman-plus-disk system, assuming that you can treat the woman as a point.

27. •• A certain drawbridge can be modeled as a uniform 15,000 N bar, 12.0 m long, pivoted about its lower end. When this bridge is raised to an angle of 60.0° above the horizontal, the cable holding it suddenly breaks, allowing the bridge to fall. At the instant after the cable breaks, (a) what is the torque on this bridge about the pivot and (b) at what rate is its angular momentum changing?

5 Conservation of Angular Momentum

28. • On an old-fashioned rotating piano stool, a woman sits holding a pair of dumbbells at a distance of 0.60 m from the axis of rotation of the stool. She is given an angular velocity of 3.00 rad/s, after which she pulls the dumbbells in until they are only 0.20 m distant from the axis. The woman's moment of inertia about the axis of rotation is 5.00 kg · m² and may be considered constant. Each dumbbell has a mass of 5.00 kg and may be considered a point mass. Neglect friction. (a) What is the initial angular momentum of the system? (b) What is the angular velocity of the system after the dumbbells are pulled in toward the axis? (c) Compute the kinetic energy of the system before and after the dumbbells are pulled in. Account for the difference, if any.

29. • **The spinning figure skater.** The outstretched hands and arms of a figure skater preparing for a spin can be considered a slender rod pivoting about an axis through its center. (See Figure 53.) When the skater's hands and arms are brought in and wrapped around his body to execute the spin, the hands and arms can be considered a thin-walled hollow cylinder. His hands and arms have a combined mass of 8.0 kg. When outstretched, they span 1.8 m; when wrapped, they form a cylinder of radius 25 cm. The moment of inertia about the axis of rotation of the remainder of his body is constant and equal to 0.40 kg · m². If the skater's original angular speed is 0.40 rev/s, what is his final angular speed?

▲ FIGURE 53 Problem 29.

30. •• A small block on a frictionless horizontal surface has a mass of 0.0250 kg. It is attached to a massless cord passing through a hole in the surface. (See Figure 54.) The block is originally revolving at a distance of 0.300 m from the hole with an angular speed of 1.75 rad/s. The cord is then pulled from below, shortening the radius of the circle in which the block revolves to 0.150 m. You may treat the block as a particle. (a) Is angular momentum conserved? Why or why not? (b) What is the new angular speed? (c) Find the change in kinetic energy of the block. (d) How much work was done in pulling the cord?

▲ FIGURE 54 Problem 30.

31. •• A uniform 4.5 kg square solid wooden gate 1.5 m on each side hangs vertically from a frictionless pivot at the center of its upper edge. A 1.1 kg raven flying horizontally at 5.0 m/s flies into this gate at its center and bounces back at 2.0 m/s in the opposite direction. (a) What is the angular speed of the gate just after it is struck by the unfortunate raven? (b) During the collision, why is the angular momentum conserved, but not the linear momentum?

32. •• A diver comes off a board with arms straight up and legs straight down, giving her a moment of inertia about her rotation axis of 18 kg · m². She then tucks into a small ball, decreasing this moment of inertia to 3.6 kg · m². While tucked, she makes two complete revolutions in 1.0 s. If she hadn't tucked at all, how many revolutions would she have made in the 1.5 s from board to water?

33. •• A large turntable rotates about a fixed vertical axis, making one revolution in 6.00 s. The moment of inertia of the turntable about this axis is 1200 kg · m². A child of mass 40.0 kg, initially standing at the center of the turntable, runs out along a radius. What is the angular speed of the turntable when the child is 2.00 m from the center, assuming that you can treat the child as a particle?

34. •• A large wooden turntable in the shape of a flat disk has a radius of 2.00 m and a total mass of 120 kg. The turntable is initially rotating at 3.00 rad/s about a vertical axis through its center. Suddenly, a 70.0 kg parachutist makes a soft landing on the turntable at a point on its outer edge. Find the angular speed of the turntable after the parachutist lands. (Assume that you can treat the parachutist as a particle.)

6 Equilibrium of a Rigid Body

35. • Which of the objects shown in Figure 55 are in only translational equilibrium, only rotational equilibrium (about the axis A), both translational and rotational equilibrium (about A), or neither equilibrium?

36. • (a) In each of the objects indicated in Figure 56, what magnitude of force *F* (if any) is needed to put the object into rotational equilibrium about the axis A shown? (b) After you have found the *F* required to put the object into rotational equilibrium, find out which (if any) of these objects is also in translational equilibrium.

37. •• **Supporting a broken leg.** A therapist tells a 74 kg patient
BIO with a broken leg that he must have his leg in a cast suspended horizontally. For minimum discomfort, the leg should be sup-

(e)

▲ FIGURE 55 Problem 35.

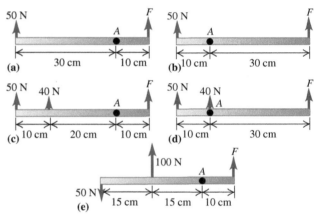

▲ FIGURE 56 Problem 36.

ported by a vertical strap attached at the center of mass of the leg–cast system. (See Figure 57.) In order to comply with these instructions, the patient consults a table of typical mass distributions and finds that both upper legs

▲ FIGURE 57 Problem 37.

(thighs) together typically account for 21.5% of body weight and the center of mass of each thigh is 18.0 cm from the hip joint. The patient also reads that the two lower legs (including the feet) are 14.0% of body weight, with a center of mass 69.0 cm from the hip joint. The cast has a mass of 5.50 kg, and its center of mass is 78.0 cm from the hip joint. How far from the hip joint should the supporting strap be attached to the cast?

38. •• Two people are carrying a uniform wooden board that is 3.00 m long and weighs 160 N. If one person applies an upward force equal to 60 N at one end, at what point and with

what force does the other person lift? Start with a free-body diagram of the board.

39. •• **Push-ups.** To strengthen his arm and chest muscles, an
BIO 82 kg athlete 2.0 m tall is doing a series of push-ups as shown in Figure 58. His center of mass is 1.15 m from the bottom of his feet, and the centers of his palms are 30.0 cm from the top of his head. Find the force that the floor exerts on each of his feet and on each hand, assuming that both feet exert the same force and both palms do likewise. Begin with a free-body diagram of the athlete.

▲ **FIGURE 58** Problem 39.

40. •• Two people carry a heavy electric motor by placing it on a light board 2.00 m long. One person lifts at one end with a force of 400.0 N, and the other lifts at the opposite end with a force of 600.0 N. (a) Start by making a free-body diagram of the motor. (b) What is the weight of the motor? (c) Where along the board is its center of gravity located?

41. •• A 60.0-cm, uniform, 50.0-N shelf is supported horizontally by two vertical wires attached to the sloping ceiling (Fig. 59). A very small 25.0-N tool is placed on the shelf midway between the points where the wires are attached to it. Find the tension in each wire. Begin by making a free-body diagram of the shelf.

▲ **FIGURE 59** Problem 41.

42. •• The horizontal beam in Figure 60 weighs 150 N, and its center of gravity is at its center. First make a free-body diagram of the beam. Then find (a) the tension in the cable and (b) the horizontal and vertical components of the force exerted on the beam at the wall.

▲ **FIGURE 60** Problem 42.

43. •• The boom in Figure 61 weighs 2600 N and is attached to a frictionless pivot at its lower end. It is not uniform; the distance of its center of gravity from the pivot is 35% of its length. Find (a) the tension in the guy wire and (b) the horizontal and vertical components of the force exerted on the boom at its lower end. Start with a free-body diagram of the boom.

▲ **FIGURE 61** Problem 43.

44. • A uniform 250 N ladder rests against a perfectly smooth wall, making a 35° angle with the wall. (a) Draw a free-body diagram of the ladder. (b) Find the normal forces that the wall and the floor exert on the ladder. (c) What is the friction force on the ladder at the floor?

45. •• A uniform ladder 7.0 m long weighing 450 N rests with one end on the ground and the other end against a perfectly smooth vertical wall. The ladder rises at 60.0° above the horizontal floor. A 750 N painter finds that she can climb 2.75 m up the ladder, measured along its length, before it begins to slip. (a) Make a free-body diagram of the ladder. (b) What force does the wall exert on the ladder? (c) Find the friction force and normal force that the floor exerts on the ladder.

46. •• A 9.0 m uniform beam is hinged to a vertical wall and held horizontally by a 5.0 m cable attached to the wall 4.0 m above the hinge, as shown in Figure 62. The metal of this cable has a test strength of 1.00 kN, which means that it will break if the tension in it exceeds that amount. (a) Draw a free-body diagram of the beam. (b) What is the heaviest beam that the cable can support with the given configuration? (c) Find the horizontal and vertical components of the force the hinge exerts on the beam.

▲ **FIGURE 62** Problem 46.

47. •• A uniform beam 4.0 m long and weighing 2500 N carries a 3500 N weight 1.50 m from the far end, as shown in Figure 63. It is supported horizontally by a hinge at the wall and a metal wire at the far end. (a) Make a free-body diagram of the beam. (b) How strong does the wire have to be? That is, what is the minimum tension it must be able to support without breaking? (c) What are the horizontal and vertical components of the force that the hinge exerts on the beam?

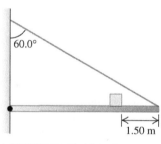

▲ **FIGURE 63** Problem 47.

48. •• **Leg raises.** In a simpli-
BIO fied version of the musculature action in leg raises, the abdominal muscles pull on the femur (thigh bone) to raise the leg by pivoting it about one end, as shown in Figure 64. When you are lying horizontally, these muscles make an angle of approximately 5° with the femur, and if you raise your legs, the muscles remain approximately horizontal, so the angle θ increases. We shall assume for simplicity that these muscles attach to the femur in only one place, 10 cm from the hip joint (although, in reality, the situation is more complicated). For a certain 80 kg person having a

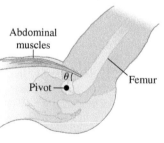

▲ **FIGURE 64** Problem 48.

leg 90 cm long, the mass of the leg is 15 kg and its center of mass is 44 cm from his hip joint as measured along the leg. If the person raises his leg to 60° above the horizontal, the angle between the abdominal muscles and his femur would also be about 60°. (a) With his leg raised to 60°, find the tension in the abdominal muscle on each leg. As usual, begin your solution with a free-body diagram. (b) When is the tension in this muscle greater, when the leg is raised to 60° or when the person just starts to raise it off the ground? Why? (Try this yourself to check your answer.) (c) If the abdominal muscles attached to the femur were perfectly horizontal when a person was lying down, could the person raise his leg? Why or why not?

49. ●● A diving board 3.00 m long is supported at a point 1.00 m from the end, and a diver weighing 500 N stands at the free end (Fig. 65). The diving board is of uniform cross section and weighs 280 N. Find (a) the force at the support point and (b) the force at the left-hand end.

▲ **FIGURE 65** Problem 49.

50. ●● Two people carry a heavy electric motor by placing it on a light board 2.00 m long. One person lifts at one end with a force of 400 N, and the other lifts the opposite end with a force of 600 N. (a) What is the weight of the motor, and where along the board is its center of gravity located? (b) Suppose the board is not light but weighs 200 N, with its center of gravity at its center, and the two people each exert the same forces as before. What is the weight of the motor in this case, and where is its center of gravity located?

51. ●● **Pumping iron.** A
BIO 72.0 kg weight lifter is doing arm raises using a 7.50 kg weight in her hand. Her arm pivots around the elbow joint, starting 40.0° below the horizontal. (See Figure 66.) Biometric measurements have shown that both forearms and the hands together account for 6.00% of a person's weight. Since the upper arm is held vertically, the

▲ **FIGURE 66** Problem 51.

biceps muscle always acts vertically and is attached to the bones of the forearm 5.50 cm from the elbow joint. The center of mass of this person's forearm–hand combination is 16.0 cm from the elbow joint, along the bones of the forearm, and the weight is held 38.0 cm from the elbow joint. (a) Make a free-body diagram of the forearm. (b) What force does the biceps muscle exert on the forearm? (c) Find the magnitude and direction of the force that the elbow joint exerts on the forearm. (d) As the weight lifter raises her arm toward a horizontal position, will the force in the biceps muscle increase, decrease, or stay the same? Why?

52. ●● **The deltoid muscle.** The deltoid muscle is the main mus-
BIO cle that allows you to raise your arm or even hold it out. It is connected to the humerus of the upper arm. (See part (a) of Figure 67.) The person shown is holding his arm out horizontally with a 2.50 kg weight in his hand. This weight is 60.0 cm from the shoulder joint. His forearm (including his hand) has a mass of 2.44 kg and is 34.0 cm long; its center of mass is 43 cm from the shoulder joint, measured along the arm. His upper arm is 26.0 cm long and has a mass of 2.63 kg; its center of mass is 13.0 cm from the shoulder joint. The deltoid muscle is attached to the humerus 15.0 cm from the shoulder joint and makes a 14.0° angle with the humerus. (See part (b) of the figure.) (a) Make a free-body diagram of the arm. (b) What is the tension in the deltoid muscle?

(a)

(b) Detail of the attachment of the deltoid muscle.

▲ **FIGURE 67** Problem 52.

53. ●● A uniform, 90.0-N table is 3.6 m long, 1.0 m high, and
BIO 1.2 m wide. A 1500-N weight is placed 0.50 m from one end of the table, a distance of 0.60 m from each of the two legs at that end. Draw a free-body diagram for the table and find the force that each of the four legs exerts on the floor.

7 Vector Nature of Angular Quantities

54. ● The rotor (flywheel) of a toy gyroscope has a mass of 0.140 kg. Its moment of inertia about its axis is $1.20 \times 10^{-4} \ \text{kg} \cdot \text{m}^2$. The mass of the frame is 0.0250 kg. The gyroscope is supported on a single pivot (see Figure 68) with its center of mass a horizontal distance of 4.00 cm from the pivot. The gyroscope is precessing in a horizontal plane at the rate of 1 revolution in 2.20 s. (a) Find the upward force exerted by the pivot. (b) Find the angular speed with which the rotor is spinning about its axis, expressed in rev/min. (c) Copy the diagram and draw vectors to show the angular momentum of the rotor and the torque acting on it.

▲ **FIGURE 68** Problem 54.

55. ●● For each of the following rotating objects, describe the direction of the angular momentum vector: (a) the minute

hand of a clock; (b) the right front tire of a car moving backwards; (c) an ice skater spinning clockwise; (d) the earth, rotating on its axis.

General Problems

56. •• **Back pains during pregnancy.** Women often suffer from
BIO back pains during pregnancy. Let us investigate the cause of these pains, assuming that the woman's mass is 60 kg before pregnancy. Typically, women gain about 10 kg during pregnancy, due to the weight of the fetus, placenta, amniotic fluid, etc. To make the calculations easy, but still realistic, we shall model the unpregnant woman as a uniform cylinder of diameter 30 cm. We can model the added mass due to the fetus as a 10 kg sphere 25 cm in diameter and centered about 5 cm *outside* the woman's original front surface. (a) By how much does her pregnancy change the horizontal location of the woman's center of mass? (b) How does the change in part (a) affect the way the pregnant woman must stand and walk? In other words, what must she do to her posture to make up for her shifted center of mass? (c) Can you now explain why she might have backaches?

57. •• You are asked to design the decorative mobile shown in Figure 69. The strings and rods have negligible weight, and the rods are to hang horizontally. (a) Draw a free-body diagram for each rod. (b) Find the weights of the balls A, B, and C. Find the tensions S_1, S_2, and S_3 in the strings. (c) What can you say about the horizontal location of the mobile's center of gravity? Explain.

▲ **FIGURE 69** Problem 57.

58. •• **A good workout.** You
BIO are doing exercises on a Nautilus machine in a gym to strengthen your deltoid (shoulder) muscles. Your arms are raised vertically and can pivot around the shoulder joint, and you grasp the cable of the machine in your hand 64.0 cm from your shoulder joint. The deltoid muscle is attached to the humerus 15.0 cm from the shoulder joint and makes a 12.0° angle with that bone. (See Figure 70.) If you have set the tension in the cable of the machine to

▲ **FIGURE 70** Problem 58.

36.0 N on each arm, what is the tension in each deltoid muscle if you simply hold your outstretched arms in place? (*Hint:* Start by making a clear free-body diagram of your arm.)

59. •• Prior to being placed in its hole, a 5700-N, 9.0-m-long, uniform utility pole makes some nonzero angle with the vertical. A vertical cable attached 2.0 m below its upper end holds it in place while its lower end rests on the ground. (a) Find the tension in the cable and the magnitude and direction of the force exerted by the ground on the pole. (b) Why don't we need to know the angle the pole makes with the vertical, as long as it is not zero?

60. •• A uniform drawbridge must be held at a 37° angle above the horizontal to allow ships to pass underneath. The drawbridge weighs 45,000 N, is 14.0 m long, and pivots about a hinge at its lower end. A cable is connected 3.5 m from the hinge, as measured along the bridge, and pulls horizontally on the bridge to hold it in place. (a) What is the tension in the cable? (b) Find the magnitude and direction of the force the hinge exerts on the bridge. (c) If the cable suddenly breaks, what is the initial angular acceleration of the bridge?

61. •• **Pyramid builders.** Ancient pyramid builders are balancing a uniform rectangular slab of stone tipped at an angle θ above the horizontal using a rope (Fig. 71). The rope is held by five workers who share the force equally. (a) If $\theta = 20.0°$, what force does each worker exert on the rope? (b) As θ increases, does each worker have to exert more or less force than in part (a), assuming they do not change the angle of the rope? Why? (c) At what angle do the workers need to exert *no force* to balance the slab? What happens if θ exceeds this value?

▲ **FIGURE 71** Problem 61.

62. •• **The farmyard gate.** A gate 4.00 m wide and 2.00 m high weighs 500 N. Its center of gravity is at its center, and it is hinged at A and B. To relieve the strain on the top hinge, a wire CD is connected as shown in Fig. 72. The tension in CD is increased until the horizontal force at hinge A is zero. (a) What is the tension in the wire CD? (b) What is the magnitude of the horizontal component of the force at hinge B? (c) What is the combined vertical force exerted by hinges A and B?

▲ **FIGURE 72** Problem 62.

63. •• **Atwood's machine.** Figure 73 illustrates an Atwood's machine. Find the linear accelerations of blocks A and B, the angular acceleration of the wheel C, and the tension in each side of the cord if there is no slipping between the cord and the surface of the wheel. Let the masses of blocks A and B be 4.00 kg and 2.00 kg, respectively, the moment of inertia of the wheel about its axis be $0.300 \text{ kg} \cdot \text{m}^2$, and the radius of the wheel be 0.120 m.

64. •• **Neck muscles.** A student bends her
BIO head at 40.0° from the vertical while intently reading her physics book, pivoting the head around the upper vertebra (point P in Figure 74). Her head has a mass of 4.50 kg (which is typical), and its center of mass is 11.0 cm from the pivot point P. Her neck muscles are 1.50 cm from point P, as measured *perpendicular* to these muscles. The neck itself and the vertebrae are held vertical. (a) Draw a free-body diagram of the student's head. (b) Find the tension in her neck muscles.

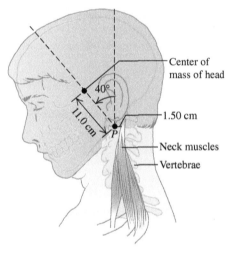

▲ **FIGURE 74** Problem 64.

65. •• **Russell traction apparatus.** The device shown in
BIO Figure 75 is one version of a Russell traction apparatus. It has two functions: to support the injured leg horizontally and at the same time provide a horizontal traction force on it. This can be done by adjusting the weight W and the angle θ. For this patient, his leg (including his foot) is 95.0 cm long (measured from the hip joint) and has a mass of 14.2 kg. Its center of mass is 41.0 cm from the hip joint. A support strap is attached to the patient's ankle 13.0 cm from the bottom of his foot. (a) What weight W is needed to support the leg horizontally? (b) If the therapist specifies that the traction force must be 12.0 N horizontally, what must be the angle θ? (c) What is the greatest traction force that this apparatus could supply to this patient's leg, and what is θ in that case?

▲ **FIGURE 73** Problem 63.

▲ **FIGURE 75** Problem 65.

66. •• **Supporting an injured**
BIO **arm: I.** A 650 N person must have her injured arm supported, with the upper arm horizontal and the forearm vertical. (See Figure 76.) According to biomedical tables and direct measurements, her upper arm is 26 cm long (measured from the shoulder joint), accounts for 3.50% of her body weight, and has a center of mass 13.0 cm from her shoulder joint. Her forearm (including the hand) is 34.0 cm long, makes up 3.25% of her body weight, and has a center of mass 43.0 cm from her shoulder joint. (a) Where is the center of mass of the person's arm when it is supported as shown? (b) What weight W is needed to support her arm? (c) Find the horizontal and vertical components of the force that the shoulder joint exerts on her arm.

▲ **FIGURE 76** Problem 66.

67. •• **Supporting an injured arm: II.** As part of therapy, the
BIO person's arm in the previous problem is later to be supported with the upper arm horizontal, but with the forearm at an angle of 55° above the horizontal, as shown in Figure 77. (a) Where is the center of mass of the person's arm? (b) What weight W is needed to support her arm this way? (c) Find the horizontal and vertical components of the force that the shoulder joint exerts on her arm.

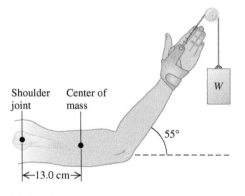

▲ **FIGURE 77** Problem 67.

68. •• **The forces on the foot.** A 750 N athlete standing on *one*
BIO foot on a very smooth gym floor lifts his body by pivoting
his foot upward through a 30.0° angle, balancing all of his
weight on the ball of the foot. The forces on the foot bones
from the rest of his body are due to the Achilles tendon and
the ankle joint. (See Figure 78.) The Achilles tendon acts perpendicular to a line through the heel and toes; it is this line
that has rotated upward through 30.0°. Assume that the
weight of the foot is negligible compared with that of the rest
of the body, and begin by making a free-body diagram of the
foot. (a) What are the magnitude and direction of the force
that the floor exerts on the athlete's foot? (b) What is the tension in the Achilles tendon? (c) Find the horizontal and vertical components of the force that the ankle joint exerts on the
foot. Then use these components to find the magnitude of
this force.

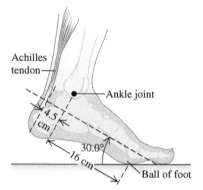

▲ **FIGURE 78** Problem 68.

69. •• A uniform solid cylinder of
mass *M* is supported on a ramp that
rises at an angle *θ* above the horizontal by a wire that is wrapped
around its rim and pulls on it tangentially parallel to the ramp (Fig.
79). (a) Show that there *must* be
friction on the surface for the cylinder to balance this way. (b) Show
that the tension in the wire must be ▲ **FIGURE 79** Problem 69.
equal to the friction force, and find
this tension.

70. •• A uniform 8.0 m, 1500 kg
beam is hinged to a wall and
supported by a thin cable
attached 2.0 m from the free
end of the beam, as shown in
Figure 80. The beam is supported at an angle of 30.0°
above the horizontal. (a) Make
a free-body diagram of the
beam. (b) Find the tension in ▲ **FIGURE 80** Problem 70.
the cable. (c) How hard does
the beam push inward on the wall?

71. •• You are trying to raise a bicycle wheel of mass *m* and
radius *R* up over a curb of height *h*. To do this, you apply a
horizontal force $\vec{F}$ (Fig. 81). What is the smallest magnitude
of the force $\vec{F}$ that will succeed in raising the wheel onto the curb

when the force is applied (a) at the center of the wheel, and (b)
at the top of the wheel? (c) In which case is less force
required?

▲ **FIGURE 81** Problem 71.

72. •• An experimental bicycle wheel is placed on a test stand so
that it is free to turn on its axle. If a constant net torque of
5.00 N · m is applied to the tire for 2.00 s, the angular speed of
the tire increases from zero to 100 rev/min. The external
torque is then removed, and the wheel is brought to rest in
125 s by friction in its bearings. Compute (a) the moment of
inertia of the wheel about the axis of rotation, (b) the friction
torque, and (c) the total number of revolutions made by the
wheel in the 125 s time interval.

73. •• Under some circumstances, a star can collapse into an
extremely dense object made mostly of neutrons and called a
neutron star. The density of a neutron star is roughly 10^{14}
times as great as that of ordinary solid matter. Suppose we represent the star as a uniform, solid, rigid sphere, both before and
after the collapse. The star's initial radius was 7.0×10^5 km
(comparable to our sun); its final radius is 16 km. If the original star rotated once in 30 days, find the angular speed of the
neutron star.

74. •• Disks *A* and *B* are
mounted on shaft *SS* and
may be connected or dis-
connected by clutch *C*.
(See Figure 82.) Disk *A* is
made of a lighter material
than disk *B*, so the moment ▲ **FIGURE 82** Problem 74.
of inertia of disk *A* about
the shaft is one-third that of disk *B*. The moments of inertia of
the shaft and clutch are negligible. With the clutch discon-
nected, *A* is brought up to an angular speed ω_0. The accelerating torque is then removed from *A*, and *A* is coupled to disk *B*
by the clutch. (You can ignore bearing friction.) It is found that
2400 J of thermal energy is developed in the clutch when the
connection is made. What was the original kinetic energy of
disk *A*?

75. •• While exploring a castle, Exena the Exterminator is spot-
ted by a dragon who chases her down a hallway. Exena runs
into a room and attempts to swing the heavy door shut before
the dragon gets her. The door is initially perpendicular to the
wall, so it must be turned through 90° to close. The door is
3.00 m tall and 1.25 m wide, and it weighs 750 N. You can
ignore the friction at the hinges. If Exena applies a force of
220 N at the edge of the door and perpendicular to it, how
much time does it take her to close the door?

76. •• **Downward-Facing Dog.** One yoga exercise, known as the
BIO "Downward-Facing Dog," requires stretching your hands
straight out above your head and bending down to lean against
the floor. This exercise is performed by a certain 750 N person,

as shown in the simplified model in Figure 83. When he bends his body at the hip to a 90° angle between his legs and trunk, his legs, trunk, head and arms have the dimensions indicated. Furthermore, his legs and feet weigh a total of 277 N, and their center of mass is 41 cm from his hip, measured along his legs. The person's trunk, head, and arms weigh 473 N, and their center of gravity is 65 cm from his hip, measured along the upper body. (a) Find the normal force that the floor exerts on each foot and on each hand, assuming that the person does not favor either hand or either foot. (b) Find the friction force on each foot and on each hand, assuming that it is the same on both feet and on both hands (but not necessarily the same on the feet as on the hands). [*Hint:* First treat his entire body as a system; then isolate his legs (or his upper body).]

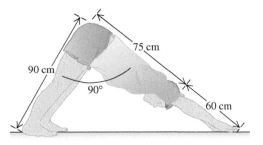

▲ **FIGURE 83** Problem 76.

77. •• A uniform, 7.5-m-long beam weighing 9000 N is hinged to a wall and supported by a thin cable attached 1.5 m from the free end of the beam. The cable runs between the beam and the wall and makes a 40° angle with the beam. What is the tension in the cable when the beam is at an angle of 30° above the horizontal?

Passage Problems

BIO Rotating space station. A space station, in the form of a rotating hollow cylinder, is designed to provide a comfortable living environment, complete with artificial gravity, for astronauts in orbit around the earth. The space station has a length of 1000 m, an outer radius of 250 m, an inner radius of 240 m, and is fabricated using an ultra light aluminum and graphite fiber composite. Forty small, adjustable rockets attached to the outer shell of the space station will provide the angular acceleration needed to spin the space station up to the required final angular velocity of 0.20 rad/s. According to design specifications, the moment of inertia of the space station about its longitudinal axis is 10^{12} kg·m².

78. What would be the radial (centripetal) acceleration of an astronaut standing on the inner surface of the space station, which is at a distance of 240 m from the axis of rotation, once the space station reaches its final angular velocity of 0.20 rad/s?
   A. 0 m/s²
   B. 4.8 m/s²
   C. 9.6 m/s²
   D. 48 m/s²

79. What would be the total torque produced by all 40 rockets? Assume that each rocket is adjusted so that its thrust is 1000 newtons in a direction that will provide maximum torque about the longitudinal axis of the space station.
   A. 2.40×10^5 N·m
   B. 2.50×10^5 N·m
   C. 1.00×10^7 N·m
   D. 1.0×10^{10} N·m

80. What would be the resulting angular acceleration of the space station when all 40 rockets provide maximum torque?
   A. 10^{-5} rad/s²
   B. 10^{-2} rad/s²
   C. 10^2 rad/s²
   D. 10^{22} rad/s²

81. How long will the rockets need to operate in order to bring the rotational velocity of the space station up from 0 rad/s to the final required value of 0.20 rad/s?
   A. 2×10^4 s
   B. 20 s
   C. 0.002 s
   D. 2×10^{-6} s

ANSWERS TO SELECTED PROBLEMS

Conceptual Questions

1. The extra length increases the torque applied to the bolt; the force exerted on the wrench by the mechanic acts with a longer moment arm. The increased torque can shear the bolt.

3. To prevent the bricks from falling, two criteria must be met. First, the center of gravity of the top brick cannot extend past the right-hand edge of the brick beneath it, so the minimum overlap is 6 inches. Second, the center of gravity of the two-brick combination cannot lie beyond the edge of the table. To determine the maximum *x*, assume the first criteria is just met—the top brick extends 6 in.

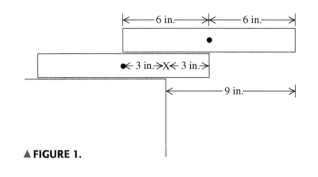

▲ **FIGURE 1.**

beyond the bottom brick. As Figure 1 shows, the center of gravity of the two-brick combination is then 9 in. to the left of the right-hand edge of the top brick. Therefore, the greatest x can be is 9.0 in.

5. (a) Yes, you can change the location of your center of mass by changing the shape of your body. This changes the way that your mass is distributed. (b) Yes, you can change your moment of inertia with respect to some axis by moving your arms or legs to change how your mass is distributed with respect to the axis.

7. The refrigerator starts to slide when the horizontal applied force exceeds the maximum possible static friction force. The size of the static friction force is proportional to the weight of the refrigerator and to the coefficient of static friction between the refrigerator and the floor. Consider an axis at the forward, lower corner of the refrigerator. The refrigerator starts to tip when the torque due to the applied force exceeds the torque due to the weight of the refrigerator. The torque due to the applied force depends on the applied force and on where the force is applied. The gravity torque depends on the weight of the refrigerator and the width of the refrigerator. Therefore, whether the refrigerator starts to slide or starts to tip first depends on: μ_s, the width of the refrigerator and the height at which the force is applied. The higher up you push, the more likely the refrigerator is to tip.

9. A glass tips when its center of gravity is pushed beyond the edge of its base. The answer to both questions depends on the location of the center of gravity. For a given base, the glass is easier to tip the higher its center of gravity. For a center of gravity at a given height, the more narrow the base the easier it is for the glass to tip. If the water lowers the center of gravity, it makes the glass harder to tip. If the water raises the center of gravity, it makes the glass easier to tip. The water also increases the weight of the object so more force is required to tilt it.

11. Torques tending to close the door are opposed by torques applied by the object. The moment arm for the force exerted by the object is very small, so the force is very large and pulls horizontally against the hinges.

13. A free-body diagram for the hammer is sketched in Figure 2. The person using the hammer to pull the nail exerts a force

$\vec{P}$ at the end of the handle. The nail exerts a downward force with magnitude F on the claw of the hammer and by Newton's third law the hammer exerts an upward force with magnitude $F' = F$ on the nail. The magnitude of the torque due to $\vec{P}$ equals the magnitude of the torque due to $\vec{F}$. But the force $\vec{P}$ has a much larger moment arm than $\vec{F}$, so $F \gg P$ and F' is large.

▲ **FIGURE 2.**

15. Since angular momentum is given by $L = I\omega$ and rotational kinetic energy is given by $K_{rot} = \frac{1}{2}I\omega^2$, $K_{rot} = \dfrac{L^2}{2I}$. If they have the same L they will have the same K_{rot} only if they have the same I. And since $L = \sqrt{2I(K_{rot})}$, if they have the same rotational kinetic energy they will have the same angular momentum only if they have the same I. And rotational kinetic energy is a scalar whereas angular momentum is a vector. Even if they have the same magnitude of angular momentum, the angular momenta of the two objects could be different if they are in different directions.

Multiple-Choice Problems

1. C
3. E
5. B
7. A
9. D
11. C
13. C
15. D

Problems

1. (a) 40.0 N · m, counterclockwise
   (b) 34.6 N · m, counterclockwise
   (c) 20.0 N · m, counterclockwise
   (d) 17.3 N · m, clockwise (e) 0 (f) 0
3. −0.31 N · m, clockwise
5. 2.50 N · m, counterclockwise

7. 3.22 rad/s^2
9. 0.482
11. (a) 2.23 m/s^2 (b) 15.2 N (c) 4.46 rad/s^2
13. (a) 3.16 × 10^4 N (b) 2.60 × 10^4 N; 2.67 × 10^4 N
15. −0.0524 N · m
17. 2.20 s
19. (a) 8.98 rad/s (b) 9.88 × 10^3 J (c) 494 W
21. (a) 358 N · m (b) 1.79 × 10^3 N (c) 83.8 m/s
23. (a) 2.67 × 10^{40} kg · m^2/s (b) 7.07 × 10^{33} kg · m^2/s
25. (a) 0 (b) 44.8 kg · m^2/s, counterclockwise
27. (a) 45,000 N · m (b) 45,000 kg · m^2/s^2
29. 1.14 rev/s
31. (a) 1.71 rad/s (b) external force but no external torque
33. 0.924 rad/s
35. (a) only rotational equilibrium (b) neither (c) only translational equilibrium (d) only translational equilibrium (e) both
37. 49.9 cm
39. hand: 272 N; foot: 130 N
41. left: 25.0 N; right: 50.0 N
43. (a) 3.41 × 10^3 N (b) 7600 N
45. (b) 300 N (c) 1200 N
47. (b) 6880 N (c) 2560 N
49. (a) 1920 N (b) 1140 N
51. (b) 569 N (c) 474 N (d) same
55. (a) perpendicular to face of clock and directed inward (b) perpendicular to hubcap of wheel and pointed outward (c) perpendicular to ice and pointed downward (d) aligned with earth's axis and pointing upward from north pole
57. (b) $W_A = 3.0$ N; $W_B = 15.0$ N; $W_C = 8.0$ N; $S_1 = 32.0$ N; $S_2 = 24.0$ N; $S_3 = 9.0$ N
59. (a) 3.7 kN, 2.0 kN vertically upward
61. (a) 0.012W (b) less (c) 25.0°; tips
63. 0.730 m/s^2; 6.09 rad/s^2; 36.3 N; 21.1 N
65. (a) 69.6 N (b) 85.1° (c) 139 N
67. (a) 24.0 cm to the right; 6.7 cm above the shoulder joint
    (b) 49.4 N (c) $F_v = 3.4$ N; $F_h = 28.3$ N
69. (b) $(Mg/2) \sin\theta$
71. (a) $mg\dfrac{\sqrt{2Rh - h^2}}{R - h}$
    (b) $(mg)\sqrt{2Rh - hv}/(2R - h)$
    (c) at top of wheel
73. 4.6 × 10^3 rad/s
75. 0.675 s
77. 7600 N

Elasticity and Periodic Motion

Ahmad Masood/Reuters

We have often used idealized models to represent objects as particles or rigid bodies. A rigid body doesn't bend, stretch, or squash when forces act on it. But the rigid body is an idealized model; all real materials do deform to some extent. In this chapter we'll introduce concepts and principles that help us predict the deformations that occur when forces are applied to a real (not perfectly rigid) body. Elastic properties of materials are tremendously important. You want the wings of an airplane to be able to bend a little, but you don't want them to break off. The steel frame of an earthquake-resistant building has to be able to flex, but not too much. Many of the necessities of everyday life, from rubber bands to suspension bridges, depend on the elastic properties of materials.

Next we'll study a class of problems, including some that involve elastic behavior, in which an object repeats the same motion over and over again in a cyclic pattern. Any such motion is called a *periodic motion* or an *oscillation*. Many familiar examples of oscillating objects come to mind: the pendulum of a grandfather's clock, the vibrating strings of a musical instrument, the pistons in a gasoline engine, a child playing on a swing. Less obvious oscillatory phenomena are the vibrations of the quartz crystal in a watch, the electromagnetic waves of radio and television transmission, and the vibrations of atoms in the crystal structure of a solid material. Periodic motion plays a vital role in many areas of physics, and studying it will give us an important foundation for later work in several areas.

One topic we'll cover in this chapter is the motion of pendulums such as these swings. We'll learn that the frequency of a swing—how often it moves back and forth per unit of time—depends on the length of the ropes or chains suspending it but not on the mass of the rider. Whether one child or several use a swing, its frequency will be the same.

1 Stress, Strain, and Elastic Deformations

The rigid body is a useful idealized model, but the stretching, squeezing, and twisting of real objects when forces are applied are often too important to ignore. Figure 1 shows examples of these types of forces. For each case, we'll study

From Chapter 11 of *College Physics*, Ninth Edition, Hugh D. Young. Copyright © 2012 by Pearson Education, Inc. Published by Pearson Addison-Wesley. All rights reserved.

Tensile stress:
Opposed forces stretch the bone.

Shear stress:
Opposed forces twist the bone.

Compressive stress:
Opposed forces compress the bone.

Volume stress:
Water pressure squeezes the swimmer.

▲ **FIGURE 1** Four types of stress that we will study.

the relation between forces and deformations. We'll introduce a quantity called **stress** that characterizes the strength of the forces associated with the stretch, squeeze, or twist, usually on a "force per unit area" basis. Another quantity, **strain,** describes the deformation that occurs. When the stress and strain are small enough, we often find that the two are directly proportional. The harder you pull on something, the more it stretches; and the more you squeeze it, the more it compresses. The general pattern that emerges can be formulated as

$$\frac{\text{Stress}}{\text{Strain}} = \text{Constant}. \tag{1}$$

The proportionality between stress and strain (under certain conditions) is called **Hooke's law,** after Robert Hooke (1635–1703), a contemporary of Newton. We saw a special case of Hooke's law already: The elongation of a spring is approximately proportional to the stretching forces involved. The constant in Equation 1 is often called an *elastic modulus*.

Tensile and Compressive Stress and Strain

The simplest elastic behavior to understand is the stretching of a bar, rod, or wire when its ends are pulled. Figure 2a shows a bar with uniform cross-sectional area A, with equal and opposite forces with magnitude $F_\perp$ pulling at its ends. We say that the bar is in **tension.** We've already talked a lot about tensions in ropes and strings; it's the same concept here. Figure 2b shows a cross section through the bar; the part to the right of the section pulls on the part to the left with a force with magnitude $F_\perp$ and vice versa. The force is distributed uniformly over the section, as shown by the short arrows in the figure. (This is always the case if the forces at the *ends* are uniformly distributed.)

We define the **tensile stress** at the cross section as the ratio of the force magnitude $F_\perp$ to the cross-sectional area A:

$$\text{Tensile stress} = \frac{F_\perp}{A}. \tag{2}$$

The SI unit of stress is the newton per square meter (N/m^2). This unit is also called the **pascal** (abbreviated Pa):

$$1 \text{ pascal} = 1 \text{ Pa} = 1 \text{ N}/\text{m}^2.$$

In the British system, the logical unit of stress would be the pound per square foot, but the pound per square inch (lb/in.², or psi) is more commonly used.

The units of stress are the same as those of *pressure,* which we'll encounter often in later chapters. Steel cables are commonly required to withstand tensile stresses on the order of 10^8 Pa (about 150,000 psi).

Cross-sectional area A

$F_\perp$ $F_\perp$

(a) A bar in tension

We assume that the tension force is distributed evenly over any cross section through the bar.

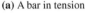

$F_\perp$ $F_\perp$

(b) Force on a cross section through the bar

▲ **FIGURE 2** Tensile stress.

Cross-sectional area A

$F_\perp$ $F_\perp$

(a) A bar in compression

$F_\perp$ $F_\perp$

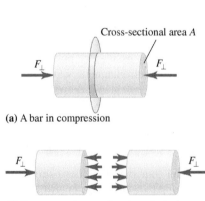

(b) Force on a cross section through the bar

▲ **FIGURE 3** Compressive stress.

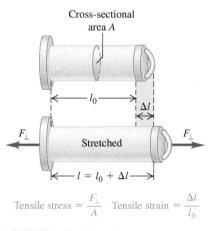

Cross-sectional area A

l_0 Δl

$F_\perp$ Stretched $F_\perp$

$l = l_0 + \Delta l$

$$\text{Tensile stress} = \frac{F_\perp}{A} \qquad \text{Tensile strain} = \frac{\Delta l}{l_0}$$

▲ **FIGURE 4** Tensile strain.

▶ **Application** **Bridging the gap.** The modern cable-stayed bridge is not only beautiful, but also a study in tension and compression. In this type of bridge, the weight of the roadway is carried by sets of diagonal cables attached to tall towers. The cables are in tension, while the roadway and the towers are in compression. Because the cables are oriented at angles to the vertical, they experience very high tensile stress and are thus quite stiff, making this a desirable type of bridge for windy conditions. In addition, the cables act as guy wires to stabilize the towers in the direction parallel to the roadway. This photo shows the Millau Viaduct in France while it was under construction. It is currently the world's tallest bridge.

Eric Cabanis/AFP/ Getty Images

When the forces on the ends of a bar are pushes rather than pulls (Figure 3a), the bar is in **compression,** and the stress is a **compressive stress.** At the cross section shown, each side pushes, rather than pulls, on the other.

The fractional change in length (the stretch) of an object under a tensile stress is called the **tensile strain.** Figure 4 shows a bar with unstretched length l_0 that stretches to a length $l = l_0 + \Delta l$ when equal and opposite forces with magnitude $F_\perp$ are applied to its ends. The elongation Δl, measured along the same line as l_0, doesn't occur only at the ends; every part of the bar stretches in the same proportion. The tensile strain is defined as the ratio of the elongation Δl to the original length l_0:

$$\text{Tensile strain} = \frac{l - l_0}{l_0} = \frac{\Delta l}{l_0}. \tag{3}$$

Tensile strain is the amount of stretch per unit length. It is a ratio of two lengths, always measured in the same units, so strain is a pure (dimensionless) number with no units. The **compressive strain** of a bar in compression is defined in the same way as tensile strain, but Δl has the opposite direction (Figure 5). In this case, it is often convenient to treat Δl as a negative quantity.

Experiments have shown that, for a sufficiently small tensile or compressive stress, stress and strain are proportional, as stated by Hooke's law, Equation 1. The corresponding proportionality constant, called **Young's modulus** (denoted by Y), is given by

$$Y = \frac{\text{Tensile stress}}{\text{Tensile strain}} \quad \text{or} \quad \frac{\text{Compressive stress}}{\text{Compressive strain}},$$

or

$$Y = \frac{F_\perp/A}{\Delta l/l_0} = \frac{l_0}{A} \frac{F_\perp}{\Delta l}. \tag{4}$$

Strain is a pure number, so the units of Young's modulus are the same as those of stress: force per unit area. Young's modulus is a property of a specific material, rather than of any particular object made of that material. A material with a large value of Y is relatively *unstretchable;* a large stress is required for a given strain. For example, steel has a much larger value of Y than rubber. Table 1 lists values of Y for a few representative materials.

When you stretch a wire or a rubber band, it gets *thinner* as well as longer. When Hooke's law holds, the fractional decrease in width is found to be proportional to the tensile strain, typically 0.2 to 0.4 times the tensile strain. Similarly, a material under compressive stress bulges at the sides, and again the fractional change in width is proportional to the compressive strain. For many materials, though not all, Young's modulus has the same values for both tensile and compressive stress.

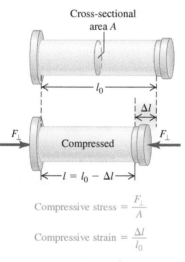

Cross-sectional area A

Compressive stress $= \dfrac{F_\perp}{A}$

Compressive strain $= \dfrac{\Delta l}{l_0}$

▲ **FIGURE 5** Compressive strain.

TABLE 1	Young's modulus
Material	**Y (Pa)**
Aluminum	0.70×10^{11}
Brass	0.91×10^{11}
Copper	1.1×10^{11}
Glass	0.55×10^{11}
Iron	1.9×10^{11}
Steel	2.0×10^{11}
Tungsten	3.6×10^{11}

EXAMPLE 1 A stretching elevator cable

A small elevator with a mass of 550 kg hangs from a steel cable that is 3.0 m long when not loaded. The wires making up the cable have a total cross-sectional area of 0.20 cm², and with a 550 kg load, the cable stretches 0.40 cm beyond its unloaded length. Determine the cable's stress and strain. Assuming that the cable is equivalent to a rod with the same cross-sectional area, determine the value of Young's modulus for the cable's steel.

SOLUTION

SET UP AND SOLVE Figure 6 shows our diagram. The tension in the cable is $F_\perp = mg = (550\ \text{kg})(9.8\ \text{m/s}^2)$. We use the definitions of tensile stress and strain, and Young's modulus, given by Equations 2, 3, and 4:

$$\text{Stress} = \frac{F_\perp}{A} = \frac{(550\ \text{kg})(9.8\ \text{m/s}^2)}{2.0 \times 10^{-5}\ \text{m}^2} = 2.7 \times 10^8\ \text{Pa},$$

$$\text{Strain} = \frac{\Delta l}{l_0} = \frac{0.0040\ \text{m}}{3.0\ \text{m}} = 0.00133,$$

$$Y = \frac{\text{Stress}}{\text{Strain}} = \frac{2.7 \times 10^8\ \text{Pa}}{0.00133} = 2.0 \times 10^{11}\ \text{Pa}.$$

REFLECT The cable stretches by about 0.1% of its original length.

Practice Problem: If we want the elongation of the cable to be no greater than 0.001 m, what cross-sectional area must the cable have? *Answer:* 0.80 cm².

▲ **FIGURE 6** Our sketch for this problem.

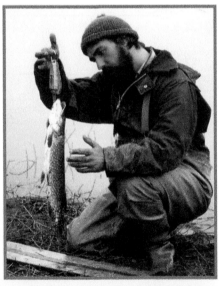

Lowell Georgia/Corbis

▲ Application **Hooke, line, and sinker.** In addition to weighing a northern pike, this biologist is also demonstrating the relationship between stress and strain. Within reasonable limits, the spring inside the scale obeys Hooke's law: The displacement of the end of the spring (strain) is proportional to the force applied at the end by the weight of the fish (stress). Because the spring constant (force divided by elongation) does not vary, you can measure the displacement of the end of the spring and determine the mass of the fish.

Modeling an Elastic Material as a Spring

Young's modulus characterizes the elastic properties of a material under tension or compression in a way that is independent of the size or shape of the particular object. To find the relation of force to elongation of any specific rod, cable, or spring, we solve Equation 4 for the magnitude $F_\perp$ of the force at each end causing the elongation; we obtain

$$F_\perp = \frac{YA}{l_0}\Delta l.$$

Now let $k = YA/l_0$, call the elongation x instead of Δl, and call the force magnitude F_x instead of $F_\perp$; then we have

$$F_x = kx.$$

We recognize k as the force constant (or spring constant) for a spring. When Hooke's law is obeyed, the force F_x needed (on each end) to stretch a spring a distance x beyond its undistorted length is directly proportional to x, and the ratio of F_x to x is the force constant k. Similarly, the shortening of an object in compression is directly proportional to the compressing force. Hooke's law was originally stated in this form; it was reformulated in terms of stress and strain much later by other physicists.

Volume Stress and Strain

When you dive under water, the water exerts nearly uniform pressure everywhere on your surface and squeezes you to a slightly smaller volume (Figure 1). This situation is different from tensile and compressive stresses and strains. The stress is now a uniform pressure on all sides, and the resulting deformation is a change in volume. We use the terms **volume stress** and **volume strain** to describe these quantities. Another familiar example is the compression of a gas under pressure, such as the air in a car's tires. We'll use the terms *volume stress* and *pressure* interchangeably.

The **pressure** in a fluid, denoted by p, is the force $F_\perp$ per unit area A transmitted across any cross section of the fluid, against a wall of its container, or against a surface of an immersed object:

$$p = \frac{F_\perp}{A}. \tag{5}$$

When a solid object is immersed in a fluid and both are at rest, **the forces that the fluid exerts on the surface of the object are always perpendicular to the surface at each point.** If they were not, the fluid would move relative to the object.

When we apply pressure to the surface of a fluid in a container, such as the cylinder and piston shown in Figure 7, the pressure is transmitted through the fluid and also acts on the surface of any object immersed in the fluid. This principle is called **Pascal's law.** If pressure differences due to differences in depth within the fluid can be neglected, the pressure is the same at every point in the fluid and at every point on the surface of any submerged object.

Pressure has the same units as stress; commonly used units include 1 Pa (or 1 N/m^2) and 1 lb/in.^{2} (or 1 psi). Also in common use is the **atmosphere,** abbreviated atm. One atmosphere is defined to be the average pressure of the earth's atmosphere at sea level:

$$1 \text{ atmosphere} = 1 \text{ atm} = 1.013 \times 10^5 \text{ Pa} = 14.7 \text{ lb/in}^2.$$

Pressure is a scalar quantity, not a vector quantity; it has no direction.

We've noted that pressure plays the role of volume stress in a volume deformation. The corresponding strain, called **volume strain,** is defined as the fractional change in volume (Figure 8)—that is, the ratio of the change in volume, ΔV, to the original volume V_0:

$$\text{Volume strain} = \frac{\Delta V}{V_0}. \tag{6}$$

Volume strain is change in volume per unit volume. Like tensile or compressive strain, it is a pure number, without units.

When Hooke's law is obeyed, the volume strain is *proportional* to the volume stress (change in pressure). The corresponding constant ratio of stress to strain is called the **bulk modulus,** denoted by B. When the pressure on an object changes by a small amount Δp, from p_0 to $p_0 + \Delta p$, and the resulting volume strain is $\Delta V/V_0$, Hooke's law takes the form

$$B = -\frac{\Delta p}{\Delta V/V_0}. \tag{7}$$

The force applied to the piston is distributed over the surface of the object.

At each point on the object, the force applied by the fluid is perpendicular to the object's surface.

▲ **FIGURE 7** Volume stress.

Initial volume V_0 at initial pressure p_0 Final volume V at pressure $p = p_0 + \Delta p$

Volume stress $= \Delta p$ Volume strain $= \dfrac{\Delta V}{V_0}$

▲ **FIGURE 8** Volume strain.

Ken Robinson

TABLE 2 **Bulk modulus**

Material	B (Pa)
Aluminum	0.70×10^{11}
Brass	0.61×10^{11}
Copper	1.4×10^{11}
Glass	0.37×10^{11}
Iron	1.0×10^{11}
Steel	1.6×10^{11}
Tungsten	2.0×10^{11}

We include a minus sign in this equation because an *increase* in pressure always causes a *decrease* in volume. In other words, when Δp is positive, ΔV is negative. The negative sign in Equation 7 makes B itself a positive quantity.

Table 2 lists values of the bulk modulus for several solid materials. Values for liquids are usually considerably smaller, typically between 1×10^9 Pa and 5×10^9 Pa. (I.e., in general, liquids are more easily compressed than solids). For small pressure changes in a solid or a liquid, we consider B to be constant. The bulk modulus of a *gas,* however, depends on the initial pressure p_0. The units of B—force per unit area, or pascals—are the same as those of pressure (and of tensile or compressive stress).

EXAMPLE 2   **Squeezing water**

The bulk modulus of water is 2.2×10^9 Pa $(= 2.2 \times 10^9 \, \text{N/m}^2)$. By how much does a cubic meter of water decrease in volume when it is taken from the surface of the ocean down to a depth of 1.0 km, where the pressure is 9.8×10^6 Pa greater than at the surface?

SOLUTION

SET UP AND SOLVE From Equation 7, the bulk modulus is

$$B = -\frac{\Delta p}{\Delta V/V_0}.$$

We solve this equation for ΔV:

$$\Delta V = -\frac{\Delta p V_0}{B} = -\frac{(9.8 \times 10^6 \, \text{Pa})(1.0 \, \text{m}^3)}{(2.2 \times 10^9 \, \text{N/m}^2)}$$
$$= -4.5 \times 10^{-3} \, \text{m}^3 = -4500 \, \text{cm}^3.$$

REFLECT The negative sign indicates that the volume has decreased while the pressure has increased. Although the pressure at a 1 km depth is roughly 100 times that at the surface, the fractional change in volume is only about 0.5%.

Practice Problem: A fluid with an initial volume of 0.35 m³ is subjected to a pressure decrease of 3.2×10^3 Pa. The volume is then found to have increased by 0.20 cm³. What is the bulk modulus of the fluid? *Answer:* $B = 5.6 \times 10^9$ Pa.

A block subjected to shear stress from two directions

▲ **FIGURE 9** Shear stress.

Shear stress $= \dfrac{F_{\parallel}}{A}$ Shear strain $= \dfrac{x}{h}$

▲ **FIGURE 10** Shear strain.

Shear Stress and Strain

Another kind of stress–strain situation shown in Figure 1 is called shear. The block in Figure 9 is under **shear stress,** which we define as the force $F_{\parallel}$ tangent to a material surface, divided by the area A of the surface on which the force acts:

$$\text{Shear stress} = \frac{F_{\parallel}}{A}. \tag{8}$$

Shear stress, like the other two types of stress, is a force per unit area. For systems in equilibrium, shear stress can exist only in *solid* materials; a fluid would simply flow in response to the tangential force.

Figure 10 shows an object deformed by shear. We define **shear strain** as the ratio of the displacement x to the transverse dimension h; that is,

$$\text{Shear strain} = \frac{x}{h} = \tan\phi, \tag{9}$$

with x and h defined as in Figure 10. In real-life situations, x is nearly always much smaller than h, $\tan\phi$ is very nearly equal to ϕ, and the strain is simply the angle ϕ, measured in radians. Like all strains, shear strain is a dimensionless number because it is a ratio of two lengths.

If the forces are small enough so that Hooke's law is obeyed, the shear strain is *proportional* to the shear stress. The corresponding proportionality constant (ratio of shear stress to shear strain), is called the **shear modulus,** denoted by S:

$$S = \frac{\text{Shear stress}}{\text{Shear strain}} = \frac{F_{\parallel}/A}{x/h} = \frac{h}{A}\frac{F_{\parallel}}{x} = \frac{F_{\parallel}/A}{\phi}. \tag{10}$$

For a given material, S is usually a third to a half as large as Y. A few representative values of S for common materials are listed in Table 3.

TABLE 3   Shear modulus

Material	S (Pa)
Aluminum	0.30×10^{11}
Brass	0.36×10^{11}
Copper	0.42×10^{11}
Glass	0.23×10^{11}
Iron	0.70×10^{11}
Steel	0.84×10^{11}
Tungsten	1.5×10^{11}

> **NOTE** ▸ Keep in mind that only a *solid* material has a shear modulus. A liquid or gas flows freely under the action of a shear stress, so a fluid at rest cannot sustain such a stress. ◂

EXAMPLE 3   Minor earthquake damage

Suppose the brass baseplate of an outdoor sculpture experiences shear forces as a result of a mild earthquake. The plate is a square, 0.80 m on a side and 0.50 cm thick. How large a force $F_\parallel$ must be exerted on each of its edges if the displacement x in Figure 10b is 0.016 cm? The shear modulus of brass is listed in Table 3.

SOLUTION

SET UP Figure 11 shows our sketch. The shear stress at each edge of the plate is the force divided by the area of the edge:

$$\text{Shear stress} = \frac{F_\parallel}{A} = \frac{F_\parallel}{(0.80\ \text{m})(0.0050\ \text{m})} = (250\ \text{m}^{-2})F_\parallel.$$

The shear strain is

$$\text{Shear strain} = \frac{x}{h} = \frac{1.6 \times 10^{-4}\ \text{m}}{0.80\ \text{m}} = 2.0 \times 10^{-4}.$$

SOLVE From Table 3, the shear modulus S is

$$S = \frac{\text{Shear stress}}{\text{Shear strain}} = 0.36 \times 10^{11}\ \text{Pa} = \frac{(250\ \text{m}^{-2})F_\parallel}{2.0 \times 10^{-4}}.$$

Solving for $F_\parallel$, we obtain

$$F_\parallel = 2.9 \times 10^4\ \text{N}.$$

▲ **FIGURE 11** Our sketch for this problem.

REFLECT This force is nearly 7000 lb, or roughly twice the weight of a medium-size car.

Practice Problem: We replace the plate with another brass plate that has the same horizontal dimensions (0.80 m on a side), but a different thickness. If the shear forces have magnitude 1.2×10^5 N and the shear strain is the same as before, what is the plate's thickness? *Answer:* 2.1 cm.

Elasticity and Plasticity

Hooke's law, the proportionality between stress and strain in elastic deformations, has a limited range of validity. We know that if you pull, squeeze, or twist *anything* hard enough, it will bend or break. Just what *are* the limitations of Hooke's law?

Let's look at tensile stress and strain again. Suppose we gradually increase the tensile stress on an object, measure the corresponding strain, and plot a graph of stress as a function of strain. Figure 12 shows a typical stress–strain graph for a metal such as copper or soft iron subjected to tensile stress. The strain is shown as the *percent* elongation ($\Delta l/l_0 \times 100\%$).

The first part of the graph (to point A) is a straight line. During this phase, the object (say, a piece of copper wire) obeys Hooke's law: stress is proportional to strain, and the proportionality constant is Young's modulus. At point A, the plot ceases to be a straight line; strain is no longer exactly proportional to stress. However, up to point B, the wire still returns to its original, unstrained length if you release the stress. We call this reversible behavior an **elastic deformation.** (Note that an object can behave elastically without following Hooke's law.) This is the behavior you see when you pluck a guitar string; when it finishes vibrating, its length is unchanged.

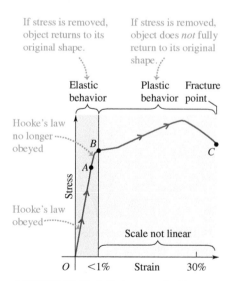

▲ **FIGURE 12** Typical stress–strain diagram for a ductile metal under tension.

Hans Pfletschinger/Peter Arnold/Photolibrary

◄ **BIO** Application **As strong as silk.** This photograph shows silk fibers emerging from the spinning glands on a spider's abdomen. Spider silk has a unique combination of high strength and high elasticity. It can have a tensile strength of up to 17×10^8 Pa, comparable to some of the strongest high-tensile steels we can produce. Considering that its density is only about 20% that of steel, spider's silk has sometimes been called "five times stronger" than steel. It is also quite elastic, having a Young's elastic modulus of only 3×10^8 Pa, less than 1% that of steel. Therefore, in addition to being very strong, spider silk can stretch to at least twice its length before breaking, allowing it to absorb large amounts of energy from flying insects. It has even been proposed that a web made from pencil-thick spider's silk would be able to stop a jet airplane in flight!

At greater stresses, the object does *not* fully return to its original shape when the stress is removed; it has undergone some degree of permanent deformation. If you subject a copper wire to a stress in this range, then, when you release the stress, the wire springs back somewhat, but not all the way back to its original length. We say that the wire undergoes **plastic deformation.** Finally, at point C, the wire breaks.

For some materials, a large amount of plastic deformation takes place between the elastic limit and the fracture (breaking) point. Such a material is said to be *ductile.* But if fracture occurs soon after the elastic limit is passed, the material is said to be *brittle.* A soft iron wire that can undergo considerable permanent stretch without breaking is ductile; a steel piano string that breaks soon after its elastic limit is reached is brittle.

The stress required to cause actual fracture of a material is called the **breaking stress** or (in the case of tensile stress) the **tensile strength.** Two materials, such as two types of steel, may have very similar values of Young's modulus but vastly different breaking stresses. Table 4 gives a few typical values of breaking stress for several materials in tension. The conversion factor 6.9×10^8 Pa = 100,000 psi will help put these numbers in perspective. For example, if the breaking stress of a particular steel is 6.9×10^8 Pa, then a bar or cable with a 1 in.^{2} cross section has a breaking strength of 100,000 lb.

2 Periodic Motion

An object such as a vibrating guitar string or the swinging pendulum of a grandfather clock repeats the same motion over and over. We refer to such motion as **periodic motion** or **oscillation.** A mechanical system that undergoes periodic motion always has a stable equilibrium position. When it is moved away from this position and released, a force comes into play to pull it back toward equilibrium. But by the time it gets there, it has picked up some kinetic energy, so it overshoots, stopping somewhere on the other side, and is again pulled back toward equilibrium. If this cycle repeats over and over, we say that the motion is periodic.

Simple Harmonic Motion

One of the simplest systems that can have periodic motion is shown in Figure 13. A glider with mass m moves along the x axis on a frictionless horizontal air track. It is attached to a spring that can be either stretched or compressed. The spring obeys Hooke's law and has force constant k. (You may want to review the definition of the force constant in Section 1.) The left end of the spring is held stationary. The spring force is the only horizontal force acting on the object. (We neglect the very small friction force on the air track.) The two vertical forces (the normal and weight forces) always add to zero.

It is simplest to define our coordinate system so that the origin O is at the equilibrium position, where the spring is neither stretched nor compressed. Then x is the displacement of the object from equilibrium and is also the change in length of the spring. The x component of acceleration is given by $a_x = F_x/m$.

TABLE 4 Breaking stresses of materials

Material	Breaking stress (N/m^2 or Pa)
Aluminum	2.2×10^8
Arterial wall	2.0×10^6
Bone	$1–2 \times 10^8$
Brass	4.7×10^8
Collagen	1.0×10^8
Glass	10×10^8
Iron	3.0×10^8
Phosphor bronze	5.6×10^8
Steel	11.0×10^8
Wood	$1–2 \times 10^8$

▲ **FIGURE 13** A system for demonstrating periodic motion.

Figure 14 shows complete free-body diagrams for three different positions of the object:

1. **x is negative** (Figure 14a). The object is to the left of O, so the spring is compressed. The spring pushes toward the right (toward the equilibrium point) on the object, so the acceleration is also toward the right. Thus, F_x and a_x are both positive. (The object may be *moving* toward either the left or right, however.)
2. **$x = 0$** (Figure 14b). The object is at O, the equilibrium position. The spring is neither stretched nor compressed; it exerts no force on the object. The acceleration is zero, and the object is instantaneously moving with constant velocity toward either the right or left.
3. **x is positive** (Figure 14c). The object is to the right of O, so the spring is stretched. The spring pulls toward the left (toward the equilibrium point) on the object, so the acceleration is also toward the left. Thus, F_x and a_x are both negative. (The object may be *moving* toward either the left or right, however.)

The force acting on the object tends always to restore it to the equilibrium position, and we call it a **restoring force. On either side of the equilibrium position, F_x and x always have opposite signs.** In Section 4, we represented the force acting *on* a stretched spring as $F_x = kx$. The force the spring exerts *on the object* is the negative of this, so the x component of force F_x acting on the body is

$$F_x = -kx. \tag{11}$$

This equation gives the correct magnitude and sign of the force, whether x is positive, negative, or zero. The force constant k is always positive and has units of N/m. A useful alternative set of units for k is kg/s^2.

The x component of acceleration, a_x, of the body at any point is determined by $\sum \vec{F} = m\vec{a}$, with the x component of force given by Equation 11:

$$a_x = \frac{F_x}{m} = -\frac{k}{m}x. \tag{12}$$

The acceleration is *not* constant, so don't even think of using constant-acceleration equations! Figure 15 shows a complete cycle of simple harmonic motion. If we displace the object to the right a distance A (so that $x = A$) and release it, its initial acceleration, from Equation 12, is $-kA/m$. As it approaches the equilibrium position, its acceleration decreases in magnitude, but its speed increases. It overshoots the equilibrium position and comes to a stop on the other side; we'll show later that the stopping point is at $x = -A$. Then it accelerates to the right, overshoots equilibrium again, and stops at the starting point $x = A$, ready to repeat the whole process. If there is no friction or other force to remove mechanical energy from the system, this motion repeats forever.

The motion that we've just described—periodic motion under the action of a restoring force that is *directly proportional* to the displacement from equilibrium, as given by Equation 11—is called **simple harmonic motion,** abbreviated **SHM.** Many periodic motions, such as the vibration of the quartz crystal in a watch, vibrations of molecules, the motion of a tuning fork, and the electric current in an alternating-current circuit, are approximately simple harmonic motion. However, not *all* periodic motions are simple harmonic.

Here are several terms that we'll use in discussing periodic motions:

Definitions of quantities that describe periodic motion

- The **amplitude** of the motion, denoted by A, is the maximum magnitude of displacement from equilibrium—that is, the maximum value of $|x|$. It is always positive. The total overall range of the motion is $2A$.

$x < 0$: glider displaced to the left from the equilibrium position.　$F_x > 0$, so $a_x > 0$: Compressed spring pushes glider toward equilibrium position.

(a)

$x = 0$: The relaxed spring exerts no force on the glider, so the glider has zero acceleration.

(b)

$x > 0$: glider displaced to the right from the equilibrium position.　$F_x < 0$, so $a_x < 0$: stretched spring pulls glider toward equilibrium position.

(c)

▲ **FIGURE 14** A model for periodic motion. If the spring obeys Hooke's law, the motion of the glider is simple harmonic motion.

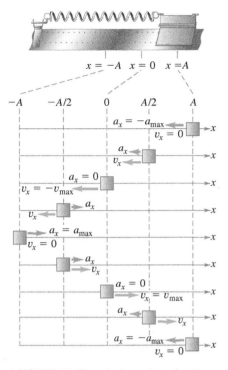

FIGURE 15 The velocity and acceleration of the glider at different points in one cycle of harmonic motion. The maximum acceleration is $a_{max} = kA/m$ and the maximum speed is v_{max}.

- A **cycle** is one complete round trip—for example, from A to $-A$ and back to A, or from O to A, back through O to $-A$, and back to O. Note that motion from one side to the other (say, from $-A$ to A) is a half-cycle, not a whole cycle.
- The **period,** T, is the time for one whole cycle. It is always positive; the SI unit is the second, but it is sometimes expressed as "seconds per cycle."
- The **frequency,** f, is the number of cycles in a unit of time. It is always positive; the SI unit of frequency is the hertz, defined as follows:

$$1 \text{ hertz} = 1 \text{ Hz} = 1 \text{ cycle/s} = 1 \text{ s}^{-1}.$$

This unit is named in honor of Heinrich Hertz, one of the pioneers investigating electromagnetic waves during the late 19th century.

- The **angular frequency,** ω, is 2π times the frequency:

$$\omega = 2\pi f.$$

We'll learn later why ω is a useful quantity. It represents the rate of change of an angular quantity (not necessarily related to a rotational motion) that is always measured in radians, so its units are rad/s.

From the definitions of period T and frequency f, we see that each is the reciprocal of the other:

$$f = \frac{1}{T}, \qquad T = \frac{1}{f}. \tag{13}$$

Also, from the definition of ω,

$$\omega = 2\pi f = \frac{2\pi}{T}. \tag{14}$$

EXAMPLE 4 **Ultrasound for medical imaging**

An ultrasonic transducer (a kind of ultrasonic loudspeaker) used for medical diagnosis is oscillating at a frequency of 6.7 MHz $(6.7 \times 10^6 \text{ Hz})$ (Figure 16). How much time does each oscillation take, and what is the angular frequency?

FIGURE 16 Ultrasonic vibrations for medical diagnosis are produced by an electronic transducer.

Gabe Palmer/Corbis

SOLUTION

SET UP We first identify the frequency: $f = 6.7 \times 10^6 \text{ Hz} = 6.7 \times 10^6 \text{ s}^{-1}$.

SOLVE The period T is given by Equation 13 and the angular frequency by Equation 14:

$$T = \frac{1}{f} = \frac{1}{6.7 \times 10^6 \text{ Hz}} = 1.5 \times 10^{-7} \text{ s} = 0.15 \text{ } \mu\text{s},$$
$$\omega = 2\pi f = 2\pi (6.7 \times 10^6 \text{ Hz}) = 4.2 \times 10^7 \text{ rad/s}.$$

REFLECT The transducer's rapid vibration corresponds to large values of f and ω and small values of T. The reverse would be true for a slow oscillator, such as the pendulum of a large grandfather clock.

Not all periodic motion is simple harmonic. **Only in SHM is the restoring force *directly proportional* to the displacement.** In more complex types of periodic motion, the force may depend on the displacement in a more complicated way. However, many periodic motions are *approximately* simple harmonic if the amplitude is small enough that the force is approximately proportional to the displacement. Thus, we can use SHM as an approximate model for many different periodic motions, such as the motion of a pendulum and the vibrations of atoms in molecules and solids.

3 Energy in Simple Harmonic Motion

In this section and the next, we'll analyze the spring–mass model of SHM that we've just described. What questions shall we ask? Given the mass m of the object and the force constant k of the spring, we'd like to be able to predict the period T and the frequency f. We also want to know how fast the object is moving at each point in its motion. That is, we want to know its x component of velocity, v_x, and its x component of acceleration a_x, as functions of position x (the x component of displacement from the equilibrium position). Best of all would be to have expressions for x, v_x, and a_x as functions of *time*, so that we can find where the object is and how it is moving at any specified time. In the next few pages we'll work all these things out.

We'll approach these questions first by using energy considerations and then by using $\Sigma \vec{F} = m\vec{a}$ along with a geometric construction called the circle of reference. Let's start with energy. We've already noted that the spring force is the only horizontal force on the object. It is a *conservative* force, and the vertical forces do no work, so the total mechanical energy of the system is conserved. We'll also assume that the mass of the spring itself is negligible.

The kinetic energy of the object is $K = \frac{1}{2}mv_x^2$, and the potential energy of the spring is $U = \frac{1}{2}kx^2$. The equation for the conservation of mechanical energy is $K + U = E =$ constant, or

$$E = \tfrac{1}{2}mv_x^2 + \tfrac{1}{2}kx^2 = \text{constant.} \tag{15}$$

The total mechanical energy E is also directly related to the amplitude A of the motion. When the object reaches the point $x = A$ or $x = -A$ (its maximum displacement from equilibrium), it stops momentarily as it turns back toward the equilibrium position. That is, when $x = \pm A$, $v_x = 0$. At this point, the energy is entirely potential energy and $E = \frac{1}{2}kA^2$. Because E is constant, this quantity also equals E at any other point; combining the preceding expression for E with Equation 15, we get

$$E = \tfrac{1}{2}kA^2 = \tfrac{1}{2}mv_x^2 + \tfrac{1}{2}kx^2. \tag{16}$$

Solving Equation 16 for v_x, we find the following relationship:

Velocity of an object in SHM as a function of position
From the basic energy relation in Equation 16,

$$v_x = \pm\sqrt{\frac{k}{m}}\sqrt{A^2 - x^2}. \tag{17}$$

We can use this equation to find the magnitude of the velocity (but not its sign) for any given position x. For example, when $x = \pm A/2$,

$$v_x = \pm\sqrt{\frac{k}{m}}\sqrt{A^2 - \left(\pm\frac{A}{2}\right)^2} = \pm\sqrt{\frac{3}{4}}\sqrt{\frac{k}{m}}A.$$

Mastering**PHYSICS**

PhET: Motion in 2D
PhET: Masses & Springs
ActivPhysics 9.3: Vibrational Energy
ActivPhysics 9.5: Ape Drops Tarzan

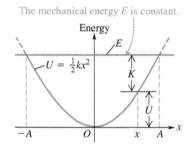

▲ FIGURE 17 In simple harmonic motion, the total energy E is constant, continually transforming from potential energy U to kinetic energy K and back again.

The mechanical energy E is constant.

(a) The potential energy U and total energy E of an object in SHM as a function of x position.

(b) The same graph as in **(a)**, showing kinetic energy K as well.

▲ FIGURE 18 Kinetic, potential, and total energies as functions of position for SHM. At each value of x, the sum of K and U equals the constant total energy E.

Equation 17 also shows that the *maximum* speed v_{max} occurs at $x = 0$ and is given by

$$v_{max} = \sqrt{\frac{k}{m}}A. \qquad (18)$$

Figure 17 is a pictorial display of the energy quantities at several x positions, and Figure 18 is a graphical display of Equation 15. Mechanical energy (kinetic, potential, and total) is plotted vertically, and the coordinate x is plotted horizontally. The parabolic curve in Figure 18a represents the potential energy $U = \frac{1}{2}kx^2$. The horizontal line represents the constant total energy E (which doesn't vary with x). This line intersects the potential-energy curve at $x = -A$ and $x = A$, where the energy is entirely potential.

Suppose we start on the horizontal axis at some value of x between $-A$ and A. The vertical distance from the x axis to the parabola is U, and since $E = K + U$, the remaining vertical distance up to the horizontal line is K. Figure 18b shows both K and U as functions of x. As the object oscillates between $-A$ and A, the mechanical energy is continuously transformed from potential to kinetic to potential and back. At $x = \pm A$, $E = U$ and $K = 0$.

We see again why A is the maximum displacement. If we tried to make x greater than A (or less than $-A$), U would be greater than E, and K would have to be negative. K can never be negative, so x can't be greater than A or less than $-A$. (In quantum mechanics, it *is* possible in some circumstances for a particle to traverse regions where classically it would have negative kinetic energy. This concept is important in alpha decay of nuclei and in the tunneling electron microscope, but it plays no role in the mechanics of macroscopic objects.)

Quantitative Analysis 1

Energy of a spring

A mass attached to a spring oscillates with SHM. If the maximum displacement from equilibrium is A and the total mechanical energy of the system is E, what is the system's kinetic energy when the position of the mass is half its maximum displacement?

A. $\frac{1}{2}E$. B. $\frac{3}{4}E$. C. E.

SOLUTION The total mechanical energy E of an oscillator is the sum of its kinetic and potential energies: $E = K + U$. But $U = \frac{1}{2}kx^2$. If $x = A$, then $U = E$ and $K = 0$. At $x = \frac{1}{2}A$, $U = \frac{1}{4}E$ and $K = E - U = \frac{3}{4}E$.

EXAMPLE 5 **Simple harmonic motion on an air track**

A spring is mounted horizontally on an air track (Figure 19a), with the left end held stationary. We attach a spring balance to the free end of the spring, pull toward the right, and measure the elongation. We determine that the stretching force is proportional to the displacement and that a force of 6.0 N causes an elongation of 0.030 m. We remove the spring balance and attach a 0.50 kg object to the end, pull it a distance of 0.040 m, release it, and watch it oscillate in SHM (Figure 19b). Find the following quantities:

(a) the force constant of the spring.
(b) the maximum and minimum velocities attained by the vibrating object.
(c) the maximum and minimum acceleration.
(d) the velocity and acceleration when the object has moved halfway to the center from its initial position.
(e) the kinetic energy, the potential energy, and the total energy in the halfway position.

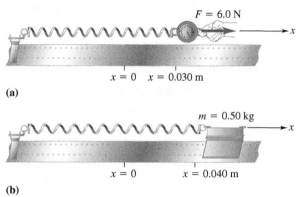

$F = 6.0\ \text{N}$

$x = 0 \quad x = 0.030\ \text{m}$

(a)

$m = 0.50\ \text{kg}$

$x = 0 \quad\quad x = 0.040\ \text{m}$

(b)

▲ **FIGURE 19**

SOLUTION

SET UP AND SOLVE For this glider, the amplitude is $A = 0.040$ m.

Part (a): When $x = 0.030$ m, the force the spring exerts on the object is $F_x = -6.0$ N. From Equation 11, the force constant k is

$$k = -\frac{F_x}{x} = -\frac{-6.0\ \text{N}}{0.030\ \text{m}} = 200\ \text{N/m}.$$

Part (b): From Equation 18, the maximum velocity occurs at the equilibrium position, $x = 0$:

$$v_{\text{max}} = \sqrt{\frac{k}{m}}A = \sqrt{\frac{200\ \text{N/m}}{0.50\ \text{kg}}}(0.040\ \text{m}) = 0.80\ \text{m/s}.$$

The minimum (most negative) velocity also occurs at $x = 0$ and is the negative of the maximum value. The minimum *magnitude* of velocity, occurring at $x = \pm A$, is zero.

Part (c): The acceleration for any x is given by Equation 12:

$$a_x = -\frac{k}{m}x.$$

The maximum (most positive) acceleration a_{max} occurs at the most negative value of x, that is, $x = -A$; therefore,

$$a_{\text{max}} = -\frac{k}{m}(-A) = -\frac{200\ \text{N/m}}{0.50\ \text{kg}}(-0.040\ \text{m}) = 16.0\ \text{m/s}^2.$$

The minimum (most negative) acceleration is $-16.0\ \text{m/s}^2$, occurring at $x = +A = +0.040$ m.

Part (d): The velocity v_x at any position x is given by Equation 17:

$$v_x = \pm\sqrt{\frac{k}{m}}\sqrt{A^2 - x^2}.$$

At the halfway point, $x = A/2 = 0.020$ m. We find that

$$v_x = -\sqrt{\frac{200\ \text{N/m}}{0.50\ \text{kg}}}\sqrt{(0.040\ \text{m})^2 - (0.020\ \text{m})^2} = -0.69\ \text{m/s}.$$

We've chosen the negative square root because the object is moving in the negative x direction, from $x = A$ toward $x = 0$. From Equation 12,

$$a_x = -\frac{k}{m}x = -\frac{200\ \text{N/m}}{0.50\ \text{kg}}(0.020\ \text{m}) = -8.0\ \text{m/s}^2.$$

Part (e): The energy quantities are the terms in Equation 16. From (d), when $x = A/2 = (0.040\ \text{m})/2$, $v_x = \pm 0.69$ m/s. At this point, the kinetic energy is

$$K = \tfrac{1}{2}mv_x^2 = \tfrac{1}{2}(0.50\ \text{kg})(0.69\ \text{m/s})^2 = 0.12\ \text{J},$$

the potential energy is

$$U = \tfrac{1}{2}kx^2 = \tfrac{1}{2}(200\ \text{N/m})(0.020\ \text{m})^2 = 0.040\ \text{J},$$

and the total energy is $E = K + U = 0.12\ \text{J} + 0.040\ \text{J} = 0.16\ \text{J}$. Alternatively,

$$E = \tfrac{1}{2}kA^2 = \tfrac{1}{2}(200\ \text{N/m})(0.040\ \text{m})^2 = 0.16\ \text{J}.$$

The conditions at $x = 0$, $\pm A/2$, and $\pm A$ are shown in Figure 15.

REFLECT The equations we've used in this solution enable us to find relations among position, velocity, acceleration, and force. But they don't help us to find directly how these quantities vary with time. In the next section, we'll work out relations that enable us to do just that and also to relate the period and frequency of the motion to the mass and force constant of the system.

4 Equations of Simple Harmonic Motion

Simple harmonic motion is closely related to uniform circular motion, which we've studied several times. By examining this relationship, we can gain additional insight into both kinds of motion. In this section we'll derive equations for the position, velocity, and acceleration of an object undergoing SHM, as functions of time. We'll also show how the period and frequency of the motion are determined by the mass m and force constant k of the system.

Circle of Reference

Our analysis is based on a geometric representation called the **circle of reference.** The basic idea is shown in Figure 20 First, imagine the apparatus shown in Figure 20a. We glue a small ball to the rim of a rotating turntable on a flat horizontal tabletop (viewed from above in the figure). Behind the turntable, we set up a vertical screen. Then we illuminate the turntable from in front by a flat, horizontal beam of light placed at the level of the turntable. As the ball rotates, its shadow appears on the screen. And, while the ball moves in uniform circular motion, we find that **the shadow moves from side to side in SHM!**

Figure 20b shows the circle of reference—an abstract representation of the phenomenon in Figure 20a. Point Q (representing the ball) moves counterclockwise around a circle whose radius is equal to the amplitude A of the shadow's simple harmonic motion. The constant angular velocity ω of the ball (measured in rad/s) is equal to the angular frequency of the shadow's SHM. Thus, ω is the rate of change of the angle ϕ with time: $\omega = \Delta\phi/\Delta t$.

The vector from the origin O to point Q (which we can denote as OQ) is the position vector of point Q relative to O. This vector has constant magnitude A, and at time t it is at an angle ϕ (measured counterclockwise from the positive x axis). As Q moves, vector OQ rotates counterclockwise with constant angular velocity $\omega = \Delta\phi/\Delta t$. As we'll soon see, the x component of this vector represents the actual motion of the object under study.

Now let's prove that the horizontal component of the vector OQ represents the actual motion of the shadow. In Figure 20b, point P represents the ball's

Illuminated vertical screen

Shadow of ball on screen

Ball's shadow

Ball on rotating turntable

While the ball on the turntable moves in uniform circular motion, its *shadow* moves back and forth on the screen in simple harmonic motion.

Illumination

Table

Light beam

(a) Apparatus for creating the reference circle

Ball moves in uniform circular motion.

Shadow moves back and forth on x axis in SHM.

$x = A \cos \phi$

(b) An abstract representation of the motion in **(a)**.

▲ **FIGURE 20** The circle of reference relates simple harmonic motion to uniform circular motion.

shadow; it lies on the diameter of the circle that coincides with the x axis, directly below point Q, just as the shadow in Figure 20a is always directly in line with the ball. We call Q the *reference point,* the circle itself the *circle of reference,* and P the *projection* of Q onto the diameter. As Q revolves, P moves back and forth along the diameter, staying always directly below (or above) Q.

The position of P with respect to the origin O at any time t is the coordinate x; from Figure 20a,

$$x = A \cos \phi.$$

If point Q is at the extreme right end of the diameter at time $t = 0$, then $\phi = 0$ when $t = 0$. Because ω is constant, ϕ increases uniformly with time; that is,

$$\phi = \omega t,$$

and

$$x = A \cos \omega t. \tag{19}$$

Now ω, the angular velocity of Q (in radians per second) is related to f, the number of complete revolutions of Q per second. There are 2π radians in one complete revolution, so $\omega = 2\pi f$. Furthermore, the point P makes one complete back-and-forth vibration (one cycle) for each revolution of Q. Hence f is also the number of vibrations per second or the *frequency* of vibration of point P. Thus we can also write Equation 19 as

$$x = A \cos 2\pi f t. \tag{20}$$

We can find the instantaneous velocity of P with the help of Fig. 21a. The reference point Q moves with a tangential speed $v_Q = v_\parallel$ given by the equation below:

$$v_\parallel = \omega A = 2\pi f A.$$

Point P is always directly below or above the reference point, so the velocity v_x of P at each instant must equal the x component of the velocity of Q. That is, from Figure 21a,

$$v_x = -v_\parallel \sin \phi = -\omega A \sin \phi,$$

and it follows that

$$v_x = -\omega A \sin \omega t = -2\pi f A \sin 2\pi f t. \tag{21}$$

The minus sign is needed because, at the instant shown, the direction of the velocity is toward the left. When Q is below the horizontal diameter, the velocity of P is toward the right, but $\sin \phi$ is negative at such points. So the minus sign is needed in both cases, and Equation 21 gives the velocity of point P at any time.

We can also find the acceleration of point P. Because P is always directly below or above Q, its x component of acceleration must equal the x component of the acceleration of Q. Point Q moves in a circular path with constant angular velocity ω, and its acceleration is toward the center of the circle, with magnitude $a_Q = a_{\mathrm{rad}}$ given by the equation below:

$$a_{\mathrm{rad}} = \omega^2 A = 4\pi^2 f^2 A.$$

From Figure 21b, the x component of this acceleration is

$$a_x = -a_{\mathrm{rad}} \cos \phi;$$

or

$$a_x = -\omega^2 A \cos \omega t = -4\pi^2 f^2 A \cos 2\pi f t. \tag{22}$$

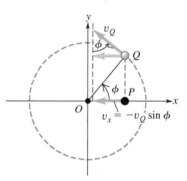

(a) Using the reference circle to determine the velocity of point P.

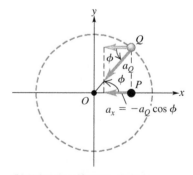

(b) Using the reference circle to determine the acceleration of point P.

▲ **FIGURE 21** The velocity and acceleration of point P are the horizontal components of the velocity and acceleration, respectively, of point Q.

The minus sign is needed because, at the instant shown, the acceleration is toward the left. When Q is to the left of the center, the acceleration of P is toward the right, but since $\cos\phi$ is negative at such points, the minus sign is still needed. Therefore, Equation 22 gives the acceleration of P at any time.

Now comes the reward for our lengthy analysis—the crucial step in showing that the motion of P is simple harmonic. We combine Equations 19 and 22, obtaining

$$a_x = -\omega^2 x. \tag{23}$$

Because ω is constant, **the acceleration a_x at each instant equals a negative constant times the displacement x at that instant.** But this is just the essential feature of simple harmonic motion, as given by Equation 12: Force and acceleration are proportional to the negative of the displacement from equilibrium. This shows that **the motion of P is indeed simple harmonic.**

Quantitative Analysis 2   **Using equations of motion**

An object undergoing simple harmonic motion along the x axis obeys the equation $x = 12.0\cos 0.25t$, where x is in cm and t is in seconds. Which of the following choices correctly gives the position, velocity, and acceleration of the object at the moment it is released (i.e., at time $t = 0$)?

A. $x = +12$ cm, $v_x = 0.00$ cm/s, $a_x = -0.75$ cm/s^2.
B. $x = 0.00$ cm, $v_x = 3.0$ cm/s, $a_x = 0.00$ cm/s^2.
C. $x = -12$ cm, $v_x = 0.00$ cm/s, $a_x = -0.75$ cm/s^2.
D. $x = 0.00$ cm, $v_x = -3.0$ cm/s, $a_x = 0.00$ cm/s^2.

SOLUTION At the initial time $t = 0$, the object has its maximum positive displacement, so at that instant $x = 12$ cm. The object is released from rest (i.e., with zero initial velocity), so $v_x = 0$. Only answer A is consistent with these two results. To confirm this choice, we can find the value of a_x at time $t = 0$. From Equation 19, $\omega = 0.25$ s^{-1}, and from Equation 22 at time $t = 0$, $a_x = -\omega^2 A = -(0.25\text{ s}^{-1})^2(12\text{ cm}) = -0.75$ cm/s^2 (also consistent with answer A). So answer A is correct.

Wald De Heer

▲ Application Hanging in the balance. Scientists recently used a single carbon nanotube to create a device to measure the mass of incredibly tiny objects, such as a tiny graphite particle with a mass of only 22 femtograms $(22 \times 10^{-15}$ g$)$. Although submicroscopic, this "nanobalance" was shown to obey the same physical laws as a macroscopic mass oscillating on the end of an elastic beam—in particular, the period and frequency of oscillation depend on the mass at the end. The nanotube's resonant frequency of oscillation in response to an applied voltage was measured with and without the tiny graphite particle attached at the end. This procedure allowed the scientists to determine the particle's mass, and the value agreed well with the calculated mass for a graphite particle of that size. Thus, someday soon it may be possible to determine directly the mass of individual cells and even virus particles.

Frequency and Period of an Object in Simple Harmonic Motion

We're now ready to find how the frequency f and angular frequency ω of simple harmonic motion are related to the physical properties of the system (the spring constant k and the mass m). To make Equations 12 and 23 agree completely, we must choose an angular velocity ω for the reference point Q such that

$$\omega^2 = \frac{k}{m}, \quad \text{or} \quad \omega = \sqrt{\frac{k}{m}}. \tag{24}$$

With this choice, the frequency of motion of Q is equal to that of the simple harmonic motion of the actual particle P:

Frequency and period of SHM in terms of mass m and force constant k

$$f = \frac{\omega}{2\pi} = \frac{1}{2\pi}\sqrt{\frac{k}{m}}. \tag{25}$$

The period T of the motion (the time for one cycle) is the reciprocal of the frequency: $T = 1/f$. From Equation 25,

$$T = \frac{1}{f} = 2\pi\sqrt{\frac{m}{k}}. \tag{26}$$

The general form of Equations 25 and 26 can be understood intuitively. When m is large, a given displacement (and force) causes a relatively small acceleration, and we expect the motion to be slow and ponderous, corresponding to small f and large T. A large value of k means a very stiff spring, corresponding to a relatively large restoring force for a given displacement, resulting in large f and small T.

It may be surprising that these equations *do not* contain the amplitude A of the motion. Suppose we give our spring–mass system some initial displacement, release it, and measure its frequency. Then we stop it, give it a *different* initial displacement, and release it again. We find that the two frequencies are the same. To be sure, the maximum displacement, maximum speed, and maximum acceleration are all different in the two cases, but *not* the frequency. When the amplitude is increased, the mass has a greater distance to travel during each cycle, but the force and acceleration are also greater, on the average. In SHM, these two effects exactly cancel.

> **NOTE** ▶ The preceding paragraph sums up one of the most important characteristics of simple harmonic motion: **The frequency of the motion does not depend on its amplitude.** For instance, a tuning fork vibrates with the same frequency, regardless of how hard you hit it (i.e., regardless of the amplitude of its vibration). The pitch of a musical tone is determined primarily by the frequency of vibration. Thus, tuning forks always produce the same note. Indeed, if it were not for this property of simple harmonic motion, it would be impossible to play most musical instruments in tune. ◀

Quantitative Analysis 3

Frequency of a spring–mass system

An object with mass $m = 4 \text{ kg}$ is attached to a spring and vibrates in simple harmonic motion with frequency f. When this object is replaced by one with mass 1 kg, the new object vibrates at a frequency of

A. f.
B. $2f$.
C. $4f$.
D. $\frac{1}{2}f$.

SOLUTION Equation 25 states that the frequency is related to the inverse square root of the mass. If the mass is reduced, then the frequency must increase, so B and C are possible answers. (This also makes sense physically, since the same force applied to a lighter mass produces a greater acceleration at any given point.) When the mass changes from 4 kg to 1 kg, the square root of the mass changes from 2 to 1 and its reciprocal from 1 to 2. So B is the correct answer.

We can simplify many of the relationships in simple harmonic motion by using the angular frequency $\omega = 2\pi f$ rather than the frequency f. In terms of ω, we can rewrite Equations 12 and 17 respectively as

$$
\begin{aligned}
a_x &= -\frac{k}{m}x = -\omega^2 x, \\
v_x &= \pm\omega\sqrt{A^2 - x^2}.
\end{aligned}
\tag{27}
$$

In these and most of the other equations of simple harmonic motion, using ω instead of f lets us avoid a lot of factors of 2π. By convention, the hertz is *not* used as a unit of angular frequency; the usual unit for ω is the radian per second, or simply s^{-1}.

Equations for position, velocity, and acceleration of a simple harmonic oscillator as functions of time

Here's a summary of our results for the position x, velocity v_x, and acceleration a_x of a simple harmonic oscillator as functions of time:

$$
\begin{aligned}
x &= A\cos\omega t = A\cos(2\pi ft), & (19, 20) \\
v_x &= -\omega A\sin\omega t = -2\pi fA\sin(2\pi ft), & (21) \\
a_x &= -\omega^2 A\cos\omega t = -(2\pi f)^2 A\cos(2\pi ft). & (22)
\end{aligned}
$$

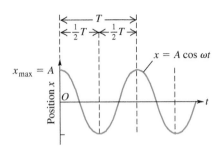

(a) Position as a function of time

(b) Velocity as a function of time

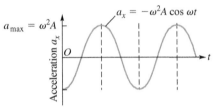

(c) Acceleration as a function of time

▲ **FIGURE 22** Graphs of position, velocity, and acceleration as functions of time for a particle in simple harmonic motion.

The strip chart pen moves in SHM on the spring while writing on the strip chart. The shadow of the peg follows the pen's motion exactly.

Pen trace

Strip chart pen mounted on spring

Light beam

Peg on rotating turntable

▲ **FIGURE 23** The strip chart pen, moving in simple harmonic motion, draws a curve of position as a function of time (the same curve as in Figure 22a). Meanwhile, the shadow of the peg on the turntable matches the motion of the pen.

Figure 22 shows graphs of these equations—for the position, velocity, and acceleration—as functions of time. We invite you to check that v_x at any time is the slope of the curve of x versus t and that a_x at any time is the slope of the curve of v_x versus t. We can plot a graph of x as a function of t with the help of an apparatus shown schematically in Figure 23.

Throughout this discussion, we've assumed that the initial position x_0 of the particle (at time $t = 0$) is its maximum positive displacement A (i.e., $x_0 = A$), but our analysis can be adapted to different starting conditions. Different initial positions correspond to different initial positions of the reference point Q. For example, if at time $t = 0$ the radial line OQ makes an angle ϕ_0 with the positive x axis, then the angle ϕ at time t is given, not by $\phi = \omega t$ as before, but by

$$\phi = \phi_0 + \omega t.$$

The object's position is then given as a function of time by

$$x = A\cos\left(\omega t + \phi_0\right).$$

With appropriate choices of the two quantities A and ϕ_0, this more general expression can be used to describe motion with any initial position and initial velocity. As before, the period and frequency are independent of the amplitude.

PROBLEM-SOLVING STRATEGY 1 Simple harmonic motion

SET UP

1. Be careful to distinguish between quantities that represent basic physical properties of the system and quantities that describe a particular motion that occurs when the system is set in motion in a specific way. The physical properties include the mass m, the force constant k, and the quantities derived from these, including the period T, the frequency f, and the angular frequency $\omega = 2\pi f$. In some problems, m or k, or both, can be determined from other information given about the system. Quantities that describe a particular motion include the amplitude A, the maximum velocity v_{max}, and any quantity that represents the position, velocity, or acceleration at a particular time.

SOLVE

2. If the problem involves a relation among position, velocity, and acceleration without reference to time, it is usually easier to use Equations 12 or 17 than to use the general expression for position as a function of time, Equation 19 or 20.
3. When detailed information about positions, velocities, and accelerations at various times is required, then Equations 20 through 22 must be used.
4. The energy equation, Equation 16, which includes the relation $E = \frac{1}{2}kA^2$, sometimes provides a convenient alternative to relations between velocity and position, especially when energy quantities are also required.

REFLECT

5. Try changing a value of one of the given quantities, and check whether the resulting changes in your answers make sense. Are they in the direction you would expect? Remember always to check for consistency of units in your results.

EXAMPLE 6   SHM on an air track, II: physical properties

Consider the oscillating air-track glider from Example 5 (Figure 24). As in that example, the force constant of the spring is $k = 200 \, \text{N/m}$ and the glider mass is $m = 0.50 \, \text{kg}$. Find the angular frequency, frequency, and period of the glider's motion.

▲ **FIGURE 24**

SOLUTION

SET UP AND SOLVE All the necessary relations are contained in Equations 24 through 26. From Equation 24,

$$\omega = \sqrt{\frac{k}{m}} = \sqrt{\frac{200 \, \text{N/m}}{0.50 \, \text{kg}}} = \sqrt{\frac{200 \, (\text{kg} \cdot \text{m/s}^2)/\text{m}}{0.50 \, \text{kg}}} = 20 \, \text{s}^{-1},$$

and from Equation 25,

$$f = \frac{\omega}{2\pi} = 3.2 \, \text{Hz}, \qquad T = \frac{1}{f} = 0.31 \, \text{s}.$$

REFLECT The angular frequency is not directly proportional to the force constant, as one might naively guess. To double the value of ω, we would have to increase k by a factor of four.

Practice Problem: Suppose we could "tune" this system by varying the mass; what mass would be required for a period of 1.0 s? *Answer:* 5.1 kg.

EXAMPLE 7   SHM on an air track, III: position vs. time

Suppose the object in Example 6 is released from rest at $x = 0.040 \, \text{m}$. How much time is required for it to move halfway to the center from the initial position?

SOLUTION

SET UP We can use the circle of reference, as shown in Figure 25. We need to find the angle ϕ of the radial line OQ when the glider has moved from the initial position $x = A$ to the later position $x = A/2$. Then we need to find the time required for ϕ to change by the corresponding amount.

SOLVE From Figure 25, we see that $x = A/2$ when $\cos\phi = 1/2$ and $\phi = 60° = \pi/3$. Also, $\phi = \omega t$, so we find that

$$t = \frac{\phi}{\omega} = \frac{\pi/3}{20 \, \text{s}^{-1}} = 0.052 \, \text{s}.$$

REFLECT The radial line OQ rotates through an angle of $\pi/3$ (1/6 revolution) in 0.052 s, corresponding to a time equal to the period, $T = 0.31 \, \text{s}$, needed for a full revolution. Note that we *must* express the angular quantity ϕ in radians.

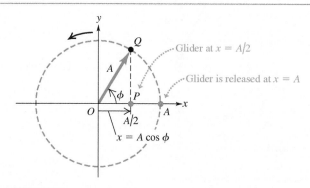

▲ **FIGURE 25**

Practice Problem: How much time is required for the glider to move from $x = A/2$ to $x = 0$? *Answer:* 0.026 s.

---

5 The Simple Pendulum

A **simple pendulum** is an idealized model consisting of a point mass suspended by a weightless, unstretchable string in a uniform gravitational field. When the mass is pulled to one side of its straight-down equilibrium position and released, it oscillates about the equilibrium position. Familiar situations such as a wrecking ball on a crane's cable, the plumb bob on a surveyor's transit, and a child on a swing can be modeled as simple pendulums. We can now analyze the motion of such systems, asking in particular whether it is simple harmonic.

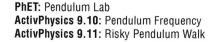

PhET: Pendulum Lab
ActivPhysics 9.10: Pendulum Frequency
ActivPhysics 9.11: Risky Pendulum Walk

The path of the object (modeled as a point mass) is an arc of a circle with radius L equal to the length of the string (Figure 26). We use as our coordinate the distance x measured along the arc. If the motion is simple harmonic, the restoring force must be directly proportional to x, or (because $x = L\theta$) to θ. Is it?

In Figure 26, we represent the forces on the mass in terms of tangential and radial components. The restoring force F at each point is the component of force tangent to the circular path at that point:

$$F = -mg\sin\theta. \tag{28}$$

The restoring force is therefore proportional *not* to θ, but to $\sin\theta$, so the motion is *not* simple harmonic. However, *if the angle θ is small*, $\sin\theta$ is very nearly equal to θ (in radians). For example, when $\theta = 0.1$ rad (about 6°), $\sin\theta = 0.0998$, a difference of only 0.2%. With this approximation, Equation 28 becomes

$$F = -mg\theta = -mg\frac{x}{L}, \qquad \text{or}$$

$$F = -\frac{mg}{L}x. \tag{29}$$

The restoring force F is then proportional to the coordinate x *for small displacements,* and the constant mg/L represents the force constant k. From Equation 24, the angular frequency ω of a simple pendulum with small amplitude is given by the following expressions:

Frequency and period of simple pendulum with length L:

$$\omega = \sqrt{\frac{k}{m}} = \sqrt{\frac{mg/L}{m}} = \sqrt{\frac{g}{L}}. \tag{30}$$

The corresponding frequency and period relations are

$$f = \frac{\omega}{2\pi} = \frac{1}{2\pi}\sqrt{\frac{g}{L}}, \tag{31}$$

$$T = \frac{2\pi}{\omega} = \frac{1}{f} = 2\pi\sqrt{\frac{L}{g}}. \tag{32}$$

Note that these expressions don't contain the *mass* of the particle. This is because the restoring force, a component of the particle's weight, is proportional to m. Thus, the mass appears on *both* sides of $\sum \vec{F} = m\vec{a}$ and cancels out. **For small oscillations, the period of a pendulum for a given value of g is independent of its mass and is determined entirely by its length.**

Galileo invented an elegant argument four centuries ago to show that the period should be independent of the mass. Make a simple pendulum, said Galileo, measure its period, and then split the pendulum down the middle, string and all. Because of the symmetry, neither half could have been pushing or pulling on the other before it was split. So splitting it can't change the motion, and each half must swing with the same period as the original. Therefore, the period cannot depend on the mass!

The dependence of the angular frequency, the frequency, and the period on L and g in Equations 30 through 32, respectively, is just what we should expect on the basis of everyday experience. A long pendulum has a longer period than a shorter one. Increasing g increases the restoring force, causing the frequency to increase and the period to decrease.

(a) A real pendulum

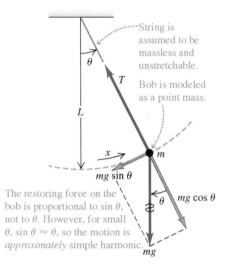

String is assumed to be massless and unstretchable.

Bob is modeled as a point mass.

θ

T

L

x

m

$mg \sin\theta$

$mg \cos\theta$

θ

mg

The restoring force on the bob is proportional to $\sin\theta$, not to θ. However, for small θ, $\sin\theta \approx \theta$, so the motion is *approximately* simple harmonic.

(b) An idealized simple pendulum

▲ **FIGURE 26** The simple pendulum, an idealized model of a real pendulum.

▶ **Application As the world turns.** In 1848, Jean-Bernard-Léon Foucault used a very long pendulum, now known as a Foucault pendulum, to demonstrate the rotation of the Earth itself. Newton's first law tells us that a pendulum tends to oscillate in a single plane in space unless a force deflects it. However, the plane of rotation of a Foucault pendulum seems to *rotate* in space: If the pendulum starts out swinging north–south, later in the day it will be swinging east–west. Is Newton wrong? No; the pendulum's plane of motion does not change, but the surface of the *earth* rotates beneath it. We humans see the pendulum as rotating because we mistake the earth's surface for an inertial frame of reference.

The simple pendulum is also a precise and convenient method for measuring the acceleration due to gravity (g), since L and T can be measured easily. Such measurements are often used in geophysics. Local deposits of ore or oil affect the local value of g because their density differs from that of their surroundings. Precise measurements of g over an area being surveyed often furnish valuable information about the nature of the underlying deposits.

NOTE ▶ We emphasize again that **the motion of a pendulum is only** *approximately* **simple harmonic.** For very small displacements, the approximation is quite precise. For example, when the angular amplitude is 15°, the actual period differs from the prediction of our approximate analysis by less than 0.5%. Indeed, the usefulness of the pendulum in clocks depends on the fact that, for small amplitudes, the motion is very nearly independent of amplitude. ◀

Javier Larrea/AGE Fotostock

Quantitative Analysis 4

Changing the length of a pendulum

A pendulum with a string of length L swings with a period T. If the string is made twice as long, the pendulum's period will be about

A. T.
B. $\sqrt{2}T$.
C. $2T$.

SOLUTION By now you should be able to work problems like this in your head quickly with thinking like the following: Since T is proportional to $\sqrt{L}$ (see Equation 32), if L is changed to $2L$, then T changes to $\sqrt{2}T$. Thus, the answer is B. In more detail, Equation 23 can also be written as

$$\frac{T_{new}}{T_{old}} = \frac{\sqrt{L_{new}}}{\sqrt{L_{old}}} = \frac{\sqrt{2L_{old}}}{\sqrt{L_{old}}} = \sqrt{2}.$$

EXAMPLE 8 **Period and frequency of a simple pendulum**

Find the period and frequency of a simple pendulum 1.000 m long in Pittsburgh, where $g = 9.801$ m/s².

SOLUTION

SET UP AND SOLVE From Equation 32,

$$T = 2\pi\sqrt{\frac{1.000 \text{ m}}{9.801 \text{ m/s}^2}} = 2.007 \text{ s}$$

and

$$f = \frac{1}{T} = 0.4983 \text{ Hz}.$$

REFLECT The period is almost exactly 2 s; at one time there was a proposal to define the second as half the period of a 1-meter pendulum.

EXAMPLE 9 **The lost Martian**

A Martian who frequently gets lost in the solar system keeps a ball on a string so that he can always figure out what planet he happens to be on. On Mars, where the acceleration due to gravity is $g_{Mars} = 0.38g_{earth}$, the ball oscillates with a period of 1.5 s when it is swung like a pendulum bob (Figure 27). During one journey, the Martian finds himself on a planet where the ball oscillates with a period of 0.92 s. What planet is he on?

Continued

SOLUTION

SET UP Each planet has a different value of the gravitational acceleration g near its surface. The Martian can measure g at his location, and from this he can determine what planet he's on. First we use the information about Mars to find the length L of the string that the Martian is swinging. Then we use that length to find the acceleration due to gravity on the unknown planet.

SOLVE First we use the Mars data to determine L. We solve Equation 32 for L:

$$T_{\text{Mars}} = 2\pi\sqrt{\frac{L}{g_{\text{Mars}}}} \quad \text{and}$$

$$L = \frac{T^2 g_{\text{Mars}}}{4\pi^2} = \frac{T^2(0.38 g_{\text{earth}})}{4\pi^2} = \frac{(1.5\ \text{s})^2(0.38 \times 9.8\ \text{m/s}^2)}{4\pi^2}$$
$$= 0.21\ \text{m}.$$

Now we use this value of L with $T = 0.92$ s to solve for the acceleration due to gravity on the unknown planet, g_{planet}:

$$g_{\text{planet}} = \frac{4\pi^2 L}{T^2} = \frac{4\pi^2(0.21\ \text{m})}{(0.92\ \text{s})^2} = 9.8\ \text{m/s}^2.$$

The Martian is surprised to find that he is on planet earth!

REFLECT In principle, the Martian can use this method to measure the acceleration due to gravity of any planet or satellite while traveling around the universe.

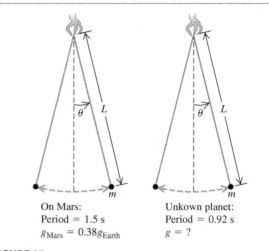

On Mars:
Period = 1.5 s
$g_{\text{Mars}} = 0.38 g_{\text{Earth}}$

Unkown planet:
Period = 0.92 s
$g = ?$

▲ **FIGURE 27**

Practice Problem: The acceleration due to gravity near the surface of the moon is about 1.6 m/s². If the Martian arrives there and swings the same pendulum bob, what will be the period of the pendulum? *Answer:* $T = 2.3$ s.

6 Damped and Forced Oscillations

The idealized oscillating systems that we've discussed thus far are frictionless. There are no nonconservative forces, the total mechanical energy is constant, and a system set into motion continues oscillating forever with no decrease in amplitude.

Real-world systems always have some friction, however, and oscillations do die out with time unless we provide some means for replacing the mechanical energy lost to friction. A pendulum clock continues to run because the potential energy stored in the spring or a hanging weight system replaces the mechanical energy lost because of friction in the pendulum and the gears. But the spring eventually runs down, or the weights reach the bottom of their travel. Then no more energy is available, and the pendulum swings decrease in amplitude and stop.

Pixtal/Age Fotostock

◄ **BIO Application Don't get hammered.** The oscillation of this construction worker's jackhammer is very effective at breaking up hard surfaces, such as concrete and asphalt. However, the repetitive motion can also damage the nerves and blood vessels in the hands, leading to the pain, tingling, and numbness characteristic of Raynaud's syndrome, or "white finger." It is not just the mechanical pounding on the tissue that causes the damage, but also the frequency of the vibration itself, which can set up damaging resonances in the human body. As little as five minutes of exposure to vibrations of 60 Hz can damage small arteries, and slower vibrations of 2 to 4 Hz can cause whole-body resonance as they are transmitted through the human skeleton. Occupational safety experts are designing new equipment and protective gear to minimize vibration-induced injury for workers using oscillating equipment.

The decrease in amplitude caused by dissipative forces is called **damping,** and the corresponding motion is called **damped oscillation.** The suspension system of an automobile is a familiar example of damped oscillations. The shock absorbers (Figure 28) provide a velocity-dependent damping force. The direction of the force always opposes the car's up-and-down motion, so that when the car goes over a bump, it doesn't continue bouncing forever. For optimal passenger comfort, the system should have enough damping that it bounces only once or twice after each bump. As the shocks get old and worn, the damping decreases and the bouncing is more persistent. Not only is this nauseating, but it is bad for steering, because the front wheels have less positive contact with the ground. Thus, damping is an advantage in this kind of system. But in a system such as a clock or an electrical oscillating system in a radio transmitter, it is often desirable to have as little damping as possible.

Figure 29 shows graphs of position x as a function of time for a damped oscillator—one graph for a relatively small damping force, the other for greater damping.

What happens when an additional periodically varying force is applied to an oscillating system? A factory floor supported by a slightly flexible steel framework may begin to vibrate when an oscillating machine rests on it. Or consider your little brother on a playground swing. You can keep him swinging with constant amplitude by giving him a little push once each cycle. More generally, we can maintain a constant-amplitude oscillation in a damped harmonic oscillator by applying a force that varies with time in a periodic or cyclic way, with a definite period and frequency. We call this additional force a **driving force.**

We denote the angular frequency of the driving force by ω_d. This angular frequency doesn't have to equal the angular frequency ω with which the system would naturally oscillate without a driving force. When a periodically varying driving force is present, the mass can undergo a periodic motion *with the same angular frequency ω_d as that of the driving force.* We call this motion a **forced oscillation,** or a *driven oscillation;* it is different from the motion that occurs when the system is simply set into motion and then left alone to oscillate with its natural frequency ω. The frequency of a forced oscillation is that of the driving force, not the system's natural frequency.

When the angular frequency of the driving force is nearly *equal* to the natural angular frequency $\omega = \sqrt{k/m}$ of the system, we are forcing the system to vibrate with a frequency that is close to the frequency it would have even with no driving force. In this case, we expect the amplitude of the resulting oscillation to be larger than it is when the two frequencies ω and ω_d are very different. This expectation is borne out by more detailed analysis and by experimental observation.

If we vary the frequency ω_d of the driving force, the amplitude of the resulting forced oscillation varies in an interesting way (Figure 30). When there is very little damping, the amplitude goes through a sharp peak as the driving angular frequency ω_d nears the natural oscillation angular frequency ω. When the damping is increased, the peak becomes broader and smaller in height and shifts toward lower frequencies.

The fact that there is an amplitude peak at driving frequencies close to the natural frequency of the system is called **resonance.** Physics is full of examples of resonance; building up the oscillations of a child on a swing by pushing with a frequency equal to the swing's natural frequency is one. A vibrating rattle in a car that occurs only at a certain engine speed or wheel-rotation speed is an all-too-familiar example. You may have heard of the dangers of a band marching in step

Upper cylinder attached to frame of car: remains relatively stationary

Piston

Viscous fluid

Pushed up

Pushed down

Lower cylinder attached to axle and wheel: moves up and down

▲ **FIGURE 28** A shock absorber used in a car. The top part, connected to the piston, is attached to the car's frame; the bottom part, connected to the lower cylinder, is connected to the axle. The viscous fluid causes a damping force that depends on the relative velocity of the two ends of the unit. The device helps control wheel bounce and jounce.

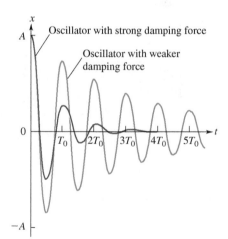

Oscillator with strong damping force

Oscillator with weaker damping force

▲ **FIGURE 29** Graph showing damped harmonic oscillation for two oscillators, one strongly damped and one more weakly damped.

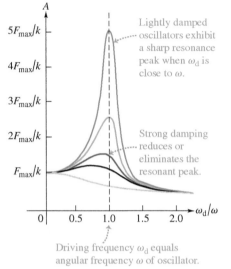

Lightly damped oscillators exhibit a sharp resonance peak when ω_d is close to ω.

Strong damping reduces or eliminates the resonant peak.

Driving frequency ω_d equals angular frequency ω of oscillator.

▲ **FIGURE 30** Graph of the amplitude A of the forced oscillation of a damped harmonic oscillator as a function of the angular frequency ω_d of the driving force. (The latter is plotted on the horizontal axis as the ratio of ω_d to the angular frequency $\omega = \sqrt{k/m}$ of an undamped oscillator.)

across a bridge. If the frequency of their steps is close to a natural vibration frequency of the bridge, dangerously large oscillations can build up. Inexpensive loudspeakers often have an annoying buzz or boom when a musical note happens to coincide with the resonant frequency of the speaker cone.

Finally, we mention the famous collapse of the Tacoma Narrows suspension bridge in 1940; nearly everyone has seen the film of this catastrophe (Figure 31). This is usually cited as an example of resonance, but there's some doubt as to whether it should be called that. The wind didn't have to vary *periodically* with a frequency close to a natural frequency of the bridge. The air flow past the bridge is turbulent, and vortices are formed with a regular frequency that depends on the flow speed. It is conceivable that this frequency may have resonated with a natural frequency of the bridge. But the cause may well have been something more subtle called a *self-excited oscillation,* in which the aerodynamic forces caused by a *steady* wind blowing on the bridge tended to displace it farther from equilibrium at times when it was already moving away from equilibrium.

It is as though we had a velocity-dependent damping force, but with the direction reversed. In that case, the force always has the *same* direction as the velocity and becomes an *anti-damping* force. Instead of draining mechanical energy away from the system, this force pumps energy into the system, building up the oscillations to destructive amplitudes. A similar phenomenon is the flapping of a flag in a wind.

The Tacoma Narrows bridge has been rebuilt, and engineers have now learned how to stabilize suspension bridges, both structurally and aerodynamically, to prevent such disasters.

AP Photo   AP Photo

▲ **FIGURE 31** The Tacoma Narrows Bridge collapsed four months and six days after it was opened for traffic. The main span was 2800 ft long and 39 ft wide, with 8-ft-high steel stiffening girders on both sides. The maximum amplitude of the twisting vibrations was 35°; the frequency was about 0.2 Hz.

CHAPTER SUMMARY

Stress, Strain, and Elastic Deformation

(Section 1) Forces that tend to stretch, squeeze, or twist an object constitute **stress.** The resulting deformation is called **strain.** Particularly for small deformations, stress and strain may be directly proportional: Stress/Strain = constant (Equation 1). We call this relationship **Hooke's law.**

Tensile and compressive stresses stretch and compress an object, respectively. Tensile stress is tensile force per unit area, $F_\perp/A$ (Equation 2). Tensile strain is the fractional change in length, $\Delta l/l_0$ (Equation 3).

Pressure or **volume stress** is force per unit area: $p = (F_\perp/A)$ (Equation 5). The force is a uniform force around an object and acts to increase or decrease its volume. The resulting deformation is volume **strain,** $\Delta V/V_0$ (Equation 6).

Shear stress is tangent force per unit area: $F_\parallel/A$ (Equation 8). The resulting deformation is **shear strain.**

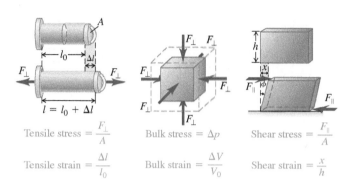

Tensile stress $= \dfrac{F_\perp}{A}$ Bulk stress $= \Delta p$ Shear stress $= \dfrac{F_\parallel}{A}$

Tensile strain $= \dfrac{\Delta l}{l_0}$ Bulk strain $= \dfrac{\Delta V}{V_0}$ Shear strain $= \dfrac{x}{h}$

Elasticity and Plasticity

(Section 1) For small stresses, the strain of many materials is elastic; when the stress is removed, an object returns to its original size and shape. For stresses beyond a particular value, the deformation becomes **plastic:** when the stress is removed, the object does not return to its original shape. At a high enough stress, the object breaks.

Periodic Motion

(Section 2) Periodic motion is motion that repeats itself in a definite cycle. Periodic motion occurs whenever an object has a stable equilibrium position and is subject to a restoring force that acts when the object is displaced from equilibrium. When the restoring force is directly proportional to the displacement $(F_x = -kx)$, which is often the case for small displacements, the resulting motion is called **simple harmonic motion.**

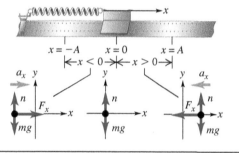

Energy in Simple Harmonic Motion

(Section 3) In simple harmonic motion, the total mechanical energy is constant: $E = \frac{1}{2}mv_x^2 + \frac{1}{2}kx^2 = $ constant (Equation 15). At points of maximum displacement, where $x = A$ and $v_x = 0$, all of the energy is in the form of elastic potential energy, so the (constant) total mechanical energy can be expressed as $E = \frac{1}{2}kA^2$ (Equation 16).

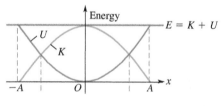

Equations of Simple Harmonic Motion

(Section 4) We obtain equations describing simple harmonic motion by using the **circle of reference.** We consider a point that moves counterclockwise with constant angular velocity ω around a circle of radius A. By evaluating the x components of the point's position, velocity, and acceleration, we find that

$$x = A\cos\omega t = A\cos(2\pi f t), \qquad (19, 20)$$
$$v_x = -\omega A\sin\omega t = -2\pi f A\sin(2\pi f t), \qquad (21)$$
$$a_x = -\omega^2 A\cos\omega t = -(2\pi f)^2 A\cos(2\pi f t). \qquad (22)$$

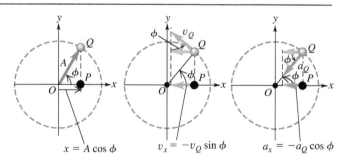

$x = A\cos\phi$ $v_x = -v_Q\sin\phi$ $a_x = -a_Q\cos\phi$

Continued

The Simple Pendulum

(Section 5) A **simple pendulum** is an idealized model consisting of a point mass suspended from a string with length L. For small amplitudes, the motion is nearly simple harmonic and the angular frequency is nearly independent of the amplitude and the object's mass: $\omega = \sqrt{g/L}$ (Equation 30). For larger displacements, the frequency depends on the amplitude.

Damped and Forced Oscillations

(Section 6) Real-world systems always have some friction (damping); oscillations die out with time, unless the lost mechanical energy is replaced.

When a periodically varying force is added to a harmonic oscillator, the resulting motion is called a **forced oscillation.** The system can then oscillate with a frequency equal to that of the driving force ω_d, not the system's natural oscillation frequency $\omega = \sqrt{k/m}$. The amplitude peaks as ω_d nears the natural frequency ω; this phenomenon is called **resonance.**

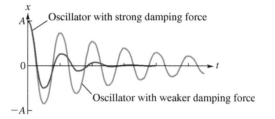

Oscillator with strong damping force

Oscillator with weaker damping force

Elasticity and Periodic Motion: Problem Set

(MP) For instructor-assigned homework, go to www.masteringphysics.com

Conceptual Questions

1. Think of several examples in everyday life of motion that is at least approximately simple harmonic. In what respects does each differ from SHM?

2. The analysis of simple harmonic motion in this chapter neglected the mass of the spring. How would the spring's mass affect the period and frequency of the motion? Explain your reasoning.

3. In any periodic motion, unavoidable friction always causes the amplitude to decrease with time. Does friction also affect the *period* of the motion? Give a qualitative argument to support your answer. (*Hint:* Does the friction affect the kinetic energy? If so, how does this affect the speed, and therefore the period, of a cycle?)

4. A mass attached by a light spring to the ceiling of an elevator oscillates vertically while the elevator ascends with constant acceleration. Is the period greater than, less than, or the same as when the elevator is at rest? Why?

5. A pendulum is mounted in an elevator that moves upward with constant acceleration. Is the period greater than, less than, or the same as when the elevator is at rest? Why?

6. At what point in the motion of a simple pendulum is (a) the tension in the string greatest, (b) the string tension least, (c) the radial acceleration greatest, (d) the angular acceleration least, (e) the speed greatest?

7. Looking at the molecular structure of matter, discuss why gases are generally more compressible than liquids and solids.

8. Why do short dogs (like Chihuahuas) walk with quicker strides than do tall dogs (like Great Danes)?

9. Which could you use as a timekeeping device in an orbiting satellite, a pendulum or a mass on a spring? Or could you use them both? Why?

10. What happens to the original energy as a damped pendulum (or spring) "runs down"? Explain *how* this energy gets dissipated.

11. Distinguish clearly between the angular frequency (ω) and the angular velocity (also ω) of a pendulum. Which of the two quantities is constant?

12. It is easy to get mixed up and think that the angular frequency ω of a pendulum is equal to $\sqrt{L/g}$ instead of $\sqrt{g/L}$. How can you use dimensional analysis to find out which version is the correct formula? Would such an analysis help to identify missing (or extra) factors of 2π? Why?

13. If a metal wire has its length doubled and its diameter tripled, by what factor does its Young's modulus change?

14. Would you expect a rubber band to have a larger or a smaller force constant than that of an iron wire? Why? How would you think that Young's modulus for these two materials would compare?

15. In designing structures in an earthquake-prone region, how should the natural frequencies of oscillation of a structure relate to typical earthquake frequencies? Why? Should the structures have a large or a small amount of damping?

Multiple-Choice Problems

1. A spring–mass system is undergoing simple harmonic motion of amplitude 2.0 cm and angular frequency 10.0 s^{-1}. The acceleration of the mass as it passes through the equilibrium position is
   A. 0.00 m/s^2. B. 0.20 m/s^2.
   C. 2.0 m/s^2. D. 31.4 m/s^2.

2. In a design for a piece of medical apparatus, you need a material that is easily compressed when a pressure is applied to it.
   A. This material should have a large bulk modulus.
   B. This material should have a small bulk modulus.
   C. The bulk modulus is not relevant to this situation.

3. If the force F in Figure 32 is constant over the area A, the pressure on that area is
   A. 2.50 Pa.
   B. 4.33 Pa.
   C. 5.00 Pa.

   $F = 10.0 \text{ N}$
   $60.0°$
   $A = 2.00 \text{ m}^2$

   ▲ **FIGURE 32** Multiple-choice problem 3.

4. A box with a mass of 5 kg, whose bottom measures 10×10 cm, sits on a table. The pressure the box exerts on the tabletop is approximately
   A. 0.5 Pa B. 50 Pa C. 500 Pa D. 5000 Pa

5. When a mass attached to a spring is released from rest 3.0 cm from its equilibrium position, it oscillates with frequency f. If this mass were instead released from rest 6.0 cm from its equilibrium position, it would oscillate with frequency
   A. $2f$. B. $\sqrt{2}f$ C. f. D. $f/2$

6. As the bob on a pendulum swings down toward its lowest point, its angular frequency ω
   A. increases.
   B. decreases.
   C. does not change.

7. Suppose you increase the amplitude of oscillation of a mass vibrating on a spring. Which of the following statements about this mass are correct? (There may be more than one correct choice.)
   A. Its maximum speed increases.
   B. Its period of oscillation increases.
   C. Its maximum acceleration increases.
   D. Its maximum kinetic energy increases.

8. An object of mass M suspended by a spring vibrates with period T. If this object is replaced by one of mass $4M$, the new object vibrates with a period
   A. T. B. $2T$. C. $4T$. D. $16T$.

9. When two wires of identical dimensions are used to hang 25 kg weights, wire A is observed to stretch twice as much as wire B. From this observation, you can make the following conclusions about the Young's moduli of these wires:
   A. $Y_A = 4Y_B$. B. $Y_A = 2Y_B$.
   C. $Y_A = \frac{1}{2}Y_B$. D. $Y_A = \frac{1}{4}Y_B$.

10. A mass on a spring oscillates with a period T. If both the mass and the force constant of the spring are doubled, the new period will be
    A. $4T$. B. $\sqrt{2}T$. C. T.
    D. $T/\sqrt{2}$. E. $T/4$.

11. A pendulum oscillates with a period T. If both the mass of the bob and the length of the pendulum are doubled, the new period will be
    A. $4T$. B. $\sqrt{2}T$. C. T.
    D. $T/\sqrt{2}$. E. $T/4$.

12. When a 100-kg mass is hung from a cable made of a certain material, the cable is observed to lengthen by 1%. If the cable is now replaced by one with twice the cross-sectional area and made of a material with twice the Young's modulus of the original one, and the mass hung from it is also doubled, how much stretching will be observed?
    A. 1% B. 0.5% C. 4% D. 8%

13. An object with mass M suspended by a spring vibrates with frequency f. When a second object is attached to the first, the system now vibrates with frequency $f/2$. The mass of the second object is
    A. $4M$. B. $3M$. C. $2M$. D. M.

14. A pendulum on earth swings with angular frequency ω. On an unknown planet, it swings with angular frequency $\omega/2$. The acceleration due to gravity on this planet is
    A. $4g$. B. $2g$. C. $g/2$. D. $g/4$.

15. A mass oscillates with simple harmonic motion of amplitude A. The kinetic energy of the mass will equal the potential energy of the spring when the position is
    A. $x = 0$. B. $x = A/2$.
    C. $x = A/\sqrt{2}$. D. $x = A/4$.

Problems

1 Stress, Strain, and Elastic Deformations

1. • A thin, light wire 75.0 cm long having a circular cross section 0.550 mm in diameter has a 25.0 kg weight attached to it, causing it to stretch by 1.10 mm. (a) What is the stress in this wire? (b) What is the strain of the wire? (c) Find Young's modulus for the material of the wire.

2. • A petite young woman distributes her 500 N weight equally over the heels of her high-heeled shoes. Each heel has an area of 0.750 cm². (a) What pressure is exerted on the floor by each heel? (b) With the same pressure, how much weight could be supported by two flat-bottomed sandals, each of area 200 cm²?

3. •• Two circular rods, one steel and the other copper, are joined end to end. Each rod is 0.750 m long and 1.50 cm in diameter. The combination is subjected to a tensile force with

magnitude 4000 N. For each rod, what are (a) the strain and (b) the elongation?

4. • A 5.0 kg mass is hung by a vertical steel wire 0.500 m long and 6.0×10^{-3} cm² in cross-sectional area. Hanging from the bottom of this mass is a similar steel wire, from which in turn hangs a 10.0 kg mass. For each wire, compute (a) the tensile strain and (b) the elongation.

5. • **Biceps muscle.** A relaxed biceps muscle requires a force of
   BIO 25.0 N for an elongation of 3.0 cm; under maximum tension, the same muscle requires a force of 500 N for the same elongation. Find Young's modulus for the muscle tissue under each of these conditions if the muscle can be modeled as a uniform cylinder with an initial length of 0.200 m and a cross-sectional area of 50.0 cm².

6. • **Stress on a mountaineer's rope.** A nylon rope used by mountaineers elongates 1.10 m under the weight of a 65.0 kg climber. If the rope is 45.0 m in length and 7.0 mm in diameter, what is Young's modulus for this nylon?

7. • A steel wire 2.00 m long with circular cross section must stretch no more than 0.25 cm when a 400.0 N weight is hung from one of its ends. What minimum diameter must this wire have?

8. • **Achilles tendon.** The Achilles tendon, which connects the
   BIO calf muscles to the heel, is the thickest and strongest tendon in the body. In extreme activities, such as sprinting, it can be subjected to forces as high as 13 times a person's weight. According to one set of experiments, the average area of the Achilles tendon is 78.1 mm², its average length is 25 cm, and its average Young's modulus is 1474 MPa. (a) How much tensile stress is required to stretch this muscle by 5.0% of its length? (b) If we model the tendon as a spring, what is its force constant? (c) If a 75 kg sprinter exerts a force of 13 times his weight on his Achilles tendon, by how much will it stretch?

9. •• **Artificial tendons.** The largest Young's modulus measured
   BIO for any biological material is 30 GPa, for the S-layer of cell walls. Suppose that in the future we are able to use this material to construct an artificial Achilles tendon (see previous problem) for an athlete who has damaged his. The artificial Achilles tendon should be just as long as the original one so that it can connect at the proper places. (a) If the artificial tendon has a circular cross section, what should be its diameter be so that it will have the same force constant as the natural Achilles tendon? (b) How does this diameter compare with that of a natural Achilles tendon?

10. •• **Human hair.** According to one set of measurements, the
    BIO tensile strength of hair is 196 MPa, which produces a maximum strain of 0.40 in the hair. The thickness of hair varies considerably, but let's use a diameter of 50 μm. (a) What is the magnitude of the force giving this tensile stress? (b) If the length of a strand of the hair is 12 cm at its breaking point, what was its unstressed length?

11. •• **The effect of jogging on the knees.** High-impact activities
    BIO such as jogging can cause considerable damage to the cartilage at the knee joints. Peak loads on each knee can be eight times body weight during jogging. The bones at the knee are separated by cartilage called the medial and lateral meniscus. Although it varies considerably, the force at impact acts over approximately 10 cm² of this cartilage. Human cartilage has a Young's modulus of about 24 MPa (although that also varies). (a) By what percent does the peak load impact of jogging compress the knee cartilage of a 75 kg person? (b) What would be

the percentage for a lower-impact activity, such as power walking, for which the peak load is about four times body weight?

12. • A solid gold bar is pulled up from the hold of the sunken RMS *Titanic*. (a) What happens to its volume as it goes from the pressure at the ship to the lower pressure at the ocean's surface? (b) The pressure difference is proportional to the depth. How many times greater would the volume change have been had the ship been twice as deep? (c) The bulk modulus of lead is one-fourth that of gold. Find the ratio of the volume change of a solid lead bar to that of a gold bar of equal volume for the same pressure change.

13. • In the Challenger Deep of the Marianas Trench, the depth of seawater is 10.9 km and the pressure is 1.16×10^8 Pa (about 1150 atmospheres). (a) If a cubic meter of water is taken to this depth from the surface (where the normal atmospheric pressure is about 1.0×10^5 Pa), what is the change in its volume? Assume that the bulk modulus for seawater is the same as for freshwater $(2.2 \times 10^9$ Pa$)$. (b) At the surface, seawater has a density of 1.03×10^3 kg/m^3. What is the density of seawater at the depth of the Challenger Deep?

14. • **Effect of diving on blood.** It is reasonable to assume that
BIO the bulk modulus of blood is about the same as that of water (2.2 GPa). As one goes deeper and deeper in the ocean, the pressure *increases* by 1.0×10^4 Pa for every meter below the surface. (a) If a diver goes down 33 m (a bit over 100 ft) in the ocean, by how much does each cubic centimeter of her blood change in volume? (b) How deep must a diver go so that each drop of blood compresses to half its volume at the surface? Is the ocean deep enough to have this effect on the diver?

15. • Shear forces are applied to a rectangular solid. The same forces are applied to another rectangular solid of the same material, but with three times each edge length. In each case the forces are small enough that Hooke's law is obeyed. What is the ratio of the shear strain for the larger object to that of the smaller object?

16. •• **Compression of human bone.** The bulk modulus for bone
BIO is 15 GPa. (a) If a diver-in-training is put into a pressurized suit, by how much would the pressure have to be raised (in atmospheres) above atmospheric pressure to compress her bones by 0.10% of their original volume? (b) Given that the pressure in the ocean increases by 1.0×10^4 Pa for every meter of depth below the surface, how deep would this diver have to go for her bones to compress by 0.10%? Does it seem that bone compression is a problem she needs to be concerned with when diving?

17. • In Figure 33, suppose the object is a square steel plate, 10.0 cm on a side and 1.00 cm thick. Find the magnitude of force required on each of the four sides to cause a shear strain of 0.0400.

▲ FIGURE 33
Problem 17.

18. • In lab tests on a 9.25 cm cube of a certain material, a force of 1375 N directed at 8.50° to the cube, as shown in Figure 34, causes the cube to deform through an angle of 1.24°. What is the shear modulus of the material?

▲ **FIGURE 34** Problem 18.

▲ **FIGURE 35**
Problem 19.

19. • **Downhill hiking.** During vigorous downhill hiking, the
BIO force on the knee cartilage (the medial and lateral meniscus) can be up to eight times body weight. Depending on the angle of descent, this force can cause a large shear force on the cartilage and deform it. The cartilage has an area of about 10 cm^2 and a shear modulus of 12 MPa. If the hiker plus his pack have a combined mass of 110 kg (not unreasonable), and if the maximum force at impact is 8 times his body weight (which, of course, includes the weight of his pack) at an angle of 12° with the cartilage (see Figure 35), through what angle (in degrees) will his knee cartilage be deformed? (Recall that the bone below the cartilage pushes upward with the same force as the downward force.)

20. • A steel wire has the following properties:

Length $= 5.00$ m
Cross-sectional area $= 0.040$ cm^2
Young's modulus $= 2.0 \times 10^{11}$ Pa
Shear modulus $= 0.84 \times 10^{11}$ Pa
Proportional limit $= 3.60 \times 10^8$ Pa
Breaking stress $= 11.0 \times 10^8$ Pa

The wire is fastened at its upper end and hangs vertically. (a) How great a weight can be hung from the wire without exceeding the proportional limit? (b) How much does the wire stretch under this load? (c) What is the maximum weight that can be supported?

21. •• A steel cable with cross-sectional area of 3.00 cm^2 has an elastic limit of 2.40×10^8 Pa. Find the maximum upward acceleration that can be given to a 1200 kg elevator supported by the cable if the stress is not to exceed one-third of the elastic limit.

22. •• **Weight lifting.** The legs of a weight lifter must ultimately
BIO support the weights he has lifted. A human tibia (shinbone) has a circular cross section of approximately 3.6 cm outer diameter and 2.5 cm inner diameter. (The hollow portion contains marrow.) If a 90 kg lifter stands on both legs, what is the heaviest weight he can lift without breaking his legs, assuming that the breaking stress of the bone is 200 MPa?

2 Periodic Motion

23. • (a) **Music.** When a person sings, his or her vocal cords
BIO vibrate in a repetitive pattern having the same frequency of the note that is sung. If someone sings the note B flat that has a

frequency of 466 Hz, how much time does it take the person's vocal cords to vibrate through one complete cycle, and what is the angular frequency of the cords? (b) **Hearing.** When sound waves strike the eardrum, this membrane vibrates with the same frequency as the sound. The highest pitch that typical humans can hear has a period of 50.0 μs. What are the frequency and angular frequency of the vibrating eardrum for this sound? (c) **Vision.** When light having vibrations with angular frequency ranging from 2.7×10^{15} rad/s to 4.7×10^{15} rad/s strikes the retina of the eye, it stimulates the receptor cells there and is perceived as visible light. What are the limits of the period and frequency of this light? (d) **Ultrasound.** High-frequency sound waves (ultrasound) are used to probe the interior of the body, much as x rays do. To detect a small objects such as tumors, a frequency of around 5.0 MHz is used. What are the period and angular frequency of the molecular vibrations caused by this pulse of sound?

24. • Find the period, frequency, and angular frequency of (a) the second hand and (b) the minute hand of a wall clock.

25. • If an object on a horizontal frictionless surface is attached to a spring, displaced, and then released, it oscillates. Suppose it is displaced 0.120 m from its equilibrium position and released with zero initial speed. After 0.800 s, its displacement is found to be 0.120 m on the opposite side and it has passed the equilibrium position once during this interval. Find (a) the amplitude, (b) the period, and (c) the frequency of the motion.

26. • The graph shown in Figure 36 closely approximates the displacement x of a tuning fork as a function of time t as it is playing a single note. What are (a) the amplitude, (b) period, (c) frequency, and (d) angular frequency of this fork's motion?

▲ FIGURE 36 Problem 26.

27. • The wings of the Blue-throated Hummingbird (*Lampornis*
BIO *clemenciae*), which inhabits Mexico and the southwestern United States, beat at a rate of up to 900 times per minute. Calculate (a) the period of vibration of the bird's wings, (b) the frequency of the wings' vibration, and (c) the angular frequency of the bird's wingbeats.

3 Energy in Simple Harmonic Motion

28. • A 0.500 kg glider on an air track is attached to the end of an ideal spring with force constant 450 N/m; it undergoes simple harmonic motion with an amplitude of 0.040 m. Compute (a) the maximum speed of the glider, (b) the speed of the glider when it is at $x = -0.015$ m, (c) the magnitude of the maximum acceleration of the glider, (d) the acceleration of the glider at $x = -0.015$ m, and (e) the total mechanical energy of the glider at any point in its motion.

29. • A 0.150 kg toy is undergoing SHM on the end of a horizontal spring with force constant 300.0 N/m. When the object is 0.0120 m from its equilibrium position, it is observed to have a speed of 0.300 m/s. Find (a) the total energy of the object at any point in its motion, (b) the amplitude of the motion, and (c) the maximum speed attained by the object during its motion.

30. • A 2.00 kg frictionless block is attached to an ideal spring with force constant 315 N/m. Initially the spring is neither stretched nor compressed, but the block is moving in the negative direction at 12.0 m/s. Find (a) the amplitude of the motion, (b) the maximum acceleration of the block, and (c) the maximum force the spring exerts on the block.

31. • Repeat the previous problem, but assume that initially the block has velocity -4.00 m/s and displacement $+0.200$ m.

32. •• You are watching an object that is moving in SHM. When the object is displaced 0.600 m to the right of its equilibrium position, it has a velocity of 2.20 m/s to the right and an acceleration of 8.40 m/s^2 to the left. How much farther from this point will the object move before it stops momentarily and then starts to move back to the left?

33. •• A mass is oscillating with amplitude A at the end of a spring. How far (in terms of A) is this mass from the equilibrium position of the spring when the elastic potential energy equals the kinetic energy?

34. •• (a) If a vibrating system has total energy E_0, what will its total energy be (in terms of E_0) if you double the amplitude of vibration? (b) If you want to triple the total energy of a vibrating system with amplitude A_0, what should its new amplitude be (in terms of A_0)?

4 Equations of Simple Harmonic Motion

35. • A 2.40 kg ball is attached to an unknown spring and allowed to oscillate. Figure 37 shows a graph of the ball's position x as a function of time t. For this motion, what are (a) the period, (b) the frequency, (c) the angular frequency, and (d) the amplitude? (e) What is the force constant of the spring?

▲ FIGURE 37 Problem 35.

36. • A proud deep-sea fisherman hangs a 65.0 kg fish from an ideal spring having negligible mass. The fish stretches the spring 0.120 m. (a) What is the force constant of the spring? (b) What is the period of oscillation of the fish if it is pulled down 3.50 cm and released?

37. •• One end of a stretched ideal spring is attached to an airtrack and the other is attached to a glider with a mass of 0.355 kg. The glider is released and allowed to oscillate in SHM. If the distance of the glider from the fixed end of the spring varies between 1.80 m and 1.06 m, and the period of the oscillation is 2.15 s, find (a) the force constant of the spring, (b) the maximum speed of the glider, and (c) the magnitude of the maximum acceleration of the glider.

38. • A mass of 0.20 kg on the end of a spring oscillates with a period of 0.45 s and an amplitude of 0.15 m. Find (a) the velocity when it passes the equilibrium point, (b) the total energy of the system, and (c) the equation describing the motion of the mass, assuming that x was a maximum at time $t = 0$.

39. •• A harmonic oscillator is made by using a 0.600 kg frictionless block and an ideal spring of unknown force constant.

The oscillator is found to have a period of 0.150 s. Find the force constant of the spring.

40. •• **Weighing astronauts.** In order to study the long-term effects
BIO of weightlessness, astronauts in space must be weighed (or at least *"massed"*). One way in which this is done is to seat them in a chair of known mass attached to a spring of known force constant and measure the period of the oscillations of this system. If the 35.4 kg chair alone oscillates with a period of 1.25 s, and the period with the astronaut sitting in the chair is 2.23 s, find (a) the force constant of the spring and (b) the mass of the astronaut.

41. •• A mass m is attached to a spring of force constant 75 N/m and allowed to oscillate. Figure 38 shows a graph of its velocity v_x as a function of time t. Find (a) the period, (b) the frequency, and (c) the angular frequency of this motion. (d) What is the amplitude (in cm), and at what times does the mass reach this position? (e) Find the maximum acceleration of the mass and the times at which it occurs. (f) What is the mass m?

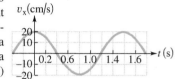

▲ **FIGURE 38** Problem 41.

42. •• An object of unknown mass is attached to an ideal spring with force constant 120 N/m and is found to vibrate with a frequency of 6.00 Hz. Find (a) the period, (b) the angular frequency, and (c) the mass of this object.

43. •• **Weighing a virus.** In February 2004, scientists at Purdue
BIO University used a highly sensitive technique to measure the mass of a vaccinia virus (the kind used in smallpox vaccine). The procedure involved measuring the frequency of oscillation of a tiny sliver of silicon (just 30 nm long) with a laser, first without the virus and then after the virus had attached itself to the silicon. The difference in mass caused a change in the frequency. We can model such a process as a mass on a spring. (a) Show that the ratio of the frequency with the virus attached (f_{S+V}) to the frequency without the virus (f_S) is given by the formula

$$\frac{f_{S+V}}{f_S} = \frac{1}{\sqrt{1 + \dfrac{m_V}{m_S}}},$$

where m_V is the mass of the virus and m_S is the mass of the silicon sliver. Notice that it is *not* necessary to know or measure the force constant of the spring. (b) In some data, the silicon sliver has a mass of 2.10×10^{-16} g and a frequency of 2.00×10^{15} Hz without the virus and 2.87×10^{14} Hz with the virus. What is the mass of the virus, in grams and femtograms?

5 The Simple Pendulum

44. • A science museum has asked you to design a simple pendulum that will make 25.0 complete swings in 85.0 s. What length should you specify for this pendulum?

45. • A simple pendulum in a science museum entry hall is 3.50 m long, has a 1.25 kg bob at its lower end, and swings with an amplitude of 11.0°. How much time does the pendulum take to swing from its extreme right side to its extreme left side?

46. • You've made a simple pendulum with a length of 1.55 m, and you also have a (very light) spring with force constant 2.45 N/m. What mass should you add to the spring so that its period will be the same as that of your pendulum?

47. •• **A pendulum on Mars.** A certain simple pendulum has a period on earth of 1.60 s. What is its period on the surface of Mars, where the acceleration due to gravity is 3.71 m/s²?

48. •• In the laboratory, a student studies a pendulum by graphing the angle θ that the string makes with the vertical as a function of time t, obtaining the graph shown in Figure 39. (a) What are the period, frequency, angular frequency, and amplitude of the pendulum's motion? (b) How long is the pendulum? (c) Is it possible to determine the mass of the bob?

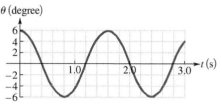

▲ **FIGURE 39** Problem 48.

49. •• (a) If a pendulum has period T and you double its length, what is its new period in terms of T? (b) If a pendulum has a length L and you want to triple its frequency, what should be its length in terms of L? (c) Suppose a pendulum has a length L and period T on earth. If you take it to a planet where the acceleration of freely falling objects is ten times what it is on earth, what should you do to the length to keep the period the same as on earth? (d) If you do *not* change the pendulum's length in part (c), what is its period on that planet in terms of T? (e) If a pendulum has a period T and you triple the mass of its bob, what happens to the period (in terms of T)?

6 Damped and Forced Oscillations

50. • A 1.35 kg object is attached to a horizontal spring of force constant 2.5 N/cm and is started oscillating by pulling it 6.0 cm from its equilibrium position and releasing it so that it is free to oscillate on a frictionless horizontal air track. You observe that after eight cycles its maximum displacement from equilibrium is only 3.5 cm. (a) How much energy has this system lost to damping during these eight cycles? (b) Where did the "lost" energy go? Explain physically how the system could have lost energy.

51. • A 2.50 kg rock is attached at the end of a thin, very light rope 1.45 m long and is started swinging by releasing it when the rope makes an 11° angle with the vertical. You record the observation that it rises only to an angle of 4.5° with the vertical after $10\frac{1}{2}$ swings. (a) How much energy has this system lost during that time? (b) What happened to the "lost" energy? Explain *how* it could have been "lost."

52. •• A mass is vibrating at the end of a spring of force constant 225 N/m. Figure 40 shows a graph of its position x as a function of time t. (a) At what times is the mass not moving? (b) How much energy did this system originally contain? (c) How much energy did the system lose between $t = 1.0$ s and $t = 4.0$ s? Where did this energy go?

▲ **FIGURE 40** Problem 52.

General Problems

53. • What is the maximum kinetic energy of the vibrating ball in Problem 35, and when does it occur?

54. •• Inside a NASA test vehicle, a 3.50-kg ball is pulled along by a horizontal ideal spring fixed to a friction-free table. The force constant of the spring is 225 N/m. The vehicle has a steady acceleration of 5.00 m/s², and the ball is not oscillating. Suddenly, when the vehicle's speed has reached 45.0 m/s, its engines turn off, thus eliminating its acceleration but not its velocity. Find (a) the amplitude and (b) the frequency of the resulting oscillations of the ball. (c) What will be the ball's maximum speed relative to the vehicle?

55. •• Four passengers with a combined mass of 250 kg compress the springs of a car with worn-out shock absorbers by 4.00 cm when they enter it. Model the car and passengers as a single body on a single ideal spring. If the loaded car has a period of vibration of 1.08 s, what is the period of vibration of the empty car?

56. •• An astronaut notices that a pendulum which took 2.50 s for a complete cycle of swing when the rocket was waiting on the launch pad takes 1.25 s for the same cycle of swing during liftoff. What is the acceleration of the rocket? (*Hint:* Inside the rocket, it appears that g has increased.)

57. •• An object suspended from a spring vibrates with simple harmonic motion. At an instant when the displacement of the object is equal to one-half the amplitude, what fraction of the total energy of the system is kinetic and what fraction is potential?

58. •• On the planet Newtonia, a simple pendulum having a bob with a mass of 1.25 kg and a length of 185.0 cm takes 1.42 s, when released from rest, to swing through an angle of 12.5°, where it again has zero speed. The circumference of Newtonia is measured to be 51,400 km. What is the mass of the planet Newtonia?

59. •• An apple weighs 1.00 N. When you hang it from the end of a long spring of force constant 1.50 N/m and negligible mass, it bounces up and down in SHM. If you stop the bouncing and let the apple swing from side to side through a small angle, the frequency of this simple pendulum is half the bounce frequency. (Because the angle is small, the back-and-forth swings do not cause any appreciable change in the length of the spring.) What is the unstretched length of the spring (with the apple removed)?

60. •• A block with mass M rests on a frictionless surface and is connected to a horizontal spring of force constant k, the other end of which is attached to a wall

▲ **FIGURE 41** Problem 60.

(Figure 41). A second block with mass m rests on top of the first block. The coefficient of static friction between the blocks is μ_s. Find the maximum amplitude of oscillation such that the top block will not slip on the bottom block.

61. •• In Fig. 42 the upper ball is released from rest, collides with the stationary lower ball, and sticks to it. The strings are both 50.0 cm long. The upper ball has mass 2.00 kg, and it is initially 10.0 cm higher than the lower ball, which has mass 3.00 kg. Find the frequency and maximum angular displacement of the motion after the collision.

▲ **FIGURE 42** Problem 61.

62. •• A 15.0 kg mass fastened to the end of a steel wire with an unstretched length of 0.50 m is whirled in a vertical circle with angular velocity 2.00 rev/s at the bottom of the circle. The cross-sectional area of the wire is 0.010 cm². Calculate the elongation of the wire when the mass is at the lowest point of the path. (See table below.)

TABLE Young's modulus

Material	Y (Pa)
Aluminum	0.70×10^{11}
Brass	0.91×10^{11}
Copper	1.1×10^{11}
Glass	0.55×10^{11}
Iron	1.9×10^{11}
Steel	2.0×10^{11}
Tungsten	3.6×10^{11}

63. •• **Stress on the shinbone.** The compressive strength of our BIO bones is important in everyday life. Young's modulus for bone is approximately 14 GPa. Bone can take only about a 1.0% change in its length before fracturing. If Hooke's law were to hold up to fracture: (a) What is the maximum force that can be applied to a bone whose minimum cross-sectional area is 3.0 cm². (This is approximately the cross-sectional area of a tibia, or shinbone, at its narrowest point.) (b) Estimate the maximum height from which a 70 kg man can jump and not fracture the tibia. Take the time between when he first touches the floor and when he has stopped to be 0.030 s, and assume that the stress is distributed equally between his legs.

64. •• You hang a floodlamp from the end of a vertical steel wire. The floodlamp stretches the wire 0.18 mm and the stress is proportional to the strain. How much would it have stretched (a) if the wire were twice as long? (b) If the wire had the same length but twice the diameter? (c) For a copper wire of the original length and diameter?

65. •• **Tendon-stretching exer-** BIO **cises.** As part of an exercise program, a 75 kg person does toe raises in which he raises his entire body weight on the ball of one foot, as shown in Figure 43. The Achilles tendon pulls straight upward on the heel bone of his foot. This tendon is 25 cm long and has a cross-sectional area of 78 mm² and a Young's modu-

▲ **FIGURE 43** Problem 68.

lus of 1470 MPa. (a) Make a free-body diagram of the person's foot (everything below the ankle joint). You can neglect the weight of the foot. (b) What force does the Achilles tendon exert on the heel during this exercise? Express your answer in newtons and in multiples of his weight. (c) By how many millimeters does the exercise stretch his Achilles tendon?

66. •• A 100 kg mass suspended from a wire whose unstretched length is 4.00 m is found to stretch the wire by 6.0 mm. The wire has a uniform cross-sectional area of 0.10 cm². (a) If the load is pulled down a small additional distance and released,

find the frequency at which it vibrates. (b) Compute Young's modulus for the wire.

67. •• A brass rod with a length of 1.40 m and a cross-sectional area of 2.00 cm^2 is fastened end to end to a nickel rod with length L and cross-sectional area 1.00 cm^2. The compound rod is subjected to equal and opposite pulls of magnitude 4.00×10^4 N at its ends. (a) Find the length L of the nickel rod if the elongations of the two rods are equal. (b) What is the stress in each rod? (c) What is the strain in each rod?

68. •• **Rapunzel, Rapunzel, let down your golden hair.** In the Grimms' fairy tale *Rapunzel,* she lets down her golden hair to a length of 20 yards (we'll use 20 m, which is not much different) so that the prince can climb up to her room. Human hair has a Young's modulus of about 490 MPa, and we can assume that Rapunzel's hair can be squeezed into a rope about 2.0 cm in

cross-sectional diameter. The prince is described as young and handsome, so we can estimate a mass of 60 kg for him. (a) Just after the prince has started to climb at constant speed, while he is still near the bottom of the hair, by how many centimeters does he stretch Rapunzel's hair? (b) What is the mass of the heaviest prince that could climb up, given that the maximum tensile stress hair can support is 196 MPa? (Assume that Hooke's law holds up to the breaking point of the hair, even though that would not actually be the case.)

69. •• Crude oil with a bulk modulus of 2.35 GPa is leaking from a deep-sea well 2250 m below the surface of the ocean, where the water pressure is 2.27×10^7 Pa. Suppose 35,600 barrels of oil leak from the wellhead; assuming all that oil reaches the surface, how many barrels will it be on the surface?

ANSWERS TO SELECTED PROBLEMS

Conceptual Questions

1. Swinging of a playground swing; this motion is simple harmonic only for small amplitudes and the motion also loses mechanical energy due to dissipative forces. Pistons in a car engine; force doesn't precisely obey Hooke's law.

3. The negative work done by friction removes kinetic energy from the object. The object slows down and takes more time to complete one cycle, for example more time to move from the initial maximum displacement to equilibrium, than when friction is absent. The period is increased by friction.

5. The period decreases. The effect is the same as increasing g by taking pendulum to another planet; the restoring force is increased.

7. Molecules in a gas have space in between them and can be pushed closer together. In a liquid or solid the molecules are more closely packed together. An attempt to push them together is opposed by a large repulsive force.

9. In a satellite the pendulum is in free-fall. There is no restoring force and the pendulum does not swing back and forth when released with an initial displacement. For a mass on a spring the restoring force is applied by the spring, and this force is not affected by being in orbit. The period of a mass on a spring could be used as a time-keeping device but a pendulum could not.

11. The circular frequency $\omega = \dfrac{2\pi}{T} = 2\pi f$ is proportional to the number of complete swings the pendulum makes each second.

It is inversely proportional to the time for one complete swing. The angular velocity is the rate at which the angular position of the pendulum is changing and is proportional to the linear speed of the pendulum bob along its path. The circular frequency describes a full cycle of the motion and is constant during the motion. The angular velocity changes during the motion. It is zero at the maximum displacement and is a maximum as the pendulum bob passes through its lowest point.

Multiple-Choice Problems

1. A
3. B
5. C
7. A, C, D
9. C
11. B
13. B
15. C

Problems

1. (a) 1.03×10^9 Pa (b) 1.47×10^{-3} (c) 7.01×10^{11} Pa
3. (a) steel: 1.1×10^{-4}; copper: 2.1×10^{-4} (b) steel: 8.3×10^{-5} m; copper: 1.6×10^{-4} m
5. relaxed: 3.3×10^4 Pa; maximum tension: 6.7×10^5 Pa
7. 1.4 mm
9. (a) 2.2 mm (b) smaller
11. (a) 24% (b) 12%
13. (a) -0.0531 m^3 (b) $1.09 \times 10^3 \text{ kg/m}^3$
15. 1/9
17. 3.4×10^6 N
19. 8.6°
21. 10.2 m/s^2
23. (a) 2.15×10^{-3} s; 2.93×10^3 rad/s

(b) 2.00×10^4 Hz; 1.26×10^5 rad/s
(c) 1.3×10^{-15} s to 2.3×10^{-15} s; 4.3×10^{14} Hz to 7.5×10^{14} Hz
(d) 2.0×10^{-7} s; 3.1×10^7 rad/s
25. (a) 0.120 m (b) 1.60 s (c) 0.625 Hz
27. (a) 0.067 s (b) 15 Hz (c) 94 rad/s
29. (a) 0.0284 J (b) 0.0138 m (c) 0.615 m/s
31. (a) 0.376 m (b) 59.2 m/s^2 (c) 118 N
33. $A/\sqrt{2}$
35. (a) 0.80 s (b) 1.25 Hz (c) 7.85 rad/s (d) 3.0 cm (e) 148 N/m
37. (a) 3.03 N/m (b) 1.08 m/s (c) 3.16 m/s^2
39. 1.05×10^3 N/m
41. (a) 1.60 s (b) 0.625 Hz (c) 3.93 rad/s (d) 5.1 cm; 0.4 s, 1.2 s, 1.8 s (e) 79 cm/s²; 0.4 s, 1.2 s, 1.8 s (f) 4.9 kg
43. (b) 9.99×10^{-15} g = 9.99 fg
45. 1.88 s
47. 2.60 s
49. (a) $\sqrt{2}T$ (b) $L/9$ (c) $L_{\text{new}} = 10L$ (d) $T/\sqrt{10}$ (e) $T_{\text{new}} = T$
51. (a) 0.543 J (b) converted to other forms by dissipative forces
53. (a) 0, 0.80 s, 1.60 s, 2.40 s, 3.20 s (b) 0.0533 J (c) 0.0218 J; converted to other forms by nonconservative forces
55. (a) $6.72 \times 10^3 \text{ m/s}^2$ (b) 3.02×10^3 N (c) 18.3 m/s; 75.6 J
57. 29.4 m/s^2
59. 2.00 m
61. 0.705 Hz; 14.5°
63. (a) 4.2×10^4 N (b) 64 m
65. (b) 2000 N; 2.72 times his weight (c) 4.4 mm
67. (a) 1.63 m (b) brass: 2.00×10^8 Pa; nickel: 4.00×10^8 Pa (c) brass: 2.2×10^{-3}; nickel: 1.9×10^{-3}
69. 35,900 barrels

Mechanical Waves and Sound

Why do male frogs inflate their throats? These pouches serve as resonating chambers, amplifying the frog's voice.

W hen you go to the beach to enjoy the ocean surf, you're experiencing a wave motion. Ripples on a pond, musical sounds, sounds we *can't* hear, the wiggles of a Slinky® stretched out on the floor—all these are *wave* phenomena. Waves can occur whenever a system has an equilibrium position and when a disturbance away from that position can travel, or *propagate,* from one region of the system to another. Sound, light, ocean waves, radio and television transmission, and earthquakes are all wave phenomena. Waves occur in all branches of physical and biological science, and the concept of waves is one of the most important unifying threads running through the entire fabric of the natural sciences.

1 Mechanical Waves

This chapter is about mechanical waves. Every type of mechanical wave is associated with some material or substance called the **medium** for that type. As the wave travels through the medium, the particles that make up the medium undergo displacements of various kinds, depending on the nature of the wave. Figure 1 shows waves produced by drops falling on a water surface. The speed of travel of a wave depends on the mechanical properties of the medium. Some waves are *periodic,* meaning that the particles of the medium undergo periodic motion during wave propagation. If the motion of each particle is simple harmonic (i.e., a sinusoidal function of time), the wave is called a *sinusoidal* wave.

Figure 2 shows three examples of mechanical waves. In Figure 2a, the medium is a stretched rope. (It could also be a spring or Slinky®.) If we give the left end a small up-and-down wiggle, the resulting pulse travels down the

From Chapter 12 of *College Physics*, Ninth Edition, Hugh D. Young. Copyright © 2012 by Pearson Education, Inc. Published by Pearson Addison-Wesley. All rights reserved.

Shutterstock

▲ FIGURE 1 A series of drops falling vertically into water produces a wave pattern that moves radially outward from its source. The wave crests and troughs are concentric circles.

length of the rope. Successive sections of rope undergo the same up-and-down motion that we gave to the end, but at successively later times. Because the displacements of particles of the medium are perpendicular (transverse) to the direction of travel of the wave along the medium, this type of wave is called a **transverse wave.**

In Figure 2b, the medium is a liquid or gas in a tube with a rigid wall at the right end and a movable piston at the left end. If we give the piston a back-and-forth motion, a displacement and a pressure fluctuation travel down the length of the medium. This time, the particles of the medium move back and forth parallel to the wave's direction of travel; we call this type of wave a **longitudinal wave.**

Longitudinal waves are familiar to you as sound. Your ears are designed to detect longitudinal waves carried by air, but sound waves can also be carried by liquids such as water (you can hear under water) and by solid objects such as walls.

In Figure 2c, the medium is water in a trough. When we move the flat board at the left end back and forth, a disturbance travels down the length of the trough. In this case, the displacements of the water particles are found to have *both* longitudinal and transverse components. The familiar waves of oceans and lakes are of this type; they are most often generated by wind moving over the water surface.

Earthquake waves have both longitudinal and transverse displacements. The longitudinal components travel faster and so give advance warning of the arrival of the more destructive transverse components—as much as 60 seconds at a distance of 200 miles from the source.

All the waves in Figure 2 have several characteristics in common. For each, there is an equilibrium state. For the stretched rope, it is the state in which the rope is at rest, stretched out along a straight line (if we neglect the sag due to gravity). For the fluid in a tube, it is a state of rest with uniform pressure, and for the water in a trough it is a smooth, level water surface. In each case, the wave motion is a disturbance from the equilibrium state that travels from one region of the medium to another. In each case, there are forces that tend to restore the system to its equilibrium position when it is displaced, just as the force of gravity tends to pull a pendulum toward its straight-down equilibrium position when it is displaced.

In each of these situations, the medium as a whole does not travel through space; its individual particles undergo back-and-forth motions around their equi-

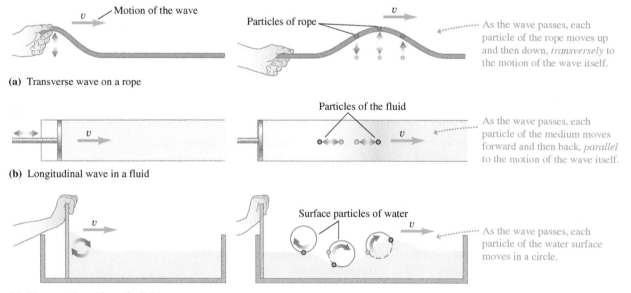

(a) Transverse wave on a rope

As the wave passes, each particle of the rope moves up and then down, *transversely* to the motion of the wave itself.

(b) Longitudinal wave in a fluid

As the wave passes, each particle of the medium moves forward and then back, *parallel* to the motion of the wave itself.

(c) Waves on the surface of a fluid

As the wave passes, each particle of the water surface moves in a circle.

▲ FIGURE 2 Examples of (a) a transverse wave on a rope, (b) a longitudinal wave in a cylinder containing a gas or liquid, and (c) a surface wave with transverse and longitudinal components.

▶ Application **Two-minute warning.** Earthquakes are caused by large-scale movements of the Earth's crust; these movements generate both transverse and longitudinal waves in the crust. Using monitoring instruments known as seismographs, scientists can record these waves and detect the presence and location of distant earthquakes. The low-amplitude longitudinal waves travel faster than the more destructive transverse waves and arrive at a seismograph station sooner—several minutes sooner for an earthquake 1000 km away. Thus, prompt detection of the longitudinal waves from an earthquake can provide an early warning of the arrival of the destructive transverse waves. Often, even a minute or two of advance notice can be critical to safeguard life and property.

Photolibrary

librium positions. What *does* travel is the pattern of the wave disturbance. To set any of these systems in motion, we have to put in energy by doing mechanical work on the system. The wave motion transports this energy from one region of the medium to another. **Waves transport energy, but not matter, from one region to another.** In each case, the disturbance is found to travel, or *propagate,* with a definite speed through the medium. This speed is called the speed of propagation or simply the **wave speed.** It is determined by the mechanical properties of the medium. We'll use the symbol v for wave speed.

Conceptual Analysis 1

Making waves

You and a friend hold the ends of a Slinky® that lies straight between you on a table. You create a wave by suddenly moving your hand toward and then away from your friend. The resulting wave

A. is purely transverse.
B. is purely longitudinal.
C. has both transverse and longitudinal components.

SOLUTION As the wave travels toward your friend, successive particles in the Slinky® undergo the same to-and-fro motion that you gave to the end. Since this motion is parallel to the direction in which the wave itself travels, the wave is longitudinal. (However, you could also cause the Slinky® to carry transverse waves by moving its end transversely.)

---

2 Periodic Mechanical Waves

The easiest kind of wave to demonstrate is a transverse wave on a stretched rope or flexible cable. Suppose we tie one end of a long, flexible rope to a stationary object and pull on the other end, stretching the rope out horizontally. In Figure 2a, we saw what happens when we give the end a single up-and-down shake. The resulting wiggle, or *wave pulse,* travels down the length of the rope. The tension in the rope restores the rope's straight-line shape once the wiggle has passed. (We are neglecting any sag in the rope due to the rope's weight.) Later we'll discuss what happens when the wiggle reaches the far end of the rope.

A more interesting situation develops when we give the free end of the rope a repetitive, or *periodic,* motion. In particular, suppose we use the setup in Figure 3 to move the end up and down with simple harmonic motion having ampli-

MasteringPHYSICS

ActivPhysics 10.1: Properties of Mechanical Waves

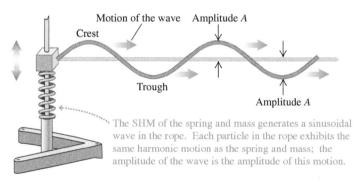

The SHM of the spring and mass generates a sinusoidal wave in the rope. Each particle in the rope exhibits the same harmonic motion as the spring and mass; the amplitude of the wave is the amplitude of this motion.

▲ **FIGURE 3** The simple harmonic motion of the spring–mass system produces a sinusoidal transverse wave on the rope.

The rope is shown at time intervals of $\frac{1}{8}$ period for a total of one period T. The highlighting shows the motion of one wave.

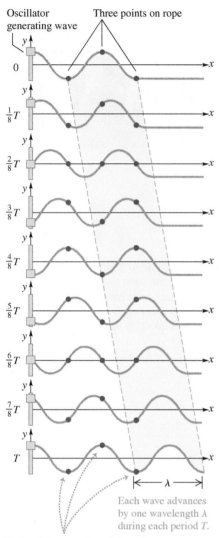

Oscillator generating wave

Three points on rope

Each wave advances by one wavelength λ during each period T.

Each point moves up and down in place. Particles one wavelength apart move in phase with each other.

▲ **FIGURE 4** A sinusoidal transverse wave shown at intervals of one-eighth of a period.

tude A, frequency f, and period T. As usual, $f = 1/T = \omega/2\pi$, where ω is the angular frequency. A *continuous succession* of transverse sinusoidal waves then advances along the rope.

Figure 4 shows the shape of a part of the rope near the left end, at intervals of one-eighth of a period, for a total time of one period. The waveform advances steadily toward the right, while any one point on the rope oscillates up and down about its equilibrium position with simple harmonic motion. Be very careful to distinguish between the motion of a *waveform* (the shape of the displaced rope at any time), which moves with constant speed v *along* the rope, and the motion of *a particle of the rope,* which is simple harmonic and transverse (perpendicular) to the length of the rope. The **amplitude** A of the wave is defined as the amplitude of the transverse simple harmonic (sinusoidal) motion of a particle of the medium; it corresponds to the amplitude of the harmonic oscillation that creates the wave. As Figure 3 shows, for a periodic transverse wave, the amplitude is the distance from the equilibrium position to a peak or trough.

The shape of the rope at any instant is a repeating pattern—a series of identical shapes. For a periodic wave, the length of one complete wave pattern is the distance between any two points at corresponding positions on successive repetitions in the wave shape. We call this the **wavelength** of the wave, denoted by λ. The waveform travels with constant speed v and advances a distance of one wavelength λ in a time interval of one period T. We can relate these quantities as follows:

Relation among the speed, wavelength, period, and frequency of a transverse wave
The wave advances a distance of one wavelength λ during one period T, so the wave speed v is given by $v = \lambda/T$. Because frequency $f = 1/T$, the wave speed also equals the product of wavelength and frequency:

$$v = \lambda f = \frac{\lambda}{T}. \tag{1}$$

Note the familiar pattern: Speed equals distance divided by time.

To understand the mechanics of a *longitudinal* wave such as a sound wave in air, we consider a long tube filled with air, with a plunger at the left end, as shown in Figure 5. The cone of a loudspeaker is simply a sophisticated version of a plunger like this. If we push the plunger in, we compress the air near it, increasing the pressure in this region. The air in the region then pushes against the neighboring region of air, and so on, forming a wave pulse that moves along the tube.

Super Stock/AGE Fotostock

◀ **Application Surf's up!** Thanks to the study of physics and the marvels of engineering, this surfer can enjoy a wild ride in a pool hundreds of miles from the ocean. This surf pool takes advantage of the physics of wave generation by repetitive motion to produce realistic "ocean" waves. The waves are generated by giant water cannons that fire repetitively at one end of the pool. By altering the shape of the cannon outlet and the pool floor and by changing the timing of the impulses, waves of different heights (up to 3 m), shapes, and angles can be generated. By studying a combination of oceanography and physics, engineers have even been able to duplicate the waves found in specific surfing hot spots such as California, Hawaii, and Indonesia.

The pressure fluctuations play the role of the restoring force, tending to restore the air to equilibrium and uniform pressure.

Now, suppose we move the plunger back and forth with simple harmonic motion along a line parallel to the direction of the tube. This motion forms regions where the pressure and density are alternately greater and less than the equilibrium values. We call a region of increased pressure a *compression*. A region of reduced pressure is an *expansion* (or *rarefaction*).

Figure 6 shows the waves in our apparatus at intervals of one-eighth of a period. The compressions and expansions move to the right with constant speed v. The motion of the individual particles of the medium (air) is simple harmonic, parallel to the direction of propagation. As we found for transverse waves, the amplitude A of a longitudinal wave is the amplitude of the periodic motion of the particles of the medium. That is, A represents the maximum displacement of a particle of the medium from its equilibrium position.

Earlier we mentioned that your ears detect longitudinal waves as sound. For a musical tone, you detect the amplitude of sound waves as loudness and their frequency as pitch—the higher pitched a sound, the greater its frequency. The wavelength is the distance between two successive compressions or two successive expansions. The same fundamental equation that we found for periodic transverse waves, $v = \lambda f$, also holds for periodic longitudinal waves and, indeed, for *all* types of periodic waves.

Forward motion of the plunger creates a compression (a zone of high pressure); backward motion creates an expansion (a zone of low pressure).

The wavelength λ is the distance between corresponding points on successive cycles.

▲ **FIGURE 5** A piston creating a sinusoidal longitudinal wave in a tube.

Quantitative Analysis 2

Distance from a sound source

A World War I infantryman sees the flash of a fired artillery gun; 20 s later he hears the gun's sound. The speed of sound in air is about a fifth of a mile per second. Which of the following is a reasonable estimate for the distance to the gun?

A. 1 mi.
B. 2 mi.
C. 4 mi.

SOLUTION The speed of *light* in air is roughly a million times as great as the speed of *sound* in air. Thus, in this example, the time between the creation of the flash and seeing it from a distance of several miles is negligible. In air, sound travels a fifth of a mile each second, or one mile in five seconds. It would take 20 seconds to travel 4 miles. A useful rule of thumb is that each mile gives a time delay of 5 seconds. If you see a lightning flash, and if you hear the accompanying thunder 10 seconds later, the flash was about 2 miles away.

EXAMPLE 1   Frequencies of musical notes

What is the wavelength of a sound wave in air at 20°C if the frequency is $f = 262$ Hz (the approximate frequency of the note "middle C" on the piano)? Assume that the speed of sound in air is 344 m/s.

SOLUTION

SET UP AND SOLVE The relation of wavelength λ to frequency f is given by Equation 1:

$$\lambda = \frac{v}{f} = \frac{344 \text{ m/s}}{262 \text{ s}^{-1}} = 1.31 \text{ m}.$$

REFLECT The "high C" sung by coloratura sopranos is two octaves above middle C (a factor of four in frequency), or about 1050 Hz. The corresponding wavelength is $(1.31 \text{ m})/4 = 0.327$ m.

Practice Problem: The frequency of the lowest note on large pipe organs is about 16 Hz. What is the corresponding wavelength? *Answer:* 21 m.

3 Wave Speeds

The speed of propagation of a wave depends on the mechanical properties of the medium. For transverse waves on a rope, these are the rope's tension and mass. Intuition suggests that increasing the tension should increase the restoring forces

ActivPhysics 10.2: Speed of Waves on a String

Longitudinal waves shown at intervals of $\frac{1}{8}T$ for one period T.

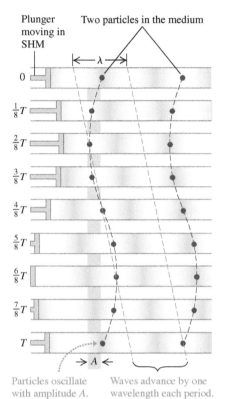

Particles oscillate with amplitude A.   Waves advance by one wavelength each period.

▲ **FIGURE 6** A sinusoidal longitudinal wave shown at intervals of one-eighth of a period.

that tend to straighten the rope when it is disturbed and thus increase the wave speed. We might also guess that increasing the rope's mass should make the motion more sluggish and decrease the speed.

Both of these expectations are confirmed by more detailed analysis. The inertial property of the rope is best described not just by its total mass m (which depends on its length L), but on the mass *per unit length,* which we'll denote by μ. That is, $\mu = m/L$. We denote the tension in the rope by F_T. Analysis then shows that the wave speed v is given by the following expression:

Speed of a transverse wave
The speed of a transverse wave in a rope under tension is proportional to the square root of the tension, divided by the mass per unit length:

$$v = \sqrt{\frac{F_T}{\mu}}. \qquad (2)$$

This result confirms our prediction that the wave speed v should increase when the tension F_T increases, but decrease when the mass per unit length μ increases.

NOTE ► The wave speed v is *directly* proportional, *not* to the tension F_T, but rather to the *square root* of F_T. Similarly, it is inversely proportional, not to the mass per unit length, μ, but to the square root of that quantity. ◄

 Waves on a string

An oscillator creates periodic waves on a stretched rope. Which of the following parameters *cannot* be changed by altering the motion of the oscillator?

A. Wave frequency.
B. Wave speed.
C. Wavelength.

SOLUTION As we've just seen, the speed of a wave depends on the properties of the medium alone. Thus, at least choice B is correct. The frequency of the wave is determined only by the frequency of the oscillator, so choice A is *not* correct. What about wavelength (choice C)? Remember that wavelength equals wave speed divided by frequency: $\lambda = v/f$. Thus, wavelength depends partly on the medium and partly on the oscillator, so choice C, too, is incorrect.

 A vibrating string

An oscillator creates periodic waves on a stretched string. If the oscillator frequency doubles, what happens to the wavelength and wave speed?

A. Wavelength doubles; wave speed is unchanged.
B. Wavelength is unchanged; wave speed doubles.
C. Wavelength is halved; wave speed is unchanged.

SOLUTION The speed of a wave depends only on the properties of the medium, so changing the frequency of the oscillator does not change the wave speed. Wavelength depends on frequency and wave speed: $\lambda = v/f$. As this equation shows, doubling the frequency will *halve* the wavelength, so C is the right answer. This conclusion makes intuitive sense: If you double the frequency without changing the wave speed, you must fit twice as many waves into a given length of string, so the waves must be half as long.

EXAMPLE 2 **Mineral samples in a mine shaft**

One end of a nylon rope is tied to a stationary support at the top of a vertical mine shaft that is 80.0 m deep (Figure 7). The rope is stretched taut by a box of mineral samples with mass 20.0 kg suspended from the lower end. The mass of the rope is 2.00 kg. The geologist at the bottom of the mine signals to his colleague at the top by jerking the rope sideways. What is the speed of a transverse wave on the rope? If a point on the rope is given a transverse simple harmonic motion with a frequency of 20 Hz, what is the wavelength of the wave?

SOLUTION

SET UP We can calculate the wave speed v from the tension F_T and the mass per unit length, $\mu = m/L$. The tension at the bottom of the rope is equal to the weight of the 20.0 kg load:

$$F_T = (20.0 \text{ kg})(9.80 \text{ m/s}^2)$$
$$= 196 \text{ N},$$

and the mass per unit length is

$$\mu = \frac{m}{L} = \frac{2.00 \text{ kg}}{80.0 \text{ m}} = 0.0250 \text{ kg/m}.$$

SOLVE The wave speed is given by Equation 2:

$$v = \sqrt{\frac{F_T}{\mu}} = \sqrt{\frac{196 \text{ N}}{0.0250 \text{ kg/m}}} = 88.5 \text{ m/s}.$$

From Equation 1,

$$\lambda = \frac{v}{f} = \frac{88.5 \text{ m/s}}{20.0 \text{ s}^{-1}} = 4.43 \text{ m}.$$

REFLECT We have neglected the 10% increase in tension in the rope between bottom and top due to the rope's own weight. Can you verify that the wave speed at the top is 92.9 m/s?

▶ **FIGURE 7**

$m_{\text{rope}} = 2.00 \text{ kg}$

80.0 m

$m_{\text{samples}} = 20.0 \text{ kg}$

Practice Problem: Another box of samples is hoisted by the same rope. If the rope is shaken with the same frequency as before, and the wavelength is found to be 8.85 m, what is the mass of this box of samples? *Answer:* 80.0 kg.

A transverse wave traveling along a rope carries *energy* from one region of the rope to another. If the wave is traveling from left to right, then the part of the rope to the left of a given point exerts a transverse force on the part to the right of the point as the point undergoes vertical displacements. Thus, the left part does *work* on the right part and transfers energy to it. A detailed calculation of the rate of doing work (power) shows that, for a sinusoidal wave with amplitude A and frequency f, the rate of energy transfer is proportional to the *square* of the amplitude and to the square of the frequency. (We'll return to this discussion later, in the context of sound waves.)

Longitudinal waves can occur in solid, liquid, and gaseous materials. In all cases, the wave speed is determined by the mechanical characteristics of the material. Ordinarily, the wave speed is proportional to the square root of an elastic factor (such as the bulk or shear modulus) and inversely proportional to the square root of the density of the material. Table 1 lists the speed of sound in several familiar materials. Notice that the speed of sound in a medium depends on temperature; in both air and water, the speed increases with increasing temperature.

4 Mathematical Description of a Wave

We've described several characteristics of periodic waves, using the concepts of wave speed, period, frequency, and wavelength. Sometimes, though, we need a more detailed description of the positions and motions of individual particles of the medium at particular times during wave propagation. As a specific example, let's look again at waves on a stretched string. If we ignore the sag of the string

TABLE 1   Speed of sound in various materials

Material	Speed of sound (m/s)
Gases	
Air (20°C)	344
(25°C)	347
(30°C)	350
Helium (20°C)	999
Hydrogen (20°C)	1330
Liquids	
Liquid helium (4 K)	211
Water (0°C)	1402
Water (100°C)	1543
Mercury (20°C)	1451
Solids	
Polystyrene	1840
Bone	3445
Brass	3480
Pyrex™ glass	5170
Steel	5000
Beryllium	12,870

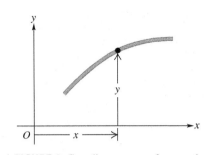

▲ FIGURE 8 Coordinate system for a mathematical description of transverse waves on a string.

due to gravity, the equilibrium position of the string is along a straight line. We take this to be the x axis of a coordinate system. Waves on a string are *transverse:* During wave motion, a particle with equilibrium position x is displaced some distance y in the direction perpendicular to the x axis (Figure 8). The value of y depends on which particle we are talking about (i.e, on x) and also on the time t when we look at it. Thus, y is a *function* of x and t: $y = f(x, t)$. If we know this function for a particular wave motion, we can use it to find the displacement (from equilibrium) of any particle at any time.

Let's consider the application of the concept we've just described to a sinusoidal wave on a string. Suppose the left end of the string is at $x = 0$. We give this end a transverse displacement y that varies sinusoidally with time:

$$y = A\sin\omega t = A\sin 2\pi f t. \tag{3}$$

The resulting wave disturbance travels with speed v from $x = 0$ to all the points to the right of the origin (with positive values of x). Every such point undergoes simple harmonic motion with the same amplitude and frequency as the endpoint $(x = 0)$, but the motion of each point has a time delay x/v equal to the time required for a point on the wave shape to travel from $x = 0$ to the point x. Thus, the motion of point x at time t is the same as the motion of point $x = 0$ at the earlier time $t - x/v$. Therefore, we can find the displacement of any point x at any time t simply by replacing t in Equation 3 by $(t - x/v)$. We obtain

$$y(x, t) = A\sin\omega\left(t - \frac{x}{v}\right) = A\sin 2\pi f\left(t - \frac{x}{v}\right). \tag{4}$$

The notation $y(x, t)$ is a reminder that the displacement y is a function of both the equilibrium location x of the point and the time t. If we know the amplitude, frequency, and wave speed, we can use this equation to find the displacement y of *any* point on the string (i.e., any value of x) by substituting the appropriate values.

We can rewrite Equation 4 in several useful ways, presenting the same relationship in different forms. Here's one of the most useful forms expressing the wave properties in terms of the period $T = 1/f$ and the wavelength $\lambda = v/f$:

$$y(x, t) = A\sin 2\pi\left(\frac{t}{T} - \frac{x}{\lambda}\right). \tag{5}$$

If we use Equation 5 to plot y as a function of x for time $t = 0$, the curve shows the shape of the string at $t = 0$.

(a)

At any specific instant of time t, Equation 4 or 5 gives the displacement y of a particle from its equilibrium position as a function of the *coordinate* x of the particle. If the wave is a transverse wave on a string, the equation represents the *shape* of the string at that instant, as if we had taken a stop-action photograph of the string. In particular, at time $t = 0$, Equation 5 becomes

$$y(x, 0) = A\sin 2\pi\left(0 - \frac{x}{\lambda}\right) = A\sin 2\pi\left(-\frac{x}{\lambda}\right).$$

This equation, which gives the shape of the string at time $t = 0$, is plotted in Figure 9a.

One period later, at time $t = T$, Equation 5 becomes

$$y(x, T) = A\sin 2\pi\left(1 - \frac{x}{\lambda}\right) = A\sin 2\pi\left(-\frac{x}{\lambda}\right).$$

(We've used the formula for the sine of the difference of two quantities.) This is the same expression as that for time $t = 0$, confirming the fact that the shape of the string varies periodically with period T, as we should expect. After a time T (and therefore also after $2T$, $3T$, and so on), the string instantaneously has the same shape that it had at time $t = 0$.

We can show that Equation 5 represents a periodic wave having a repeating pattern with wavelength λ. To do this, we replace x by $x + \lambda$ in Equation 5 and

If we use Equation 5 to plot y as a function of t for position $x = 0$, the curve shows the displacement y of the particle at that coordinate as a function of time.

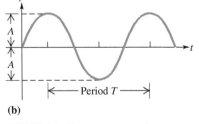

(b)

▲ FIGURE 9 Two ways to graph Equation 5.

again use the formula for the sine of the difference of two quantities. The result is that, at any time, point x has the same displacement as point $x + \lambda$, confirming that the wave shape is a repeating pattern with wavelength λ.

At any specific *coordinate x*, Equation 4 or Equation 5 gives the displacement y of the particle at that coordinate as a function of *time*. That is, it describes the motion of that particle. In particular, at the position $x = 0$,

$$y = A\sin\omega t = A\sin 2\pi \frac{t}{T}.$$

This equation is consistent with our original assumption that the motion at $x = 0$ is simple harmonic. The curve of the equation is plotted in Figure 9b; it is *not* a picture of the shape of the string, but rather a graph of the position y of a particle as a function of time.

5 Reflections and Superposition

In our study of mechanical waves thus far, we haven't been concerned with what happens when a wave arrives at an end or boundary of its medium. But there are many wave phenomena in which boundaries play a significant role. When you yell at a flat wall some distance away, the sound wave is reflected from the rigid surface, and an echo comes back. When you send a wave pulse down the length of a rope whose far end is tied to a rigid support, a reflected pulse comes back to you. In both cases, the initial and reflected waves overlap in the same region of the medium. Figure 10 is a multiflash photograph showing the reflection of a pulse at a stationary end of a stretched spring. Both the displacement and the direction of propagation of the reflected pattern are opposite to those of the initial pulse.

Figure 11 shows reflection of a wave pulse from an end that is held stationary and from one that is free to move transversely. In Figure 11a, a wave

▲ **FIGURE 10** Successive strobe images of a stretched spring. The photos show a wave pulse traveling to the right, reflecting at the fixed end of the spring, and traveling back to the left.

(a) Wave reflects from a fixed end   **(b)** Wave reflects from a free end

▲ **FIGURE 11** Reflection of a wave pulse (a) at a fixed end of a string and (b) at a free end.

As the pulses overlap, the displacement of the string at any point is the vector sum of the displacements due to the individual pulses.

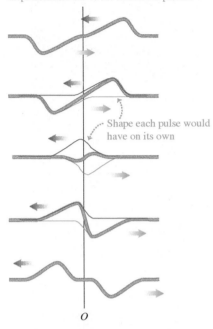

Shape each pulse would have on its own

O

▲ **FIGURE 12** An encounter between two waves traveling in opposite directions, one inverted with respect to the other.

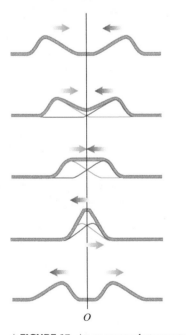

O

▲ **FIGURE 13** An encounter between two identical waves traveling in opposite directions.

MasteringPHYSICS

PhET: Fourier: Making Waves
PhET: Waves on a String
ActivPhysics 10.4: Standing Waves on Strings
ActivPhysics 10.5: Tuning a Stringed Instrument: Standing Waves
ActivPhysics 10.6: String Mass and Standing Waves

pulse arrives at an end of the rope that is fastened to a rigid support so that the end point of the rope can't move. The arriving wave exerts a force on the support; the reaction to this force, exerted *by* the support *on* the rope, "kicks back" on the rope and sets up a *reflected* pulse or wave traveling in the reverse direction, inverted with respect to the incoming pulse. We would see the same result for a sinusoidal wave arriving at a fixed end.

The opposite extreme (Figure 11b) is an end that is perfectly free to move in the direction transverse to the length of the rope. For example, the rope might be tied to a light ring that slides on a smooth rod perpendicular to the length of the rope. The ring and rod maintain the tension, but exert no transverse force. When a wave arrives at a free end, where there is no transverse force, the end "overshoots," and again a reflected wave is set up, this time *not* inverted. The conditions at the end of the rope, such as the presence of a rigid support or the complete absence of a transverse force, are called **boundary conditions.**

The formation of the reflected pulse is similar to the overlap of two pulses traveling in opposite directions. Figure 12 shows two pulses with the same shape, but one inverted with respect to the other, traveling in opposite directions. As the pulses overlap and pass each other, the total displacement of any point of the string is the *vector sum* of the displacements at that point in the individual pulses. At points along the vertical line in the middle of the figure, the total displacement is zero at all times. Thus, the motion of the left half of the string would be the same if we cut the string at point O, threw away the right side, and held the end at O stationary. The two pulses on the left side then correspond to the incident and reflected pulses, combining so that the total displacement at the end of the string is *always* zero. For this to occur, the reflected pulse must be inverted relative to the incident pulse.

Figure 13 shows two pulses with the same shape, traveling in opposite directions, but *not* inverted relative to each other. The displacement at the midpoint is not zero, but the slope of the string at that point is always zero. In this case, the motion of the left half of the string would be the same if we cut the string at point O and anchored the end with a sliding ring (Figure 11b) to maintain tension without exerting any transverse force. This situation corresponds to the reflection of a pulse at a free end of a string at the point in question. In this case, the reflected pulse is *not* inverted.

In each case, the actual displacement of any point on the rope is the vector sum of the displacements corresponding to the two separate pulses at that point. This is an example of the **principle of superposition,** which states that **whenever two waves overlap, the actual displacement of any point on the string, at any time, is obtained by vector addition of the following two displacements: the displacement the point would have if only the first wave were present and the displacement it would have with only the second wave present.** This principle holds for the overlap of sinusoidal waves as well as for individual wave pulses. Later in the chapter, we'll see that the principle applies to both longitudinal and transverse waves and also to the addition of three or more waves.

6 Standing Waves and Normal Modes

Now let's look in more detail at what happens when a *sinusoidal* transverse wave is reflected by a stationary point on a string (such as a fixed end of a string). When the original wave combines with the reflected wave, the resulting motion no longer looks like two waves traveling in opposite directions. Instead, the string appears to be subdivided into a number of segments, as in the time-exposure photographs of Figure 14. Figure 14e shows the shape of the string in Figure 14b at two different instants. Let's compare this behavior with that of the waves we studied earlier in the chapter. (We'll refer to those as *traveling waves,* because when there are no reflections, they travel in one direction through the medium.)

(a) String is one-half wavelength long.

(b) String is one wavelength long.

(c) String is one and a half wavelengths long.

(d) String is two wavelengths long.

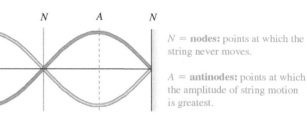

N = **nodes:** points at which the string never moves.

A = **antinodes:** points at which the amplitude of string motion is greatest.

(e) The shape of the string in **(b)** at two different instants.

▲ **FIGURE 14** (a–d) Standing waves in a stretched string (time exposure). (e) A standing wave, with nodes at the center and at the ends.

Richard Megna/Fundamental Photographs

In a traveling wave, the amplitude is constant and the waveform moves with a speed equal to the wave speed. In the kind of wave we are examining here, the waveform remains in the same position along the string, and its amplitude fluctuates. There are particular points called **nodes** (labeled N in Figure 14e) that never move at all. Midway between the nodes are points called **antinodes** (labeled A in the figure), where the amplitude of motion is greatest. Because the wave pattern doesn't appear to be moving in either direction along the string, it is called a **standing wave.**

A standing wave, unlike a traveling wave, *does not* transfer energy from one end to the other. The two waves that form a standing wave would individually carry equal amounts of power in opposite directions. There is a local flow of energy from each node to the adjacent antinodes and back, but the *average* rate of energy transfer is zero at every point.

Figure 15 shows how we can use the superposition principle to understand the formation of a sinusoidal standing wave. The figure shows the waveform at instants one-sixteenth of a period apart. The thin red curves show a wave traveling to the left. The thin blue curves show a wave with the same propagation speed, wavelength, and amplitude, traveling to the right. (It could be a reflection of the red wave.) The brown curves show the resultant waveform—the actual shape a string would have at each given instant—obtained by applying the principle of superposition. At each point, the actual displacement of the string (the position of the brown curve) represents the vector sum of the displacements due to the two separate waves (i.e., the values of y for the two separate waves). The resultant (total) displacement at each node (marked N) is always zero. Midway between the nodes, the antinodes (marked A) have the greatest amplitude of displacement. We can see from the figure that **the distance between successive nodes or between successive antinodes is one half-wavelength, or $\lambda/2$.**

Normal Modes

We've mentioned that an echo of a sound wave can be produced by reflection at a rigid wall. Now suppose we have two parallel walls. If we stand between the walls and produce a sharp sound pulse (for example, by clapping our hands), the result is a series of regularly spaced echoes caused by repeated back-and-forth

Andrew Davidhazy

▲ **Application Just passing through.**
These two sets of ripples on water demonstrate the principle of superposition of mechanical waves. Notice how the two set of waves pass through each other without changing each other's overall shape or speed. At each point of intersection of individual waves, the vertical motion of the water is the vector sum of the motions of the two waves. Where the waves intersect exactly in step, they reinforce each other, resulting in a crest or trough height that is the sum of the heights of the individual waves. Where they intersect exactly out l of step, they cancel each other and there is no vertical displacement of the water. This principle also holds true for a series of waves that are reflected from a boundary and return to interact with themselves.

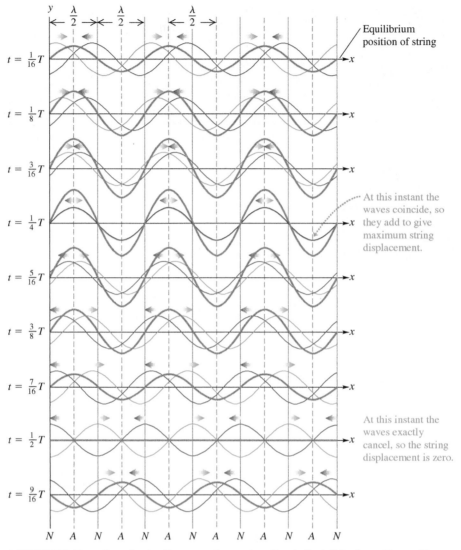

▲ **FIGURE 15** Formation of a standing wave. A wave traveling to the left (red) combines with an identical wave traveling to the right (blue) to form a standing wave on a string (brown). We see successive instants at intervals of $1/16$ of a period.

reflection between the walls. In room acoustics, this phenomenon is called "flutter echo"; it is the bane of acoustical engineers.

The analogous situation with transverse waves on a string is a string with some definite length L, rigidly held at *both* ends. If we produce a sinusoidal wave on a guitar string, the wave is reflected and re-reflected from the ends. The waves combine to form a standing wave like one of the waves shown in Figure 14. Both ends must be nodes, and adjacent nodes are one half-wavelength $(\lambda/2)$ apart. The length L of the string, therefore, has to be some integer multiple of $\lambda/2$ (i.e., $(\lambda/2), 2(\lambda/2), 3(\lambda/2), \dots$), that is, an integer number of half-wavelengths:

$$L = n\frac{\lambda}{2} \qquad (n = 1, 2, 3, \dots).$$

A standing wave can exist on a string with length L, held stationary at both ends, only when its wavelength satisfies the preceding equation. When we solve the equation for λ and label the possible values of λ as λ_n, we obtain the following expression:

Wavelengths for standing waves on a string

On a string that is fixed at both ends, the only possible standing waves have wavelengths λ_n that are related to the string length L by the formula

$$\lambda_n = \frac{2L}{n} \qquad (n = 1, 2, 3, \dots).\qquad (6)$$

When the wavelength is *not* equal to one of these values, no standing wave is possible.

Corresponding to this series of possible wavelengths is a series of possible frequencies f_n, each related to its corresponding wavelength by $f_n = v/\lambda_n$. The smallest frequency, f_1, corresponds to the largest wavelength (when $n = 1$), $\lambda = 2L$:

$$f_1 = \frac{v}{2L} \qquad \text{(string, held at both ends)}.$$

This frequency is called the **fundamental frequency.** The other frequencies are $f_2 = 2v/2L$, $f_3 = 3v/2L$, and so on. These are all integer multiples of f_1, such as $2f_1$, $3f_1$, $4f_1$, and so on, and we can express *all* the frequencies as follows:

Frequencies for standing waves on a string

On a string of length L that is held stationary at both ends, standing waves can have only frequencies f_n that are related to L and the wave speed v by the formula

$$f_n = n\frac{v}{2L} = nf_1, \qquad (n = 1, 2, 3, \dots).\qquad (7)$$

These frequencies, all integer multiples of f_1, are called **harmonics,** and the series is called a **harmonic series.** Musicians sometimes call f_2, f_3, and so on **overtones;** f_2 is the second harmonic or the first overtone, f_3 is the third harmonic or the second overtone, and so on. (You can think of overtones as the first, second, third, etc., "tones over" the fundamental frequency.)

A **normal mode** is a motion in which all particles of the string move sinusoidally (i.e., with simple harmonic motion) with the same frequency. Each of the frequencies given by Equation 7 corresponds to a possible normal-mode pattern. There are infinitely many normal modes, each with its characteristic frequency and vibration pattern. Figure 16 shows the four lowest-frequency normal-mode

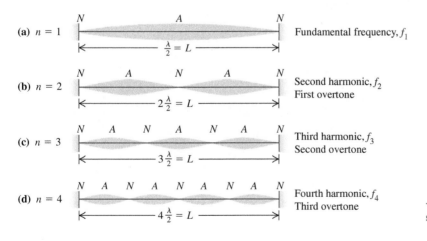

◀ FIGURE 16 The first four normal modes of a string fixed at both ends.

407

patterns and their associated frequencies and wavelengths. We can contrast this situation with a simpler vibrating system, the harmonic oscillator, which has only one normal mode and one characteristic frequency.

If we displace a string so that its shape is the same as one of the normal-mode patterns and then release it, it vibrates with the frequency of that mode. But when a piano string is struck or a guitar string is plucked, not only is the fundamental frequency present in the resulting vibration, but also many overtones. This motion is therefore a combination, or *superposition,* of many normal modes. Several frequencies and motions are present simultaneously, and the displacement of any point on the string is the vector sum (or superposition) of displacements associated with the individual modes.

As we've seen, the fundamental frequency of a vibrating string is $f_1 = v/2L$. The wave speed v is determined by Equation 2, $v = \sqrt{F_T/\mu}$. Combining these equations, we obtain the following expression:

Fundamental frequency of a vibrating string

The fundamental frequency f_1 of a vibrating string with length L, held at both ends, is

$$f_1 = \frac{1}{2L}\sqrt{\frac{F_T}{\mu}},\tag{8}$$

where the string tension is F_T and the mass per unit length is μ.

All string instruments are "tuned" to the correct frequencies by varying the tension F_T. An increase in tension increases the wave speed v and thus also increases the frequency (and the pitch) for a string of any fixed length L. The inverse dependence of frequency on length L is illustrated by the long strings of the bass (low-frequency) section of the piano or the string bass, compared with the shorter strings of the piano treble or the violin (Figure 17). One reason for winding the bass strings of a piano with wire is to increase the mass per unit length μ so as to obtain the desired low frequency without resorting to a string that is inconveniently long or inflexible. In playing the violin or guitar, the usual means of varying the pitch is to press the strings against the fingerboard with the fingers to change the length L of the vibrating portion of the string. As Equation 8 shows, decreasing L increases f_1.

▲ **FIGURE 17** The ranges of a bass, cello, viola, and violin compared with that of a concert grand piano. In all cases, longer strings give lower notes.

PROBLEM-SOLVING STRATEGY 1 **Standing waves and normal modes**

In all wave problems, it's useful to distinguish between the purely kinematic quantities, such as the wave speed v, wavelength λ, and frequency f, and the dynamic quantities involving the properties of the medium, including F_T and μ. You can compute the wave speed if you know either λ and f or F_T and μ. Try to determine whether the properties of the medium are involved in the problem at hand or whether the problem is only kinematic in nature.

To visualize nodes and antinodes in standing waves, it's always helpful to draw a diagram. For a string, you can draw the shape at one instant and label the nodes N and the antinodes A. For longitudinal waves (discussed in the next section), it's not so easy to draw the shape, but you can still label the nodes and antinodes. The distance between two adjacent nodes or two adjacent antinodes is always $\lambda/2$, and the distance between a node and the adjacent antinode is always $\lambda/4$. For a string held at both ends, the fundamental mode has nodes only at the ends and one antinode in the middle.

Quantitative Analysis 5 — Changing the fundamental frequency

In the apparatus shown in Figure 18, the wire is tensioned by the weight of the hanging block. If the vibrating portion of the wire has a fundamental frequency f when the block has mass m, what should the block's mass be in order to give a fundamental frequency of $2f$?

A. $\sqrt{2}\,m$
B. $2m$
C. $4m$

SOLUTION The frequency is related to the tension in the wire by Equation 8:

$$f_1 = \frac{1}{2L}\sqrt{\frac{F_T}{\mu}}.$$

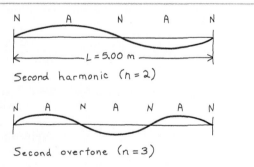

Vibrating portion of wire

▲ **FIGURE 18**

This equation says that the fundamental frequency is directly proportional to the square root of the tension F_T in the wire. We can assume that the tension is equal to the block's weight and thus is directly proportional to its mass. Thus, f_1 is directly proportional to the square root of the block's mass. In that case, to double the frequency, you must increase the mass by a factor of four—so C is the correct answer.

EXAMPLE 3 **A giant bass viol**

In an effort to get your name in the *Guinness Book of World Records,* you set out to build a bass viol with strings that have a length of 5.00 m between fixed points. One of the strings has a mass per unit length of 40.0 g/m and a fundamental frequency of 20.0 Hz. **(a)** Calculate the tension in this string. **(b)** Calculate the frequency and wavelength of the second harmonic. **(c)** Calculate the frequency and wavelength of the second overtone.

SOLUTION

SET UP Figure 19 shows our diagram. Remember that the second overtone is the third harmonic. (Refer to Figure 16 if you're confused.)

SOLVE Part (a): To find the tension F_T in the string, we first solve Equation 8 for F_T:

$$F_T = 4\mu L^2 f_1^2.$$

We are given that $\mu = 4.00 \times 10^{-2}$ kg/m, $L = 5.00$ m, and $f_1 = 20.0$ s^{-1}. Substituting these values, we find that

$$F_T = 4(4.00 \times 10^{-2}\ \text{kg/m})(5.00\ \text{m})^2(20.0\ \text{s}^{-1})^2 = 1600\ \text{N}.$$

N   A   N   A   N

$L = 5.00$ m

Second harmonic $(n = 2)$

N   A   N   A   N   A   N

Second overtone $(n = 3)$

▲ **FIGURE 19** Our sketch for this problem.

Continued

(In a real bass viol, the tension in each string is typically a few hundred newtons.)

Part (b): From Equation 7, the second harmonic frequency $(n = 2)$ is

$$f_2 = 2f_1 = 2(20.0 \text{ Hz}) = 40.0 \text{ Hz}.$$

From Equation 6, the wavelength of the second harmonic is

$$\lambda_2 = \frac{2L}{2} = 5.00 \text{ m}.$$

Part (c): The second overtone is the "second tone over" (above) the fundamental; that is, $n = 3$, and

$$f_3 = 3f_1 = 3(20.0 \text{ Hz}) = 60.0 \text{ Hz}.$$

The wavelength is

$$\lambda_3 = \frac{2L}{3} = 3.33 \text{ m}.$$

REFLECT The 20.0 Hz fundamental frequency for this string is approximately the frequency of the E below the lowest C on the piano and is roughly at the threshold for human hearing. The second and third harmonics have higher frequencies and would thus be easier to hear.

Practice Problem: With the same values of μ and F_T, what length of string would be needed for a fundamental frequency of 33.0 Hz (the lowest C on the piano)? *Answer:* 3.03 m.

7 Longitudinal Standing Waves

When longitudinal waves propagate in a fluid (such as air or water) contained in a pipe with finite length, the waves are reflected from the ends in the same way that transverse waves on a string are reflected at its ends. The superposition of the waves traveling in opposite directions again forms a standing wave.

When reflection takes place at a *closed* end (an end with a rigid barrier or plug), the displacement of the particles at this end must always be zero. Just as with a stationary end of a string, there is no displacement at the end, and the end is a *node.* If the pipe is closed at both ends, then each end is a node; there may also be nodes at intermediate positions within the pipe. If an end of a pipe is *open* and the pipe is narrow in comparison with the wavelength (which is true for most wind instruments, including some organ pipes), the open end is an *antinode*—a point at which the displacement of the medium is maximal. (If this doesn't seem right, recall that a free end of a stretched string, like that in Figure 11b, is also a displacement antinode.) Thus, longitudinal waves in a column of fluid are reflected at the closed and open ends of a pipe in the same way that transverse waves in a string are reflected at stationary and free ends, respectively. A closed end is always a node, and an open end is always an antinode.

A standing longitudinal wave in a pipe always has alternating nodes and antinodes. The pressure variations in the pipe also have an alternating pattern. It turns out that the antinodes (points of maximum displacement) correspond to points where there is *no* pressure variation. We can call these *pressure nodes.* To distinguish the two kinds of nodes, we sometimes speak of *displacement nodes* and *pressure nodes,* and similarly for the antinodes. A displacement node is always a pressure antinode, and a displacement antinode is always a pressure node. The relationship will become clearer in the next section, where we discuss normal modes for longitudinal waves.

We can demonstrate longitudinal standing waves in a column of gas, and also measure the wave speed, with an apparatus called a Kundt's tube (Figure 20). A horizontal glass tube a meter or so long is closed at one end and at the other end has a flexible diaphragm that can transmit vibrations. As our sound source, we use a small loudspeaker, driven by a sinusoidal oscillator whose frequency we can vary. We place a small amount of light powder or cork dust inside the pipe and distribute it uniformly along the bottom side of the pipe. As we vary the frequency of the sound, we pass through frequencies at which the amplitude of the standing waves becomes large enough for the moving gas to sweep the cork dust along the pipe at all points where the gas is in motion. The powder therefore

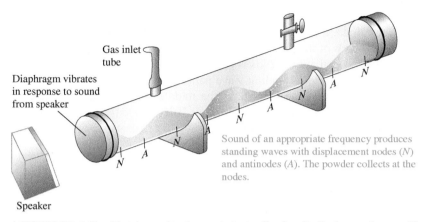

Gas inlet tube

Diaphragm vibrates in response to sound from speaker

Speaker

Sound of an appropriate frequency produces standing waves with displacement nodes (N) and antinodes (A). The powder collects at the nodes.

▲ **FIGURE 20** A Kundt's tube used to demonstrate standing longitudinal waves in a gas. The dust collects at the displacement nodes, where the displacement of gas due to the standing wave is minimal.

collects at the displacement nodes (where the gas is not moving). Adjacent nodes are separated by a distance equal to $\lambda/2$, and we can measure this distance. We read the frequency f from the oscillator dial, and we can then calculate the speed v of the waves from the relation $v = \lambda f$.

EXAMPLE 4 **Speed of sound in hydrogen**

At a frequency of 25 kHz, the distance from a closed end of a tube of hydrogen gas to the nearest displacement node of a standing wave is 0.026 m. Calculate the wave speed.

SOLUTION

SET UP AND SOLVE Figure 21 shows our sketch. This is a common way to represent a longitudinal standing wave in a tube. While the curves *look* like the real shape of a transverse standing wave on a string, for a longitudinal wave they don't show directly what the medium is doing. Rather, you can think of them as a graph of displacement (on the vertical axis) versus position (on the horizontal axis). As our sketch shows, the closed end of the tube is a displacement node. The statement of the problem tells us that the next displacement node is 0.026 m away. Adjacent nodes are always a half-wavelength apart, so we have $\lambda/2 = 0.026$ m and $\lambda = 0.052$ m. Then the wave speed is

$$v = \lambda f = (0.052 \text{ m})(25,000 \text{ s}^{-1}) = 1300 \text{ m/s}.$$

▲ **FIGURE 21** Our sketch for this problem.

REFLECT This result is close to the value given in Table 1 for the speed of sound in hydrogen at 20°C (1330 m/s). Either value is about four times the speed of sound in air at 20°C.

Practice Problem: If the hydrogen in the tube is replaced by air at 20°C, what frequency would be needed to produce standing waves with the same wavelength? *Answer:* 6600 Hz.

Normal Modes

Many musical instruments, including organ pipes and all the woodwind and brass instruments, use longitudinal standing waves (normal modes) in vibrating air columns to produce musical tones. Organ pipes are one of the simplest examples. Air is supplied by a blower, at a pressure typically on the order of 10^3 Pa, or 10^{-2} atm (above normal atmospheric pressure), to the bottom end of the pipe (Figure 22). A stream of air is directed against the mouth of each pipe, as shown in the figure. The column of air in the pipe is set into vibration, and there is a series of possible normal modes, just as with a stretched string. The mouth always acts as an open end; thus, it is a displacement antinode. The top of a pipe may be either open or closed. Figure 23 shows three normal modes in a schematic organ pipe open at the top end. (The pipes are shown on their sides.)

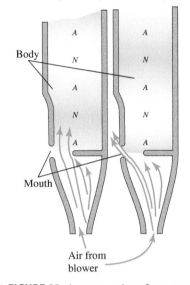

Vibrations from turbulent airflow set up standing waves in the pipe.

▲ FIGURE 22 A cross section of an organ pipe. Vibrations from the turbulent air flow set up standing waves in the pipe.

Let's consider the general problem of normal modes in an air column. The pipe may be a flute, a clarinet, an organ pipe, or any other wind instrument. In Figure 23, both ends of the pipe are open, so both are displacement antinodes. An organ pipe that is open at both ends is called an *open pipe*. The fundamental frequency f_1 corresponds to a standing-wave pattern with a displacement anti-node at each end and a displacement node in the middle (Figure 23a). The distance between adjacent nodes is always equal to one half-wavelength, and in this case that is equal to the length L of the pipe: $\lambda/2 = L$. The corresponding frequency, obtained from the relation $f = v/\lambda$, is

$$f_1 = \frac{v}{2L} \qquad \text{(open pipe)}. \tag{9}$$

The other two parts of Figure 23 show the second and third harmonics (first and second overtones); their vibration patterns have two and three displacement nodes, respectively. For these patterns, the length L of the pipe is equal to two or three half-wavelengths, so $\lambda/2$ is equal to $L/2$ and $L/3$, respectively, and the frequencies are twice and three times the fundamental frequency, respectively (i.e., $f_2 = 2f_1$ and $f_3 = 3f_1$). For *every* normal mode, the length L must be an integer number of half-wavelengths, and the possible wavelengths λ_n are given by

$$L = n\frac{\lambda_n}{2}, \qquad \text{or} \qquad \lambda_n = \frac{2L}{n} \qquad (n = 1, 2, 3, \dots).$$

The corresponding frequencies f_n are given by $f_n = v/\lambda_n$, so all the normal-mode frequencies for a pipe that is open at both ends are given by

$$f_n = n\frac{v}{2L} = nf_1 \qquad (n = 1, 2, 3, \dots). \qquad \text{(open pipe)}. \tag{10}$$

The value $n = 1$ corresponds to the fundamental frequency, $f_1 = v/2L$, $n = 2$ to the second harmonic (or first overtone), and so on.

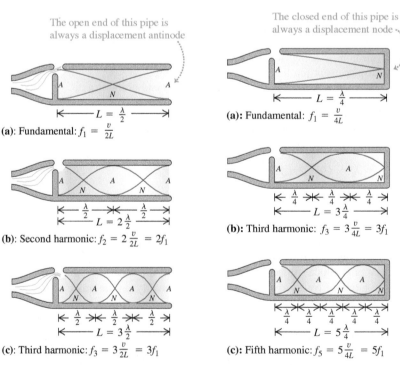

The open end of this pipe is always a displacement antinode

(a): Fundamental: $f_1 = \frac{v}{2L}$

(b): Second harmonic: $f_2 = 2\frac{v}{2L} = 2f_1$

(c): Third harmonic: $f_3 = 3\frac{v}{2L} = 3f_1$

▲ FIGURE 23 A cross section of an open pipe, showing the first three normal modes as well as the displacement nodes and antinodes.

The closed end of this pipe is always a displacement node

(a): Fundamental: $f_1 = \frac{v}{4L}$

(b): Third harmonic: $f_3 = 3\frac{v}{4L} = 3f_1$

(c): Fifth harmonic: $f_5 = 5\frac{v}{4L} = 5f_1$

▲ FIGURE 24 A cross section of a stopped pipe, showing the first three normal modes as well as the displacement nodes and antin-odes. Only odd harmonics are possible.

Figure 24 shows a pipe open at the left (mouth) end but closed at the right end. We call this a *stopped pipe.* The left (open) end is an antinode, but the right (closed) end is a node. The distance between a node and the adjacent antinode is always one quarter-wavelength. Figure 24a shows the fundamental frequency; the length of the pipe is a quarter-wavelength $(L = \lambda_1/4)$. The fundamental frequency is $f_1 = v/\lambda_1$, or

$$f_1 = \frac{v}{4L} \qquad \text{(stopped pipe).} \qquad (11)$$

This is one-half the fundamental frequency for an *open* pipe of the same length. In musical language, the *pitch* of a stopped pipe is one octave lower (a factor of two in frequency) than that of an open pipe of the same length. Figure 24b shows the next mode, for which the length of the pipe is *three-quarters* of a wavelength, corresponding to a frequency $3f_1$. In Figure 24c, $L = 5\lambda/4$ and the frequency is $5f_1$. The possible wavelengths are given by

$$L = n\frac{\lambda_n}{4} \qquad \text{or} \qquad \lambda_n = \frac{4L}{n} \qquad (n = 1, 3, 5, \dots).$$

The normal-mode frequencies are given by $f_n = v/\lambda_n$, or

$$f_n = n\frac{v}{4L} = nf_1 \qquad (n = 1, 3, 5, \dots), \qquad \text{(stopped pipe),} \qquad (12)$$

with the fundamental frequency f_1 given by Equation 11. We see that the second, fourth, and, indeed, all *even* harmonics are missing. In a pipe that is closed at one end, the fundamental frequency is $f_1 = v/4L$, and only the odd harmonics in the series $(3f_1, 5f_1, 7f_1, \dots)$ are possible.

EXAMPLE 5   Harmonics of an organ pipe

On a day when the speed of sound is 345 m/s, the fundamental frequency of an open organ pipe is 690 Hz. If the second *harmonic* of this pipe has the same wavelength as the second *overtone* of a stopped pipe, what is the length of each pipe?

SOLUTION

SET UP Figure 25 shows our sketch. Note that the frequency of the second harmonic of the open pipe is twice its fundamental frequency, but the second overtone of the stopped pipe has a frequency five times that of the fundamental. Do you see why?

SOLVE For an open pipe, $f_1 = v/2L$, so the length of the open pipe is

$$L_{\text{open}} = \frac{v}{2f_1} = \frac{345 \text{ m/s}}{2(690 \text{ s}^{-1})} = 0.250 \text{ m.}$$

The second harmonic of the open pipe has a frequency of

$$f_2 = 2f_1 = 2(690 \text{ Hz}) = 1380 \text{ Hz.}$$

If the wavelengths are the same, the frequencies are the same, so the frequency of the second overtone of the stopped pipe is also 1380 Hz. The first overtone of a stopped pipe is at $3f_1$, and the second at $5f_1 = 5(v/4L)$. If this equals 1380 Hz, then

$$1380 \text{ Hz} = 5\left(\frac{345 \text{ m/s}}{4L_{\text{stopped}}}\right) \qquad \text{and} \qquad L_{\text{stopped}} = 0.313 \text{ m.}$$

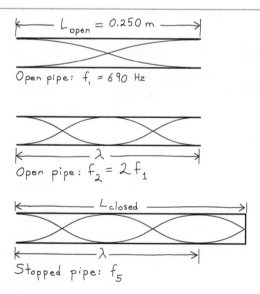

▲ **FIGURE 25** Our sketch for this problem.

REFLECT A final possibility is a pipe that is closed at *both* ends and therefore has nodes at both ends. This pipe wouldn't be of much use as a musical instrument, because there would be no way for the vibrations to get out of it.

Practice Problem: An open pipe and a stopped pipe have the same length. Does any harmonic of the open pipe have the same frequency as any harmonic of the stopped pipe? *Answer:* No.

AP Photo

▲ Application **Boning up on physics.** You don't need a physicist's knowledge of standing waves to learn how to make a flute. This photo shows 9000-year-old bone flutes from Jiahu, China. The bone flute is one of the earliest known musical instruments. Blowing into the hollow bone causes a longitudinal wave to form in the internal air space. The wave produces a note with a fundamental frequency corresponding to a standing wave with a displacement antinode at each end of the flute. By placing their fingers over holes carved into the bone, these early musicians could change the effective length of the flute, thus varying the frequency of the waves produced and allowing them to play notes of different pitch.

In an actual organ pipe, several modes are always present at once. The situation is analogous to a string that is struck or plucked, producing several modes at the same time. In each case, the motion is a *superposition* of various modes. The extent to which modes higher than the fundamental mode are present depends on the cross section of the pipe, the proportion of the length to width, the shape of the mouth, and other, more subtle factors. The harmonic content of the tone is an important factor in determining its tone quality, or timbre. A very narrow pipe produces a tone that is rich in higher harmonics, which we hear as a thin and "stringy" tone; a fatter pipe produces mostly the fundamental mode, heard as a softer, more flutelike tone.

In this section we've talked mostly about organ pipes, but our discussion is also applicable to other wind instruments. The flute and the recorder are directly analogous. The most significant difference is that those instruments have holes along the pipe. Opening and closing the holes with the fingers changes the effective length L of the air column and thus changes the pitch. Any individual organ pipe, by comparison, plays only a single note. The flute and recorder behave as *open* pipes, but the clarinet acts as a *stopped* pipe (closed at the reed end, open at the bell).

Equations 9 and 11 show that the frequencies of any such instrument are proportional to the speed of sound v in the air column inside the instrument. In all gases (including air), v increases when the temperature increases. Thus, the pitch of all wind instruments rises with increasing temperature. An organ that has some of its pipes at one temperature and others at a different temperature is bound to sound out of tune.

8 Interference

Wave phenomena that occur when two or more periodic waves with the same frequency overlap in the same region of space are grouped under the heading of *interference.* As we have seen, standing waves are a simple example of an interference effect. Two waves with the same frequency and amplitude, traveling in opposite direction in a medium, combine to produce a standing-wave pattern, with nodes and antinodes that do not move.

Figure 26 shows an example of interference involving waves that spread out in space. Two speakers, driven by the same amplifier, emit identical sinusoidal sound waves with the same constant frequency. We place a microphone at point P in the figure, equidistant from the speakers. Wave crests emitted from the speakers at the same time travel equal distances and arrive at point P at the same time. The amplitudes add according to the principle of superposition. The total wave amplitude at P is twice the amplitude from each individual wave, and we can measure this combined amplitude with the microphone. (If you put your ear where the microphone is, the sound is *louder* than the sound from either speaker alone.) When interference causes an increase in amplitude, we call it **constructive interference,** and we say that the two waves *reinforce* each other.

Now let's move the microphone to point Q, where the distances from the two speakers to the microphone differ by a half-wavelength. Then the two waves arrive a half-cycle out of step; a positive crest from one speaker arrives at the same time as a negative crest from the other, and the net amplitude measured by the microphone at Q is much *smaller* than when only one speaker is present. When interference causes a decrease in amplitude, we call it **destructive interference** or *cancellation.*

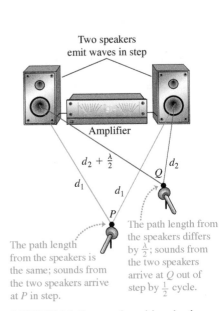

Two speakers emit waves in step

Amplifier

$d_2 + \frac{\lambda}{2}$

d_2

d_1

d_1

Q

P

The path length from the speakers is the same; sounds from the two speakers arrive at P in step.

The path length from the speakers differs by $\frac{\lambda}{2}$; sounds from the two speakers arrive at Q out of step by $\frac{1}{2}$ cycle.

▲ **FIGURE 26** Two speakers driven by the same amplifier produce sound waves that interfere. The waves are in step as they emerge from the speakers; they interfere constructively at point P, destructively at point Q.

EXAMPLE 6 Interference from two loudspeakers

Two small loudspeakers A and B (Figure 27) are driven by the same amplifier and emit pure sinusoidal waves; crests from the speakers are emitted simultaneously ("in step"). If the speed of sound is 350 m/s, for what frequencies does maximum constructive interference occur at point P? For what frequencies does destructive interference (cancellation) occur at point P?

► **FIGURE 27**

SOLUTION

SET UP First we need to find the difference in path lengths from points A and B to point P. Maximum constructive interference occurs when the path difference d is an integer number of wavelengths; maximum destructive interference occurs when the path difference is a half-integer number of wavelengths. Once the wavelengths are known, the corresponding frequencies can be found from $f = v/\lambda$.

SOLVE The distance from speaker A to point P is $[(2.00\text{ m})^2 + (4.00\text{ m})^2]^{1/2} = 4.47$ m, and the distance from speaker B to point P is $[(1.00\text{ m})^2 + (4.00\text{ m})^2]^{1/2} = 4.12$ m. The path difference is $d = 4.47\text{ m} - 4.12\text{ m} = 0.35$ m.

Maximum constructive interference occurs when the path difference d is an integer multiple of λ: $d = 0, v/f, 2v/f, \ldots = nv/f$ ($n = 0, 1, 2, \ldots$). So the possible frequencies for maximum constructive interference are

$$f_n = n\frac{v}{d} = n\frac{350\text{ m/s}}{0.35\text{ m}} \quad (n = 1, 2, 3, \ldots)$$
$$= 1000\text{ Hz}, 2000\text{ Hz}, 3000\text{ Hz}, \ldots.$$

Maximum destructive interference (cancellation) occurs when the path difference for the two waves is a half-integer number of wavelengths:

$$d = \lambda/2, 3\lambda/2, 5\lambda/2, \ldots, \quad \text{or}$$
$$d = v/2f, 3v/2f, 5v/2f, \ldots.$$

The possible frequencies for destructive interference are

$$f_n = n\frac{v}{2d} = n\frac{350\text{ m/s}}{2(0.35\text{ m})} \quad (n = 1, 3, 5, \ldots)$$
$$= 500\text{ Hz}, 1500\text{ Hz}, 2500\text{ Hz}, \ldots.$$

REFLECT As we increase the frequency, the sound at point P alternates between large and small amplitudes; the maxima and minima occur at the frequencies we have found. It would be hard to notice this effect in an ordinary room because of multiple reflections from the walls, floor, and ceiling. Such an experiment is best done in an anechoic chamber (Figure 28)—a room with walls that are almost completely nonreflecting for sound.

▲ **FIGURE 28** An anechoic chamber.

Roger Ressmeyer/Corbis

9 Sound and Hearing

Sound can travel in gases (such as air), liquids (such as water), and solid materials. The simplest sound waves are sinusoidal waves, which have definite frequency, amplitude, and wavelength. The human ear is sensitive to waves in the frequency range from about 20 to 20,000 Hz, but we also use the term *sound* for similar waves with frequencies above (**ultrasonic**) and below (**infrasonic**) the range of human hearing.

Sound waves may also be described in terms of variations of *pressure* at various points. In a sinusoidal sound wave in air, the pressure fluctuates above and below atmospheric pressure p_a with a sinusoidal variation having the same frequency as the motions of the air particles. The *maximum* variation in pressure above and below atmospheric pressure is called the *pressure amplitude,* denoted by p_{max}. Microphones and similar devices usually sense pressure variations, not displacements.

▲ **BIO** Application **Not so loud!** The human ear is a marvelous instrument for detecting the vibrations caused by sound waves. This highly magnified photo shows the tiny hairs inside the cochlea of the inner ear that sense these vibrations. (Technically, these hairs are the stereocilia of cochlear hair cells.) When these microscopic hairs bend, the hair cells send nerve signals to the brain, and we perceive those signals as different sounds. Between the threshold of hearing and the sound of a raging rock concert, these hairs are sensitive to sounds ranging in power over 14 orders of magnitude. They can sense very faint, low-power sounds, but can be damaged by prolonged exposure to loud, high-power sounds. Therefore, it's important to minimize one's exposure to sources of very loud sound waves and to wear proper ear protection if exposure is unavoidable.

Amplitude

Measurements of sound waves show that, in the loudest sounds the human ear can tolerate without pain, the maximum pressure variations are on the order of $p_{max} = 30$ Pa above and below atmospheric pressure p_a (nominally, 1.013×10^5 Pa at sea level). If the frequency is 1000 Hz, the corresponding amplitude A (maximum displacement) is about $A = 0.012$ mm.

Thus, the displacement amplitude of even the loudest sound is *extremely* small. The maximum pressure variation in the *faintest* audible sound, of frequency 1000 Hz, is only about 3×10^{-5} Pa. The corresponding displacement amplitude is about 10^{-11} m. For comparison, the wavelength of yellow light is 6×10^{-7} m, and the diameter of a molecule is about 10^{-10} m. The ear is an extremely sensitive organ!

The Human Ear

Figure 29 shows the anatomy of the human ear. When a sound wave enters the auditory canal, it causes the eardrum to vibrate. The vibration is transmitted to the three small bones called the incus, the malleus, and the stapes. This motion is in turn transmitted to the fluid-filled *cochlea* of the inner ear. The motion of the cochlear fluid is then imparted to specialized hair cells in the cochlea, and the resulting nerve impulses are transmitted to the brain.

10 Sound Intensity

Like all other waves, sound waves transfer energy from one region to another. We define the **intensity** of a wave, denoted by I, as *the time-averaged rate at which energy is transported by the wave, per unit area,* across a surface perpendicular to the direction of propagation. That is, the intensity I is the average *power* transported per unit area. The intensity of the faintest sound wave that can be heard by a person with normal hearing is about 10^{-12} W/m^2, or 10^{-16} W/cm^2.

The average *total* power (energy per unit time) carried across a surface by a sound wave equals the product of the intensity (power per unit area) at the surface and the surface area (assuming that the intensity over the surface is uniform). The average total sound power emitted by a person speaking in an ordinary conversational tone is about 10^{-5} W, and a loud shout corresponds to about 3×10^{-2} W. If all the residents of New York City were to talk at the same time, the total sound power would be about 100 W, equivalent to the electric power requirement of a medium-sized light bulb! Yet the power required to fill a large auditorium with loud sound is considerable. The intensity at an individual point is proportional to the square of the amplitude of the sound wave and also proportional to the frequency of the wave.

▲ **FIGURE 29** The structure of the human ear. The eardrum and the bones of the middle ear transmit sound waves into the cochlea, where the information is coded into nerve impulses.

EXAMPLE 7   **An auditorium sound system**

For a sound system for a 2000-seat auditorium, suppose we want the sound intensity over the surface of a hemisphere 20 m in radius to be 1.0 W/m^2. What acoustic power output would be needed from an array of speakers at the center of the sphere?

SOLUTION

SET UP AND SOLVE The total power needed is the intensity (power per unit area) times the area of the hemisphere. The area of the hemispherical surface is $\frac{1}{2}(4\pi R^2) = \frac{1}{2}(4\pi)(20 \text{ m})^2$, or about 2500 m². The total acoustic power needed is

$$(1.0 \text{ W/m}^2)(2500 \text{ m}^2) = 2500 \text{ W} = 2.5 \text{ kW}.$$

REFLECT The efficiency of loudspeakers in converting electrical energy into sound is not very high (typically a few percent for ordinary speakers and up to 25% for horn-type speakers). The

electrical power input to the speakers would need to be considerably larger than 2.5 kW.

However, 1.0 W/m^2 is *very* loud sound, at the threshold of pain and definitely in the range where permanent hearing damage is likely.

Practice Problem: In a smaller auditorium, we want the sound intensity over the surface of a hemisphere 10 m in radius to be 1.0 W/m^2. If the speakers have an efficiency of 20% (i.e., 20% of the electrical energy is converted into sound), what total electrical power input is required? *Answer:* 3.1 kW.

If a source of sound can be considered as a point, the intensity at a distance r from the source is inversely proportional to r^2. This relationship follows directly from energy conservation: If the power output of the source is P, then the average intensity I_1 through a sphere with radius r_1 and surface area $4\pi r_1^2$ is

$$I_1 = \frac{P}{4\pi r_1^2}.$$

The average intensity I_2 through a sphere with a different radius r_2 is given by a similar expression. If no energy is absorbed between the two spheres, the power P must be the same for both, and we have

$$4\pi r_1^2 I_1 = 4\pi r_2^2 I_2$$
$$\frac{I_1}{I_2} = \frac{r_2^2}{r_1^2}. \tag{13}$$

The intensity I at any distance r is therefore inversely proportional to r^2. This inverse-square relationship also holds for various other energy-flow situations involving a point source, such as light emitted by a point source.

Decibels

Because the ear is sensitive over such a broad range of intensities, a *logarithmic* intensity scale is usually used. The **intensity level** (or *sound level*) β of a sound wave is defined by the equation

$$\beta = (10 \text{ dB})\log\frac{I}{I_0}. \tag{14}$$

In this equation, I_0 is a reference intensity chosen to be 10^{-12} W/m^2, and "log" denotes the logarithm to the base 10, not the natural logarithm (ln). The units of β are **decibels,** abbreviated dB. A sound wave with an intensity I equal to I_0 $(=10^{-12} \text{ W/m}^2)$ has an intensity level of 0 dB. This level corresponds roughly to the faintest sound that can be heard by a person with normal hearing, although that depends on the frequency of the sound. The intensity at the pain threshold, about 1 W/m^2, corresponds to an intensity level of 120 dB.

Table 2 gives the intensity levels in decibels of several familiar noises. It is taken from a survey made by the New York City Noise Abatement Commission.

TABLE 2 Noise levels due to various sources (representative values)

Type of noise	Sound level, dB	Intensity, W/m²
Rock concert	140	100
Threshold of pain	120	1
Riveter	95	3.2×10^{-3}
Elevated train	90	10^{-3}
Busy street traffic	70	10^{-5}
Ordinary conversation	65	3.2×10^{-6}
Quiet automobile	50	10^{-7}
Quiet radio in home	40	10^{-8}
Average whisper	20	10^{-10}
Rustle of leaves	10	10^{-11}
Threshold of hearing	0	10^{-12}

PROBLEM-SOLVING STRATEGY 2 Sound intensity

Quite a few quantities are involved in characterizing the amplitude and intensity of a sound wave, and it's easy to get lost in the maze of relationships. It helps to put them into categories: The amplitude is described by A or p_{max}; the frequency f is related to the wavelength λ and the wave speed v, which in turn is determined by the properties of the medium. Take a hard look at the problem at hand, identifying which of these quantities are given and which you have to find; then start looking for relationships that take you where you want to go.

In using Equation 14 for the sound intensity level, remember that I and I_0 must be in the same units, usually W/m^2. If they aren't, convert!

EXAMPLE 8 Temporary deafness

A 10-minute exposure to 120 dB sound typically shifts your threshold of hearing temporarily from 0 dB up to 28 dB. Studies have shown that, on average, 10 years of exposure to 92 dB sound causes a *permanent* shift of up to 28 dB. What intensities correspond to 28 dB and 92 dB?

SOLUTION

SET UP AND SOLVE We rearrange Equation 14, dividing both sides by 10 dB and then taking inverse logarithms of both sides:

$$I = I_0 10^{(\beta/10\,\text{dB})}.$$

When $\beta = 28$ dB,

$$I = (10^{-12}\,\text{W/m}^2)\,10^{(28\,\text{dB}/10\,\text{dB})} = (10^{-12}\,\text{W/m}^2)(10^{2.8})$$
$$= 6.3 \times 10^{-10}\,\text{W/m}^2.$$

When $\beta = 92$ dB,

$$I = (10^{-12}\,\text{W/m}^2)\,10^{(92\,\text{dB}/10\,\text{dB})} = (10^{-12}\,\text{W/m}^2)(10^{9.2})$$
$$= 1.6 \times 10^{-3}\,\text{W/m}^2.$$

REFLECT If your answers are a factor of 10 too large, you may have entered 10×10^{-12} in your calculator instead of 1×10^{-12}. Be careful! Also, note that the human ear is sensitive to an extremely broad range of intensities.

EXAMPLE 9 A bird sings in a meadow

Consider an idealized model with a point source emitting a sound with constant power with an intensity inversely proportional to the square of the distance from the bird (Figure 30). By how many dB does the sound intensity level drop when you move to a point twice as far away from the bird?

Continued

SOLUTION

SET UP AND SOLVE We label the two points 1 and 2 (Figure 30), and we use Equation 14 twice. The difference in sound intensity level, $\beta_2 - \beta_1$, is given by

$$\beta_2 - \beta_1 = (10 \text{ dB})\left(\log\frac{I_2}{I_0} - \log\frac{I_1}{I_0}\right)$$
$$= (10 \text{ dB})[(\log I_2 - \log I_0) - (\log I_1 - \log I_0)]$$
$$= (10 \text{ dB})\log\frac{I_2}{I_1}.$$

Now we use Equation 13, inverted: $I_2/I_1 = r_1^2/r_2^2$. Then

$$\beta_2 - \beta_1 = (10 \text{ dB})\log\frac{r_1^2}{r_2^2} = (10 \text{ dB})\log\frac{r_1^2}{(2r_1)^2}$$
$$= (10 \text{ dB})\log\frac{1}{4} = -6.0 \text{ dB}.$$

A decrease in intensity of a factor of four corresponds to a 6 dB decrease in sound intensity level.

REFLECT The decibel scale is logarithmic; a factor of two in intensity corresponds to a 3 dB difference in sound intensity level,

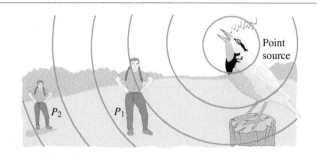

▲ **FIGURE 30** When you double your distance from a point source of sound, how much does the sound intensity level drop?

a factor of eight to a 9 dB difference, and so on. In this problem, if two birds are singing, the sound intensity level increases by 3 dB.

Practice Problem: If the listener moves to a point four times the original distance from the bird, how many birds would have to sing in order to produce the same intensity level at this point as in the initial problem? *Answer:* 16 birds.

We invite you to prove that an increase in intensity of a factor of two corresponds to about a 3 dB increase in intensity level. This change is barely perceptible to the human ear. An increase of 8 to 10 dB in intensity level is usually interpreted by the ear as a doubling of loudness.

11 Beats

In several earlier sections, we've talked about *interference* effects that occur when two different waves with the same frequency overlap in the same region of space. Now let's look at the superposition of two waves with equal amplitude but slightly different frequencies. This phenomenon occurs, for example, when two guitar strings with slightly different frequencies are sounded together or when two organ pipes that are supposed to sound exactly the same pitch are slightly "out of tune." What you hear from two sound waves with slightly different frequencies is a slow pulsing or beating sound called **beats.**

Consider a particular point in space where the two waves overlap. The displacements of the individual waves at this point are plotted as functions of time in Figure 31a. The total length of the time axis represents about 1 s, and the frequencies are 16 Hz and 18 Hz. Applying the principle of superposition, we add the two displacements at each instant of time to find the total displacement at that time, obtaining the graph in Figure 31b. At certain times, the two waves are "in step": Their maxima coincide, and their amplitudes add. But as time goes on, they become more and more out of step because of their slightly different frequencies. Eventually, a maximum of one wave coincides with a maximum in the opposite direction for the other wave. The two waves then cancel each other, and the total amplitude is zero.

The resulting wave looks like a single sinusoidal wave with a varying amplitude that goes from a maximum to zero and back, as Figure 31b shows. In this

MasteringPHYSICS

ActivPhysics 10.7: Beats and Beat Frequency

▲ FIGURE 31 When two waves with slightly different frequency interfere, the resultant wave fluctuates in amplitude. We hear these fluctuations as beats. (a) Two interacting waves; (b) the resultant wave formed by superposition of the two original waves.

Shutterstock

▲ BIO Application Prey location by barn owls. Barn owls locate their prey by making use of the fact that each ear receives sounds at slightly different times if the owl's head is turned away from the source, due to the small difference in the distances traveled by the sound to reach each ear. This small difference is processed by the neural circuitry of the brain; the owl swivels its head until the waves reach both ears at the same time. At that null point, the head and eyes are facing directly toward the sound source. Owls are capable of detecting time differences in the sound waves received by each ear as small as 10 μs.

example, the amplitude goes through two maxima and two minima in 1 s; thus, the frequency of this amplitude variation is 2 Hz. The resulting variations in amplitude (loudness) are beats, and the frequency with which the amplitude varies is called the **beat frequency.** In this example the beat frequency is the *difference* of the two frequencies. If the beat frequency is a few hertz, we hear it as a waver or pulsation in the tone.

We can show that the beat frequency is *always* the difference of the two frequencies f_1 and f_2. Suppose f_1 is larger than f_2; then the corresponding periods are T_1 and T_2, with $T_1 < T_2$. If the two waves start out in step at time $t = 0$, they will be in step again at a time T_{beat} such that the first wave has gone through exactly one more cycle than the second. Let n be the number of cycles of the first wave in time T_{beat}; then the number of cycles of the second wave in the same time is $(n - 1)$, and we have the relations

$$T_{\text{beat}} = nT_1 \qquad \text{and} \qquad T_{\text{beat}} = (n - 1)T_2.$$

We solve the second equation for n and substitute the result back into the first equation (to eliminate n), obtaining

$$T_{\text{beat}} = \frac{T_1 T_2}{T_2 - T_1}.$$

Now, T_{beat} is just the *period* of the beat, and its reciprocal is the beat *frequency* $f_{\text{beat}} = 1/T_{\text{beat}}$. So

$$f_{\text{beat}} = \frac{T_2 - T_1}{T_1 T_2} = \frac{1}{T_1} - \frac{1}{T_2},$$

and finally,

$$f_{\text{beat}} = f_1 - f_2. \tag{15}$$

Beats between two tones can be heard up to a beat frequency of 6 or 7 Hz. Two piano strings or two organ pipes differing in frequency by 2 or 3 Hz sound wavery and "out of tune," although some organ stops contain two sets of pipes deliberately tuned to beat frequencies of about 1 to 2 Hz for a gently undulating effect. Listening for beats (or their absence) is an important technique in tuning all musical instruments.

At higher frequency differences, we no longer hear individual beats, and the sensation merges into one of *consonance* or *dissonance,* depending on the frequency ratio of the two tones. In some cases the ear perceives a tone called a *difference tone,* with a pitch equal to the beat frequency of the two tones.

In multiengine aircraft, the engines have to be synchronized so that the sounds don't cause annoying beats, which are heard as loud throbbing sounds. On some planes this is done electronically; on others the pilot does it by ear, just like tuning a piano.

12 The Doppler Effect

You've probably noticed that when a car approaches you with its horn sounding, the pitch seems to drop as the car passes. This phenomenon is called the **Doppler effect.** When a source of sound and a listener are in motion relative to each other, the frequency of the sound heard by the listener is not the same as the source frequency. We can work out a relation between the frequency shift and the source and listener velocities.

To keep things simple, we'll consider only the special case in which the velocities of both source and listener lie along the line joining them. We'll take this line to be the x axis, with the positive direction to the right, and we'll assume that the source S is to the right (at greater x) of the listener L. We assume that this coordinate system is at rest with respect to the air. Let v_S and v_L be the x components of velocity of source and listener, respectively, with respect to this coordinate system. Thus, the direction from the listener L to the source S is the positive direction for both v_S and v_L The speed of sound v is always considered positive, but v_S and v_L can be either positive or negative because they are components of velocity, a vector quantity. If $v_L > 0$, the listener is moving to the right; if $v_L < 0$, the listener is moving to the left. The same rules apply to v_S.

Moving Listener

Let's think first about a listener L moving with velocity v_L toward a stationary source S (Figure 32). The source emits a sound wave with frequency f_S and wavelength $\lambda = v/f_S$. The figure shows several wave crests, separated by equal

▲ **Application Found at sea.** Another important application of the physics of wave formation and propagation is sonar, which was used to find the long-lost steam ship Portland shown above, which sank in 1898. Sonar (SOund Navigation And Ranging) works by transmitting an ultrasonic pulse of sound waves through air or water and sensing the waves reflected from objects in the path of these waves. The frequency of the sound transmitted is about 50 kHz, well above the upper limit of the human ear, which is about 20 kHz. When the sound waves reach an object, they are reflected in various ways, depending on the position, shape, orientation, and surface characteristics of the object. The images from this shipwreck clearly show the side-by-side smokestacks and the diamond-shaped metal walking beam that provided power to the ship's side paddle wheels.

MasteringPHYSICS

ActivPhysics 10.8: Doppler Effect: Conceptual Introduction
ActivPhysics 10.9: Doppler Effect: Problems

▲ **FIGURE 32** A listener moving toward a stationary sound source hears a frequency that is higher than the source frequency because the relative velocity of listener and wave is greater than the wave speed v.

distances λ. The waves approaching the moving listener have a speed of propagation of $v + v_L$ *relative to the listener,* so the frequency f_L with which the wave crests arrive at the listener's position (the frequency the listener hears) is

$$f_L = \frac{v + v_L}{\lambda} = \frac{v + v_L}{v/f_S} = \frac{v + v_L}{v} f_S. \tag{16}$$

So a listener moving toward a source $(v_L > 0)$ hears a sound that has a greater frequency (higher pitch) than a stationary listener hears. A listener moving away from the source $(v_L < 0)$ hears a sound that has a lesser frequency (lower pitch).

Moving Source

Now suppose the source is also moving, with velocity v_S (Figure 33). The wave speed relative to the air is still v; it is determined by the properties of the wave medium and is not changed by the motion of the source. But the wavelength is no longer equal to v/f_S. Here's why: The time for the emission of one cycle of the wave is the period $T = 1/f_S$. During this time, the wave travels a distance $vT = v/f_S$ and the displacement of the source is $v_S T = v_S/f_S$ (where v_s may be either positive or negative). The wavelength is the distance between successive wave crests and is determined by the *relative* displacement of source and wave. As Figure 33 shows, this is different in front of and behind the source. In the region to the right of the source in the figure, the wavelength is

$$\lambda = \frac{v}{f_S} - \frac{v_S}{f_S} = \frac{v - v_S}{f_S}. \tag{17}$$

In the region to the left of the source, the wavelength is

$$\lambda = \frac{v + v_S}{f_S}. \tag{18}$$

When v_S is positive (as it is in Figure 33), the waves are compressed in front of the source and stretched out behind it.

To find the frequency heard by the listener, we substitute Equation 18 into the first form of Equation 16 to obtain

$$f_L = \frac{v + v_L}{\lambda} = (v + v_L) \frac{f_S}{v + v_S},$$

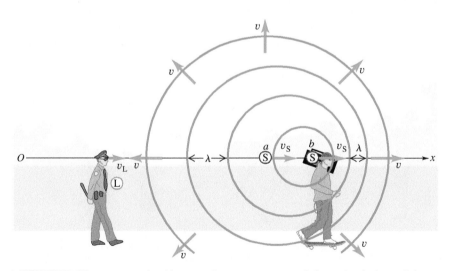

▲ **FIGURE 33** Wave crests emitted by a moving source are crowded together in front of the source and stretched out behind it.

which we can rewrite as follows:

Doppler effect when both listener and source may be moving

For a listener L and source S moving along the line joining them, the frequency f_L heard by the listener is related to the frequency f_S produced by the source as follows:

$$f_L = \frac{v + v_L}{v + v_S} f_S. \tag{19}$$

In this equation, v is the speed of sound and v_L and v_S are the x components of velocity of the listener and source, respectively.

Equation 19 includes all possibilities for the motion of source and listener (relative to the medium) along the line joining them. If the source happens to be at rest in the medium, v_S is zero; if the listener is at rest in the medium, v_L is zero. When both source and listener are at rest or have the same velocity relative to the medium, then $v_L = v_S$ and $f_L = f_S$. Whenever the source's or listener's velocity is in the negative x direction (opposite to the direction from listener toward source), the corresponding component of velocity (v_L or v_S) in Equation 19 is negative. But the wave speed v is always positive.

PROBLEM-SOLVING STRATEGY 3   **Doppler effect**   (MP)

SET UP

1. Establish a coordinate system. Define the positive direction to be the direction from listener to source, and make sure that you know the signs of all the relevant velocities. A velocity in the direction from listener to source has a positive x component; a velocity in the opposite direction has a negative x component. Also, the velocities must all be measured relative to the air in which the sound is traveling.

2. Use consistent notation to identify the various quantities: subscript S for source, L for listener.

SOLVE

3. When a wave is reflected from a surface, either stationary or moving, the analysis can be carried out in two steps. In the first, the surface plays the role of listener; the frequency with which the wave crests arrive at the surface is f_L. Then think of the surface as a new source, emitting waves with this same frequency f_L. Finally, determine what frequency is heard by a listener detecting these new waves.

REFLECT

4. Ask whether your final result makes sense. If the source and listener are moving toward each other, f_L is always greater than f_S; if they are moving apart, f_L is always less than f_S. If source and listener have zero relative velocity, then $f_S = f_L$.

EXAMPLE 10   **Police car chasing a speeder**

A police siren emits a sinusoidal wave with frequency $f_S = 300$ Hz. The speed of sound is 340 m/s. **(a)** Find the wavelength of the waves if the siren is at rest in the air. **(b)** If the siren is moving with velocity $v_S = 30.0$ m/s, find the wavelengths of the waves ahead of and behind the source.

Continued

SOLUTION

SET UP (a) When the siren is at rest, $\lambda = v/f_s$. Figure 34 shows the situation for part (b). For the moving siren, we use Equations 17 and 18 with $v_S = 30.0 \text{ m/s}$.

SOLVE Part (a): When the source is at rest,

$$\lambda = \frac{v}{f_S} = \frac{340 \text{ m/s}}{300 \text{ Hz}} = 1.13 \text{ m}.$$

Part (b): We use Equations 17 and 18. In front of the siren,

$$\lambda = \frac{v - v_S}{f_S} = \frac{340 \text{ m/s} - 30.0 \text{ m/s}}{300 \text{ Hz}} = 1.03 \text{ m}.$$

Behind the siren,

$$\lambda = \frac{v + v_S}{f_S} = \frac{340 \text{ m/s} + 30.0 \text{ m/s}}{300 \text{ Hz}} = 1.23 \text{ m}.$$

▲ **FIGURE 34** Wavelengths ahead of and behind the police siren when the siren is moving relative to the air.

REFLECT The wavelength is smaller in front of the moving siren, and greater behind it, than when the siren is at rest.

Practice Problem: If the siren speeds up until the wavelength in front of it is 1.00 m, what is its speed? *Answer:* 40.0 m/s.

EXAMPLE 11   A bystander observes the chase

If the listener is at rest and the siren is moving away from the listener at 30.0 m/s, what frequency does the listener hear?

SOLUTION

SET UP Figure 35 shows our diagram. We use Equation 19, with $v_L = 0$ and $v_S = 30.0 \text{ m/s}$.:

SOLVE From Equation 19,

$$f_L = \frac{v + v_L}{v + v_S} f_S = \frac{340 \text{ m/s} + 0}{340 \text{ m/s} + 30.0 \text{ m/s}} (300 \text{ Hz}) = 276 \text{ Hz}.$$

REFLECT As the siren recedes, the listener hears sound of smaller frequency than when the siren is at rest.

▲ **FIGURE 35** Our sketch for this problem.

Practice Problem: What frequency does the policeman hear? Answer: 300 Hz.

EXAMPLE 12   Driving past the stationary police car

If the siren is at rest and the listener is in a car moving away from the siren at 30 m/s, what frequency does the listener hear?

SOLUTION

SET UP Figure 36 shows our sketch. The positive direction is still from the listener toward the source, so this time $v_L = -30.0 \text{ m/s}$ and $v_S = 0$.

SOLVE From Equation 19,

$$f_L = \frac{v + v_L}{v + v_S} f_S$$

$$= \frac{340 \text{ m/s} + (-30.0 \text{ m/s})}{340 \text{ m/s} + 0} (300 \text{ Hz}) = 274 \text{ Hz}.$$

▲ **FIGURE 36** Our sketch for this problem.

REFLECT The listener again hears sound of smaller frequency than when he and the siren are at rest, but not by the same amount as when the siren is moving.

EXAMPLE 13 **Following the police car**

If the siren is moving away from the listener with a speed of 45.0 m/s relative to the air, and the listener is moving in the same direction as the siren with a speed of 15.0 m/s relative to the air, what frequency does the listener hear?

SOLUTION

SET UP Figure 37 shows our sketch. In this case, $v_L = 15.0$ m/s and $v_s = 45.0$ m/s. (Both velocities are positive because both velocity vectors point in the $+x$ direction, from listener to source.)

▲ **FIGURE 37** Our sketch for this problem.

SOLVE From Equation 17,

$$f_L = \frac{v + v_L}{v + v_S}f_S = \frac{340 \text{ m/s} + 15.0 \text{ m/s}}{340 \text{ m/s} + 45.0 \text{ m/s}}(300 \text{ Hz}) = 277 \text{ Hz}.$$

REFLECT When the source and listener are moving apart, the frequency f_L heard by the listener is always *less than* the frequency f_S emitted by the source. This is the case in all of the last three examples. Note that the *relative velocity* of source and listener (30.0 m/s) is the same in all three, but the Doppler shifts are all different because the velocities relative to the air are different.

Doppler Effect for Light

In our discussion thus far, the velocities v_L and v_S have always been measured *relative to the air* or whatever medium we are considering. There is also a Doppler effect for electromagnetic waves in empty space, such as light waves or radio waves. According to the special theory of relativity, the speed of light c is the same in all inertial frames of reference. When a source emits radiation with frequency f_S, a listener moving away from the source with speed v observes a smaller frequency f_L given by

$$f_L = \sqrt{\frac{c - v}{c + v}}f_S.$$

When the listener is moving directly toward the source, v is negative and f_L is *greater* than f_S.

A familiar application of the Doppler effect with radio waves is the radar device used in police cars to check other cars' speeds. The electromagnetic wave emitted by the device is reflected from a moving car, which then acts as a moving source, and the wave reflected back to the device is Doppler shifted in frequency. The transmitted and reflected signals are combined to produce beats, and the speed can be computed from the frequency of the beats.

The Doppler effect for light is of fundamental importance in astronomy. Light emitted by elements in stars of distant galaxies shows shifts toward longer wavelength and smaller frequency, compared with light from the same elements on earth. These shifts are Doppler shifts caused by the receding motion of the galaxies containing the stars. Because the shift is nearly always toward the longer wavelength (red end) of the visible spectrum, it is called a *red shift*. These observations provide solid evidence for the "big bang" theory, which describes a universe that has been expanding for about 14 billion years.

13 Applications of Acoustics

The importance of acoustic principles goes far beyond human hearing. Several animals use sound for navigation. Bats depend primarily on sound rather than sight for guidance during flight. That's how they can fly in the total darkness of a cave. They emit short pulses of ultrasonic sound, typically 30 to 150 kHz; the returning echoes give the bats information about the location and size of obstacles and potential prey such as flying insects.

Dolphins use an analogous system for underwater navigation. The frequencies are again ultrasonic, about 100 kHz. With such a system, the animal can

Jim Reed/Corbis

▲ Application **Take cover!** Meteorologists studying severe weather use radar (RAdio Detection And Ranging) and take advantage of the Doppler effect to monitor the occurrence and movement of thunderstorms, hurricanes, and tornadoes. Doppler radar towers transmit radio-frequency waves and can detect rain, hail, and snow by recording the waves reflected by these types of atmospheric moisture. Doppler radar also compares the frequencies of the transmitted and reflected waves to determine the movement of the moisture. Waves reflected from moisture moving toward the tower have a higher frequency than that of the transmitted wavelength, and the frequency of waves reflected from receding moisture is lower. Thus, knowledge of the physics of wave propagation allows us to receive advance warning of severe weather and can prevent unnecessary damage and injury.

sense objects of about the size of the wavelength of the sound (1.4 cm) or larger. The corresponding human-designed systems, used for submarine navigation, depth measurements, finding the locations of fish or wrecked ships, and so on, are called **sonar.** Sonar systems using the Doppler effect can measure the motion, as well as position, of submerged objects.

Analysis of elastic waves in the earth provides important information about its structure. The interior of the earth may be pictured crudely as being made of concentric spherical shells around a solid inner core. Mechanical properties such as density and elastic moduli are different in different shells. Waves produced by explosions or earthquakes are reflected and refracted at the interfaces between these shells, and analysis of these waves helps geologists measure the dimensions and properties of the shells. Local anomalies such as oil deposits can also be detected by studying wave propagation.

Acoustic phenomena have many important medical applications. Shock waves are used to break up kidney stones and gallstones without invasive surgery, by means of a technique with the impressive name *extracorporeal shock-wave lithotripsy.* A shock wave is produced outside the body and is then focused by a reflector or acoustic lens so that as much of its energy as possible converges on the stone. When the resulting stresses in the stone exceed its tensile strength, it breaks into small pieces and can be eliminated. This technique requires accurate determination of the location of the stone.

Ultrasonic imaging (the reflection of ultrasonic waves from regions in the interior of the body) is used for prenatal examinations, the detection of anomalous conditions such as tumors, and the study of heart-valve action, to name a few applications. Ultrasound is more sensitive than x rays in distinguishing various kinds of tissues, and it does not have the radiation hazards associated with x rays. At much higher power levels, ultrasound appears to have promise as a selective destroyer of pathological tissue in the treatment of arthritis and certain cancers. The sound is always produced by first generating an electrical wave and then using this wave to drive a loudspeakerlike device called a **transducer** that converts electrical waves to sound. Techniques have been developed in which transducers move over, or *scan,* the region of interest and a computer-reconstructed image is produced. An example of such an image is shown in Figure 38.

Acoustic principles have many important applications to environmental problems, such as noise control. The design of quiet mass-transit vehicles, for example, involves detailed study of the generation and propagation of sound in the motors, wheels, and supporting structures. Excessive noise levels often lead to permanent hearing impairment; studies have shown that many young rock musicians have hearing that is typical of persons 65 years of age. Prolonged listening to music at high intensity levels (100 to 120 dB) can lead to permanent hearing loss. Stereo headsets used at high volume levels pose similar threats to hearing. Be careful!

▲ **FIGURE 38** An ultrasound image of an unborn fetus.

14 Musical Tones

Several aspects of musical sound are directly related to the physical characteristics of sound waves. The **pitch** of a musical tone is the quality that lets us classify it as "high" or "low." Middle C on the piano has a frequency of 262 Hz. The musical interval of an *octave* corresponds to a factor of two in frequency. The C note an octave above middle C has a frequency of $2 \times 262 \text{ Hz} = 524 \text{ Hz}$, and the "high C" sung by coloratura sopranos, two octaves above middle C, has a frequency of $4 \times 262 \text{ Hz}$, or 1048 Hz. The ear can be fooled, however: When a listener hears two sinusoidal tones with the same frequency but different intensities, the louder one usually seems to be slightly lower in pitch.

Musical tones usually contain many frequencies. A plucked, bowed, or struck string or the column of air in a wind instrument vibrates with a fundamental frequency and many harmonics at the same time. Two tones may have the same fundamental frequency (and thus the same pitch) but may sound different because of the presence of different intensities of the various harmonics. The difference is called *tone color, quality,* or **timbre,** often described in subjective terms such as reedy, golden, round, mellow, or tinny. A tone that is rich in harmonics usually sounds thin and "stringy" or "reedy," and a tone containing mostly a fundamental is more mellow and flutelike.

Another factor in determining tone quality is the behavior at the beginning and end of a tone. A piano tone begins percussively with a thump and then dies away gradually. A harpsichord tone, in addition to having different harmonic content, begins much more quickly and incisively with a click, and the higher harmonics begin before the lower ones. The ending of the tone, when the key is released, is also much more incisive on the harpsichord than the piano. Similar effects are present with other musical instruments; with wind and string instruments, the player has considerable control over the attack and decay of the tone, and these characteristics help to define the unique characteristics of each instrument.

When combinations of musical tones are heard together or in succession, even a listener with no musical training hears a relationship among them; they sound comfortable together, or they clash. Musicians use the terms *consonant* and *dissonant* to describe these effects. A *consonant interval* is a combination of two tones that sound comfortable or pleasing together. The most consonant interval is the *octave,* consisting of two tones with a frequency ratio of 2 : 1. An example is middle C on the piano and the next C above it. Another set of consonant tones is obtained by playing C, E, and G. These form what is called a *major triad,* and the frequencies are in the ratio 4 : 5 : 6. The interval from C to G, with a frequency ratio of 3 : 2, is a perfect fifth; C to E, with 5 : 4, is a major third; and so on. These combinations sound good together because they have many harmonics in common. For example, for the interval of the octave, every harmonic in the harmonic series of the lower-frequency tone is also present in the harmonic series of the upper tone. For other intervals, the overlap of harmonics is only partial, but it is there.

If we want to be able to play major triads starting on various tones on a keyboard instrument such as the piano or organ, complications arise. Either we add a lot of extra keys in each octave to get the exact frequencies we need, or else we compromise a little on the frequencies. The most common compromise in piano tuning is called *equal temperament,* in which every pair of adjacent keys (white and black) is tuned to the same frequency ratio of $2^{1/12}$. This interval is called a *semitone* or a *halftone;* a succession of 12 of these intervals then forms an exact 2 : 1 octave. The perfect fifth is seven semitones; the corresponding frequency ratio is $2^{7/12} = 1.4983$. This ratio is close to the ideal one of 3 : 2, or 1.5000, but a sensitive ear can hear the difference.

Thus, a piano tuned in equal temperament is not quite in tune, in terms of the ideal ratios, in *any* key, but it is equally good (or bad) in all keys. An alternative would be to tune the white keys to form ideal intervals. Doing this would make the instrument sound better for music in the key of C, but music in some other keys would sound worse in comparison with music played in equal temperament. So an instrument that is intended to be used for compositions in all keys is usually tuned to equal temperament.

In the Baroque period, however, keys with more than three sharps or flats were seldom used, and various compromise temperaments were invented to favor the commonly used keys. Organs and harpsichords that are intended primarily for music of this period are often tuned to one of these unequal temperaments. The great J. S. Bach favored such temperaments rather than equal temperament. His composition "The Well-Tempered Clavier" contains preludes and fugues in all the major and minor keys, but it is important not to misconstrue *well tempered* as meaning *equally tempered!*

CHAPTER SUMMARY

Mechanical Waves

(Sections 1–4) A mechanical wave is any disturbance from an equilibrium condition that propagates from one region of space to another through some material called the medium. In a periodic wave, the motion of each particle of the medium is periodic; the period T, frequency f, wavelength λ, and wave speed v are related by $v = \lambda f = \lambda/T$. For a string with mass per unit length μ and tension F_T, the speed of transverse waves is

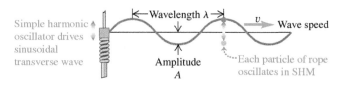

$$v = \sqrt{\frac{F_T}{\mu}}. \tag{2}$$

Superposition, Standing Waves, and Normal Modes

(Sections 5–6) The **principle of superposition** states that when two waves overlap, the resulting displacement at any point is obtained by vector addition of the displacements that would be caused by the two individual waves. When a sinusoidal wave is reflected at a stationary or free end, the original and reflected wave combine to make a **standing wave**. At the **nodes** of a standing wave, the displacement is always zero; the **antinodes** are the points of maximum displacement. Fixed string ends are nodes; ends that are free to move transversely are antinodes.

Standing waves on a string of length L can have only certain specific frequencies. When both ends are held stationary, the allowed frequencies f_n are

$$f_n = n\frac{v}{2L} = nf_1, \qquad (n = 1, 2, 3, \dots) \tag{7}$$

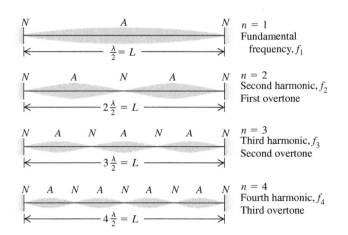

A **normal mode** is a motion in which all particles on the string move sinusoidally with one of the frequencies f_n. Each value of f_n corresponds to a different normal mode.

Longitudinal Standing Waves

(Section 7) When a longitudinal wave propagates in a fluid in a pipe with a finite length, the waves reflect and form a standing wave. The closed end of a pipe is a *node,* and the open end is an *antinode.* For an open pipe of length L, the lowest frequency with antinodes at both ends is the fundamental frequency $f_1 = v/2L$ (Equation 9), and the harmonics are integer multiples of this fundamental frequency: $f_n = nf_1$. If a pipe is closed at one end, the fundamental frequency is $f_1 = v/4L$ (Equation 11) and the harmonics are

$$f_n = n\frac{v}{4L} = nf_1, \qquad (n = 1, 3, 5, \dots) \tag{12}$$

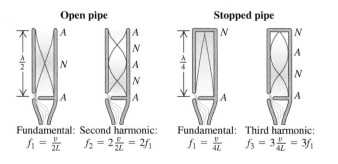

Interference

(Section 8) Wave phenomena that occur when two or more waves overlap in the same region of space are grouped under the heading *interference.* According to the principle of superposition, if two periodic waves are *in step* at a point, then their amplitudes add together. This phenomenon is called **constructive interference**. If the waves are a half-cycle *out of step* at a point, the resulting amplitude is smaller and the phenomenon is called **destructive interference**.

Continued

Sound, Intensity, and Beats

(Sections 9–11) A *logarithmic* intensity scale is usually used to measure the **intensity level** β of a sound wave:

$$\beta = (10 \text{ dB}) \log \frac{I}{I_0}. \tag{14}$$

In this equation, I_0 is a reference intensity chosen to be 10^{-12} W/m^2, and the units of β are **decibels,** abbreviated dB. When two sound waves of slightly different frequency interfere, alternating constructive and destructive interference produces **beats.** The beat frequency is $f_{\text{beat}} = f_1 - f_2$ (Equation 15).

The Doppler Effect

(Section 12) The **Doppler effect** is the frequency shift that occurs when a listener is in motion relative to a source of sound. The source and listener frequencies f_S and f_L and their velocity components v_S and v_L are related by

$$f_L = \frac{v + v_L}{v + v_S} f_S. \tag{19}$$

Applications of Acoustics

(Section 13) The importance of acoustic principles goes far beyond human hearing. Bats locate insects, and dolphins navigate, using ultrasonic waves. We study properties of the earth by measuring the reflected and refracted elastic waves passing through its interior. Ultrasonic shock waves are used to break up kidney stones or gallstones without invasive surgery. Ultrasonic imaging is used to view a fetus or tumor without the dangerous radiation associated with x-ray imaging.

Musical Tones

(Section 14) Several aspects of musical sound are directly related to the physical characteristics of sound waves. Musical tones usually contain many frequencies. A plucked, bowed, or struck string or the column of air in a wind instrument vibrates with a fundamental frequency and many harmonics at the same time. Two tones may have the same fundamental frequency (and thus the same pitch), but sound different because of the presence of different intensities of the various harmonics.

Mechanical Waves and Sound: Problem Set

(MP) For instructor-assigned homework, go to www.masteringphysics.com

Conceptual Questions

1. What kinds of energy are associated with waves on a stretched string? How could such energy be detected experimentally?
2. In most modern wind instruments, the pitch is changed by using keys or valves to change the length of the vibrating air column. The bugle, however, has no valves or keys, yet it can play many notes. How might this be possible? Are there restrictions on what notes a bugle can play?
3. Sci-fi movies sometimes show the explosion of a star accompanied by a great surge of noise. What is wrong with that picture?
4. Which of the characteristics of a sound wave (amplitude or frequency) is most closely related to musical pitch? To loudness?
5. Musical notes produced by different instruments (such as a flute and an oboe) may have the same pitch and loudness and yet sound different. What is the difference, in physical terms?
6. Energy can be transferred along a string by wave motion. However, in a standing wave, no energy can ever be transferred past a node. Why not?
7. Some opera singers, such as Enrico Caruso, have been reputed to be able to break a glass by singing the appropriate note. What physical phenomenon could account for such a feat? (In fact, this is a legend and is not known ever to have occurred.)
8. Lane dividers on highways sometimes have regularly spaced ridges or ripples. When the tires of a moving car roll along such a divider, a musical note is produced. Why? Could this phenomenon be used to measure the car's speed? How?
9. Two tuning forks have identical frequencies, but one is stationary while the other is mounted on a rotating record turntable. Describe the sound that a listener hears from these forks.
10. (a) Does a sound level of zero decibels mean that there is no sound? (b) Is there any physical meaning to a sound having a negative intensity level? What is it? (c) Does a sound intensity of zero mean that there is no sound? (d) Is there any physical meaning to a sound having a negative intensity? Why?
11. Players of stringed instruments tune them by tightening the string. Why does this work? How does a piano tuner tune the instrument?
12. You are standing several meters from the railroad tracks with a train approaching, sounding its whistle. (a) As the train gets closer and closer, what happens to the loudness of the sound? Why? (b) As the train gets closer and closer, the pitch you hear from the whistle gets lower and lower. Why? (c) Would both observations in parts (a) and (b) hold true if you were standing *on* the tracks? Why?
13. An organist in a cathedral plays a loud chord and then releases the keys. The sound persists for a few seconds and gradually dies away. Why does it persist? What happens to the sound energy when the sound dies away?
14. TV weather forecasters often refer to *Doppler radar* in predicting advancing storms. How do you think Doppler radar works?
15. A wire under tension and vibrating in its first overtone produces sound of wavelength λ. What is the new wavelength of the sound (in terms of λ) if the tension is doubled?

Multiple-Choice Problems

1. A hiker sees a lightning flash; 15 s later he hears the sound of the thunder. Recalling from his study of physics that the speed of sound in air is approximately $\frac{1}{3}$ km/s, he estimates that the distance to where the lightning flash occurred is approximately
   A. 5 km.   B. 10 km.   C. 15 km.   D. 45 km.
2. A segment A of wire stretched tightly between two posts a distance L apart vibrates in its fundamental mode with frequency f. A segment B of an identical wire is stretched with the same tension, but between two different posts. You observe that the frequency of the second harmonic of wire B is the same as the fundamental frequency of wire A. The length of wire B must be
   A. L.   B. $2L$.   C. $4L$.
3. Two pulses of exactly the same size and shape are traveling toward each other along a stretched rope. They differ only in that one is upright while the other is inverted. Superposition tells us that when the pulses meet each other, they will cancel each other exactly at that instant and the rope will show no evidence of a pulse. What happens *afterwards?*
   A. Each pulse continues as though it had never met the other one.
   B. The rope remains straight, since the pulses have cancelled each other.
   C. The pulses rebound from each other, each going back in the direction from which it came.
4. An organ pipe open at one end, but closed at the other, is vibrating in its fundamental mode, producing sound of frequency 1000 Hz. If you now open the closed end, the new fundamental frequency will be
   A. 2000 Hz.   B. 1000 Hz.   C. 500 Hz.   D. 250 Hz.

5. A person listening to a siren from a stationary police car observes the frequency and wavelength of that sound. This person now moves rapidly toward the police car.
   A. The wavelength of the sound the person observes is shorter than it was, but the frequency does not change.
   B. The frequency of the sound the person observes is higher than it was, but the wavelength does not change.
   C. The wavelength of the sound the person observes is shorter than it was, and the frequency is higher than it was.

6. A person listening to a siren from a stationary police car observes the frequency and wavelength of that sound. The car now drives rapidly toward the person.
   A. The wavelength of the sound the person observes will be shorter than it was, but the frequency will not be changed.
   B. The frequency of the sound the person observes will be higher than it was, but the wavelength will not be changed.
   C. The wavelength of the sound the person observes will be shorter than it was, and the frequency will also be higher than it was.

7. A string of length 0.600 m is vibrating at 100.0 Hz in its second harmonic and producing sound that moves at 340 m/s. What is true about the frequency and wavelength of this sound? (There may be more than one correct choice.)
   A. The wavelength of the sound is 0.600 m.
   B. The wavelength of the sound is 3.40 m.
   C. The frequency of the sound is 100.0 Hz.
   D. The frequency of the sound is 567 Hz.

8. When a 15 kg mass is hung vertically from a thin, light wire, pulses take time t to travel the full length of the wire. If an additional 15 kg mass is added to the first one without changing the length of the wire, the time taken for pulses to travel the length of the wire will be
   A. $2t$.   B. $\sqrt{2}t$.   C. $t/2$.   D. $t/\sqrt{2}$.

9. An omnidirectional loudspeaker produces sound waves uniformly in all directions. The total power received by a sphere of radius 2.0 m centered on the speaker is 100 W. A sphere of radius 4.0 m will receive a total power of
   A. 100 W.   B. 50 W.   C. 25 W.

10. An organ pipe open at both ends is resonating in its fundamental mode at frequency f. If you close both ends, the fundamental frequency will now be
    A. $2f$.   B. f.   C. $f/2$.   D. $f/4$.

11. You are standing between two stereo speakers that are emitting sound of wavelength 10.0 cm in step with each other. They are very far apart compared with that wavelength. If you start in the middle and walk a distance x directly toward one speaker, you observe that the sound from these speakers first cancels when x is equal to
    A. 20.0 cm.   B. 10.0 cm.   C. 5.0 cm.   D. 2.5 cm.

12. On a cold day, a siren emits sound waves with a wavelength of 17 cm. On a hot day, the wavelength of the sound produced by the same siren oscillating at the same frequency will be
    A. greater than 17 cm.
    B. less than 17 cm.
    C. 17 cm.

13. Traffic noise on Beethoven Boulevard has an intensity level of 80 dB; the traffic noise on Mozart Alley is only 60 dB. Compared to the sound intensity on Beethoven Boulevard, the sound intensity on Mozart Alley is
    A. 25% lower   B. 20 times lower
    C. 100 times lower   D. 20 W/m² lower

14. A thin, light string supports a weight W hanging from the ceiling. In this situation, the string produces a note of frequency f when vibrating in its fundamental mode. In order to cause this string to produce a note one octave higher in its fundamental mode without stretching it, we must change the weight to
    A. $4W$.   B. $2W$.   C. $\sqrt{2}W$.
    D. $W/2$.   E. $W/4$.

15. String A weighs twice as much as string B. Both strings are thin and light and have the same length. If you hang equal weights at the bottom of each of these strings, the ratio of the speed of waves on string A to the speed of waves on string B will be
    A. $v_A/v_B = 2$.   B. $v_A/v_B = \sqrt{2}$.
    C. $v_A/v_B = 1/\sqrt{2}$.   D. $v_A/v_B = \frac{1}{2}$.

Problems

Unless otherwise indicated, assume that the speed of sound in air is 344 m/s.

2 Periodic Mechanical Waves

1. • (a) **Audible wavelengths.** The range of audible frequencies
   BIO is from about 20 Hz to 20,000 Hz. What is range of the wavelengths of audible sound in air? (b) **Visible light.** The range of visible light extends from 400 nm to 700 nm. What is the range of visible frequencies of light? (c) **Brain surgery.** Surgeons can remove brain tumors by using a cavitron ultrasonic surgical aspirator, which produces sound waves of frequency 23 kHz. What is the wavelength of these waves in air? (d) **Sound in the body.** What would be the wavelength of the sound in part (c) in bodily fluids in which the speed of sound is 1480 m/s, but the frequency is unchanged?

2. • **The electromagnetic spectrum.** Electromagnetic waves, which include light, consist of vibrations of electric and magnetic fields, and they all travel at the speed of light. (a) **FM radio.** Find the wavelength of an FM radio station signal broadcasting at a frequency of 104.5 MHz. (b) **X rays.** X rays have a wavelength of about 0.10 nm. What is their frequency? (c) **The Big Bang.** Microwaves with a wavelength of 1.1 mm, left over from soon after the Big Bang, have been detected. What is their frequency? (d) **Sunburn.** Sunburn (and skin cancer) are caused by ultraviolet light waves having a frequency of around 10^{16} Hz. What is their wavelength? (e) **SETI.** It has been suggested that extraterrestrial civilizations (if they exist) might try to communicate by using electromagnetic waves having the same frequency as that given off by the spin flip of the electron in hydrogen, which is 1.43 GHz. To what wavelength should we tune our telescopes in order to search for such signals? (f) **Microwave ovens.** Microwave ovens cook food with electromagnetic waves of frequency around 2.45 GHz. What wavelength do these waves have?

3. • If an earthquake wave having a wavelength of 13 km causes the ground to vibrate 10.0 times each minute, what is the speed of the wave?

4. •• A fisherman notices that his boat is moving up and down periodically, owing to waves on the surface of the water. It takes 2.5 s for the boat to travel from its highest point to its lowest, a total distance of 0.62 m. The fisherman sees that the wave crests are spaced 6.0 m apart. (a) How fast are the waves traveling? (b) What is the amplitude of each wave? (c) If the total vertical distance traveled by the boat were 0.30 m, but the other data remained the same, how would the answers to parts (a) and (b) be affected?

3 Wave Speeds

5. • A steel wire 4.00 m long has a mass of 0.0600 kg and is stretched with a tension of 1000 N. What is the speed of propagation of a transverse wave on the wire?

6. • With what tension must a rope with length 2.50 m and mass 0.120 kg be stretched for transverse waves of frequency 40.0 Hz to have a wavelength of 0.750 m?

7. • One end of a horizontal rope is attached to a prong of an electrically driven tuning fork that vibrates at 120 Hz. The other end passes over a pulley and supports a 1.50 kg mass. The linear mass density of the rope is 0.0550 kg/m. (a) What is the speed of a transverse wave on the rope? (b) What is the wavelength? (c) How would your answers to parts (a) and (b) change if the mass were increased to 3.00 kg?

8. •• (a) If the amplitude in a sound wave is doubled, by what factor does the intensity of the wave increase? (b) By what factor must the amplitude of a sound wave be increased in order to increase the intensity by a factor of 9?

9. •• When a mass M hangs from a vertical wire of length L, waves travel on this wire with a speed V. What will be the speed of these waves (in terms of V) if (a) we double M without stretching the wire? (b) we replace the wire with an identical one, except twice as long? (c) we replace the wire with one of the same length, but three times as heavy? (d) we stretch the wire to twice its original length? (e) we increase M by a factor of 10, which stretches the wire to double its original length?

4 Mathematical Description of a Wave

10. • A certain transverse wave is described by the equation

$$y(x, t) = (6.50 \text{ mm}) \sin 2\pi \left(\frac{t}{0.0360 \text{ s}} - \frac{x}{0.280 \text{ m}} \right).$$

Determine this wave's (a) amplitude, (b) wavelength, (c) frequency, (d) speed of propagation, and (e) direction of propagation.

11. • Transverse waves on a string have wave speed 8.00 m/s, amplitude 0.0700 m, and wavelength 0.320 m. These waves travel in the x direction, and at $t = 0$ the $x = 0$ end of the string is at $y = 0$ and moving downward. (a) Find the frequency, period, and wave number of these waves. (b) Write the equation for $y(x, t)$ describing these waves. (c) Find the transverse displacement of a point on the string at $x = 0.360$ m at time $t = 0.150$ s.

12. • The equation describing a transverse wave on a string is

$$y(x, t) = (1.50 \text{ mm}) \sin[(157 \text{ s}^{-1})t - (41.9 \text{ m}^{-1})x].$$

Find (a) the wavelength, frequency, and amplitude of this wave, (b) the speed and direction of motion of the wave, and (c) the transverse displacement of a point on the string when $t = 0.100$ s and at a position $x = 0.135$ m.

13. •• Transverse waves are traveling on a long string that is under a tension of 4.00 N. The equation describing these waves is

$$y(x, t) = (1.25 \text{ cm}) \sin[(415 \text{ s}^{-1})t - (44.9 \text{ m}^{-1})x].$$

Find the linear mass density of this string.

5 Reflections and Superposition
6 Standing Waves and Normal Modes

14. • **Mapping the ocean floor.** The ocean floor is mapped by sending sound waves (sonar) downward and measuring the time it takes for their echo to return. From this information, the ocean depth can be calculated if one knows that sound travels at 1531 m/s in seawater. If a ship sends out sonar pulses and records their echo 3.27 s later, how deep is the ocean floor at that point, assuming that the speed of sound is the same at all depths?

15. • In Figure 39, each pulse is traveling on a string at 1 cm/s, and each square represents 1 cm. Draw the shape of the string at the end of 6 s, 7 s, and 8 s.

16. • A 1.50-m-long rope is stretched between two supports with a tension that makes the speed of transverse waves 48.0 m/s. What are the wavelength and frequency of (a) the fundamental tone? (b) the second overtone? (c) the fourth harmonic?

▲ **FIGURE 39** Problem 15.

17. • A piano tuner stretches a steel piano wire with a tension of 800 N. The wire is 0.400 m long and has a mass of 3.00 g. (a) What is the frequency of its fundamental mode of vibration? (b) What is the number of the highest harmonic that could be heard by a person who is capable of hearing frequencies up to 10,000 Hz?

18. • A wire with mass 40.0 g is stretched so that its ends are tied down at points 80.0 cm apart. The wire vibrates in its fundamental mode with frequency 60.0 Hz and with an amplitude of 0.300 cm at the antinodes. (a) What is the speed of propagation of transverse waves in the wire? (b) Compute the tension in the wire.

19. •• The portion of string between the bridge and upper end of the fingerboard (the part of the string that is free to vibrate) of a certain musical instrument is 60.0 cm long and has a mass of 2.00 g. The string sounds an A_4 note (440 Hz) when played. (a) Where must the player put a finger (at what distance x from the bridge) to play a D_5 note (587 Hz)? (See Figure 40.) For both notes, the string vibrates in its fundamental mode. (b) Without retuning, is it possible to play a G_4 note (392 Hz) on this string? Why or why not?

▲ **FIGURE 40** Problem 19.

20. •• **Voiceprints.** In this chapter, we have been concentrating
BIO on sinusoidal waves. But most waves in the real world are far more complicated. However, many complicated waves can be created by adding together sine waves of varying amplitude and frequency. When a singer, for example, sings a note, the pitch we hear is the fundamental frequency at which his or her larynx is vibrating. But the larynx also vibrates in other frequencies (the overtones) at the same time. So the sound we hear is a superposition of the fundamental frequency plus all the overtones. This set of all the frequencies (with their respective amplitudes) is called the person's *voiceprint.* (a) To see how this works, carefully graph a sine wave of frequency 440 Hz (concert A), with time on the horizontal axis and displacement on the vertical axis. Let the amplitude be 1 unit. On the same set of axes, graph the first overtone of 880 Hz, but with an amplitude of $\frac{1}{2}$ unit. (b) Now add the two waves to find their superposition. Notice that the shape is no longer a sine wave.

21. •• **Voiceprints.** Suppose a singer singing F# (370 Hz, the
BIO fundamental frequency) has one overtone of frequency 740 Hz with half the amplitude of the fundamental and another overtone of frequency 1110 Hz having one-third the amplitude of the fundamental. Using the previous problem as a guide, graph the superposition of these three waves to show the complex sound wave produced by this singer.

22. •• **Guitar string.** One of the 63.5-cm-long strings of an ordinary guitar is tuned to produce the note B$_3$ (frequency 245 Hz) when vibrating in its fundamental mode. (a) Find the speed of transverse waves on this string. (b) If the tension in this string is increased by 1.0%, what will be the new fundamental frequency of the string? (c) If the speed of sound in the surrounding air is 344 m/s, find the frequency and wavelength of the sound wave produced in the air by the vibration of the B$_3$ string. How do these compare to the frequency and wavelength of the standing wave on the string?

7 Longitudinal Standing Waves

23. • Standing sound waves are produced in a pipe that is 1.20 m long. For the fundamental frequency and the first two overtones, determine the locations along the pipe (measured from the left end) of the displacement nodes if (a) the pipe is open at both ends; (b) the pipe is closed at the left end and open at the right end.

24. • Find the fundamental frequency and the frequency of the first three overtones of a pipe 45.0 cm long (a) if the pipe is open at both ends; (b) if the pipe is closed at one end. (c) For each of the preceding cases, what is the number of the highest harmonic that may be heard by a person who can hear frequencies from 20 Hz to 20,000 Hz?

25. • The longest pipe found in most medium-size pipe organs is 4.88 m (16 ft) long. What is the frequency of the note corresponding to the fundamental mode if the pipe is (a) open at both ends, (b) open at one end and closed at the other?

26. •• The fundamental frequency of a pipe that is open at both ends is 594 Hz. (a) How long is this pipe? If one end is now closed, find (b) the wavelength and (c) the frequency of the new fundamental.

27. • **The role of the mouth in sound.** The production of sound
BIO during speech or singing is a complicated process. Let's concentrate on the mouth. A typical depth for the human mouth is about 8.0 cm, although this number can vary. (Check it against your own mouth.) We can model the mouth as an organ pipe that is open at the back of the throat. What are the wavelengths and frequencies of the first four harmonics you can produce if your mouth is (a) open, (b) closed? Use $v = 354$ m/s.

28. •• A certain pipe produces a fundamental frequency of 262 Hz in air at 20°C. (a) If the pipe is filled with helium at the same temperature, what fundamental frequency does it produce? (b) Does your answer to part (a) depend on whether the pipe is open or stopped? Why or why not?

29. •• **The vocal tract.** Many opera singers (and some pop
BIO singers) have a range of about $2\frac{1}{2}$ octaves or even greater. Suppose a soprano's range extends from A below middle C (frequency 220 Hz) up to E^b above high C (frequency 1244 Hz). Although the vocal tract is quite complicated, we can model it as a resonating air column, like an organ pipe, that is open at the top and closed at the bottom. The column extends from the mouth down to the diaphragm in the chest cavity, and we can also assume that the lowest note is the fundamental. How long is this column of air if $v = 354$ m/s? Does your result seem reasonable, on the basis of observations of your own body?

30. •• **Singing in the shower!** We all sound like great singers in the shower, due to standing waves. Assume that your shower is 2.45 m (about 8 ft) tall and can be modeled as an organ pipe. (a) What will we have at the floor and ceiling, displacement nodes or antinodes? (b) What are the wavelength and frequency of the fundamental harmonic for standing waves in this shower? (See the answer to Problem 28.) (c) What are the wavelength and frequency of the first two overtones for this shower?

31. •• **French horn.** The French horn, one of the most beautiful-sounding instruments in the orchestra, consists of about 3.7 m (roughly 12 ft) of thin tubing, rolled into a spiral shape (although sizes do vary). The player blows into the mouthpiece, which can be treated as a closed end, and places his hand in the opposite end, which has a large flared opening. In brass instruments, the fundamental note is not normally playable. Instead the *first overtone* is the lowest playable note. (a) If the player's hand keeps the large end open, what is the frequency of the lowest *playable* note? (b) If the player now closes the large end with his hand, what is the frequency of the lowest playable note? See the answer to Problem 28. (*Note:* The physics of the French horn is much more complex than is indicated here. The player's hand in the open end also changes the effective length of the tube, which then affects the frequency of the sound.)

▲ **FIGURE 41** Problem 31.

32. •• You blow across the open mouth of an empty test tube and produce the fundamental standing wave of the air column inside the test tube. The speed of sound in air is 344 m/s and the test tube acts as a stopped pipe. (a) If the length of the air column in the test tube is 14.0 cm, what is the frequency of this standing wave? (b) What is the frequency of the fundamental standing wave in the air column if the test tube is half filled with water?

8 Interference

33. • Two small speakers A and B are driven in step at 725 Hz by the same audio oscillator. These speakers both start out 4.50 m from the listener, but speaker A is slowly moved away. (See Figure 42.) (a) At what distance d will the sound from the speakers first produce destructive interference at the location of the listener? (b) If A keeps moving, at what distance d will the speakers next produce destructive interference at the listener? (c) After A starts moving away, at what distance will the speakers first produce constructive interference at the listener?

▲ **FIGURE 42** Problem 33.

34. •• In a certain home sound system, two small speakers are located so that one is 45.0 cm closer to the listener than the other. For what frequencies of audible sound will these speakers produce (a) destructive interference at the listener, (b) constructive interference at the listener? In each case, find only the three lowest audible frequencies.

35. •• Two small stereo speakers are driven in step by the same variable-frequency oscillator. Their sound is picked up by a microphone arranged as shown in Figure 43. For what frequencies does their sound at the speakers produce (a) constructive interference, (b) destructive interference?

▲ **FIGURE 43** Problem 35.

9 Sound and Hearing

36. • **Human hearing.** The human
BIO outer ear contains a more-or-less cylindrical cavity called the *auditory canal* that behaves like a resonant tube to aid in the hearing process. One end terminates at the eardrum (tympanic membrane), while the other opens to the outside. (See Figure 44.) Typically, this canal is approximately 2.4 cm long. (a) At what frequencies would it resonate in its first two harmonics? (b) What are the corresponding sound wavelengths in part (a)?

▲ **FIGURE 44** Problem 36.

Auditory canal

Tympanic membrane (eardrum)

37. • **Ultrasound and infrasound.** (a) **Whale communication.**
BIO Blue whales apparently communicate with each other using sound of frequency 17 Hz, which can be heard nearly 1000 km away in the ocean. What is the wavelength of such a sound in

seawater, where the speed of sound is 1531 m/s? (b) **Dolphin clicks.** One type of sound that dolphins emit is a sharp click of wavelength 1.5 cm in the ocean. What is the frequency of such clicks? (c) **Dog whistles.** One brand of dog whistles claims a frequency of 25 kHz for its product. What is the wavelength of this sound? (d) **Bats.** While bats emit a wide variety of sounds, one type emits pulses of sound having a frequency between 39 kHz and 78 kHz. What is the range of wavelengths of this sound? (e) **Sonograms.** Ultrasound is used to view the interior of the body, much as x rays are utilized. For sharp imagery, the wavelength of the sound should be around one-fourth (or less) the size of the objects to be viewed. Approximately what frequency of sound is needed to produce a clear image of a tumor that is 1.0 mm across if the speed of sound in the tissue is 1550 m/s?

38. •• A 75.0 cm wire of mass 5.625 g is tied at both ends and adjusted to a tension of 35.0 N. When it is vibrating in its second overtone, find (a) the frequency and wavelength at which it is vibrating and (b) the frequency and wavelength of the sound waves it is producing.

10 Sound Intensity

39. • A small omnidirectional stereo speaker produces waves in all directions that have an intensity of 6.50 W/m^2 at a distance of 2.50 m from the speaker. (a) At what rate does this speaker produce energy? (b) What is the intensity of this sound 7.00 m from the speaker? (c) What is the *total* amount of energy received each second by the walls (including windows and doors) of the room in which this speaker is located?

40. • Find the intensity (in W/m^2) of (a) a 55.0 dB sound, (b) a 92.0 dB sound, (c) a −2.0 dB sound.

41. • Find the noise level (in dB) of a sound having an intensity of (a) 0.000127 W/m^2, (b) 6.53 × 10^{-10} W/cm^2, (c) 1.5 × 10^{-14} W/m^2.

42. • (a) By what factor must the sound intensity be increased to raise the sound intensity level by 13.0 dB? (b) Explain why you don't need to know the original sound intensity.

43. •• **Eavesdropping!** You are trying to overhear a juicy conversation, but from your distance of 15.0 m, it sounds like only an average whisper of 20.0 dB. So you decide to move closer to give the conversation a sound level of 60.0 dB instead. How close should you come?

44. •• **Energy delivered to the ear.** Sound is detected when a
BIO sound wave causes the tympanic membrane (the eardrum) to vibrate. (See Figure 29). Typically, the diameter of this membrane is about 8.4 mm in humans. (a) How much energy is delivered to the eardrum each second when someone whispers (20 dB) a secret in your ear? (b) To comprehend how sensitive the ear is to very small amounts of energy, calculate how fast a typical 2.0 mg mosquito would have to fly (in mm/s) to have this amount of kinetic energy.

45. •• **Human hearing.** A fan at a rock concert is 30 m from the
BIO stage, and at this point the sound intensity level is 110 dB. (a) How much energy is transferred to her eardrums each second? (See the previous problem.) (b) How fast would a 2.0 mg mosquito have to fly to have this much kinetic energy? Compare the mosquito's speed with that found for the whisper in part (a) of the previous problem.

46. •• The intensity due to a number of independent sound sources is the sum of the individual intensities. (a) When four

quadruplets cry simultaneously, how many decibels greater is the sound intensity level than when a single one cries? (b) To increase the sound intensity level again by the same number of decibels as in part (a), how many more crying babies are required?

47. •• (a) What is the sound intensity level in a car when the sound intensity is 0.500 $\mu W/m^2$? (b) What is the sound intensity in the air near a jackhammer when the sound intensity level is 103 dB?

11 Beats

48. • A trumpet player is tuning his instrument by playing an A note simultaneously with the first-chair trumpeter, who has perfect pitch. The first-chair player's note is exactly 440 Hz, and 2.8 beats per second are heard. What are the two possible frequencies of the other player's note?

49. • Two tuning forks are producing sounds of wavelength 34.40 cm and 33.94 cm simultaneously. How many beats do you hear each second?

50. • Two guitarists attempt to play the same note of wavelength 6.50 cm at the same time, but one of the instruments is slightly out of tune and plays a note of wavelength 6.52 cm instead. What is the frequency of the beat these musicians hear when they play together?

51. •• **Tuning a violin.** A violinist is tuning her instrument to concert A (440 Hz). She plays the note while listening to an electronically generated tone of exactly that frequency and hears a beat of frequency 3 Hz, which increases to 4 Hz when she tightens her violin string slightly. (a) What was the frequency of her violin when she heard the 3-Hz beat? (b) To get her violin perfectly tuned to concert A, should she tighten or loosen her string from what it was when she heard the 3-Hz beat?

12 The Doppler Effect

52. • A railroad train is traveling at 25.0 m/s in still air. The frequency of the note emitted by the locomotive whistle is 400 Hz. What is the wavelength of the sound waves (a) in front of the locomotive? (b) behind the locomotive? What is the frequency of the sound heard by a stationary listener (c) in front of the locomotive? (d) behind the locomotive?

53. • Two train whistles, A and B, each have a frequency of 392 Hz. A is stationary and B is moving toward the right (away from A) at a speed of 35.0 m/s. A listener is between the two whistles and is moving toward the right with a speed of 15.0 m/s. (See Figure 45.) (a) What is the frequency from A as heard by the listener? (b) What is the frequency from B as heard by the listener? (c) What is the beat frequency detected by the listener?

▲ FIGURE 45 Problem 53.

54. • On the planet Arrakis, a male ornithoid is flying toward his stationary mate at 25.0 m/s while singing at a frequency of 1200 Hz. If the female hears a tone of 1240 Hz, what is the speed of sound in the atmosphere of Arrakis?

55. • A car alarm is emitting sound waves of frequency 520 Hz. You are on a motorcycle, traveling directly away from the car. How fast must you be traveling if you detect a frequency of 490 Hz?

56. • A railroad train is traveling at 30.0 m/s in still air. The frequency of the note emitted by the train whistle is 262 Hz. What frequency is heard by a passenger on a train moving in the opposite direction to the first at 18.0 m/s and (a) approaching the first; and (b) receding from the first?

57. •• The siren of a fire engine that is driving northward at 30.0 m/s emits a sound of frequency 2000 Hz. A truck in front of this fire engine is moving northward at 20.0 m/s. (a) What is the frequency of the siren's sound that the fire engine's driver hears reflected from the back of the truck? (b) What wavelength would this driver measure for these reflected sound waves?

58. •• A stationary police car emits a sound of frequency 1200 Hz that bounces off of a car on the highway and returns with a frequency of 1250 Hz. The police car is right next to the highway, so the moving car is traveling directly toward or away from it. (a) How fast was the moving car going? Was it moving towards or away from the police car? (b) What frequency would the police car have received if it had been traveling toward the other car at 20.0 m/s?

59. •• A container ship is traveling westward at a speed of 5.00 m/s. The waves on the surface of the ocean have a wavelength of 40.0 m and are traveling eastward at a speed of 16.5 m/s. (a) At what time intervals does the ship encounter the crest of a wave? (b) At what time intervals will the ship encounter wave crests if it turns around and heads eastward?

60. •• While sitting in your car by the side of a country road, you see your friend, who happens to have an identical car with an identical horn, approaching you. You blow your horn, which has a frequency of 260 Hz; your friend begins to blow his horn as well, and you hear a beat frequency of 6.0 Hz. How fast is your friend approaching you?

61. •• **Moving source vs. moving listener.** (a) A sound source producing 1.00 kHz waves moves toward a stationary listener at one-half the speed of sound. What frequency will the listener hear? (b) Suppose instead that the source is stationary and the listener moves toward the source at one-half the speed of sound. What frequency does the listener hear? How does your answer compare with that in part (a)? Did you expect to get the same answer in both cases? Explain on physical grounds why the two answers differ.

62. •• How fast (as a percentage of light speed) would a star have to be moving so that the frequency of the light we receive from it is 10.0% higher than the frequency of the light it is emitting? Would it be moving away from us or toward us? (Assume it is moving either directly away from us or directly toward us.)

General Problems

63. •• One end of a 14.0-m-long wire having a total mass of 0.800 kg is fastened to a fixed support in the ceiling, and a 7.50 kg object is hung from the other end. If the wire is struck a transverse blow at one end, how much time does the pulse take to reach the other end? Neglect the variation in tension along the length of the wire.

64. •• **Ultrasound in medicine.** A 2.00 MHz sound wave travels
BIO through a pregnant woman's abdomen and is reflected from

the fetal heart wall of her unborn baby. The heart wall is moving toward the sound receiver as the heart beats. The reflected sound is then mixed with the transmitted sound, and 85 beats per second are detected. The speed of sound in body tissue is 1500 m/s. Calculate the speed of the fetal heart wall at the instant this measurement is made.

65. •• A very noisy chain saw operated by a tree surgeon emits a total acoustic power of 20.0 W uniformly in all directions. At what distance from the source is the sound level equal to (a) 100 dB, (b) 60 dB?

66. •• **Tuning a cello.** A cellist tunes the C-string of her instrument to a fundamental frequency of 65.4 Hz. The vibrating portion of the string is 0.600 m long and has a mass of 14.4 g. (a) With what tension must she stretch that portion of the string? (b) What percentage increase in tension is needed to increase the frequency from 65.4 Hz to 73.4 Hz, corresponding to a rise in pitch from C to D?

67. •• A person is playing a small flute 10.75 cm long, open at one end and closed at the other, near a taut string having a fundamental frequency of 600.0 Hz. If the speed of sound is 344.0 m/s, for which harmonics of the flute will the string resonate? In each case, which harmonic of the string is in resonance?

68. •• A bat flies toward a wall, emitting a steady sound of frequency 2000 Hz. The bat hears its own sound, plus the sound reflected by the wall. How fast should the bat fly in order to hear a beat frequency of 10.0 Hz? (*Hint:* Break this problem into two parts, first with the bat as the source and the wall as the listener and then with the wall as the source and the bat as the listener.)

69. •• You're standing between two speakers that are driven by the same amplifier and are emitting sound waves with frequency 229 Hz. The two speakers are facing each other, 15 meters apart. (a) You begin walking away from one speaker toward the other one, and as you walk, you hear what sounds like beats, with a frequency of 2.50 Hz. How fast are you walking? (b) If the frequency of the sound emitted by the speakers increases to 573 Hz and you continue to walk at the same speed, what frequency of beats will you hear? [*Hint:* You can model this situation as a tube open at both ends; alternatively, you can treat it as a Doppler effect problem.]

70. •• The sound source of a ship's sonar system operates at a frequency of 22.0 kHz. The speed of sound in water (assumed to be at a uniform 20° C) is 1482 m/s. (a) What is the wavelength of the waves emitted by the source? (b) What is the difference in frequency between the directly radiated waves and the waves reflected from a whale traveling straight toward the ship at 4.95 m/s? The ship is at rest in the water.

71. •• **The range of human hearing.** A young person with nor-
BIO mal hearing can hear sounds ranging from 20 Hz to 20 kHz. How many octaves can such a person hear? (Recall that if two tones differ by an octave, the higher frequency is twice the lower frequency.)

72. •• A person leaning over a 125-m-deep well accidentally drops a siren emitting sound of frequency 2500 Hz. Just before this siren hits the bottom of the well, find the frequency and wavelength of the sound the person hears (a) coming directly from the siren, (b) reflected off the bottom of the well. (c) What beat frequency does this person perceive?

73. •• A police siren of frequency f_{siren} is attached to a vibrating platform. The platform and siren oscillate up and down in simple

harmonic motion with amplitude A_P and frequency f_P. (a) Find the maximum and minimum sound frequencies that you would hear at a position directly above the siren. (b) At what point in the motion of the platform is the maximum frequency heard? The minimum frequency? Explain.

74. •• A flexible stick can oscillate in a standing-wave pattern, much as a string does. (a) Are the ends of the stick displacement nodes or antinodes? Why? (If in doubt, use a handy stick at home or in the laboratory and try it out.) (b) A flexible stick 3.00 m long is free to wiggle. Using the conditions from part (a), find the wavelengths of the first five harmonics for this stick.

75. •• A turntable 1.50 m in diameter rotates at 75 rpm. Two speakers, each giving off sound of wavelength 31.3 cm, are attached to the rim of the table at opposite ends of a diameter. A listener stands in front of the turntable. (a) What is the greatest beat frequency the listener will receive from this system? (b) Will the listener be able to distinguish individual beats?

76. •• **Musical scale.** The frequency ratio of a semitone interval on the equally tempered scale is $2^{1/12}$. (a) Show that this ratio is 1.059. (b) Find the speed of an automobile passing a listener at rest in still air if the pitch of the car's horn drops a semitone between the times when the car is coming directly toward him and when it is moving directly away from him.

77. •• Two organ pipes, open at one end but closed at the other, are each 1.14 m long. One is now lengthened by 2.00 cm. Find the frequency of the beat they produce when playing together in their fundamental.

Passage Problems

BIO **Temperature and instrument tuning.** The speed of a longitudinal sound wave in a gas depends on both the temperature and composition of the gas. For a given gas the speed of sound typically increases with increasing temperature: for instance, the speed of sound in air increases from about 330 m/s at 0°C to 350 m/s at 30°C. In addition, the speed of sound tends to be higher in gases composed of lightweight monatomic molecules (such as helium) and lower in gases composed of heavy polyatomic molecules (such as carbon dioxide)—for example, at 20°C, the speed of sound in helium is 999 m/s and the speed of sound in carbon dioxide is 260 m/s.

The flute is a musical instrument that behaves as a pipe that is open at both ends, while the violin is a musical instrument based on a tuned string. Initially a flute and a violin are tuned so that they both play middle C at 262 Hz, when the speed of sound in the air in the room is 350 m/s.

After the initial tuning, the temperature in the room drops so that the speed of sound in the air decreases by 2%. The instruments are not retuned to compensate.

78. By how much does middle C on the flute change?
   A. There is no change.
   B. It increases by 2%.
   C. It decreases by 2%.
   D. It increases by 4%.
   E. It decreases by 4%.

79. By how much does middle C on the violin change?
   A. There is no change.
   B. It increases by 2%.
   C. It decreases by 2%.
   D. It increases by 4%.
   E. It decreases by 4%.

80. Roughly, what would be the resulting beat frequency between the two instruments when played at the reduced temperature?
    A. 0 Hz
    B. 2 Hz
    C. 5 Hz
    D. 7 Hz
    E. 10.5 Hz

ANSWERS TO SELECTED PROBLEMS

Conceptual Questions

1. There is kinetic energy of the moving string and the elastic potential energy of the string when it is displaced from equilibrium. The kinetic energy could be transferred to an object attached to the end of the string.

3. Sound waves require a medium and cannot propagate through empty space.

5. The harmonic content (the extent to which frequencies higher than the fundamental are present) is different for the same note produced by different instruments.

7. This would be an example of resonance. When the sung note has the same frequency as one of the normal-mode frequencies of the glass, large amplitude standing waves can be set up in the glass.

9. The observed frequency of the rotating fork is shifted by the Doppler effect. Its pitch is increased when it is moving toward the listener and is decreased when it is moving away from the listener. The listener therefore hears two different frequencies from the two forks and beats occur.

11. Changing the tension in the string changes the speed of transverse waves on the string and this alters the standing wave frequencies for the string. The notes of a piano are produced by mallets striking stretched wires and the piano is tuned by adjusting the tension in these wires.

Multiple-Choice Problems

1. A
3. A
5. B
7. B, C
9. A
11. D
13. C
15. C

Problems

1. (a) 1.7 cm to 17 m (b) 4.3×10^{14} Hz to 7.5×10^{14} Hz (c) 1.5 cm (d) 6.4 cm
3. 2.2 km/s
5. 258 m/s
7. (a) 16.3 m/s (b) 0.136 m (c) 23.1 m/s; 0.192 m (both increase by a factor of $\sqrt{2}$)
9. (a) $\sqrt{2}V$ (b) V (c) $V/\sqrt{3}$ (d) $\sqrt{2}V$ (e) $2\sqrt{5}V$
11. (a) 25.0 Hz, 0.0400 s, 19.6 rad/m (b) $y(x, t) = -(0.0700 \text{ m}) \sin 2\pi \cdot \left(\dfrac{t}{0.0400 \text{ s}} - \dfrac{x}{0.320 \text{ m}} \right)$ (c) 0.0495 m
13. 0.469 g/cm
17. (a) 408 Hz (b) 24th
19. (a) 45.0 cm (b) no; 440 Hz is lowest frequency possible
23. (a) fundamental: 0.60 m; 1st overtone: 0.30 m, 0.90 m; 2nd overtone: 0.20 m, 0.60 m, 1.00 m (b) fundamental: 0; 1st overtone: 0, 0.80 m; 2nd overtone: 0, 0.48 m, 0.96 m
25. (a) 35.2 Hz (b) 17.6 Hz

27. (a) 16.0 cm, 8.0 cm, 5.3 cm, 4.0 cm; 2210 Hz, 4420 Hz, 6630 Hz, 8840 Hz (b) 32.0 cm, 10.7 cm, 6.4 cm, 4.6 cm; 1110 Hz, 3330 Hz, 5550 Hz, 7770 Hz
29. 39.1 cm; yes
31. (a) 70 Hz (b) 93 Hz
33. (a) 0.237 m (b) 0.711 m (c) 0.474 m
35. (a) $n(820 \text{ Hz})$, $n = 1, 2, 3, \ldots$ (b) $(2n + 1)(410 \text{ Hz})$, $n = 0, 1, 2, \ldots$
37. (a) 90 m (b) 102 kHz (c) 1.4 cm (d) 4.4 mm to 8.8 mm (e) 6.2 MHz
39. (a) 511 W (b) 0.829 W/m^2 (c) 511 J
41. (a) 81.0 dB (b) 28.1 dB (c) -18.2 dB
43. 15.0 cm
47. (a) 57 dB (b) 2.00×10^{-2} W/m^2
49. 14 beats
51. (a) 433 Hz (b) loosen
53. (a) 375 Hz (b) 371 Hz (c) 4 Hz
55. 19.8 m/s
57. (a) 2120 Hz (b) 0.172 m
59. (a) 1.86 s (b) 3.48 s
61. (a) 2000 Hz (b) 1500 Hz
63. 0.390 s
65. (a) 12.6 m (b) 1.26 km
67. flute harmonic $3N$ ($N = 1, 3, \ldots$) resonates with string harmonic $4N$
69. (a) 1.88 m/s (b) 6.26 Hz
71. 10 octaves
73. (a) $f_{\text{L-max}} = f_{\text{siren}} v/(v - 2\pi f_{\text{P}}A_{\text{P}})$; $f_{\text{L-min}} = f_{\text{siren}} v/(v + 2\pi f_{\text{P}}A_{\text{P}})$
75. (a) 38 Hz (b) no
77. 1.3 Hz

Fluid Mechanics

Shutterstock

Fluids play a vital role in many aspects of everyday life. We drink them, breathe them, and swim in them; they circulate through our bodies, they control our weather, airplanes fly through them, and ships float in them. A fluid is any substance that can flow; we use the term for both liquids and gases. Usually, gases are easily compressed while liquids are quite incompressible. We'll see some of the consequences of this difference.

We begin our study with *fluid statics,* the study of fluids at rest (in equilibrium). Like the analysis of other equilibrium situations, the study of fluid statics is based on Newton's first and third laws. The key concepts include density, pressure, buoyancy, and surface tension. *Fluid dynamics* is the study of fluids in motion. Fluid dynamics is much more complex and indeed is one of the most complex branches of mechanics. Fortunately, we can analyze many important situations with simple idealized models and familiar principles such as Newton's laws and conservation of energy. Even so, we will barely scratch the surface of this broad and interesting topic.

To sail well, the crew must understand how their boat interacts with two fluids, the water and the air.

Different mass, same density
Because the wrench and nail are both made of steel, they have the same density (mass per unit volume)

Steel wrench   Steel nail

▲ **FIGURE 1** Density is mass per unit volume.

1 Density

A block of Styrofoam™ can have the same mass as a steel nail, but a much greater volume. To express this difference, we need the concept of *density.* The **density** of a material is defined as its mass per unit volume (Figure 1). Because density is defined as *mass divided by volume,* all objects made of a given material have the same density, irrespective of their size.

Shutterstock

▲ **Application Layers of liquids.** This coffee concoction was made by using liquids of differing densities and a steady hand. The liquid with the highest specific gravity (density relative to water) was poured first and the lighter liquid was carefully poured on top of the previous, more dense layer. As you know, any liquid will float on top of another liquid with a greater density, as long as no mixing occurs.

Definition of density

We use the Greek letter ρ (rho) for density. If a mass m of material has volume V, its density is

$$\rho = \frac{m}{V}. \tag{1}$$

Units: The SI unit of density is the kilogram per cubic meter ($1\ \text{kg/m}^3$). The cgs unit, the gram per cubic centimeter ($1\ \text{g/cm}^3$), is also widely used. (Notice that $1\ \text{g/cm}^3 = 1000\ \text{kg/m}^3$.)

A homogeneous material such as ice or iron has the same density throughout. Table 1 gives the densities of several common solids and liquids at ordinary temperatures. Note the wide range of magnitudes. The densest material found on earth is the metal osmium ($22,500\ \text{kg/m}^3$, or $22.5\ \text{g/cm}^3$). The density of air at sea level is about $1.2\ \text{kg/m}^3$ ($0.0012\ \text{g/cm}^3$), but the density of white-dwarf stars is on the order of $10^{10}\ \text{kg/m}^3$, and that of neutron stars is on the order of $10^{18}\ \text{kg/m}^3$!

The **specific gravity** of a material is the ratio of its density to the density of water; it is a pure (unitless) number. For example, the specific gravity of aluminum is 2.7; this means that the density of aluminum is 2.7 times as great as that of water. ("Specific gravity" is a poor term, since it has nothing to do with gravity; "relative density" would be better.)

Density measurements are an important analytical technique. For example, an auto mechanic can determine the freezing point of antifreeze by measuring its density. Antifreeze used in car engines is usually a solution of ethylene glycol (density $1.12 \times 10^3\ \text{kg/m}^3$) in water. The glycol concentration determines the freezing point of the solution; it can be found from a simple density measurement, performed routinely in service stations with the aid of a *hydrometer*. The auto mechanic measures density with this instrument by observing the level at which a calibrated body floats in a sample of the solution. (The hydrometer is discussed in Section 3.)

TABLE 1 Densities of Some Common Substances

Material	Density (kg/m³) *	Material	Density (kg/m³) *
Gases		Concrete	2×10^3
Air (1 atm, 20° C)	1.20	Aluminum	2.7×10^3
		Iron, steel	7.8×10^3
Liquids		Brass	8.6×10^3
Benzene	0.90×10^3	Copper	8.9×10^3
Ethanol	0.81×10^3	Silver	10.5×10^3
Water	1.00×10^3	Lead	11.3×10^3
Seawater	1.03×10^3	Gold	19.3×10^3
Blood	1.06×10^3	Platinum	21.4×10^3
Solids		Mercury	13.6×10^3
Glycerin	1.26×10^3	White-dwarf star	10^{10}
Ice	0.92×10^3	Neutron star	10^{18}

*To obtain the densities in grams per cubic centimeter, simply divide by 10^3.

Conceptual Analysis 1 **Changing density?**

If you cut a block of modeling clay in half, the density of each half is _____ the density of the original block.

A. twice   B. the same as   C. half

SOLUTION Because the clay in the block is a homogeneous material, its density (mass per unit volume) is the same for pieces of any size. Thus, B is the right answer.

EXAMPLE 1   The weight of a roomful of air

Find the mass of air, and its weight, in a living room with a 4.0 m × 5.0 m floor and a ceiling 3.0 m high. What would be the mass and weight of an equal volume of water?

SOLUTION

SET UP AND SOLVE Even for a problem like this, a simple sketch such as the one in Figure 2 helps to prevent mistakes. First we'll find the volume of the room; then we'll use the density of air to find the mass of air it contains. The room's volume is $V = l \times w \times h = (4.0 \text{ m})(5.0 \text{ m})(3.0 \text{ m}) = 60 \text{ m}^3$.

From Table 1, air has a density of $\rho = 1.2 \text{ kg/m}^3$. From Equation 1, $\rho = m/V$, so the mass of air in the room is $m = \rho V = (1.2 \text{ kg/m}^3)(60 \text{ m}^3) = 72 \text{ kg}$. The weight of the air is $w = mg = (72 \text{ kg})(9.8 \text{ m/s}^2) = 710 \text{ N}$.

From Table 1, the density of water is $\rho = 1.0 \times 10^3 \text{ kg/m}^3$. Thus, the mass of a volume of water that would fill the room is $m = \rho V = (1000 \text{ kg/m}^3)(60 \text{ m}^3) = 6.0 \times 10^4 \text{ kg}$. The weight is $w = (6.0 \times 10^4 \text{ kg})(9.8 \text{ m/s}^2) = 5.9 \times 10^5 \text{ N}$.

▲ **FIGURE 2** Our sketch for this problem.

REFLECT The weight of the air is about 160 lb. Does it surprise you that a roomful of air weighs this much? But the weight of the same volume of water is about 1.3×10^5 lb, or 66 tons! This much weight would certainly collapse the floor of an ordinary house. (We'll learn later why the weight of the room's air doesn't stress the floor.)

Practice Problem: What volume of water would have a mass equal to the mass of air in the room? *Answer:* $7.2 \times 10^{-2} \text{ m}^3$, or 72 L.

2 Pressure in a Fluid

When a fluid (either a liquid or a gas) is at rest, it exerts a force perpendicular to any surface in contact with it, such as the wall of a container or the surface of a body immersed in it. To see that this must be so, imagine a surface located *within* the fluid (Figure 3a). The fluid on either side of this surface exerts forces on it. Because the fluid is at rest, we know that the forces acting on the two sides must be equal in magnitude and opposite in direction (otherwise the surface would accelerate and the fluid would not remain at rest), and they must be oriented perpendicular to the surface. Similarly, any surface of an object immersed in the fluid is acted upon by a force perpendicular to the surface.

Pressure is force per unit area. We define the **pressure** p at a point in a fluid as the ratio of the normal force $F_\perp$ on a small area A around that point to the area.

Definition of pressure

The pressure p on a plane surface of area A is the magnitude $F_\perp$ of the force exerted on that surface, divided by the area:

$$p = \frac{F_\perp}{A}, \qquad F_\perp = pA. \qquad \text{(if } p \text{ is the same at all points on the surface)} \qquad (2)$$

Units: The SI unit of pressure is N/m^2. This unit is given a special name: the pascal (Pa). That is, $1 \text{ N/m}^2 = 1 \text{ Pa}$. Two related units, used principally in meteorology, are the *bar,* equal to 10^5 Pa, and the *millibar,* equal to 100 Pa. The British unit pounds per square inch (lb/in.^{2}, or psi) is still in common use in the United States. Another unit of pressure is the *atmosphere,* defined next. Later in this chapter, we'll encounter additional units used in specific situations.

The force exerted by the fluid on any surface must be perpendicular to the surface, otherwise it would have a component of shear that would cause the surface to accelerate.

(a) Why forces due to fluid pressure must act normal to a surface.

Although these two surfaces differ in area and orientation, the pressure on them (force divided by area) is the same.

Note that pressure is a scalar—it has no direction.

(b) Pressure equals force divided by area.

▲ **FIGURE 3** The forces due to pressure on arbitrary surfaces within a fluid.

Atmospheric pressure p_{atm} is the pressure of the earth's atmosphere—the pressure in the sea of air in which we live. This pressure varies with weather changes and with elevation. The average atmospheric pressure at sea level is used as a unit of pressure called the **atmosphere** (atm), defined as

$$1 \text{ atm} = 1.013 \times 10^5 \text{ Pa} = 14.7 \text{ psi} = 1.013 \text{ bars} = 1013 \text{ millibars}.$$

EXAMPLE 2   **The force of a roomful of air**

In the room described in Example 1, what is the total force on the floor due to the air above the surface if the air pressure is 1.00 atm?

SOLUTION

SET UP The total force on the floor has magnitude equal to the pressure multiplied by the area. We're given 1.00 atm of pressure—that is, $p = 1.013 \times 10^5$ Pa.

SOLVE The floor area is $A = (4.0 \text{ m})(5.0 \text{ m}) = 20 \text{ m}^2$. From Equation 3, the magnitude $F_\perp$ of the total force is

$$F_\perp = pA = (1.013 \times 10^5 \text{ Pa})(20 \text{ m}^2)$$
$$= 2.0 \times 10^6 \text{ N } (= 4.5 \times 10^5 \text{ lb} = 225 \text{ tons}).$$

REFLECT This force is equal to the total weight of all the air in a column directly above the floor. It is more than enough force to

collapse the floor. So why doesn't it collapse? Because there is an upward force on the underside of the floor. If we neglect the thickness of the floor, this upward force is exactly equal in magnitude to the downward force on the top surface, and the total force due to air pressure is zero.

Practice Problem: If the room has a window with dimensions 0.50 m $\times$ 1.0 m, what is the total force on the window due to the air inside? Why doesn't this force push the window out? *Answer:* 5.1×10^4 N; there is equal pressure on the outside surface.

Pascal's Law

If the weight of the fluid can be neglected, the pressure in a fluid at rest is the same throughout. We used that assumption in our discussion of bulk stress and strain. But often the fluid's weight is *not* negligible. The reason atmospheric pressure is greater at sea level than on a high mountain is that there is more air above you at sea level and greater weight pushing down on you. And when you dive into deep water, your ears tell you that the pressure increases rapidly with increasing depth below the surface.

We can derive a general relation between the pressure p at any point in a fluid in a gravitational field and the elevation h of that point relative to some reference level (where $h = 0$ and the pressure is p_0). We define h to be positive for points above the reference level. If the fluid is in equilibrium, every portion of it is in equilibrium. Consider the rectangular volume element shown in Figure 4. The bottom surface of the element is at $h = 0$, and the top surface is a distance h above that. The area of each of these surfaces is A. The height of the element is h, its volume is $V = hA$, its mass is $m = \rho V = \rho h A$, and its weight has magnitude $w = mg = \rho g h A$.

Let the pressure at the bottom surface of the volume element be p_0; then the total upward force on this surface (due to the fluid underneath pushing up) has magnitude $p_0 A$. The pressure at the top surface is p, and the total downward force on the top surface (due to the fluid above pushing down) has magnitude pA. The fluid in this volume is in equilibrium, so the total vertical component of force, including the weight of the fluid in the volume element and the forces at the bottom and top surfaces, must be zero. This condition gives

$$p_0 A - pA - \rho g h A = 0.$$

We can divide out the area A and rearrange terms, obtaining the following relation:

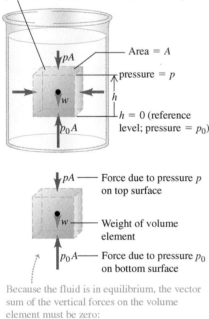

Arbitrary volume element of fluid
(forces on front and back sides not shown)

pA
Area = A
pressure = p
w
h
$p_0 A$
$h = 0$ (reference level; pressure = p_0)

pA —— Force due to pressure p on top surface

w —— Weight of volume element

$p_0 A$ —— Force due to pressure p_0 on bottom surface

Because the fluid is in equilibrium, the vector sum of the vertical forces on the volume element must be zero:

$$p_0 A - pA - w = 0$$

▲ **FIGURE 4** The forces on an arbitrary volume element in a fluid.

Variation of pressure with height in a fluid

If the pressure at a point in a fluid is p_0, then, at a point in the fluid at a distance h above this point, the pressure is $p_0 - \rho gh$; that is,

$$p = p_0 - \rho gh. \quad \text{(variation of pressure with height)} \quad \text{(A)}$$

When h is positive, p is less than p_0; when h is negative (i.e., a point deeper in the fluid than the reference level $h = 0$), p is greater than p_0, as we would expect. Pressure increases with depth: When we decrease h, we increase p.

Let's apply this equation to a liquid in an open container, as shown in Figure 5. Again, we let p_0 be the pressure at $h = 0$ (a distance h below the surface). At the surface of the liquid, the pressure is atmospheric pressure, so $p = p_{atm}$. We're interested in the pressure p_0 at a depth h below the surface. In Equation 3, we substitute p_{atm} for p; we obtain $p_{atm} - p_0 = -\rho gh$, or

$$p_0 = p_{atm} + \rho gh. \quad \text{(4)}$$

The pressure p_0 at a depth h below the surface is greater than the pressure p_{atm} at the surface by an amount ρgh. It also follows from Equation 4 that if the pressure at the top surface is increased in any way—say, by inserting a piston on the top surface and pressing down on it—the pressure p_0 at any depth must increase by exactly the same amount. This fact was recognized in 1653 by the French scientist Blaise Pascal (1623–1662) and is called **Pascal's law:**

Pascal's law

Pressure applied to an enclosed fluid is transmitted undiminished to every portion of the fluid and the walls of the containing vessel. The pressure depends only on depth; the shape of the container does not matter.

For instance, notice that the liquid in Figure 6 rises to the same height in all of the arms, regardless of their shape. This is the level at which $p = p_{atm}$. At any level below the surface, the pressure is the same in all four arms.

The hydraulic jack shown schematically in Figure 7 illustrates Pascal's law. A piston with a small cross-sectional area A_1 exerts a force with magnitude F_1 on the surface of a liquid such as oil. The pressure $p = F_1/A_1$ is transmitted through the connecting pipe to a larger piston with area A_2. In this case, the two pistons are at the same height, so they experience the same pressure p:

$$p = \frac{F_1}{A_1} = \frac{F_2}{A_2} \quad \text{and} \quad F_2 = \frac{A_2}{A_1}F_1. \quad \text{(5)}$$

Therefore, the hydraulic jack is a force-multiplying device with a multiplication factor equal to the ratio (A_2/A_1) of the areas of the two pistons. Dentists' chairs, car lifts and jacks, some elevators, and hydraulic brakes all use this principle.

FIGURE 5 The pressure at a depth h in a liquid is greater than the surface pressure by ρgh.

FIGURE 6 The pressure in a fluid is the same at all points having the same elevation, regardless of the container's shape.

FIGURE 7 The principle of the hydraulic lift, an application of Pascal's law.

EXAMPLE 3 The hydraulic lift: an application of Pascal's law

Suppose the hydraulic lift shown in Figure 7 has a small cylindrical piston with radius 5.0 cm and a larger piston with radius 20 cm. The mass of a car placed on the larger piston platform is 1000 kg. **(a)** Assuming that the two pistons are at the same height, what force must be applied to the small piston to lift the car? **(b)** How far must the small piston move down to lift the car through a height of 0.10 m?

Continued

SOLUTION

SET UP A downward external force with magnitude F_1 is applied on the smaller piston, and a downward force with magnitude F_2 equal to the weight of the car is applied on the larger piston. The weight of the car is $F_2 = w = mg = (1000 \text{ kg})(9.8 \text{ m/s}^2) = 9800 \text{ N}$.

SOLVE Part (a): From Pascal's law, the pressure at any given level is the same throughout the hydraulic fluid. Since the pistons are at the same level, we can use Equation 5. The downward force on the smaller piston needed to lift the car is

$$F_1 = \frac{A_1}{A_2}F_2 = \frac{\pi r_1^2}{\pi r_2^2}F_2 = \frac{\pi(0.050 \text{ m})^2}{\pi(0.20 \text{ m})^2}(9800 \text{ N}) = 610 \text{ N}.$$

So a force of 610 N can lift a car weighing 9800 N.

Part (b): If the small piston moves a distance d_1, the volume of fluid displaced is $V_1 = d_1 A_1$. Because the total volume of fluid is constant, V_1 must equal the volume V_2 displaced by the large piston. It follows that $d_1 A_1 = d_2 A_2$. If the car is hoisted a distance $d_2 = 0.10$ m, the small piston moves a distance d_1 given by

$$d_1 = \frac{\pi r_2^2}{\pi r_1^2}d_2 = \frac{\pi(0.20 \text{ m})^2}{\pi(0.05 \text{ m})^2}(0.10 \text{ m}) = 1.6 \text{ m}.$$

ALTERNATIVE SOLUTION Part (b) may also be solved by using conservation of energy. If we neglect friction, the amount of work done by the applied force must equal the work done to lift the car. Thus,

$$W_1 = W_2 \quad \text{or} \quad F_1 d_1 = F_2 d_2,$$
$$(610 \text{ N})(d_1) = (9800 \text{ N})(0.10 \text{ m}),$$
$$d_1 = 1.6 \text{ m}.$$

REFLECT The hydraulic lift is a force-multiplying device. The multiplication factor is the ratio of the areas of the pistons. It seems as though we get something for nothing. But the much larger weight is lifted through a much smaller distance, and the two quantities of work are the same in magnitude. The device multiplies force, but it can't multiply *energy*.

Practice Problem: Engineers are designing a hydraulic lift that can be used to repair trucks with a mass of 5000 kg. What ratio of piston areas would you suggest for the design if the maximum available external force is to be 3000 N? *Answer:* $A_2/A_1 = 16.3$.

Conceptual Analysis 2 | **Atmospheric pressure**

Atmospheric pressure is about 1.013×10^5 Pa at sea level. This means that

A. the weight of a column of air 1 square meter in cross section extending up to the top of the atmosphere is about 1.013×10^5 N.
B. the weight of 1 cubic meter of air at sea level is about 1.013×10^5 N.
C. the density of air at sea level is about 1.013×10^5 times the density of water at sea level.

SOLUTION As we've just learned, the pressure at a given level in a fluid (such as air) is caused by the weight of the overlying fluid, plus any external pressure applied to the fluid. In the case of earth's atmosphere, there is no external pressure, because the atmosphere is open to outer space at the top. Remember also that pressure is force divided by area. In the case of the atmosphere, the force is the weight of the overlying air. If atmospheric pressure is 1.013×10^5 Pa, then the air exerts a weight force of 1.013×10^5 N per square meter. Thus, choice A is correct and choices B and C are not.

The assumption that the density ρ of a fluid is constant is often reasonable for liquids, which are relatively incompressible, but it is realistic for gases only over short vertical distances. When we calculated the weight of air in a room of known volume, it was reasonable to assume that the density of the air was the same throughout the room. To justify this assumption, we note that, in a room with a ceiling height of 3.0 m filled with air of density 1.2 kg/m³, the difference in pressure between floor and ceiling, given by Equation 3, is

◀ **BIO Application A close look at pressure.** Fluid pressure in the human body is highly regulated, not just in the veins and arteries, but within the eye as well. This instrument, called a *tonometer,* is being used to measure the pressure of the fluid inside the eyeball as a means of diagnosing glaucoma, an eye disease characterized by a loss of vision from damage to the retina and the optic nerve. Glaucoma is often caused by excessive pressure within the eyeball. As Pascal's law states, if the weight of a fluid at rest can be neglected, the pressure in the fluid at rest is the same at all points. Therefore, using a tonometer to measure the pressure in the front of the eyeball, doctors can determine the pressure against the optic nerve at the back and diagnose whether excess pressure is the cause of vision problems.

Richard T. Nowitz/Photo Researchers, Inc.

$$\rho gh = (1.2\ \text{kg/m}^3)(9.8\ \text{m/s}^2)(3.0\ \text{m}) = 35\ \text{Pa},$$

or about 0.00035 atm, a very small difference. The resulting difference in density between floor and ceiling is correspondingly very small. But between sea level and the summit of Mount Everest (8850 m), the density of air changes by a factor of nearly three. In such situations, it wouldn't be correct to use Equation 3 $(p - p_0 = -\rho gh)$.

At great enough pressures, even liquids are compressed appreciably. The deepest point in the oceans is the Marianas Trench, which is 10,920 m deep. If the density of seawater were constant, the pressure at this depth would be 1.10×10^8 Pa (about 1000 atm or 16,000 lb/in.^{2}). But because seawater is compressed to greater density under high pressures, the actual pressure at this depth is 1.16×10^8 Pa (nearly 17,000 lb/in.^{2}).

If the pressure inside a car tire is equal to atmospheric pressure, the tire is flat. The pressure has to be *greater than* atmospheric to support the car, and the significant quantity is the *difference* between the inside and outside pressures. When we say that the pressure in a car tire is "32 pounds" (actually, 32 lb/in.^{2} = 32 psi, equal to 220 kPa, or 2.2×10^5 Pa), we mean that it is *greater* than atmospheric pressure $(14.7\ \text{lb/in.}^2$, or 1.01×10^5 Pa) by that amount.

The *total* pressure in the tire is 47 lb/in.^{2}, or 320 kPa. The excess pressure above atmospheric pressure is usually called the **gauge pressure,** and the total pressure is called the **absolute pressure.** Engineers use the abbreviations psig and psia for "pounds per square inch gauge" and "pounds per square inch absolute," respectively. If the pressure is *less than* atmospheric, as in a partial vacuum, the gauge pressure is negative.

Alan Becker/Getty Images

▲ Application **On top of the situation.** Snowshoes have been used for centuries to allow travel on foot in deep snow, long before we had defined pressure as force divided by area. If you try to walk in fresh snow without snowshoes, your feet sink in because you exert too much pressure for the snow to support. Snowshoes reduce the pressure you exert by distributing your weight over a larger area, allowing you to walk atop the snow without sinking in significantly.

Conceptual Analysis 3

An open U-tube

The equilibrium state of two nonmixing liquids in an open U-tube is shown in Figure 8. At which level(s) must the pressure be the same in both sides of this tube?

A. h_1.
B. h_2.
C. h_3.
D. The pressure at h_1 must equal the pressure at h_2.

SOLUTION The two liquids rise to different heights in the tube because the brown liquid is denser than the blue liquid. At level h_1, if the pressure in the two sides of the tube were *different*, the liquids would respond by moving. Since the liquids are in equilibrium (motionless), the pressure at h_1 is the same on both sides of the tube—so A is correct. (This argument also tells us that D is not correct.) At h_3, the pressure on both sides of the tube is atmospheric, so C is also correct. At h_2, the pressure on the left

▲ **FIGURE 8**

side is atmospheric, but the pressure on the right side equals the atmospheric pressure *plus* the pressure due to the weight of the blue liquid above h_2. Thus, B is not correct.

EXAMPLE 4   **Finding absolute and gauge pressures**

A solar water-heating system uses solar panels on the roof, 12.0 m above the storage tank. The pressure at the level of the panels is 1 atmosphere. What is the absolute pressure at the top of the tank? The gauge pressure?

SOLUTION

SET UP Figure 9 shows our sketch.

SOLVE To find the absolute pressure p_{tank} at the tank, 12 m below the panels, we use Equation 4, with $p_0 = p_{tank}$:

$$\begin{aligned} p_{tank} &= p_{atm} + \rho gh \\ &= (1.01 \times 10^5\ \text{Pa}) \\ &\quad + (1.00 \times 10^3\ \text{kg/m}^3)(9.80\ \text{m/s}^2)(12.0\ \text{m}) \\ &= 2.19 \times 10^5\ \text{Pa}. \end{aligned}$$

Continued

The gauge pressure is the amount by which p_{tank} exceeds atmospheric pressure—that is, $p_{tank} - p_{atm}$:

$$p_{tank} - p_{atm} = (2.19 - 1.01) \times 10^5 \, \text{Pa} = 1.18 \times 10^5 \, \text{Pa}$$
$$= 1.16 \, \text{atm} = 17.1 \, \text{lb/in}^2 = 17.1 \, \text{psig}.$$

REFLECT If the tank has a pressure gauge, it is usually calibrated to read gauge pressure rather than absolute pressure. As we have mentioned, the variation in *atmospheric* pressure over this height is negligibly small.

Practice Problem: At what distance below the panels is the gauge pressure equal to 1 atmosphere? *Answer:* 10.3 m.

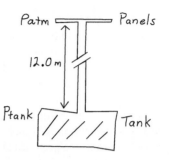

▲ **FIGURE 9** Our sketch for this problem.

Pressure Gauges

The simplest pressure gauge is the **open-tube manometer,** shown in Figure 10a. The U-shaped tube contains a liquid; one end of the tube is connected to the container in which the pressure is to be measured, and the other end is open to the atmosphere at pressure p_{atm}. According to Pascal's law, the pressures on the two sides of the tube at the level labeled $h = 0$ must be equal. On the left side, the pressure at this height is p_0, and on the right side (from Equation 4), it is $p_{atm} + \rho g h$. Equating these two expressions, we find that

$$p_0 = p_{atm} + \rho g h \qquad \text{and} \qquad p_{gauge} = \rho g h. \tag{6}$$

In Equation 6, the pressure p_0 is the absolute pressure; the difference $p - p_{atm}$ between absolute and atmospheric pressure is the gauge pressure. Thus, the gauge pressure is proportional to the difference in height h of the liquid columns on the two sides.

Another common pressure gauge is the **mercury barometer;** it consists of a long glass tube, closed at one end, that has been filled with mercury and then inverted in a dish of mercury, as shown in Figure 10b. The space above the mercury column contains only mercury vapor; the pressure of the vapor is negligibly small, so the pressure above the mercury column is practically zero. From Equation 3, $(p = p_0 - \rho g h)$, with $p = 0$ and $p_0 = p_{atm}$,

$$p_{atm} = \rho g h.$$

NOTE ▶ The *shape* and *diameter* of the tubes in the open-tube manometer and mercury barometer don't matter. As we found in deriving Pascal's law, the fact that pressure is defined as force *per unit area* means that it is independent of area. ◀

Pressures are sometimes described in terms of the height of the corresponding mercury column as so many "inches of mercury" or "millimeters of mercury" (abbreviated mm Hg). Thus, the mercury barometer reads atmospheric pressure in mm Hg directly from the height of the mercury column. A pressure of 1 mm Hg is sometimes called 1 torr, after Evangelista Torricelli, inventor of the mercury barometer. The mm Hg and the torr depend on the density of mercury, which varies with temperature, and on the value of g, which varies with location, so the pascal is the preferred unit of pressure. As we noted earlier in this section, two related units are the *bar,* defined as 10^5 Pa, and the *millibar,* defined as 10^{-3} bar, or 10^2 Pa. Atmospheric pressures are on the order of 1000 millibars; the National Weather Service usually reports atmospheric pressures in this unit. The conversions are as follows:

$$1.013 \times 10^5 \, \text{Pa} = 1.013 \, \text{bars} = 1013 \, \text{millibars} = 1 \, \text{atm}.$$

(a) Open-tube manometer

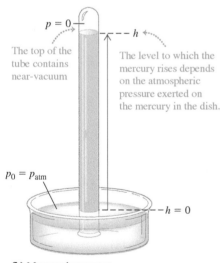

(b) Mercury barometer

▲ **FIGURE 10** Two types of pressure gauges.

Quantitative Analysis 4 — Two-liquid barometer

The barometer in Figure 11 contains two liquids, A and B, differing in density. According to this device, the barometric pressure is

A. $\rho_A g h_A$.
B. $\rho_B g h_B$.
C. $\rho_A g h_A + \rho_B g h_B$.
D. $g(h_A + h_B)(\rho_A + \rho_B)/2$.

SOLUTION In the open dish, the surface of the liquid is at atmospheric pressure. Therefore, by Pascal's law, the liquid at that level inside the tube must also be at atmospheric pressure. But the pressure at this level in the tube *also* equals the pressure due to the weights of the overlying liquids. This pressure is given by the sum in choice C. Therefore, C gives the atmospheric (barometric) pressure.

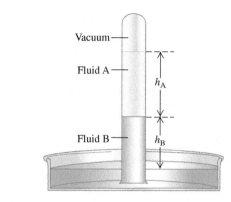

▲ **FIGURE 11**

EXAMPLE 5 Atmospheric pressure

Compute the atmospheric pressure p_{atm} on a day when the height of mercury in a barometer is 76.0 cm.

SOLUTION

SET UP Figure 12 shows our sketch; from Table 1, the density of mercury is $\rho = 13.6 \times 10^3$ kg/m^3. We assume that the pressure in the volume above the mercury column is zero.

SOLVE We use Equation 3 with $p = 0$, $p_0 = p_{atm}$:

$$p_{atm} = \rho g h = (13.6 \times 10^3 \text{ kg/m}^3)(9.80 \text{ m/s}^2)(0.760 \text{ m})$$
$$= 101,300 \text{ N/m}^2 = 1.013 \times 10^5 \text{ Pa} = 1.013 \text{ bars}.$$

REFLECT This is about 14.7 lb/in.^{2}. With weather variations, atmospheric pressure typically varies from about 0.97 bar to 1.03 bars; in the eye of a hurricane, it can be as little as 0.90 bar.

Practice Problem: On a very stormy day, the pressure is 0.950 bar. What is the height of mercury in a barometer? *Answer:* 71.3 cm (pressure 713 torr).

▲ **FIGURE 12** Our sketch for this problem.

Measuring Blood Pressure

Blood-pressure measurements are an important diagnostic tool in medicine. Blood-pressure readings, such as 130/80, refer to the maximum and minimum gauge pressures in the arteries, measured in mm Hg or torr. Blood pressure varies with height; the standard reference point is the upper arm, level with the heart.

In a commonly used blood-pressure gauge, known as a *sphygmomanometer,* an inflatable band, called a *cuff,* is placed around the upper arm, at heart level, as shown in Figure 13. The band is inflated by squeezing a flexible bulb, increasing the pressure on the arm. A stethoscope is used to detect the pulse at the elbow. When the pressure in the cuff exceeds the blood pressure, an artery under the cuff collapses and the pulse is no longer detectable. The pressure itself is measured with a mercury manometer or a mechanical pressure gauge.

To measure blood pressure, you listen through the stethoscope for arterial flow while letting the cuff deflate. Flow starts when the pressure in the deflating cuff reaches the arterial pressure.

▶ **FIGURE 13** Measuring blood pressure with a pressure cuff and a stethoscope. (In practice, one measures two pressures: the *systolic* pressure, at which blood first starts to spurt discontinuously through the compressed vessel, and the lower *diastolic* pressure, at which blood flows continuously.)

EXAMPLE 6 Feeling light-headed?

Suppose you have a healthy systolic (maximum) blood pressure of 1.30×10^4 Pa (about 100 mm Hg), measured at the level of your heart. **(a)** If the density of blood is 1.06×10^3 kg/m³, find the blood pressure at a point in your head, 35.0 cm above your heart. **(b)** Find the difference in blood pressure between your head and your feet when you are sitting down, a distance of 1.10 m. (Ignore the fact that the blood is in motion and is not in equilibrium.)

SOLUTION

SET UP Figure 14 shows our sketch. We put the reference level $h = 0$ at the level of the heart, where the pressure is p_0. Notice that h_2, the distance to the foot, is *negative*.

SOLVE We use Equation 3, $p - p_0 = -\rho g h$, for the variation in pressure with height.

Part (a): Let p_1 be the pressure at the level of the head; p_0 is the pressure at the level of the heart, and the height h_1 is 35.0 cm = 0.350 m. From Equation 3,

$$p_1 = p_0 - \rho g h_1$$
$$= 1.30 \times 10^4 \text{ Pa}$$
$$- (1.06 \times 10^3 \text{ kg/m}^3)(9.80 \text{ m/s}^2)(0.350 \text{ m})$$
$$= 9.4 \times 10^3 \text{ Pa}.$$

As expected, we get a blood pressure for the head that is lower than that at heart level. (If our result had been *greater* than the blood pressure at heart level, we would know we had made a mistake.)

Part (b): This time, p_2 is the pressure at the level of the foot, and the height is $h_2 = -1.10$ m. Then

$$p_2 = p_0 - \rho g h_2$$
$$= 1.30 \times 10^4 \text{ Pa}$$
$$- (1.06 \times 10^3 \text{ kg/m}^3)(9.80 \text{ m/s}^2)(-1.10 \text{ m})$$
$$= 2.44 \times 10^4 \text{ Pa}.$$

▲ **FIGURE 14** Our sketch for this problem.

As expected, the blood pressure at foot level is greater than that at heart level.

REFLECT Notice that we didn't need to know anything about the shape or volume of the blood vessels—just the relative heights of head, heart, and feet. If you lie down, then your head and feet are at the same level as your heart, and the differences we calculated disappear. Also, our results are somewhat simplistic because Pascal's law is valid only for fluids in equilibrium. As we will see later in the chapter, the viscosity of circulating blood has effects on its local pressure, in addition to the pressure differences due to relative height.

Practice Problem: When a person 1.70 m tall stands up, what is the difference in blood pressure between head and feet? *Answer:* 1.8×10^4 Pa.

3 Archimedes's Principle: Buoyancy

Buoyancy is a familiar phenomenon: An object immersed in water seems to weigh less than when it is in air. When the object is less dense than the fluid, it floats. Rafts inflated with air float in water, and a helium-filled balloon floats in air. Buoyancy is described by Archimedes's principle:

Archimedes's principle
When an object is completely or partially immersed in a fluid, the fluid exerts an upward force on the object equal to the weight of the fluid that is displaced by the object.

To derive this principle, we consider an arbitrary volume element of fluid at rest (in equilibrium), as shown in Figure 15a. The forces labeled $\vec{F}_\perp$ represent the forces exerted on the surface of the element by the surrounding fluid—that is, the forces due to the pressure of the fluid.

Because the entire beaker of fluid is in equilibrium, the sum of all the y components of force acting on the chosen element of fluid must be zero. Therefore, the sum of the y components of the surface forces must be an upward force equal in magnitude to the weight mg of the fluid inside the surface. Also, the sum of

Arbitrary element of fluid in equilibrium

Fluid element replaced with solid object of the same size and shape.

The forces on the fluid element due to pressure must sum to a buoyancy force equal in magnitude to the element's weight.

The forces due to pressure are the same, so the object must be acted upon by the same buoyancy force as the fluid element, *regardless of the object's weight.*

(a)

(b)

▲ **FIGURE 15** The origin of the buoyancy force. (a) The forces on a volume element of fluid in equilibrium. (b) The fluid element is replaced with a solid object having the same shape and size.

the torques of these forces must be zero, so the line of action of the resultant y component of surface forces must pass through the center of gravity of this portion of fluid.

Now, suppose that we remove the chosen element of fluid and replace it with a solid object having exactly the same shape (Figure 15b). The pressure at each point on the surface of this object is exactly the same as before, so the total upward force exerted on the object by the surrounding fluid is also the same, again equal in magnitude to the weight mg of the fluid that formerly occupied this spot. We call this upward force the **buoyant force** on the solid object.

NOTE ▶ Notice that the object *need not have the same weight as the fluid it replaces.* If the object's weight is greater than that of the displaced fluid, the object sinks; if less, then it rises. Thus, objects that are denser than the surrounding fluid sink; those that are less dense rise. ◀

Notice also that the center of gravity of the object need not coincide with that of the fluid that's replaced. As we just explained, the line of action of the buoyant force passes through the center of gravity of the replaced portion of fluid. If the *object's* center of gravity does not lie along this line (as in Figure 16), the buoyant force exerts a torque on the object.

As a helium balloon loses helium, it passes through a condition in which it neither floats nor sinks, but is in equilibrium with the surrounding air. At this point, the balloon's weight must be the same as the weight of the air it displaces. That is, the average density of a balloon floating in equilibrium must be the same as that of the surrounding air. Similarly, when a submerged submarine is in equilibrium, its weight must equal the weight of the water it displaces.

An object whose average density is less than that of a liquid can float partially submerged at the free upper surface of the liquid. The greater the density of the liquid, the less far the object is submerged. When you swim in seawater (density 1030 kg/m^3), your body floats higher than in fresh water (1000 kg/m^3). Unlikely as it may seem, lead floats in mercury. Very flat surfaced "float glass" is made by floating glass on molten tin and then letting it cool.

Another familiar example is the hydrometer, shown in Figure 17a. The calibrated float sinks into the fluid until the weight of the fluid it displaces is exactly equal to its own weight. The hydrometer floats *higher* in denser liquids than in less dense liquids. It is weighted at its bottom end so that the upright position is stable, and a scale in the top stem permits direct density readings.

The cg of this object does not coincide with the cg of the displaced fluid.

BEFORE

Thus, the buoyant force exerts a torque about the object's cg, causing the object to rotate.

Because the object's weight is greater in magnitude than the buoyant force, the object also sinks.

AFTER

▲ **FIGURE 16** A case in which the buoyancy force does not act through the center of gravity of an immersed object.

The depth to which the weighted scale sinks tells you the density of the fluid.

(a) A simple hydrometer

(b) Using a hydrometer to measure the density of battery acid or antifreeze

▲ **FIGURE 17** Hydrometers, for measuring the density of a fluid.

Dallas and John Heaton/Stock Connection

◀ **BIO Application The physics of floating.** These vacationers in the very salty Dead Sea are demonstrating Archimedes's principle. When you float in equilibrium, your body displaces an amount of water that weighs exactly as much as you do. You float low in fresh water because your body's density (even with inflated lungs) is only slightly less than that of fresh water; to achieve equilibrium, you must displace a volume of water nearly equal to your own volume. Very salty water is considerably denser than fresh water, so when you float in it, your body displaces less of it—you float higher. In salty enough water, you can even read while swimming (if you don't mind a crusty book).

Figure 17b shows a hydrometer that is commonly used to measure the density of battery acid or antifreeze. The bottom of the tube is immersed in the liquid; the bulb is squeezed to expel air and is then released, like a giant medicine dropper. The liquid rises into the outer tube, and the hydrometer floats in this sample of the liquid.

 Floating lead

A lead ball floats in liquid mercury and sinks in water. Which statement is true about the buoyant force acting on the lead ball?

A. It is greater when the ball is floating in the mercury.
B. It is greater when the ball is totally submerged in the water.
C. It is the same in both cases.

SOLUTION The ball's behavior depends on the difference in magnitude between its weight and the buoyant force. The ball's weight mg is the same in both experiments. The ball floats partially submerged in mercury, so the buoyant force equals the magnitude of the ball's weight. (It would be greater if the ball were completely submerged.) In water the ball sinks, so the buoyant force is less in magnitude than the ball's weight. Thus, A is correct: Mercury exerts a greater buoyant force on the ball than water does.

 Buoyant Ping-Pong™ ball

A Ping-Pong™ ball is held submerged in a bucket of water by a string attached to the bucket's bottom. What happens to the tension in the string as water is added to the bucket, increasing the distance between the ball and the surface?

A. The tension does not change.
B. The tension increases.
C. The tension decreases.

SOLUTION The buoyant force is equal in magnitude to the weight of the water displaced by the Ping-Pong™ ball. As water is added to the bucket, the *pressure* at the level of the ball increases. We'll assume that water is nearly incompressible, so this pressure change is too small to cause a significant change in the *density* of water. Therefore, the weight of the displaced water remains the same, and so does the buoyant force. Thus, the tension doesn't change. (If the fluid were a compressible gas rather than water, changing the pressure might indeed have a significant effect on the buoyancy force.)

EXAMPLE 7 Raising sunken treasure

A 15.0 kg solid-gold statue is being raised from a sunken treasure ship, as shown in Figure 18a. **(a)** Find the tension in the hoisting cable when the statue is completely immersed. **(b)** Find the tension when the statue is completely out of the water.

SOLUTION

SET UP When immersed in water, the statue is acted upon by an upward buoyant force with magnitude F_B. From Archimedes's principle, this force is equal in magnitude to the weight of water displaced. Figure 18b shows a free-body diagram for the statue, including its weight, the tension T, and the upward buoyant force F_B.

SOLVE Part (a): To find F_B, we first find the volume of the statue, using its mass and the density of gold from Table 1:

$$V = \frac{m_{statue}}{\rho_{gold}} = \frac{15.0 \text{ kg}}{19.3 \times 10^3 \text{ kg/m}^3} = 7.77 \times 10^{-4} \text{ m}^3.$$

Continued

The weight of an equal volume of water is

$$m_{water}g = \rho_{water}Vg$$
$$= (1.00 \times 10^3 \text{ kg/m}^3)(7.77 \times 10^{-4} \text{ m}^3)(9.80 \text{ m/s}^2)$$
$$= 7.61 \text{ N}.$$

This weight is equal to the magnitude F_B of the buoyant force. In equilibrium, the tension in the cable equals the weight of the statue minus the magnitude of the buoyant force. Taking the positive y direction as upward, we find that

$$T + F_B - w = 0,$$
$$T + 7.61 \text{ N} - 147 \text{ N} = 0,$$
$$T = 139 \text{ N}.$$

We note that this tension is less than the weight of the statue.

Part (b): To find the tension when the statue is in air, we neglect the very small buoyant force of *air* (as we have done in earlier chapters). The tension when the block is in air is just equal to its weight:

$$m_{statue}g = (15.0 \text{ kg})(9.80 \text{ m/s}^2) = 147 \text{ N}.$$

REFLECT The tensions calculated here are for a statue at rest or being hoisted at *constant* speed. Here is a shortcut leading to the same result for the buoyant force: The density of water is less than that of gold by a factor of

$$\frac{1.00 \times 10^3 \text{ kg/m}^3}{19.3 \times 10^3 \text{ kg/m}^3} = \frac{1}{19.3} = 0.0518.$$

Conceptual Analysis 7

Weighing in water

Suppose you place a beaker of water on a scale, weigh it, and then immerse the statue from Example 7 in the water, suspending it so that it is under water, but does not touch the bottom of the beaker (Figure 19). Does the scale reading increase, decrease, or stay the same?

A. Increase.
B. Decrease.
C. Stay the same.

SOLUTION Consider the water and the statue together as a system; its total weight does not change when the statue is immersed. Thus, the total supporting force—the vector sum of the tension $\vec{T}$ and the upward force $\vec{F}$ of the scale on the container (equal to the reading on the scale)—is the same in both cases. But T decreases when the statue is immersed, so the scale reading F must *increase* by the same amount. Thus, A is correct. Alternatively, we can see that the scale force *must* increase because, when the statue is immersed, the water level

▲ FIGURE 18

(a) Immersed statue in equilibrium   **(b)** Free-body diagram of statue

That is, the weight of a given volume of water is 0.0518 times that of an equal volume of gold, and the weight of the displaced water is $(1.00/19.3)(147 \text{ N}) = 7.62 \text{ N}$.

Practice Problem: A brass statue with a mass of 0.500 kg and a density of $8.00 \times 10^3 \text{ kg/m}^3$ is suspended from a string. What is the tension in the string when the statue is completely immersed in water? *Answer: $T = 4.29$ N.*

▲ FIGURE 19

in the container rises, increasing the pressure of water on the bottom of the container.

4 Surface Tension and Capillarity

What do the following observations (Figure 20) have in common? A liquid emerges from the tip of a pipette or medicine dropper as a succession of drops, not as a continuous stream. A paper clip, if placed carefully on a water surface, makes a small depression in the surface and rests there without sinking, even

Mario Beauregard/Stock Connection Adam Hart-Davis/ Photo Researchers, Inc. Shaun Lowe/iStockphoto

(a) **(b)** **(c)**

▲ **FIGURE 20** Three examples of surface tension. (a) Surface tension causes the drops at the ends of these pipettes to adopt a near-spherical shape. (b) A paperclip rests on water, supported by surface tension. (c) water striders spend their life walking on water.

(a)

(b)

▲ **FIGURE 21** A flexible loop of thread in a wire ring that has been dipped in a soap solution (a) before and (b) after puncturing the film inside the loop.

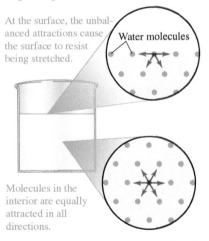

▲ **FIGURE 22** The physical origin of surface tension.

though its density is several times that of water. Some insects can walk on the surface of water; their feet make indentations in the surface, but do not penetrate it. When a small, clean glass tube is dipped into water, the water rises in the tube, but when the tube is dipped in mercury, the mercury is depressed.

In all these situations, the surface of the liquid seems to be under *tension.* Here's another example: We attach a loop of thread to a wire ring, as shown in Figure 21a. We dip the ring and thread into a soap solution and remove them, forming a thin film of liquid in which the thread "floats" freely. When we puncture the film inside the loop, the thread springs out into a circular shape (Figure 21b) as the tension of the liquid surface pulls radially outward on it.

Why does the surface of a liquid behave this way? The key is that water molecules attract each other. (That's what makes liquid water cohere.) Figure 22 compares the forces of attraction on a water molecule on the surface with those on a molecule below the surface. Below the surface, a molecule is equally attracted in all directions. At the surface, a molecule is attracted to the molecules around and below it, but not to the overlying air. If you place a paper clip on the water surface, these forces cause the surface to resist being stretched; the resulting tension supports the clip.

A drop of liquid in free fall in vacuum is always spherical in shape (*not* teardrop shaped), because a surface under tension tends to have the minimum possible area. A sphere has a smaller surface area for a given volume than any other geometric shape has. Figure 23 is a beautiful example of the formation of spherical droplets in a very complex phenomenon: the impact of a drop on a liquid surface.

Figure 24 shows another example of surface tension. A piece of wire is bent into a U shape, and a second piece of wire slides on the arms of the U. When the apparatus is dipped into a soap solution and removed, the upward surface tension force may be greater in magnitude than the weight of the wire. If it is, the slider is pulled up toward the top of the inverted U by the upward surface tension force. To hold the slider in equilibrium, there must be a total downward force with a magnitude greater than the weight of the wire. When we apply a large enough downward force, we can pull the slider down, increasing the area of the film. Molecules move from the interior of the liquid (which is many molecules thick, even in a thin film) into the surface layers, which are not stretched like a rubber sheet. Instead, more surface is created by molecules moving from the bulk liquid.

Let l be the length of the wire slider. The film has two surfaces, so the surface force acts along a total length $2l$. The **surface tension** γ in the film is defined as *the ratio of the magnitude F of the surface force to the length d* (perpendicular to the force) *along which the force acts:*

Definition of surface tension (γ)

Surface tension is a *force per unit length*:

$$\gamma = \frac{F}{d}. \tag{7}$$

Units: The SI unit of surface tension is the newton per meter (N/m), but the cgs unit, the dyne per centimeter (dyn/cm), is more commonly used: $1 \text{ dyn/cm} = 10^{-3} \text{ N/m}$.

In the case of the sliding wire, $d = 2l$ and

$$\gamma = \frac{F}{2l}.$$

Typical values of γ for familiar liquids are in the range from 20 to 100 dyn/cm. Surface tension for a particular liquid usually decreases as temperature increases.

Surface tension tends to pull the surface of a soap bubble inward, collapsing it. Excess pressure inside the bubble is needed to maintain its spherical shape. Detailed analysis shows that the excess pressure $p - p_{\text{atm}}$ inside a soap bubble with radius R, due to surface tension, is

$$p - p_{\text{atm}} = \frac{4\gamma}{R}. \quad \text{(bubble)} \tag{8}$$

For a liquid drop, which has only *one* surface film, the difference between the pressure of the liquid and that of the outside air is half that for a soap bubble:

$$p - p_{\text{atm}} = \frac{2\gamma}{R} \quad \text{(liquid drop).} \tag{9}$$

▲ **FIGURE 23** Aftermath of a drop splashing on a liquid surface.

▲ **FIGURE 24** The horizontal slide wire is in equilibrium under the action of the upward surface-tension force $2\gamma l$ and downward pull $w + T$.

EXAMPLE 8 **A drop of mercury**

Mercury has an unusually large surface tension, about 465 dyn/cm. Calculate the excess pressure inside a drop of mercury 4.00 mm in diameter.

SOLUTION

SET UP AND SOLVE We first convert the surface tension γ to SI units:

$$\gamma = 465 \text{ dyn/cm} = 465 \times 10^{-3} \text{ N/m}.$$

Now we have, from Equation 9,

$$p - p_{\text{atm}} = \frac{2\gamma}{R} = \frac{(2)(465 \times 10^{-3} \text{ N/m})}{0.00200 \text{ m}}$$
$$= 465 \text{ Pa}$$
$$= 0.00459 \text{ atm.}$$

REFLECT The excess pressure (the difference between the inside and outside pressures) is a very small fraction of atmospheric pressure.

Practice Problem: What would the diameter of the drop be if the inside pressure were 2 atm? *Answer:* 0.009 mm.

When a gas–liquid interface meets a solid surface, such as the wall of a container (Figure 25), surface tension causes the interface to curve upward in a concave shape or curve downward in a convex shape, near the line where it meets the solid surface. The interface is concave if the fluid *wets* the solid surface—that is, if the surface attracts the fluid at a molecular level. It is convex if the solid does not attract the fluid (allowing surface tension to pull the fluid toward a spherical shape). As you can see from Figure 25a, water wets glass and forms a concave interface; mercury does not wet glass, and it forms a convex interface.

If you push a thin glass tube into water, the attraction of the glass actually causes the water to climb a certain distance up into the tube, as shown in Figure 25b. Conversely, if you push a glass tube into mercury, surface tension makes it difficult for the mercury to enter the tube, so the tube pushes the mercury down. These two phenomena, called **capillarity,** are responsible for the absorption of water by paper towels, the rise of melted wax in a candle wick, and many other everyday phenomena.

Related to surface tension is the phenomenon of *negative pressure.* The stress in a liquid is ordinarily *compressive,* but in some circumstances liquids can sustain *tensile* stresses. Consider a cylindrical tube that is closed at one end and has a tight-fitting piston at the other. We fill the tube completely with a liquid that wets and adheres to both the inner surface of the tube and the piston face; the molecules of liquid adhere to all the surfaces. If the surfaces are very clean and the liquid very pure, then, when we pull the piston face, we observe a *tensile* stress and a slight *increase* in volume; we are *stretching* the liquid! Adhesive forces prevent it from pulling away from the walls of the container.

With water, tensile stresses as large as 300 atm have been observed in the laboratory. This situation is highly unstable: A liquid under tension tends to break up into many small droplets. In tall trees, however, negative pressures are a regular occurrence. Negative pressure is believed to be an important mechanism for the transport of water and nutrients from the roots to the leaves in the small xylem tubes (diameter on the order of 0.1 mm) in the tree's outer wood.

5 Fluid Flow

We're now ready to consider *motion* of a fluid. Fluid flow can be extremely complex, as shown by the flow of a river in flood or the swirling flames of a campfire. Despite this complexity, some situations can be represented by relatively simple idealized models. An **ideal fluid** is a fluid that is *incompressible* (i.e., that has constant density) and has no internal friction or viscosity. The assumption of incompressibility is usually a good approximation for liquids, and we may also treat a gas as incompressible whenever the pressure differences from one region to another are not too great. Internal friction in a fluid causes shear stresses when two adjacent layers of fluid move relative to each other, such as when the fluid flows inside a tube or around an obstacle. In some cases, these shear forces are negligible in comparison with forces arising from gravitation and pressure differences.

The path of an individual element of a moving fluid is called a **flow line.** If the overall flow pattern does not change with time, the flow is called **steady flow.** In steady flow, every element passing through a given point follows the same flow line. In this case the "map" of the fluid velocities at various points in space remains constant, although the velocity of a particular particle of the fluid changes in both magnitude and direction during its motion.

Figure 26 shows groups of flow lines for motion of a fluid flowing from left to right around a number of obstacles. The photographs were made by injecting dye into water flowing between two closely spaced glass plates. These patterns are typical of

Water wets (is attracted to) glass: concave interface.

Mercury does not wet glass: convex interface.

(a) Gas–liquid interface in contact with a solid

Water climbs up a glass tube because glass attracts it.

Mercury is pushed down by a glass tube because glass does not attract it.

(b) Capillarity

▲ **FIGURE 25** Two effects of surface tension when a gas–liquid interface meets a solid surface that the liquid either wets or does not wet.

Creatas/Thinkstock

◀ **BIO Application How does water get up there?** How do plants supply water all the way from the soil to the leaves at their highest points? It is especially mysterious how trees like the giant redwoods can lift water as high as 100 m, which requires a pressure of 10 atm. The answer is a kind of micro-capillarity in the leaves. As the conducting pipes of the tree (xylem) terminate in the leaves, the water flows into the spaces around the cells and evaporates through pores in the leaves, producing a thin layer of water on the surface of the cells. The irregular fibers outside the cell walls force the water to have very sharp radii of curvature of less than 100 nm as it conforms to the fibers. This generates pressure in the leaves as much as 30 atm less than that in the roots, sufficient to pull water to the tops of the highest trees and overcome the resistance to flow through the xylem. This process works only if the pores in the leaves are open so that the water evaporates continuously, thus maintaining the thin layer and the sharp curvature of the remaining water. At night, the pores in the leaves close and the flow of water stops.

(a)   **(b)**   **(c)**

▲ **FIGURE 26** (a)–(c) Laminar flow around obstacles of different shapes.

laminar flow, in which adjacent layers of fluid slide smoothly past each other. At sufficiently high flow rates or when boundary surfaces cause abrupt changes in velocity, the flow becomes irregular and chaotic; this is called **turbulent flow.** Smoke rising from a candle or an incense stick typically exhibits laminar flow near the bottom and then breaks up into chaotic swirls as the flow becomes turbulent. (Figure 27). In turbulent flow, *there is no steady-state pattern;* the flow pattern continuously changes.

Conservation of mass in fluid flow gives us an important relationship called the **continuity equation.** The essence of this relation is contained in the familiar maxim "Still waters run deep." If the flow rate of a river with constant width is the same everywhere along a certain length, the water must run faster where it is shallow than where it is deep. As another example, the stream of water from a faucet tapers down in width because the water speeds up as it falls and a smaller diameter is needed to carry the same volume flow rate as at the top.

We can turn these observations into a quantitative relation. We'll consider only incompressible fluids, for which the density is constant. Figure 28 shows a fluid flowing through a gradually narrowing tube. We'll look at two points along the tube at which the cross-sectional areas are, respectively, A_1 and A_2 and the speeds of fluid flow are v_1 and v_2. During a small time interval Δt, the fluid at A_1 moves a distance $v_1 \Delta t$. The volume of fluid ΔV_1 that flows into the tube across A_1 during this interval is the fluid in the cylindrical element with base A_1 and height $v_1 \Delta t$; that is, $\Delta V_1 = A_1 v_1 \Delta t$.

If the density of the fluid is ρ, the mass Δm_1 that flows into the tube across A_1 during time Δt is the density ρ multiplied by the volume ΔV_1; that is, $\Delta m_1 = \rho \, \Delta V_1 = \rho A_1 v_1 \Delta t$. Similarly, the mass Δm_2 that flows out across A_2 in the same time is $\Delta m_2 = \rho A_2 v_2 \Delta t$. In steady flow the total mass in the tube is constant, so these two masses must be equal: $\Delta m_1 = \Delta m_2$, and

$$\rho A_1 v_1 \Delta t = \rho A_2 v_2 \Delta t, \qquad \text{or} \qquad A_1 v_1 = A_2 v_2.$$

Thus, we find the following:

Continuity equation

This equation expresses conservation of mass for an incompressible fluid flowing in a tube or some other channel. It says that the amount (either mass or volume) of fluid flowing through a cross section of the tube in a given time interval must be the same for all cross sections, or

$$\frac{\Delta V}{\Delta t} = A_1 v_1 = A_2 v_2. \tag{10}$$

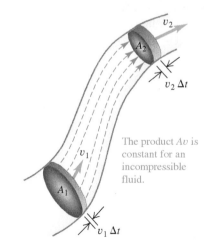

▲ **FIGURE 27** Smoke rising from incense shows laminar flow near the bottom and turbulent flow farther up.

The product Av is constant for an incompressible fluid.

▲ **FIGURE 28** Flow in a tube with changing cross-sectional area.

Peter/Georgina Bowater/Creative Eye/Mira

◄ **Application Meandering along.** In a relatively straight, slow-moving waterway, the movement of the water approximates laminar flow; adjacent layers of water slide smoothly past each other with little mixing. As the flow approaches a bend in the river, it becomes slightly turbulent, and water on the outside of the bend travels faster than water on the inside. The turbulence causes erosion of the outside riverbank due to the higher flow rate and results in the deposition of suspended sediment on the inside riverbank as the water there slows. These combined processes lead to an ever-widening series of bends and turns, a phenomenon known as *meandering* that is characteristic of rivers on flat plains. So, if you're traveling by boat on this mature river, the shortest distance between two points may not be a straight line!

The product Av is the **volume flow rate** $(\Delta V/\Delta t = Av)$, the time rate at which a given volume crosses any section of the tube. Similarly, the product $\Delta m/\Delta t = \rho Av$ is the **mass flow rate,** the time rate at which a given mass crosses a section of the tube.

Equation 10 shows that the volume flow rate and the mass flow rate are constant along any given tube. When the cross section of the tube decreases, the speed of flow increases. The shallow part of a river has a smaller cross section and a faster current than the deep part, but the volume flow rates are the same in both. The stream from the faucet narrows as it gains speed during its fall, but $\Delta V/\Delta t$ is the same everywhere along the stream. If a water pipe with a 2 cm diameter is connected to a pipe with a 1 cm diameter, the flow speed is four times as great in the 1 cm part as in the 2 cm part (because the cross-sectional area is proportional to the square of the diameter).

We derived the continuity equation for a steady flow in a physically distinct tube, pipe, or channel. However, a larger steady flow pattern can be thought of as a bundle of side-by-side tubes with imaginary boundaries separating adjacent tubes. If there is no mixing across boundaries of the individual tubes, then the fluid in each tube behaves according to Equation 10. For instance, if a river has slowly moving water near the banks and swifter water in the middle, with little mixing between the two, the continuity equation can be applied separately to the faster-moving central portion and to a more slowly moving channel near the bank. In the discussion that follows, we'll use the term **flow tube** to describe the flow patterns in a fluid, even when the tube isn't bounded by a real physical wall.

Conceptual Analysis 8

Flow through a tube

Water flows steadily through a horizontal pipe that has a narrowed section. What happens to the volume flow rate as the water passes through the narrow section?

A. It decreases because the speed of the fluid decreases.
B. It remains constant.
C. It increases because the speed of the fluid increases.

SOLUTION As we've just seen, when an incompressible fluid such as water flows steadily through a pipe, the *same amount* of water must pass through each portion of the pipe in any given amount of time. This is equivalent to saying that the volume flow rate, $\Delta V/\Delta t$, is constant (choice B). For the product Av to be constant, the flow speed v must increase when the cross-sectional area A decreases. Thus, narrowing the pipe increases the flow speed.

6 Bernoulli's Equation

According to the continuity equation, the speed of fluid flow can vary along the paths of the fluid particles. The pressure can also vary; it depends on height, as in the static situation, and it also depends on the speed of flow. We can now use the concepts introduced in Section 5, along with the work–energy theorem, to derive an important relationship called **Bernoulli's equation** that relates the pressure, flow speed, and height for flow in an ideal fluid.

The dependence of pressure on fluid speed follows from Equation 10. When an incompressible fluid flows along a flow tube with varying cross section, the flow speed *must* change. Therefore, each element of fluid must have an acceleration, and the force that causes this acceleration has to be applied by the surrounding fluid. When an element of the fluid speeds up, we know that it is moving from a region of higher pressure to one of lower pressure; the pressure difference provides the net forward force needed to accelerate it. So when the cross section of a flow tube changes, the pressure *must* vary along the tube, even when there is no difference in elevation. If the elevation also changes, this causes an additional pressure difference.

To derive the Bernoulli equation, we use the work–energy theorem. We'll use the general form. Let's review that relationship; it is

$$\Delta K + \Delta U = W_{\text{other}},$$

where ΔK is the change in kinetic energy of an object during the motion we're considering, ΔU is the change in its potential energy (in this case, gravitational potential energy ΔU_{grav}), and W_{other} is the work done by the forces whose work is not included in ΔU_{grav}. We'll compute each of these three pieces for a system consisting of a segment of fluid in a flow tube; then we'll combine the pieces according to the work–energy theorem.

In Figure 29, we consider as our system the segment of fluid that lies between the two cross sections a and c at some initial time. The speed at the upstream end is v_1, and the pressure there is p_1. In a small time interval Δt, the fluid initially at a moves to b, a distance $\Delta s_1 = v_1 \Delta t$, where v_1 is the speed at this end of the tube. In the same time interval, the fluid initially at c moves to d, a distance $\Delta s_2 = v_2 \Delta t$. The cross-sectional areas at the two ends are A_1 and A_2, as shown. Because of the continuity relation, the volume ΔV of fluid passing *any* cross section during time Δt is the same at both ends: $\Delta V = A_1 \Delta s_1 = A_2 \Delta s_2$.

Note that the fluid between cross sections a and b is part of our system at the beginning of Δt, but not at the end, and that the fluid between cross sections c and d are part of our system at the end of Δt, but not at the beginning.

To apply the work–energy theorem, let's first compute W_{other}, which is the work done on this segment of fluid during Δt by the fluid adjacent to it. The pressure on the segment at cross section a is p_1; the total force exerted on this cross section by the adjacent fluid has magnitude $p_1 A_1$, and the displacement of the segment during the interval Δt is Δs_1. Thus, the work done on the segment by the force at cross section a during time Δt (force times displacement) has magnitude $p_1 A_1 \Delta s_1$. Similarly, the magnitude of the work done on the segment at cross section c is $p_2 A_2 \Delta s_2$. Therefore, the net work W_{other} done on the segment by the adjacent fluid during this displacement is

$$\begin{aligned} W_{\text{other}} &= p_1 A_1 \Delta s_1 - p_2 A_2 \Delta s_2 \\ &= (p_1 - p_2) \Delta V. \end{aligned}$$

We need the negative sign in the second term because the force at c is opposite in direction to the displacement.

Next, let's find the change in gravitational potential energy during time Δt. The gravitational potential energy of the mass between a and b at the beginning of Δt is $\Delta m\, gy_1 = \rho\, \Delta V\, gy_1$, where y is the height of the mass above some reference level at which $y = 0$. At the end of the interval Δt, this mass has left our system, and there's a corresponding decrease in the potential energy of the system. But during the same interval, the mass between c and d has been added to the system, bringing with it a potential-energy increase $\Delta m\, gy_2 = \rho\, \Delta V\, gy_2$. Thus, the *net* change in potential energy ΔU_{grav} during Δt is

$$\Delta U_{\text{grav}} = \rho\, \Delta V\, g(y_2 - y_1).$$

Finally, we compute the change ΔK in kinetic energy of our system during Δt. At the beginning of Δt, the fluid between a and b has volume $A_1 \Delta s_1$, mass $\rho A_1 \Delta s_1$, and kinetic energy $\frac{1}{2}mv^2 = \frac{1}{2}\rho(A_1 \Delta s_1)v_1^2 = \frac{1}{2}\rho \Delta V v_1^2$. At the end of Δt, this fluid is no longer in the system, but the fluid between c and d is now included; it brings in kinetic energy $\frac{1}{2}\rho(A_2 \Delta s_2)v_2^2 = \frac{1}{2}\rho \Delta V v_2^2$. The net *change* in kinetic energy ΔK during time Δt is the difference of these quantities:

$$\Delta K = \tfrac{1}{2}\rho\, \Delta V(v_2^2 - v_1^2).$$

Mark Wilson/Getty Images

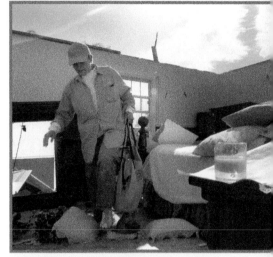

▲ **Application Raising the roof.** In severe weather accompanied by high winds, the roofs of houses may be blown completely off. At first you might think that the direct force of the wind pushed this roof off. In fact, the wind *pulled* the roof off—or, alternatively, the pressure inside the house blew it off. The wind that flowed up and over the house was forced to take a longer path than wind that did not meet the house. Therefore, it flowed faster. Bernoulli's principle tells us that the pressure in this fast-moving air was lower than the pressure elsewhere—such as inside the house. After a severe storm, you will often see that the windows of houses are blown out rather than in.

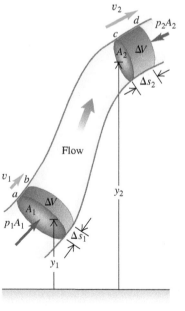

▲ **FIGURE 29** The net work done by the pressure equals the change in the kinetic energy plus the change in the gravitational potential energy.

(Note that there is no net change in kinetic energy of the fluid between cross sections b and c: There is just as much of our system contained between these sections at the end of the interval as at the beginning, and the flow velocity at any point doesn't change.)

Now we combine all these pieces in the work–energy theorem:

$$\Delta K + \Delta U_{grav} = W_{other},$$

$$\tfrac{1}{2}\rho\,\Delta V(v_2^2 - v_1^2) + \rho\,\Delta V g(y_2 - y_1) = (p_1 - p_2)\,\Delta V,$$

or

$$p_1 - p_2 = \tfrac{1}{2}\rho(v_2^2 - v_1^2) + \rho g(y_2 - y_1). \tag{11}$$

This is **Bernoulli's equation.** We may interpret it in terms of pressures. The second term on the right is the pressure difference between any two points in the fluid, caused by the weight of the fluid and the difference in elevation of the two ends. The first term on the right is the additional pressure difference associated with the change in speed of the fluid.

Equation 11 can also be written as follows:

Bernoulli's equation: pressure, flow speed, and height in a fluid

$$p_1 + \rho g y_1 + \tfrac{1}{2}\rho v_1^2 = p_2 + \rho g y_2 + \tfrac{1}{2}\rho v_2^2. \tag{12}$$

The subscripts 1 and 2 refer to *any* two points along the flow tube, so Bernoulli's equation may also be written as

$$p + \rho g y + \tfrac{1}{2}\rho v^2 = \text{constant}. \tag{13}$$

PROBLEM-SOLVING STRATEGY 1 **Bernoulli's equation**

Bernoulli's equation is derived from the work–energy relationship.

SET UP

1. Always begin by identifying points 1 and 2 clearly, with reference to Bernoulli's equation.
2. Write down (or show on a sketch) the known and unknown quantities in Equation 12. The variables are p_1, p_2, v_1, v_2, y_1, and y_2, and the constants are ρ and g. What is given? What do you need to determine? Be sure that your pressures are either all gauge pressures or all absolute pressures; don't mix them. Be careful about consistency of units. In SI units, pressure is expressed in pascals, density in kilograms per cubic meter, and speed in meters per second.

SOLVE

3. In some problems you'll need to use the continuity equation, Equation 10, to get a relation between the two speeds in terms of cross-sectional areas of pipes or containers. Or perhaps you will know both speeds and will need to determine one of the areas.
4. The volume flow rate $\Delta V/\Delta t$ across any area A is given by $\Delta V/\Delta t = Av$, and the corresponding mass flow rate $\Delta m/\Delta t$ is $\Delta m/\Delta t = \rho A v$. These relations sometimes come in handy.

REFLECT

5. Always try to estimate comparative magnitudes of your results. Are they what you expected? Do they agree with commonsense predictions or estimates?

EXAMPLE 9   **Water pressure in the home**

Water enters a house through a pipe with an inside diameter of 2.0 cm at a gauge pressure of 4.0×10^5 Pa (about 4 atm, or 60 lb/in^2). The cold-water pipe leading to the second-floor bathroom 5.0 m above is 1.0 cm in diameter (Figure 30). Find the flow speed and gauge pressure in the bathroom when the flow speed at the inlet pipe is 2.0 m/s. How much time would be required to fill a 100 L bathtub?

SOLUTION

SET UP Let point 1 be at the inlet pipe and point 2 at the bathroom. The speed v_2 of the water at the bathroom is obtained from the continuity equation, Equation 10. We take $y_1 = 0$ at the inlet and $y_2 = 5.0$ m at the bathroom. We are given p_1 and v_1; we can find p_2 from Bernoulli's equation, Equation 12. To find the time to fill the bathtub, we use the volume flow-rate relation $\Delta V / \Delta t = Av$. The bathtub's volume is 100 L $= 100 \times 10^{-3}$ m^3.

SOLVE From the continuity equation, the flow speed v_2 in the bathroom is

$$v_2 = \frac{A_1}{A_2} v_1 = \frac{\pi (1.0 \text{ cm})^2}{\pi (0.50 \text{ cm})^2} (2.0 \text{ m/s}) = 8.0 \text{ m/s}.$$

From Bernoulli's equation, the gauge pressure p_2 in the bathroom is

$$\begin{aligned}
p_2 &= p_1 - \tfrac{1}{2}\rho(v_2^2 - v_1^2) - \rho g(y_2 - y_1) \\
&= 4.0 \times 10^5 \text{ Pa} \\
&\quad - \tfrac{1}{2}(1.0 \times 10^3 \text{ kg/m}^3)(64 \text{ m}^2/\text{s}^2 - 4.0 \text{ m}^2/\text{s}^2) \\
&\quad - (1.0 \times 10^3 \text{ kg/m}^3)(9.8 \text{ m/s}^2)(5.0 \text{ m}) \\
&= 3.2 \times 10^5 \text{ Pa} \\
&= 3.2 \text{ atm} = 47 \text{ lb/in}^2. \quad \text{(gauge pressure)}.
\end{aligned}$$

The volume flow rate is

$$\begin{aligned}
\Delta V / \Delta t &= A_2 v_2 = \pi (0.50 \times 10^{-2} \text{ m})^2 (8.0 \text{ m/s}) \\
&= 6.3 \times 10^{-4} \text{ m}^3/\text{s} = 0.63 \text{ L/s}.
\end{aligned}$$

The time needed to fill the tub is 100 L$/(0.63$ L/s$) = 160$ s.

▲ **FIGURE 30** What is the water pressure in the second-story bathroom of this house?

REFLECT Note that when the water is turned off, the second term on the right of the pressure equation vanishes, and the pressure rises to 3.5×10^5 Pa. In fact, when the fluid is not moving, Bernoulli's equation (Equation 12) reduces to the pressure relation that we derived for a fluid at rest, Equation 3.

7 Applications of Bernoulli's Equation

The sections that follow discuss several practical applications of Bernoulli's equation.

Speed of Efflux; Torricelli's Theorem

Figure 31 shows a gasoline storage tank with cross-sectional area A_1 filled to a depth h with a liquid of density ρ. The space above the gasoline is vented to the atmosphere, so it contains air at atmospheric pressure p_{atm}, and the gasoline flows out through a short pipe with cross-sectional area A_2. How fast does the gasoline run out?

To answer this question, we consider the entire volume of moving liquid as a single flow tube; v_1 and v_2 are the speeds at points 1 and 2, respectively. The pressure at both points is atmospheric pressure p_{atm}, so the pressure differential is zero. We apply Bernoulli's equation to points 1 and 2 and take $y_2 = 0$ at the bottom of the tank.

When we set $y_1 = h$, Bernoulli's equation becomes

$$p_{atm} + \tfrac{1}{2}\rho v_1^2 + \rho g h = p_{atm} + \tfrac{1}{2}\rho v_2^2.$$

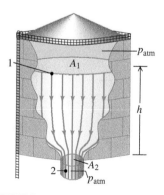

▲ **FIGURE 31** How fast does the gasoline run out of this storage tank?

force on the underside of the wing is greater than the downward force on the top side, there is a net upward force, or *lift*. (This highly simplified discussion ignores the effect of turbulent flow and the formation of vortices; a more complete discussion would take these into account.)

We can also understand the lift force on the basis of momentum changes. Figure 34 shows that there is a net *downward* change in the vertical component of momentum of the air flowing past the wing, corresponding to the downward force the wing exerts on it. The reaction force *on* the wing is *upward*, as we concluded in the previous paragraph.

The Curveball

Does a curveball *really* curve? Yes, it certainly does. Figure 35 shows a ball moving through air from left to right. To an observer moving with the center of the ball, the air stream appears to move from right to left, as shown by the flow lines in the figure. Because of the large speeds that are ordinarily involved (up to 100 mi/h for a baseball or a served tennis ball), there is a region of turbulent flow behind the ball.

Figure 35b shows a spinning ball with "top spin," viewed from the side. When the ball is spinning, the viscosity of air causes layers of air near the ball's surface to be pulled around in the direction of spin. Therefore, the speed of the air relative to the ball's surface is smaller at the top of the ball than at the bottom (Also, the region of turbulence becomes asymmetric; turbulence occurs farther forward on the top side than on the bottom.) The difference in the speed of the air between the top and bottom of the ball causes a pressure difference: The average pressure at the top of the ball becomes greater than that at the bottom. The corresponding net downward force deflects the ball downward, as shown. This could be a side view of a tennis ball (Figure 35d) moving from left to right with "top spin." In a baseball curve pitch, the ball spins about a nearly vertical axis, and the actual deflection is mostly sideways. In that case, Figure 35c is a *top* view of the situation. Note that a curveball thrown by a left-handed pitcher curves *toward* a right-handed batter, making it harder to hit than the same ball thrown to a left-handed batter (in which case the ball would curve *away from* the batter).

A similar effect occurs with golf balls, which always have "backspin" from impact with the slanted face of the golf club. The resulting pressure difference

This side of the ball moves opposite to the air flow.

This side moves in the direction of the air flow.

A moving ball drags the adjacent air with it. So, when air moves past a spinning ball:

On one side the ball **slows the air**, creating a region of **high pressure**.

On the other side, the ball **speeds the air**, creating a region of **low pressure**.

The resultant force points in the direction of the low-pressure side.

(a) Motion of air relative to a nonspinning ball

(b) Motion of a spinning ball

(c) Force generated when a spinning ball moves through air

(d) Spin pushing a tennis ball downward

(e) Spin causing a curveball to be deflected sideways

▲ **FIGURE 35** How spin on a ball creates forces that cause the ball to follow a nonparabolic trajectory.

▲ **FIGURE 36** Strobe photo of a golf ball being struck by a club. The picture was taken at 1000 flashes per second. The ball rotates about once in eight pictures, corresponding to an angular velocity of 125 rev/s, or 7500 rpm.

▲ **FIGURE 37** Velocity profile for a viscous fluid in a cylindrical pipe.

between the top and bottom of the ball causes a "lift" force that keeps the ball in the air considerably longer than would be possible without spin. From the tee, a well-hit drive appears to float, or even curve *upward,* during the initial portion of its flight. This is a real effect, not an illusion. The dimples on the ball play an essential role: Because of effects associated with the viscosity of air, a ball without dimples has a much shorter trajectory than a dimpled ball, given the same initial velocity and spin. One manufacturer even claims that the *shape* of the dimples is significant: Polygonal dimples are alleged to be more effective than round ones. Figure 36 shows the backspin of a golf ball just after it is struck by a club.

8 Real Fluids: Viscosity and Turbulence

Viscosity is internal friction in a fluid; viscous forces oppose the motion of one portion of a fluid relative to another. Viscosity is the reason that paddling a canoe through calm water requires effort, but it is also the reason the paddle works. Viscosity plays a vital role in the flow of fluids in pipes, the flow of blood, the lubrication of engine parts, and many other areas of practical importance. An ideal fluid, the model we used to derive the Bernoulli equation, has no viscosity, but in real-life fluids, especially liquids, effects associated with viscosity are often significant.

A viscous fluid always tends to cling to a solid surface that is in contact with it. There is always a thin *boundary layer* of fluid near the surface in which the fluid is nearly at rest with respect to the surface. That's why dust particles can cling to a fan blade even when it is rotating rapidly and why you can't get all the mud off your car by just squirting a hose at it.

Viscosity plays an important role in the flow of fluids through pipes. Let's think first about a fluid with zero viscosity, so that we can apply Bernoulli's equation, Equation 12. For a pipe of uniform cross section, if the two ends are at the same height (so that $y_1 = y_2$) and have the same flow speed ($v_1 = v_2$) and the fluid has zero acceleration, then the Bernoulli equation states that the pressure is the same at the two ends. But if viscosity is taken into account, the pressure must be greater at the upstream end than at the downstream end. To see why, let's consider the velocity profile for flow of a viscous fluid in a cylindrical pipe (Figure 37). The flow velocity is different at different points of a cross section. The outermost layer of fluid clings to the walls, so the speed is zero at the pipe walls. The walls exert a backward drag on this layer, which in turn drags backward on the next layer inward, and so on. The flow speed is greatest along the axis of the pipe.

The motion is like that of many coaxial telescoping tubes sliding relative to one another, with the central tube moving fastest and the outermost tube at rest. The viscous forces between the tubes resist this motion, so, for the fluid to keep moving, the pressure p_1 at the back end has to be greater than the pressure p_2 at the front end. The strength of the viscous resisting forces is characterized by a quantity called the *coefficient of viscosity,* or simply the *viscosity,* denoted by η (Greek eta). Very viscous fluids, such as molasses, have large values of η; gases have much smaller values, and water is in between. The coefficient of viscosity is strongly dependent on temperature, decreasing with increasing temperature for liquids, but increasing with temperature for gases.

Detailed analysis of the flow pattern of a viscous fluid in a cylindrical pipe shows that the volume flow rate $\Delta V/\Delta t$ is proportional to the pressure difference $p_1 - p_2$ between the ends and inversely proportional to the length L of the pipe. That is, the volume flow rate is proportional to the pressure change *per unit length,* which is called the *pressure gradient.* The volume flow rate is also proportional to the *fourth power* of the pipe's radius R. The specific relationship, called **Poiseuille's law,** is

$$\frac{\Delta V}{\Delta t} = \frac{\pi R^4}{8\eta}\frac{p_1 - p_2}{L}.$$

If the radius R is doubled, the volume flow rate increases by a factor of 16. This relation is familiar to physicians in connection with hypodermic needles. Needle size is much more important than thumb pressure in determining the flow rate from the needle; doubling the needle diameter has the same effect as increasing the thumb force by a factor of 16. Similarly, blood flow in arteries and veins can be controlled over a wide range by relatively small changes in diameter, an important temperature-control mechanism in warm-blooded animals. Relatively slight narrowing of arteries due to arteriosclerosis can result in elevated blood pressure and added strain on the heart muscle.

One more useful relation in viscous fluid flow is the expression for the magnitude F of force exerted on a sphere of radius r that moves with speed v through a fluid with viscosity η. When v is small enough that there is no turbulence, the relationship is simple:

$$F = 6\pi\eta rv.$$

This relation is called **Stokes's law.**

A sphere falling in a viscous fluid reaches a *terminal speed* v_t for which the total force, including the weight of the sphere and the viscous retarding force, is zero, and the sphere no longer accelerates. (We neglect the effect of buoyancy of the sphere in the fluid.) Let ρ be the density of the sphere; then the weight of the sphere is $\frac{4}{3}\pi r^3\rho g$. When the sphere reaches terminal speed, the total force on it is zero:

$$6\pi\eta rv_t - \tfrac{4}{3}\pi r^3\rho g = 0,$$

or

$$v_t = \tfrac{2}{9}\frac{r^2 g\rho}{\eta}.$$

The Stokes's-law force is what keeps clouds in the air. The terminal speed for a water droplet of radius 10^{-5} m is on the order of 1 mm/s. At higher speeds the flow often becomes turbulent, and Stokes's law is no longer valid. In air, the drag force at highway speeds is approximately proportional to v^2. Raindrops have terminal speeds of a few meters per second because of air drag; otherwise, they would smash everything in their path!

As we've mentioned previously, flow can be either laminar, with layers of fluid slipping smoothly past each other, or turbulent—irregular, complex, and ever changing. Figure 27 showed rising smoke changing from laminar to turbulent flow. Figure 38 compares laminar and turbulent flow in streams of water.

The transition from laminar to turbulent flow is often very sudden. A flow pattern that is stable at low speeds suddenly becomes unstable when a critical speed is reached. Irregularities in the flow pattern can be caused by roughness in a pipe wall, variations in density of the fluid, and many other factors. At small flow speeds, these disturbances are damped out and the flow pattern tends to

Laminar flow   Turbulent flow

▲ **FIGURE 38** Laminar and turbulent flow in a stream of water.

maintain its laminar nature. But when the critical speed is reached, the disturbances no longer damp out; instead, they grow until they destroy the entire laminar-flow pattern.

Turbulence poses some profound questions for theoretical physics. The motion of any particular particle in a fluid is presumably determined by Newton's laws. If we know the motion of the fluid at some initial time, shouldn't we be able to predict the motion at any later time? After all, when we launch a projectile, we can compute the entire trajectory if we know the initial position and velocity. How is it that a system that obeys well-defined and supposedly deterministic physical laws can have unpredictable, chaotic behavior?

There is no simple answer to these questions. Indeed, the study of chaotic behavior in deterministic systems is a highly active field of research in theoretical physics. The development of supercomputers in recent years has enabled scientists to carry out computer simulations of the behavior of physical systems on a scale that would have been hopeless only a few years ago. The results of such simulations have often guided new developments in the theory of chaotic behavior. A particularly significant result of these studies has been the discovery of common characteristics in the behavior of widely divergent kinds of systems, including turbulent fluid flow, population fluctuations in ecosystems, the growth of crystals, the shapes of coastlines, and many others.

CHAPTER SUMMARY

Density and Pressure in a Fluid

(Sections 1 and 2) Density is mass per unit volume. If a mass m of material has volume V, its density ρ is $\rho = m/V$ (Equation 1). **Specific gravity** is the ratio of the density of a material to the density of water.

Pressure is force per unit area. Assuming that the pressure is constant over the area in question, we express pressure as $p = F_\perp/A$ (Equation 2). **Pascal's law** states that the pressure applied to the surface of an enclosed fluid is transmitted undiminished to every portion of the fluid. The total pressure at any level in a fluid is the external pressure plus the pressure due to the weight of the overlying fluid. The pressure p at a height h above or below a reference level where $h = 0$, relative to the pressure p_0 at the reference level, is $p - p_0 = -\rho gh$ (where ρ is the density of the fluid) (Equation 3).

Absolute pressure is the total pressure in a fluid; **gauge pressure** is the difference between absolute pressure and atmospheric pressure. The SI unit of pressure is the pascal (Pa), where $1\text{ Pa} = 1\text{ N/m}^2$. Additional units of pressure are the bar $(1\text{ bar} = 10^5\text{ Pa})$, the torr $[1\text{ torr} = 1\text{ millimeter of mercury (mm Hg)}]$, and the atmosphere (atm) $(1\text{ atm} = 1.013 \times 10^5\text{ Pa} = 760\text{ torrs} = 1.013\text{ bar})$

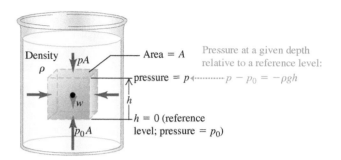

Density ρ — Area $= A$

Pressure at a given depth relative to a reference level:

pressure $= p$ ········ $p - p_0 = -\rho gh$

$h = 0$ (reference level; pressure $= p_0$)

Archimedes's Principle: Buoyancy

(Section 3) Archimedes's principle states that when an object is immersed in a fluid, the fluid exerts an upward buoyant force on the object equal in magnitude to the weight of the fluid the object displaces. Thus, an object denser than the surrounding fluid sinks; one less dense than the surrounding fluid floats.

The pressure on any volume element of a fluid produces a buoyancy force $\vec{F}_B$ that exactly cancels the element's weight.

The buoyancy force on a solid object is equal in magnitude to the weight of the displaced fluid.

Surface Tension and Capillarity

(Section 4) A boundary surface between a liquid and a gas behaves like a surface under tension (**surface tension**). Where a liquid–gas interface meets a solid surface, the interface is concave if the liquid is attracted to (wets) the solid and convex if not. In the related phenomenon of **capillarity**, a liquid climbs up a narrow tube if it wets the tube's material, but is pushed down by the tube if it does not.

Why liquids exhibit surface tension

Surface molecules— asymmetric attraction

Interior molecules— symmetric attraction

Fluid Flow, Bernoulli's Equation

(Sections 5–7) An ideal fluid is an incompressible fluid with no viscosity. A flow line is the path of a fluid particle. In **laminar flow**, layers of fluid slide smoothly past each other. In **turbulent flow**, there is disorder and a constantly changing flow pattern.

Conservation of mass for an incompressible fluid is expressed by the **equation of continuity:** For a liquid flowing in a tube with varying cross section, the flow speeds v_1 and v_2 at two cross sections with areas A_1 and A_2, respectively, are related by $A_1v_1 = A_2v_2$ (Equation 10). The product Av is the **volume flow rate**, $\Delta V/\Delta t$, the rate at which volume crosses a section of the tube: $\Delta V/\Delta t = Av$.

Bernoulli's equation relates the pressure p, flow speed v, and elevation y in an ideal fluid. For any two points, indicated by subscripts 1 and 2, $p_1 + \rho gy_1 + \frac{1}{2}\rho v_1^2 = p_2 + \rho gy_2 + \frac{1}{2}\rho v_2^2$ (Equation 12). This equation states that faster flow is associated with lower pressure. That fact underlies the working of Venturi meters and is also responsible for the lift on airplane wings and for the nonparabolic trajectories of spinning baseballs and golf balls.

Lift due to Bernoulli's principle: Air travels farther and therefore faster over the top than the bottom of the wing; the result is lower pressure over the top of the wing.

Continued

Real Fluids: Viscosity and Turbulence

(Section 8) Real fluids have viscosity. Consequently, the boundary layer fluid in contact with a stationary wall or surface is nearly at rest, whereas flow speeds peak in the center of a pipe or channel. Flow is typically laminar at low speeds; at higher speeds, flow tends to become turbulent.

Fluid Mechanics: Problem Set

MP For instructor-assigned homework, go to www.masteringphysics.com

Conceptual Questions

1. A clear plastic hose is attached to the narrow end of a funnel, and its free end is bent around to point upward (Figure 39). When water is poured into the funnel, it rises in the hose to the same level as in the funnel, despite the fact that the funnel has a lot more water in it than the hose. Why does it do this? Where does the force come from to support the weight of the extra water in the funnel?

▲ FIGURE 39
Question 1.

2. In describing the size of a large ship, one uses the expression "It displaces 20,000 tons." What does this expression mean? Can the weight of the ship be obtained from this information?

3. A popular, though expensive, sport is hot-air ballooning, in which a large nylon balloon is filled with air heated by a gas burner at the bottom. Why must the air be heated? How does the balloonist control the balloon's ascent and descent?

4. Equation A below shows that an area ratio of 100 to 1 can give 100 times more output force than input force. Doesn't this violate conservation of energy? Explain.

$$p = \frac{F_1}{A_1} = \frac{F_2}{A_2} \quad \text{and} \quad F_2 = \frac{A_2}{A_1}F_1. \tag{A}$$

5. Suppose the door of a room makes an airtight, but frictionless, fit in its frame. Do you think you could open the door if the air pressure on one side were standard atmospheric pressure and that on the other side differed from standard by 1%? Back up your answer with a simple but reasonable calculation.

6. When a smooth-flowing stream of water comes out of a faucet, it narrows as it falls. Why does it do this?

7. You push an empty glass jar into a tank of water with the open mouth downward, so that the air inside the jar is trapped and cannot get out. If you push the jar deeper into the water, does the buoyant force on the jar stay the same? If not, does it increase or decrease? Explain your answer.

8. A very smooth wooden block is pressed against the bottom of a container of water so that no water remains under the block. Will this block rise to the surface when it is released? Why? (*Hint:* Can the water exert a force on the bottom of the block?)

9. A marble is in a little box that is floating in a beaker of water. The marble is then removed from the box and dropped into the water, sinking to the bottom. What happens to the water level

in the beaker when you do this? Does it go up, go down, or stay the same? Why? (It might help to draw a figure.)

10. A beaker of water rests on a scale. You slowly lower a piece of metal into the water, using a string attached to the metal, but you do not allow the metal to touch the walls or bottom of the beaker. (a) What happens to the reading on the scale when you do this? (b) How does the scale "know" that the metal is in the water, since the metal never touches either the beaker or the scale? (It might help to draw a figure.)

11. If a rocketship traveling through the vacuum of space is hit by a small asteroid, it could lose its air through the hole caused by the collision. Many people would describe this situation by saying that the air was *sucked out* by the vacuum. Is this a good *physical* explanation of what is happening? Does the vacuum actually suck out the air? What does make the air go out?

12. If you walk along a coastal seaport, you often see recently caught fish that are enormously bloated. These are fish that live very deep in the sea. What caused them to be so bloated? Were they that way deep down where they normally live?

13. Submarines can remain at equilibrium at various depths in the ocean, and they are made of rigid metal to withstand great pressures. (a) What must be the average density of a submarine? (b) Devise a simple way that a submarine could cause itself to go up (or down) without using its propellers.

14. You are told, "Bernoulli's equation tells us that where there is higher fluid speed, there is lower fluid pressure, and vice versa." Is this statement always true, even for an idealized fluid?

15. A helium-filled balloon is tied to a light string inside of a car at rest. The other end of the string is attached to the floor of the car, so the balloon pulls the string vertical. You now accelerate forward. Which way does the balloon move, forward or backward, or does it not move? Justify your reasoning with reference to buoyancy. (If you have a chance, try this experiment yourself—but with someone else doing the driving!)

Multiple-Choice Problems

1. Which has a greater buoyant force on it, a 25 cm³ piece of wood floating with part of its volume above water or a 25 cm³ piece of submerged iron?
   A. The floating wood.
   B. The submerged iron.
   C. They have the same buoyant force on them.
   D. It is impossible to tell without knowing their weights.

2. As a rigid (i.e., constant volume), lighter-than-air balloon leaves the ground and rises, the buoyant force on it
   A. increases.　　B. decreases.　　C. stays the same.

From Chapter 13 of *College Physics*, Ninth Edition, Hugh D. Young. Copyright © 2012 by Pearson Education, Inc. Published by Pearson Addison-Wesley. All rights reserved.

3. A mass of sunken lead is resting against the bottom in a glass of water. You take this lead, put it in a small boat of negligible mass, and float the boat in the water. Which of the following statements are true? (There may be more than one correct choice.)
   A. The sunken lead displaces a volume of water equal to the lead's own volume.
   B. The floating lead displaces a volume of water equal to the lead's own volume.
   C. The sunken lead displaces a volume of water whose weight equals the lead's weight.
   D. The floating lead displaces a volume of water whose weight equals the lead's weight.

4. Two equal-sized buckets are filled to the brim with water, but one of them has a piece of wood floating in it. Which bucket of water weighs more?
   A. The bucket with the wood.
   B. The bucket without the wood.
   C. They weigh the same amount.

5. Two equal *mass* pieces of metal are sitting side by side at the bottom of a deep lake. One piece is aluminum and the other is lead. Which piece has the greater buoyant force acting on it?
   A. The aluminum.
   B. The lead.
   C. They both have the same buoyant force acting on them.

6. If a 5 lb force is required to keep a block of wood 1 ft beneath the surface of water, the force needed to keep it 2 ft beneath the surface is
   A. 2.5 lb.   B. 5 lb.   C. 10 lb.

7. A horizontal pipe with water flowing through it has a circular cross section that varies in diameter. The diameter at the wide section is 3 times that of the diameter at the narrow section. If the rate of flow of the water in the narrow section is 9.0 L/min, the rate of flow of the water in the wide section is
   A. 1.0 L/min.   B. 3.0 L/min.   C. 9.0 L/min.
   D. 18 L/min.   E. 36 L/min.

8. A horizontal cylindrical pipe has a part with a diameter half that of the rest of the pipe. If V is the speed of the fluid in the wider section of pipe, then the speed of the fluid in the narrower section is
   A. $V/4$.   B. $V/2$.   C. $2V$.   D. $4V$.

9. If the *absolute* pressure at a depth d in a lake is P, the absolute pressure at a depth $2d$ will be
   A. $2P$.   B. P.
   C. Greater than $2P$.   D. Less than $2P$.

10. If the *gauge* pressure at a depth d in a lake is P, the gauge pressure at a depth $2d$ will be
    A. $2P$.   B. P.
    C. Greater than $2P$.   D. Less than $2P$.

11. There is a great deal of ice floating on the oceans near the North Pole. If this ice were to melt due to global warming, what would happen to the level of the oceans?
    A. The level would rise.
    B. The level would fall.
    C. The level would stay the same.

12. A rigid metal object is dropped into a lake and sinks to the bottom. The density of the water in this lake is the same everywhere. As the object sinks deeper and deeper below the surface, the buoyant force on it
    A. gets greater and greater.
    B. gets less and less.

C. does not change.
D. is equal to the weight of this object.

13. A spherical object has a density ρ. If it is compressed under high pressure to half of its original diameter, its density will now be
    A. $\rho/8$.   B. $\rho/4$.   C. 2ρ.
    D. 4ρ.   E. 8ρ.

14. Identical-size cubes of lead and aluminum are suspended at different depths by two wires in a tank of water. Which wire will have a greater tension?
    A. The wire holding the lead cube
    B. The wire holding the aluminum cube
    C. The tensions in the two wires will be equal.

15. Two small holes are drilled in the side of a barrel filled with water. One hole is twice as far below the surface as the other. If the speed of the water flowing from the upper hole is V, the speed of the water flowing from the lower hole is
    A. V B. $V/2$ C. $2V$ D. $\sqrt{2}V$

Problems

1 Density

1. • You purchase a rectangular piece of metal that has dimensions 5.0 mm $\times$ 15.0 mm $\times$ 30.0 mm and mass 0.0158 kg. The seller tells you that the metal is gold. To check this, you compute the average density of the piece. What value do you get? Were you cheated?

2. • A kidnapper demands a 40.0 kg cube of platinum as a ransom. What is the length of a side?

3. • Calculate the weight of air at 20°C in a room that measures 5.00 $\times$ 4.50 $\times$ 3.25 m. Give your answer in newtons and in pounds.

4. • By how many newtons do you increase the weight of your car when you fill up your 11.5 gal gas tank with gasoline? A gallon is equal to 3.788 L and the density of gasoline is 737 kg/m³.

5. •• **How big is a million dollars?** At the time this problem was written, the price of gold was about $1239 per ounce, while that of platinum was about $1508 an ounce. The "ounce" in this case is the *troy ounce,* which is equal to 31.1035 g. (The more familiar *avoirdupois ounce* is equal to 28.35 g.) The density of gold is 19.3 g/cm³ and that of platinum is 21.4 g/cm³. (a) If you find a spherical gold nugget worth 1.00 million dollars, what would be its *diameter?* (b) How much would a platinum nugget of this size be worth?

6. •• A cube 5.0 cm on each side is made of a metal alloy. After you drill a cylindrical hole 2.0 cm in diameter all the way through and perpendicular to one face, you find that the cube weighs 7.50 N. (a) What is the density of this metal? (b) What did the cube weigh before you drilled the hole in it?

7. •• A cube of compressible material (such as Styrofoam™ or balsa wood) has a density ρ and sides of length L. (a) If you keep its mass the same, but compress each side to half its length, what will be its new density, in terms of ρ? (b) If you keep the mass and shape the same, what would the length of each side have to be (in terms of L) so that the density of the cube was three times its original value?

8. • A hollow cylindrical copper pipe is 1.50 m long and has an outside diameter of 3.50 cm and an inside diameter of 2.50 cm. How much does it weigh?

9. • A uniform lead sphere and a uniform aluminum sphere have the same mass. What is the ratio of the radius of the aluminum sphere to the radius of the lead sphere?

2 Pressure in a Fluid

10. • **Blood pressure.** Systemic blood pressure is defined as the
BIO ratio of two pressures, both expressed in millimeters of mercury. Normal blood pressure is about $\frac{120 \text{ mm}}{80 \text{ mm}}$, which is usually just stated as $\frac{120}{80}$. (See also Problem 24.) What would normal systemic blood pressure be if, instead of millimeters of mercury, we expressed pressure in each of the following units, but continued to use the same ratio format? (a) atmospheres, (b) torr, (c) Pa, (d) N/m², (e) psi.

11. • **Blood.** (a) **Mass of blood.** The human body typically con-
BIO tains 5 L of blood of density 1060 kg/m³. How many kilograms of blood are in the body? (b) The average blood pressure is 13,000 Pa at the heart. What average force does the blood exert on each square centimeter of the heart? (c) **Red blood cells.** Red blood cells have a specific gravity of 5.0 and a diameter of about 7.5 μm. If they are spherical in shape (which is not quite true), what is the mass of such a cell?

12. • **Landing on Venus.** One of the great difficulties in landing on Venus is dealing with the crushing pressure of the atmosphere, which is 92 times the earth's atmospheric pressure. (a) If you are designing a lander for Venus in the shape of a hemisphere 2.5 m in diameter, how many newtons of inward force must it be prepared to withstand due to the Venusian atmosphere? (Don't forget about the bottom!) (b) How much force would the lander have to withstand on the earth?

13. • You are designing a diving bell to withstand the pressure of seawater at a depth of 250 m. (a) What is the gauge pressure at this depth? (You can ignore the small changes in the density of the water with depth.) (b) At the 250 m depth, what is the net force due to the water outside and the air inside the bell on a circular glass window 30.0 cm in diameter if the pressure inside the diving bell equals the pressure at the surface of the water? (You may ignore the small variation in pressure over the surface of the window.)

14. • **Glaucoma.** Under normal circumstances, the vitreous
BIO humor, a jelly-like substance in the main part of the eye, exerts a pressure of up to 24 mm of mercury that maintains the shape of the eye. If blockage of the drainage duct for aqueous humor causes this pressure to increase to about 50 mm of mercury, the condition is called *glaucoma*. What is the *increase* in the total force (in newtons) on the walls of the eye if the pressure increases from 24 mm to 50 mm of mercury? We can quite accurately model the eye as a sphere 2.5 cm in diameter.

15. • By means of physiological adaptations that are still not very well understood, sperm whales are thought to be able to hunt for their food at depths of between 400 m and 3000 m. (a) What range of gauge pressures (in Pa and atm) do the whales withstand at these depths? (b) Estimate the total inward force of water pressure on the surface of a sperm whale at a depth of 3000 m, modeling the whale as a cylinder 16 m long and 4 m in diameter.

16. • What gauge pressure must a pump produce to pump water from the bottom of the Grand Canyon (elevation 730 m) to Indian Gardens (elevation 1370 m)? Express your result in pascals and in atmospheres.

17. • **Intravenous feeding.** A hospital
BIO patient is being fed intravenously with a liquid of density 1060 kg/m³. (See Figure 40.) The container of liquid is raised 1.20 m above the patient's arm where the fluid enters his veins. What is the pressure this fluid exerts on his veins, expressed in millimeters of mercury?

▲ FIGURE 40
Problem 17.

18. •• A 975-kg car has its tires each inflated to "32.0 pounds." (a) What are the absolute and gauge pressures in these tires in lb/in.², Pa, and atm? (b) If the tires were perfectly round, could the tire pressure exert any force on the pavement? (Assume that the tire walls are flexible so that the pressure exerted by the tire on the pavement equals the air pressure inside the tire.) (c) If you examine a car's tires, it is obvious that there is some flattening at the bottom. What is the total contact area for all four tires of the flattened part of the tires at the pavement?

19. •• An electrical short cuts off all power to a submersible diving vehicle when it is 30 m below the surface of the ocean. The crew must push out a hatch of area 0.75 m² and weight 300 N on the bottom to escape. If the pressure inside is 1.0 atm, what downward force must the crew exert on the hatch to open it?

20. • **Standing on your head.** (a) When you stand on your head,
BIO what is the *difference* in pressure of the blood in your brain compared with the pressure when you stand on your feet if you are 1.85 m tall? The density of blood is 1060 kg/m³. (b) What effect does the increased pressure have on the blood vessels in your brain?

21. •• You are designing a machine for a space exploration vehicle. It contains an enclosed column of oil that is 1.50 m tall, and you need the pressure difference between the top and the bottom of this column to be 0.125 atm. (a) What must be the density of the oil? (b) If the vehicle is taken to Mars, where the acceleration due to gravity is 0.379g, what will be the pressure difference (in earth atmospheres) between the top and bottom of the oil column?

22. •• **Ear damage from diving.** If the force on the tympanic
BIO membrane (eardrum) increases by about 1.5 N above the force from atmospheric pressure, the membrane can be damaged. When you go scuba diving in the ocean, below what depth could damage to your eardrum start to occur? The eardrum is typically 8.2 mm in diameter. (Consult Table 1 at the end of this problem set.)

23. •• A barrel contains a 0.120 m layer of oil of density 600 kg/m³ floating on water that is 0.250 m deep. (a) What is the gauge pressure at the oil–water interface? (b) What is the gauge pressure at the bottom of the barrel?

24. •• **Blood pressure.** Systemic blood pressure is expressed as
BIO the ratio of the *systolic* pressure (when the heart first ejects blood into the arteries) to the *diastolic* pressure (when the heart is relaxed):

$$\text{systemic blood pressure} = \frac{\text{systolic pressure}}{\text{diastolic pressure}}$$

Both pressures are measured at the level of the heart and are expressed in millimeters of mercury (or torr), although the units are not written. Normal systemic blood pressure is $\frac{120}{80}$. (a) What are the maximum and minimum forces (in newtons) that the blood exerts against each square centimeter of the heart for a person with normal blood pressure? (b) As pointed out in the text, blood pressure is normally measured on the upper arm at the same height as the heart. Due to therapy for an injury, a patient's upper arm is extended 30.0 cm above his heart. In that position, what should be his systemic blood pressure reading, expressed in the standard way, if he has normal blood pressure? The density of blood is 1060 kg/m^3.

25. •• **Blood pressure on the moon.** When we eventually estab-
BIO lish lunar colonies, people living there will need to have their blood pressure taken. Assume that we continue to express the systemic blood pressure as we now do on earth (see previous problem) and that the density of blood does not change. Suppose also that normal blood pressure on the moon is still $\frac{120}{80}$ (which may not actually be true). If a lunar colonizer has her blood pressure taken at her upper arm when it is raised 25 cm above her heart, what will be her systemic blood pressure reading, expressed in the standard way, if she has normal blood pressure? The acceleration due to gravity on the moon is 1.67 m/s^2.

26. • The piston of a hydraulic automobile lift is 0.30 m in diameter. What gauge pressure, in pascals, is required to lift a car with a mass of 1200 kg? Now express this pressure in atmospheres.

27. •• **Hydraulic lift.** You are designing a hydraulic lift for an automobile garage. It will consist of two oil-filled cylindrical pipes of different diameters. A worker pushes down on a piston at one end, raising the car on a platform at the other end. (See Figure 41.) To handle a full range of jobs, you must be able to lift cars up to 3000 kg, plus the 500 kg platform on which they are parked. To avoid injury to your workers, the maximum amount of force a worker should need to exert is 100 N. (a) What should be the diameter of the pipe under the platform? (b) If the worker pushes down with a stroke 50 cm long, by how much will he raise the car at the other end?

▲ FIGURE 41 Problem 27.

28. •• There is a maximum depth at which a diver can breathe through a snorkel tube (Fig. 42), because as the depth increases, so does the pressure difference, which tends to collapse the diver's lungs. Since the snorkel connects the air in the lungs to the atmosphere at the surface, the pressure inside the lungs is atmospheric pressure. What is the external–internal pressure difference when the diver's lungs are at a depth of 6.1 m (about 20 ft)? Assume that the diver is in freshwater. (A scuba diver breathing from compressed air tanks can operate at greater depths than can a snorkeler, since the pressure of the air inside the scuba diver's lungs increases to match the external pressure of the water.)

p_a

6.1 m

▲ FIGURE 42 Problem 28.

3 Archimedes's Principle: Buoyancy

29. • A solid aluminum ingot weighs 89 N in air. (a) What is its volume? (See Table 1.) (b) The ingot is suspended from a rope and totally immersed in water. What is the tension in the rope (the *apparent* weight of the ingot in water)?

30. •• **Fish navigation.** (a) As you can tell by watching them in
BIO an aquarium, fish are able to remain at any depth in water with no effort. What does this ability tell you about their density? (b) Fish are able to inflate themselves using a sac (called the *swim bladder*) located under their spinal column. These sacs can be filled with an oxygen–nitrogen mixture that comes from the blood. If a 2.75 kg fish in fresh water inflates itself and increases its volume by 10%, find the *net* force that the *water* exerts on it. (c) What is the net *external* force on it? Does the fish go up or down when it inflates itself?

31. •• When an open-faced boat has a mass of 5750 kg, including its cargo and passengers, it floats with the water just up to the top of its gunwales (sides) on a freshwater lake. (a) What is the volume of this boat? (b) The captain decides that it is too dangerous to float with his boat on the verge of sinking, so he decides to throw some cargo overboard so that 20% of the boat's volume will be above water. How much mass should he throw out?

32. •• An ore sample weighs 17.50 N in air. When the sample is suspended by a light cord and totally immersed in water, the tension in the cord is 11.20 N. Find the total volume and the density of the sample.

33. •• A slab of ice floats on a freshwater lake. What minimum volume must the slab have for a 45.0 kg woman to be able to stand on it without getting her feet wet?

34. • Calculate the average density of the planet Saturn. How does your answer compare to the density of water, and what does this imply about the buoyancy of Saturn, if you could find an ocean big enough to drop it into?

35. •• A hollow plastic sphere is held below the surface of a freshwater lake by a cord anchored to the bottom of the lake. The sphere has a volume of 0.650 m^3 and the tension in the cord is 900 N. (a) Calculate the buoyant force exerted by the water on the sphere. (b) What is the mass of the sphere? (c) The cord breaks and the sphere rises to the surface. When the sphere comes to rest, what fraction of its volume will be submerged?

36. •• (a) Calculate the buoyant force of air (density $1.20 \, \text{kg/m}^3$) on a spherical party balloon that has a radius of 15.0 cm. (b) If the rubber of the balloon itself has a mass of 2.00 g and the balloon is filled with helium (density $0.166 \, \text{kg/m}^3$), calculate the net upward force (the "lift") that acts on it in air.

37. •• **The tip of the iceberg.** Icebergs consist of freshwater ice and float in the ocean with only about 10% of their volume above water (the "tip of the iceberg," so to speak). This percentage can vary, depending on the condition of the ice. Assume that the ice has the density given in Table 1, although, in reality, this can vary considerably, depending on the condition of the ice and the amount of impurities in it. (a) What does this 10% observation tell us is the density of seawater? (b) What percentage of the icebergs' volume would be above water if they were floating in a large freshwater lake such as Lake Superior?

4 Surface Tension and Capillarity

38. • At 20° C, the surface tension of water is 72.8 dynes/cm. Find the excess pressure inside of (a) an ordinary-size water drop of radius 1.50 mm and (b) a fog droplet of radius 0.0100 mm.

39. • Find the gauge pressure in pascals inside a soap bubble 7.00 cm in diameter. The surface tension of this soap is 25.0 dynes/cm.

40. • What radius must a water drop have for the difference between the inside and outside pressures to be 0.0200 atm? The surface tension of water is 72.8 dynes/cm.

41. •• At 20° C, the surface tension of water is 72.8 dynes/cm and that of carbon tetrachloride (CCl_4) is 26.8 dynes/cm. If the gauge pressure is the same in two drops of these liquids, what is the ratio of the *volume* of the water drop to that of the CCl_4 drop?

5 Fluid Flow

42. • At a point where an irrigation canal having a rectangular cross section is 18.5 m wide and 3.75 m deep, the water flows at 2.50 cm/s. At a point downstream, but on the same level, the canal is 16.5 m wide, but the water flows at 11.0 cm/s. How deep is the canal at this point?

43. • Water is flowing in a pipe with a varying cross-sectional area, and at all points the water completely fills the pipe. At point 1, the cross-sectional area of the pipe is $0.070 \, \text{m}^2$ and the magnitude of the fluid velocity is 3.50 m/s. What is the fluid speed at points in the pipe where the cross-sectional area is (a) $0.105 \, \text{m}^2$, (b) $0.047 \, \text{m}^2$?

44. • Water is flowing in a cylindrical pipe of varying circular cross-sectional area, and at all points the water completely fills the pipe. (a) At one point in the pipe, the radius is 0.150 m. What is the speed of the water at this point if the volume flow rate in the pipe is $1.20 \, \text{m}^3/\text{s}$? (b) At a second point in the pipe, the water speed is 3.80 m/s. What is the radius of the pipe at this point?

45. •• A shower head has 20 circular openings, each with radius 1.0 mm. The shower head is connected to a pipe with radius 0.80 cm. If the speed of water in the pipe is 3.0 m/s, what is its speed as it exits the shower-head openings?

46. •• You're holding a hose at waist height and spraying water horizontally with it. The hose nozzle has a diameter of 1.80 cm, and the water splashes on the ground a distance of 0.950 m horizontally from the nozzle. Suppose you now constrict the nozzle to a diameter of 0.750 cm; how far horizontally from the nozzle will the water travel before hitting the ground? (Ignore air resistance.)

6 Bernoulli's Equation
7 Applications of Bernoulli's Equation

47. • A small circular hole 6.00 mm in diameter is cut in the side of a large water tank, 14.0 m below the water level in the tank. The top of the tank is open to the air. Find the speed at which the water shoots out of the tank.

48. • A sealed tank containing seawater to a height of 11.0 m also contains air above the water at a gauge pressure of 3.00 atm. Water flows out from the bottom through a small hole. Calculate the speed with which the water comes out of the tank.

49. •• What gauge pressure is required in the city water mains for a stream from a fire hose connected to the mains to reach a vertical height of 15.0 m? (Assume that the mains have a much larger diameter than the fire hose.)

50. • At one point in a pipeline, the water's speed is 3.00 m/s and the gauge pressure is $4.00 \times 10^4 \, \text{Pa}$. Find the gauge pressure at a second point in the line 11.0 m lower than the first if the pipe diameter at the second point is twice that at the first.

51. •• **Lift on an airplane.** Air streams horizontally past a small airplane's wings such that the speed is 70.0 m/s over the top surface and 60.0 m/s past the bottom surface. If the plane has a mass of 1340 kg and a wing area of $16.2 \, \text{m}^2$, what is the net vertical force (including the effects of gravity) on the airplane? The density of the air is $1.20 \, \text{kg/m}^3$.

52. •• A golf course sprinkler system discharges water from a horizontal pipe at the rate of $7200 \, \text{cm}^3/\text{s}$. At one point in the pipe, where the radius is 4.00 cm, the water's absolute pressure is $2.40 \times 10^5 \, \text{Pa}$. At a second point in the pipe, the water passes through a constriction where the radius is 2.00 cm. What is the water's absolute pressure as it flows through this constriction?

53. •• Water discharges from a horizontal cylindrical pipe at the rate of $465 \, \text{cm}^3/\text{s}$. At a point in the pipe where the radius is 2.05 cm, the absolute pressure is $1.60 \times 10^5 \, \text{Pa}$. What is the pipe's radius at a constriction if the pressure there is reduced to $1.20 \times 10^5 \, \text{Pa}$?

54. •• **Artery blockage.** A medical technician is trying to determine what percentage of a patient's artery is blocked by plaque. To do this, she measures the blood pressure just before the region of blockage and finds that it is $1.20 \times 10^4 \, \text{Pa}$, while in the region of blockage it is $1.15 \times 10^4 \, \text{Pa}$. Furthermore, she knows that blood flowing through the normal artery just before the point of blockage is traveling at 30.0 cm/s, and the specific gravity of this patient's blood is 1.06. What percentage of the cross-sectional area of the patient's artery is blocked by the plaque?

BIO

55. •• At a certain point in a horizontal pipeline, the water's speed is 2.50 m/s and the gauge pressure is $1.80 \times 10^4 \, \text{Pa}$. Find the gauge pressure at a second point in the line if the cross-sectional area at the second point is twice that at the first.

8 Real Fluids: Viscosity and Turbulence

56. • With what terminal speed would a steel ball bearing 2.00 mm in diameter fall in a liquid of viscosity $0.150 \, \text{N} \cdot \text{s/m}^2$ if we could neglect buoyancy?

57. •• What speed must a gold sphere of radius 3.00 mm have in castor oil for the viscous drag force to be one-fourth of the weight of the sphere? The density of gold is $19,300 \, \text{kg/m}^3$ and the viscosity of the oil is $0.986 \, \text{N} \cdot \text{s/m}^2$.

58. •• A copper sphere with a mass of 0.20 g and a density of 8900 kg/m³ is observed to fall with a terminal speed of 6.0 cm/s in an unknown liquid. Find the viscosity of the unknown liquid if its buoyancy can be neglected.

59. •• **Clogged artery.** Viscous blood is flowing through an
BIO artery partially clogged by cholesterol. A surgeon wants to remove enough of the cholesterol to double the flow rate of blood through this artery. If the original diameter of the artery is D, what should be the new diameter (in terms of D) to accomplish this for the same pressure gradient?

General Problems

60. •• Advertisements for a certain small car claim that it floats in water. (a) If the car's mass is 900 kg and its interior volume is 3.0 m³, what fraction of the car is immersed when it floats? You can ignore the volume of steel and other materials. (b) Water gradually leaks in and displaces the air in the car. What fraction of the interior volume is filled with water when the car sinks?

61. •• A U-shaped tube open to the air at both ends contains some mercury. A quantity of water is carefully poured into the left arm of the U-shaped tube until the vertical height of the water column is 15.0 cm (Figure 43). (a) What is the gauge pressure at the water–mercury interface? (b) Calculate the vertical distance h from the top of the mercury in the right-hand arm of the tube to the top of the water in the left-hand arm.

▲ **FIGURE 43** Problem 61.

62. •• An open barge has the dimensions shown in Figure 44. If the barge is made out of 4.0-cm-thick steel plate on each of its four sides and its bottom, what mass of coal can the barge carry in fresh water without sinking? Is there enough room in the barge to hold this amount of coal? (The density of coal is about 1500 kg/m³.)

▲ **FIGURE 44** Problem 62.

63. •• A piece of wood is 0.600 m long, 0.250 m wide, and 0.080 m thick. Its density is 600 kg/m³. What volume of lead must be fastened underneath it to sink the wood in calm water so that its top is just even with the water level? What is the mass of this volume of lead?

64. •• A hot-air balloon has a volume of 2200 m³. The balloon fabric (the envelope) weighs 900 N. The basket with gear and full propane tanks weighs 1700 N. If the balloon can barely lift an additional 3200 N of passengers, breakfast, and champagne when the outside air density is 1.23 kg/m³, what is the average density of the heated gases in the envelope?

65. •• In seawater, a life preserver with a volume of 0.0400 m³ will support a 75.0 kg person (average density 980 kg/m³), with 20% of the person's volume above water when the life preserver is fully submerged. What is the density of the material composing the life preserver?

66. •• Block A in Figure 45 hangs by a cord from spring balance D and is submerged in a liquid C contained in beaker

B. The mass of the beaker is 1.00 kg; the mass of the liquid is 1.80 kg. Balance D reads 3.50 kg and balance E reads 7.50 kg. The volume of block A is 3.80×10^{-3} m³. (a) What is the density of the liquid? (b) What will each balance read if block A is pulled up out of the liquid?

▲ **FIGURE 45** Problem 66.

67. •• A hunk of aluminum is completely covered with a gold shell to form an ingot of weight 45.0 N. When you suspend the ingot from a spring balance and submerge the ingot in water, the balance reads 39.0 N. What is the weight of the gold in the shell?

68. •• A liquid is used to make a mercury-type barometer. The barometer is intended for spacefaring astronauts. At the surface of the earth, the column of liquid rises to a height of 2185 mm, but on the surface of Planet X, where the acceleration due to gravity is one-fourth of its value on earth, the column rises to only 725 mm. Find (a) the density of the liquid and (b) the atmospheric pressure at the surface of Planet X.

69. •• An open cylindrical tank of acid rests at the edge of a table 1.4 m above the floor of the chemistry lab. If this tank springs a small hole in the side at its base, how far from the foot of the table will the acid hit the floor if the acid in the tank is 75 cm deep?

70. •• Water stands at a depth H in a large, open tank whose side walls are vertical (Fig. 46). A hole is made in one of the walls at a depth h below the water surface. (a) At what distance R from the foot of the wall does the emerging stream strike the floor? (b) How far above the bottom of the tank could a second hole be cut so that the stream emerging from it could have the same range as for the first hole?

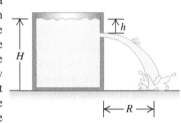

▲ **FIGURE 46** Problem 70.

71. •• **Exploring Europa's oceans.** Europa, a satellite of Jupiter, appears to have an ocean beneath its icy surface. Proposals have been made to send a robotic submarine to Europa to see if there might be life there. There is no atmosphere on Europa, and we shall assume that the surface ice is thin enough that we can neglect its weight and that the oceans are fresh water having the same density as on the earth. The mass and diameter of Europa have been measured to be 4.78×10^{22} kg and 3130 km, respectively. (a) If the submarine intends to submerge to a depth of 100 m, what pressure must it be designed to withstand? (b) If you wanted to test this submarine before sending it to Europa, how deep would it have to go in our oceans to experience the same pressure as the pressure at a depth of 100 m on Europa?

72. •• The horizontal pipe shown in Figure 47 has a cross-sectional area of 40.0 cm² at the wider portions and 10.0 cm² at the constriction. Water is flowing in the pipe, and the discharge

from the pipe is $6.00 \times 10^{-3} \text{ m}^3/\text{s}$ (6.00 L/s). Find (a) the flow speeds at the wide and the narrow portions; (b) the pressure difference between these portions; (c) the difference in height between the mercury columns in the U-shaped tube.

▲ **FIGURE 47** Problem 72.

73. •• **Venturi meter.** The Venturi meter is a device used to measure the speed of a fluid traveling through a pipe. Two cylinders are inserted in small holes in the pipes, as shown in

▲ **FIGURE 48** Problem 73.

Figure 48. Since the cross-sectional area is different at the two places, the speed and pressure will be different there also. The difference (h) in the heights of the two columns can easily be measured, as can the cross-sectional areas A_1 and A_2. Notice that points 1 and 2 in the figure are both at the same vertical height. (a) Show that $\Delta p = \rho gh$, where ρ is the density of the fluid and Δp is the pressure difference between points 1 and 2. (b) Apply Bernoulli's equation and the continuity condition to show that the speed at point 1 is given by the equation

$$v_1 = \sqrt{\frac{2gh}{(A_1/A_2)^2 - 1}}.$$ (c) How would you find the speed at point 2?

74. •• **Compressible fluids.** Throughout this chapter, we have dealt only with incompressible fluids. But under very high pressure, fluids do, in fact, compress. (a) Show that the continuity condition for compressible fluids is $\rho_1 A_1 v_1 = \rho_2 A_2 v_2$, where ρ is the density of the fluid. (b) Show that your result reduces to the familiar result for incompressible fluids.

Passage Problems

BIO Measuring blood pressure. The standard procedure for measuring blood pressure determines both the systolic (maximum) and diastolic (minimum) pressures in the brachial artery during the

▲ **FIGURE 49** Problems 75–78.

cardiac cycle. (The brachial artery is the major artery that runs down the arm and provides blood to both the hand and arm.) See Figure 49.

First, the cuff is inflated to stop the flow of blood. As the pressure in the cuff is reduced to the patient's systolic blood pressure, some blood will begin to flow past the cuff, but in a turbulent fashion because the artery is still not fully open. This turbulence generates characteristic Korotkoff sounds that allow the physician to determine when to make the systolic pressure reading using the manometer. When the pressure is further reduced to the patient's diastolic blood pressure, the cuff no longer restricts arterial blood flow and the Korotkoff sounds disappear (as the blood flow becomes laminar again). A healthy patient typically has a systolic pressure that is between 90 and 120 mm Hg and a diastolic pressure of 60 to 80 mm. Note that all blood-pressure measurements are gauge pressures (i.e., they are the pressure difference between the arterial pressure and the ambient air pressure).

75. Roughly speaking, arteries carry blood from the heart and veins return blood to the heart. From your experience with small cuts or skinned knees, what can you say about the pressure in the venous system (veins)?
    A. It is much less than atmospheric pressure.
    B. It is slightly more than atmospheric pressure.
    C. It is approximately the same as atmospheric pressure.
    D. It is much greater than atmospheric pressure.
    E. It is slightly greater than atmospheric pressure.

76. Blood pressure is normally measured on the arm of a patient at a point that is nearly at the same height as the heart. If we were to measure the blood pressure on the lower leg of a standing patient, we would expect the measurement to be
    A. lower than
    B. higher than
    C. the same as the measurement on the arm.

77. On the earth, the pressure generated by the heart is sufficient to pump blood to a height of 1.3 m. (The density of blood is 1.04 g/cm³.) If the top of your head were 0.5 m above your heart, what would be the strongest gravitational acceleration that you could endure on another planet before your heart would be unable to pump blood to your brain?
    A. 2g
    B. 3g
    C. 5g
    D. 10g

78. The cross-sectional area of the aorta is 3 cm², and the average velocity of blood leaving the heart into the aorta is 30 cm/s. If the combined effective cross sectional area of the body's capillaries is 600 cm², what is the average flow rate in a capillary?
    A. 1 cm/s
    B. 2 cm/s
    C. 0.01 cm/s
    D. 0.15 cm/s
    E. 0.2 cm/s

TABLE 1 Densities of Some Common Substances

Material	Density (kg/m^3)*	Material	Density (kg/m^3)*
Gases		Concrete	2×10^3
Air (1 atm, 20° C)	1.20	Aluminum	2.7×10^3
		Iron, steel	7.8×10^3
Liquids		Brass	8.6×10^3
Benzene	0.90×10^3	Copper	8.9×10^3
Ethanol	0.81×10^3	Silver	10.5×10^3
Water	1.00×10^3	Lead	11.3×10^3
Seawater	1.03×10^3	Gold	19.3×10^3
Blood	1.06×10^3	Platinum	21.4×10^3
Solids		Mercury	13.6×10^3
Glycerin	1.26×10^3	White-dwarf star	10^{10}
Ice	0.92×10^3	Neutron star	10^{18}

*To obtain the densities in grams per cubic centimeter, simply divide by 10^3.

ANSWERS TO SELECTED PROBLEMS

Conceptual Questions

1. The pressure in a fluid depends only on height, not the shape of the container. The height of both columns is the same because the pressure at the bottom of each column of water must be the same, if the water is not flowing in either direction. The water in the funnel is supported partly by the rest of the water and partly by the sides of the funnel.

3. Hot air has a smaller density than the surrounding air so the buoyancy force is larger than the weight when the balloon is filled with hot air. The density of the air in the balloon depends on the temperature of this air; the ascent or descent of the balloon is controlled by varying the temperature of the air in the balloon.

5. The pressure difference would be $(0.01)(1.0 \times 10^5 \text{ Pa}) = 1.0 \times 10^3 \text{ Pa}$. For a door with area 2 m² the net force keeping the door closed would be 2×10^3 N. This is about 450 pounds. It would take a very strong person to pull the door open. But all that would be required would be to open it slightly, so air can move from the high pressure to the low pressure side. Once the pressure is equalized the door will easily open the rest of the way.

9. When the marble is sitting in the floating box it must cause an amount of water to be displaced that is equal to the weight of the marble. When the marble is sitting at the bottom of the beaker the buoyant force on it is less than its weight, since it sinks, so it is displacing less than its weight of water. The marble causes less water to be displaced when it has been dropped into the water, so the water level in the beaker falls.

11. The pressure inside the rocket ship pushes the air through the hole. The vacuum doesn't pull the air out; the vacuum exerts no force.

13. (a) The average density of the submarine must equal that of the surrounding water when the submarine floats at equilibrium at some depth. The density of water increases with depth below the surface, so the average density of the submarine is different when it is floating at different depths. (b) The submarine could rise by decreasing its average density and descend by increasing its average density. It could do this either by pushing some water out of tanks within the submarine and replacing that water by air, or by letting more water into these tanks.

15. The balloons move forward toward the front of the car. The air in the car has the same acceleration as the car. The force that produces this acceleration for a volume of the air is exerted by the surrounding air. When this volume is replaced by a helium-filled balloon, the force on the balloon exerted by the surrounding air is the same as when just air was in the volume. But the helium-filled balloon has less mass than the same volume of air (the balloon rises if released), so the same force produces a greater acceleration when applied to the balloon and the balloon has a greater forward acceleration than does the air inside the car.

Multiple-Choice Problems

1. B
3. A, D
5. A
7. C
9. D
11. C
13. E
15. D

Problems

1. $7.02 \times 10^3 \text{ kg/m}^3$; yes
3. 860 N; 193 lb
5. (a) 19.3 cm (b) 2.29 million dollars
7. (a) 8ρ (b) $L/3^{1/3}$
9. 1.6
11. (a) 5.25 kg (b) 1.3 N (c) 1.1×10^{-9} g
13. (a) 2.52×10^6 Pa (b) 1.78×10^5 N
15. (a) From 4×10^6 Pa (40 atm) to 3×10^7 Pa (300 atm) (b) 7×10^9 N
17. 93.5 mm of Hg
19. 2.27×10^5 N
21. (a) 864 kg/m^3 (b) 0.0475 atm
23. (a) 706 Pa (b) 3160 Pa
25. 117/77
27. (a) 4.64 m (b) 1.45 mm
29. (a) 3.4 L (b) 56 N
31. (a) 5.75 m^3 (b) 1150 kg
33. 0.562 m^3
35. (a) 6370 N (b) 558 kg (c) 85.9%
37. (a) $1.02 \times 10^3 \text{ kg/m}^3$ (b) 8.0%
39. 2.86 Pa
41. 20.0
43. (a) 2.33 m/s (b) 5.21 m/s
45. 9.6 m/s
47. 16.6 m/s
49. 1.47×10^5 Pa
51. 500 N, downward
53. 0.41 cm
55. 2.03×10^4 Pa
57. 9.59 cm/s
59. $(2^{1/4})D$
61. (a) 1.47×10^3 Pa (b) 13.9 cm
63. $4.66 \times 10^{-4} \text{ m}^3$; 5.27 kg
65. 732 kg/m^3
67. 33.5 N
69. 2.05 m
71. (a) 1.30×10^5 Pa (b) 13.3 m
73. (c) Use $v_1A_1 = v_2A_2$.

Temperature and Heat

Rick & Nora Bowers/Alamy

Which season do you like better, summer or winter? Whatever your choice, you use a lot of physics to keep comfortable in changing weather conditions. Your body's core needs to be kept at constant temperature. The body has effective temperature-control mechanisms, but sometimes it needs help. On a hot day, you wear less clothing, to improve heat transfer from your body to the air and to allow better cooling by evaporation of perspiration. You probably drink cold beverages, possibly with ice in them, and sit near a fan or in an air-conditioned room. On a cold day, you wear more clothes or stay indoors where it's warm. When you're outside, you keep active and drink hot liquids to stay warm. The concepts in this chapter will help you understand the basic physics of keeping warm or cool.

First we need to define temperature, including temperature scales and ways to measure temperature. Next we discuss changes in dimensions and in the volumes of materials caused by temperature changes. We'll encounter the concept of *heat*, which describes energy transfer caused by temperature differences, and we'll learn to calculate the *rates* of such energy transfers. This chapter lays the groundwork for our later study of *thermodynamics*, the study of energy transformations and their relationships to the properties of matter. Thermodynamics forms an indispensable part of the foundation of physics, chemistry, and the life sciences, and its applications turn up in such diverse places as car engines, refrigerators, biochemical processes, and the structure of stars.

Large animals have a relatively small ratio of heat-dissipating surface area to heat-producing internal volume, so they often have special systems to help them get rid of unwanted heat. People sweat, dogs pant, and antelope jackrabbits send blood into their large, thin-skinned, highly vascularized ears.

1 Temperature and Thermal Equilibrium

The concept of **temperature** is rooted in qualitative ideas of "hot" and "cold" based on our sense of touch. An object that feels hot usually has a higher temperature than when

From Chapter 14 of *College Physics*, Ninth Edition, Hugh D. Young. Copyright © 2012 by Pearson Education, Inc. Published by Pearson Addison-Wesley. All rights reserved.

it feels cold. That's pretty vague, of course, but many properties of matter that we can measure quantitatively depend on temperature. The length of a metal rod increases as the rod becomes hotter. The pressure of gas in a container increases with temperature; a steam boiler may explode if it gets too hot. When a material is extremely hot, it glows "red hot" or "white hot," the color depending on its temperature.

Temperature is also related to the kinetic energies of the molecules of a material. It's important to understand, however, that temperature and heat can and must be defined independently of any detailed molecular picture.

Thermometers

Temperature is a measure of "hotness" or "coldness" on some scale. But *what* scale? We can use any measurable property of a system that varies with its hotness or coldness to assign numbers to various states of hotness and coldness. Figure 1a shows a familiar type of **thermometer** (a device used to measure temperature). When the system becomes hotter, the liquid (usually mercury or ethanol) expands and rises in the tube, and the value of L increases. Another simple system is a quantity of gas in a constant-volume container (Figure 1b). The pressure p, measured by the gauge, increases or decreases as the gas becomes hotter or colder. A third example is the electrical resistance R of a conducting wire, which also varies when the wire becomes hotter or colder. Each of these properties gives us a number (L, p, or R) that varies with hotness and coldness, so each property can be used to make a thermometer.

Thermal Equilibrium

To measure the temperature of an object, you place the thermometer in contact with the object. If you want to know the temperature of a cup of hot coffee, you stick the thermometer in the coffee. As the two interact, the thermometer becomes hotter and the coffee cools off a little. After the thermometer settles down to a steady value, you read the temperature. The system has reached an *equilibrium* condition, in which the interaction between the thermometer and the coffee causes no further change in the temperature of any part of the system. We call this a state of **thermal equilibrium.**

In a state of thermal equilibrium, the thermometer and the coffee have the same temperature. How do we know this? Consider the interaction of any two systems A and B. System A might be a hot potato and B a pan of cold water. We may use any kind of thermometer to monitor their temperatures; for example, we could use the tube-and-liquid system (Figure 1a) for system A and the container of gas and pressure gauge (Figure 1b) for system B. In general, when the two systems come into contact, the values of L and p change as the systems move toward thermal equilibrium. Initially, one system is hotter than the other; during the interaction, each system changes the temperature of the other.

If the systems are separated by an insulating material, or **insulator,** such as wood, plastic foam, or fiberglass, they influence each other more slowly. An *ideal* insulator is a material that permits *no* interactions at all between the two systems. It *prevents* the systems from attaining thermal equilibrium if they aren't in thermal equilibrium at the start. This is why camping coolers are made with insulating materials. We don't want the ice and cold food inside to warm up and attain thermal equilibrium with the hot summer air outside; the insulation delays this process, although not forever.

Zeroth Law of Thermodynamics

Now consider three systems A, B, and C that are initially *not* in thermal equilibrium (Figure 2). We surround them with an ideal insulating box so that they cannot interact with anything except each other. We separate A and B with an ideal insulating wall (the green slab in Figure 2a), but we let system C interact

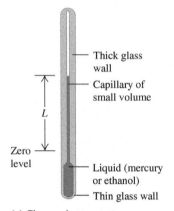

Thick glass wall

Capillary of small volume

L

Zero level

Liquid (mercury or ethanol)

Thin glass wall

(a) Changes in temperature cause the liquid's volume to change.

p

Container of gas at constant volume

(b) Changes in temperature cause the pressure of the gas to change.

▲ **FIGURE 1** Two types of thermometer.

with both *A* and *B*. This interaction is shown in the figure by a gold slab representing a thermal **conductor**—a material that *permits* thermal interactions through it. We wait until thermal equilibrium is attained; then *A* and *B* are each in thermal equilibrium with *C*. But are they in thermal equilibrium *with each other?*

To find out, we separate *C* from *A* and *B* with an ideal insulating wall (see Figure 2b), and then we replace the insulating wall between *A* and *B* with a *conducting* wall that lets *A* and *B* interact. What happens? Experiment shows that *nothing* happens: The states of *A* and *B* do not change. We thus conclude that if *C* is initially in thermal equilibrium with both *A* and *B*, then *A* and *B* are also in thermal equilibrium with each other. This principle is called the **zeroth law of thermodynamics.** It may seem trivial and obvious, but even so, it needs to be verified by experiment.

(a) If systems *A* and *B* are each in thermal equilibrium with system *C* ...

Zeroth law of thermodynamics

Two systems that are each in thermal equilibrium with a third system are in thermal equilibrium with each other.

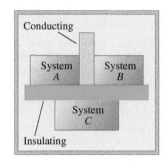

(b) ... then systems *A* and *B* are in thermal equilibrium with each other.

▲ **FIGURE 2** The zeroth law of thermodynamics.

The importance of this law was recognized only after the first, second, and third laws of thermodynamics had been named. Since it is fundamental to all of them, the label "zeroth" is appropriate.

The temperature of a system determines whether the system is in thermal equilibrium with another system. **Two systems are in thermal equilibrium if and only if they have the same temperature.** When the temperatures of two systems are different, the systems *cannot* be in thermal equilibrium. A thermometer actually measures *its own* temperature, but when a thermometer is in thermal equilibrium with another object, the temperatures of the two must be equal. A temperature scale, such as the Celsius or Fahrenheit scale, is just a particular scheme for assigning numbers to temperatures.

2 Temperature Scales

To make the thermometer in Figure 1a useful, we need to give it a scale with numbers on it. These numbers are arbitrary; historically, many different schemes have been used. Suppose we label the thermometer's liquid level when it is at the freezing temperature of pure water "zero" and the level at the boiling temperature "100"; then we divide the distance between these two points into 100 equal intervals called *degrees*. The result is the **Celsius temperature scale** (formerly called the *centigrade scale* in English-speaking countries). We interpolate between these reference temperatures 0°C and 100°C, or extrapolate beyond them, by using the liquid-in-tube thermometer or one of the other thermometers mentioned in Section 1. The temperature for a state colder than freezing water is a negative number. The Celsius scale, shown on the left side of Figure 3, is used, both in everyday life and in science and industry, everywhere in the world except the United States and a few other English-speaking countries.

The right side of Figure 3 shows the **Fahrenheit temperature scale,** still used in everyday life in the United States. The freezing temperature of water is assigned the value 32°F (32 degrees Fahrenheit), and the boiling temperature of water is 212°F, both at normal atmospheric pressure. Thus, there are 180 degrees between freezing and boiling, compared with 100 on the Celsius scale. One Fahrenheit degree represents only $\frac{100}{180}$, or $\frac{5}{9}$ as large a temperature change as one Celsius degree.

To convert temperatures from Celsius to Fahrenheit, we note that a Celsius temperature T_C is the number of Celsius degrees above freezing; to obtain the number of Fahrenheit degrees above freezing, we must multiply T_C by $\frac{9}{5}$. But freezing on the Fahrenheit scale is 32°F, so to obtain the actual Fahrenheit

▲ **FIGURE 3** The Celsius and Fahrenheit temperature scales compared.

▲ **Applications Some like it hot.** We usually think of the boiling point of water as being 100°C, but remember that this is true only at normal atmospheric pressure. At higher pressures, water remains liquid at temperatures above 100°C. The photo shows hydrothermal vents on the ocean floor. The water emerging from such vents may be as hot as 400°C, but it remains liquid because of the great pressure due to the overlying water. Amazingly, the mineral "chimneys" built by these "smokers" host a rich population of microorganisms that can survive at temperatures higher than 110°C. Indeed, some *grow best* at temperatures above 100°C and find temperatures below 80°C (176°F) too cold for growth.

temperature T_F, we must first multiply the Celsius value by $\frac{9}{5}$ and then add 32°. Symbolically,

$$T_F = \frac{9}{5}T_C + 32°. \tag{1}$$

To convert Fahrenheit to Celsius, we first subtract 32° to obtain the number of Fahrenheit degrees above freezing and then multiply by $\frac{5}{9}$ to obtain the number of Celsius degrees above freezing—that is, the Celsius temperature. In symbols,

$$T_C = \frac{5}{9}(T_F - 32°). \tag{2}$$

We don't recommend memorizing Equations 1 and 2. Instead, try to understand the reasoning that led to them well enough that you can derive them on the spot when you need them. Check your reasoning with the relation 100°C = 212°F.

It's useful to distinguish between an actual temperature on a certain scale and a temperature *interval,* representing a *difference,* or change, in temperature. To make this distinction, we state an actual temperature of 20° as 20°C (20 degrees Celsius) and a temperature *interval* of 10° as 10 C° (10 Celsius degrees). Thus, a beaker of water heated from 20°C to 30°C undergoes a temperature change of 10 C°. We'll use this notation consistently throughout this text.

When we calibrate two thermometers, such as a liquid-in-tube system and a gas thermometer, so that they agree at 0°C and 100°C, they may not agree exactly at intermediate temperatures. The expansion properties of a gas may not match exactly the properties of a liquid. Ideally, we'd like to define a temperature scale that doesn't depend on the properties of a particular material. The gas thermometer, which we'll discuss next, comes close.

The Kelvin Scale

In Section 1, we mentioned a thermometer that makes use of the variation in pressure of a gas with changing temperature. The gas, often helium, is placed in a constant-volume container (Figure 4a), and its pressure is measured. To calibrate a constant-volume gas thermometer, we measure the pressure at two

(a) A constant-volume gas thermometer

(b) Graphs of pressure versus temperature at constant volume for three gases

▲ **FIGURE 4** Use of a constant-volume gas thermometer to find the temperature at which a gas would have zero pressure (if it were still gaseous). This is the zero temperature on the Kelvin scale.

temperatures, say, 0°C and 100°C, plot these points on a graph, and draw a straight line between them (Figure 4b). Then, from the graph, we can read the temperature corresponding to any other pressure.

By extrapolating this graph to lower and lower pressures, we see that there is a hypothetical temperature at which the gas pressure would become zero. We might expect that this temperature would be different for different gases, but it actually turns out to be the same for many different gases (at least in the limit of very low gas concentrations), namely, $-273.15°C$. We'll call this temperature *absolute zero*. We can't actually observe this zero-pressure condition, because gases liquefy and even solidify at very low temperatures; then the proportional relationship between pressure and temperature no longer holds. However, we can use this extrapolated zero-pressure temperature as the basis for a new temperature scale with its zero at that temperature.

This is the **Kelvin temperature scale,** named for Lord Kelvin (1824–1907). The units are the same size as those of the Celsius scale, but the zero is shifted so that the zero point is at absolute zero: $0 \text{ K} = -273.15°C$ and $273.15 \text{ K} = 0°C$; thus,

$$T_K = T_C + 273.15° \tag{3}$$

A common room temperature, $20°C \ (= 68°F)$, is $20 + 273.15$, or about 293 K. In SI nomenclature, "degree" is not used with the Kelvin scale; the room temperature 20°C is read "293 kelvins," not "293 degrees Kelvin." We capitalize Kelvin when it refers to the temperature scale, but the *unit* of temperature is the *kelvin*, not capitalized, but abbreviated K.

Figure 5 summarizes the relations among the Celsius, Fahrenheit, and Kelvin scales. The Kelvin scale is called an **absolute temperature scale,** and its zero point is called **absolute zero.**

▲ **FIGURE 5** Relationships among Kelvin, Celsius, and Fahrenheit temperature scales. Temperatures have been rounded off to the nearest degree.

EXAMPLE 1 **Body temperature**

Normal internal body temperature for an average healthy human is 98.6°F. **(a)** Find this temperature in degrees Celsius and in kelvins. **(b)** When a human is relaxing on a couch, the skin temperature is about 2 C° lower than the internal temperature. How much lower is the skin temperature, in Fahrenheit degrees and in kelvins?

SOLUTION

SET UP AND SOLVE Part (a): To convert from Fahrenheit to Celsius temperatures, we first subtract 32° to obtain the number of Fahrenheit degrees above freezing and then multiply by $\frac{5}{9}$ to find the number of Celsius degrees above freezing (i.e., the Celsius temperature). Thus, in degrees Celsius, normal body temperature is

$$T_C = \tfrac{5}{9}(T_F - 32°) = \tfrac{5}{9}(98.6° - 32°) = 37.0°C.$$

Continued

To find this temperature in kelvins, we add 273.15 K:

$$T_K = T_C + 273.15° = 37.0° + 273.15°$$
$$= 310.1 \text{ K } (= 310.1 \text{ kelvins}).$$

Part (b): To convert the number of Celsius degrees to the number of Fahrenheit degrees in a temperature interval, we multiply by 1 in the form $(9 \text{ F°}/5 \text{ C°})$. But one Celsius degree equals one kelvin, so to find the same interval on the Kelvin scale, we just multiply by 1:

$$2 \text{ Celsius degrees} = 2 \text{ C°} = (9 \text{ F°}/5 \text{ C°})2 \text{ C°} = 3.6 \text{ F°}$$

and

$$2 \text{ C°} = 2 \text{ K}.$$

REFLECT Note again that the degree symbol and the word *degree* are not used for the Kelvin scale. Also, for any calculations of temperature *changes*, the numbers of degrees on the Celsius and Kelvin scales are equal, but the number of degrees on the Fahrenheit scale is $\frac{9}{5}$ as great as either of these.

Practice Problem: On a stormy day in Orlando, Florida, the temperature dropped by 31.5 F°. What is this temperature change in Celsius degrees and in kelvins? *Answer:* $\Delta T = -17.5 \text{ C°} = -17.5 \text{ K}.$

For moderate temperature changes, ΔL is directly proportional to ΔT:

ΔL is also directly proportional to L_0:

▲ **FIGURE 6** The dependence of linear thermal expansion on the change in temperature and the initial length.

▲ **FIGURE 7** We can envision the forces between neighboring atoms in a solid by imagining the atoms to be connected by springs.

3 Thermal Expansion

Most materials expand when their temperatures increase. Bridge decks need special joints and supports to allow for expansion. A completely filled and tightly capped bottle of water cracks when it is heated, but you can loosen a metal jar lid by running hot water on it. These are all examples of *thermal expansion*.

Linear Expansion

Suppose a rod of material has a length L_0 at some initial temperature T_0. When the temperature changes by a small amount ΔT, the length changes by ΔL (Figure 6). Experiment shows that if ΔT is not too large (say, less than 100 C° or so), ΔL is *directly proportional* to ΔT. If two rods made of the same material have the same temperature change, but one is twice as long as the other, then the *change* in its length is also twice as great. Therefore, ΔL must also be proportional to L_0. Introducing a proportionality constant α (which is different for different materials), we may express this relation in an equation:

Thermal expansion

When the temperature of a solid object changes, the change in length, ΔL, is proportional to the change in temperature, ΔT:

$$\Delta L = \alpha L_0 \Delta T. \quad (4)$$

The proportionality constant α is called the **coefficient of linear expansion.** If an object has length L_0 at temperature T_0, then its length L at a temperature $T = T_0 + \Delta T$ is

$$L = L_0 + \Delta L = L_0(1 + \alpha \Delta T). \quad (5)$$

Units: The units of α are K^{-1} or $(C°)^{-1}$. (Remember that a temperature *interval* is the same in Celsius and Kelvin.) In the discussion that follows, we'll usually use K^{-1}.

We can think of α as the fractional change in length of an object during a temperature change of 1 C°. For many materials, every linear dimension changes according to Equation 4 or 5. Thus, L could be the thickness of a rod, the length of the side of a square sheet, or (as we'll see in a minute) the diameter of a hole. Some materials, such as wood or single crystals, expand differently in different directions. We won't consider this complication.

We can understand thermal expansion qualitatively on a molecular basis. Picture the interatomic forces in a solid as springs (Figure 7). Each atom vibrates

▶ **Application Bimaterial strips.** While coefficient of linear expansion may seem like a textbook concept, we depend on it daily. Many instruments, including mechanical thermostats and some thermometers and circuit breakers, employ sensors made of a *bimaterial strip*—that is, a strip made by welding together two thin strips of different materials so that the two materials form the two faces of the strip. The photo shows a sensor that uses such strips to measure temperature and humidity. In the temperature-sensing coil, the two faces of the strip consist of metals with different coefficients of linear expansion; changes in temperature cause the strip to either coil up or uncoil. In the humidity sensor, one face consists of paper or plastic that expands with increasing humidity, causing the strip to uncoil. In a mechanical thermostat, the coiling and uncoiling of a temperature-sensitive bimetallic strip makes and breaks electrical connections.

Jeff Daly/Fundamental Photographs

about its equilibrium position. When the temperature increases, the average distance between molecules also increases. As the atoms get farther apart, every dimension increases.

When you heat an object that has a hole in it, the hole gets bigger. Figure 8 shows what happens. If you heat a flat plate of material, its area increases. If you now cut a section from the center of the plate, both the cutout and the remaining plate (with a hole in it) behave as they did previously: The cut-out piece and the hole it came from both get bigger. When you heat an object with a hole in it, the *hole gets bigger*.

The direct proportionality between ΔL and ΔT expressed by Equation 4 isn't exact; it's *approximately* correct for sufficiently small temperature changes. For a given material, α varies somewhat with the initial temperature T_0 and the size of the temperature interval. We'll ignore this complication. Average values of α for several materials are listed in Table 1. Within the precision of these values, we don't need to worry about whether the initial temperature T_0 is 0°C, 20°C, or some other temperature. We also note that α is usually a very small number; even for a temperature change of $100\,\mathrm{C}°$, the fractional change in length $\Delta L/L_0$ is on the order of $\frac{1}{1000}$. But don't be misled by this small number: The expansion of a 100 m bridge by 0.1 m has to be taken seriously!

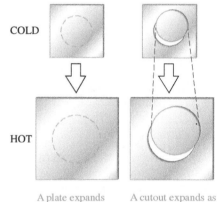

COLD

HOT

A plate expands when heated. (Expansion exaggerated!)

A cutout expands as it would have done if still part of the plate—so the *hole must expand, too.*

▲ **FIGURE 8** One way to understand why a hole in a solid object expands (rather than shrinks) when the object is heated.

PROBLEM-SOLVING STRATEGY 1 **Thermal expansion**

This strategy also applies to problems involving an expansion in *volume*, which we'll consider later in this section.

SET UP
1. Identify which of the quantities in Equation 4 or 5 are known and which are unknown. Often, you will be given two temperatures and will have to compute ΔT. Or you may be given an initial temperature T_0 and may have to find a final temperature corresponding to a given change in length or volume. In this case, find ΔT first; then the final temperature is $T_0 + \Delta T$.

SOLVE
2. Consistency of units is crucial, as always. L_0 and ΔL (or V_0 and ΔV) must have the same units, and if you use a value of α in K^{-1}, then ΔT must be in kelvins.

REFLECT
3. Remember that dimensions of holes in a material expand with temperature just the same way as any other linear dimensions do.

TABLE 1 Coefficients of linear expansion for selected materials

Material	α (K^{-1} or $\mathrm{C}°^{-1}$)
Quartz (fused)	0.04×10^{-5}
Invar (nickel–iron alloy)	0.09×10^{-5}
Glass	$0.4–0.9 \times 10^{-5}$
Steel	1.2×10^{-5}
Copper	1.7×10^{-5}
Brass	2.0×10^{-5}
Aluminum	2.4×10^{-5}

EXAMPLE 2   Change in length of a measuring tape

A surveyor uses a steel measuring tape that is exactly 50.000 m long at a temperature of 20°C. What is its length on a hot summer day when the temperature is 35°C?

SOLUTION

SET UP AND SOLVE We have $L_0 = 50.000$ m, $T_0 = 20°C$, and $T = 35°C$. We use Equation 4 to find ΔL (Note that because ΔL is usually much smaller than L_0, we need to keep more significant figures in the lengths than in the temperatures.) From Table 1, the coefficient of linear expansion for steel is 1.2×10^{-5} K^{-1}. From Equation 4,

$$\Delta L = \alpha L_0 \Delta T$$
$$= (1.2 \times 10^{-5} \text{ K}^{-1})(50 \text{ m})(35°C - 20°C)$$
$$= 9.0 \times 10^{-3} \text{ m} = 9.0 \text{ mm}.$$

The new length is

$$L = L_0 + \Delta L = 50.000 \text{ m} + 0.0090 \text{ m} = 50.009 \text{ m}.$$

REFLECT The measuring tape lengthens by 9 mm, or 0.018%. In surveying a baseball field, this amount is negligible, but not when measuring the length of a steel bridge. Note that, although L_0 is given to five significant figures, we need only two of them to compute ΔL.

Practice Problem: A concrete slab forming part of a driveway is 20.000 m long when the temperature is 20°C. How much does the driveway increase in length when the temperature increases to 30°C? The coefficient of linear expansion for concrete is 1.2×10^{-5} K^{-1}. *Answer:* $\Delta L = 2.4$ mm.

EXAMPLE 3   Measuring a true distance

The surveyor in Example 2 measures a distance when the temperature is 35°C and obtains the result 35.794 m. What is the actual distance?

SOLUTION

SET UP AND SOLVE From Equation 5, the ratio L/L_0 for any specific material depends only on the temperature change. At 35°C, the distance between two successive meter marks on the tape is a little more than a meter, by the ratio

$$\frac{L}{L_0} = \frac{L_0(1 + \alpha T)}{L_0} = \frac{50.009 \text{ m}}{50.000 \text{ m}}.$$

Thus, the true distance is

$$\frac{50.009 \text{ m}}{50.000 \text{ m}}(35.794 \text{ m}) = 35.800 \text{ m}.$$

REFLECT The term $(1 + \alpha \Delta T)$ for a particular material depends only on the temperature change, within the limits of precision of Equation 5.

Volume Expansion

Increases in temperature usually cause increases in *volume* for both solid and liquid materials. Experiments show that if the temperature change ΔT is not too great (less than 100 C° or so), the increase in volume, ΔV, is approximately proportional to the temperature change. The change in volume is also proportional to the initial volume V_0, just as with linear expansion, so we obtain the following relationship:

Volume expansion

When the temperature of an object changes, the change ΔV in its volume is proportional to the temperature change ΔT. That is,

$$\Delta V = \beta V_0 \Delta T \tag{6}$$

and

$$V = V_0(1 + \beta \Delta T). \tag{7}$$

The constant β characterizes the volume expansion properties of a particular material; it is called the **coefficient of volume expansion.** The units of β are

TABLE 2   Coefficients of volume expansion

Material	β (K^{-1})
Solids	
Quartz (fused)	0.12×10^{-5}
Invar	0.27×10^{-5}
Glass	$1.2–2.7 \times 10^{-5}$
Steel	3.6×10^{-5}
Copper	5.1×10^{-5}
Brass	6.0×10^{-5}
Aluminum	7.2×10^{-5}
Liquids	
Mercury	18×10^{-5}
Glycerin	49×10^{-5}
Ethanol	75×10^{-5}
Carbon disulfide	115×10^{-5}

K^{-1}. As with linear expansion, β varies somewhat with temperature, and Equation 6 is an approximate relation that works well for small temperature changes. For many substances, β decreases at low temperatures. Table 2 lists values of β in the neighborhood of room temperature for several substances. Note that the values for liquids are much larger than those for solids.

For solid materials that expand equally in all directions, there is a simple relation between the volume expansion coefficient β and the linear expansion coefficient α. Expansion in each of the three directions contributes to changes in volume. Detailed analysis shows that the two coefficients are related simply by $\beta = 3\alpha$. We invite you to check this relationship for a few materials listed in Tables 1 and 2.

EXAMPLE 4   **Expansion of mercury**

A glass flask filled with a volume of 200 cm^3 is filled to the brim with mercury at 20°C. When the temperature of the system is raised to 100°C, does the mercury overflow? If so, by how much? The coefficient of volume expansion of the glass is $1.2 \times 10^{-5}\,K^{-1}$.

SOLUTION

SET UP Both the flask and the mercury expand. The mercury overflows because its coefficient of volume expansion (from Table 2) is much greater than that of the glass: $18 \times 10^{-5}\,K^{-1}$ versus $1.2 \times 10^{-5}\,K^{-1}$.

SOLVE The increase in volume of the flask is $\Delta V_{\text{flask}} = \beta_{\text{flask}} V_0 \Delta T$, and the increase in the volume of mercury is $\Delta V_{\text{mercury}} = \beta_{\text{mercury}} V_0 \Delta T$:

$$\Delta V_{\text{mercury}} = (18 \times 10^{-5}\,K^{-1})(200\,\text{cm}^3)(100°C - 20°C)$$
$$= 2.9\,\text{cm}^3;$$
$$\Delta V_{\text{flask}} = (1.2 \times 10^{-5}\,K^{-1})(200\,\text{cm}^3)(100°C - 20°C)$$
$$= 0.19\,\text{cm}^3.$$

The volume of mercury that overflows is the difference between these values:

$$\Delta V_{\text{mercury}} - \Delta V_{\text{flask}} = 2.9\,\text{cm}^3 - 0.19\,\text{cm}^3 = 2.7\,\text{cm}^3.$$

REFLECT This is basically the way a mercury-in-glass thermometer works, except that instead of letting the mercury overflow and run all over the place, the thermometer has it rise inside a sealed tube as T increases.

Practice Problem: Suppose we replace the mercury with ethanol (less poisonous than mercury and more suitable for very cold weather). How much ethanol runs over? *Answer:* 11.8 cm^3

Thermal Expansion of Water

Above 4°C, liquid water expands with increasing temperature. However, between 0°C (the freezing point) and 4°C, water *decreases* in volume with increasing temperature; in this range, its coefficient of volume expansion is *negative*. Thus, water has its greatest density at 4°C. Water also expands when it freezes; that's why ice humps up in the middle of the compartments in an ice cube tray and why pipes full of water burst if allowed to freeze. Most other materials contract when they freeze.

This anomalous behavior of water has an important effect on plant and animal life in lakes. When a lake cools, the cooled water at the surface flows to the bottom because of its greater density. But when the temperature goes below 4°C, this flow ceases, and the water near the surface remains colder (and less dense) than that at the bottom. As the surface freezes, the ice floats because it is less dense than water. The water at the bottom remains at 4°C until nearly the entire lake is frozen. If water behaved like most substances, contracting continuously on cooling and freezing, lakes would freeze from the bottom up. Circulation due to density differences would continuously carry warmer (less dense) water to the surface for efficient cooling, and lakes would freeze solid much more easily. This would destroy all plant and animal life that can withstand cold water, but not freezing. All life forms known on earth depend on chemical systems based on aqueous solutions; if water did not have this special property, the evolution of various life-forms would have taken a very different course.

The anomalous expansion of water in the temperature range from 0°C to 10°C is shown in Figure 9.

Thermal Stress

If we clamp the ends of a rod rigidly to prevent expansion or contraction and then raise or lower the temperature, a compressive or tensile stress called **thermal stress** develops. The rod would like to expand or contract, but the clamps won't let it. The resulting stress may become large enough to strain the rod irreversibly or even break it. Concrete highways and bridge decks usually have gaps between sections, filled with a flexible material or bridged by interlocking teeth (Figure 10), to permit expansion and contraction of the concrete. If one end of a steel bridge is rigidly fastened to its abutment, the other end usually rests on rollers.

To calculate the thermal stress in a clamped rod, we compute the amount the rod *would* expand (or contract) if it were not held and then find the stress needed to compress (or stretch) it back to its original length. Suppose a rod with length L_0 and cross-sectional area A is held at constant length while the temperature is reduced (negative ΔT), causing a tensile stress. Then the fractional change in length if the rod were free to contract would be

$$\frac{\Delta L}{L_0} = \alpha \, \Delta T.$$

Both ΔL and ΔT are negative. The tension F must increase enough to produce an equal and opposite fractional change in length. From the definition of Young's modulus Y (Equation 4),

$$Y = \frac{F/A}{\Delta L/L_0} \quad \text{and} \quad \frac{\Delta L}{L_0} = \frac{F}{AY}.$$

If the *total* fractional change in length is zero, then

$$\alpha \, \Delta T + \frac{F}{AY} = 0, \quad \text{or} \quad F = -AY\alpha \, \Delta T. \tag{8}$$

For a decrease in temperature, ΔT is negative, so F is positive. The tensile *stress* F/A in the rod is

$$\frac{F}{A} = -Y\alpha \, \Delta T. \tag{9}$$

If ΔT is positive, F and F/A are negative, corresponding to *compressive* force and stress.

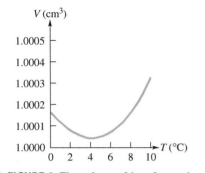

V (cm³)

▲ **FIGURE 9** The volume of 1 g of water in the temperature range from 0°C to 10°C. The fact that water is denser at about 4°C than at the freezing point is vitally important for the ecology of lakes and streams.

Shutterstock

▲ **FIGURE 10** The interlocking teeth of an expansion joint on a bridge. These joints are needed to accommodate changes in length that result from thermal expansion.

EXAMPLE 5   Stress on a spacer

An aluminum cylinder 10 cm long, with a cross-sectional area of 20 cm², is to be used as a spacer between two steel walls. At 17.2°C, it just slips in between the walls. Then it warms to 22.3°C. Calculate the stress in the cylinder and the total force it exerts on each wall, assuming that the walls are perfectly rigid and a constant distance apart.

SOLUTION

SET UP Figure 11 shows our sketch. We use Equation 9, which relates the stress F/A (compressive in this case) to the temperature change. From Table 1, $Y = 0.70 \times 10^{11}$ Pa, and from Table 1, $\alpha = 2.4 \times 10^{-5}$ K⁻¹. The temperature change is $\Delta T = 5.1$ K, and the cross-sectional area of the cylinder is $20 \text{ cm}^2 = 20 \times 10^{-4} \text{ m}^2$.

$A = 20$ cm²

10 cm

▲ **FIGURE 11** Our sketch for this problem.

Continued

SOLVE From Equation 9, the stress F/A is

$$\frac{F}{A} = -Y\alpha\,\Delta T$$
$$= -(0.70 \times 10^{11}\,\text{Pa})(2.4 \times 10^{-5}\,\text{K}^{-1})(5.1\,\text{K})$$
$$= -8.6 \times 10^{6}\,\text{Pa} \ (\text{about} -1240\,\text{lb/in.}^2).$$

The total force F exerted by the cylinder on a wall is

$$F = -AY\alpha\,\Delta T = (20 \times 10^{-4}\,\text{m}^2)(-8.6 \times 10^{6}\,\text{Pa})$$
$$= -1.7 \times 10^{4}\,\text{N} \ (\text{about } 3800\,\text{lb}).$$

REFLECT The negative sign indicates compressive rather than tensile stress. The stress is independent of the length and cross-sectional area of the cylinder. The total force is nearly 2 tons.

Thermal stresses can be induced by non-uniform expansion due to temperature differences. Have you ever broken a glass jar by pouring boiling water into it? Thermal stress caused by temperature differences exceeded the breaking stress of the material, and it cracked. The same phenomenon makes ice cubes crack when they're dropped into a hot liquid. Heat-resistant glasses such as Pyrex™ have exceptionally low expansion coefficients and high strength.

4 Quantity of Heat

When you put a cold spoon into a cup of hot coffee, the spoon warms up and the coffee cools off as they approach thermal equilibrium. What kind of interaction is taking place to cause these temperature changes? During this interaction, *something* is transferred from the coffee to the spoon. We'll call this interaction a **heat transfer** or a *heat flow* from the coffee to the spoon. But what *is* this "something" that flows from the coffee to the spoon?

The answer to this question emerged gradually during the 18th and 19th centuries. Sir James Joule (1818–1889) discovered that water can be warmed by vigorous stirring with a paddle wheel (Figure 12a) and that *the rise in temperature is directly proportional to the work done* (and energy added) in turning the wheel. Since the same temperature change could have been caused by putting the water in contact with some hotter object (Figure 12b), that interaction must also involve an energy exchange. This experiment and many similar ones, have established the fact that heat flow is *energy transfer* and that there is an equivalence between heat and work: The same change of state of a system (such as a change in temperature or volume) can be produced by heat flow, work, or a combination of the two.

Energy transfer that takes place solely because of a temperature difference is called *heat flow,* or *heat transfer,* and energy transferred in this way is called **heat.** For example, cold water in a steam boiler is converted to steam by contact with a metal pipe kept at a high temperature by a hot flame from burning coal or gas. Having received energy from the flame, the water (as steam) has a greater ability to do *work* (by pushing against a turbine blade or the piston in a steam engine) than does an equal mass of cold liquid water.

NOTE ▶ The term *heat* always refers to the *transfer* of energy from one object or system to another due to a temperature difference, never to the amount of energy *contained within* a particular system. There is no such thing as "the heat *in* an object"; **the concept of heat has meaning only as energy in transit.** A detailed study of the relationship between heat and work leads to the *first law of thermodynamics.* ◀

Because heat is energy transferred from one system to another, the SI unit of quantity of heat is the joule. The International Committee on Weights and Measures recommends use of the joule as the basic unit of energy in all forms, including heat. We'll follow that recommendation in this text. However, several older,

The water warms as the paddle does work on it; the temperature rise is proportional to the amount of work done.

(a) Raising the temperature of water by doing work on it

Direct heating can produce the same temperature change as doing work on the water.

(b) Raising the temperature of water by direct heating

▲ **FIGURE 12** The temperature of a system may be changed by either (a) doing work on the system or (b) adding heat to it.

non-SI units are also in common use for heat. The most familiar of these is the calorie.

Definition of the calorie

The **calorie** (abbreviated cal) is defined as *the amount of heat required to raise the temperature of 1 gram of water from* 14.5°C *to* 15.5°C.

The familiar "Calorie" found on food labels is actually a kilocalorie (kcal), equal to 1000 cal. The kilocalorie, also called the food calorie, is sometimes written with a capital C (Calorie) to distinguish it from the calorie just defined. But as Figure 13 shows, much of the world worries about the joule content of their food, not the calorie (or Calorie) content.

A corresponding unit of quantity of heat that uses Fahrenheit degrees and British units is the **British thermal unit,** or Btu. One Btu is defined as the quantity of heat required to raise the temperature of 1 standard pound (weight) of water 1 F° from 63°F to 64°F.

Because heat is energy in transit, there must be a definite relation between the preceding units and the familiar energy unit, the joule. Experiments similar in concept to Joule's have shown that

$$1 \text{ cal} = 4.186 \text{ J},$$
$$1 \text{ kcal} = 1000 \text{ cal} = 4186 \text{ J},$$
$$1 \text{ Btu} = 778 \text{ ft} \cdot \text{lb} = 252 \text{ cal} = 1055 \text{ J}.$$

Hugh D. Young

▲ **FIGURE 13** Packaged foods sold in many countries outside the United States, such as these sugar cubes from Germany, list their energy content in joules as well as calories.

Specific Heat Capacity

We use the symbol Q for quantity of heat (amount of energy transferred). The quantity of heat Q required to increase the temperature T of a mass m of a certain material by a small amount from T_1 to T_2 is found to be approximately proportional to the temperature change $\Delta T = T_2 - T_1$. To raise the temperature of a certain mass of substance from 20°C to 40°C ($\Delta T = 20$ K) requires approximately twice as much heat as the amount needed to raise it from 20°C to 30°C ($\Delta T = 10$ K). The heat required for a given temperature change is also proportional to the mass m of substance. Thus, when you heat water to make tea, you need twice as much heat for two cups as for one if the temperature interval is the same. Finally, the quantity of heat needed also depends on the nature of the material; to raise the temperature of 1 kilogram of water by 1 C° requires almost five times as much heat as for 1 kilogram of aluminum and the same temperature change.

Putting all these relationships together, we have the definition of specific heat capacity:

Specific heat capacity

The amount of heat Q needed for a certain temperature change ΔT is proportional to the temperature change and to the mass m of substance being heated; that is,

$$Q = mc \, \Delta T, \tag{10}$$

where c is a quantity, different for different materials, called the **specific heat capacity** (or sometimes *specific heat*) of the material. The SI unit of specific heat capacity is the joule per kilogram per kelvin [J/(kg · K)]. Also, 1 K = 1 C°.

In Equation 10, Q and ΔT can be either positive or negative. When they are positive, heat enters the object and its temperature increases; when they are negative, heat leaves the object and its temperature decreases.

NOTE ▶ Remember that Q does not represent a change in the amount of heat *contained* in an object; that is a meaningless concept. Heat is always energy *in transit* as a result of a temperature difference. There is no such thing as "the amount of heat in an object." The term *heat capacity* is unfortunate because it tends to suggest the erroneous idea that an object *contains* a certain amount of heat. ◀

The specific heat capacity of water is approximately

$$c_{\text{water}} = 4190 \text{ J}/(\text{kg} \cdot \text{K}), 1 \text{ cal}/(\text{g} \cdot \text{K}), \text{ or } 1 \text{ Btu}/(\text{lb} \cdot \text{F}°).$$

Specific heat capacities vary somewhat with the initial temperature and the temperature interval. For example, the specific heat capacity of water varies by almost 1% in the temperature range from 0°C to 100°C. In the problems and examples in this chapter, we'll usually ignore this small variation. Table 3 lists specific heat capacities for several common materials.

TABLE 3 Mean specific heat capacities (constant pressure, temperature range 0°C to 100°C)

Material	Specific heat capacity (c)	
	J/(kg·K)	cal/(g·K)
Solids		
Lead	0.13×10^3	0.031
Mercury	0.14×10^3	0.033
Silver	0.23×10^3	0.056
Copper	0.39×10^3	0.093
Iron	0.47×10^3	0.112
Marble ($CaCO_3$)	0.88×10^3	0.21
Salt	0.88×10^3	0.21
Aluminum	0.91×10^3	0.217
Beryllium	1.97×10^3	0.471
Ice (-25°C to 0°C)	2.01×10^3	0.48
Liquids		
Ethylene glycol	2.39×10^3	0.57
Ethanol	2.43×10^3	0.58
Water	4.19×10^3	1.00

Quantitative Analysis 1

The meaning of c

In the equation $Q = mc \, \Delta T$, m represents the mass in kilograms of the sample and c represents

A. the amount of heat required to raise the temperature of m kilograms of sample by 1 C°.
B. the amount of heat required to raise the temperature of 1 kilogram of the sample by 1 C°.
C. the amount of heat required to raise the temperature of m kilograms of the sample by ΔT.

SOLUTION The specific heat capacity c is a property of a particular material; it doesn't depend on *how much* of the material is present. It's also independent of the temperature interval: if we double ΔT, the total amount of heat doubles, but c doesn't change. Thus, neither A nor C can be right. The correct answer is B: c is the amount of heat needed *per unit mass* and *per unit temperature change*.

EXAMPLE 6 Running a fever

During a bout with the flu, an 80 kg man ran a fever of 2.0 C°; that is, his body temperature was 39.0°C (or 102.2°F) instead of the normal 37.0°C (or 98.6°F). Assuming that the human body is mostly water, how much heat was required to raise his temperature by that amount?

SOLUTION

SET UP AND SOLVE The temperature change is $\Delta T = 39.0°C - 37.0°C = 2.0 \text{ C}° = 2.0 \text{ K}$. From Table 3, the specific heat capacity of water is 4190 J/(kg·K). From Equation 10,

$$Q = mc \, \Delta T = (80 \text{ kg})[4190 \text{ J}/(\text{kg} \cdot \text{K})](2.0 \text{ K}) = = 6.7 \times 10^5 \text{ J}.$$

REFLECT This amount of heat is equal to 1.6×10^5 cal, or 160 kcal (160 food calories). This is roughly half the calorie intake from eating 1 ounce of milk chocolate.

Practice Problem: If a 35 kg child has a temperature of 104°F = 40°C, how much heat was needed to raise her temperature to that value from an initial value of 37°C? *Answer:* 4.4×10^5 J.

EXAMPLE 7 Circuit meltdown

You are designing an electronic circuit element made of 23 mg of silicon. The electric current through it adds energy at the rate of 7.4 mW $= 7.4 \times 10^{-3}$ J/s. If your design doesn't allow any heat transfer out of the element, at what rate does its temperature increase? The specific heat capacity of silicon is 705 J/(kg·K).

Continued

SOLUTION

SET UP AND SOLVE In 1 second, $Q = (7.4 \times 10^{-3} \text{ J/s})(1 \text{ s}) = 7.4 \times 10^{-3}$ J. From Equation 10, the temperature change in 1 second is

$$\Delta T = \frac{Q}{mc} = \frac{7.4 \times 10^{-3} \text{ J}}{(23 \times 10^{-6} \text{ kg})[705 \text{ J}/(\text{kg} \cdot \text{K})]} = 0.46 \text{ K}.$$

Alternatively, we can divide both sides of this equation by Δt and rearrange factors:

$$\frac{\Delta T}{\Delta t} = \frac{Q/\Delta t}{mc}$$

$$= \frac{7.4 \times 10^{-3} \text{ J/s}}{(23 \times 10^{-6} \text{ kg})[705 \text{ J}/(\text{kg} \cdot \text{K})]} = 0.46 \text{ K/s}.$$

REFLECT At this rate of temperature rise (27 K every minute), the circuit element would quickly self-destruct. Heat transfer is an important design consideration in electronic circuit elements.

NOTE ▶ We conclude this section with a short sermon. It is absolutely essential for you to keep clearly in mind the distinction between *temperature* and *heat*. Temperature depends on the physical state of a material and is a quantitative description of its hotness or coldness. Heat is energy transferred from one object to another because of a temperature difference. We can change the temperature of an object by adding heat to it or taking heat away from it or by adding or subtracting energy in other ways, such as doing mechanical work. If we cut an object in half, each half has the same temperature as the whole; but to raise the temperature of each half by a given interval, we add *half* as much heat as for the whole. ◀

Conceptual Analysis 2

Heat versus temperature

As Table 3 shows, the specific heat capacity of water is about 10 times that of iron. If you take equal masses of water and iron, initially in thermal equilibrium, and add 50 J of heat to each, which of the following statements is true?

A. They remain in thermal equilibrium.
B. They are no longer in thermal equilibrium; the iron is warmer.
C. They are no longer in thermal equilibrium; the water is warmer.

SOLUTION Because water has a larger specific heat capacity than iron, a greater amount of heat is needed to cause a given temperature change for a given mass of water than for an equal mass of iron. If the heat added is the same for both, it follows that the temperature change of the water is less than that of the iron. If they were initially at the same temperature, then, after the additions of heat, the iron is warmer than the water. The correct answer is B.

5 Phase Changes

We've discussed the energy transfer (heat) involved in changing an object's temperature. Heat is also involved in *phase changes,* such as the melting of ice or boiling of water. Once we understand these additional heat relationships, we can analyze a variety of problems involving quantity of heat Q.

We use the term **phase** to describe a specific state of matter, such as solid, liquid, or gas. The compound H_2O exists in the *solid phase* as ice, in the *liquid phase* as water, and in the *gaseous phase* as steam. A transition from one phase to another is called a **phase change** or phase transition. For any given pressure, a phase change usually takes place at a definite temperature and is usually accompanied by the absorption or emission of heat and a change in volume and density.

A familiar example of a phase change is the melting of ice. When we add heat to ice at 0°C and normal atmospheric pressure, the temperature of the ice *does not* increase. Instead, some of the ice melts to form liquid water. If we add the heat slowly, to maintain the system very close to thermal equilibrium, the temperature remains at 0°C until all the ice is melted. The effect of adding heat to this system is not to raise its temperature, but to change its *phase* from solid to liquid.

▶ **Application Flaking out?** Snow and ice are two familiar forms of the solid phase of water. Why do they look so different? Air always contains water vapor. When air above the freezing temperature of water cools to the point that it can't retain all its water vapor (i.e., the relative humidity exceeds 100%), some vapor condenses to liquid in the form of rain, fog, or dew. If the air cools further, the liquid water freezes to form hail or sleet. But if the temperature is below the freezing point of water, the water vapor goes directly from the gaseous to the solid phase. (This is the reverse of *sublimation*, where a solid material goes directly into the vapor phase.) Suspended in air, the ice crystals grow slowly, preserving their natural six-fold symmetry and forming snowflakes. A similar process causes frost to form on the cooling coils of a refrigerator.

Ted Kinsman/Photo Researchers, Inc.

To change 1 kg of ice at 0°C to 1 kg of liquid water at 0°C and normal atmospheric pressure requires 3.34×10^5 J of heat. The heat required, per unit mass is called the **heat of fusion** (or sometimes *latent* heat of fusion), denoted by L_f. Thus, the heat of fusion L_f of water, at normal atmospheric pressure, is

$$L_f = 3.34 \times 10^5 \text{ J/kg} = 79.6 \text{ cal/g} = 143 \text{ Btu/lb}.$$

More generally, to melt a mass m of material that has a heat of fusion L_f requires a quantity of heat Q given by

$$Q = mL_f.$$

This process is *reversible*: To freeze liquid water to ice at 0°C, we have to *remove* heat. The magnitude is the same, but in this case Q is negative because heat is removed rather than added. To cover both possibilities and to include other kinds of phase changes, we write

$$Q = \pm mL. \tag{11}$$

The plus sign (heat entering) is used when the material melts, the minus sign (heat leaving) when it freezes. The heat of fusion is different for different materials, and it also varies somewhat with pressure.

At any given pressure, there is a unique temperature at which liquid water and ice can coexist in a condition called **phase equilibrium.** The freezing temperature is always the same as the melting temperature.

We can tell this whole story again, changing the names of the characters, for *boiling*, or *evaporation*, a phase transition between the liquid and gaseous phases. The corresponding heat (per unit mass) is called the **heat of vaporization,** L_v. At normal atmospheric pressure, the heat of vaporization L_v for water is

$$L_v = 2.26 \times 10^6 \text{ J/kg} = 539 \text{ cal/g} = 970 \text{ Btu/lb}.$$

Richard Megna/Fundamental Photographs

Note that over five times as much heat is required to vaporize a quantity of water at 100°C as is required to raise its temperature from 0°C to 100°C.

Both L_v and the boiling temperature of a material depend on pressure. Water boils at a lower temperature (about 95°C) in Denver than in Pittsburgh because Denver is at a higher elevation and the average atmospheric pressure is less. The heat of vaporization is somewhat greater at this lower pressure, about 2.27×10^6 J/kg.

Like melting, boiling is a reversible transition. When heat is removed from a gas at the boiling temperature, the gas returns to the liquid phase, or *condenses*, giving up to its surroundings the same quantity of heat (heat of vaporization) as was needed to vaporize it. At a given pressure, the boiling and condensation temperatures are the same.

Table 4 lists heats of fusion and vaporization for several materials, with the corresponding melting and boiling temperatures at normal atmospheric pressure. Very few *elements* have melting temperatures in the vicinity of ordinary room temperatures; one of the few is the metal gallium, shown in Figure 14.

▲ **FIGURE 14** The metal gallium melts in your hand. This element is one of the few having a melting temperature near room temperature.

TABLE 4 Heats of fusion and vaporization

Substance	Normal melting point* K	Normal melting point* °C	Heat of fusion, L_f, J/kg	Normal boiling point* K	Normal boiling point* °C	Heat of vaporization, L_v, J/kg
Helium	†	†	†	4.216	−268.93	20.9×10^3
Hydrogen	13.84	−259.31	58.6×10^3	20.26	−252.89	452×10^3
Nitrogen	63.18	−209.97	25.5×10^3	77.34	−195.81	201×10^3
Oxygen	54.36	−218.79	13.8×10^3	90.18	−182.97	213×10^3
Ethyl alcohol	159	−114	104.2×10^3	351	78	854×10^3
Mercury	234	−39	11.8×10^3	630	357	272×10^3
Water	273.15	0.00	334×10^3	373.15	100.00	2256×10^3
Sulfur	392	119	38.1×10^3	717.75	444.60	326×10^3
Lead	600.5	327.3	24.5×10^3	2023	1750	871×10^3
Antimony	903.65	630.50	165×10^3	1713	1440	561×10^3
Silver	1233.95	960.80	88.3×10^3	2466	2193	2336×10^3
Gold	1336.15	1063.00	64.5×10^3	2933	2660	1578×10^3
Copper	1356	1083	134×10^3	1460	1187	5069×10^3

* At normal atmospheric pressure.

†A pressure in excess of 25 atmospheres is required to make helium solidify. At 1 atmosphere pressure, helium remains a liquid down to absolute zero.

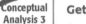

Getting burned

As a theoretical possibility, which (if any) of the following choices would transfer more heat to your skin and thus cause a worse burn?

A. Allowing 1 g of boiling water (at 100°C) to cool to body temperature in your hand.
B. Allowing 1 g of steam at 100°C to condense to liquid water at 100°C in your hand.
C. The heat transfer is the same in both cases.

SOLUTION When 1 g of liquid water cools from 100°C to 20°C, it gives off 4.186 J for each C° drop in temperature, for a total of 335 J. When 1 g of steam at 100°C condenses to liquid water at the same temperature, it gives off an amount of heat equal to the heat of vaporization, about 2260 J. The total amount of heat given off by the condensing steam is over six times as great as the amount given off by the cooling water. Answer B is correct.

Figure 15 shows how temperature varies with time when heat is added continuously to a specimen of ice with an initial temperature below 0°C. The temperature rises (from *a* to *b*) until the melting point is reached. Then, as more heat is

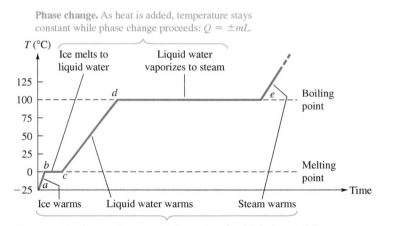

▲ **FIGURE 15** A plot of temperature versus time for a sample of ice to which heat is added continuously.

added (from *b* to *c*), the temperature remains constant until all the ice has melted. Next, the temperature starts to rise again (from *c* to *d*) until the boiling temperature is reached. At that point, the temperature is again constant (from *d* to *e*) until all the water is transformed into the vapor phase. If the rate of heat input is constant, the slope of the line for the liquid phase is smaller than that of the solid phase because, as Table 3 indicates, the specific heat capacity of ice is only about half that of liquid water.

Conceptual Analysis 4

Water and ice

What happens when a lump of ice at 0°C is placed in a beaker of water at 0°C in a room at 0°C?

A. Nothing.
B. All the ice melts.
C. Only some of the ice melts.
D. Only some of the water freezes.

SOLUTION The system is in thermal equilibrium; all parts are at the same temperature, and there is no heat transfer when the ice is placed in the beaker of water. If there were freezing or melting, there would have to be heat transfer. Therefore, nothing happens; the correct answer is A.

A substance can sometimes evaporate directly from the solid to the gaseous phase; this process is called **sublimation,** and the solid is said to *sublime*. The corresponding heat is called the **heat of sublimation,** L_s. Liquid carbon dioxide cannot exist at a pressure lower than about 5×10^5 Pa (about 5 atm), so "dry ice" (solid carbon dioxide) sublimes at atmospheric pressure. Sublimation of water from frozen food causes freezer burn, and it is the reason clothes can dry on a clothesline even at subfreezing temperatures. The reverse process, a phase change from gas to solid, occurs when frost forms on cold objects such as the cooling coils in a refrigerator.

The temperature-control mechanisms of many warm-blooded animals make use of the heat of vaporization, removing heat from the body by sweating or panting, both of which depend on evaporating water from the body. Evaporative cooling enables humans to maintain normal body temperature in hot, dry desert climates, where the air temperature may reach 55°C (about 130°F). The skin temperature may be as much as 30 C° cooler than the surrounding air. Under these conditions, a normal person may perspire several liters per day. Unless this lost water is replaced, dehydration, heat stroke, and death result. Old-time desert rats (such as the author) state that in the desert, any canteen that holds less than a gallon should be viewed as a toy!

Evaporative cooling is also used to cool buildings in hot, dry climates and to condense and recirculate "used" steam in coal-fired or nuclear-powered electric-generating plants. That's what is going on in the large cone-shaped concrete towers that you see at such plants.

Chemical reactions such as combustion involve definite quantities of heat. Complete combustion of 1 gram of gasoline produces about 46,000 J, or 11,000 cal, so the **heat of combustion** L_c of gasoline is

$$L_c = 46,000 \text{ J/g} = 46 \times 10^6 \text{ J/kg}.$$

Earlier, we mentioned that the energy value of food is measured in kilocalories (or Calories with a capital C), where 1 kcal = 1000 cal = 4186 J. When we say that a gram of peanut butter "contains 6 Calories," we mean that if we burned it completely—allowed it to undergo complete combustion with oxygen—it would release 6 kcal (25,000 J) of heat. In the body, essentially the same combustion takes place, although slowly and by means of enzyme-mediated reactions in cells. Not all of the energy liberated in the body's "burning" of food is available for mechanical work. We'll study the *efficiency* of energy conversion.

Image Source/Photolibrary

▲ **BIO Application Heat stroke and hot tubs** At hot ambient temperatures above 30°C, the body loses heat more by evaporation of water than by radiation and convection. When body temperature rises above normal, feedback systems activate blood vessel dilation and increased blood flow to the skin. This leads to a drop in blood pressure and decreased blood flow to the brain and internal organs. In a hot tub or a sauna, where evaporative cooling cannot occur, the body's response fails to lower the core temperature and the body responds by further increasing surface blood flow. Because the water temperature is above normal body temperature, this leads to further warming of the blood and the body. Numerous deaths have been reported as a result of overheated hot tubs, often exacerbated by alcohol, which also increases blood flow to the skin. The body's feedback mechanisms for maintaining core temperature are complex and powerful, but they can be overcome in extreme situations, sometimes with disastrous results.

USDA/ARS.

▲ BIO Application Meat, not heat.
A calorimeter is a device used to measure heat production or consumption by an isolated system. Typically, the calorimeter is a benchtop piece of equipment used in an analytical laboratory to study, for example, the amount of heat generated by chemical reactions. However, the calorimeter can also be used to measure heat production in a much larger isolated system, such as the farm animal shown here. The cow is fed a strictly controlled diet in this room-sized calorimeter for several days, and the amount of heat produced by the animal's metabolism is carefully measured. In this way, agricultural scientists have been able to determine which types of animal feed are most efficient at promoting weight gain without excessive loss of energy as heat.

6 Calorimetry

"Calorimetry" means "measuring heat." We've discussed the energy transfer (heat) involved in temperature changes and in phases changes. Now we're ready to look at some examples of calorimetry calculations (calculations with heat). The basic principle is simple: When heat flow occurs between two objects that are isolated from their surroundings, the amount of heat lost by one object must equal the amount of heat gained by the other. Heat is energy in transit, so this principle is really just another form of conservation of energy. We take each quantity of heat *added to* an object as *positive* and each quantity *leaving* an object as *negative*. When several objects interact, the *algebraic sum* of the quantities of heat transferred to *all* of them must be zero. The basic principle can be stated very simply as

$$\Sigma Q = 0.$$

Calorimetry, dealing entirely with one conserved scalar quantity, is in many ways the simplest of all physical theories!

PROBLEM-SOLVING STRATEGY 2   Calorimetry problems   (MP)

SET UP

1. To avoid confusion about algebraic signs when calculating quantities of heat, use Equations 10 and 11 consistently for each object. Each Q is positive when heat enters an object and negative when it leaves. The algebraic sum of all the Q's must be zero.

SOLVE

2. Often you will need to find an unknown temperature. Represent it by an algebraic symbol such as T. Then, if an object has an initial temperature of 20°C and an unknown final temperature T, the temperature change for the object is $\Delta T = T_{\text{final}} - T_{\text{initial}} = T - 20°C$ (*not* $20°C - T$) . . . and so on.
3. Compute the heat added to each interacting object, and then equate the algebraic sum of all the quantities of heat to zero (representing conservation of energy). When heat leaves an object, consider it as negative heat added to the object.

REFLECT

4. In problems in which a phase change takes place, as when ice melts, you may not know in advance whether *all* of the material undergoes a phase change or only part of it does. You can always assume one or the other, and if the resulting calculation gives an absurd result (such as a final temperature that is higher or lower than *all* of the initial temperatures), you know that the initial assumption was wrong. Back up and try again!

EXAMPLE 8   Coffee in a metal cup

A Turkish restaurant serves coffee in copper mugs (with the inside tin plated to avoid copper poisoning). A waiter fills a cup having a mass of 0.100 kg and initially at 20.0°C with 0.300 kg of coffee that is initially at 70.0°C. What is the final temperature after the coffee and the cup attain thermal equilibrium? (Assume that coffee has the same specific heat capacity as water and that there is no heat exchange with the surroundings.)

Continued

492

SOLUTION

SET UP AND SOLVE Call the final temperature T. The (negative) change in temperature of the coffee is $\Delta T_{coffee} = T - 70°C$, and the (positive) change in temperature of the cup is $\Delta T_{copper} = T - 20°C$. We need to find the heat lost by the coffee and gained by the copper cup and then set the algebraic sum equal to zero. Because the coffee loses heat, it has a negative value of Q:

$$Q_{coffee} = mc_{water}\Delta T_{coffee}$$
$$= (0.300 \text{ kg})[4190 \text{ J}/(\text{kg} \cdot \text{K})](T - 70.0°C).$$

(Note that ΔT_{coffee} is negative in this expression.) The heat gained by the copper cup is

$$Q_{copper} = mc_{copper}\Delta T_{copper}$$
$$= (0.100 \text{ kg})[390 \text{ J}/(\text{kg} \cdot \text{K})](T - 20.0°C).$$

(Note that ΔT_{copper} is positive in this expression.) We equate the sum of these two quantities of heat to zero, obtaining an algebraic equation for T:

$$Q_{coffee} + Q_{copper} = 0,$$
or
$$(0.300 \text{ kg})[4190 \text{ J}/(\text{kg} \cdot \text{K})](T - 70.0°C)$$
$$+ (0.100 \text{ kg})[390 \text{ J}/(\text{kg} \cdot \text{K})](T - 20.0°C) = 0.$$

Solving this equation for T, we find $T = 68.5°C$.

REFLECT The final temperature is much closer to the initial temperature of the coffee than to that of the cup; water has a much larger specific heat capacity than copper, and we have three times as much mass of water. We can also find the quantities of heat by substituting this value for T back into the original equations. When we do this, we find that $Q_{coffee} = -1890 \text{ J}$ and $Q_{copper} = +1890 \text{ J}$; Q_{coffee} is negative, as expected.

Practice Problem: Find the final temperature if the cup is a heavy ceramic cup with a mass of 0.200 kg and specific heat capacity $c = 800 \text{ J}/(\text{kg} \cdot \text{K})$. *Answer:* 64.3°C.

EXAMPLE 9   Chilling your soda

A physics student wants to cool 0.25 kg of Diet Omni-Cola (mostly water) initially at 20°C by adding ice initially at −20°C. How much ice should she add so that the final temperature will be 0°C with all the ice melted? Assume that the heat capacity of the paper container may be neglected.

SOLUTION

SET UP AND SOLVE The ice *gains* the heat (positive Q) required to warm it from −20°C to 0°C and to melt all of it. The cola *loses* (negative Q) the same amount of heat. Let the unknown mass of ice be m. The (negative) heat transfer to the Omni-Cola is

$$Q_{Omni} = m_{Omni}c_{water}\,\Delta T_{Omni}$$
$$= (0.25 \text{ kg})[4190 \text{ J}/(\text{kg} \cdot \text{K})](0°C - 20°C)$$
$$= -21,000 \text{ J}.$$

The specific heat capacity of ice (not the same as that for liquid water) is about $2.0 \times 10^3 \text{ J}/\text{kg} \cdot \text{K}$. The heat needed to warm a mass m of ice from −20°C to 0°C is

$$Q_{ice} = mc_{ice}\,\Delta T_{ice}$$
$$= m[2.0 \times 10^3 \text{ J}/(\text{kg} \cdot \text{K})][0°C - (-20°C)]$$
$$= m(4.0 \times 10^4 \text{ J}/\text{kg}).$$

The additional heat needed to melt the ice is the mass of the ice times the heat of fusion:

$$Q_{melt} = mL_f$$
$$= m(3.34 \times 10^5 \text{ J}/\text{kg.})$$

The sum of these three quantities must equal zero:

$$Q_{Omni} + Q_{ice} + Q_{melt} = -21,000 \text{ J} + m(40,000 \text{ J}/\text{kg})$$
$$+ m(334,000 \text{ J}/\text{kg}) = 0.$$

Solving this equation for m, we get $m = 0.056 \text{ kg} = 56 \text{ g}$ (two or three medium-size ice cubes).

REFLECT A final state with all the ice melted isn't a very satisfying outcome. We probably want to add a couple of extra ice cubes so that the drink will stay cold for a while even though the temperature of the surrounding air may be considerably higher than 0°C.

7 Heat Transfer

In Section 1, we spoke qualitatively about *conductors* and *insulators*—materials that permit or prevent heat transfer between objects. We weren't concerned with how quickly or slowly the transfer takes place. But if you're boiling water to make tea or trying to build an energy-efficient house, you need to know how quickly or slowly heat is transferred. In this section, we'll study the three mechanisms of heat transfer—conduction, convection, and radiation—and the relation of the rate of heat transfer to the properties of the system. *Conduction* occurs within an object or between two objects that are in actual contact with each other.

▲ FIGURE 16 Steady-state heat flow due to conduction in a uniform rod.

Heat current $H = kA\dfrac{T_H - T_C}{L}$

Doubling the cross-sectional area of the conductor doubles the heat current ($H \propto A$):

Doubling the length of the conductor halves the heat current ($H \propto 1/L$):

▲ FIGURE 17 The relationship of heat current to the area and length of a conductor.

TABLE 5   Thermal conductivities

Material	$k \, (\mathrm{W}/(\mathrm{m} \cdot \mathrm{K}))$
Metals	
Lead	34.7
Steel	50.2
Brass	109
Aluminum	205
Copper	385
Silver	406
Other solids (representative values)	
Styrofoam™	0.01
Fiberglass	0.04
Wood	0.12–0.04
Insulating brick	0.15
Red brick	0.6
Concrete	0.8
Glass	0.8
Ice	1.6
Gases	
Air	0.024
Helium	0.14

Convection depends on the motion of mass (such as air or water) from one region of space to another, and *radiation* is heat transfer by electromagnetic radiation, such as sunshine, with no need for matter to be present in the space between objects. We'll consider these three kinds of processes in turn.

Conduction

If you hold one end of a copper rod and place the other end in a flame, the end you are holding gets hotter and hotter, even though it isn't in direct contact with the flame. Heat reaches the cooler end by **conduction** through the material. On the atomic level, the atoms in the hotter regions have more kinetic energy, on the average, than their cooler neighbors. They jostle their neighbors, giving them some of their energy. The neighbors then jostle *their* neighbors, and so it goes through the material. The atoms themselves do not move from one region of the material to another, but their energy does.

In metals, electron motion provides another mechanism for heat transfer. Most metals are good conductors of electricity because some electrons can leave their parent atoms and wander through the crystal lattice. These free electrons can carry energy from the hotter to the cooler regions of the metal. Good thermal conductors such as silver, copper, aluminum, and gold are also good electrical conductors.

Heat transfer occurs only between regions at different temperatures, and the direction of heat flow is always from higher to lower temperature. Figure 16 shows a rod of conducting material with cross-sectional area A and length L. The left end of the rod is kept at a temperature T_H and the right end at a lower temperature T_C, and heat flows from left to right. We assume that the rod is insulated, so that heat flows only from one end to the other, not in or out at the sides.

In discussing the rate of heat transfer with time, we'll change our notation slightly: We'll use ΔQ (rather than just Q) for the quantity of heat transferred in a time Δt. Then the rate of heat flow with time (heat transferred per unit time) is $\Delta Q/\Delta t$. We call this rate the **heat current** and denote it by H. That is, $H = \Delta Q/\Delta t$. Experiments show that the heat current is proportional to the cross-sectional area A. If we place two identical rods side by side, the total heat flow is twice as great as for each individual rod (Figure 17). It is also proportional to the temperature difference $(T_H - T_C)$. Finally, it is *inversely* proportional to the length L: Roughly speaking, if the heat has twice as far to go, it takes twice as long to get there.

Introducing a proportionality constant k called the **thermal conductivity** of the material, we have

$$H = \frac{\Delta Q}{\Delta t} = kA\frac{T_H - T_C}{L}. \tag{12}$$

The quantity $(T_H - T_C)/L$ is the temperature difference *per unit length*; it is called the **temperature gradient.** The numerical value of k depends on the material of the rod. Materials with large k are good conductors of heat; materials with small k are poor conductors (and thus good insulators). Equation 12 also gives the heat current through a slab, or *any* homogeneous object with uniform cross-sectional area A perpendicular to the direction of flow; L is the length of the heat-flow path.

The units of heat current H are units of energy per unit time, or power; the SI unit of heat current is the joule per second, or watt (W). We can find the units of k by solving Equation 12 for k. We invite you to verify that the SI units of k are $\mathrm{W}/(\mathrm{m} \cdot \mathrm{K})$. Some numerical values of k are given in Table 5. This table makes it clear why copper and aluminum are often used in the bottoms of cooking pans.

The thermal conductivity of "dead" (nonmoving) air is very small. A wool sweater is warm because it traps air between the fibers. In fact, many insulating

▶ **BIO Application Hot-and-cold fish.** Most fish are the same temperature as the surrounding water because the heat their bodies generate is lost by conduction to the water as their blood circulates through the gills. However, some large predatory fishes, such as these bluefin tuna, use a special technique to warm key body parts—their central swimming muscles, their brains, and the retinas of their eyes, for example. Warming these organs allows the fishes to hunt effectively in cold water. To keep a body part warm, the arteries entering it run in intimate contact with the veins leaving it, allowing rapid transfer of heat by conduction between the vessels. The heat in the venous blood leaving the body part passes to the cold arterial blood approaching it; by the time the arterial blood reaches the part in question, it is warm. Thus, the "countercurrent" flow of blood in the adjoining vessels traps heat in a particular region.

Nature Picture Library

materials, such as Styrofoam™ and fiberglass, are mostly dead air. Figure 18 shows a "space-age" ceramic material with highly unusual thermal properties, including very small conductivity.

Quantitative Analysis 5

Big house, little house

Two neighboring houses are built of the same materials, but one is twice as long, high, and wide as the other and also has walls twice as thick. To keep the two houses equally warm on a cold day, at what rate must the heater in the big house supply heat, compared with the heater in the small house?

A. at twice the rate.
B. at four times the rate.
C. at 16 times the rate.

SOLUTION We assume that the walls, roofs, and basement floors (if any) participate equally in the heat loss from the houses. The larger house is twice as large in each dimension, so it has four times the surface area as the smaller one. If the walls of the two houses were the same thickness, the larger one would lose heat at four times the rate of the small one. But its walls are twice as thick; therefore, the rate of heat flow for a given area is only half as great. We conclude that the larger house loses heat at a rate two times as great as the smaller one. The correct answer is A.

Russ Underwood/Lockheed Martin

PROBLEM-SOLVING STRATEGY 3 Heat conduction

SET UP

1. Identify the direction of heat flow in the problem (from hot to cold). In Equation 12, L is always measured along that direction and A is always an area perpendicular to that direction. Often, when a box or other container has an irregular shape, but uniform wall thickness, you can approximate it as a flat slab with the same thickness and total wall area.

SOLVE

2. In some problems, the heat flows through two different materials in succession. The temperature at the interface between the two materials is then intermediate between T_H and T_C; represent it by a symbol such as T. The temperature differences for the two materials are then $(T_H - T)$ and $(T - T_C)$. In steady-state heat flow, the same heat has to pass through both materials in succession, so the heat current H must be *the same* in both materials.

3. If there are two *parallel* heat flow paths, so that some heat flows through each, then the total H is the sum of the quantities H_1 and H_2 for the separate paths. An example is heat flow from inside to outside a house, both through the glass in a window and through the surrounding frame. In this case, the temperature difference is the same for the two paths, but L, A, and k may be different.

4. As always, it is essential to use a consistent set of units. If you use a value of k expressed in $W/(m \cdot K)$, don't use distances in cm, heat in calories, or T in °F!

REFLECT

5. Ask whether your results make sense. If you find that Styrofoam™ conducts heat better than copper, you've made a mistake!

▲ **FIGURE 18** This protective tile, developed for use in the space shuttle, has extraordinary thermal properties. The extremely small thermal conductivity and small heat capacity of the material make it possible to hold the tile by its edges, even though it is hot enough to emit the light needed for this photograph.

EXAMPLE 10   Conduction through a Styrofoam™ cooler

The Styrofoam™ box in Figure 19 is used to keep drinks cold at a picnic. The total wall area (including the lid) is 0.80 m², and the wall thickness is 2.0 cm. The box is filled with ice and cans of Omni-Cola, keeping the inner surface at 0°C. What is the rate of heat flow into the box if the temperature of the outside surface is 30°C? How much ice melts in one day (24 h)?

▶ **FIGURE 19**

SOLUTION

SET UP Figure 20 shows our sketch. We assume that the total heat flow is approximately the same as it would be through a flat slab of area 0.80 m² and thickness 2.0 cm = 0.020 m. We find k from Table 5. The heat of fusion of ice is 3.34×10^5 J/kg. There are 86,400 s in one day.

SOLVE From Equation 12, the heat current H (rate of heat flow) is

$$H = kA\frac{T_2 - T_1}{L}$$

$$= [0.010 \text{ W}/(\text{m} \cdot \text{K})](0.80 \text{ m}^2)\frac{30°C - 0°C}{0.020 \text{ m}}$$

$$= 12 \text{ W}.$$

The total heat flow Q in one day is

$$Q = Ht = (12 \text{ J/s})(86,400 \text{ s}) = 1.04 \times 10^6 \text{ J}.$$

The mass of ice melted by this quantity of heat is

$$m = \frac{Q}{L_f} = \frac{1.04 \times 10^6 \text{ J}}{3.34 \times 10^5 \text{ J/kg}} = 3.1 \text{ kg}.$$

▲ **FIGURE 20** Our sketch for this problem.

REFLECT A typical bag of ice you buy at the market is 8 lb = 3.6 kg. So this amount is roughly equal to one 8 lb bag of ice.

Practice Problem: This same Styrofoam™ cooler is sitting in the sun, and the outside temperature reaches 40°C. How much time passes before the 8 lb of ice is completely melted? *Answer:* $t = 21$ h.

EXAMPLE 11   Conduction in two bars in series

A steel bar 10.0 cm long is welded end to end to a copper bar 20.0 cm long. Each bar has a square cross section 2.00 cm on a side. The free end of the steel bar is in contact with steam at 100°C, and the free end of the copper bar is in contact with ice at 0°C. Find the temperature at the junction of the two bars and the total rate of heat flow.

SOLUTION

SET UP Figure 21 shows our sketch; we use the subscripts s and c for steel and copper, respectively. The key to the solution is the fact that the heat currents in the two bars must be equal; otherwise, some sections would have more heat flowing in than out, or the reverse, and steady-state conditions could not exist.

SOLVE Let T be the unknown junction temperature; we use Equation 12 for each bar and equate the two expressions:

$$\frac{k_s A(100°C - T)}{L_s} = \frac{k_c A(T - 0°C)}{L_c}.$$

▲ **FIGURE 21** Our sketch for this problem.

Continued

The areas A are equal and may be divided out. Substituting numerical values, we find that

$$\frac{[50.2 \text{ W}/(\text{m} \cdot \text{K})](100°\text{C} - T)}{0.100 \text{ m}}$$
$$= \frac{[385 \text{ W}/(\text{m} \cdot \text{K})](T - 0°\text{C})}{0.200 \text{ m}}.$$

Rearranging and solving for T, we obtain

$$T = 20.7°\text{C}.$$

To find the total heat current H, we substitute this value for T back into either of the previous expressions:

$$H = \frac{[50.2 \text{ W}/(\text{m} \cdot \text{K})](0.0200 \text{ m})^2(100°\text{C} - 20.7°\text{C})}{0.100 \text{ m}}$$
$$= 15.9 \text{ W}$$

or

$$H = \frac{[385 \text{ W}/(\text{m} \cdot \text{K})](0.0200 \text{ m})^2(20.7°\text{C} - 0°\text{C})}{0.200 \text{ m}}$$
$$= 15.9 \text{ W}.$$

REFLECT Even though the steel bar is shorter, the temperature drop across it is much greater than that across the copper bar because steel is a much poorer conductor of heat.

Practice Problem: If we change the length of the steel bar, what length is needed in order to make the temperature at the junction 50.0°C? *Answer:* 2.60 cm.

EXAMPLE 12 **Conduction in two bars in parallel**

Suppose the two bars in Example 11 are separated. One end of each bar is placed in contact with steam at 100°C, and the other end of each bar contacts ice at 0°C. What is the *total* rate of heat flow in the two bars?

SOLUTION

SET UP Figure 22 shows our sketch. In this case the bars are in parallel rather than in series. As before, we use the subscripts s and c for steel and copper, respectively.

SOLVE The total heat current H is now the *sum* of the currents in the two bars. The temperature difference between ends is the same for both bars: $T_H - T_C = 100°\text{C} - 0°\text{C} = 100 \text{ K}$. We find that

$$H = \frac{\Delta Q}{\Delta t} = k_c A_c \frac{T_{H,c} - T_{C,c}}{L_c} + k_s A_s \frac{T_{H,s} - T_{C,s}}{L_s}$$
$$= \frac{[385 \text{ W}/(\text{m} \cdot \text{K})](0.0200 \text{ m})^2(100 \text{ K})}{0.200 \text{ m}}$$
$$+ \frac{[50.2 \text{ W}/(\text{m} \cdot \text{K})](0.0200\text{m})^2(100 \text{ K})}{0.100 \text{ m}}$$
$$= 77.0 \text{ W} + 20.1 \text{ W} = 97.1 \text{ W}.$$

REFLECT The heat flow in the copper bar is much greater than that in the steel bar, even though the copper bar is longer, because its thermal conductivity is much larger. The total heat flow is

▲ **FIGURE 22** Our sketch for this problem.

much greater than that in Example 11, partly because the total cross section for heat flow is greater and partly because the full 100 C° temperature difference acts across each bar.

Practice Problem: Suppose we increase the cross-sectional area of the steel bar. What cross-sectional area would be needed to make the heat currents in the two bars equal? *Answer:* 15.3 cm².

Convection

Convection is the transfer of heat by the motion of a mass of fluid from one region of space to another. Familiar examples include hot-air and hot-water home heating systems, the cooling system of an automobile engine, and the heating and cooling of the body by the flow of blood. If the fluid is circulated by a blower or pump, the process is called *forced convection;* if the flow is caused by differences in density due to thermal expansion, such as hot air rising, the process is called *natural convection* or *free convection.*

Day: The land is warmer than the water; convection draws a sea breeze onshore.

Night: The land is colder than the water; convection sends a land breeze offshore.

▲ **FIGURE 23** Convective currents in the air determine daytime sea breezes and nighttime land breezes near shore.

Getty Images Inc.—Punchstock

▲ **FIGURE 24** Heat transfer by radiation from the sun. The heat is not dangerous to human skin, but the ultraviolet radiation is.

Convection in the atmosphere plays a dominant role in determining weather patterns (Figure 23), and convection in the oceans is an important global heat-transfer mechanism. On a smaller scale, glider pilots make use of thermal updrafts from the warm earth. But sometimes the air cools enough as it rises to form thunderheads, which contain convection currents that can tear a glider to pieces.

The most important mechanism for heat transfer within the human body is forced convection of blood, with the heart serving as the pump. The total rate of heat loss from the body is on the order of 100 to 200 W (2000 to 4000 kcal per day). A dry, unclothed body in still air loses about 75 W by radiation, but during vigorous exercise and plentiful perspiration, evaporative cooling with convection is the dominant mechanism.

Convective heat transfer is a complex process, and there is no simple equation to describe it. Here are a few experimental facts: The heat current due to convection is directly proportional to the surface area involved. This is the reason for the large surface areas of radiators and cooling fins. In some cases, it is approximately proportional to the $\frac{5}{4}$ power of the temperature difference between the surface and the main body of fluid. The viscosity of fluids slows natural convection near a stationary surface. In air, this effect produces a surface film; forced convection decreases the thickness of this film, increasing the rate of heat transfer. This is the reason for the "wind-chill factor": You get cold faster in a cold wind than in still air with the same temperature.

Radiation

Heat transfer by **radiation** depends on electromagnetic waves such as visible light, infrared, and ultraviolet radiation. Everyone has felt the warmth of the sun's radiation (Figure 24) and the intense heat from a charcoal grill or the glowing coals in a fireplace. Heat from these very hot objects reaches you not by conduction or convection in the intervening air, but by *radiation*. This kind of heat transfer would occur even if there were nothing but vacuum between you and the source of heat.

Every object, even at ordinary temperatures, emits energy in the form of electromagnetic radiation. At ordinary temperatures, say, 20°C, nearly all the energy is carried by infrared waves with wavelengths much longer than those of visible light. As the temperature rises, the wavelengths shift to shorter values. At 800°C, an object emits enough visible radiation to be self-luminous and appears "red hot," although even at this temperature most of the energy is carried by infrared waves. At 3000°C, the temperature of an incandescent lamp filament, the radiation contains enough visible light that the object appears "white hot."

The rate of energy radiation from a surface is proportional to the surface area A. The rate increases very rapidly with temperature, in proportion to the fourth power of the absolute (Kelvin) temperature. The rate also depends on the nature of the surface; this dependence is described by a quantity e called the **emissivity,** a dimensionless number between 0 and 1. The heat current $H = \Delta Q/\Delta t$ due to radiation from a surface area A with emissivity e at absolute (Kelvin) temperature T can be expressed as

$$H = Ae\sigma T^4, \tag{13}$$

where σ is a fundamental physical constant called the **Stefan–Boltzmann constant.** This relation is called the **Stefan–Boltzmann law,** in honor of its late-19th-century discoverers. The numerical value of σ is found experimentally to be

$$\sigma = 5.6705 \times 10^{-8} \, \mathrm{W}/(\mathrm{m^2 \cdot K^4}).$$

▶ Application **Baked in a convection oven?** The volcanic Hawaiian Islands are a by-product of the earth's convective cooling system. Earth's deep interior generates heat, mainly by the decay of radioactive elements and the slow solidification of the liquid core. The temperature difference between the hot interior and the cold crust sets up density differences that cause the solid rock of the earth's crust and mantle to flow in (very) slow convective motions, carrying heat from the interior to the surface. The Hawaiian islands are built by a dramatic type of convective flow called a *mantle plume*—a vertical jet of hot rock that may rise from near the core itself. As this plume approaches the surface, the reduction in pressure causes some of the plume's rock to melt, creating the lava that builds the islands. In the foreground we see a cinder cone on the peak of Mauna Kea; in the background is the silhouette of Mauna Loa.

We invite you to check for consistency of units in Equation 13. Emissivity *e* is often larger for dark surfaces than for light ones. The emissivity of a smooth copper surface is about 0.3, but *e* for a dull black surface is nearly unity.

Philip Rosenberg/Pacific Stock/Photolibrary

Quantitative Analysis 6

Raising the temperature

If the Kelvin temperature of a spherical object were increased by 20%, by approximately what factor would the rate of radiated energy emitted from its surface be changed?

A. 1.2.
B. 1.4.
C. 1.7.
D. 2.0.

SOLUTION The rate of radiation of energy is proportional to the fourth power of the absolute temperature. If the temperature increases by a factor of 1.2, the rate of radiation increases by a factor of $(1.2)^4$, or 2.07 (to three significant figures). The closest answer to this is D, the correct answer.

EXAMPLE 13 **Radiation from a hot plate**

A thin, square steel plate 10 cm on a side is heated in a blacksmith's forge to a temperature of 800°C. If the emissivity is 0.60, what is the plate's rate of radiation of energy?

SOLUTION

SET UP The total surface area of the plate, including both sides, is $2(0.10 \text{ m})^2 = 0.020 \text{ m}^2$. We must convert the temperature to the Kelvin scale: 800°C = 1073 K.

SOLVE Equation 13 gives

$$H = Ae\sigma T^4$$
$$= (0.020 \text{ m}^2)(0.60)[5.67 \times 10^{-8} \text{ W}/(\text{m}^2 \cdot \text{K}^4)](1073 \text{ K})^4$$
$$= 900 \text{ W}.$$

REFLECT This rate of emission of energy is comparable to the output of a small electric space heater.

Practice Problem: What temperature would be required for this plate to radiate at the rate of 1500 W? *Answer:* 950°C.

While an object at absolute (Kelvin) temperature T is radiating, its surroundings, at temperature T_s, are also radiating, and the object *absorbs* some of this radiation. If it is in thermal equilibrium with its surroundings, the rates of radiation and absorption must be equal. For this to be true, the rate of absorption must be given in general by $H = Ae\sigma T_s^4$. Then the *net* rate of radiation from an object at temperature T with surroundings at temperature T_s is

$$H_{\text{net}} = Ae\sigma T^4 - Ae\sigma T_s^4 = Ae\sigma(T^4 - T_s^4). \tag{14}$$

In this equation, a positive value of H means a net heat flow *out of* the object. Equation 14 shows that, for radiation, as for conduction and convection, the heat current depends on the temperature *difference* between two objects.

EXAMPLE 14 **Radiation from the human body**

If the total surface area of a woman's body is 1.2 m^2 and her skin temperature is 30°C, find the total rate of radiation of energy from her body. She also *absorbs* radiation from her surroundings. If the surroundings are at a temperature of 20°C, what is her *net* rate of heat loss by radiation? The emissivity of the body is very close to unity, irrespective of skin pigmentation.

SOLUTION

SET UP We need to convert the temperatures to absolute (Kelvin) temperatures: 30°C = 303 K and 20°C = 293 K. The rate of radiation of energy per unit area is given by Equation 13.

SOLVE Taking $e = 1$, we find that

$$H = Ae\sigma T^4$$
$$= (1.2 \text{ m}^2)(1)[5.67 \times 10^{-8} \text{ W}/(\text{m}^2 \cdot \text{K}^4)](303 \text{ K})^4$$
$$= 574 \text{ W}.$$

This loss is partly offset by the *absorption* of radiation, which depends on the temperature of the surroundings. The *net* rate of radiative energy transfer is given by Equation 14:

$$H = Ae\sigma(T^4 - T_s^4)$$
$$= (1.2 \text{ m}^2)(1)[(5.67 \times 10^{-8} \text{ W}/(\text{m}^2 \cdot \text{K}^4)]$$
$$\cdot [(303 \text{ K})^4 - (293 \text{ K})^4]$$
$$= 72 \text{ W}.$$

REFLECT The heat produced by the human body at rest is about 75 W. Thus, this net rate of radiation is sufficient to prevent overheating. But when additional heat is produced by even mild exertion, heat must be removed by other means, such as evaporative cooling.

OSF/Photolibrary

▲ **BIO Application** **See my heat.** Just as an ordinary photograph captures visible light from an object, an infrared image captures heat released in the form of long-wavelength infrared radiation (infrared light). We cannot see infrared light without the help of special cameras or goggles. However, the venomous snakes known as pit vipers, which include the rattlesnakes and water moccasins, have special "pit organs" on their snout that are sensitive to infrared radiation. These snakes hunt mostly at night; their pit organs help them to "see" their warm-blooded prey in the cool darkness.

An object that is a good absorber must also be a good emitter. An ideal radiator, with an emissivity of unity, is also an ideal absorber, absorbing *all* of the radiation that strikes it. Such an ideal surface is called an ideal blackbody, or simply a **blackbody.** Conversely, an ideal *reflector,* which absorbs *no* radiation at all, is a highly ineffective radiator. This is the reason for the silver coatings on vacuum, or thermos, bottles, which were invented by Sir James Dewar (1842–1923). A vacuum bottle has double glass walls, and the air is pumped out of the spaces between the walls, eliminating nearly all heat transfer by conduction and convection. The silver coating on the walls reflects most of the radiation from the contents back into the container, and the wall itself is a very poor emitter. Thus, a vacuum bottle can keep coffee or soup hot for several hours. The Dewar flask, used to store very cold liquefied gases, is exactly the same in principle.

Heat transfer by radiation is important in some surprising places. A premature baby in an incubator can be cooled dangerously by radiation if the walls of the incubator happen to be cold, even when the *air* in the incubator is warm. Some incubators regulate the air temperature by measuring the baby's skin temperature.

We can study the infrared radiation emitted by an object by using a camera with infrared-sensitive film or by means of a device, similar to a television camera, that is sensitive to infrared radiation. The resulting picture is called a *thermograph.* The rate of emission of energy depends strongly on temperature, so thermography permits the detailed study of temperature distributions, with a precision as great as 0.1 C°. Thermography is used to study energy losses in heated buildings, and it has several important medical applications. Various tumors, such as breast cancer, cause local temperature variations, and growths as small as 1 cm can be detected. Circulatory disorders that cause local temperature anomalies can be studied, and thermography has many other applications.

8 Solar Energy and Resource Conservation

The principles of heat transfer that we've studied in this chapter have many practical applications in a civilization such as ours, with growing energy consumption and dwindling energy resources. A substantial fraction of all the energy consumption in the United States is used to heat and cool homes and other buildings, to maintain a comfortable temperature and humidity inside when the outside temperature is much hotter or much colder.

For space heating, the objective is to prevent as much heat flow as possible from inside to outside; heating units replace the inevitable loss of heat. Walls insulated with material of low thermal conductivity, storm windows, and multiple-layer glass windows all help to reduce heat loss. It has been estimated that if all buildings used such materials, the total energy needed for space heating would be reduced by at least one-third.

Air-conditioning in summer poses the reverse problem: Heat flows from outside to inside, and energy must be expended in refrigeration units to remove it. Again, appropriate insulation can decrease this energy cost considerably.

Direct conversion of solar energy is a promising development in energy technology. Near the earth, the rate of energy transfer due to solar radiation is about 1400 W for each square meter of surface area. Not all of this energy reaches the earth's surface; even on a clear day, about one-fourth of the energy is absorbed by the earth's atmosphere. In a typical household solar heating system, large black plates facing the sun are backed with pipes through which water circulates. The black surface absorbs most of the sun's radiation; the heat is transferred by conduction to the water and then by forced convection to radiators inside the house. Heat loss by convection of air near the solar collecting panels is reduced by covering them with glass, with a thin air space between the glass and the panel. An insulated heat reservoir stores the energy collected for use at night and on cloudy days. Many larger-scale solar-energy conversion systems, including windmills, are also currently under study.

From an environmental standpoint, solar energy has multiple advantages over the use of fossil fuels (burning of coal or oil) or nuclear power. Fossil fuels are being used up; solar power continues indefinitely. Obtaining fossil fuels may involve strip mining, with its associated destruction of landscape and elimination of other useful land functions, such as farming or timber. Offshore oil drilling is a source of ocean water pollution. Air pollution from combustion products is a familiar problem, as is acid rain, which is directly attributable to coal smoke in many cases. Excess atmospheric carbon dioxide produced by the combustion of hydrocarbons is a major contributor to the so-called greenhouse effect. Many responsible scientists believe that the long-range effects on our climate will be serious or even catastrophic unless greenhouse gas emission is substantially reduced.

Nuclear power poses radiation hazards and the problem of disposing of radioactive waste material. Solar power avoids all these problems. Some practical problems still need to be worked out, however, including high installation costs and the need for energy storage facilities for nighttime and cloudy days.

Intelligent consideration of the effects of solar radiation in the design of buildings can also reduce energy consumption in heating and cooling. In recent years, there has been considerable growth in awareness of the need to design buildings with energy conservation in mind. The need to conserve is pressing and will undoubtedly become more so in years to come.

David Mauriuz/Corbis

▲ Application **Driving off using the sunset.** Solar energy represents an almost limitless source of energy if we can figure out how to convert it efficiently into usable forms such as mechanical, chemical, or electrical energy. Thanks to ultralight materials and efficient solar panels and energy converters, the Nuna 2, pictured here, can reach speeds of over 100 mph (160 km/hr)! This car, designed and built in the Netherlands by physics and engineering students, shows how limitless human imagination, creativity, and innovation can be with enough study and hard work.

CHAPTER SUMMARY

Temperature and Temperature Scales

(Sections 1 and 2) Two objects in **thermal equilibrium** must have the same temperature. A conducting material between two objects permits interaction leading to thermal equilibrium; an insulating material prevents or impedes this interaction. The **Celsius** and **Fahrenheit** temperature scales are based on the freezing $(0°C = 32°F)$ and boiling $(100°C = 212°F)$ temperatures of water, related by the formulas $T_F = \frac{9}{5}T_C + 32°$ and $T_C = \frac{5}{9}(T_F - 32°)$ (Equations 1 and 2).

The **Kelvin** scale has its zero at the extrapolated zero-pressure temperature for a gas thermometer, which is $-273.15°C$. Thus, $0\ K = -273.15°C$, and $T_K = T_C + 273.15$ (Equation 3).

If A and B are each in thermal equilibrium with C ...

... then A and B are in thermal equilibrium with each other.

Thermal Expansion

(Section 3) The change ΔL in any linear dimension L_0 of a solid object with a temperature change ΔT is approximately $\Delta L = \alpha L_0 \Delta T$ (Equation 4), where α is the **coefficient of linear expansion.** The change ΔV in the volume V_0 of any solid or liquid material with a temperature change ΔT is approximately $\Delta V = \beta V_0 \Delta T$ (Equation 6), where β is the **coefficient of volume expansion.** For many solids, $\beta = 3\alpha$.

$L = L_0 + \Delta L$
$= L_0(1 + \alpha \Delta T)$

Heat, Phase Changes, and Calorimetry

(Sections 4–6) Heat is energy transferred from one object to another as a result of a temperature difference. The quantity of heat Q required to raise the temperature of a mass m of material by a small amount ΔT is $Q = mc\Delta T$ (Equation 10), where c is the **specific heat capacity** of the material.

To change a mass m of a material to a different phase (such as liquid to solid or liquid to vapor) at the same temperature requires the addition or subtraction of a quantity of heat Q given by $Q = \pm mL$ (Equation 11), where L is the **heat of fusion, heat of vaporization,** or **heat of sublimation.**

Calculations with heat are called **calorimetry calculations:** In an isolated system whose parts interact by heat exchange, the algebraic sum of the Q's for all parts of the system must be zero.

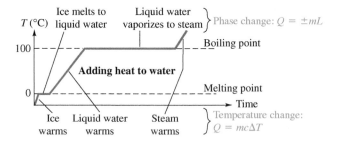

Phase change: $Q = \pm mL$

Temperature change: $Q = mc\Delta T$

Heat Transfer

(Section 7) The three mechanisms of heat transfer are conduction, convection, and radiation. **Conduction** is transfer of energy of molecular motion within materials without bulk motion of the materials. **Convection** involves the motion of a mass from one region to another. **Radiation** is energy transfer through electromagnetic radiation.

The **heat current** H for conduction depends on the area A through which the heat flows, the length L of the heat path, the temperature difference $(T_H - T_C)$, and the thermal conductivity k of the material, according to the equation

$$H = kA\frac{T_H - T_C}{L}. \qquad (12)$$

The heat current H due to radiation is given by $H = Ae\sigma T^4$ (Equation 13), where A is the surface area, e is the **emissivity** of the surface (a pure number between 0 and 1), T is the absolute (Kelvin) temperature, and σ is the Stefan–Boltzmann constant.

Continued

Solar Energy and Resource Conservation

(Section 8) A substantial fraction of all energy consumption in the United States is used to heat and cool homes and other buildings. Insulation in walls and multiple-layer glass windows can reduce heat flow by at least a third.

In a typical household solar heating system, large black plates facing the sun are backed with pipes through which water circulates. The black surface absorbs most of the sun's radiation; the heat is transferred by conduction to the water and then by forced convection to radiators inside the house.

Temperature and Heat: Problem Set

Conceptual Questions

1. When a block with a hole in it is heated, why doesn't the material around the hole expand into the hole and make it smaller? Explain this behavior by looking at the forces operating at the molecular level.

2. You have a drink that you want to cool off. You could put in 100 g of ice or 100 g of water, both at 0°C. Which one would be more effective in cooling your drink? Why?

3. A thermostat for controlling household heating systems often contains a bimetallic element consisting of two parallel strips of different metals welded together along their length. When the temperature changes, this composite strip bends one way or the other. Why?

4. Why is it sometimes possible to loosen caps on screw-top bottles by dipping the capped bottle briefly into hot water?

5. Galileo supposedly designed a thermometer consisting of hollow metal spheres suspended in a liquid inside a vertical glass cylinder. At a low temperature, all the spheres were at the top of the liquid. As the temperature of the room (and hence of the liquid and the spheres) rose, the spheres, one by one, would descend from the top. Each sphere was marked with the temperature at which it descended. (Replicas of this thermometer are available today, one of which sits on the author's fireplace mantel.) Explain the physical principles behind the operation of this device. What do you suppose is different about the properties of the spheres?

6. Builders usually put steel bars (called *rebar*) inside of concrete slabs for reinforcement. Since the concrete and rebar are made of different materials, it might seem that they should expand at different rates when heated and that the rebar should actually *weaken* the concrete. So why does adding rebar strengthen concrete? What might happen if a metal other than steel were used?

7. To raise the temperature of an object, must you add heat to it? If you add heat to an object, must you raise its temperature? Explain.

8. You've probably seen what happens to lettuce or other vegetables if they freeze accidentally in the refrigerator. Freezing cells, as opposed to just making them cold, can kill them by causing them to burst. Why does a cell burst when frozen?

9. True or false? When two objects at different temperatures are placed in contact, the rise in temperature of the cooler object must equal the drop in temperature of the warmer one.

10. If you have wet hands and pick up a piece of metal that is below the freezing point of water, you may stick to it. This doesn't happen with wood. Why this difference in behavior?

11. If you add heat slowly to ice at 0°C, why doesn't the temperature of the ice increase? What becomes of this heat energy? Likewise, if you add heat to boiling water, the temperature remains at 100°C. What is happening to the heat you add?

12. In some household air conditioners used in dry climates, air is cooled by blowing it through a water-soaked filter, evaporating some of the water. How does this cool the air? Would such a system work well in a high-humidity climate? Why or why not?

13. A person pours a cup of hot coffee, intending to drink it 5 minutes later. To have it as hot as possible for drinking, should she put the cold milk into it now or wait until just before she drinks it? Explain your reasoning.

14. If you put your hand into boiling water at 212°F, you will immediately get a serious burn. Yet you readily reach into a much hotter 400°F oven without danger. Why the difference? (*Hint:* What are the significant differences between the properties of the air in the oven and the boiling water?)

15. You are going away for the weekend and plan to turn down your home thermostat to conserve energy. Your neighbor suggests that you not turn it down, because the walls and floors of your home will get cold and have to be reheated when you get back, which will take more energy than you save. Should you follow your neighbor's advice? Consider all three forms of heat transfer (conduction, convection, and radiation).

16. Why is snow, which is made up of ice crystals, a much better insulator than ice?

17. A cold block of metal feels colder than a block of wood at the same temperature. Why? A *hot* block of metal feels hotter than a block of wood at the same temperature. Again, why? Is there any temperature at which the two blocks feel equally hot or cold? What temperature is this?

18. Give some good reasons why the equation $H = e\sigma A T^4$ is valid only if the temperature is expressed in kelvins (rather than degrees Fahrenheit or Celsius).

From Chapter 14 of *College Physics*, Ninth Edition, Hugh D. Young. Copyright © 2012 by Pearson Education, Inc.
Published by Pearson Addison-Wesley. All rights reserved.

Multiple-Choice Problems

1. If heat Q is required to increase the temperature of a metal object from 4°C to 6°C, the amount of heat necessary to increase its temperature from 6°C to 12°C is most likely
   A. Q. B. $2Q$. C. $3Q$. D. $4Q$.

2. A metal bar expands by 1.0 mm when its temperature is increased by 1.0 C°. Which of the following statements about this bar must be true? (There may be more than one correct choice.)
   A. It will expand by more than 1.0 mm if its temperature is increased by 1.0 K.
   B. It will expand by less than 1.0 mm if its temperature is increased by 1.0 F°.
   C. It will expand by 2.00 mm if its temperature is increased by 2.0 K.
   D. It will expand by more than 2.0 mm if its temperature is increased by 2.0 F°.

3. If an amount of heat Q is needed to increase the temperature of a solid metal sphere of diameter D from 4°C to 7°C, the amount of heat needed to increase the temperature of a solid sphere of diameter $2D$ of the same metal from 4°C to 7°C is
   A. Q. B. $2Q$. C. $4Q$. D. $8Q$.

4. If you mix 100 g of ice at 0°C with 100 g of boiling water at 100°C in a perfectly insulated container, the final stabilized temperature will be
   A. 0°C.   B. between 0°C and 50°C.
   C. 50°C.   D. between 50°C and 100°C.

5. A sphere radiates energy at a rate of 1.00 J/s when its temperature is 100°C. At what rate will it radiate energy if its temperature is increased to 200°C? (Neglect any heat transferred back into the sphere.)
   A. 1.27 J/s. B. 2.00 J/s. C. 2.59 J/s. D. 16.0 J/s.

6. Two identical closed, insulated containers hold equal amounts of water at a temperature of 50°C. One kilogram of ice at 0°C is added to the water in container A; one kilogram of steam at 100°C is added to container B. After all the ice has melted and all the steam has condensed, which container's temperature will have changed more?
   A. Container A   B. Container B
   C. Their temperatures change by the same amount.

7. The wall of a furnace conducts 1000 cal/min of heat out of the furnace and into the factory. If the wall's thickness is doubled, but nothing else changes (including the inner and outer surface temperatures), the amount of heat it conducts into the factory will be
   A. 4000 cal/min.   B. 2000 cal/min.
   C. 500 cal/min.   D. 250 cal/min.

8. A thin metal rod expands 1.5 mm when its temperature is increased by 2.0 C°. If an identical rod of the same material, except *twice as long,* also has its temperature increased by 2.0 C°, it will expand
   A. 0.75 mm. B. 1.0 mm. C. 3.0 mm. D. 6.0 mm.

9. Water has a specific heat capacity nearly 9 times that of iron. Suppose a 50-g pellet of iron at a temperature of 200°C is dropped into 50 g of water at a temperature of 20°C. When the system reaches thermal equilibrium, its temperature will be
   A. closer to 20°C.
   B. closer to 200°C.
   C. halfway between the two initial temperatures.

10. A cylindrical metal bar conducts heat at a rate R from a hot reservoir to a cold reservoir. If both its *length* and *diameter* are doubled, it will conduct heat at a rate
    A. R.   B. $2R$.   C. $4R$.   D. $8R$.

11. Two rods P and Q of identical shape and size, but made of different metals, are joined end to end. The left end of rod P is kept at 100°C while the right end of rod Q is at 0°C, causing heat to flow down the rods. The graph in Figure 25 shows the temperature distribution along the rods from the hot end to the cold end. Which rod has the higher thermal conductivity?
    A. rod P.
    B. rod Q.
    C. We cannot tell from the available data.

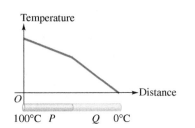

▲ **FIGURE 25** Multiple-choice problem 11.

12. The thermal conductivity of concrete is 0.80 W/(m · K), and the thermal conductivity of a certain wood is 0.10 W/(m · K). How thick would a solid concrete wall have to be to have the same rate of heat flow as an 8.0-cm-thick solid wall of this wood? Both walls have the same surface area and the same interior and exterior temperatures.
    A. 1.0 cm.   B. 16 cm.   C. 32 cm.   D. 64 cm.

13. The graph in Figure 26 shows the temperature as a function of time for a sample of material being heated at a constant rate. What segment or segments of this graph show the sample existing in two phases (or states)?
    A. OA.
    B. AB.
    C. OA and BC.

Temperature

▲ **FIGURE 26** Multiple-choice problem 13.

14. For the sample in the previous question, what segment of the graph shows the specific heat capacity of the sample to be *greatest?*
    A. OA.   B. AB.   C. BC.

15. You enter a cold room containing a wooden table and a steel table; both have been there for a long time. Why does the steel table feel much colder than the wooden one?
    A. Steel is a much better conductor of heat than wood is.
    B. The steel stores much more cold than the wood does.
    C. Steel has a higher specific heat capacity than wood has.
    D. The temperature of the steel table is lower than that of the wooden table.

Problems

2 Temperature Scales

1. ● (a) While vacationing in Europe, you feel sick and are told that you have a temperature of 40.2°C. Should you be concerned? What is your temperature in °F? (b) The morning weather report in Sydney predicts a high temperature of 12°C. Will you need to bring a jacket? What is this temperature in °F? (c) A friend has suggested that you go swimming in a pool having water of temperature 350 K. Is this safe to do? What would this temperature be on the Fahrenheit and Celsius scales?

2. ● **Temperatures in biomedicine.** (a) **Normal body temper-**
BIO **ature.** The average normal body temperature measured in the mouth is 310 K. What would Celsius and Fahrenheit thermometers read for this temperature? (b) **Elevated body temperature.** During very vigorous exercise, the body's temperature can go as high as 40°C. What would Kelvin and Fahrenheit thermometers read for this temperature? (c) **Temperature difference in the body.** The surface temperature of the body is normally about 7 C° lower than the internal temperature. Express this temperature difference in kelvins and in Fahrenheit degrees. (d) **Blood storage.** Blood stored at 4.0°C lasts safely for about 3 weeks, whereas blood stored at −160°C lasts for 5 years. Express both temperatures on the Fahrenheit and Kelvin scales. (e) **Heat stroke.** If the body's temperature is above 105°F for a prolonged period, heat stroke can result. Express this temperature on the Celsius and Kelvin scales.

3. ● (a) On January 22, 1943, the temperature in Spearfish, South Dakota, rose from −4.0°F to 45.0°F in just 2 minutes. What was the temperature change in Celsius degrees and in kelvins? (b) The temperature in Browning, Montana, was 44.0°F on January 23, 1916, and the next day it plummeted to −56.0°F. What was the temperature change in Celsius degrees and in kelvins?

4. ● **Inside the earth and the sun.** (a) Geophysicists have estimated that the temperature at the center of the earth's core is 5000°C (or more), while the temperature of the sun's core is about 15 million K. Express both of these temperatures in Fahrenheit degrees.

5. ●● (a) At what temperature do the Fahrenheit and Celsius scales coincide? (b) Is there any temperature at which the Kelvin and Celsius scales coincide?

6. ● Convert the following Kelvin temperatures to the Celsius and Fahrenheit scales: (a) the midday temperature at the surface of the moon (400 K); (b) the temperature at the tops of the clouds in the atmosphere of Saturn (95 K); (c) the temperature at the center of the sun $(1.55 \times 10^7 \text{ K})$.

3 Thermal Expansion

7. ● The Eiffel Tower in Paris is 984 ft tall and is made mostly of steel. If this is its height in winter when its temperature is −8.00°C, how much additional vertical distance must you cover if you decide to climb it during a summer heat wave when its temperature is 40.0°C? (b) Express the coefficient of linear expansion of steel in terms of Fahrenheit degrees.

8. ● A steel bridge is built in the summer when its temperature is 35.0°C. At the time of construction, its length is 80.00 m. What is the length of the bridge on a cold winter day when its temperature is −12.0°C?

9. ● A metal rod is 40.125 cm long at 20.0°C and 40.148 cm long at 45.0°C. Calculate the average coefficient of linear expansion of the rod's material for this temperature range.

10. ● (a) Steel train rails are laid in 12.0-m-long segments placed end to end. The rails are laid on a winter day when their temperature is −2.00°C. How much space must be left between adjacent rails if they are just to touch on a summer day when their temperature is 33.0°C? (b) If the rails are mistakenly laid in contact with each other, what is the stress in them on a summer day when their temperature is 33.0°C?

11. ● An underground tank with a capacity of 1700 L (1.70 m³) is completely filled with ethanol that has an initial temperature of 19.0°C. After the ethanol has cooled off to the temperature of the tank and ground, which is 10.0°C, how much air space will there be above the ethanol in the tank? (See Table A at the end of this problem set, and assume that the volume of the tank doesn't change appreciably.)

12. ● A copper cylinder is initially at 20.0°C. At what temperature will its volume be 0.150% larger than it is at 20.0°C?

13. ●● A geodesic dome constructed with an aluminum framework is a nearly perfect hemisphere; its diameter measures 55.0 m on a winter day at a temperature of −15°C. How much more interior space does the dome have in the summer, when the temperature is 35°C?

14. ●● The outer diameter of a glass jar and the inner diameter of its iron lid are both 725 mm at room temperature (20.0°C). What will be the size of the mismatch between the lid and the jar if the lid is briefly held under hot water until its temperature rises to 50.0°C, without changing the temperature of the glass?

15. ●● A glass flask whose volume is 1000.00 cm³ at 0.0°C is completely filled with mercury at this temperature. When flask and mercury are warmed to 55.0°C, 8.95 cm³ of mercury overflow. Compute the coefficient of volume expansion of the glass. (Consult Table A.)

16. ●● **Ensuring a tight fit.** Aluminum rivets used in airplane construction are made slightly larger than the rivet holes and cooled by "dry ice" (solid CO_2) before being driven. If the diameter of a hole is 4.500 mm, what should be the diameter of a rivet at 23.0°C, if its diameter is to equal that of the hole when the rivet is cooled to −78.0°C, the temperature of dry ice? Assume that the expansion coefficient remains constant at the value given in Table B at the end of this problem set.

17. ●● The markings on an aluminum ruler and a brass ruler begin at the left end; when the rulers are at 0.00°C, they are perfectly aligned. How far apart will the 20.0 cm marks be on the two rulers at 100.0°C if the left-hand ends are kept precisely aligned?

4 Quantity of Heat

18. ● (a) How much heat is required to raise the temperature of 0.250 kg of water from 20.0°C to 30.0°C? (b) If this amount of heat is added to an equal mass of mercury that is initially at 20.0°C, what is its final temperature?

19. ● One of the moving parts of an engine contains 1.60 kg of aluminum and 0.300 kg of iron and is designed to operate at 210°C. How much heat is required to raise its temperature from 20.0° to 210°C?

20. ● In an effort to stay awake for an all-night study session, a student makes a cup of coffee by first placing a 200.0 W electric immersion heater in 0.320 kg of water. (a) How much heat must be added to the water to raise its temperature from 20.0°C to 80.0°C? (b) How much time is required if all of the heater's power goes into heating the water?

21. • **Heat loss during breathing.** In very cold weather, a significant mechanism for heat loss by the human body is energy expended in warming the air taken into the lungs with each breath. (a) On a cold winter day when the temperature is $-20°C$, what is the amount of heat needed to warm to internal body temperature ($37°C$) the 0.50 L of air exchanged with each breath? Assume that the specific heat capacity of air is $1020 \text{ J}/(\text{kg} \cdot \text{K})$ and that 1.0 L of air has a mass of 1.3 g. (b) How much heat is lost per hour if the respiration rate is 20 breaths per minute?

22. • A nail driven into a board increases in temperature. If 60% of the kinetic energy delivered by a 1.80 kg hammer with a speed of 7.80 m/s is transformed into heat that flows into the nail and does not flow out, what is the increase in temperature of an 8.00 g aluminum nail after it is struck 10 times?

23. • You are given a sample of metal and asked to determine its specific heat. You weigh the sample and find that its weight is 28.4 N. You carefully add 1.25×10^4 J of heat energy to the sample and find that its temperature rises 18.0 C°. What is the sample's specific heat?

24. •• A 25,000-kg subway train initially traveling at 15.5 m/s slows to a stop in a station and then stays there long enough for its brakes to cool. The station's dimensions are 65.0 m long by 20.0 m wide by 12.0 m high. Assuming all the work done by the brakes in stopping the train is transferred as heat uniformly to all the air in the station, by how much does the air temperature in the station rise? Take the density of the air to be 1.20 kg/m^3 and its specific heat to be $1020 \text{ J}/(\text{kg} \cdot \text{K})$.

25. •• You add 8950 J of heat to 3.00 mol of iron. (a) What is the temperature increase of the iron? (b) If this same amount of heat is added to 3.00 kg of iron, what is the iron's temperature increase? (c) Explain the difference in your results for parts (a) and (b).

26. • From a height of 35.0 m, a 1.25 kg bird dives (from rest) into a small fish tank containing 50.0 kg of water. What is the maximum rise in temperature of the water if the bird gives it all of its mechanical energy?

27. •• A 15.0 g bullet traveling horizontally at 865 m/s passes through a tank containing 13.5 kg of water and emerges with a speed of 534 m/s. What is the maximum temperature increase that the water could have as a result of this event?

28. •• **Maintaining body temperature.** While running, a 70 kg student generates thermal energy at a rate of 1200 W. To maintain a constant body temperature of 37°C, this energy must be removed by perspiration or other mechanisms. If these mechanisms failed and the heat could not flow out of the student's body, for what amount of time could a student run before irreversible body damage occurred? (Protein structures in the body are damaged irreversibly if the body temperature rises to 44°C or above. The specific heat capacity of a typical human body is $3480 \text{ J}/(\text{kg} \cdot \text{K})$, slightly less than that of water. The difference is due to the presence of protein, fat, and minerals, which have lower specific heat capacities.)

29. •• A technician measures the specific heat capacity of an unidentified liquid by immersing an electrical resistor in it. Electrical energy is converted to heat, which is then transferred to the liquid for 120 s at a constant rate of 65.0 W. The mass of the liquid is 0.780 kg, and its temperature increases from 18.55°C to 22.54°C. (a) Find the average specific heat capacity of the liquid in this temperature range. Assume that negligible heat is transferred to the container that holds the liquid and that no heat is lost to the surroundings. (b) Suppose that in this experiment heat transfer from the liquid to the container or its surroundings cannot be ignored. Is the result calculated in part (a) an overestimate or an underestimate of the average specific heat capacity? Explain.

30. •• Much of the energy of falling water in a waterfall is converted into heat. If all the mechanical energy is converted into heat that stays in the water, how much of a rise in temperature occurs in a 100 m waterfall?

5 Phase Changes

31. • Consult Table C at the end of this problem set. (a) How much heat is required to melt 0.150 kg of lead at 327.3°C? (b) How much heat would be needed to evaporate this lead at 1750°C? (c) If the total heat added from parts (a) and (b) were put into ice at 0.00°C, how many grams of the ice would it melt?

32. •• A blacksmith cools a 1.20-kg chunk of iron, initially at a temperature of 650.0°C, by trickling 15.0°C water over it. All the water boils away, and the iron ends up at a temperature of 120.0°C. How much water did the blacksmith trickle over the iron?

33. • **Treatment for a stroke.** One suggested treatment for a person who has suffered a stroke is to immerse the patient in an ice-water bath at 0°C to lower the body temperature, which prevents damage to the brain. In one set of tests, patients were cooled until their internal temperature reached 32.0°C. To treat a 70.0 kg patient, what is the minimum amount of ice (at 0°C) that you need in the bath so that its temperature remains at 0°C? The specific heat capacity of the human body is $3480 \text{ J}/(\text{kg} \cdot \text{C}°)$, and recall that normal body temperature is 37.0°C.

34. • A container holds 0.550 kg of ice at $-15.0°C$. The mass of the container can be ignored. Heat is supplied to the container at the constant rate of 800.0 J/min for 500.0 min. (a) After how many minutes does the ice *start* to melt? (b) After how many minutes, from the time when the heating is first started, does the temperature begin to rise above 0.00°C? (c) Plot a curve showing the temperature as a function of the time elapsed.

35. •• An asteroid with a diameter of 10 km and a mass of 2.60×10^{15} kg impacts the earth at a speed of 32.0 km/s, landing in the Pacific Ocean. If 1.00% of the asteroid's kinetic energy goes to boiling the ocean water (assume an initial water temperature of 10.0°C), what mass of water will be boiled away by the collision? (For comparison, the mass of water contained in Lake Superior is about 2×10^{15} kg.)

36. • **Evaporative cooling.** The evaporation of sweat is an important mechanism for temperature control in some warm-blooded animals. (a) What mass of water must evaporate from the skin of a 70.0 kg man to cool his body 1.00 C°? The heat of vaporization of water at body temperature (37°C) is 2.42×10^6 J/kg. The specific heat capacity of a typical human body is $3480 \text{ J}/(\text{kg} \cdot \text{K})$. (b) What volume of water must the man drink to replenish the evaporated water? Compare this result with the volume of a soft-drink can, which is 355 cm³.

37. •• An ice-cube tray contains 0.350 kg of water at 18.0°C. How much heat must be removed from the water to cool it to 0.00°C and freeze it? Express your answer in joules and in calories.

38. •• How much heat is required to convert 12.0 g of ice at $-10.0°C$ to steam at 100.0°C? Express your answer in joules and in calories.

39. ●● **Steam burns vs. water burns.** What is the amount of
BIO heat entering your skin when it receives the heat released
(a) by 25.0 g of steam initially at 100.0°C that cools to
34.0°C? (b) by 25.0 g of water initially at 100.0°C that cools
to 34.0°C? (c) What do these results tell you about the relative
severity of steam and hot-water burns?

40. ●● **Bicycling on a warm day.** If the air temperature is the
BIO same as the temperature of your skin (about 30°C), your body
cannot get rid of heat by transferring it to the air. In that case, it
gets rid of the heat by evaporating water (sweat). During bicycling, a typical 70 kg person's body produces energy at a rate
of about 500 W due to metabolism, 80% of which is converted
to heat. (a) How many kilograms of water must the person's
body evaporate in an hour to get rid of this heat? The heat of
vaporization of water at body temperature is 2.42×10^6 J/kg.
(b) The evaporated water must, of course, be replenished, or
the person will dehydrate. How many 750 mL bottles of water
must the bicyclist drink per hour to replenish the lost water?
(Recall that the mass of a liter of water is 1.0 kg.)

41. ●● **Overheating.** (a) By how much would the body tempera-
BIO ture of the bicyclist in the previous problem increase in an
hour if he were unable to get rid of the excess heat? (b) Is this
temperature increase large enough to be serious? To find out,
how high a fever would it be equivalent to, in °F? [Recall that
the normal internal body temperature is 98.6°F and the specific
heat capacity of the body is 3480 J/(kg · C°).]

6 Calorimetry

42. ● You have 750 g of water at 10.0°C in a large insulated beaker.
How much boiling water at 100.0°C must you add to this beaker
so that the final temperature of the mixture will be 75°C?

43. ●● A 0.500 kg chunk of an unknown metal that has been in
boiling water for several minutes is quickly dropped into an
insulating Styrofoam™ beaker containing 1.00 kg of water at
room temperature (20.0°C). After waiting and gently stirring
for 5.00 minutes, you observe that the water's temperature has
reached a constant value of 22.0°C. (a) Assuming that the Sty-
rofoam™ absorbs a negligibly small amount of heat and that
no heat was lost to the surroundings, what is the specific heat
capacity of the metal? (b) Which is more useful for storing
energy from heat, this metal or an equal weight of water?
Explain. (c) What if the heat absorbed by the Styrofoam™
actually is not negligible. How would the specific heat capacity you calculated in part (a) be in error? Would it be too large,
too small, or still correct? Explain your reasoning.

44. ●● A copper pot with a mass of 0.500 kg contains 0.170 kg of
water, and both are at a temperature of 20.0°C. A 0.250 kg block
of iron at 85.0°C is dropped into the pot. Find the final temperature of the system, assuming no heat loss to the surroundings.

45. ●● In a physics lab experiment, a student immersed 200 one-cent
coins (each having a mass of 3.00 g) in boiling water. After they
reached thermal equilibrium, she quickly fished them out and
dropped them into 0.240 kg of water at 20.0°C in an insulated
container of negligible mass. What was the final temperature of
the coins? [One-cent coins are made of a metal alloy—mostly
zinc—with a specific heat capacity of 390 J/(kg · K).]

46. ●● A laboratory technician drops an 85.0 g solid sample of
unknown material at a temperature of 100.0°C into a calorimeter. The calorimeter can is made of 0.150 kg of copper and contains 0.200 kg of water, and both the can and water are initially

at 19.0°C. The final temperature of the system is measured to be
26.1°C. Compute the specific heat capacity of the sample.
(Assume no heat loss to the surroundings.)

47. ●● A 4.00 kg silver ingot is taken from a furnace, where its
temperature is 750°C, and placed on a very large block of ice
at 0.00°C. Assuming that all the heat given up by the silver is
used to melt the ice and that not all the ice melts, how much
ice is melted?

48. ●● An insulated beaker with negligible mass contains 0.250 kg
of water at a temperature of 75.0°C. How many kilograms of
ice at a temperature of −20.0°C must be dropped in the water
so that the final temperature of the system will be 30.0°C?

49. ●● A Styrofoam™ bucket of negligible mass contains 1.75 kg
of water and 0.450 kg of ice. More ice, from a refrigerator at
−15.0°C, is added to the mixture in the bucket, and when thermal equilibrium has been reached, the total mass of ice in the
bucket is 0.778 kg. Assuming no heat exchange with the surroundings, what mass of ice was added?

7 Heat Transfer

50. ● A slab of a thermal insulator with a cross-sectional area of
100 cm² is 3.00 cm thick. Its thermal conductivity is
0.075 W/(m · K). If the temperature difference between opposite faces is 80 C°, how much heat flows through the slab in
1 day?

51. ●● You are asked to design a cylindrical steel rod 50.0 cm long,
with a circular cross section, that will conduct 150.0 J/s from
a furnace at 400.0°C to a container of boiling water under
1 atmosphere of pressure. What must the rod's diameter be?

52. ● **Conduction through the skin.** The blood plays an impor-
BIO tant role in removing heat from the body by bringing this heat
directly to the surface where it can radiate away. Nevertheless,
this heat must still travel through the skin before it can radiate
away. We shall assume that the blood is brought to the bottom
layer of skin at a temperature of 37°C and that the outer surface
of the skin is at 30.0°C. Skin varies in thickness from 0.50 mm
to a few millimeters on the palms and soles, so we shall assume
an average thickness of 0.75 mm. A 165 lb, 6 ft person has a
surface area of about 2.0 m² and loses heat at a net rate of 75 W
while resting. On the basis of our assumptions, what is the
thermal conductivity of this person's skin?

53. ●● A pot with a steel bottom 8.50 mm thick rests on a hot
stove. The area of the bottom of the pot is 0.150 m². The water
inside the pot is at 100.0°C, and 0.390 kg are evaporated every
3.00 min. Find the temperature of the lower surface of the pot,
which is in contact with the stove.

54. ●● A carpenter builds an exterior house wall with a layer of
wood 3.0 cm thick on the outside and a layer of Styrofoam™
insulation 2.2 cm thick on the inside wall surface. The wood
has a thermal conductivity of 0.080 W/(m · K), and the Sty-
rofoam™ has a thermal conductivity of 0.010 W/(m · K).
The interior surface temperature is 19.0°C, and the exterior
surface temperature is −10.0°C. (a) What is the temperature at
the plane where the wood meets the Styrofoam™? (b) What is
the rate of heat flow per square meter through this wall?

55. ●● A picture window has dimensions of 1.40 m × 2.50 m and
is made of glass 5.20 mm thick. On a winter day, the outside
temperature is −20.0°C, while the inside temperature is a comfortable 19.56°C. (a) At what rate is heat being lost through the

window by conduction? (b) At what rate would heat be lost through the window if you covered it with a 0.750-mm-thick layer of paper (thermal conductivity 0.0500 W/(m · K))?

56. •• One end of an insulated metal rod is maintained at 100°C, while the other end is maintained at 0°C by an ice–water mixture. The rod is 60.0 cm long and has a cross-sectional area of 1.25 cm². The heat conducted by the rod melts 8.50 g of ice in 10.0 min. Find the thermal conductivity k of the metal.

57. •• **Mammal insulation.** Animals in cold climates often
BIO depend on *two* layers of insulation: a layer of body fat [of thermal conductivity 0.20 W/(m · K)] surrounded by a layer of air trapped inside fur or down. We can model a black bear (*Ursus americanus*) as a sphere 1.5 m in diameter having a layer of fat 4.0 cm thick. (Actually, the thickness varies with the season, but we are interested in hibernation, when the fat layer is thickest.) In studies of bear hibernation, it was found that the outer surface layer of the fur is at 2.7°C during hibernation, while the inner surface of the fat layer is at 31.0°C. (a) What is the temperature at the fat–inner fur boundary, and (b) how thick should the air layer (contained within the fur) be so that the bear loses heat at a rate of 50.0 W?

58. • A box-shaped wood stove has dimensions of 0.75 m × 1.2 m × 0.40 m, an emissivity of 0.85, and a surface temperature of 205°C. Calculate its rate of radiation into the surrounding space.

59. • **Radiation by the body.** The amount of heat radiated by the
BIO body depends on its surface temperature and area. Typically, this temperature is about 30°C (although it can vary). The surface area depends on the person's height and weight. An empirical formula for the surface area of a person's body is

$$A(\text{in m}^2) = (0.202)M^{0.425} h^{0.725},$$

where M is the person's mass (in kilograms) and h is his or her height (in meters). (a) What would be the surface area of a 165 lb (75 kg), 6 ft (1.83 m) person? (This is a good chance to use the y^x key of your calculator.) (b) How much heat would the person radiate away per second at a skin temperature of 30°C? (At the low temperatures of room-temperature objects, nearly all the heat radiated is infrared radiation, for which the emissivity is essentially 1, regardless of the amount of skin pigment.) (c) How much *net* heat would radiation remove from the person's body if the air temperature is 20°C? (d) Take measurements on your own body to test the validity of the area formula. Treat yourself as a sphere and several cylinders.

60. • **How large is the sun?** By measuring the spectrum of wavelengths of light from our sun, we know that its surface temperature is 5800 K. By measuring the rate at which we receive its energy on earth, we know that it is radiating a total of 3.92 × 10²⁶ J/s and behaves nearly like an ideal blackbody. Use this information to calculate the diameter of our sun.

61. •• **Basal metabolic rate.** The basal metabolic rate is the rate
BIO at which energy is produced in the body when a person is at rest. A 75 kg (165 lb) person of height 1.83 m (6 ft) would have a body surface area of approximately 2.0 m². (a) What is the net amount of heat this person could radiate per second into a room at 18°C (about 65°F) if his skin's surface temperature is 30°C? (At such temperatures, nearly all the heat is infrared radiation, for which the body's emissivity is 1.0, regardless of the amount of pigment.) (b) Normally, 80% of

the energy produced by metabolism goes into heat, while the rest goes into things like pumping blood and repairing cells. Also normally, a person at rest can get rid of this excess heat just through radiation. Use your answer to part (a) to find this person's basal metabolic rate.

62. • The emissivity of tungsten is 0.35. A tungsten sphere with a radius of 1.50 cm is suspended within a large evacuated enclosure whose walls are at 290 K. What power input is required to maintain the sphere at a temperature of 3000 K if heat conduction along the supports is negligible?

63. • **Size of a lightbulb filament.** The operating temperature of a tungsten filament in an incandescent lightbulb is 2450 K, and its emissivity is 0.35. Find the surface area of the filament of a 150 W bulb if all the electrical energy consumed by the bulb is radiated by the filament as light. (In reality, only a small fraction of the radiation appears as visible light.)

64. •• A spherical pot of hot coffee contains 0.75 L of liquid (essentially water) at an initial temperature of 95°C. The pot has an emissivity of 0.60, and the surroundings are at a temperature of 20.0°C. Calculate the coffee's rate of heat loss by radiation.

General Problems

65. •• An 8.50 kg block of ice at 0°C is sliding on a rough horizontal icehouse floor (also at 0°C) at 15.0 m/s. Assume that half of any heat generated goes into the floor and the rest goes into the ice. (a) How much ice melts after the speed of the ice has been reduced to 10.0 m/s? (b) What is the maximum amount of ice that will melt?

66. •• Use Fig. A at the end of this problem set to find the approximate coefficient of volume expansion of water at 2.0°C and at 8.0°C.

67. •• **Global warming.** As the earth warms, sea level will rise due to melting of the polar ice and thermal expansion of the oceans. Estimates of the expected temperature increase vary, but 3.5 C° by the end of the century has been plausibly suggested. If we assume that the temperature of the oceans also increases by this amount, how much will sea level rise by the year 2100 due only to the thermal expansion of the water? Assume, reasonably, that the ocean basins do not expand appreciably. The average depth of the ocean is 4000 m, and the coefficient of volume expansion of water at 20°C is 0.207 × 10⁻³(C°)⁻¹.

68. •• A Foucault pendulum consists of a brass sphere with a diameter of 35.0 cm suspended from a steel cable 10.5 m long (both measurements made at 20.0°C). Due to a design oversight, the swinging sphere clears the floor by a distance of only 2.00 mm when the temperature is 20.0°C. At what temperature will the sphere begin to brush the floor?

69. •• **On-demand water heaters.** Conventional hot-water heaters consist of a tank of water maintained at a fixed temperature. The hot water is to be used when needed. The drawback is that energy is wasted because the tank loses heat when it is not in use, and you can run out of hot water if you use too much. Some utility companies are encouraging the use of *on-demand* water heaters (also known as *flash heaters*), which consist of heating units to heat the water as you use it. No water tank is involved, so no heat is wasted. A typical household shower flow rate is 2.5 gal/min (9.46 L/min) with the tap water

being heated from 50°F (10°C) to 120°F (49°C) by the on-demand heater. What rate of heat input (either electrical or from gas) is required to operate such a unit, assuming that all the heat goes into the water?

70. •• **Burning fat by exercise.** Each pound of fat contains
BIO 3500 *food* calories. When the body metabolizes food, 80% of this energy goes to heat. Suppose you decide to run without stopping, an activity that produces 1290 W of metabolic power for a typical person. (a) For how many hours must you run to burn up 1 lb of fat? Is this a realistic exercise plan? (b) If you followed your planned exercise program, how much heat would your body produce when you burn up a pound of fat? (c) If you needed to get rid of all of this excess heat by evaporating water (i.e., sweating), how many liters would you need to evaporate? The heat of vaporization of water at body temperature is 2.42×10^6 J/kg.

71. •• **Shivering.** You have no doubt noticed that you usually
BIO shiver when you get out of the shower. Shivering is the body's way of generating heat to restore its internal temperature to the normal 37°C, and it produces approximately 290 W of heat power per square meter of body area. A 68 kg (150 lb), 1.78 m (5 foot, 10 inch) person has approximately 1.8 m^2 of surface area. How long would this person have to shiver to raise his or her body temperature by 1.0 C°, assuming that none of this heat is lost by the body? The specific heat capacity of the body is about 3500 J/(kg · K).

72. •• A steel ring with a 2.5000-in. inside diameter at 20.0°C is to be warmed and slipped over a brass shaft with a 2.5020-in. outside diameter at 20.0°C. (a) To what temperature should the ring be warmed? (b) If the ring and the shaft together are cooled by some means such as liquid air, at what temperature will the ring just slip off the shaft?

73. •• **Pasta time!** You are making pesto for your pasta and have a cylindrical measuring cup 10.0 cm high made of ordinary glass $(\beta = 2.7 \times 10^{-5}(C°)^{-1})$ and that is filled with olive oil $(\beta = 6.8 \times 10^{-4}(C°)^{-1})$ to a height of 1.00 mm below the top of the cup. Initially, the cup and oil are at a kitchen temperature of 22.0°C. You get a phone call and forget about the olive oil, which you inadvertently leave on the hot stove. The cup and oil heat up slowly and have a common temperature. At what temperature will the olive oil start to spill out of the cup?

74. •• A copper calorimeter can with mass 0.100 kg contains 0.160 kg of water and 0.018 kg of ice in thermal equilibrium at atmospheric pressure. If 0.750 kg of lead at a temperature of 255°C is dropped into the can, what is the final temperature of the system if no heat is lost to the surroundings?

75. •• A piece of ice at 0°C falls from rest into a lake whose temperature is 0°C, and 1.00% of the ice melts. Compute the minimum height from which the ice has fallen.

76. •• **Hot air in a physics lecture.** (a) A typical student listening attentively to a physics lecture has a heat output of 100 W. How much heat energy does a class of 90 physics students release into a lecture hall over the course of a 50 min lecture? (b) Assume that all the heat energy in part (a) is transferred to the 3200 m^3 of air in the room. The air has a specific heat capacity of 1020 J/(kg · K) and a density of 1.20 kg/m^3. If none of the heat escapes and the air-conditioning system is off, how much will the temperature of the air in the room rise during the 50 min lecture? (c) If the class is taking an exam, the heat output per student rises to 280 W. What is the temperature rise during 50 min in this case?

77. •• **"The Ship of the Desert."** Camels require very little water because they are able to tolerate relatively large changes in their body temperature. While humans keep their body temperatures constant to within one or two Celsius degrees, a dehydrated camel permits its body temperature to drop to 34.0°C overnight and rise to 40.0°C during the day. To see how effective this mechanism is for saving water, calculate how many liters of water a 400-kg camel would have to drink if it attempted to keep its body temperature at a constant 34.0°C by evaporation of sweat during the day (12 hours) instead of letting it rise to 40.0°C. (*Note:* The specific heat of a camel or other mammal is about the same as that of a typical human, 3480 J/(kg · K). The heat of vaporization of water at 34°C is 2.42×10^6 J/kg.)

78. •• A worker pours 1.250 kg of molten lead at a temperature of 327.3°C into 0.5000 kg of water at a temperature of 75.00°C in an insulated bucket of negligible mass. Assuming no heat loss to the surroundings, calculate the mass of lead and water remaining in the bucket when the materials have reached thermal equilibrium.

79. •• **Time for a lake to freeze over.** When the air temperature is below 0°C, the water at the surface of a lake freezes to form a sheet of ice. If the upper surface of an ice sheet 25.0 cm thick is at −10.0°C and the bottom surface is at 0.00°C, calculate the time it will take to add 2.0 mm to the thickness of this sheet.

80. •• **Jogging in the heat of the day.** You have probably seen
BIO people jogging in extremely hot weather and wondered "Why?" As we shall see, there are good reasons not to do this! When jogging strenuously, an average runner of mass 68 kg and surface area 1.85 m^2 produces energy at a rate of up to 1300 W, 80% of which is converted to heat. The jogger radiates heat, but actually absorbs more from the hot air than he radiates away. At such high levels of activity, the skin's temperature can be elevated to around 33°C instead of the usual 30°C. (We shall neglect conduction, which would bring even more heat into his body.) The only way for the body to get rid of this extra heat is by evaporating water (sweating). (a) How much heat per second is produced just by the act of jogging? (b) How much *net* heat per second does the runner gain just from radiation if the air temperature is 40.0°C (104°F)? (Remember that he radiates out, but the environment radiates back in.) (c) What is the *total* amount of excess heat this runner's body must get rid of per second? (d) How much water must the jogger's body evaporate every minute due to his activity? The heat of vaporization of water at body temperature is 2.42×10^6 J/kg. (e) How many 750 mL bottles of water must he drink after (or preferably before!) jogging for a half hour? Recall that a liter of water has a mass of 1.0 kg.

81. •• **Overheating while jogging.** (a) If the jogger in the previ-
BIO ous problem were not able to get rid of the excess heat, by how much would his body temperature increase above the normal 37°C in a half hour of jogging? The specific heat capacity for a human is about 3500 J/(kg · K). (b) How high a fever (in °F) would this temperature increase be equivalent to? Is the increase large enough to be of concern? (Recall that normal body temperature is 98.6°F.)

82. •• A thirsty nurse cools a 2.00 L bottle of a soft drink (mostly water) by pouring it into a large aluminum mug of mass 0.257 kg and adding 0.120 kg of ice initially at −15.0°C. If the

soft drink and mug are initially at 20.0°C, what is the final temperature of the system, assuming no heat losses?

83. •• One experimental method of measuring an insulating material's thermal conductivity is to construct a box of the material and measure the power input to an electric heater inside the box that maintains the interior at a measured temperature above the outside surface. Suppose that in such an apparatus a power input of 180 W is required to keep the interior surface of the box 65.0 C° (about 120 F°) above the temperature of the outer surface. The total area of the box is 2.18 m², and the wall thickness is 3.90 cm. Find the thermal conductivity of the material in SI units.

84. •• The icecaps of Greenland and Antarctica contain about 1.75% of the total water (by mass) on the earth's surface; the oceans contain about 97.5%, and the other 0.75% is mainly groundwater. Suppose the icecaps, currently at an average temperature of about −30°C, somehow slid into the ocean and melted. What would be the resulting temperature decrease of the ocean? Assume that the average temperature of ocean water is currently 5.00°C.

85. •• **The effect of urbanization on plant growth.** A study
BIO published in July 2004 indicated that temperature increases in urban areas in the eastern United States are causing plants to bud up to 7 days early compared with plants in rural areas just a few miles away, thereby disrupting biological cycles. Average temperatures in the urban areas were up to 3.5 C° higher than in the rural areas. By what percent will the radiated heat per square meter increase due to such a temperature difference if the rural temperature was 0°C on the average?

86. •• **Basal metabolic rate.** The energy output of an animal
BIO engaged in an activity is called the basal metabolic rate (BMR) and is a measure of the conversion of food energy into other forms of energy. A simple calorimeter to measure the BMR consists of an insulated box with a thermometer to measure the temperature of the air. The air has a density of 1.29 kg/m³ and a specific heat capacity of 1020 J/(kg · K). A 50.0 g hamster is placed in a calorimeter that contains 0.0500 m³ of air at room temperature. (a) When the hamster is running in a wheel, the temperature of the air in the calorimeter rises 1.8 C° per hour. How much heat does the running hamster generate in an hour? (Assume that all this heat goes into the air in the calorimeter. Neglect the heat that goes into the walls of the box and into the thermometer, and assume that no heat is lost to the surroundings.) (b) Assuming that the hamster converts seed into heat with an efficiency of 10% and that hamster seed has a food energy value of 24 J/g, how many grams of seed must the hamster eat per hour to supply the energy found in part (a)?

87. •• **A thermos for liquid helium.** A physicist uses a cylindrical metal can 0.250 m high and 0.090 m in diameter to store liquid helium at 4.22 K; at that temperature the heat of vaporization of helium is 2.09×10^4 J/kg. Completely surrounding the metal can are walls maintained at the temperature of liquid nitrogen, 77.3 K, with vacuum between the can and the surrounding walls. How much helium is lost per hour? The emissivity of the metal can is 0.200. The only heat transfer between the metal can and the surrounding walls is by radiation.

TABLE A Coefficients of volume expansion

Material	β (K^{-1})
Solids	
Quartz (fused)	0.12×10^{-5}
Invar	0.27×10^{-5}
Glass	$1.2-2.7 \times 10^{-5}$
Steel	3.6×10^{-5}
Copper	5.1×10^{-5}
Brass	6.0×10^{-5}
Aluminum	7.2×10^{-5}
Liquids	
Mercury	18×10^{-5}
Glycerin	49×10^{-5}
Ethanol	75×10^{-5}
Carbon disulfide	115×10^{-5}

TABLE B Coefficients of linear expansion for selected materials

Material	α (K^{-1} or C$^{\circ-1}$)
Quartz (fused)	0.04×10^{-5}
Invar (nickel– iron alloy)	0.09×10^{-5}
Glass	$0.4-0.9 \times 10^{-5}$
Steel	1.2×10^{-5}
Copper	1.7×10^{-5}
Brass	2.0×10^{-5}
Aluminum	2.4×10^{-5}

TABLE C   Heats of fusion and vaporization

Substance	Normal melting point*		Heat of fusion, L_f, J/kg	Normal boiling point*		Heat of vaporization, L_v, J/kg
	K	**°C**		**K**	**°C**	
Helium	†	†	†	4.216	−268.93	20.9×10^3
Hydrogen	13.84	−259.31	58.6×10^3	20.26	−252.89	452×10^3
Nitrogen	63.18	−209.97	25.5×10^3	77.34	−195.81	201×10^3
Oxygen	54.36	−218.79	13.8×10^3	90.18	−182.97	213×10^3
Ethyl alcohol	159	−114	104.2×10^3	351	78	854×10^3
Mercury	234	−39	11.8×10^3	630	357	272×10^3
Water	273.15	0.00	334×10^3	373.15	100.00	2256×10^3
Sulfur	392	119	38.1×10^3	717.75	444.60	326×10^3
Lead	600.5	327.3	24.5×10^3	2023	1750	871×10^3
Antimony	903.65	630.50	165×10^3	1713	1440	561×10^3
Silver	1233.95	960.80	88.3×10^3	2466	2193	2336×10^3
Gold	1336.15	1063.00	64.5×10^3	2933	2660	1578×10^3
Copper	1356	1083	134×10^3	1460	1187	5069×10^3

* At normal atmospheric pressure.

†A pressure in excess of 25 atmospheres is required to make helium solidify. At 1 atmosphere pressure, helium remains a liquid down to absolute zero.

▲ **FIGURE A** The volume of 1 g of water in the temperature range from 0°C to 10°C. The fact that water is denser at about 4°C than at the freezing point is vitally important for the ecology of lakes and streams.

ANSWERS TO SELECTED PROBLEMS

Conceptual Questions

1. When the material is heated the average distance between the atoms or molecules in the material increases uniformly in all directions. The piece of material with the hole expands just like the piece without the hole, and the hole expands just like a solid piece of the material.

3. The two metals have different coefficients of linear expansion. The strips are in good thermal contact, so when the temperature changes both strips have the same ΔT. The strip with the larger α has a greater change of length. If ΔT is positive the composite strip bends such that the material with the larger α is on the outside of the curve. If ΔT is negative the composite strip bends such that the material with the larger α is on the inside of the curve.

5. The spheres have an average density that is slightly less than the density of the liquid at low temperatures. And the spheres differ a little from one another in their average densities. As the temperature of the liquid increases, it expands and its density decreases. When the average density of a particular sphere exceeds that of the liquid, that sphere sinks to the bottom of the cylinder. This occurs at different temperatures for different spheres, with the ones with the greater average density descending first. The volume of each sphere also increases as the temperature increases, so its average density decreases, but the coefficient of volume expansion for the liquid is much larger than for the solid spheres and the expansion of the liquid dominates.

9. False. Conservation of energy requires that the amount of heat that flows into the cooler object equals the amount of heat energy that flows out of the warmer object. But the temperature changes associated with these heat flows depend on the mass and specific heat capacities of the objects. Equal heat flows need not mean equal temperature changes.

11. Phase transitions happen at fixed temperatures. As long as two phases are present the temperature of the system remains at the phase transition temperature. The heat added during the phase change is required for the phase change and doesn't produce a temperature change.

13. There will be small effects due to different emissivity of the coffee when its color changes. But the predominant effect on the rate of heat transfer is the temperature difference between the coffee and its surroundings; the greater the temperature difference the greater the rate of heat loss to the environment. The heat loss during the five minutes is less if the cream is added at the beginning of the period, so the coffee is cooler as it sits during the five-minute period.

15. No. The heat your furnace must provide equals the heat that passes out of the house into the environment. The rate of heat transfer decreases when the temperature difference between the house and its surroundings is less. Less heat is lost while you are away if the house is at a lower temperature during that time.

Multiple-Choice Problems

1. C
3. D
5. C
7. C
9. A
11. A
13. B
15. A

Problems

1. (a) Yes. 104.4°F (b) Yes. 54°F (c) No. 77°C, 171°F
3. (a) 27.2 C° 27.2 K (b) −55.6 C°, −55.6 K
5. (a) −40.0° (b) No
7. (a) 6.8 in. (b) 6.7×10^{-6} $(F°)^{-1}$
9. 2.3×10^{-5} $(C°)^{-1}$
11. 11 L
13. 160 m^3
15. 1.7×10^{-5} $(C°)^{-1}$
17. 0.008 cm
19. 3.03×10^5 J
21. (a) 38 J (b) 4.5×10^4 J
23. 240 J/kg · K
25. (a) 113 C° (b) 6.35 C°
27. 0.0613 C°
29. (a) 2.51×10^3 J/(kg · K) (b) overestimate
31. (a) 3680 J (b) 1.31×10^5 J (c) 0.404 kg
33. 3.7 kg
35. 5.05×10^{15} kg
37. 1.43×10^5 J, 34.2 kcal
39. (a) 6.33×10^4 J (b) 6.91×10^3 J (c) steam burns are more severe
41. (a) 5.9 C° (b) 109°F; yes
43. (a) 215 J/(kg · K) (b) water (c) too small
45. 35.1°C
47. 2.10 kg
49. 3.08 g
51. 8.0 cm
53. 105.5 C°
55. (a) 2.1×10^4 W (b) 6.4×10^3 W
57. (a) 29.6°C (b) 9.1 cm
59. (a) 1.96 m^2 (b) 937 W (c) 118 W
61. (a) 140 W (b) 180 W
63. 2.1 cm^2
65. (a) 0.793 g (b) 1.43 g
67. 2.9 m
69. 26 kW
71. 456 s
73. 37.5°C
75. 341 m
77. 3.45 L
79. 2.7 h
81. (a) 8.6 C° (b) 114° F
83. 5.0×10^{-2} W/m · k
85. 5.2 %
87. 5.82 g

Thermal Properties of Matter

Shutterstock

Y ou can't see air molecules, but they're moving all around you. Did you
know that in one day you are hit 10^{32} times by air molecules? And did
you know that the average speed of an air molecule is about 1000 mi/h?
Or that the impacts of these molecules on a surface are responsible for
the pressure that air exerts on that surface?

To understand and relate such facts, we need to be able to use both *macroscopic*
(bulk) and *microscopic* viewpoints. The **macroscopic** perspective deals with large-
scale variables such as pressure, volume, temperature, and mass of substance. In
contrast, the **microscopic** point of view investigates small-scale quantities such as
the speeds, kinetic energies, momenta, and masses of the individual molecules that
make up a substance. Where these two perspectives overlap, they must be consistent. For example, the (microscopic) collision forces that occur when air molecules
strike a surface (such as your skin) cause (macroscopic) atmospheric pressure.

In this chapter, we'll use both macroscopic and microscopic approaches to gain an
understanding of the thermal properties and behavior of matter. One of the simplest
kinds of matter to understand is the *ideal gas*. For this class of materials, we'll relate
pressure, volume, temperature, and amount of substance to one another and to the
speeds and masses of individual molecules. We will explore the molecular basis of the
heat capacities of both gases and solids, and we will take a look at the various *phases*
of matter—gas, liquid, and solid—and the conditions under which each occurs.

As we'll learn in this chapter,
unconfined gases expand
when heated. When hot
ground heats the overlying
air, the air expands and rises,
forming a *thermal*. Thermals
can lift soaring birds to great
heights.

1 The Mole and Avogadro's Number

In our study of mechanics, we've usually described a quantity of a material or
substance in terms of the *mass* of material. In this chapter, where we explore the
relation between mechanics and thermal phenomena, we'll often find it useful to

From Chapter 15 of *College Physics*, Ninth Edition, Hugh D. Young. Copyright © 2012 by Pearson Education, Inc.
Published by Pearson Addison-Wesley. All rights reserved.

Richard Megna/Fundamental Photographs

NASA

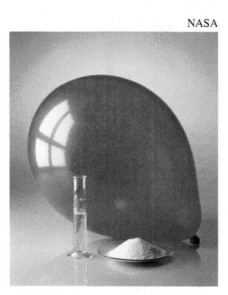

▲ **FIGURE 1** One mole each of several familiar substances.

◀ **Application** **One trillionth of a mole of stars.** A typical fair-sized spiral galaxy like our own Milky Way contains roughly 100 billion (10^{11}) stars. That's a lot of stars . . . But remember that a mole of any substance contains 6.022×10^{23} (Avogadro's number) of molecules. A mole of water, which you can hold in your hand, thus contains *one trillion* (10^{12}) times more molecules than there are stars in our galaxy.

describe a quantity of material in terms of the number of *moles* of the material rather than the mass. So we'll begin by discussing what we mean by a mole.

One **mole** of any pure chemical element or compound contains **a definite number of molecules**—the same number for all elements and compounds. The official SI definition of the mole is as follows:

Definition of the mole
One mole (1 mol) is the amount of substance that contains as many elementary entities as there are atoms in 0.012 kilogram of carbon 12.

In our discussion, the "elementary entities" are molecules. (In a monatomic substance such as carbon or helium, each molecule is a single atom, but in this discussion we'll still call it a molecule.)

The number of molecules in a mole is called **Avogadro's number,** denoted by N_A. The numerical value is

$$N_A = 6.022 \times 10^{23} \text{ molecules/mol.}$$

Figure 1 shows 1 mole of each of several familiar substances.

The **molar mass** M of a substance is the mass of 1 mole; this is equal to the mass m of a single molecule, multiplied by Avogadro's number N_A:

$$M = N_A m. \tag{1}$$

Molar mass is sometimes called "molecular mass" or "molecular weight." Both these terms are unfortunate, the first because M is *not* the mass of a molecule, the second because we are talking about mass, not weight. In this chapter, we'll use "molar mass" consistently.

We'll denote the number of moles of substance by n. In this chapter, we'll usually denote the total mass of substance by m_{total} (because later we'll want to use m as the mass of a single molecule). The total mass is equal to the number of moles multiplied by the mass per mole:

$$m_{total} = nM. \tag{2}$$

EXAMPLE 1   **Mass of a hydrogen atom**

Find the mass of a single hydrogen atom and the mass of an oxygen molecule (consisting of two oxygen atoms and written O_2).

SOLUTION

SET UP From the periodic table of the elements (Appendix D), we find that the molar mass of hydrogen (i.e., the mass per mole of hydrogen atoms) is 1.008 g/mol. The molar mass of oxygen is 16.0 g/mol, so the molar mass of O_2 is 32.0 g/mol.

SOLVE We use Equation 1. The mass m_H of a single hydrogen atom is

$$m_H = \frac{M_H}{N_A} = \frac{1.008 \text{ g/mol}}{6.022 \times 10^{23} \text{ molecules/mol}}$$
$$= 1.674 \times 10^{-24} \text{ g/atom.}$$

The mass of a single molecule of O_2 is

$$m_{O_2} = \frac{32.0 \text{ g/mol}}{6.022 \times 10^{23} \text{ molecules/mol}}$$
$$= 53.1 \times 10^{-24} \text{ g/molecule.}$$

REFLECT A water molecule (H_2O) consists of one oxygen atom and two hydrogen atoms, but we can now see that the oxygen atom accounts for nearly 90% of its mass.

Practice Problem: Find the total mass of a molecule of nitrogen dioxide (NO_2), a component of smog. What fraction of this total mass is the mass of the nitrogen atom? *Answers:* 7.64×10^{-23} g/molecule, 0.30.

2 Equations of State

The conditions in which a particular material exists are described by physical quantities such as pressure, volume, and temperature. Usually we also need to specify the amount of substance in a system. For example, a tank of oxygen in a welding outfit has a pressure gauge and a label stating its volume. We could add a thermometer and place the tank on a scale. These variables (pressure, volume, and temperature) describe the **state** of the material, and they are called **state variables** or **state coordinates.** The amount of substance can be described by its total mass or the number of moles.

The volume V of a substance usually depends on its pressure p, temperature T, and amount of substance, measured either as mass m_{total} or number of moles n. Ordinarily, we can't change one of these variables without causing a change in another. When the tank of oxygen gets hotter, the pressure increases. When the tank gets too hot, the pressure causes it to explode; this happens occasionally with overheated steam boilers (Figure 2).

In a few cases, the relationship among p, V, T, and m_{total} (or n) is simple enough that we can express it as an equation called the **equation of state.** When it's too complicated for that, we can use graphs or numerical tables. Even then, the relation among the variables still exists; we call it an equation of state even when we don't know the actual equation.

In this discussion, we'll consider only **equilibrium states**—that is, states in which the temperature and pressure are uniform throughout the system. In principle, when a system changes from one state to another, *non-equilibrium* states must occur during the transition. For example, when a material expands, there must be mass in motion; this requires acceleration and non-uniform pressure. Similarly, when heat conduction occurs, different regions must have different temperatures. We'll assume that such changes occur so slowly that the system is always very nearly in an equilibrium state.

▲ **FIGURE 2** An overheated steam boiler can explode with great violence. This photo shows the rusted wreckage of a steam locomotive destroyed by a boiler explosion.

The Ideal-Gas Equation

Gases at low pressures have particularly simple equations of state. Figure 3 shows an experimental setup to study the behavior of a gas. The cylinder has a movable piston and is equipped with a pressure gauge and a thermometer. We can vary the pressure, volume, and temperature, and we can pump any desired mass of any gas into the cylinder. Measurements of the behavior of various gases at low pressures lead to several conclusions:

- First, **the volume V is proportional to the number of moles n and thus to the number of molecules.** Thus, if we double the number of moles, keeping the pressure and temperature constant, the volume doubles.
- Second, **the volume varies *inversely* with the pressure p.** Hence, if we double the pressure, holding the temperature T and amount of substance n constant, we compress the gas to one-half of its initial volume. This relation is called **Boyle's law,** after Robert Boyle (1627–1691), a contemporary of Newton. It states that $pV = $ constant when n and T are constant.
- Third, **the pressure is directly proportional to the absolute (Kelvin) temperature.** Thus, if we double the absolute temperature, keeping the volume and quantity of material constant, the pressure doubles. This is called **Charles's law,** after Jacques Charles (1746–1823). It states that $p = (\text{constant})T$ when n and V are constant.

▲ **FIGURE 3** A hypothetical setup for studying the behavior of gases.

NASA

These three relationships can be combined neatly into a single equation:

Ideal-gas equation

For an ideal gas (defined in the following paragraphs), and as an approximation of real gas behavior, the product of pressure p and volume V is proportional to the product of the number n of moles of gas and the absolute temperature T:

$$pV = nRT. \tag{3}$$

The proportionality constant R is called the **ideal-gas constant.** Its numerical value depends on the units used for p, V, and T. In SI units, in which the unit of p is the Pa ($= N/m^2$) and the unit of V is the cubic meter (m^3), $R = 8.3145 \ J/(mol \cdot K)$.

We call Equation (3) the **ideal-gas equation.** We might expect that the constant R in this equation would have different values for different gases, but it turns out to have the same value for *all* gases, at least at sufficiently high temperatures and low pressures. Note that the units of pressure times volume are the same as the units of work or energy (e.g., N/m^2 times m^3); that's why R has units of energy per mole per unit of absolute temperature.

In chemical calculations, volumes are sometimes expressed in liters (L) and pressures in atmospheres (atm). In this system,

$$R = 0.08206 \ L \cdot atm/(mol \cdot K).$$

We can express Equation 3 in terms of the mass m_{total} of material, using Equation 2:

$$pV = \frac{m_{total}}{M} RT.$$

From this relationship, we can get an expression for the density (mass per unit volume, $\rho = m_{total}/V$) of the gas:

$$\rho = \frac{pM}{RT}. \tag{4}$$

We can now define an ideal gas as **a gas for which Equation 3 holds precisely for *all* pressures and temperatures.** This is an idealized model; no real gas behaves exactly like an ideal gas. However, most real gases show nearly ideal behavior at very low pressures and high temperatures, when the gas molecules are far apart and in rapid motion. The match is reasonably good (within a few percent) at moderate pressures (such as a few atmospheres) and at temperatures well above those at which the gas liquefies.

For a *constant mass* (or constant number of moles) of an ideal gas, the product nR is constant, so the quantity pV/T is also constant. Thus, using the subscripts 1 and 2 to refer to any two states of the same mass of a gas, we have

$$\frac{p_1 V_1}{T_1} = \frac{p_2 V_2}{T_2} = \text{constant.} \tag{5}$$

▲ **Application Martian dust devil.** This photo shows a dust devil that was caught on film while passing the *Mars Spirit Rover*. Although Mars is bitterly cold and has an atmosphere much thinner than earth's, the physics of dust devils is the same on both planets. First, a patch of sun-warmed ground transfers heat to the overlying air. By the ideal-gas equation ($pV = nRT$), this increase in the temperature of the air must increase the product pV. The air is not confined, so its volume V increases, lowering its density and causing it to rise buoyantly. As it rises, surrounding air flows in to take its place. If this surrounding air has a net rotation (as it often does), conservation of angular momentum causes the air to spin faster as it moves inward, creating the dust devil. On earth, where heating can be strong and the atmosphere is dense and energetic, this basic process results not just in dust devils, but in tornadoes and in great storms such as hurricanes and typhoons.

Quantitative Analysis 1

A compressed gas

If a gas in a 1.0 L box at 800 K is compressed to a volume of 0.50 L while its pressure changes from 1.0 atm to 0.5 atm, what is the resulting temperature in kelvins? (Assume no phase change.)

A. 800 K.　　B. 600 K.　　C. 400 K.　　D. 200 K.

The amount of gas doesn't change, so nR is constant, and we can use Equation 5, $p_1V_1/T_1 = p_2V_2/T_2$. Now we notice that the change of state involves *halving* both the volume and the pressure. If we rearrange the equation to solve for T_2/T_1, we see that $T_2/T_1 = p_2V_2/p_1V_1 = \frac{1}{4}$. Thus, the final absolute temperature is one-quarter of the original temperature, or 200 K. (Because our equation did not use the ideal-gas constant, the units used for pressure and volume did not matter, as long as they were the same for both states. However, for any ideal-gas calculation, temperature *must* be in kelvins.)

Using the ideal-gas law (MP)

SET UP

1. List your known and unknown quantities. If the problem involves two different states of the same quantity of gas, designate one as state 1 and the other as state 2.

2. As always, be sure to use a consistent set of units. First decide which value of the gas constant R you are going to use, and then convert the units of the other quantities accordingly. You may have to convert atmospheres to pascals or liters to cubic meters. Sometimes the statement of the problem will make one system of units clearly more convenient than others. Decide on your system, and stick to it!

3. Don't forget that T must always be an *absolute* temperature. If you are given temperatures in degrees Celsius, be sure to add 273 to convert to kelvins.

4. You may sometimes have to convert between total mass m_{total} and number of moles n. The relationship is $m_{total} = Mn$, where M is the molar mass. Here's a tricky point: If you replace n in Equation 3 by (m_{total}/M), you *must* use the same mass units for m_{total} and M. So if M is in grams per mole (the usual units for molar mass), then m must also be in grams. If you want to use m_{total} in kilograms, then you must convert M to kilograms per mole. For example, the molar mass of oxygen is 32 g/mol or 32×10^{-3} kg/mol. Be careful!

SOLVE

5. If you are dealing with only one state of the system, you will use Equation 3, the ideal-gas equation. If you are dealing with two states of the same quantity of gas, *and* you know all but one of the p, V, and T values, you can use Equation 5; otherwise you have to use Equation 3.

REFLECT

6. The mathematical relations are simple, but it's easy to make mistakes with units and conversions of units. Be sure to carry units through your calculations; be especially careful to distinguish between grams, kilograms, and moles.

Shutterstock

▲ **BIO Application Why do aircraft cabins have to be pressurized?** When we breathe in, air is warmed to 37° C and becomes saturated with water vapor, which has a "partial pressure" of 47 torr. In comparison, the partial pressure of O_2 in air is about 150 torr. Because the gases behave independently and the total pressure of the inhaled air does not change, the water displaces on a mole-to-mole basis an equal amount of air. The partial pressure of inhaled O_2 becomes $0.2P_B - 47$ torr, where P_B is barometric or ambient air pressure. As one goes up in altitude, P_B declines, but the partial pressure of the water vapor stays the same. Thus, at an altitude of between 50,000 and 60,000 ft, when P_B falls to 47 torr or less, a person can breathe in only water vapor even if breathing from an unpressurized source of 100% O_2. The amount of O_2 inspired becomes intolerably small even at lower altitudes. For this reason, commercial aircraft cabins require pressurization at altitudes higher than 9800 ft, and airlines must provide oxygen through drop-down masks in case of loss of pressurization.

EXAMPLE 2 **Volume of a gas at STP**

The condition called **standard temperature and pressure** (STP) for a gas is defined to be a temperature of 0°C = 273 K and a pressure of 1 atm = 1.013×10^5 Pa. If you want to keep a mole of an ideal gas in your room at STP, how big a container do you need?

SOLUTION

SET UP If we use the ideal-gas equation with SI units, we need to express R in units of J/(mol · K). The temperature in the ideal-gas equation must be an absolute temperature, expressed in kelvins.

SOLVE We rearrange the ideal-gas equation, solving for volume:

$$pV = nRT,$$
$$V = \frac{nRT}{p} = \frac{(1 \text{ mol})[8.314 \text{ J}/(\text{mol} \cdot \text{K})](273 \text{ K})}{1.013 \times 10^5 \text{ Pa}}$$
$$= 0.0224 \text{ m}^3 = 22.4 \text{ L}.$$

REFLECT This is about the size of a 5-gallon gasoline can.

Practice Problem: How many moles would your entire room hold at STP if the room had dimensions of 3 m × 3 m × 2 m? *Answer:* $n = 800$ mol.

EXAMPLE 3 Mass of air in a scuba tank

A typical tank used for scuba diving (Figure 4) has a volume of 11.0 L (about 0.4 ft³) and a maximum gauge pressure of 2.10×10^7 Pa (about 3000 lb/in² gauge). The "empty" tank contains 11.0 L of air at 21°C and 1 atm (1.013×10^5 Pa). The air is hot when it comes out of the compressor; when the tank is filled, the temperature is 42°C and the gauge pressure is 2.10×10^7 Pa. What mass of air was added? (Air is a mixture of gases: about 78% nitrogen, 21% oxygen, and 1% miscellaneous gases; its average molar mass is 28.8 g/mol = 28.8×10^{-3} kg/mol.)

▶ FIGURE 4

Shutterstock

SOLUTION

SET UP First we find the number of moles in the tank, at the beginning and at the end. We must remember to convert the temperatures from Celsius to kelvin and to convert the pressures from gauge to absolute by adding 1.013×10^5 Pa.

SOLVE From Equation 3, the number of moles n_1 in the "empty" tank is

$$n_1 = \frac{pV}{RT} = \frac{(1.013 \times 10^5 \text{ Pa})(11.0 \times 10^{-3} \text{ m}^3)}{[8.314 \text{ J/(mol} \cdot \text{K)}](294 \text{ K})} = 0.456 \text{ mol}.$$

The number of moles n_2 in the "full" tank is

$$n_2 = \frac{(2.11 \times 10^7 \text{ Pa})(11.0 \times 10^{-3} \text{ m}^3)}{[8.314 \text{ J/(mol} \cdot \text{K)}](315 \text{ K})} = 88.6 \text{ mol}.$$

We added 88.6 mol − 0.456 mol = 88.1 mol to the tank. The average molar mass of air is 28.8×10^{-3} kg/mol, so the added mass is $(88.1 \text{ mol})(28.8 \times 10^{-3} \text{ kg/mol}) = 2.54$ kg.

REFLECT Because the amount of gas was not the same for the two states of the system, Equation 5 isn't applicable; we have to use the ideal-gas equation, Equation 3.

EXAMPLE 4 Density of air

Find the density of air at 20°C and normal atmospheric pressure.

SOLUTION

SET UP AND SOLVE We use Equation 4, taking care to convert T to kelvins. As in the previous example, the average molar mass of air is 28.8 g/mol = 28.8×10^{-3} kg/mol. From Equation 4,

$$\rho = \frac{pM}{RT} = \frac{(1.013 \times 10^5 \text{ Pa})(28.8 \times 10^{-3} \text{ kg/mol})}{[8.314 \text{ J/(mol} \cdot \text{K)}](293 \text{ K})}$$
$$= 1.20 \text{ kg/m}^3.$$

REFLECT Remember that the density of water is an easy-to-remember 1.00×10^3 kg/m³. Thus, the density of air at normal atmospheric pressure and ordinary temperatures is roughly a thousandth that of water.

When we deal with *mixtures* of ideal gases, the concept of **partial pressure** is useful. In a mixture, the partial pressure of each gas is the pressure that gas would exert if it occupied the entire volume by itself. The actual total pressure of the mixture is the sum of the partial pressures of the components. In air at normal atmospheric pressure, the partial pressure of nitrogen is about 0.8 atm, or 0.8×10^5 Pa, and the partial pressure of oxygen is about 0.2 atm, or 0.2×10^5 Pa.

The ability of the human body to absorb oxygen from the atmosphere depends critically on the partial pressure of oxygen. Absorption drops sharply when the partial pressure of oxygen is less than about 0.13×10^5 Pa, corresponding to an elevation above sea level of approximately 4700 m (15,000 ft). At partial pressures less than 0.11×10^5 Pa, oxygen absorption is not sufficient to maintain life. There is no permanently maintained human habitation on earth above 16,000 ft, although survival for short periods of time is possible at higher elevations. At the summit of Mount Everest (elevation 8882 m, or 29,141 ft) the partial pressure of

▶ **BIO Application Scuba hazards.** Scuba divers must breathe gas that is at the same pressure as the surrounding water; otherwise they couldn't inflate their lungs once they dove more than a short distance below the surface. However, that means that the partial pressures of the gases in the mix rise as the diver descends. Certain gases become toxic at elevated partial pressures. Nitrogen, which is harmless at its normal atmospheric partial pressure of 0.80 atm, becomes a narcotic at elevated pressures. A diver breathing ordinary compressed air begins to act drunk below about 30 m because of nitrogen narcosis. Oxygen also has toxic effects at elevated partial pressures, depending on the partial pressure and the length of exposure. To counteract these problems, technical divers sometimes use special gas mixtures (typically nitrogen–oxygen or helium–oxygen mixtures) chosen to fit the depth and duration of the intended dive.

Miguel Angelo Silva/iStockphoto

oxygen is only about 0.07×10^5 Pa, and climbers nearly always carry oxygen tanks. For similar reasons, jet airplanes, which typically fly at altitudes of 8000 to 12,000 m, *must* have pressurized cabins for passenger comfort and health.

pV Diagrams

For a given quantity of a material, the equation of state is a relation among the three state coordinates: pressure p, volume V, and temperature T. A useful graphical representation of this relation is a set of graphs of pressure as a function of volume, each for a particular constant temperature. Such a diagram is called a *pV* **diagram.** Each curve, representing behavior at a specific temperature, is called an **isotherm,** or a *pV isotherm.* ("Isotherm" means "same temperature.")

Figure 5 shows pV isotherms for a constant amount of an ideal gas. The highest temperature is T_4; the lowest is T_1. The figure is a graphical representation of the ideal-gas equation of state. We can read off the volume V corresponding to any given pressure p and temperature T in the range shown.

Figure 6 shows a pV diagram for a material that *does not* obey the ideal-gas equation. At high temperatures such as T_4, the curves resemble the ideal-gas curves of Figure 5. However, at temperatures below T_c, the isotherms develop flat parts—regions where the material can be compressed without an increase in pressure. Observation of the gas shows that it is *condensing* from the vapor (gas) to the liquid phase. The flat parts of the isotherms in the shaded area of Figure 6 represent conditions of liquid–vapor *phase equilibrium.* As the volume decreases, more and more material goes from vapor to liquid, but the pressure does not change. To keep the temperature constant, we have to remove heat.

When we compress a gas such as that in Figure 6 at a constant temperature T_2, it is vapor until point a is reached. There it begins to liquefy; as the volume decreases further and heat of vaporization is removed, more material liquefies, with *both* pressure and temperature remaining constant. At point b, *all* the material is in the liquid state. After this, any further compression results in a very rapid rise in pressure because, in general, liquids are much less compressible than gases. At a lower constant temperature T_1, the gas behaves similarly, but the onset of condensation occurs at lower pressure and greater volume than at the constant temperature T_2.

We'll use pV diagrams often in this chapter and the next. We'll show that the area under a pV curve (regardless of whether it is or is not an isotherm) represents the *work* done by the system during a change in volume. This work, in turn, is directly related to heat transfer and changes in the *internal energy* of the system, which we'll study later in this chapter.

Another diagram that's useful, especially for describing phases of matter and phase transitions, is a graph with axes p and T, called a **phase diagram.** Each phase is stable only in certain ranges of temperature and pressure. Ordinarily, a transition from one phase to another takes place under conditions of **phase equilibrium** between the two phases. For a given pressure, this occurs at only one

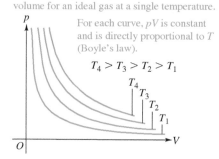

Each curve represents pressure as a function of volume for an ideal gas at a single temperature.

For each curve, pV is constant and is directly proportional to T (Boyle's law).

$$T_4 > T_3 > T_2 > T_1$$

▲ **FIGURE 5** Isotherms, or constant-temperature curves, for a constant amount of an ideal gas.

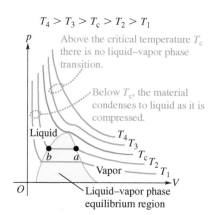

$$T_4 > T_3 > T_c > T_2 > T_1$$

Above the critical temperature T_c there is no liquid–vapor phase transition.

Below T_c, the material condenses to liquid as it is compressed.

Liquid–vapor phase equilibrium region

▲ **FIGURE 6** A pV diagram for a non-ideal gas, showing pV isotherms for temperatures above and below the critical temperature T_c.

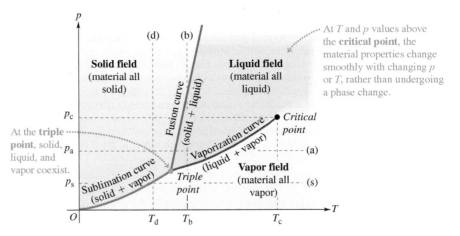

▲ **FIGURE 7** A typical pT phase diagram, showing regions of temperature and pressure in which the various phases exist and where phase changes occur.

specific temperature. A phase diagram shows what phase occurs for each possible combination of temperature and pressure.

A typical example is shown in Figure 7. Each point on the diagram represents a pair of values of p and T. The three colored areas labeled "solid field," "liquid field," and "vapor field" represent points at which the material consists of a single phase: solid, liquid, and vapor, respectively. At any point along the three colored lines separating these fields, the material consists of two coexisting phases. On the sublimation curve, solid and vapor coexist; on the fusion curve, solid and liquid coexist; and on the vaporization curve, liquid and vapor coexist. When a material is at a point on one of these lines, a phase change can proceed.

If we increase the temperature of a substance, keeping the pressure constant, it passes through a sequence of states represented by points on a horizontal line such as the dashed gray line (a) in the figure. The melting and boiling temperatures at this pressure are the temperatures at which this line intersects the fusion and vaporization curves, respectively. If we *compress* a material by increasing the pressure while we hold the temperature constant, as represented by a vertical dashed line such as line (b), the material passes from vapor to liquid and then to solid at the points where the line crosses the vaporization curve and fusion curve, respectively.

When the pressure is low enough, constant-pressure heating can transform a substance from solid directly to vapor, as shown by line (s). This process is called *sublimation;* it occurs at a pressure and temperature corresponding to the intersection of the line and the sublimation curve. At atmospheric pressure, solid carbon dioxide (dry ice) undergoes sublimation; no liquid phase can exist at this pressure. When a substance with an initial temperature lower than the temperature at the point labeled "triple point" is compressed by increasing its pressure, it goes directly from the vapor to the solid phase, as shown by line (d). The melting of ice under pressure is what makes ice skating possible.

TABLE 1 Triple-point data

Substance	Temperature, K	Pressure, Pa
Hydrogen	13.8	0.0704×10^5
Neon	24.57	0.432×10^5
Nitrogen	63.18	0.125×10^5
Oxygen	54.36	0.00152×10^5
Ammonia	195.40	0.0607×10^5
Carbon dioxide	216.55	5.17×10^5
Water	273.16	0.00610×10^5

Triple Point

The intersection point of the equilibrium curves in Figure 7 is called the **triple point.** For any substance, this point represents the unique pressure–temperature combination at which *all three* phases can coexist. We call these the triple-point pressure and temperature. Triple-point data for a few substances are given in Table 1.

Critical Point

Figure 6 shows that a liquid–vapor phase transition occurs only when the temperature and pressure are less than those at the point lying at the top of the tongue-shaped area labeled "liquid–vapor equilibrium region." This point corresponds to the endpoint at the top of the vaporization curve in Figure 7. It is called the **critical point,** and the corresponding values of p and T are called the critical pressure p_c and critical temperature T_c. A gas at a temperature *above* the critical temperature doesn't separate into two phases when it is compressed isothermally (along a vertical line to the right of the critical point in Figure 7). Instead, its properties change gradually and continuously from those we ordinarily associate with a gas (low density and high compressibility) to those of a liquid (high density and low compressibility) *without a phase transition*. Similarly, when a material is heated at a constant pressure greater than the critical-point pressure (a horizontal line above the critical point in Figure 7), its properties change gradually from liquid-like to gas-like.

If the preceding discussion stretches your credulity, here's another point of view: Look at liquid–vapor phase transitions at successively higher points on the vaporization curve. As we approach the critical point, the *differences* in physical properties, such as density, bulk modulus, optical properties, and viscosity, between the liquid and vapor phases become smaller and smaller. Exactly *at* the critical point they all become zero, and at this point the distinction between liquid and vapor disappears. The heat of vaporization also grows smaller and smaller as we approach the critical point, and it too becomes zero at the critical point.

Table 2 lists critical constants for a few substances. The very low critical temperatures of hydrogen and helium show why these gases defied attempts to liquefy them for many years. For carbon dioxide, the triple-point temperature is $-56.6°C$ and the triple-point pressure is 5.11 atm. At atmospheric pressure, CO_2 can exist only as a solid or vapor—hence the name "dry ice." Liquid CO_2 can exist only at a pressure greater than 5.11 atm.

Many substances can exist in more than one solid phase. A familiar example is carbon, which exists as noncrystalline lampblack (roughly, soot) and crystalline graphite and diamond. (Graphite is the main constituent of pencil leads; it is also used in dry lubricants.) Water is another example: At least eight types of ice, differing in crystal structure and physical properties, have been observed at very high pressures.

National Researcher Council of Canada

▲ **Application How hot is hot?** For industrial applications, we often need to measure very hot and very cold temperatures, and the measurements involved require special thermometers such as the platinum resistance thermometer. Of course, these thermometers must be calibrated with the use of reproducible temperatures other than the freezing and boiling points of pure water used by the Fahrenheit and Celsius scales. The photo shows the calibration of a platinum resistance thermometer for high temperatures, using the freezing point of molten silver $(961°C = 1234\ K)$. Calibration of thermometers for low-temperature use can be done at the triple point of argon, where solid, liquid, and gaseous phases coexist $(-189.3°C = 83.8\ K)$. Some of these platinum resistance thermometers are sensitive enough to measure temperatures with an accuracy of $\pm 0.05\ C°$ over a range of temperatures from $-190°C$ to over $1000°C$.

TABLE 2   Critical-point data

Substance	Critical temperature, K	Critical pressure, Pa
Helium ($^4_2$He)	5.3	2.29×10^5
Hydrogen	33.3	13.0×10^5
Nitrogen	126.2	33.9×10^5
Oxygen	154.8	50.8×10^5
Ammonia	405.5	112.8×10^5
Carbon dioxide	304.2	73.9×10^5
Water	647.4	221.2×10^5

3 Kinetic Theory of an Ideal Gas

We've studied several properties of matter in bulk, including elasticity, density, surface tension, equations of state, and heat capacities, with only passing references to molecular structure. Now we want to look in more detail at the relation of bulk (macroscopic) behavior to microscopic structure. We begin with a general discussion of the molecular structure of matter. Then, in the next two sections, we'll develop the *kinetic-molecular model* of an ideal gas and derive the equation of state and an expression for molar heat capacity from this molecular model.

Molecular Properties of Matter

All familiar matter is made up of atoms or groups of connected atoms. For convenience, we'll use the term **molecule** to refer to the smallest unit of a substance, even in cases where this unit is a single atom. Individual atoms are on the order of 10^{-10} m in size; the largest molecules contain many atoms and are 10,000 or more times that large. In gases, the molecules move nearly independently; in liquids and solids, they are held together by intermolecular forces that are electrical in nature, arising from interactions of the electrically charged particles that make up the molecules. Gravitational forces between molecules are negligible in comparison with electrical forces.

When molecules of a gas are far apart, the electrical forces between them are very small and usually attractive. As a gas is compressed and its molecules are brought closer together, the attractive forces increase. At sufficiently small separations, the intermolecular attractions are large enough to make the material condense into a liquid or solid.

Molecules are always in motion; their kinetic energies usually increase with temperature. In *solids,* molecules vibrate about more or less fixed centers. In a crystalline solid, these centers are arranged in a recurring *crystal lattice.* Figure 8 shows the cubic crystal structure of sodium chloride (ordinary table salt). A scanning tunneling microscope photograph of the surface of a silicon crystal is shown in Figure 9. Each "bead" is a silicon atom.

In a *liquid,* the intermolecular distances are usually only slightly greater than in the solid phase of the same substance, but the molecules have much greater freedom of movement. Liquids show regularity of structure only in the immediate neighborhood of a few molecules.

The molecules of a *gas* are usually widely separated and exert only very small attractive forces on one another. A gas molecule moves in a straight line until it collides with another molecule or with a wall of the container. In molecular terms, an *ideal gas* is a gas whose molecules exert *no* attractive forces on one another and therefore have no *potential* energy.

At low temperatures, most common substances are in the solid phase. As the temperature rises, a substance melts and then vaporizes. From a *molecular* point of view, these transitions are in the direction of increasing molecular kinetic energy. Thus, temperature and molecular kinetic energy are closely related.

Kinetic Molecular Theory of an Ideal Gas

The goal of any molecular theory of matter is to understand the *macroscopic* properties of matter in terms of its atomic or molecular structure and behavior. Such theories are of tremendous practical importance; once we have this understanding, we can *design* materials to have specific desired properties. Such analysis has led to the development of high-strength steels, glasses with special optical properties, semiconductor materials for electronic devices, and countless other materials that are essential to contemporary technology.

One of the simplest examples of a molecular theory is the kinetic-molecular model of an ideal gas. With the help of this model, we can understand the relation

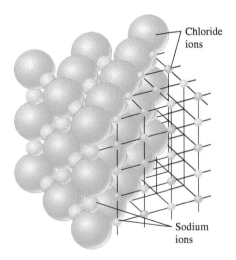

Chloride ions

Sodium ions

▲ **FIGURE 8** Schematic representation of the cubic crystal structure of sodium chloride (table salt).

ThermoMicroscopes

▲ **FIGURE 9** A scanning tunneling microscope image of silicon atoms on the surface of a silicon crystal. The regularity of the crystal structure is easy to see.

of ideal-gas behavior, including the ideal-gas equation of state (Equation 3) and the molar heat capacities of gases, to Newton's laws. The development that follows has several steps, and you may need to go over it several times to grasp how it all goes together. Don't get discouraged!

Here are the assumptions of the kinetic-molecular model:

1. A container with volume V contains a very large number N of identical molecules, each with mass m. The container has perfectly rigid walls that do not move.
2. The molecules behave as point particles; their size is small in comparison to the average distance between particles and to the dimensions of the container.
3. The molecules are in constant random motion; they obey Newton's laws. Each molecule occasionally makes a perfectly elastic (energy-conserving) collision with a wall of the container.
4. During collisions, the molecules exert *forces* on the walls of the container; these forces create the *pressure* that the gas exerts. In a typical collision (Figure 10), the velocity component v_y parallel to the wall is unchanged, and the component v_x perpendicular to the wall changes direction, but not magnitude.

Here's our program, one step at a time:

Step 1: We find the total change in momentum associated with each collision.
Step 2: We find the *number* of collisions per unit time for a certain wall area A.
Step 3: We find the total change in momentum per unit time due to these collisions and, from that, the force on area A needed to cause that change in momentum.
Step 4: Finally, we can obtain an expression for the pressure, which is force per unit area, and compare it with the ideal-gas equation.

▲ **FIGURE 10** Elastic collision of a molecule with an idealized container wall. The component v_y parallel to the wall does not change; the component v_x perpendicular to the wall reverses direction. The speed v does not change.

We'll take these steps in order. Here we go:

Step 1. Let $|v_x|$ be the magnitude of the x component of velocity of a molecule of the gas. For now, we assume that all molecules have the same $|v_x|$. That isn't right, but making this temporary assumption helps to clarify the basic ideas. We will show later that the assumption isn't really necessary. For each collision, the x component of momentum changes from $-m|v_x|$ to $+m|v_x|$, so the *change* in the x component of momentum is $m|v_x| - (-m|v_x|) = 2m|v_x|$.

Step 2. If a molecule is going to collide with a given wall area A during a small time interval Δt, then, at the beginning of Δt, it must be within a distance $|v_x| \Delta t$ from the wall (Figure 11) and it must be headed toward the wall. So the number of molecules that collide with A during Δt is equal to the number of molecules that are within a cylinder with base area A and length $|v_x| \Delta t$ and that have their v_x aimed toward the wall. The volume of such a cylinder is $A|v_x| \Delta t$.

Assuming that the number of molecules per unit volume (N/V) is uniform, the *number* of molecules in this cylinder is $(N/V)(A|v_x| \Delta t)$. On the average, half of these molecules are moving toward the wall and half away from it. So the number of collisions with wall area A during Δt is

$$\tfrac{1}{2}\left(\frac{N}{V}\right)(A|v_x| \, \Delta t).$$

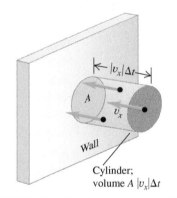

▲ **FIGURE 11** Molecules moving toward the wall with speed $|v_x|$ collide with area A during the time interval Δt only if they are within a distance $|v_x| \Delta t$ of the wall at the beginning of the interval. All such molecules are contained within a volume $A|v_x| \Delta t$.

Step 3. The total change in momentum, ΔP_x, due to all these collisions during time Δt is the *number* of collisions multiplied by the change in momentum in one collision, $2m|v_x|$:

$$\Delta P_x = \tfrac{1}{2}\left(\frac{N}{V}\right)(A|v_x| \, \Delta t)(2m|v_x|) = \frac{NAmv_x^2 \, \Delta t}{V}.$$

(We're using capital P for momentum and small p for pressure. Also, capital V denotes volume, and small v represents a velocity component. Be careful!) The *rate* of change of the momentum component P_x with time is the preceding expression divided by Δt:

$$\frac{\Delta P_x}{\Delta t} = \frac{NAmv_x^2}{V}.$$

According to Newton's second law, this rate of change of momentum equals the force exerted by the wall area A on the molecules. From Newton's *third* law, this force is equal and opposite to the force exerted *on* the wall *by* the molecules.

Step 4. The pressure p of the gas is the magnitude of the force per unit area, and we obtain

$$p = \frac{F}{A} = \frac{Nmv_x^2}{V}, \qquad pV = Nmv_x^2. \tag{6}$$

Now we need one additional step: We need to express v_x^2 in this equation in terms of the average value of v^2 for all the molecules. First, the square of the speed of an individual molecule (v^2) is related to the sum of the squares of the components $(v_x, v_y$ and $v_z)$: $v^2 = v_x^2 + v_y^2 + v_z^2$. Second, we can take the *average* of this expression for all the molecules in the gas: When we do, we get $(v^2)_{av} = (v_x^2)_{av} + (v_y^2)_{av} + (v_z^2)_{av}$. Third, there is no distinction among the x, y, and z axis directions, so it must be true that $(v_x^2)_{av} = (v_y^2)_{av} = (v_z^2)_{av}$, and it follows that $(v^2)_{av} = 3(v_x^2)_{av}$, or $(v_x^2)_{av} = \left(\frac{1}{3}\right)(v^2)_{av}$.

We see that we didn't really need the initial assumption that all molecules had the same value of $|v_x|$, because in this step we work with *average values* of the velocity components. When we replace v_x^2 with $(v_x^2)_{av}$ in Equation 6, we get

$$pV = \tfrac{1}{3}Nm(v^2)_{av} = \tfrac{2}{3}N[\tfrac{1}{2}m(v^2)_{av}].$$

We notice that $\tfrac{1}{2}m(v^2)_{av}$ is the average *translational kinetic energy* of a single molecule. The product of this quantity and the total number N of molecules equals the *total* random kinetic energy K_{tr} of translational motion of *all* the molecules. (The notation K_{tr} reminds us that this energy is associated with *translational* motion and anticipates the possibility of additional energies associated with rotational and vibrational motion of molecules.) Hence, the product pV equals two-thirds of the total translational kinetic energy:

$$pV = \tfrac{2}{3}K_{tr}.$$

Now here comes the *coup de grace:* We compare this result with the ideal-gas equation, $pV = nRT$, which is based on experimental studies of gas behavior. For the two equations to agree, we must have the following relationship:

Kinetic energy of gas molecules
For an ideal gas, the total translational kinetic energy K_{tr} of all the molecules is proportional to the absolute (Kelvin) temperature T and to the quantity of gas (as measured by the number of moles, n):

$$K_{tr} = \tfrac{3}{2}nRT. \tag{7}$$

We'll use this important result several times in the discussion that follows.

The average translational kinetic energy of a *single* molecule is the total translational kinetic energy K_{tr} of *all* the molecules, divided by the number N of molecules:

$$K_{av} = \frac{K_{tr}}{N} = \tfrac{1}{2}m(v^2)_{av} = \frac{3nRT}{2N}.$$

▶ **Application** **Hold your hydrogen.** The cloud of gas and dust from which our solar system formed consisted mostly of diatomic hydrogen gas (H_2). However, earth and its sister rocky planets have practically no hydrogen gas in their atmospheres, whereas the gas giants, such as Jupiter, have a lot. Why? The main reason concerns mass—of hydrogen and of planets. Hydrogen is the least massive element; H_2 has a molar mass of 2.01 g/mol. Therefore, H_2 molecules have a higher average speed at a given temperature than more massive molecules. On a small planet like earth, a significant fraction of any H_2 molecules in the atmosphere are moving faster than the planet's escape speed and can simply fly off into outer space. Thus, small planets leak hydrogen until essentially none remains in their atmospheres. The gas giants, being far more massive, have enough gravity to keep their hydrogen.

Earth and Jupiter to scale

NASA

Also, the total number of molecules, N, is the number of moles, n, multiplied by Avogadro's number N_A (i.e., $N = nN_A$), so the average translational kinetic energy per molecule is

$$K_{av} = \frac{3nRT}{2(nN_A)} = \tfrac{3}{2}\frac{R}{N_A}T.$$

The ratio R/N_A occurs frequently in molecular theory. It is called the **Boltzmann constant,** denoted by k and defined as

$$k = \frac{R}{N_A} = \frac{8.314 \text{ J}/(\text{mol} \cdot \text{K})}{6.022 \times 10^{23} \text{ molecules}/\text{mol}}$$
$$= 1.381 \times 10^{-23} \text{ J}/(\text{molecule} \cdot \text{K}).$$

We can rewrite the expression for K_{av} (the average translational kinetic energy of a single molecule) in terms of k as

$$K_{av} = \tfrac{1}{2}m(v^2)_{av} = \tfrac{3}{2}kT. \qquad (8)$$

This result shows that, for an ideal gas, the average translational kinetic energy *per molecule* depends only on the temperature, not on the pressure, volume, or kind of molecule involved. We can obtain an equivalent statement by using the relation $M = N_A m$. The average translational kinetic energy *per mole* (which also depends only on T) is

$$N_A \tfrac{1}{2}m(v^2)_{av} = N_A(\tfrac{3}{2}kT) = \tfrac{3}{2}RT.$$

Finally, it's often useful to rewrite the ideal-gas equation on a molecular basis. We use $N = N_A n$ and $R = N_A k$ to obtain the following alternative form:

$$pV = NkT. \qquad (9)$$

This equation shows that we can think of k as a gas constant on a "per molecule" basis instead of the usual "per-mole" basis with the gas constant R.

Quantitative Analysis 2

A cooled gas

An ideal gas is cooled at constant volume until the pressure is half the original pressure. When this happens, the average translational kinetic energy of the gas molecules is

A. twice the original.
B. unchanged.
C. half the original.

SOLUTION According to the ideal-gas equation, $pV = nRT$, if V is constant and p is reduced by a factor of one-half, the absolute temperature must also decrease by a factor of one-half. According to Equation 8, the average translational kinetic energy is proportional to the absolute temperature, so it too decreases by a factor of one-half. The correct answer is C.

Calvin Hamilton

◀ Application **It could have been so nice there!** Science fiction authors once envisioned Venus as a cloud-shrouded tropical swamp planet—and indeed, when it formed, Venus probably had at least as much water as our own world. But Venus is now utterly dry, with a dense carbon dioxide atmosphere that keeps it hotter than a pizza oven. Where did the water go? Being closer to the sun, Venus was always warmer than earth. If it ever had oceans, they soon vaporized. With no oceans, carbon dioxide could not form limestone (as it does on earth), but instead stayed in the atmosphere. The thick, hot atmosphere let water vapor rise to altitudes at which UV light could split water molecules, releasing hydrogen atoms. Because of their low mass, these atoms easily reached escape speed and disappeared into outer space. Eventually, the water was gone. That is how our sister planet became an arid furnace. We're so lucky . . . .

Molecular Speeds in an Ideal Gas

From Equations 8 and 9, we can obtain an expression for the square root of $(v^2)_{av}$, called the **root-mean-square speed** v_{rms} of molecules in an ideal gas:

$$v_{rms} = \sqrt{(v^2)_{av}} = \sqrt{\frac{3kT}{m}} = \sqrt{\frac{3RT}{M}}. \tag{10}$$

This quantity increases with temperature, as we should expect; it also varies inversely with the square root of the molecular or molar mass.

To compute the rms speed, we square each molecular speed, add, divide by the number of molecules, and take the square root. That is, v_{rms} is the *root* of the *mean* of the *squares*. Example 6 illustrates this procedure.

We've mentioned that the molecules in a gas don't all have the same speed. Figure 12 is a graph of the relative numbers of molecules with various speeds for three different temperatures. As the temperature increases, the curve flattens and the peak moves to higher speed. This speed distribution curve is called the *Maxwell–Boltzmann* distribution.

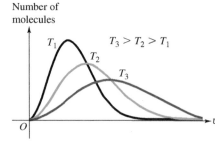

▲ **FIGURE 12** The distribution of speeds for the molecules of a gas at three different temperatures.

PROBLEM-SOLVING STRATEGY 2 **Kinetic-molecular theory**

As usual, using a consistent set of units is essential. Following are several places where caution is needed:

1. The usual units for molar mass M are grams per mole; the molar mass of O_2 is 32 g/mol, for example. These units are often omitted in tables. When you use SI units in equations, such as Equation 10, you *must* express M in kilograms per mole by multiplying the value shown in the table by $(1 \text{ kg}/10^3 \text{ g})$. Thus, in SI units, M for O_2 is 32×10^{-3} kg/mol.

2. Are you working on a "per molecule" basis or a "per mole" basis? Remember that m is the mass of a molecule and M is the mass of a mole. N is the number of molecules, and n is the number of moles; k is the gas constant per molecule, and R is the gas constant per mole. Although N, the number of molecules, is in one sense a dimensionless number, you can do a complete unit check if you think of N as having the unit "molecules;" then m has the unit "mass per molecule" and k has the unit "joules per molecule per kelvin."

3. Remember that T is always *absolute* (Kelvin) temperature.

EXAMPLE 5 **Kinetic energy of a molecule**

(a) What is the average translational kinetic energy of a molecule of oxygen (O_2) at a temperature of 27°C, assuming that oxygen can be treated as an ideal gas? **(b)** What is the *total* translational kinetic energy of the molecules in 1 mole of oxygen at this temperature? **(c)** Compare the root-mean-square speeds of oxygen and nitrogen (N_2) molecules at this temperature (assuming that they can be treated as ideal gases). The mass of an oxygen molecule is $m_{O_2} = 5.31 \times 10^{-26}$ kg, and the mass of a molecule of nitrogen is $m_{N_2} = 4.65 \times 10^{-26}$ kg.

Continued

SOLUTION

SET UP AND SOLVE **Part (a):** First we convert the temperature to kelvins: $27°C = 300$ K. Then we use Equation 8: For one molecule,

$$K_{av} = \tfrac{1}{2}m(v^2)_{av} = \tfrac{3}{2}kT$$
$$= \tfrac{3}{2}(1.38 \times 10^{-23} \text{ J/K})(300 \text{ K}) = 6.21 \times 10^{-21} \text{ J}.$$

Part (b): Using Equation 7 (for 1 mole), we obtain

$$K_{tr} = \tfrac{3}{2}nRT = \tfrac{3}{2}(1 \text{ mol})[8.315 \text{ J}/(\text{mol} \cdot \text{K})](300 \text{ K}) = 3740 \text{ J}.$$

Part (c): From Equation 10, we find that

$$v_{\text{rms},O_2} = \sqrt{\frac{3kT}{m_{O_2}}} = \sqrt{\frac{3(1.38 \times 10^{-23} \text{ J/K})(300 \text{ K})}{5.31 \times 10^{-26} \text{ kg}}}$$
$$= 484 \text{ m/s},$$

$$v_{\text{rms},N_2} = \sqrt{\frac{3kT}{m_{N_2}}} = \sqrt{\frac{3(1.38 \times 10^{-23} \text{ J/K})(300 \text{ K})}{4.65 \times 10^{-26} \text{ kg}}}$$
$$= 517 \text{ m/s}.$$

Thus, the ratio of the rms speed of N_2 molecules to that of O_2 molecules is 1.07.

ALTERNATIVE SOLUTION

$$v_{\text{rms},O_2} = \sqrt{\frac{3RT}{M_{O_2}}} = \sqrt{\frac{3(8.314 \text{ J/mol} \cdot \text{K})(300 \text{ K})}{32 \times 10^{-3} \text{ kg/mol}}} = 484 \text{ m/s},$$

$$v_{\text{rms},N_2} = \sqrt{\frac{3RT}{M_{N_2}}} = \sqrt{\frac{3(8.314 \text{ J/mol} \cdot \text{K})(300 \text{ K})}{28 \times 10^{-3} \text{ kg/mol}}} = 517 \text{ m/s}.$$

REFLECT These speeds are roughly 1000 mi/h. At any temperature, rms molecular speeds are inversely proportional to the square root of molar mass. Note that we have to be careful throughout to distinguish between "per molecule" and "per mole" quantities.

Practice Problem: What is the root-mean-square speed of a diatomic hydrogen molecule (H_2) at 300 K, assuming that it can be treated as an ideal gas? The mass of a hydrogen molecule is 3.348×10^{-27} kg. *Answer:* $v_{\text{rms}} = 1930$ m/s.

EXAMPLE 6 **Gang of five**

Five ideal-gas molecules chosen at random are found to have speeds of 500, 600, 700, 800, and 900 m/s, respectively. Find the rms speed for this collection. Is it the same as the *average* speed of these molecules?

SOLUTION

SET UP AND SOLVE The average value of v^2 for the molecules is

$$(v^2)_{av} = [(500 \text{ m/s})^2 + (600 \text{ m/s})^2 + (700 \text{ m/s})^2$$
$$+ (800 \text{ m/s})^2 + (900 \text{ m/s})^2]/5$$
$$= 5.10 \times 10^5 \text{ m}^2/\text{s}^2.$$

The square root of this is v_{rms}:

$$v_{\text{rms}} = 714 \text{ m/s}.$$

The *average* speed v_{av} is given by

$$v_{av} = \frac{500 \text{ m/s} + 600 \text{ m/s} + 700 \text{ m/s} + 800 \text{ m/s} + 900 \text{ m/s}}{5}$$
$$= 700 \text{ m/s}.$$

REFLECT In general, v_{rms} and v_{av} are not the same. Roughly speaking, v_{rms} gives greater weight to the larger speeds than does v_{av}.

Practice Problem: Suppose we double all the speeds in this example. How do v_{av} and v_{rms} change? *Answers:* $v_{av} = 1400$ m/s, $v_{\text{rms}} = 1428$ m/s.

EXAMPLE 7 **Volume of a gas at STP, revisited**

Find the number of molecules and the number of moles in 1 cubic meter of air at atmospheric pressure and $0°C$.

SOLUTION

SET UP AND SOLVE We use the alternative form of the ideal-gas equation, $pV = NkT$ (Equation 9):

$$N = \frac{pV}{kT} = \frac{(1.013 \times 10^5 \text{ Pa})(1 \text{ m}^3)}{(1.38 \times 10^{-23} \text{ J/K})(273 \text{ K})}$$
$$= 2.69 \times 10^{25}.$$

The number of moles n is

$$n = \frac{N}{N_A} = \frac{2.69 \times 10^{25} \text{ molecules}}{6.022 \times 10^{23} \text{ molecules/mol}} = 44.7 \text{ mol}.$$

Continued

The total volume is 1.00 m³, so the volume of 1 mole is

$$\frac{1.00 \text{ m}^3}{44.7 \text{ mol}} = 0.0224 \text{ m}^3/\text{mol} = 22.4 \text{ L}/\text{mol}.$$

REFLECT This is the same result that we obtained in Example 2 (Section 2), using only macroscopic quantities.

4 Heat Capacities

We defined specific heat capacities in terms of the measured amount of heat needed to change the temperature of a specified quantity of material by a particular amount (in SI units, 1 K and 1 kg). We didn't attempt to *predict* heat capacities on the basis of more fundamental considerations. In some simple cases, these numbers *can* be predicted on theoretical grounds, using the relation between heat and molecular energy.

Especially when we deal with heat capacities of gases, it's often more convenient to describe the quantity of substance in terms of the number of *moles* rather than the mass m_{total} of material. We define the **molar heat capacity** (also called molar specific heat) of a substance as follows:

Molar heat capacity

The amount of heat Q needed for a certain temperature change ΔT is proportional to the temperature change and to the number of moles of substance; that is,

$$Q = nC\,\Delta T, \tag{11}$$

where C is a quantity, different for different materials, called the *molar heat capacity* for the material. The SI units of C are $\text{J}/(\text{mol} \cdot \text{K})$.

Comparing the equation $Q = m_{total}c\,\Delta T$ and Equation 11 ($Q = nC\,\Delta T$), and recalling that $m_{total} = Mn$, we see that the molar heat capacity C of a material is related to its specific heat capacity c by the equation

$$C = Mc, \quad \text{(Relation of specific and molar heat capacities)} \tag{12}$$

where M is the molar mass of the material. That is, heat per mole equals heat per unit mass times amount of mass per mole. For example, the molar heat capacity of liquid water is about $(4186 \text{ J}/(\text{kg} \cdot \text{K}))(18 \times 10^{-3} \text{ kg}/\text{mol}) = 75 \text{ J}/(\text{mol} \cdot \text{K})$.

In our discussion of heat capacities in this chapter, we'll keep the volume of material constant so that there is no energy transfer through mechanical work. If we were to let a gas expand, it would do work (force times distance) on the moving walls of its container. We'll return to this more general case in Section 7. For now, with the volume held constant, we'll denote the molar heat capacity at constant volume as C_V.

Molar Heat Capacities of Gases

In this section, we present a brief introduction to the analysis of heat capacities of gases on the basis of the simple kinetic-molecular model we discussed in the last section. In that model, the molecular energy consists only of the kinetic energy K_{tr} associated with the translational motion of pointlike molecules. This energy is directly proportional to the absolute temperature T, as shown by Equation 7: $K_{tr} = \frac{3}{2}nRT$. When the temperature changes by a small amount ΔT, the corresponding change in kinetic energy is

$$\Delta K_{tr} = \tfrac{3}{2}nR\,\Delta T.$$

From the definition of molar heat capacity at constant volume, C_V, we also have

$$Q = nC_V \Delta T,$$

where Q is the heat input needed for a temperature change ΔT. Now if K_{tr} represents the total molecular energy, as we have assumed, then Q and ΔK_{tr} must be *equal*. Equating the last two equations, we get

$$nC_V \Delta T = \tfrac{3}{2}nR \Delta T, \tag{13}$$
$$C_V = \tfrac{3}{2}R \qquad (\text{monatomic gas})$$

This surprisingly simple result says that the molar heat capacity (at constant volume) of *every* gas whose molecules can be represented as points is equal to $3R/2$. In SI units,

$$C_V = \tfrac{3}{2}[8.314 \text{ J}/(\text{mol} \cdot \text{K})] = 12.47 \text{ J}/(\text{mol} \cdot \text{K}).$$

For comparison, Table 3 gives *measured* values of C_V for several gases. We see that, for monatomic gases, our prediction is right on the money, but that it is way off for diatomic and polyatomic gases.

Thus, our point-molecule model works for monatomic gases, but for diatomic and polyatomic molecules we need something more sophisticated. For example, we can picture a diatomic molecule as *two* point masses, like a little elastic dumbbell. Such a molecule can have additional kinetic energy associated with *rotation* about axes through its center of mass, and the atoms may also have a back-and-forth *vibrating* motion along the line joining them, with additional kinetic and potential energies. Hence, the molar heat capacities for diatomic gases should be greater than those for monatomic gases. These possibilities are shown in Figure 13.

Equation 7 $\left(K_{tr} = \tfrac{3}{2}nRT\right)$ shows that the average random *translational* kinetic energy of the molecules of an ideal gas is proportional to the absolute temperature T of the gas. It turns out that the additional energy of rotational and vibrational motion is also proportional to T. A diatomic molecule has an additional average *rotational* kinetic energy of kT per molecule or RT per mole. Thus, we expect a diatomic molecule to have an average kinetic energy of $K = \tfrac{3}{2}kT + kT = \tfrac{5}{2}kT$ per molecule or $\tfrac{5}{2}RT$ per mole, and the molar heat capacity should be $\tfrac{5}{2}R$. In SI units,

$$C_V = \tfrac{5}{2}R = \tfrac{5}{2}[8.314 \text{ J}/(\text{mol}\cdot\text{K})] = 20.8 \text{ J}/(\text{mol}\cdot\text{K}) \qquad (\text{diatomic gas}). \tag{14}$$

We note that this value agrees, within a few percent, with the measured molar heat capacities of the diatomic gases listed in Table 3.

Vibrational motion can also contribute to the heat capacities of gases. Molecular bonds are not rigid; they can stretch and bend, and the resulting vibrations lead to additional degrees of freedom and additional energies. Because of quantum effects, including these energies in our formulation would be more complex than for the rotational energies of diatomic molecules, and we won't attempt a quantitative discussion. In Table 3, the large values of C_V for some polyatomic molecules show the contributions of vibrational energy. In addition, a molecule with three or more atoms that are not in a straight line has an average rotational kinetic energy of $\tfrac{3}{2}kT$ rather than just kT.

5 The First Law of Thermodynamics

Energy relationships are of central importance in the study of energy-conversion devices such as engines, batteries, and refrigerators and also in the functioning of living organisms. We've studied energy transfer through mechanical work and

TABLE 3 Molar heat capacities of gases

Type of gas	Gas	$C_V(\text{J}/(\text{mol}\cdot\text{K}))$
Monatomic	He	12.47
	Ar	12.47
Diatomic	H_2	20.42
	N_2	20.76
	O_2	21.10
	CO	20.85
Polyatomic	CO_2	28.46
	SO_2	31.39
	H_2S	25.95

(a) Translational motion

(b) Rotational motion

(c) Vibrational motion

▲ **FIGURE 13** A diatomic molecule can move in three ways: (a) by translational motion of the whole molecule through space, (b) by rotation of the molecule about an axis, and (c) by vibration of the two atoms on their springlike mutual bond.

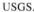

Heat is positive when it *enters* the system, negative when it *leaves* the system.

Work is positive when it is done *by* the system, negative when it is done *on* the system.

▲ **FIGURE 14** A thermodynamic system may exchange energy with its surroundings by means of heat (which may enter or leave the system) and work (which may be done by or on the system).

USGS.

▲ **FIGURE 15** The catastrophic eruption of Mt. St. Helens on May 18, 1980, a dramatic illustration of the enormous pressure developed in a confined hot gas. The eruption column is driven in part by this pressure and in part by the buoyancy of the hot gas, which is much less dense than the surrounding air.

through heat transfer. Now we're ready to combine and generalize those principles. *Thermodynamics* is the study of energy relationships that involve heat, mechanical work, and other aspects of energy and energy transfer. The first law of thermodynamics extends the principle of conservation of energy to include heat as well as mechanical energy.

Energy, Heat, and Work

To state energy relationships precisely, we'll always use the concept of a *thermodynamic system,* and we'll discuss *heat* and *work* as two means of transferring energy into or out of such a system. The system might be a quantity of expanding steam in a turbine, the refrigerant in an air conditioner, some other specific quantity of material, or, sometimes, a particular device or an organism. A **thermodynamic system** (Figure 14) is a system that can interact (and exchange energy) with its surroundings, or environment, in at least two ways, one of which is heat transfer. A familiar example of a thermodynamic system is a quantity of gas confined in a cylinder with a piston, similar to the cylinders in internal-combustion engines. Energy can be added to the system by conduction of heat, and the system can also do *work* as the gas exerts a force on the piston and moves it through a displacement. With thermodynamic systems, as with all others, it's essential to define clearly at the start exactly what is and is not included in the system. Only then can we describe unambiguously the energy transfers into and out of that system.

Thermodynamics has its roots in practical problems. The engine in an automobile and the jet engines in an airplane use the heat of combustion of their fuel to perform mechanical work in propelling the vehicle. Muscle tissue in living organisms metabolizes chemical energy in food and performs mechanical work on the organism's surroundings. A steam engine or steam turbine uses the heat of combustion of coal or some other fuel to perform mechanical work such as driving an electric generator or pulling a train.

In all these situations, we describe the energy relations in terms of the quantity of heat Q added *to* the system and the work W done *by* the system. Both Q and W may be positive or negative. Figure 14 shows the sign conventions we'll use. As in the preceding chapter, a positive value of Q represents heat flow *into* the system, with a corresponding input of energy to it. Negative Q represents heat flow *out of* the system. A positive value of W represents work done *by* the system as it pushes outward against its surroundings, such as work done by an expanding gas. Thus, positive work corresponds to energy *leaving* the system. Negative W, such as work done *on a gas* by its surroundings while the gas is being compressed, represents energy *entering* the system. We'll use these rules consistently in the examples in this chapter.

NOTE ▶ There is no uniformity in the literature concerning the signs of Q and W. In particular, W is sometimes defined with the opposite sign, as work done *on* the system rather than *by* it. The moral is, when you read other references, be careful! ◀

In this discussion, we'll be concerned mostly with *equilibrium* processes. In such processes, heat transfer takes place so slowly that the system is always very nearly in thermal equilibrium. (That is, the temperature is uniform throughout the system.). Also, changes in volume take place slowly enough so that the system is always very nearly in *mechanical equilibrium.* (That is, the pressure is uniform throughout the system.) Including both conditions, we speak of states of **thermodynamic equilibrium.** In non-equilibrium processes, there is no such thing as a single temperature or pressure for the system as a whole.

Thermal Properties of Matter

▶ **Application Your typical steamship.** It's a truism that the industrial revolution was powered by steam. In a steam engine, water is boiled to create steam, which later cools and condenses. The resulting changes in pressure and volume do work, such as moving a piston. We've all seen historical images of steam locomotives and steamships. What you may not realize is that today's nuclear submarines are . . . steamships. A reactor core is simply a source of heat. To do work with that heat—and, not incidentally, to prevent the core from overheating and melting down—the reactor uses steam. And what better method? Steam power is, after all, a mature technology.

U.S. Navy photo by Mass Communication Specialist Seaman Ryan Steinhour (Released)

Work Done during Volume Changes

A gas in a cylinder with a movable piston is a simple example of a thermodynamic system. Internal-combustion engines, steam engines, and compressors in refrigerators and air conditioners all use some version of such a system. In the next several sections, we'll use the gas-in-cylinder system to explore several kinds of processes that involve energy transformations. We'll look first at the *work* done by the system during a change in volume. When a gas expands, it pushes on its boundary surfaces as they move outward; an expanding gas always does positive work. The same thing is true of any solid or fluid material confined under pressure. Figure 15 shows an impressive example of the work done by expanding gases.

Figure 16 shows a solid or fluid in a cylinder with a movable piston. Suppose that the cylinder has cross-sectional area A and that the pressure exerted by the system at the piston face is p. Then the magnitude F of the total force exerted on the piston by the system is $F = pA$. When the piston moves out a small distance Δx, the work W done by the force is

$$W = F \Delta x = pA \Delta x. \qquad (15)$$

The change in volume is $\Delta V = A \Delta x$, so we can express the work done by the system as

$$W = p \Delta V.$$

(We assume that the process proceeds so slowly that mechanical equilibrium is maintained; then, at any instant, the pressure is the same throughout the system.) If the pressure remains constant while the volume changes by a finite amount— say, from V_1 to V_2—the total work done by the system is

$$W = p(V_2 - V_1) \qquad \text{(constant pressure only).} \qquad (16)$$

But what if the pressure is *not* constant during the expansion? Suppose, for example, that we let an ideal gas expand, keeping its temperature constant. Then the product pV is constant, so as the volume V increases, the pressure p must decrease. This situation is similar to one in which work is done by a varying force, and we can handle it in the same way. We divide the total change in volume into many small changes $\Delta V_1, \Delta V_2, \ldots,$ each so small that we can consider the pressure to be constant within each one. Calling the various pressures $p_1, p_2, \ldots,$ we represent the total work as

$$W = p_1 \Delta V_1 + p_2 \Delta V_2 + \cdots.$$

As we take the ΔV's smaller and smaller, this approximation becomes more and more precise.

We can also draw a graph showing the variation of p with V, as in Figure 17a, with pressure p on the vertical axis and volume V on the horizontal axis. Then each product $p_1 \Delta V_1$, $p_2 \Delta V_2$, and so on, corresponds to the area of one of the rectangles in Figure 17b, and the sum of these areas is approximately equal to the total area under the curve between V_1 and V_2. As the ΔV's become smaller and smaller, the approximation gets better and better. So we have the following general result:

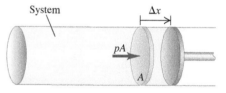

▲ **FIGURE 16** The work done by the system during the small expansion Δx is $\Delta W = F \Delta x = pA \Delta x$.

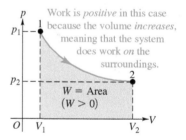

(a) pV diagram for a system undergoing a change in volume with varying pressure

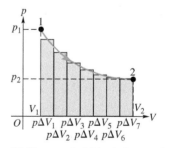

(b) The curve in (a) treated as a series of small constant-pressure intervals

▲ **FIGURE 17** The work done by a system equals the area under the curve on a pV diagram.

533

The volume *decreases* ($V_2 < V_1$), meaning that the surroundings do work on the system. Thus, work is *negative*.

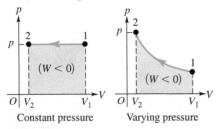

▲ FIGURE 18 Two cases in which the work is negative (meaning that work is done *on* the system, reducing its volume).

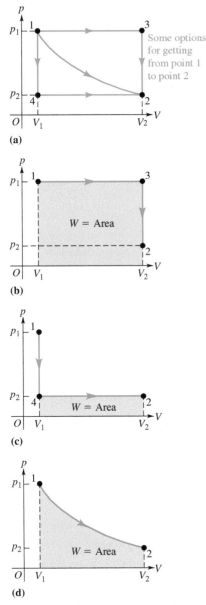

(a)

(b)

(c)

(d)

▲ FIGURE 19 (a) Three different paths between state 1 and state 2. (b)–(d) The work done by the system during a transition between two states depends on the path chosen.

Graphical representation of work during a volume change

The work W done by a system is equal to the area under the curve on a pV diagram.

According to the sign rule that we stated earlier in this section, W is always the work done *by* the system, and it is always *positive* when a system *expands*. When a system expands from state 1 to state 2 as shown in Figure 17, the area is positive. In a *compression* from state 1 to state 2 (Figure 18), the change in volume is negative, and the total work done by the system on the piston by the system is negative. This corresponds to a *negative* area; thus, when a system is compressed, its volume decreases, and it does *negative* work on its surroundings.

A particular case that occurs often in problems is the *isothermal* (constant-temperature) expansion of an ideal gas. As the gas expands, the pressure decreases, so we can't use Equation 16. Methods of calculus can be used to show that when n moles of an ideal gas expand from volume V_1 to volume V_2 at constant temperature T, the total work W done by the gas is

$$W = nRT \ln \frac{V_2}{V_1}, \tag{17}$$

where "ln" stands for the natural logarithm (i.e., the logarithm to the base e).

When a system changes from an initial state to a final state, it passes through a series of intermediate states; we call this series of states a **path.** There are always infinitely many different possibilities for these intermediate states. When they are all equilibrium states, the path can be plotted on a pV diagram (Figure 19). Point 1 represents an initial state (1) with pressure p_1 and volume V_1, and point 2 represents a final state (2) with pressure p_2 and volume V_2. For example (Figure 19b), we could keep the pressure constant at p_1 while the system expands to volume V_2 (point 3 on the diagram) and then reduce the pressure to p_2 (probably by decreasing the temperature) while keeping the volume constant at V_2 (to point 2 on the diagram). The work done by the system during this process is the area under the line $1 \rightarrow 3$; the system does no work during the constant-volume process $3 \rightarrow 2$. Or the system might traverse the path $1 \rightarrow 4 \rightarrow 2$ (Figure 19c); in that case, the work is the area under the line $4 \rightarrow 2$. The smooth curve from 1 to 2 is another possibility (Figure 19d), and the work done in that case is different from that done in each of the other paths. If the system passes through non-equilibrium states during a change of state, we may not be able to speak of a pressure or temperature for the system as a whole. There is still a path for such a change of state, but it can't be represented in terms of points and curves on a pV diagram.

We conclude that **the work done by the system depends not only on the initial and final states, but also on the intermediate states—that is, on the path.** Furthermore, we can take the system through a series of states forming a closed loop, such as $1 \rightarrow 3 \rightarrow 2 \rightarrow 4 \rightarrow 1$. In this case, the final state is the same as the initial state, but the total work done by the system is *not* zero. (In fact, it is represented on the graph by the *area* enclosed by the loop; can you prove that?) It follows that it doesn't make sense to talk about the amount of work contained in a system. In a particular state, a system may have definite values of the state coordinates p, V, and T, but it wouldn't make sense to say that it has a definite value of W.

Heat Transfer during Volume Changes

Heat transfer and work are two means by which the energy of a thermodynamic system may increase or decrease. We've just seen that when a thermodynamic system undergoes a change of state, the *work* done by the system depends not

(a) System does work on piston; hot plate adds heat to system ($W > 0$ and $Q > 0$).

(b) System does no work; no heat enters or leaves system ($W = 0$ and $Q = 0$).

▲ **FIGURE 20** (a) Slow, controlled isothermal expansion of a gas from an initial state 1 to a final state 2 with the same temperature, but lower pressure. (b) Rapid, uncontrolled expansion of the same gas starting at the same state 1 and ending at the same state 2.

only on the initial and final states, but also on the series of intermediate states through which it passes—that is, on the *path* from the initial state to the final state. Next we'll show that this is also true for the *heat* added to a system.

Here's an example: We want to change the volume of a certain quantity of an ideal gas from 2.0 L to 5.0 L while keeping the temperature constant at $T = 300$ K. Figure 20 shows two different ways we can do this. In Figure 20a, the gas is contained in a cylinder with a piston and has an initial volume of 2.0 L. We let the gas expand slowly, supplying heat from the electric heater to keep the temperature at 300 K. After expanding in this slow, controlled, isothermal manner, the gas reaches its final volume of 5.0 L; it absorbs a definite amount of heat in the process.

Figure 20b shows a different process leading to the same final state. The container is surrounded by insulating walls and is divided by a thin, breakable partition into two compartments. The lower part has a volume of 2.0 L, and the upper part has a volume of 3.0 L. In the lower compartment, we place the same amount of the same gas as in Figure 20a, again at $T = 300$ K. The initial state is the same as before. Now we break the partition; the gas undergoes a rapid, uncontrolled expansion, with no heat passing through the insulating walls. The final volume is 5.0 L, the same as in Figure 20a. This uncontrolled expansion of a gas into vacuum is called a **free expansion.** During the process, the gas is *not* in thermodynamic equilibrium.

Experiments have shown that when an ideal gas undergoes a free expansion, there is no temperature change. Therefore, the final equilibrium state of the gas is the same as that in Figure 20a. The intermediate states (pressures and volumes) during the transition from state 1 to state 2 are entirely different in the two cases; Figures 20a and 20b represent *two different paths* connecting the *same states* 1 and 2. For path (b), *no* heat is transferred into the system, and it does no work. **Like work, heat depends not only on the initial and final states, but also on the path.** The free expansion involves non-equilibrium states that can't be described by a single temperature or pressure for the system as a whole.

Because of this dependence on the path, it doesn't make sense to say that a system "contains" a certain quantity of heat. Suppose we were to assign an arbitrary value to "the heat in an object" in some standard reference state. Then, presumably, the heat in the object in some other state would equal the heat in the object in the reference state plus the heat added when the object goes into the second state. But that notion is ambiguous: The heat added depends on the *path* we take from the reference state to the second state. Thus, there is no consistent way to define "heat in an object;" it isn't a useful concept. It *does* make sense, however, to speak of the amount of *internal energy* in a body; this important concept is our next topic.

MasteringPHYSICS

ActivPhysics 8.5: Work Done by a Gas

Internal Energy and the First Law

The concept of internal energy is one of the most important concepts in thermodynamics. We can look at it in various ways, some simple, some subtle. Let's start with the simple. Matter consists of atoms and molecules, and these are made up of particles having kinetic and potential energies. We tentatively define the **internal energy** of a system as the sum of all the kinetic and potential energies of its constituent particles. We use the symbol U for internal energy. During a change of state of the system, the internal energy may change from an initial value U_1 to a final value U_2; we denote the change in internal energy as $\Delta U = U_2 - U_1$.

We also know that heat transfer is energy transfer. When we add a quantity of heat Q to a system and it does no work during the process, the internal energy should increase by an amount equal to Q; that is, $\Delta U = Q$. When a system does work W by expanding against its surroundings and no heat is added during the process, energy leaves the system and the internal energy decreases. That is, when W is positive, ΔU is negative, and conversely, so $\Delta U = -W$. When *both* heat transfer *and* work occur, the *total* change in internal energy is $U_2 - U_1 = \Delta U = Q - W$. We can rearrange this set of equations into the following form:

First law of thermodynamics

When heat Q is added to a system, some of this added energy remains within the system, changing its internal energy by an amount ΔU. The remainder leaves the system as the system does work W against its surroundings. Because W and Q may be positive, negative, or zero, we also expect ΔU to be positive, negative, or zero, depending on the process. We thus have

$$Q = \Delta U + W, \qquad \text{or} \qquad U_2 - U_1 = \Delta U = Q - W. \qquad (18)$$

The first law of thermodynamics represents a generalization of the principle of conservation of energy to include energy transfer through heat as well as mechanical work. Actually *calculating* this energy for any real system, however, would be hopelessly complicated. By contrast, if we use Equation 18 to define changes in internal energy for thermodynamic processes, then we have to ask whether these changes may depend on the path taken as the system moves from one state to another. We've already seen that both work and heat exchange depend on the path taken; might this also be true for internal energy? If so, it wouldn't make sense to speak of the internal energy of an object, and it couldn't be the basis for an enlarged conservation law.

The only way to resolve such questions is through *experiment*. We study the properties of various materials; in particular, we measure Q and W for various changes of state and various paths in order to learn whether ΔU is or is not the same for different paths. The results of many such investigations are clear and unambiguous: ΔU *is independent of the path*. The change in internal energy of a system during any thermodynamic process depends only on the initial and final states, *not* on the path leading from one to the other. An equivalent statement is that the internal energy U of a system is a function of the state coordinates p, V, and T alone (actually, of any two of these, since the three variables are related by the equation of state).

Now let's return to the first law of thermodynamics. To say that the first law, given by Equation 18, represents conservation of energy for thermodynamic processes is correct—as far as it goes. But an important *additional* part of the content of the first law is the fact that internal energy depends only on the state of a system. In changes of state, the change in internal energy is path-independent.

If we take a system through a process that eventually returns it to its initial state (a *cyclic* process), the *total* internal energy change must be zero. Then

$$U_2 = U_1 \quad \text{and} \quad Q = W.$$

If a net quantity of work W is done by the system during this process, an equal amount of energy must have flowed into the system as heat Q. But there is no reason why either Q or W individually has to be zero.

An *isolated* system is a system that does no work on its surroundings and has no heat flow. For any process taking place in an isolated system,

$$W = Q = 0 \quad \text{and} \quad U_2 - U_1 = \Delta U = 0.$$

In other words, *the internal energy of an isolated system is constant.*

Conceptual Analysis 3 · An expanding gas

When an ideal gas in a well-insulated container expands slowly by pushing a piston, the temperature of the gas drops because

A. the gas must do work, so its internal energy must decrease, and temperature is related to internal energy.

B. the molecules have more room to move around, which means that they can travel at a lower speed, and temperature is related to molecular speed.

C. pushing the piston robs the gas of heat, and loss of heat means that the temperature of the gas will drop.

SOLUTION The first law of thermodynamics says that $\Delta U = Q - W$. In this case the container is insulated, so $Q = 0$. The gas expands, so W is positive; therefore, ΔU must be negative. A is a correct answer. B is not correct: It's true that the molecules have room to move, but their slower speed is a consequence of doing work against the moving piston. C is not correct: The problem states that the container is well insulated, so there is no heat transfer.

PROBLEM-SOLVING STRATEGY 3 · First law of thermodynamics

SET UP

1. As usual, consistent units are essential. If p is in pascals and V is in cubic meters, then W is in joules. If p and V are not in pascals and cubic meters, respectively, you may want to convert them into those units. If a heat capacity is given in terms of calories, the simplest procedure is usually to convert it to joules. Be especially careful with moles. When you use $n = m_{total}/M$ to convert between mass and number of moles, remember that if m_{total} is in kilograms, M must be in *kilograms* per mole. The usual units for M are *grams* per mole; be careful!

SOLVE

2. The internal energy change ΔU in any thermodynamic process or series of processes is independent of the path, no matter whether the substance is an ideal gas or not. This is of the utmost importance in the problems in this chapter and the next. Sometimes you will be given enough information about one path between given initial and final states to calculate ΔU for that path. Then you can use the fact that ΔU is the same for every other path between the same two states to relate the various energy quantities for other paths.

3. When a process consists of several distinct steps, it often helps to make a chart showing Q, W, and ΔU for each step. Put these quantities for each step on a different line, and arrange them so that the Q's, W's, and ΔU's form columns. Then you can apply the first law to each line; in addition, you can add each column and apply the first law to the sums. Do you see why?

REFLECT

4. Ask yourself whether the entries in the table in point 3 are consistent. For example, if you find that Q for a certain process is positive, but W and ΔU are both negative, you know that there's something wrong.

EXAMPLE 8   Thermodynamics of boiling water

One gram of water (1 cm^3) becomes 1671 cm^3 of steam when boiled at a constant pressure of 1 atm $(1.013 \times 10^5 \text{ Pa})$. The heat of vaporization at this pressure is $L_v = 2.256 \times 10^6 \text{ J/kg} = 2256 \text{ J/g}$. Compute **(a)** the work done by the water when it vaporizes; **(b)** its increase in internal energy.

SOLUTION

SET UP AND SOLVE Part (a): For a constant-pressure process, we may use Equation 16, $W = p(V_2 - V_1)$, to compute the work done by the vaporizing water.

The work done by the vaporizing water is

$$W = p(V_2 - V_1)$$
$$= (1.013 \times 10^5 \text{ Pa})(1671 \times 10^{-6} \text{ m}^3 - 1 \times 10^{-6} \text{ m}^3)$$
$$= 169 \text{ J}.$$

Part (b): We find the heat added to the water and then use the first law of thermodynamics. The heat added to the water is the heat of vaporization, $Q = mL_v$:

$$Q = mL_v$$
$$= (1 \text{ g})(2256 \text{ J/g})$$
$$= 2256 \text{ J}.$$

From the first law of thermodynamics, Equation 18, the change in internal energy is

$$\Delta U = Q - W$$
$$= 2256 \text{ J} - 169 \text{ J}$$
$$= 2087 \text{ J}.$$

REFLECT To vaporize 1 gram of water, we have to add 2256 J of heat. Most (2087 J) of this added energy remains in the system as an increase in its internal energy. The remaining 169 J leaves the system as the system does work against its surroundings while expanding from liquid to vapor. The increase in internal energy is associated mostly with the intermolecular forces that hold the molecules together in the liquid state. Because these forces are attractive, the associated potential energies are greater after work has been done on the molecules to pull them apart in forming the vapor state. It's like increasing the potential energy by pulling an elevator farther from the center of the earth.

Practice Problem: Suppose water is boiled in a pressure chamber in which the pressure is 2.00 atm, the heat of vaporization is 2200 J/g, and 1.00 kg of steam has a volume of 0.824 m³. Determine the work done and the increase in internal energy. *Answers:* 167 J, 2033 J.

EXAMPLE 9   An isothermal expansion

Figure 21 shows a slow, controlled isothermal expansion of 3.0 moles of an ideal gas. The initial volume of the gas is 4.0 L and the final volume is 5.0 L. While the gas expands, heat is supplied from a flame to maintain the temperature at 300 K. How much work does the gas do during the expansion? What is the change in the internal energy of the gas?

► FIGURE 21

SOLUTION

SET UP AND SOLVE From Equation 17,

$$W = nRT \ln\!\left(\frac{V_2}{V_1}\right)$$

$$= (3.0 \text{ mol})[8.314 \text{ J/(mol} \cdot \text{K})](300 \text{ K}) \ln\!\left(\frac{5.0 \text{ L}}{4.0 \text{ L}}\right)$$

$$= 1700 \text{ J}.$$

Because the temperature is constant and the substance is an ideal gas, the change in internal energy is zero.

REFLECT Because the internal energy does not change, all of the heat entering the system goes into work.

Practice Problem: If 2000 J of heat is added isothermally to 3.5 moles of an ideal gas with an initial volume of 3.0 L and a constant temperature of 300 K, what is the final volume of the gas? *Answer:* $V_2 = 3.8$ L.

EXAMPLE 10 **A series of thermodynamic processes**

A series of thermodynamic processes is shown in the pV diagram of Figure 22. In process ab, 150 J of heat are added to the system, and in process bd, 600 J of heat are added. Find **(a)** the internal energy change in process ab; **(b)** the internal energy change in process abd; **(c)** the total heat added in process acd.

▶ **FIGURE 22** pV diagram showing various thermodynamic processes.

SOLUTION

SET UP AND SOLVE Part (a): No change in volume occurs during process ab, so $W_{ab} = 0$ and $\Delta U_{ab} = Q_{ab} = 150$ J.

Part (b): Process bd occurs at constant pressure, so the work done by the system during this expansion is

$$W_{bd} = p(V_2 - V_1)$$
$$= (8.0 \times 10^4 \text{ Pa})(5.0 \times 10^{-3} \text{ m}^3 - 2.0 \times 10^{-3} \text{ m}^3)$$
$$= 240 \text{ J}.$$

The total work for process abd is

$$W_{abd} = W_{ab} + W_{bd} = 0 + 240 \text{ J} = 240 \text{ J},$$

and the total heat added is

$$Q_{abd} = Q_{ab} + Q_{bd} = 150 \text{ J} + 600 \text{ J} = 750 \text{ J}.$$

Applying Equation 18 to process abd, we find that

$$\Delta U_{abd} = Q_{abd} - W_{abd} = 750 \text{ J} - 240 \text{ J} = 510 \text{ J}.$$

Part (c): Because ΔU is independent of the path, the internal energy change is the same for path acd as for abd; that is,

$$\Delta U_{acd} = \Delta U_{abd} = 510 \text{ J}.$$

The total work for the path acd is

$$W_{acd} = W_{ac} + W_{cd} = p(V_2 - V_1) + 0$$
$$= (3.0 \times 10^4 \text{ Pa})(5.0 \times 10^{-3} \text{ m}^3 - 2.0 \times 10^{-3} \text{ m}^3)$$
$$= 90 \text{ J}.$$

Now we apply Equation 18 to process acd:

$$Q_{acd} = \Delta U_{acd} + W_{acd} = 510 \text{ J} + 90 \text{ J} = 600 \text{ J}.$$

We see that although ΔU is the same (510 J) for abd and acd, W (240 J versus 90 J) and Q (750 J versus 600 J) are quite different for the two processes.

Here is a tabulation of the various quantities:

Step	Q	W	$\Delta U = Q - W$
ab	150 J	0	150 J
bd	600 J	240 J	360 J
abd	750 J	240 J	510 J

Step	Q	W	$\Delta U = Q - W$
ac	?	90 J	?
cd	?	0	?
acd	600 J	90 J	510 J

REFLECT The fact that ΔU is the same for all paths between given initial and final states plays a crucial role in this solution

6 Thermodynamic Processes

Here are four thermodynamic processes that occur often enough in practical problems to be worth some discussion. Their characteristics can be summarized briefly as "no heat transfer," "constant volume," "constant pressure," and "constant temperature," respectively. These four processes for an ideal gas are shown on the pV diagram in Figure 23.

Adiabatic Process

An **adiabatic process** is a process in which there is no heat transfer into or out of a system; in other words, $Q = 0$. We can prevent heat flow either by surrounding the system with thermally insulating material or by carrying out the process so quickly that there is not enough time for any appreciable heat flow. From the first law, we find that, for every adiabatic process,

$$U_2 - U_1 = \Delta U = -W \qquad \text{(adiabatic process).} \qquad (19)$$

MasteringPHYSICS

ActivPhysics 8.4: State Variables and Ideal Gas Law
ActivPhysics 8.6: Heat, Internal Energy, and First Law of Thermodynamics
ActivPhysics 8.8: Isochoric Process
ActivPhysics 8.9: Isobaric Process
ActivPhysics 8.10: Isothermal Process
ActivPhysics 8.11: Adiabatic Process

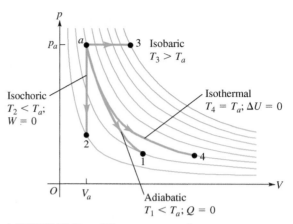

▲ **FIGURE 23** Four different processes for a constant amount of an ideal gas, all starting at state a. The temperature increases only during the isobaric expansion.

When a system expands under adiabatic conditions, W is positive, ΔU is negative, and the internal energy decreases. When a system is *compressed* adiabatically, W is negative and U increases. An increase in internal energy is often, though not always, accompanied by a rise in temperature.

The compression stroke in an internal-combustion engine is an example of a process that is approximately adiabatic. The temperature rises as the air–fuel mixture in the cylinder is compressed. Similarly, the expansion of the burned fuel during the power stroke is an approximately adiabatic expansion with a drop in temperature.

Isochoric Process

An **isochoric process** is a *constant-volume* process. When the volume of a thermodynamic system is constant, the system does no work on its surroundings. Then $W = 0$, and

$$U_2 - U_1 = \Delta U = Q \qquad \text{(isochoric process).} \qquad (20)$$

In an isochoric process, all the energy added as heat remains in the system as an increase in its internal energy. Heating a gas in a closed constant-volume container is an example of an isochoric process.

Isobaric Process

An **isobaric process** is a *constant-pressure* process. In general, for an isobaric process, *none* of the three quantities ΔU, Q, and W in the first law is zero, but calculating W is easy, as we saw in Section 5. Figure 24 shows how an isobaric process looks on a pV diagram. For an isobaric process,

$$W = p(V_2 - V_1) \qquad \text{(isobaric process).} \qquad (16)$$

Example 8 is an example of an isobaric process.

Isothermal Process

An **isothermal process** is a *constant-temperature* process. For a process to be isothermal, the system must remain in thermal equilibrium. This means that any heat flow into or out of the system must occur slowly enough to maintain thermal equilibrium. In general, *none* of the quantities ΔU, Q, and W is zero. Example 9 is an example of an isothermal process.

In some special cases (including ideal gases), the internal energy of a system depends *only* on its temperature, not on its pressure or volume. For such systems, if the temperature is constant, the internal energy is also constant; then $\Delta U = 0$

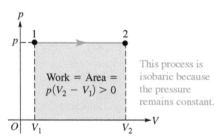

▲ **FIGURE 24** A pV diagram for an isobaric process.

This process is isobaric because the pressure remains constant.

and $Q = W$. That is, any energy entering the system as heat Q must leave it again as work W done by the system. Example 9, involving an ideal gas, is an example of an isothermal process in which U is also constant. For most systems other than ideal gases, the internal energy depends on pressure as well as temperature, so U may vary even when T is constant.

7 Properties of an Ideal Gas

We stated in Section 5 that, for an ideal gas, the internal energy U depends only on temperature, not on pressure or volume. How do we know this? Let's think again about the free-expansion experiment described in Section 5. A thermally insulated container with rigid walls is divided into two compartments by a partition (Figure 25). One compartment contains a quantity of an ideal gas, and the other is evacuated.

When the partition is removed or broken, the gas expands to fill both parts of the container. This process is called a *free expansion*. The gas does no work because the walls of the container don't move. Both Q and W are zero, so the internal energy U is constant. This is true of any substance, whether it is an ideal gas or not.

Does the temperature of a gas change during a free expansion? Suppose it *does* change, while the internal energy stays the same. In that case, the internal energy must depend on both temperature and volume, or both temperature and pressure, but certainly not on temperature alone. But if T is the *same* after the free expansion as before, a process for which we know that U is constant even though both p and V change, then we have to conclude that U depends *only* on T, not on p or V.

Many experiments have shown that when an ideal gas undergoes a free expansion, its temperature *does not* change. The conclusion is that **the internal energy of an ideal gas depends only on its temperature, not on its pressure or volume.** This property, in addition to the ideal-gas equation of state, is part of the ideal-gas model. We'll use the preceding property several times, so make sure that you understand it.

For non-ideal gases, some temperature change occurs during free expansions, even though the internal energy is constant. This shows that the internal energy cannot depend *only* on temperature; it must depend on pressure as well. From a microscopic viewpoint, this dependence on pressure is not surprising. Non-ideal gases usually have attractive intermolecular forces. When molecules move farther apart, the associated potential energies increase. If the total internal energy is constant, the kinetic energies must decrease. Temperature is directly related to molecular *kinetic* energy, so, for a non-ideal gas, a free expansion is usually accompanied by a *drop* in temperature.

Heat Capacities of an Ideal Gas

We defined molar heat capacity in Section 4. The molar heat capacity of a substance depends on the conditions under which the heat is added. It is usually easiest to measure the heat capacity of a gas in a closed container under constant-volume conditions. The corresponding heat capacity is the **molar heat capacity at constant volume,** denoted by C_V. Heat capacity measurements for solids and liquids are usually carried out in the atmosphere under constant atmospheric pressure, and we call the resulting heat capacity the **molar heat capacity at constant pressure,** denoted by C_p. If neither p nor V is constant, we have an infinite number of possible heat capacities.

To measure C_V for a gas, we add heat to raise the temperature of the gas in a rigid container with constant volume. To measure C_p, we add heat while letting the gas expand just enough to keep the pressure constant as the temperature rises.

ActivPhysics 8.7: Heat Capacity

▲ **FIGURE 25** When the partition is broken, the gas expands freely into the vacuum region.

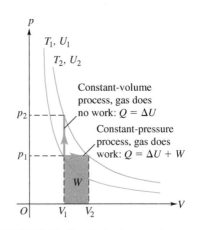

T_1, U_1
T_2, U_2

Constant-volume process, gas does no work: $Q = \Delta U$

Constant-pressure process, gas does work: $Q = \Delta U + W$

p_2
p_1

W

O V_1 V_2 V

▲ **FIGURE 26** Constant-volume and constant-pressure processes for a sample of an ideal gas. For an ideal gas, U depends only on T.

Why should these two molar heat capacities be different? The answer lies in the first law of thermodynamics. In a constant-volume temperature change, the system does no work, and the change in internal energy, ΔU, equals the heat added, Q. In a constant-pressure temperature change, by contrast, the volume *must* increase; otherwise, the pressure could not remain constant. As the material expands, it does an amount of work W. According to the first law,

$$Q = \Delta U + W.$$

For a given temperature change, the heat input for a constant-pressure process must be *greater* than that for a constant-volume process because additional energy is needed to account for the work W done during the expansion, so C_p is greater than C_V. The pV diagram in Figure 26 shows this relationship. For air, C_p is 40% greater than C_V.

In fact, there's a simple relation between C_V and C_p for an ideal gas. We'll omit the details of the derivation; the result is

$$C_p = C_V + R. \tag{21}$$

For an ideal gas, C_p is always greater than C_V; the difference is the gas constant R. (Of course, R must be expressed in the same units as C_V and C_p, such as $J/(mol \cdot K)$.)

 Conceptual Analysis 4

C_p versus C_V

The main reason more heat is needed to raise the temperature of an ideal gas by a given amount at constant pressure than at constant volume is that

A. at constant volume the molecules remain the same mean distance apart.
B. at constant pressure some energy must be provided to increase the volume occupied by the gas.

C. at constant pressure some energy must be provided to separate the molecules, which are subject to cohesive forces of attraction.

SOLUTION For an ideal gas, the molecules have no appreciable interaction, so answers A and C are eliminated. As the gas expands during the constant-pressure process, it has to do work against the walls of its container as the volume increases. This work represents an additional energy requirement; B is correct.

Measured values of C_p and C_V are given in Table 4 for several real gases at low pressures; the difference in most cases is approximately $8.31 \, J/(mol \cdot K)$, as Equation 21 predicts. The table also shows that the molar heat capacity of a gas is related to its molecular structure, as we discussed in Section 4. In fact, the first two columns of Table 4 are the same as those in Table 3.

NOTE ▶ Here's a final reminder: For an ideal gas, the change in internal energy for *any* infinitesimal process is given by $\Delta U = nC_V \Delta T$, *whether the volume is constant or not.* This relation, which comes in handy in the next conceptual analysis example, holds for other substances *only* when the volume is constant. ◀

TABLE 4 Molar heat capacities of gases at low pressure

Type of gas	Gas	$C_V(J/(mol \cdot K))$	$C_p(J/(mol \cdot K))$	$C_p - C_V(J/(mol \cdot K))$	γ
Monatomic	He	12.47	20.78	8.31	1.67
	Ar	12.47	20.78	8.31	1.67
Diatomic	H_2	20.42	28.74	8.32	1.41
	N_2	20.76	29.07	8.31	1.40
	O_2	20.85	29.17	8.31	1.40
	CO	20.85	29.16	8.31	1.40
Polyatomic	CO_2	28.46	36.94	8.48	1.30
	SO_2	31.39	40.37	8.98	1.29
	H_2S	25.95	34.60	8.65	1.33

Conceptual Analysis 5

A compressed gas

An ideal gas in a container is compressed to half its original volume with no change in temperature. The internal energy of the gas is then

A. half its original value, because of the heat released.
B. unchanged, because the temperature is unchanged.
C. twice its original value, because the energy comes from work on the gas.
D. unchanged, because no heat is absorbed or released.

SOLUTION The internal energy of an ideal gas depends only on its temperature. In this case the temperature doesn't change, so the internal energy is also unchanged (answer B). Heat is released, and work is done on the gas, but these two quantities exactly balance each other. Thus, answers A, C, and D can't be correct.

Adiabatic Process for an Ideal Gas

An adiabatic process, defined in Section 5, is a process in which no heat transfer takes place between a system and its surroundings. In an adiabatic process, $Q = 0$ and (from the first law) $\Delta U = -W$. Zero heat transfer is an idealization, but a process is approximately adiabatic if the system is well insulated or if the process takes place so quickly that there is not enough time for any appreciable heat flow to occur.

An adiabatic process for an ideal gas is shown on the pV diagram of Figure 27. As the gas expands from volume V_a to V_b, its temperature drops because it does positive work, decreasing its internal energy. If point a, representing the initial state, lies on an isotherm at temperature $T + \Delta T$, then point b for the final state is on a different isotherm at a lower temperature T. An adiabatic curve at any point is always *steeper* than the isotherm passing through the same point. For an adiabatic *compression* from V_b to V_a, the situation is reversed and the temperature rises.

The air in the output pipes of air compressors used in gasoline stations and paint-spraying equipment and to fill scuba tanks is always warmer than the air entering the compressor because of the approximately adiabatic compression. When air is compressed in the cylinders of a diesel engine during the compression stroke, it gets so hot that fuel injected into the cylinders ignites spontaneously.

The first law of thermodynamics, together with the ideal-gas equation of state, can be used to derive a relation between pressure and volume for an adiabatic process for an ideal gas. This relation depends on the ratio of the two molar heat capacities at constant pressure and at constant volume. We'll denote this ratio by γ; that is, $\gamma = C_p/C_V$. For diatomic gases, γ is approximately 1.40, as Table 4 shows.

We recall that for an *isothermal* (constant-temperature) process, the product pV is constant, so p is inversely proportional to V. It turns out that for an *adiabatic* process, the product pV^γ is constant, and p is proportional to $1/V^\gamma$. So when V increases, the pressure p decreases more rapidly for an adiabatic process than an isothermal process. This is to be expected, because the temperature of an ideal gas always decreases when it expands isothermally.

When an ideal gas expands from state (p_1, V_1) to state (p_2, V_2), the state coordinates are related by

$$p_1 V_1^\gamma = p_2 V_2^\gamma = \text{constant.} \qquad (22)$$

We can combine this result with the ideal-gas equation of state to obtain the following relation between volume and temperature:

$$T_1 V_1^{\gamma-1} = T_2 V_2^{\gamma-1}. \qquad (23)$$

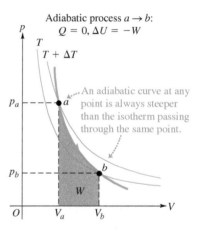

▲ FIGURE 27 A pV diagram of an adiabatic process for an ideal gas. As the gas expands from V_a to V_b, its temperature drops from $T + \Delta T$ to T, corresponding to the decrease in internal energy due to the work W done by the gas (represented by the shaded area).

EXAMPLE 11 **Adiabatic compression in a diesel engine**

The compression ratio of a certain diesel engine is 15 to 1; this means that air in the cylinders is compressed to one-fifteenth of its initial volume (Figure 28). If the initial pressure is 1.01×10^5 Pa and the initial temperature is 27°C (300 K), find the final pressure and the temperature after compression. Air is mostly a mixture of diatomic oxygen and nitrogen; treat it as an ideal gas with $\gamma = 1.40$.

Initial volume Maximum compression

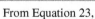

$V_2 = \frac{1}{15} V_1$

V_1

▶ **FIGURE 28**

SOLUTION

SET UP We solve Equation 22 for p_2. We don't need to know V_1 or V_2, but only their ratio. Similarly, we solve Equation 23 for T_2 and use the ratio of the initial and final volumes.

SOLVE We have $p_1 = 1.01 \times 10^5$ Pa, $T_1 = 300$ K, and $V_1/V_2 = 15$. From Equation 22,

$$p_2 = p_1\left(\frac{V_1}{V_2}\right)^{\gamma} = (1.01 \times 10^5 \text{ Pa})(15)^{1.40}$$
$$= 44.8 \times 10^5 \text{ Pa} = 44 \text{ atm}.$$

From Equation 23,

$$T_2 = T_1\left(\frac{V_1}{V_2}\right)^{\gamma-1} = (300 \text{ K})(15)^{0.40} = 886 \text{ K} = 613° \text{ C}.$$

REFLECT If the compression had been isothermal, the final pressure would have been 15 atm, but because the temperature also increases during an adiabatic compression, the final pressure is much greater, about 650 psi. The high temperature attained during compression causes the fuel to ignite spontaneously, without the need for spark plugs, when it is injected into the cylinders near the end of the compression stroke.

CHAPTER SUMMARY

The Mole and Avogadro's Number
(Section 1) **Avogadro's number** $(N_A = 6.022 \times 10^{23}$ molecules/mol$)$ is the number of molecules in a mole. The **molar mass** of a substance is the mass of the substance in 1 mole.

Equations of State
(Section 2) The pressure, volume, and temperature of a given quantity of a substance are called state variables; they are related by an equation of state. The equation of state for an ideal gas is the **ideal-gas equation:** $pV = nRT$ (Equation 3); R is the **ideal-gas constant.**

Kinetic Theory of an Ideal Gas
(Section 3) The average translational kinetic energy of n moles of an ideal gas is directly proportional to the absolute temperature of the gas: $K_{tr} = \frac{3}{2}nRT$ (Equation 7). This relation can be expressed for a single particle in the gas by using Boltzmann's constant $k = R/N_A$: $K_{av} = \frac{1}{2}m(v^2)_{av} = \frac{3}{2}kT$ (Equation 8).

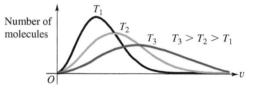

Heat Capacities
(Section 4) The **molar heat capacity** is the amount of heat required to change the temperature of 1 mole of material by 1 kelvin. The molar heat capacity at constant volume is the same for *every* ideal monatomic gas: $C_V = \frac{3}{2}R$ (Equation 13) For an ideal diatomic gas, including rotational, but not vibrational, kinetic energy, $C_V = \frac{5}{2}R$ (Equation 14).

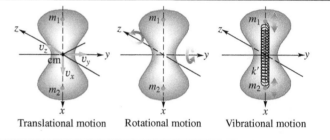

Translational motion   Rotational motion   Vibrational motion

The First Law of Thermodynamics
(Section 5) The **first law of thermodynamics** states that when heat Q is added to a system while work W is done by the system, the internal energy U changes by an amount $\Delta U = Q - W$ (Equation 18). The internal energy of any thermodynamic system depends only on its state. The change in internal energy in any process depends only on the initial and final states, not on the path taken.

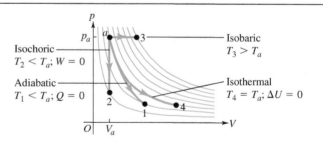

Thermodynamic Processes
(Section 6) Four common kinds of thermodynamic processes are as follows:

- **Adiabatic process:** No heat transfer in or out of a system; $Q = 0$.
- **Isochoric process:** Constant volume; $W = 0$.
- **Isobaric process:** Constant pressure; $W = p(V_2 - V_1)$.
- **Isothermal process:** Constant temperature.

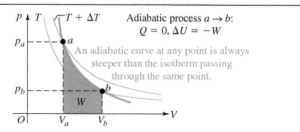

Properties of an Ideal Gas
(Section 7) The internal energy of an ideal gas depends only on its temperature, not its pressure or volume. For non-ideal gases, and for solids and liquids, the internal energy generally depends on both pressure and temperature. The molar heat capacities C_V and C_p of an ideal gas are related by $C_p = C_V + R$ (Equation 25). The ratio of C_p to C_V is denoted by γ: $\gamma = C_p/C_V$ (Equation 26). For an adiabatic process taking place in an ideal gas, the quantities $TV^{\gamma-1}$ and pV^γ are constant.

Thermal Properties of Matter: Problem Set

(MP) For instructor-assigned homework, go to www.masteringphysics.com

Conceptual Questions

1. In the ideal-gas equation, could you give the temperature in degrees Celsius rather than in kelvins if you used an appropriate numerical value of the gas constant R?
2. True or false? Equal masses of two different gases placed in containers of equal volume at equal temperature must exert equal pressures.
3. How does evaporation of perspiration from your skin cool your body?
4. The ideal-gas law is sometimes written in the form $p_1 V_1/T_1 = p_2 V_2/T_2$. Are there any extra limitations on this form of the law, or is it just as general as the form $pV = nRT$?
5. By thinking about matter on the microscopic level, explain why heat flows from a hot to a cold object, but not the other way around. (*Hint:* Look at the transfer of energy during molecular collisions.)
6. (a) If you double the absolute temperature of an ideal gas, what happens to the average kinetic energy of its molecules? To the root-mean-square speed of its molecules? (b) If you double the speeds of the molecules of an ideal gas, what happens to the absolute temperature of this gas?
7. Chemical reaction rates slow down as the temperature is decreased. (This is why we put food in the refrigerator to preserve it.) By thinking about matter on the microscopic (molecular) level, explain why this happens.
8. The *mean free path* of a gas molecule is the average distance the molecule travels before colliding with another molecule. Does this mean free path increase, decrease, or stay the same if the gas is compressed?
9. True or false? When two ideal gases are mixed, they must have the same average molecular speed when they have reached thermal equilibrium.
10. You hold an inflated balloon over a hot air vent in your house and watch it slowly expand. You then remove it and let it cool back to room temperature. During the expansion, which was larger: the heat added to the balloon or the work done by the air inside it? Explain. (Assume that air is an ideal gas.) Once the balloon has returned to room temperature, how does the net heat gained or lost by the air inside it compare to the net work done on it by the surrounding air?
11. In a constant-volume process, $\Delta U = nC_V \Delta T$; in a constant-pressure process, it is *not* true that $\Delta U = nC_p \Delta T$. Why not?

12. When a gas expands adiabatically, it does work on its surroundings. But if there is no heat input to the gas, where does the energy come from to do the work?
13. Since C_V is defined with specific reference to a constant-volume process, how can it be correct that, for an ideal gas, $\Delta U = nC_V \Delta T$ even when the volume is not constant?
14. The ratio γ found in the equations below must always be greater than 1. Why?

$$p_1 V_1^\gamma = p_2 V_2^\gamma = \text{constant.}$$

$$T_1 V_1^{\gamma-1} = T_2 V_2^{\gamma-1}.$$

15. Do the equations in Problem 14 hold for adiabatic processes for liquids and solids? Why or why not?

Multiple-Choice Problems

1. To double both the pressure and the volume of a fixed amount of an ideal gas, you would multiply its absolute temperature by
   A. 1 (i.e., keep the temperature the same).
   B. 2.   C. 4.   D. 16.
2. Oxygen molecules are 16 times more massive than hydrogen molecules. If samples of these two gases are at the *same temperature,* what must be true about the motion of the molecules? (There may be more than one correct choice.)
   A. The rms molecular speed is the same for both gases.
   B. The average kinetic energy is the same for both gases.
   C. The rms speed of the hydrogen molecules is 4 times greater than that of the oxygen molecules.
   D. The rms speed of the hydrogen molecules is 16 times greater than that of the oxygen molecules.
3. An ideal gas in a cubical box having sides of length L exerts a pressure p on the walls of the box. If all of this gas is put into a box having sides of length $2L$ without changing its temperature, the pressure it exerts on the walls of the larger box will be
   A. $4p$.   B. $p/2$.   C. $p/4$.   D. $p/8$.
4. If you mix different amounts of two ideal gases that are originally at different temperatures, what must be true of the final state after the temperature stabilizes? (There may be more than one correct choice.)
   A. Both gases will reach the same final temperature.
   B. The final rms molecular speed will be the same for both gases.
   C. The final average kinetic energy of a molecule will be the same for both gases.

From Chapter 15 of *College Physics*, Ninth Edition, Hugh D. Young. Copyright © 2012 by Pearson Education, Inc. Published by Pearson Addison-Wesley. All rights reserved.

5. If you double the rms speed of the molecules of an ideal gas, which of the following statements is or are true about the gas?
   A. Its absolute temperature is doubled.
   B. Its Celsius temperature is doubled.
   C. Its absolute temperature is quadrupled.
   D. Its Celsius temperature is quadrupled.
6. In an ideal gas, which of the following quantities can be determined by measuring *just* the temperature of the gas?
   A. The average kinetic energy of the molecules.
   B. The total kinetic energy of the molecules.
   C. The pressure of the gas.
7. You add equal amounts of heat to two identical cylinders containing equal amounts of the same ideal gas. Cylinder A is allowed to expand, while cylinder B is not. How do the temperature changes of the two cylinders compare?
   A. The two cylinders will experience the same temperature change.
   B. Cylinder A will experience a greater temperature change.
   C. Cylinder B will experience a greater temperature change.
8. When ice melts at 0°C, its volume decreases. Compared to the amount of heat added, the change in internal energy is
   A. greater.   B. less.   C. the same.
9. The formula $\Delta U = nC_V \Delta T$ for the change in the internal energy of a fixed amount of an ideal gas is valid
   A. only for constant-volume processes.
   B. only for adiabatic processes.
   C. only for isobaric processes.
   D. for *any* process involving that fixed amount of the gas.
10. For the process shown in the pV diagram in Figure 29, the total work in going from a to d along the path shown is
    A. 15×10^5 J.   B. 9×10^5 J.   C. 6×10^5 J.   D. 1×10^5 J.

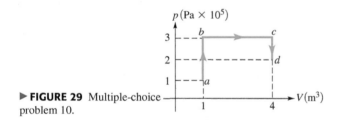

► **FIGURE 29** Multiple-choice problem 10.

11. You have two boxes, one containing some hot gas and the other containing some cold gas. *This is all you know about these boxes.* What can you validly conclude about the characteristics of the gas in the boxes? (There may be more than one correct choice.)
    A. The molecules in the hot gas are moving faster, on average, than those in the cold gas.
    B. The molecules of the hot gas have greater average kinetic energy than those of the cold gas.
    C. The molecules of the hot gas have more *total* kinetic energy than those of the cold gas.
    D. The pressure of the hot gas is greater than that of the cold gas.
12. The gas shown in Figure 30 is in a completely insulated rigid container. Weight is added to the frictionless piston, compressing the gas. As this is done,
    A. the temperature of the gas stays the same because the container is insulated.
    B. the temperature of the gas increases because heat is added to the gas.

C. the temperature of the gas increases because work is done on the gas.
D. the pressure of the gas stays the same because the temperature of the gas is constant.

13. Which of the following must be true about an ideal gas that undergoes an isothermal *expansion?* (There may be more than one correct choice.)
    A. No heat enters the gas.
    B. The pressure of the gas decreases.
    C. The internal energy of the gas does not change.
    D. The gas does positive work.

▲ **FIGURE 30** Multiple-choice problem 12.

14. An ideal gas is initially confined to one side of a perfectly insulated rigid chamber by a movable frictionless piston, as shown in Figure 31. (The other side of the chamber is evacuated.) What is true of this gas after the piston is suddenly pulled to the right end of the chamber? (There may be more than one correct choice.)

▲ **FIGURE 31** Multiple-choice problem 14.

A. The expansion causes the temperature of the gas to decrease.
B. The pressure of the gas decreases.
C. The temperature of the gas does not change.
D. The expansion causes the internal energy of the gas to decrease.

15. Suppose t.hat, in the previous problem, the piston is not pulled but instead is allowed to move slowly to the right as it is hit by the gas molecules. What is true about this gas just as the piston reaches the right end of the chamber? (There may be more than one correct choice.)
    A. The expansion causes the temperature of the gas to decrease.
    B. The pressure of the gas decreases.
    C. The temperature of the gas does not change.
    D. The expansion causes the internal energy of the gas to decrease.

Problems

1 Equations of State

1. • A cylindrical tank has a tight-fitting piston that allows the volume of the tank to be changed. The tank originally contains 0.110 m³ of air at a pressure of 3.40 atm. The piston is slowly pulled out until the volume of the gas is increased to 0.390 m³. If the temperature remains constant, what is the final value of the pressure?
2. • Helium gas with a volume of 2.60 L under a pressure of 1.30 atm and at a temperature of 41.0°C is warmed until both the pressure and volume of the gas are doubled. (a) What is the final temperature? (b) How many grams of helium are there? The molar mass of helium is 4.00 g/mol.

3. • A 3.00 L tank contains air at 3.00 atm and 20.0°C. The tank is sealed and cooled until the pressure is 1.00 atm. (a) What is the temperature then in degrees Celsius, assuming that the volume of the tank is constant? (b) If the temperature is kept at the value found in part (a) and the gas is compressed, what is the volume when the pressure again becomes 3.00 atm?

4. • A 20.0 L tank contains 0.225 kg of helium at 18.0°C. The molar mass of helium is 4.00 g/mol. (a) How many moles of helium are in the tank? (b) What is the pressure in the tank, in pascals and in atmospheres?

5. • A room with dimensions 7.00 m by 8.00 m by 2.50 m is filled with pure oxygen at 22.0°C and 1.00 atm. The molar mass of oxygen is 32.0 g/mol. (a) How many moles of oxygen are required? (b) What is the mass of this oxygen, in kilograms?

6. • Three moles of an ideal gas are in a rigid cubical box with sides of length 0.200 m. (a) What is the force that the gas exerts on each of the six sides of the box when the gas temperature is 20.0°C? (b) What is the force when the temperature of the gas is increased to 100.0°C?

7. • A large cylindrical tank contains 0.750 m³ of nitrogen gas at 27°C and 1.50×10^5 Pa (absolute pressure). The tank has a tight-fitting piston that allows the volume to be changed. What will be the pressure if the volume is decreased to 0.480 m³ and the temperature is increased to 157°C?

8. • **Planetary atmospheres.** (a) Calculate the density of the atmosphere at the surface of Mars (where the pressure is 650 Pa and the temperature is typically 253 K, with a CO_2 atmosphere), Venus (with an average temperature of 730 K and pressure of 92 atm, with a CO_2 atmosphere), and Saturn's moon Titan (where the pressure is 1.5 atm and the temperature is $-178°C$, with a N_2 atmosphere). (b) Compare each of these densities with that of the earth's atmosphere.

9. • The gas inside a balloon will always have a pressure nearly equal to atmospheric pressure, since that is the pressure applied to the outside of the balloon. You fill a balloon with helium (a nearly ideal gas) to a volume of 0.600 L at a temperature of 19.0°C. What is the volume of the balloon if you cool it to the boiling point of liquid nitrogen (77.3 K)?

10. • **Lung volume.** The total lung volume for a typical person is
BIO 6.00 L. A person fills her lungs with air at an absolute pressure of 1.00 atm. Then, holding her breath, she compresses her chest cavity, decreasing her lung volume to 5.70 L. What is the pressure of the air in her compressed lungs, assuming that the temperature of the air remains constant?

11. • A Jaguar XK8 convertible has an eight-cylinder engine. At the beginning of its compression stroke, one of the cylinders contains 499 cm³ of air at atmospheric pressure (1.01×10^5 Pa) and a temperature of 27.0°C. At the end of the stroke, the air has been compressed to a volume of 46.2 cm³ and the gauge pressure has increased to 2.72×10^6 Pa. Compute the final temperature.

12. •• A diver observes a bubble of air rising from the bottom of a lake (where the absolute pressure is 3.50 atm) to the surface (where the pressure is 1.00 atm). The temperature at the bottom is 4.0°C and the temperature at the surface is 23.0°C. (a) What is the ratio of the volume of the bubble as it reaches the surface to its volume at the bottom? (b) Would it be safe for the diver to hold his breath while ascending from the bottom of the lake to the surface? Why or why not?

13. •• At an altitude of 11,000 m (a typical cruising altitude for a jet airliner), the air temperature is $-56.5°C$ and the air density is 0.364 kg/m³. What is the pressure of the atmosphere at that altitude? The molar mass of air is 28.8 g/mol.

14. •• If a certain amount of ideal gas occupies a volume V at STP on earth, what would be its volume (in terms of V) on Venus, where the temperature is 1003°C and the pressure is 92 atm?

2 Phases of Matter

15. • Calculate the volume of 1.00 mol of liquid water at a temperature of 20°C (at which its density is 998 kg/m³), and compare this volume with the volume occupied by 1.00 mol of water at the critical point, which is 56×10^{-6} m³. Water has a molar mass of 18.0 g/mol.

16. •• Solid water (ice) is slowly warmed from a very low temperature. (a) What minimum external pressure p_1 must be applied to the solid if a melting phase transition is to be observed? Describe the sequence of phase transitions that occur if the applied pressure p is such that $p < p_1$. (b) Above a certain maximum pressure p_2, no boiling transition is observed. What is this pressure? Describe the sequence of phase transitions that occur if $p_1 < p < p_2$.

17. •• The atmosphere of the planet Mars is 95.3% carbon dioxide (CO_2) and about 0.03% water vapor. The atmospheric pressure is only about 600 Pa, and the surface temperature varies from $-30°C$ to $-100°C$. The polar ice caps contain both CO_2 ice and water ice. Could there be *liquid* CO_2 on the surface of Mars? Could there be liquid water? Why or why not?

3 Kinetic Theory of an Ideal Gas

18. • Find the mass of a single sulfur (S) atom and an ammonia (NH_3) molecule.

19. • How many water molecules are there in a 1.00 L bottle of water? The molar mass of water is 18.0 g/mol.

20. • In the air we breathe at 72°F and 1.0 atm pressure, how many molecules does a typical cubic centimeter contain, assuming that the air is all N_2?

21. •• We have two equal-size boxes, A and B. Each box contains gas that behaves as an ideal gas. We insert a thermometer into each box and find that the gas in box A is at a temperature of 50°C while the gas in box B is at 10°C. This is all we know about the gas in the boxes. Which of the following statements *must* be true? Which *could* be true? (a) The pressure in A is higher than in B. (b) There are more molecules in A than in B. (c) A and B cannot contain the same type of gas. (d) The molecules in A have more average kinetic energy per molecule than those in B. (e) The molecules in A are moving faster than those in B. Explain the reasoning behind your answers.

22. •• (a) A deuteron, ^2_1H, is the nucleus of a hydrogen isotope and consists of one proton and one neutron. The plasma of deuterons in a nuclear fusion reactor must be heated to about 300 million K. What is the rms speed of the deuterons? Is this a significant fraction of the speed of light ($c = 3.0 \times 10^8$ m/s)? (b) What would the temperature of the plasma be if the deuterons had an rms speed equal to $0.10c$?

23. • Oxygen (O_2) has a molar mass of 32.0 g/mol. (a) What is the root-mean-square speed of an oxygen molecule at a temperature of 300 K? (b) What is its average translational kinetic energy at that speed?

24. • Suppose some insects have speeds of 10.00 m/s, 8.00 m/s, 7.00 m/s, and 2.00 m/s. Find (a) the rms speed of these critters and (b) their average speed.

25. •• In a gas at standard temperature and pressure, what is the length of the side of a cube that contains a number of molecules equal to the population of the earth (about 6 billion people at present)?

26. •• At what temperature is the root-mean-square speed of nitrogen molecules equal to the root-mean-square speed of hydrogen molecules at 20.0°C? (*Hint:* The periodic table shows the molar mass (in g/mol) of each element under the chemical symbol for that element. The molar mass of H_2 is twice the molar mass of hydrogen atoms, and similarly for N_2.)

27. •• **Where is the hydrogen?** The average temperature of the atmosphere near the surface of the earth is about 20°C. (a) What is the root-mean-square speed of hydrogen molecules, H_2, at this temperature? (b) The escape speed from the earth is about 11 km/s. Is the average H_2 molecule moving fast enough to escape? (c) Compare the rms speeds of oxygen (O_2) and nitrogen (N_2) with that of H_2. (d) So why has the hydrogen been able to escape the earth's gravity, but the heavier gases (such as O_2 and N_2) have not, even though none of these gases has an rms speed equal to the escape speed of the earth? (*Hint:* Do *all* the molecules have the rms speed, or are some moving faster? Since the rms speed for H_2 is greater than that of O_2 and N_2, which gas would have a higher percentage of its molecules moving fast enough to escape?)

28. •• A flask contains a mixture of neon (Ne), krypton (Kr), and radon (Rn) gases. Compare (a) the average kinetic energies of the three types of atoms; (b) their root-mean-square speeds. (*Hint:* The periodic table in Appendix C shows the molar mass (in g/mol) of each element.)

29. •• **STP.** The conditions of standard temperature and pressure (STP) are a temperature of 0.00°C, and a pressure of 1.00 atm. (a) How many liters does 1.00 mol of any ideal gas occupy at STP? (b) For a scientist on Venus, an absolute pressure of 1 Venusian-atmosphere is 92 Earth-atmospheres. Of course she would use the Venusian-atmosphere to define STP. Assuming she kept the same temperature, how many liters would 1 mole of ideal gas occupy on Venus?

30. •• **Breathing at high altitudes.** If you have ever hiked or
BIO climbed to high altitudes in the mountains, you surely have noticed how short of breath you get. This occurs because the air is thinner, so each breath contains fewer O_2 molecules than at sea level. At the top of Mt. Everest, the pressure is only $\frac{1}{3}$ atm. Air contains 21% O_2 and 78% N_2, and an average human breath is 0.50 L of air. At the top of Mt. Everest, (a) how many O_2 molecules does each breath contain when the temperature is −15°F, and (b) what percent is this of the number of O_2 molecules you would get from a breath at sea level at −15°F?

31. •• **How often do we need to breathe?** A resting person
BIO requires 14.5 L of O_2 per hour to maintain metabolic activities. Such a person breathes in 0.50 L of air at approximately 20°C with each breath. The inhaled air is 20.9% O_2, while the exhaled air is 16.3% O_2. (a) How many breaths per minute does a resting person need to take to provide the necessary oxygen? (b) How many O_2 molecules does a resting person inhale per breath?

4 Heat Capacities

32. • (a) How much heat does it take to increase the temperature of 2.50 moles of an ideal monatomic gas from 25.0°C to 55.0°C if the gas is held at constant volume? (b) How much heat is needed if the gas is diatomic rather than monatomic? (c) Sketch a pV diagram for these processes.

33. • (a) If you supply 1850 J of heat to 2.25 moles of an ideal diatomic gas initially at 10.0°C in a perfectly rigid container, what will be the final temperature of the gas? (b) Suppose the gas in the container were an ideal monatomic gas instead. How much heat would you need to add to produce the same temperature change? (c) Sketch a pV diagram of these processes.

34. • Compute the specific heat capacity (in J/(kg · K)) at constant volume of nitrogen (N_2) gas, and compare it with the specific heat capacity of liquid water. Use Appendix C to determine the molar mass of N_2.

35. • Perfectly rigid containers each hold n moles of ideal gas, one being hydrogen (H_2) and other being neon (Ne). If it takes 100 J of heat to increase the temperature of the hydrogen by 2.50 C°, by how many degrees will the same amount of heat raise the temperature of the neon?

36. •• Assume that the gases in this problem can be treated as ideal over the temperature ranges involved, and consult Appendix C to determine the necessary molar masses. (a) How much heat is needed to raise the temperature of 75.0 g of N_2 from 12.1°C to 49.5°C at constant volume? (b) If instead you want to produce the same temperature change in 75.0 g of O_2 at constant volume, how much heat do you need?

5 The First Law of Thermodynamics

37. • A metal cylinder with rigid walls contains 2.50 mol of oxygen gas. The gas is cooled until the pressure decreases to 30.0% of its original value. You can ignore the thermal contraction of the cylinder. (a) Draw a pV diagram of this process. (b) Calculate the work done by the gas.

38. • A gas under a constant pressure of 1.50×10^5 Pa and with an initial volume of 0.0900 m^3 is cooled until its volume becomes 0.0600 m^3. (a) Draw a pV diagram of this process. (b) Calculate the work done by the gas.

39. • Two moles of an ideal gas are heated at constant pressure from $T = 27°C$ to $T = 107°C$. (a) Draw a pV diagram for this process. (b) Calculate the work done by the gas.

40. •• Three moles of an ideal monatomic gas expands at a constant pressure of 2.50 atm; the volume of the gas changes from 3.20×10^{-2} m^3 to 4.50×10^{-2} m^3. (a) Calculate the initial and final temperatures of the gas. (b) Calculate the amount of work the gas does in expanding. (c) Calculate the amount of heat added to the gas. (d) Calculate the change in internal energy of the gas.

41. •• **Work done in a cyclic process.** In Figure 32, consider the closed loop $1 \rightarrow 2 \rightarrow 3 \rightarrow 4 \rightarrow 1$. This is a *cyclic* process in which

▲ **FIGURE 32** Problem 41.

the initial and final states are the same. (a) Find the total work done by the system in this process, and show that it is equal to the area enclosed by the loop. (b) How is the work done during the process in part (a) related to the work done if the loop is traversed in the opposite direction, $1 \rightarrow 4 \rightarrow 3 \rightarrow 2 \rightarrow 1$. Explain. (c) How much work is done in the cycle $3 \rightarrow 4 \rightarrow 2 \rightarrow 3$?

42. •• **Work done by the lungs.** The graph in Figure 33 shows a
BIO pV diagram of the air in a human lung when a person is inhaling and then exhaling a deep breath. Such graphs, obtained in clinical practice, are normally somewhat curved, but we have modeled one as a set of straight lines of the same general shape. (*Important:* The pressure shown is the *gauge* pressure, *not* the absolute pressure.) (a) How many joules of *net* work does this person's lung do during one complete breath? (b) The process illustrated here is somewhat different from those we have been studying, because the pressure change is due to changes in the amount of gas in the lung, not to temperature changes. (Think of your own breathing. Your lungs do not expand because they've gotten hot.) If the temperature of the air in the lungs remains a reasonable 20°C, what is the maximum number of moles in this person's lungs during a breath?

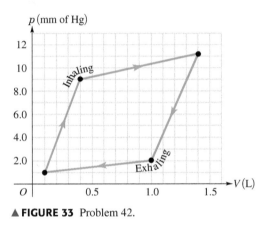

▲ **FIGURE 33** Problem 42.

43. • In a certain chemical process, a lab technician supplies 254 J of heat to a system. At the same time, 73 J of work are done on the system by its surroundings. What is the increase in the internal energy of the system?

44. • A gas in a cylinder expands from a volume of 0.110 m³ to 0.320 m³. Heat flows into the gas just rapidly enough to keep the pressure constant at 1.80×10^5 Pa during the expansion. The total heat added is 1.15×10^5 J. (a) Find the work done by the gas. (b) Find the change in internal energy of the gas.

45. • A gas in a cylinder is held at a constant pressure of 2.30×10^5 Pa and is cooled and compressed from 1.70 m³ to 1.20 m³. The internal energy of the gas decreases by 1.40×10^5 J. (a) Find the work done by the gas. (b) Find the amount of the heat that flowed into or out of the gas, and state the direction (inward or outward) of the flow.

46. • Five moles of an ideal monatomic gas with an initial temperature of 127°C expand and, in the process, absorb 1200 J of heat and do 2100 J of work. What is the final temperature of the gas?

47. •• When a system is taken from state a to state b in Figure 34 along the path acb, 90.0 J of heat flows into the system and

60.0 J of work is done by the system. (a) How much heat flows into the system along path adb if the work done by the system is 15.0 J? (b) When the system is returned from b to a along the curved path, the absolute value of the work done by the system is 35.0 J. Does the system absorb or liberate heat? How much heat? (c) If $U_a = 0$ and $U_d = 8.0$ J, find the heat absorbed in the processes ad and db.

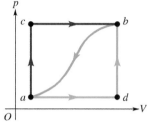

▲ **FIGURE 34** Problem 47.

6 Thermodynamic Processes
7 Properties of an Ideal Gas

48. • An ideal gas expands while the pressure is kept constant. During this process, does heat flow into the gas or out of the gas? Justify your answer.

49. • You are keeping 1.75 moles of an ideal gas in a container surrounded by a large ice-water bath that maintains the temperature of the gas at 0.00°C. (a) How many joules of work would have to be done on this gas to compress its volume from 4.20 L to 1.35 L? (b) How much heat came into (or out of) the gas during this process? Was it into or out of?

50. • Suppose you do 457 J of work on 1.18 moles of ideal He gas in a perfectly insulated container. By how much does the internal energy of this gas change? Does it increase or decrease?

51. •• A cylinder with a movable piston contains 3.00 mol of N_2 gas (assumed to behave like an ideal gas). (a) The N_2 is heated at constant volume until 1557 J of heat have been added. Calculate the change in temperature. (b) Suppose the same amount of heat is added to the N_2, but this time the gas is allowed to expand while remaining at constant pressure. Calculate the temperature change. (c) In which case, (a) or (b), is the final internal energy of the N_2 higher? How do you know? What accounts for the difference between the two cases?

52. •• Figure 35 shows a pV diagram for an ideal gas in which its pressure tripled from a to b when 534 J of heat was put into the gas. (a) How much work was done on or by the gas between a and b? (b) Without doing any calculations, decide whether the temperature of this gas increased, decreased, or remained the same between a and b. Explain your reasoning. (c) By how much did the internal energy of the gas change between a and b? Did it increase or decrease? (d) What is the temperature of the gas at point b in terms of its temperature at a, T_a?

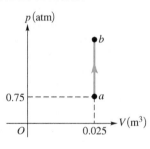

▲ **FIGURE 35** Problem 52.

53. •• Figure 36 shows a pV diagram for an ideal gas in which its absolute temperature at b is one-fourth of its absolute temperature at a. (a) What volume does this gas occupy at point b? (b) How many joules of work was done by or on the gas in this process? Was it done by or on the gas? (c) Did the internal energy of the gas

551

increase or decrease from a to b? How do you know? (d) Did heat enter or leave the gas from a to b? How do you know?

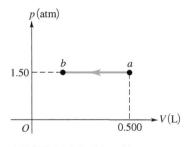

▲ FIGURE 36 Problem 53.

54. •• The pV diagram in Figure 37 shows a process abc involving 0.450 mole of an ideal gas. (a) What was the temperature of this gas at points a, b, and c? (b) How much work was done by or on the gas in this process? (c) How much heat had to be put in during the process to increase the internal energy of the gas by 15,000 J?

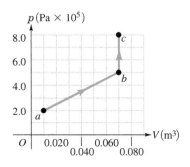

▲ FIGURE 37 Problem 54.

55. •• A volume of air (assumed to be an ideal gas) is first cooled without changing its volume and then expanded without changing its pressure, as shown by the path abc in Fig. 38. (a) How does the final temperature of the gas compare with its initial temperature? (b) How much heat does the air exchange with its surroundings during the process abc? Does the air absorb heat or release heat during this process? Explain. (c) If the air instead expands from state a to state c by the straight-line path shown, how much heat does it exchange with its surroundings?

▲ FIGURE 38 Problem 55.

56. •• In the process illustrated by the pV diagram in Figure 39, the temperature of the ideal gas remains constant at 85°C. (a) How many moles of gas are involved? (b) What volume does this gas occupy at a? (c) How much work was done by

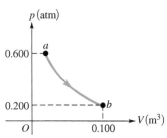

▲ FIGURE 39 Problem 56.

or on the gas from a to b? (d) By how much did the internal energy of the gas change during this process?

57. • A cylinder contains 0.250 mol of carbon dioxide (CO_2) gas at a temperature of 27.0°C. The cylinder is provided with a frictionless piston, which maintains a constant pressure of 1.00 atm on the gas. The gas is heated until its temperature increases to 127.0°C. Assume that the CO_2 may be treated as an ideal gas. (a) Draw a pV diagram of this process. (b) How much work is done by the gas in the process? (c) On what is this work done? (d) What is the change in internal energy of the gas? (e) How much heat was supplied to the gas? (f) How much work would have been done if the pressure had been 0.50 atm?

58. •• **Heating air in the lungs.** Human lung capacity varies
BIO from about 4 L to 6 L, so we shall use an average of 5.0 L. The air enters at the ambient temperature of the atmosphere and must be heated to internal body temperature at an approximately constant pressure of 1.0 atm in our model. Suppose you are outside on a winter day when the temperature is $-10°F$. (a) How many moles of air does your lung hold if the 5.0 L is at the internal body temperature of 37°C? (b) How much heat must your body have supplied to get the 5.0 L of air up to internal body temperature, assuming that the atmosphere is all N_2? (See Table A at the end of this problem set.) (c) Suppose instead that you manage to inhale the full 5.0 L of air in one breath and hold it in your lungs without expanding (or contracting) them. How much heat would your body have had to supply in that case to raise the air up to internal body temperature?

59. •• The graph in Figure 40 shows a pV diagram for 1.10 moles of *ideal* oxygen, O_2. (a) Find the temperature at points a, b, c, and d. (b) How many joules of heat enters (or leaves) the oxygen in segment (i) ab, (ii) bc, (iii) cd, (iv) da? (c) In each of the preceding segments, does the heat enter or leave the gas? How do you know?

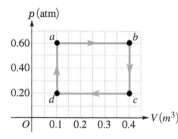

▲ FIGURE 40 Problem 59.

60. • An ideal gas at 4.00 atm and 350 K is permitted to expand adiabatically to 1.50 times its initial volume. Find the final pressure and temperature if the gas is (a) monatomic with $C_p/C_V = \frac{5}{3}$, (b) diatomic with $C_p/C_V = \frac{7}{5}$.

61. •• An experimenter adds 970 J of heat to 1.75 mol of an ideal gas to heat it from 10.0°C to 25.0°C at constant pressure. The gas does +223 J of work during the expansion. (a) Calculate the change in internal energy of the gas. (b) Calculate γ for the gas.

62. •• Heat Q flows into a monatomic ideal gas, and the volume increases while the pressure is kept constant. What fraction of the heat energy is used to do the expansion work of the gas?

63. •• A player bounces a basketball on the floor, compressing it to 80.0% of its original volume. The air (assume it is essentially N_2 gas) inside the ball is originally at a temperature of

20.2°C and a pressure of 2.00 atm. The ball's diameter is 23.9 cm. (a) What temperature does the air in the ball reach at its maximum compression? (b) By how much does the internal energy of the air change between the ball's original state and its maximum compression?

64. •• In the pV diagram shown in Figure 41, 85.0 J of work was done by 0.0650 mole of ideal gas during an adiabatic process. (a) How much heat entered or left this gas from a to b? (b) By how many joules did the internal energy of the gas change? (c) What is the temperature of the gas at b?

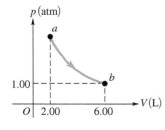

▲ FIGURE 41 Problem 64.

General Problems

65. • Modern vacuum pumps make it easy to attain pressures on the order of 10^{-13} atm in the laboratory. At a pressure of 9.00×10^{-14} atm and an ordinary temperature of 300 K, how many molecules are present in 1.00 cm³ of gas?

66. •• **How many atoms are you?** Estimate the number of atoms
BIO in the body of a 65 kg physics student. Note that the human body is mostly water, which has molar mass 18.0 g/mol, and that each water molecule contains three atoms.

67. •• **The effect of altitude on the lungs.** (a) Calculate the *change*
BIO in air pressure you will experience if you climb a 1000 m mountain, assuming that the temperature and air density do not change over this distance and that they were 22°C and 1.2 kg/m³, respectively, at the bottom of the mountain. (b) If you took a 0.50 L breath at the foot of the mountain and managed to hold it until you reached the top, what would be the volume of this breath when you exhaled it there?

68. •• (a) Calculate the mass of nitrogen present in a volume of 3000 cm³ if the temperature of the gas is 22.0°C and the absolute pressure is 2.00×10^{-13} atm, a partial vacuum easily obtained in laboratories. The molar mass of nitrogen (N_2) is 28.0 g/mol. (b) What is the density (in kg/m³) of the N_2?

69. • An automobile tire has a volume of 0.0150 m³ on a cold day when the temperature of the air in the tire is 5.0°C and atmospheric pressure is 1.02 atm. Under these conditions, the gauge pressure is measured to be 1.70 atm (about 25 lb/in²). After the car is driven on the highway for 30 min, the temperature of the air in the tires has risen to 45.0°C and the volume to 0.0159 m³. What is the gauge pressure at that time?

70. •• A cylinder 1.00 m tall with inside diameter 0.120 m is used to hold propane gas (molar mass 44.1 g/mol) for use in a barbecue. It is initially filled with gas until the gauge pressure is 1.30×10^6 Pa and the temperature is 22.0°C. The temperature of the gas remains constant as it is partially emptied out of the tank, until the gauge pressure is 2.50×10^5 Pa. Calculate the mass of propane that has been used.

71. •• **The surface of the sun.** The surface of the sun has a temperature of about 5800 K and consists largely of hydrogen atoms. (a) Find the rms speed of a hydrogen atom at this temperature. (The mass of a single hydrogen atom is 1.67×10^{-27} kg.) (b) What would be the mass of an atom that had half the rms speed of hydrogen?

72. •• **Atmosphere of Titan.** Titan, the largest satellite of Saturn, has a thick nitrogen atmosphere. At its surface, the pressure is 1.5 Earth-atmospheres and the temperature is 94 K. (a) What is the surface temperature in °C? (b) Calculate the surface density in Titan's atmosphere in molecules per cubic meter. (c) Compare the density of Titan's surface atmosphere to the density of Earth's atmosphere at 22°C. Which body has a denser atmosphere?

73. •• Helium gas expands slowly to twice its original volume, doing 300 J of work in the process. Find the heat added to the gas and the change in internal energy of the gas if the process is (a) isothermal, (b) adiabatic, (c) isobaric.

74. •• A cylinder with a piston contains 0.250 mol of ideal oxygen at a pressure of 2.40×10^5 Pa and a temperature of 355 K. The gas first expands isobarically to twice its original volume. It is then compressed isothermally back to its original volume, and finally it is cooled isochorically to its original pressure. (a) Show the series of processes on a pV diagram. (b) Compute the temperature during the isothermal compression. (c) Compute the maximum pressure. (d) Compute the total work done by the piston on the gas during the series of processes.

75. •• You blow up a spherical balloon to a diameter of 50.0 cm until the absolute pressure inside is 1.25 atm and the temperature is 22.0°C. Assume that all the gas is N_2, of molar mass 28.0 g/mol. (a) Find the mass of a single N_2 molecule. (b) How much translational kinetic energy does an average N_2 molecule have? (c) How many N_2 molecules are in this balloon? (d) What is the *total* translational kinetic energy of all the molecules in the balloon?

76. •• (a) One-third of a mole of He gas is taken along the path abc shown as the solid line in Figure 42. Assume that the gas may be treated as ideal. How much heat is transferred into or out of the gas? (b) If the gas instead went from state a to state c along the horizontal dashed line in Fig. 42, how much heat would be transferred into or out of the gas? (c) How does Q in part (b) compare against Q in part (a)? Explain.

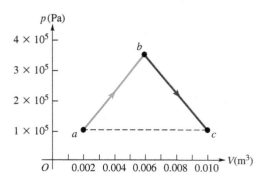

▲ FIGURE 42 Problem 76.

77. •• A bicyclist uses a tire pump whose cylinder is initially full of air at an absolute pressure of 1.01×10^5 Pa. The length of stroke of the pump (the length of the cylinder) is 36.0 cm. At what part of the stroke (i.e., what length of the air column) does air begin to enter a tire in which the gauge pressure is 2.76×10^5 Pa? Assume that the temperature remains constant during the compression.

78. •• **The bends.** If deep-sea divers rise to the surface too
BIO quickly, nitrogen bubbles in their blood can expand and prove

fatal. This phenomenon is known as the *bends*. If a scuba diver rises quickly from a depth of 25 m in Lake Michigan (which is fresh water), what will be the volume at the surface of an N_2 bubble that occupied 1.0 mm³ in his blood at the lower depth? Does it seem that this difference is large enough to be a problem? (Assume that the pressure difference is due only to the changing water pressure, not to any temperature difference, an assumption that is reasonable, since we are warm-blooded creatures.)

79. •• Figure 43 shows a *pV* diagram for 0.0040 mole of *ideal* H_2 gas. The temperature of the gas does not change during segment *bc*. (a) What volume does this gas occupy at point *c*? (b) Find the temperature of the gas at points *a*, *b*, and *c*. (c) How much heat went into or out of the gas during segments *ab*, *ca*, and *bc*? Indicate whether the heat has gone into or out of the gas. (d) Find the change in the internal energy of this hydrogen during segments *ab*, *bc*, and *ca*. Indicate whether the internal energy increased or decreased during each of these segments.

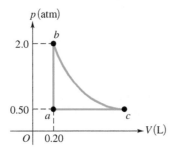

▲ **FIGURE 43** Problem 79.

80. •• The graph in Figure 44 shows a *pV* diagram for 3.25 moles of *ideal* helium (He) gas. Part *ca* of this process is isothermal. (a) Find the pressure of the He at point *a*. (b) Find the temperature of the He at points *a*, *b*, and *c*. (c) How much heat entered or left the He during segments *ab*, *bc*, and *ca*? In each segment, did the heat enter or leave? (d) By how much did the internal energy of the He change from *a* to *b*, from *b* to *c*, and from *c* to *a*? Indicate whether this energy increased or decreased.

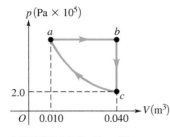

▲ **FIGURE 44** Problem 80.

81. •• A flask with a volume of 1.50 L, provided with a stopcock, contains ethane gas (C_2H_6) at 300 K and atmospheric pressure $(1.013 \times 10^5 \text{ Pa})$. The molar mass of ethane is 30.1 g/mol. The system is warmed to a temperature of 380 K, with the stopcock open to the atmosphere. The stopcock is then closed, and the flask is cooled to its original temperature. (a) What is the final pressure of the ethane in the flask? (b) How many grams of ethane remain in the flask?

82. •• **Diesel ignition.** Conventional engines ignite their fuel by using the spark from a spark plug. But in a diesel engine, the air enters the chamber at the temperature of the atmosphere and is compressed by the piston until it reaches 550°C, at which time the fuel is injected into the chamber and ignited by the hot air. There is no spark plug and no heat is put into the air. (One of the drawbacks of diesel engines is that they are hard to start in cold weather, as we shall shortly see.) Suppose that a certain chamber has a maximum

volume of 0.50 L and uses 0.050 mole of air. We can model the air as all ideal N_2 and use the appropriate values from Table A. (a) If the air temperature is 20°C, what is the volume of the air (which started at 0.50 L) when it has been compressed enough so that its temperature has risen to 550°C? (b) What is the change in the internal energy of the air during this compression? (c) How much work did the piston do on this gas while compressing it? (d) Suppose it is a cold winter morning, with the air temperature 10° F. If the piston compressed the air by the same amount as before, what will be the highest temperature the gas will reach in this case? (e) Do you now see why a diesel engine is hard to start in cold weather? Can you suggest any reasonable technological solutions to help start a diesel engine on a cold day?

83. •• Initially at a temperature of 80.0°C, 0.28 m³ of air expands at a constant gauge pressure of 1.38×10^5 Pa to a volume of 1.42 m³ and then expands further adiabatically to a final volume of 2.27 m³ and a final gauge pressure of 2.29×10^4 Pa. Draw a *pV* diagram for this sequence of processes, and compute the total work done by the air. C_V for air is 20.8 J/(mol · K).

84. •• In a cylinder, 4.00 mol of helium initially at 1.00×10^6 Pa and 300 K expands until its volume doubles. Compute the work done by the gas if the expansion is (a) isobaric, (b) adiabatic. (c) Show each process on a *pV* diagram. In which case is the magnitude of the work done by the gas the greatest? (d) In which case is the magnitude of the heat transfer greatest? (e) In which case is the magnitude of the change in internal energy greatest?

85. •• Starting with 2.50 mol of N_2 gas (assumed to be ideal) in a cylinder at 1.00 atm and 20.0°C, a chemist first heats the gas at constant volume, adding 1.52×10^4 J of heat, then continues heating and allows the gas to expand at constant pressure to twice its original volume. (a) Calculate the final temperature of the gas. (b) Calculate the amount of work done by the gas. (c) Calculate the amount of heat added to the gas while it was expanding. (d) Calculate the change in internal energy of the gas for the whole process.

86. ••• A hot-air balloon stays aloft because hot air at atmospheric pressure is less dense than cooler air at the same pressure. If the volume of the balloon is 500.0 m³ and the surrounding air is at 15.0°C, what must the temperature of the air in the balloon be for it to lift a total load of 290 kg (in addition to the mass of the hot air)? The density of air at 15.0°C and atmospheric pressure is 1.23 kg/m³.

Passage Problems

BIO Temperature and degrees of freedom. The internal energy of an ideal monatomic gas is simply the kinetic energy associated with the translational motion of its atoms as they move randomly in each of the three independent spatial dimensions. However, for a diatomic ideal gas we must also take into account the kinetic and potential energies associated with molecular vibration, and the kinetic energy associated with molecular rotation. Roughly speaking, each independent way that energy can be stored is known as a *degree of freedom*.

Although translational motion can occur at any temperature, rotational and vibrational motions typically cannot occur at lower temperatures—thus, the number of available degrees of freedom can change as the temperature changes. For example, an ideal *monatomic* gas has three degrees of freedom (one for each of its independent directions of translational motion) at all temperatures. In contrast, *diatomic* hydrogen (H_2) has five degrees of freedom near room temperature (3 translational and 2 rotational). However, at higher temperatures, where molecular vibrations can occur, diatomic hydrogen has seven degrees of freedom (3 translational, 2 rotational, and 2 vibrational).

The equipartition theorem states that at equilibrium each degree of freedom contributes $\frac{1}{2}nRT$ to the internal energy of the gas. For example, the internal energy of a monatomic gas, which has 3 degrees of freedom, would be $\frac{3}{2}nRT$.

87. Near room temperature, how does the internal energy of one mole of a diatomic ideal gas compare to that of one mole of a monatomic ideal gas?
    A. They have the same internal energy.
    B. The diatomic gas has 2 times as much internal energy as the monatomic gas.
    C. The diatomic gas has $2/3$ times as much internal energy as the monatomic gas.

D. The diatomic gas has $3/2$ times as much internal energy as the monatomic gas.
E. The diatomic gas has $5/3$ times as much internal energy as the monatomic gas.

88. For an ideal gas with 9 degrees of freedom, the *molar heat capacity* at constant volume $(J/(mol \cdot K))$ would be
    A. $\frac{3}{2}RT$
    B. $\frac{3}{2}nR$
    C. $\frac{9}{2}nR$
    D. $\frac{9}{2}R$
    E. $\frac{11}{2}R$

89. As the temperature of a monatomic gas increases, we expect its specific heat to
    A. remain the same
    B. increase
    C. decrease

90. As the temperature of a diatomic gas increases, we expect its specific heat to
    A. remain the same
    B. increase
    C. decrease

TABLE A   Molar heat capacities of gases at low pressure

Type of gas	Gas	$C_V(J/(mol \cdot K))$	$C_p(J/(mol \cdot K))$	$C_p - C_V(J/(mol \cdot K))$	γ
Monatomic	He	12.47	20.78	8.31	1.67
	Ar	12.47	20.78	8.31	1.67
Diatomic	H_2	20.42	28.74	8.32	1.41
	N_2	20.76	29.07	8.31	1.40
	O_2	20.85	29.17	8.31	1.40
	CO	20.85	29.16	8.31	1.40
Polyatomic	CO_2	28.46	36.94	8.48	1.30
	SO_2	31.39	40.37	8.98	1.29
	H_2S	25.95	34.60	8.65	1.33

ANSWERS TO SELECTED PROBLEMS

Conceptual Questions

1. No. The conversion from kelvins to Celsius degrees involves an additive rather than a multiplicative factor, so the conversion factor cannot be absorbed into the gas constant. For example, there are negative temperatures on the Celsius scale and negative values for T don't make sense in the ideal gas equation, no matter what the value is for the gas constant.

5. In a hot object the random motions of the atoms (or molecules) are more energetic than in a cold object. When the two objects are in contact their atoms collide and in the collision kinetic energy is transferred from the atoms in the hot object to the atoms in the cold object.

7. As the temperature is decreased the average kinetic energy of the molecules in the material decreases. Collisions between molecules in the material become less frequent and are less energetic.

9. False. At thermal equilibrium the two kinds of atoms have the same temperature and the same average kinetic energy. To have the same average kinetic energy, the lighter atoms have a greater speed.

11. For any process of an ideal gas, $\Delta U = nC_V \Delta T$. The constants C_V and C_p are defined by the equations for the heat flow for constant volume $(Q = nC_V \Delta T)$ and constant pressure $(Q = nC_p \Delta T)$ processes. For a constant volume process, $W = 0$ and $Q = nC_V \Delta T$ so by $\Delta U = Q - W$, $\Delta U = nC_V \Delta T$. For a constant pressure process, $Q = nC_p \Delta T$, but $W \neq 0$ and ΔU is not equal to Q.

13. For an ideal gas U depends only on T. Since $\Delta U = nC_V \Delta T$ for constant volume, ΔU is also given by this expression for any process.

15. No. To derive these equations we used the ideal gas law. The equation of state for liquids and solids differs greatly from the ideal gas law, so equations 15.22 and 15.23 don't apply.

Multiple-Choice Problems

1. C
3. D
5. C
7. B
9. D
11. B
13. B, C, D
15. A, B, D

Problems

1. 0.959 atm
3. (a) $-175°C$ (b) 1.00 L
5. (a) 5.78×10^3 mol (b) 185 kg
7. 3.36×10^5 Pa
9. 0.159 L
11. 503°C
13. 2.28×10^4 Pa
15. 18 cm³; 56 cm³
17. no; no
19. 3.35×10^{25} molecules
21. (a) could be true (b) could be true (c) not true (d) must be true (e) could be true
23. (a) 4.84×10^2 m/s (b) 6.21×10^{-21} J
25. 6.1×10^{-6} m
27. (a) 1.90 km/s (b) no (c) O_2: 0.477 km/s; N_2: 0.510 km/s (d) some molecules move faster than v_{rms}
29. (a) 22.4 L (b) 0.243 L
31. (a) 10.5 breaths/min (b) 2.62×10^{21} molecules
33. (a) 49.6°C (b) 1110 J
35. (a) 4.09 C°
37. (b) 0
39. (b) 1.33×10^3 J
41. (a) 1.2×10^3 J (b) negative of work done in (a) (c) 600 J
43. 327 J
45. (a) -1.15×10^5 J (b) 2.55×10^5 J; heat flows out of the gas

47. (a) 45.0 J (b) liberates 65.0 J (c) *ad*: 23.0 J *db*: 22.0 J
49. (a) -4510 J (b) 4510 J out of gas
51. (a) 25.0 K (b) 17.9 K (c) a
53. (a) 0.125 L (b) 57.0 J done on gas (c) decreased (d) left the gas
55. (a) same (b) absorbs 4000 J (c) absorbs 8000 J
57. (b) 208 J (c) on the piston (d) 712 J (e) 920 J (f) 208 J
59. (a) $T_a = 665$ K; $T_b = 2660$ K; $T_c = 887$ K; $T_d = 222$ K (b) (i) 6.39×10^4 J (ii) 4.05×10^4 J (iii) 2.13×10^4 J (iv) 1.01×10^4 J (c) (i) enters (ii) leaves (iii) leaves (iv) enters
61. (a) 747 J (b) 1.30
63. (a) 47.4°C (b) 345 J
65. 2.20×10^6 molecules
67. (a) 1.18×10^4 Pa (b) 0.5667
69. 1.92 atm
71. (a) 1.2×10^4 m/s (b) 6.68×10^{-27} kg
73. (a) $Q = 300$ J; $\Delta U = 0$ (b) $Q = 0$; $\Delta U = -300$ J (c) $Q = 750$ J; $\Delta U = 450$ J
75. (a) 4.65×10^{-26} kg (b) 6.11×10^{-21} J (c) 2.04×10^{24} molecules (d) 1.25×10^4 J
77. 9.6 cm
79. (a) 0.80 L (b) $T_a = 305$ K; $T_b = T_c = 1220$ K (c) *ab*: 76 J into gas; *ca*: 107 J out of gas; *bc*: 56 J into gas (d) *ab*: $\Delta U = 76$ J; *bc*: $\Delta U = 0$; *ca*: $\Delta U = -76$ J
81. (a) 8.00×10^4 Pa (b) 1.45 g
83. 4.18×10^5 J
85. (a) 1172 K (b) 1.22×10^4 J (c) 4.26×10^4 J (d) 4.56×10^4 J

Passage Problems

87. E
89. A

The Second Law of
Thermodynamics

The Second Law of Thermodynamics

Shutterstock

When you put 0.1 kg of boiling water and 0.1 kg of ice in an insulated cup, you end up with 0.2 kg of water at about 10°C. That's not surprising. But you'd be very surprised if you came back later and found that the water had turned back to 0.1 kg of ice and 0.1 kg of boiling water. That wouldn't violate the first law of thermodynamics; energy would be conserved. But it doesn't happen in nature. Why not? Why does a power plant convert less than half of the heat from burning coal into electrical energy, discarding the remainder of the heat? Why does heat always flow spontaneously from hotter places to cooler places, never the reverse? When you drop ink into water, it mixes spontaneously, coloring the water, but it never spontaneously unmixes. Why not? What do all these things have in common?

A study of inherently one-way processes, such as the flow of heat from hotter to colder regions and the conversion of work into heat by friction, leads to the *second law of thermodynamics*. This law places fundamental limitations on the efficiency of an engine or a power plant and on the minimum energy input needed to operate a refrigerator. So the second law is directly relevant to many important practical problems. We can also state the second law in terms of the concept of *entropy,* a quantitative measure of the degree of disorder, or randomness, of a system.

In this chapter we'll encounter the concept of *entropy,* which represents the fact that order tends to disintegrate spontaneously into disorder. To fend off entropy, our bodies require a constant input of energy—which we take in the form of food.

1 Directions of Thermodynamic Processes

Heat flows spontaneously from a hotter object to a cooler object, never the reverse. Spontaneous heat flow from a cool object to a hot object would not violate the first law, but it doesn't happen in nature. Or suppose all the air in a box could rush to one side, leaving vacuum in the other side, the reverse of free expansion. This phenomenon doesn't occur in nature either, although the first law doesn't forbid it. It's easy to convert mechanical energy completely into heat; we do this every time we use a car's brakes to stop it. It is not so easy to convert heat into mechanical energy. Many would-be inventors have proposed cooling some air to extract heat from it and then converting that heat to mechanical energy to propel a car or an airplane. None has ever succeeded; no one has ever built a machine that converts heat *completely* into mechanical energy.

What all these examples have in common is a preferred *direction.* In each case, a process proceeds spontaneously in one direction, but not in the other. Still, despite the fact that there is a preferred direction for every natural process, we can think of a class of idealized processes that are *reversible.* We say that a system undergoes a **reversible process** if the system is always very close to being in thermodynamic equilibrium, within itself and with its surroundings. When this is the case, any change of state that takes place can be reversed (i.e., made to go the other way) by making only an infinitesimal change in the conditions of the system. For example, heat flow between two objects whose temperatures differ only infinitesimally can be reversed by making only a very small change in one temperature or the other. Thus, a gas expanding slowly and adiabatically can be compressed slowly and adiabatically by an infinitesimal increase in pressure.

Reversible processes are thus **equilibrium processes.** In contrast, heat flow with a finite (as opposed to an infinitesimal) temperature difference, the free expansion of a gas, and the conversion of work to heat by friction are all **irreversible processes:** No small change in conditions could make any of them go to the other way. They are also all *non-equilibrium* processes.

Reversible process

A reversible process is a transition from one state of a thermodynamic system to another, during which the system is always very close to a state of mechanical and thermal equilibrium (including uniform temperature and pressure).

A reversible process is an idealization that can never be precisely attained in the real world. But by making the temperature gradients and the pressure differences in the substance very small, we can keep the system very close to equilibrium states.

Finally, we'll find that there is a relation between the direction of a process and the *disorder,* or *randomness,* of the resulting state. For example, imagine a tedious sorting job, such as alphabetizing a thousand book titles written on file cards. Throw the alphabetized stack of cards into the air. Do they come down in alphabetical order? No, their tendency is to come down in a random, or disordered, state. In the free expansion of a gas, the air is more disordered after it has expanded into the entire container than when it was confined in one side, because the molecules are scattered over more space.

Similarly, macroscopic kinetic energy is energy associated with organized, coordinated motions of many molecules in a moving macroscopic object, but heat transfer involves changes in energy of random, disordered molecular motion. Therefore the conversion of mechanical energy into heat involves an increase in randomness, or disorder.

In the sections that follow, we'll introduce the second law of thermodynamics by considering two broad classes of devices: *heat engines,* which are partly successful in converting heat into work, and *refrigerators,* which are partly successful in transporting heat from cooler to hotter objects.

Shutterstock

▲ Application **Near-reversible control.**
The energy released by the sun comes from nuclear fusion reactions in its core. The rate of these reactions depends sensitively on temperature: A slight increase in temperature would cause a large increase in energy output. For life on earth, it is essential that the sun's brightness be steady. Luckily, the rate of fusion is controlled by a "thermostat." Energy escapes from the core rather slowly. Suppose the rate of fusion increased slightly. Then the extra heat output would cause the core to swell and thus to cool down, reducing the fusion rate. (The core consists of a plasma rather than a gas per se, but thermodynamically, it behaves like a gas.) Similarly, a drop in the rate of fusion would cause the core to shrink and heat up, increasing the rate again. Inferno though it is, the core is always close to equilibrium, so that a slight change in conditions can reverse the direction of a thermodynamic process.

Reversible versus irreversible processes

Which of the following mechanical processes are not reversible, in the sense that energy converted from one form to another cannot be completely converted from the second form back to the first form?

A. A ball is tossed upward, gaining height.
B. A moving cart is caught by a spring, stretching the spring.
C. A moving block slides to a stop because of friction.

SOLUTION Processes A and B involve only mechanical energy. In each, the system is given some kinetic energy, which is then transformed into potential energy. In A, the kinetic energy is recovered as the ball falls back to its original elevation; in B, the kinetic energy is recovered when the spring is permitted to relax back to its original length. If friction can be neglected, processes A and B are reversible. Process C is not reversible, because mechanical energy is converted to internal energy and there is no way to convert it back to mechanical energy without supplying some work from outside the system.

2 Heat Engines

ActivPhysics 8.12: Cyclic Process—Strategies
ActivPhysics 8.13: Cyclic Process—Problems

iStockphoto

▲ **Application Earth power.** One type of heat engine uses the earth itself as a source of heat. At the Svartsengi geothermal power plant in Iceland, the hot reservoir is a subsurface body of hot volcanic rock. (Iceland is one of the most active volcanic regions in the world.) The rock heats the local briny groundwater to temperatures of 240°C. Drill holes bring this water to the surface as high-pressure steam. The steam is used both to power turbines for electrical generation and to heat fresh water, which is distributed by the surrounding towns for home heating and hot water. The condensed steam is then released into the Blue Lagoon next to the power plant, where bathers can relax in 40°C waters even in the middle of an Icelandic winter. The power plant pumps about 150 MJ/s (150 MW) of heat from below ground and produces about 50 MW of electricity.

The essence of a technological society is its ability to use sources of mechanical energy other than muscle power. Sometimes mechanical energy is directly available; water power is an example. But most of our energy comes from the burning of fossil fuels (coal, oil, and gas) and from nuclear reactions. These processes supply energy that is transferred as *heat*. This transformation of energy is directly useful for heating buildings, for cooking, and for chemical and metallurgical processing. But to run an electrical generator or to operate a machine or propel a vehicle, we need *mechanical* energy.

Thus, it's important to know how to take heat from a source and convert as much of it as possible into mechanical energy or work. This is what happens in gasoline and Diesel engines in automobiles and trucks, jet engines in airplanes, steam turbines in electric power plants, and many other systems. A device that transforms heat partly into work or mechanical energy is called a **heat engine.** In a heat engine, a quantity of matter inside the engine undergoes addition and subtraction of heat, expansion and compression, and, sometimes, a phase change. We call this matter the **working substance** of the engine. In internal combustion engines (such as automobile engines), the working substance is a mixture of air and fuel; in a steam engine or steam turbine, it is water.

The simplest kind of engine to analyze is one in which the working substance undergoes a **cyclic process—a sequence of processes that eventually leaves the substance in the same state as that in which it started.** In a steam turbine, the water is recycled and used over and over. Internal combustion engines do not use the same air over and over, but we can still analyze them in terms of cyclic processes that approximate their actual operation.

All the heat engines just mentioned absorb heat from a source at a relatively high temperature, perform some mechanical work, and discard some heat at a lower temperature. As far as the engine is concerned, the discarded heat is wasted. In internal combustion engines, the waste heat is discarded in the hot exhaust gases and the cooling system; in a steam engine or steam turbine, the waste heat is the heat that must be taken out of the used steam in order to condense and recycle the water.

When a system is carried through a cyclic process, its initial and final internal energies are equal, so the change ΔU in internal energy of the system is zero. Thus, for any cyclic process, the first law of thermodynamics requires that

$$\Delta U = Q - W = 0 \quad \text{and} \quad Q = W.$$

That is, **in a cyclic process, the net heat Q flowing into the engine equals the net work W done by the engine.**

When we analyze heat engines, it helps to think of two objects with which the working substance of the engine can interact. One of these, called the *hot reservoir,* can give the working substance large amounts of heat at a constant temperature T_H without appreciably changing its own temperature. The other object, called the *cold reservoir,* can absorb large amounts of discarded heat from the engine at a constant lower temperature T_C. In a steam-turbine system, the flames and hot gases in the boiler are the hot reservoir, and the cold water and air used to condense and cool the used steam are the cold reservoir.

We denote the quantities of heat transferred from the hot and cold reservoirs as Q_H and Q_C, respectively. A quantity of heat Q is positive when heat is transferred *from* a reservoir *into* the working substance. When heat leaves the working substance, Q is negative. Thus, in a heat engine, Q_H is positive, but Q_C is negative, representing heat *leaving* the working substance. When the working substance does positive work on its surroundings, W is positive. These sign conventions are consistent with the rules that we stated; we'll continue to use those rules here. Sometimes it clarifies the relationships to state them in terms of the absolute values of the Q's and W's, because absolute values are always positive. When we do this, our notation will show it explicitly.

We can represent the energy transformations in a heat engine by the *energy-flow diagram* of Figure 1. The engine itself is represented by the circle. The amount of heat Q_H supplied to the engine by the hot reservoir is proportional to the width of the incoming "pipeline" at the top of the diagram. The width of the outgoing pipeline at the bottom is proportional to the magnitude $|Q_C|$ of the heat discarded. The branch line to the right represents that portion of the heat supplied that the engine converts to mechanical work W.

When an engine repeats the same cycle over and over, Q_H and Q_C represent the quantities of heat absorbed and rejected, respectively, by the engine *during one cycle;* Q_H is positive, Q_C negative. The *net* heat Q absorbed per cycle is

$$Q = Q_H + Q_C = |Q_H| - |Q_C|. \tag{1}$$

The useful output of the engine is the net work W done by the working substance; from the first law,

$$W = Q = Q_H + Q_C = |Q_H| - |Q_C|. \tag{2}$$

Ideally, we would like to convert *all* the heat Q_H into work; in that case, we would have $Q_H = W$ and $Q_C = 0$. Experience shows that this is impossible; there is always some heat wasted, and Q_C can never be zero. We define the **thermal efficiency** of an engine, denoted by e, as the quotient of W and Q_H:

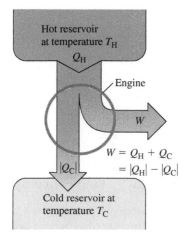

▲ **FIGURE 1** Schematic energy-flow diagram for a heat engine.

Thermal efficiency of a heat engine

The thermal efficiency of a heat engine is the useful work W done by the engine, divided by the heat input Q_H:

$$e = \frac{W}{Q_H}. \tag{3}$$

The thermal efficiency e represents the fraction of Q_H that *is* converted to work. To put it another way, e is what you get, divided by what you pay for. This is always less than 1, an all-too-familiar experience! In terms of the flow diagram of Figure 1, the most efficient engine is the one for which the branch pipeline representing the work output is as wide as possible and the exhaust pipeline representing the heat thrown away is as narrow as possible.

When we substitute the two expressions for W given by Equation 2 into Equation 3, we get the following equivalent expressions for e:

$$e = \frac{W}{Q_H} = 1 + \frac{Q_C}{Q_H} = 1 - \frac{|Q_C|}{|Q_H|}. \tag{4}$$

Note that e is a quotient of two energy quantities and thus is a pure number, without units. Of course, we must always express W, Q_H, and Q_C in the same units.

The following points may need additional emphasis:

1. Be very careful with the sign conventions for W and the various Q's. W is positive when the system expands and does work, negative when it is compressed. Each Q is positive if it represents heat entering the working substance of the engine or other system, negative when heat leaves the system. When in doubt, use the first law, if possible, to check consistency. When you know that a quantity is negative, such as Q_C in the preceding discussion, it sometimes helps to write it as $Q_C = -|Q_C|$.

2. As always, unit consistency is essential. Be careful not to mix thermal units such as calories or Btu with mechanical quantities such as joules. We suggest you convert everything to joules whenever possible. Efficiency ratings of air conditioners are usually expressed in a peculiar mix of British and SI units; be careful!

3. Some problems deal with power rather than energy quantities. Power is work done per unit time $(P = W/t)$, and the rate of heat transfer (heat current) H is heat transferred per unit time $(H = Q/t)$. Sometimes it helps to ask, "What is W or Q in 1 second (or 1 hour)?"

EXAMPLE 1   Fuel consumption in a truck

A gasoline engine in a large truck takes in 2500 J of heat and delivers 500 J of mechanical work per cycle. The heat is obtained by burning gasoline with heat of combustion $L_c = 5.0 \times 10^4$ J/g. **(a)** What is the thermal efficiency of this engine? **(b)** How much heat is discarded in each cycle? **(c)** How much gasoline is burned during each cycle? **(d)** If the engine goes through 100 cycles per second, what is its power output in watts? In horsepower? **(e)** How much gasoline is burned per second? Per hour?

SOLUTION

SET UP It's often useful to make an energy-flow sketch for heat-engine problems; Figure 2 shows what we draw. We are given that $Q_H = 2500$ J and $W = 500$ J.

SOLVE Part (a): The thermal efficiency is found from Equation 3:

$$e = \frac{W}{Q_H} = \frac{500\,\text{J}}{2500\,\text{J}} = 0.20 = 20\%.$$

Part (b): From Equation 2, the heat Q_C discarded per cycle is the difference between the heat absorbed (Q_H) and the work W done by the engine:

$$W = Q_H + Q_C,$$
$$500\,\text{J} = 2500\,\text{J} + Q_C,$$
$$Q_C = -2000\,\text{J}.$$

Thus, 2000 J of heat leaves the engine during each cycle.

Part (c): Let m be the mass of gasoline burned during each cycle; then Q_H is m times the heat of combustion: $Q_H = mL_c$. Thus,

$$m = Q_H/L_c = (2500\,\text{J})/(5.0 \times 10^4\,\text{J/g}) = 0.050\,\text{g}.$$

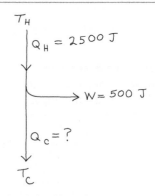

▲ FIGURE 2 Our sketch for this problem.

Part (d): The power P (rate of doing work) is the work per cycle multiplied by the number of cycles per second.

$$P = (500\,\text{J/cycle})(100\,\text{cycles/s}) = 50{,}000\,\text{W} = 50\,\text{kW}, \quad \text{or}$$
$$P = (50{,}000\,\text{W})(1\,\text{hp}/746\,\text{W}) = 67\,\text{hp}.$$

Part (e): The mass of gasoline burned per second is the mass burned per cycle multiplied by the number of cycles per second:

$$(0.050\,\text{g/cycle})(100\,\text{cycles/s}) = 5.0\,\text{g/s}.$$

Continued

The mass burned per hour is

$$(5.0 \text{ g/s})\left(\frac{3600 \text{ s}}{1 \text{ h}}\right) = 18{,}000 \text{ g/h} = 18 \text{ kg/h}.$$

REFLECT The efficiency from part (a) is a fairly typical figure for cars and trucks if W includes only the work actually delivered to the wheels. The density of gasoline is about 0.70 g/cm^3; the volume of fuel burned per hour is about $25{,}700 \text{ cm}^3$, 25.7 L, or 6.8 gallons of gasoline per hour. If the truck is traveling at 55 mi/h (88 km/h), that volume represents fuel consumption of about 8.1 miles per gallon (mpg) (3.4 km/L).

Each cylinder in the engine goes through one cycle for every two revolutions of the crankshaft. For a four-cylinder engine, 100 cycles per second corresponds to 50 crankshaft revolutions per second, or 3000 rev/min (typical for highway speeds).

Practice Problem: A gasoline engine with a thermal efficiency of 28% has a power output of 50 hp. How much heat must be supplied per second to the engine? *Answer:* $Q_{\text{H}} = 133 \text{ kJ}$.

3 Internal Combustion Engines

The gasoline engine, used in automobiles and many other types of machinery, is a familiar example of a heat engine. Figure 3 shows the sequence of processes. First, a mixture of air and gasoline vapor flows into a cylinder through an open intake valve while the piston descends, increasing the volume of the cylinder from a minimum of V (when the piston is all the way up) to a maximum of rV (when it is all the way down). The quantity r is called the **compression ratio;** for present-day automobile engines, it is typically about 8.

At the end of this *intake stroke,* the intake valve closes and the air–gasoline mixture is compressed, quickly and approximately adiabatically, to volume V during the *compression stroke.* The mixture is then ignited by the spark plug, and the heated gas expands, again approximately adiabatically, back to volume rV. As it does so, it pushes on the piston and does work on it; this is the *power stroke.* Finally, the exhaust valve opens and the combustion products are pushed out (during the *exhaust stroke*), leaving the cylinder ready for the next intake stroke.

The Otto Cycle

Figure 4 is a *pV* diagram showing an idealized model of the thermodynamic processes in a gasoline engine. This model is called the **Otto cycle.** We'll assume that the gasoline–air mixture behaves as an ideal gas. At point a, the mixture has entered the cylinder. The mixture is compressed adiabatically (line ab) and is then ignited. Heat Q_{H} (heat of combustion) is added to the system by the burning

Intake valve open   Exhaust valve closed   Both valves closed   Intake valve closed   Exhaust valve open

Spark plug fires

Cylinder — Piston — Crankshaft — Connecting rod

Intake stroke: Piston moves down, causing a partial vacuum in cylinder; gasoline–air mixture enters through intake valve.

Compression stroke: Intake valve closes; mixture is compressed as piston moves up.

Ignition: Spark plug ignites mixture.

Power stroke: Hot burned mixture expands, pushing piston down.

Exhaust stroke: Exhaust valve opens; piston moves up, expelling exhaust and leaving cylinder ready for next intake stroke.

▲ **FIGURE 3** Cycle of a four-stroke internal combustion engine.

Otto cycle

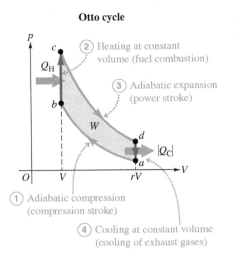

① Adiabatic compression (compression stroke)

② Heating at constant volume (fuel combustion)

③ Adiabatic expansion (power stroke)

④ Cooling at constant volume (cooling of exhaust gases)

▲ **FIGURE 4** The pV diagram for the Otto cycle, an idealized model of the thermodynamic processes that take place in a gasoline engine.

Diesel cycle

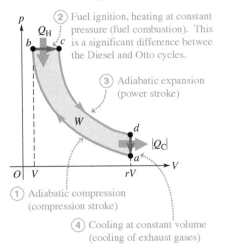

① Adiabatic compression (compression stroke)

② Fuel ignition, heating at constant pressure (fuel combustion). This is a significant difference betwee the Diesel and Otto cycles.

③ Adiabatic expansion (power stroke)

④ Cooling at constant volume (cooling of exhaust gases)

▲ **FIGURE 5** The pV diagram for the Diesel cycle.

gasoline (line bc), and the power stroke is the adiabatic expansion cd. The gas is cooled to the temperature of the outside air (da); during process (da), heat Q_C is released. In practice, this same air does not enter the engine again, but since an equivalent amount does enter, we may consider the process to be cyclic.

It's possible, although a bit complicated, to calculate the efficiency e of this idealized cycle; we'll omit the details. The result is surprisingly simple; it depends only on the compression ratio r and the ratio $\gamma = C_p/C_V$ of the molar heat capacities at constant volume and at constant pressure. It turns out that the efficiency for the idealized Otto cycle is given by

$$e = 1 - \frac{1}{r^{\gamma-1}}. \tag{5}$$

The quantities r and γ are pure numbers, and they are always greater than 1. As we would expect, the thermal efficiency given by Equation 5 is always less than 1, even for this idealized model. With $r = 8$ and $\gamma = 1.4$ (the value for air), the theoretical efficiency is $e = 0.56$, or 56%. The efficiency can be increased by increasing r. However, doing this also increases the temperature reached by the air–fuel mixture at the end of the adiabatic compression. If the temperature is too high, the mixture explodes spontaneously during compression instead of burning evenly after the spark plug ignites it. This is called *pre-ignition*, or *detonation;* it causes a knocking sound and can damage the engine. The octane rating of a gasoline is a measure of its antiknock qualities. The maximum practical compression ratio for high-octane, or "premium," gasoline is about 10. Higher ratios can be used with more exotic fuels.

The Otto cycle is a highly idealized model. It assumes that the air–fuel mixture behaves as an ideal gas; it neglects friction, turbulence, loss of heat to cylinder walls, incomplete combustion, and many other effects that combine to reduce the efficiency of a real engine. Thermal efficiencies of real gasoline engines are typically around 20%.

The Diesel Cycle

The Diesel engine is similar in operation to the gasoline engine. The most important difference is that, at the beginning of the compression stroke, the cylinder contains air, but no fuel. A little before the beginning of the power stroke, the injectors start to inject fuel directly into the cylinder, just fast enough to keep the pressure approximately constant during the first part of the power stroke. Because of the high temperature developed during the adiabatic compression, the fuel ignites spontaneously as it is injected; no spark plugs are needed.

The idealized **Diesel cycle** is shown in the pV diagram of Figure 5. Starting at point a, air is compressed adiabatically to point b, heated (by the heat of combustion) at constant pressure to point c, expanded adiabatically to point d, and cooled at constant volume to point a. Because there is no fuel in the cylinder

Mike Kepka/Corbis

◄ **Application Peanut power.** As we've learned, the key feature of the Diesel engine is that the fuel is ignited, not by a spark, but by the heat from adiabatic compression during the compression stroke. Thus, there's no real connection between Diesel engines and "diesel fuel." In fact, the original Diesel engine, invented in 1892 by Rudolph Diesel, ran on peanut oil! Diesel saw this property as a key feature of his engine: In addition to being far more efficient than steam engines, it could run on fuel produced by local agriculture, which was independent of the fossil fuel monopolies of the day. In the 1920s, the engine was modified to run on "diesel" fossil fuel, which was inexpensive. Now, however, there is renewed interest in "bio-diesel"—basically, vegetable oil. This fuel can be produced anywhere plants grow and contributes less net carbon dioxide to the atmosphere than burning fossil fuel because carbon dioxide is consumed by the plants in the creation of the oils. Unfortunately, substantial amounts of carbon dioxide can be emitted in the extraction of the oils and in the manufacture of nitrogen fertilizers for the plants used to create biodiesel. The use of filtered, cast-off cooking oil is a better solution that makes use of wasted oil and produces no sulphur emissions (unlike diesel and biodiesel fuel).

during most of the compression stroke, pre-ignition cannot occur, and the compression ratio r can be much higher than for a gasoline engine. This feature improves the efficiency of the engine and ensures reliable ignition when the fuel is injected (because of the high temperature reached during the adiabatic compression). Values of r of 15 to 20 are typical; with these values and $\gamma = 1.4$, the theoretical efficiency of the idealized Diesel cycle is about 0.65 to 0.70. As with the Otto cycle, the efficiency of any actual engine is substantially less than this. Diesel engines are usually more efficient than gasoline engines. They are also heavier (per unit power output) and often harder to start.

4 Refrigerators

We can think of a **refrigerator** as a heat engine operating in reverse. A heat engine takes heat from a hot place and gives off heat to a colder place. A refrigerator does the opposite; it takes heat from a cold place (the inside of the refrigerator) and gives it off to a warmer place (usually the air in the room where the refrigerator is located). A heat engine has a net *output* of mechanical work; the refrigerator requires a net *input* of mechanical work, as shown in Figure 6, an energy-flow diagram for a refrigerator. With the symbols we used in Section 2, Q_C is positive for a refrigerator, but both W and Q_H are negative, so $|W| = -W$ and $|Q_H| = -Q_H$.

For a cyclic process, the first law gives $\Delta U = 0$ and

$$Q_H + Q_C - W = 0, \quad \text{or} \quad -Q_H = Q_C - W.$$

Or, because both Q_H and W are negative,

$$|Q_H| = |Q_C| + |W|. \tag{6}$$

Thus, as the diagram shows, the heat $|Q_H|$ leaving the working substance and given to the hot reservoir is always *greater* than the heat Q_C taken from the cold reservoir. Note that the absolute-value relation given by Equation 6 is valid for both heat engines and refrigerators.

From an economic point of view, the best refrigeration cycle is one that removes the greatest amount of heat Q_C from the refrigerator for the least expenditure of mechanical work W. The relevant ratio is therefore $Q_C/|W|$. We call this the **performance coefficient,** denoted by K. Also, from Equation 6, we have $|W| = |Q_H| - |Q_C|$, so K can be expressed as follows:

Performance coefficient of a refrigerator

$$K = \frac{Q_C}{|W|} = \frac{|Q_C|}{|Q_H| - |Q_C|}. \tag{7}$$

As always, we measure Q_H, Q_C and W all in the same energy units; K is then a dimensionless number.

The principles of the common refrigeration cycle are shown schematically in Figure 7. The fluid "circuit" contains a refrigerant (the working substance). The left side of the circuit (including the cooling coils inside the refrigerator) is at low temperature and low pressure; the right side (including the condenser coils outside the refrigerator) is at high temperature and high pressure. Ordinarily, both sides contain liquid and vapor in phase equilibrium.

The compressor takes in fluid, compresses it adiabatically, and delivers it to the condenser coil at high pressure. The temperature of the fluid is then higher than that of the air surrounding the condenser, so the refrigerant gives off heat $|Q_H|$ and partially condenses to liquid. The fluid then expands adiabatically, at a rate controlled by the expansion valve, into the evaporator. As it does so, it cools

Lambert/Hulton Archive/Getty Images

▲ **Application** **Cooling power.** The modern refrigerator is based on the physical principle that, as a gas expands or a liquid evaporates, it absorbs heat from its surroundings. The ancient Egyptians used this principle to make ice by setting water out in clay pots on cold, windy nights and keeping the pots wet on the outside. Mechanical refrigerators from the early 20th century, like the one shown here, used alternate compression and expansion of a volatile gas, such as ether or ammonia, to cool a closed container. As the gas is compressed on the outside of the container, it heats up, and this heat is released into the room. The compressed gas is allowed to expand in cooling coils inside the container, where it absorbs heat from the container, lowering the container's temperature. The net effect is that heat is transferred from a cold area to a warm area, but not without an energy cost: the energy required to compress the gas in each cycle.

▲ **FIGURE 6** Schematic energy-flow diagram for a refrigerator.

(a)

(b)

▲ **FIGURE 7** Principle of the mechanical refrigeration cycle.

considerably, enough so that the fluid in the evaporator coil is colder than its surroundings. The fluid absorbs heat Q_C from its surroundings, cooling them while partially vaporizing. It then enters the compressor to begin another cycle. The compressor, usually driven by an electric motor, requires energy input and does work $|W|$ *on* the working substance during each cycle.

An air conditioner operates on exactly the same principle. In this case, the refrigerator box becomes a room or an entire building. The evaporator coils are inside, the condenser is outside, and fans circulate air through these components (Figure 8). In large installations, the condenser coils are often cooled by water. For air conditioners, the quantities of greatest practical importance are the *rate* of heat removal (the heat current H from the region being cooled) and the *power* input $P = W/t$ to the compressor. If heat Q_C is removed in time t, then $H = Q_C/t$. We can then express the performance coefficient as

$$K = \frac{Q_C}{|W|} = \frac{Ht}{Pt} = \frac{H}{P}.$$

▲ **FIGURE 8** An air conditioner works on the same principle as a refrigerator.

Typical room air conditioners have heat removal rates H of 5000 to 10,000 Btu/h, or about 1500 to 3000 W, and require a power input of about 500 to 1000 W. Performance coefficients are typically about 3, with somewhat larger values for larger-capacity units. Unfortunately, K is usually expressed commercially in mixed units, with H in Btu per hour and P in watts. In these units, H/P is called the **energy efficiency rating (EER).** Because $1\text{ W} = 3.413\text{ Btu/h}$, the EER is numerically 3.413 times as large as the dimensionless K. Room air conditioners typically have an EER of about 10. The units, customarily omitted, are $(\text{Btu/h})/\text{W}$.

A variation on this theme is the **heat pump,** used to heat buildings by cooling the outside. It functions like a refrigerator turned inside out. The evaporator coils are outside, where they take heat from cold air or water, and the condenser coils are inside, where they give off heat to the inside region. With proper design, the heat $|Q_H|$ delivered to the inside during each cycle can be considerably greater than the work $|W|$ required to get it there. Heat pumps are typically designed so that they can be run as air conditioners in the summer (by reversing the pumps so that the condenser becomes the evaporator and vice versa). In this mode, a heat pump has no extra efficiency over a standard air conditioner.

For example, suppose you have an air conditioner with $K = 3$. In normal use, the unit removes 300 J of heat from the inside of the house while expending 100 J of electrical energy and discarding 400 J to the outside. But if you mount the air conditioner backwards, so that 400 J goes *into* the house and 300 J is taken from the outside environment, you are getting a total of 400 J of heat into the house while paying the electric company for only 100 J of electrical energy.

Nevertheless, some work is *always* needed to transfer heat from a colder to a hotter object. Heat flows spontaneously from hotter to colder, and to reverse this flow requires the addition of work from the outside. Experience shows that it is impossible to make a refrigerator that transports heat from a cold object to a hotter object without the addition of work. If no work were needed, the performance coefficient would be infinite. We call such a device a *workless refrigerator;* it is a mythical beast, like the unicorn, the frictionless plane, and the free lunch.

Conceptual Analysis 2

Heating up or cooling down?

One method sometimes used in an attempt to cool a kitchen on a hot day is to leave the refrigerator door open. Does this actually cool the kitchen?

A. Yes, because refrigerators function on the same principle as air conditioners.
B. No, it actually warms the kitchen.
C. There is no net effect. The heat that is absorbed in the front of the refrigerator is offset by heat dissipated from the back of the refrigerator.

SOLUTION It is true that refrigerators and air conditioners function in the same way, but air conditioners move heat from the inside to the outside of the building, whereas refrigerators move heat from the refrigerator box to the rest of the kitchen. We've learned that, to move heat from the refrigerator box to the warmer kitchen, the refrigerator must convert work to heat. This additional heat is also released to the kitchen. Thus, the refrigerator *always* adds net heat to the kitchen, whether its door is open or shut. Opening the door makes the refrigerator work harder and thus heats the kitchen *more* than if you kept the door shut. Answer B is correct.

Conceptual Analysis 3

Efficient heating

Which of the following key advantages does a heat pump have over an ordinary electric (hot-wire) heater for heating a house?

A. The heat pump can be used as an air conditioner in the summer.
B. The heat pump pulls in warm air from the outside to add to the heat it produces.
C. The heat pump uses work to bring additional heat from the outside to the inside of the house.

SOLUTION As we've discussed, a heat pump is basically an air conditioner installed backward; indeed, most heat pumps are designed to switch direction and work as air conditioners when needed. Thus, A is correct. C is also correct; a standard hot-wire heater converts electrical energy to heat on a joule-for-joule basis, but a heat pump uses work (obtained from electric energy) to move heat from the outside to the inside *and also* converts this work to additional heat released inside the house. B is not correct: A heat pump moves heat, not hot air, from the outside to the inside.

5 The Second Law of Thermodynamics

Experimental evidence strongly suggests that it is impossible to build a heat engine that converts heat completely to work—that is, an engine with 100% thermal efficiency. This impossibility is the basis of one form of the **second law of thermodynamics:**

Second law of thermodynamics (engine statement)

It is impossible for any system to undergo a process in which it absorbs heat from a reservoir at a single temperature and converts the heat completely into mechanical work with the system ending in the same state in which it began.

We'll call this the "engine" statement of the second law.

The basis of the second law of thermodynamics lies in the difference between the nature of internal energy and that of macroscopic mechanical energy. In a moving object, the molecules have random motion, but superimposed on this is a coordinated motion of every molecule in the direction of the object's velocity. The kinetic energy associated with this *coordinated* macroscopic motion is what we call the kinetic energy of the moving object. The kinetic and potential energies associated with the *random* motion of the object's molecules constitute the internal energy. When a moving object comes to rest as result of friction or an inelastic collision, the organized part of the motion is converted to random motion. **Since we cannot control the motions of individual molecules, we cannot convert this random motion completely back to organized motion.** We can convert *part* of it, and that is what a heat engine does.

If the second law were *not* true, we could power an automobile or run a power plant simply by cooling the surrounding air and thus taking energy from it. Neither of these impossible scenarios violates the *first* law of thermodynamics. The second law is not a deduction from the first, but stands by itself as a separate law of nature. The first law denies the possibility of creating or destroying energy; the second law limits the *availability* of energy and the ways in which it can be used and converted.

Our analysis of refrigerators in Section 4 forms the basis for an alternative statement of the second law of thermodynamics. Heat flows spontaneously from hotter to colder objects, never the reverse. A refrigerator does take heat from a colder to a hotter object, but its operation depends on an input of mechanical energy or work. Generalizing this observation, we state the following principle:

Second law of thermodynamics (refrigerator statement)

It is impossible for any process to have as its sole result the transfer of heat from a cooler to a hotter object.

We'll call this the "refrigerator" statement of the second law. It may not seem to be very closely related to the "engine" statement. In fact, though, the two statements are completely equivalent. For example, if we could build a workless refrigerator, violating the "refrigerator" statement of the second law, we could use it in conjunction with a heat engine to pump the heat rejected by the engine back into the hot reservoir, to be reused. This composite machine (Figure 9a) would violate the "engine" statement of the second law because its net effect would be to take a net quantity of heat $Q_H - |Q_C|$ from the hot reservoir and convert it completely to work W.

Alternatively, if we could make an engine with 100% thermal efficiency, in violation of the first statement, we could run it by taking heat from the hot reservoir. Then we could use the work output to drive a refrigerator that pumps heat

If a workless refrigerator were possible, it could be used in conjunction with an ordinary heat engine to form a 100%-efficient engine, converting heat $Q_H - |Q_C|$ completely to work.

(a) The "engine" statement of the second law

If a 100%-efficient engine were possible, it could be used in conjunction with an ordinary refrigerator to form a workless refrigerator, transferring heat Q_C from the cold to the hot reservoir with no net input of work.

(b) The "refrigerator" statement of the second law

▲ **FIGURE 9** Energy-flow diagrams for equivalent forms of the second law. Since either of these machines is impossible, the other must be also.

from the cold reservoir to the hot (Figure 9b). This composite device would violate the "refrigerator" statement because its net effect would be to take heat Q_C from the cold reservoir and deliver it to the hot reservoir without requiring any input of work. Thus, any device that violates one form of the second law can also be used to make a device that violates the other form. In other words, if violations of the first form are impossible, so are violations of the second!

The conversion of work to heat, as in friction or viscous fluid flow, and heat flow from hot to cold across a finite temperature gradient are *irreversible* processes. The "engine" and "refrigerator" statements of the second law state that these processes can be only partially reversed. Here are two other examples: Gases always seep through an opening spontaneously from a region of high pressure to a region of low pressure; and gases left by themselves always tend to mix, never to unmix. Figure 10 shows two liquids mixing spontaneously.

The second law of thermodynamics is an expression of the inherent one-way aspect of these and many other irreversible processes. Energy conversion is an essential aspect of all plant and animal life and of many mechanical devices, so the second law of thermodynamics is of the utmost fundamental importance in the world we live in.

Shutterstock

▲ **FIGURE 10** These liquids mix spontaneously—and they never spontaneously unmix.

6 The Carnot Engine: The Most Efficient Heat Engine

According to the second law, no heat engine can have 100% efficiency. But how great an efficiency *can* an engine have, given two heat reservoirs at temperatures T_H and T_C? This question was answered in 1824 by the French engineer Sadi Carnot (1796–1832), who developed a hypothetical, idealized heat engine that has the *maximum possible* efficiency consistent with the second law. In his honor, the cycle of this engine is called the **Carnot cycle.**

To understand the rationale of the Carnot cycle, we return to a recurrent theme in this chapter: *reversibility* and its relation to directions of thermodynamic processes. The conversion of work to heat is an irreversible process; the purpose of a heat engine is a *partial* reversal of this process: the conversion of heat to work with as great efficiency as possible. For maximum heat-engine efficiency, therefore, *we must avoid all irreversible processes.* This requirement turns out to be enough to determine the basic sequence of steps in the Carnot cycle, as we'll show next.

Heat flow through a finite temperature drop is an irreversible process. Therefore, during heat transfer in the Carnot cycle, there must be *no* finite temperature differences. When the engine takes heat from the hot reservoir at temperature T_H, the working substance of the engine must also be at T_H; otherwise, irreversible heat flow would occur. Similarly, when the engine discards heat to the cold reservoir at T_C, the engine itself must be at T_C. That is, every process that involves heat transfer must be *isothermal* at either T_H or T_C.

Conversely, in any process in which the temperature of the working substance of the engine is intermediate between T_H and T_C, there must be *no* heat transfer between the engine and either reservoir, because such heat transfer cannot be reversible. Therefore, any process in which the temperature T of the working substance changes must be adiabatic. The bottom line is that *every process* in our idealized cycle must be either *isothermal* or *adiabatic*. In addition, thermal and mechanical equilibrium must be maintained at all times, so that each process is completely reversible.

MasteringPHYSICS

ActivPhysics 8.14: Carnot Cycle

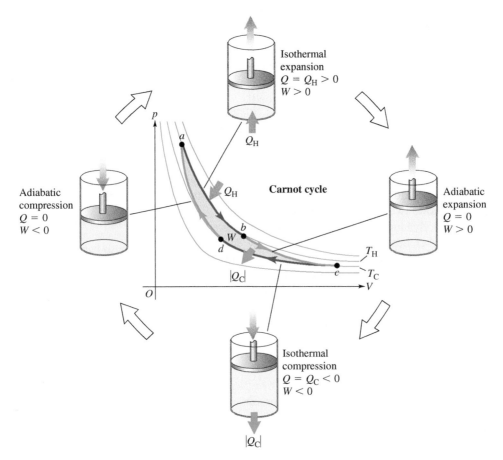

▲ FIGURE 11 The Carnot cycle for an ideal gas.

The Carnot Cycle

The Carnot cycle consists of two isothermal and two adiabatic processes. Figure 11 shows a Carnot cycle using an ideal gas in a cylinder with a piston as its working substance. It consists of the following steps:

1. The gas expands isothermally at temperature T_H, absorbing heat Q_H (ab).
2. It expands adiabatically until its temperature drops to T_C (bc).
3. It is compressed isothermally at T_C, rejecting heat $|Q_C|$ (cd).
4. It is compressed adiabatically back to its initial state at temperature T_H (da).

When the working substance in a Carnot engine is an ideal gas, it's a straightforward calculation to find the heat and work for each step. Then from these quantities we can obtain the thermal efficiency, using the definition of e (Equation 4). The details of the calculations are a little involved, so we'll simply state the results here, without any derivation.

The ratio Q_C/Q_H of the two quantities of heat turns out to be equal (apart from a negative sign) to the ratio of the absolute temperatures of the reservoirs:

$$\frac{Q_C}{Q_H} = -\frac{T_C}{T_H}. \tag{8}$$

Combining this equation with the general expression for the thermal efficiency of *any* heat engine, $e = 1 + Q_C/Q_H$ (Equation 4), we find that the thermal efficiency of the Carnot engine depends only on the temperatures T_H and T_C:

Thermal efficiency of Carnot engine

$$e_{\text{Carnot}} = 1 - \frac{T_C}{T_H} = \frac{T_H - T_C}{T_H}. \tag{9}$$

This surprisingly simple result says that the thermal efficiency of the Carnot engine depends only on the ratio T_C/T_H of the absolute temperatures of the two heat reservoirs. Note that the temperatures must be *absolute* (Kelvin). The efficiency is large when the temperature *difference* is large, and it is very small when the temperatures are nearly equal. The efficiency can never be exactly 1 unless $T_C = 0$. As we shall see later, this, too, is impossible.

EXAMPLE 2 **A Carnot engine**

A Carnot engine takes 2000 J of heat from a reservoir at 500 K, does some work, and discards some heat to a reservoir at 350 K. How much work does it do, how much heat is discarded, and what is its efficiency?

SOLUTION

SET UP AND SOLVE From Equation 8, the heat Q_C discarded by the engine is

$$Q_C = -Q_H \frac{T_C}{T_H} = -(2000 \text{ J}) \frac{350 \text{ K}}{500 \text{ K}}$$
$$= -1400 \text{ J}.$$

Then, from the first law, the work W done by the engine is

$$W = Q_H + Q_C = 2000 \text{ J} + (-1400 \text{ J})$$
$$= 600 \text{ J}.$$

From Equation 9, the thermal efficiency is

$$e_{\text{Carnot}} = 1 - \frac{T_C}{T_H} = 1 - \frac{350 \text{ K}}{500 \text{ K}} = 0.30 = 30\%.$$

Alternatively, from the basic definition of thermal efficiency,

$$e = \frac{W}{Q_H} = \frac{600 \text{ J}}{2000 \text{ J}} = 0.30 = 30\%.$$

REFLECT The efficiency of any engine is always less than 1. For the Carnot engine, the greater the ratio of T_H to T_C, the greater is the efficiency.

Practice Problem: What temperature T_H would the high-temperature reservoir need to have in order to increase the efficiency to $e = 0.50$? *Answer: 700 K.*

Carnot Refrigerator

Because each step in the Carnot cycle is reversible, the *entire cycle* may be reversed, converting the engine into a refrigerator. The performance coefficient of the Carnot refrigerator is obtained by combining the general definition of K, Equation 7, with Equation 8 for the Carnot cycle. We first rewrite Equation 7 as

$$K = \frac{|Q_C|}{|Q_H| - |Q_C|} = \frac{|Q_C|/|Q_H|}{1 - |Q_C|/|Q_H|}.$$

From Equation 8, $|Q_C|/|Q_H| = T_C/T_H$. Substituting this into the previous equation, we find that

$$K_{\text{Carnot}} = \frac{T_C}{T_H - T_C}. \tag{10}$$

When the temperature difference $T_H - T_C$ is small, K is much larger than 1; in this case, a lot of heat can be "pumped" from the lower to the higher temperature with only a little expenditure of work. But the greater the temperature difference, the smaller K is and the more work is required to transfer a given quantity of heat.

EXAMPLE 3 **A Carnot refrigerator**

If the Carnot engine described in Example 2 is run backwards as a refrigerator, what is its performance coefficient?

Continued

SOLUTION

SET UP AND SOLVE We use the values from Example 2, with all the signs reversed because the cycle is run backwards:

$$Q_C = +1400 \text{ J}, \quad Q_H = -2000 \text{ J}, \quad W = -600 \text{ J}.$$

From Equation 7, the performance coefficient K is

$$K = \frac{Q_C}{|W|} = \frac{1400 \text{ J}}{600 \text{ J}} = 2.33.$$

Because the cycle is a Carnot cycle, we may also use Equation 10:

$$K = \frac{T_C}{T_H - T_C} = \frac{350 \text{ K}}{500 \text{ K} - 350 \text{ K}} = 2.33.$$

REFLECT For a Carnot cycle, e and K depend only on the temperatures, as shown by Equations 9 and 10, and we don't need to calculate Q and W. For cycles containing irreversible processes, however, these equations are not valid, and more detailed calculations are necessary.

Practice Problem: Suppose you want to increase the performance coefficient K in Example 3. Would it be better to decrease T_H by 50 K or increase T_C by 50 K? *Answer:* Increase T_C.

▲ **BIO Application Is photosynthesis efficient?** In photosynthesis, the chloroplasts of plants and algae are the subcellular organelles that capture bits of energy emitted by the sun and convert it to useful cellular energy in the form of ATP. If the sun and the plant are viewed as thermodynamic systems, the chloroplasts can be considered machines that work between two reservoirs of different temperatures to extract useful energy. We know that the efficiency of an engine depends on the temperature difference between the reservoirs, and in this case, the difference is very large indeed. The temperature of the Sun is 5600 K whereas the temperature of a plant might be 293 K. Thus the laws of thermodynamics tell us that photosynthesis is a perfectly practical process.

The Carnot Cycle and the Second Law

We can prove that **no engine can be more efficient than a Carnot engine operating between the same two temperatures.** The key to the proof is the preceding observation that, since each step in the Carnot cycle is reversible, the *entire cycle* may be reversed. Run backward, the engine becomes a refrigerator. Suppose we have a super-efficient engine that is more efficient than a Carnot engine (Figure 12). The Carnot engine, run backward as a refrigerator with negative work $-W$, takes in heat Q_C from the cold reservoir and expels heat $|Q_H|$ to the hot reservoir. The super-efficient engine expels heat $|Q_C|$, but to do this, it takes in a greater amount of heat $Q_H + Q$. Its work output is then $W + Q$, and the net effect of the two machines together is to take a quantity of heat Q and convert it completely into work. Doing this, however, violates the "engine" statement of the second law. We could construct a similar argument that a super-efficient engine could be used to violate the "refrigerator" statement of the second law. (Note that we don't have to assume that the super-efficient engine is reversible.)

Thus, the statement that no engine can be more efficient than a Carnot engine is yet another equivalent statement of the second law of thermodynamics. It also follows directly that **all Carnot engines operating between the same two temperatures have the same efficiency, irrespective of the nature of the working substance.** Although we discussed Equation 9 in the context of a Carnot engine using an ideal gas as its working substance, that equation is in fact valid for *any* Carnot engine, no matter what its working substance.

Equation 9 also shows how to maximize the efficiency of a real engine, such as a steam turbine in an electric generating plant. The intake temperature T_H must be made as high as possible and the exhaust temperature T_C as low as possi-

If a superefficient engine were possible, it could be used in conjunction with a Carnot refrigerator to convert the heat Q completely to work, with no net transfer to the cold reservoir.

▲ **FIGURE 12** If there were a more efficient engine than a Carnot engine, it could be used in conjunction with a Carnot refrigerator to construct the impossible device shown here.

ble. The exhaust temperature can't be lower than the lowest temperature available for cooling the exhaust—usually the temperature of the air, or perhaps of river or lake water if this is available at the plant. The vapor pressures of all liquids increase rapidly with increasing temperature, so T_H is limited by the mechanical strength of the boiler. At 540°C (1000°F), the vapor pressure of water is about 125×10^5 Pa (120 atm, or 1800 psi), and this is about the maximum practical pressure in large present-day steam boilers.

The unavoidable exhaust heat loss in electric power plants creates a serious environmental problem. When a lake or river is used for cooling, the temperature of the body of water may be raised several degrees. Such a temperature change has a severely disruptive effect on the overall ecological balance, since relatively small temperature changes can have significant effects on metabolic rates in plants and animals. Because **thermal pollution,** as this effect is called, is an inevitable consequence of the second law of thermodynamics, careful planning is essential to minimize the ecological impact of new power plants.

7 Entropy

The second law of thermodynamics, as we have stated it, is a rather strange beast, compared with many familiar physical laws. It is not an equation or a quantitative relationship, but rather a statement of *impossibility*. However, the second law *can* be stated as a quantitative relation by use of the concept of *entropy*, the subject of this section.

We've talked about several processes that proceed naturally in the direction of increasing disorder. Irreversible heat flow increases disorder because the molecules are initially sorted into hotter and cooler regions, and this sorting is lost when the system comes to thermal equilibrium. Adding heat to an object increases its disorder because it increases average molecular speeds and therefore the randomness of molecular motion. Free expansion of a gas increases its disorder because the molecules have greater randomness of *position* after the expansion than before. **Entropy** provides a *quantitative* measure of disorder.

Entropy and Disorder

To introduce the concept of entropy, let's consider an infinitesimal isothermal expansion of an ideal gas. We add heat Q and let the gas expand just enough so that the temperature remains constant. Because the internal energy of an ideal gas depends only on its temperature, the internal energy is also constant. Thus, from the first law, the work W done by the gas is equal to the heat Q added. That is,

$$Q = W = p\,\Delta V = \frac{nRT}{V}\Delta V \quad \text{and} \quad \frac{Q}{T} = nR\frac{\Delta V}{V}.$$

The gas is in a more disordered state after the expansion than before because the molecules are moving in a larger volume and have more randomness of position. The fractional change in volume $\Delta V/V$ is a measure of the increase in disorder, and it is proportional to the quantity Q/T. We introduce the symbol S for the entropy of the system in a particular state, and we *define* the entropy change $\Delta S = S_2 - S_1$ during a reversible isothermal process at absolute temperature T as follows:

Definition of entropy change in a reversible isothermal process
In a reversible isothermal process from state 1 to state 2, the change in entropy $\Delta S = S_2 - S_1$ of a system equals the heat Q added to or removed from the system, divided by the absolute temperature T:

$$\Delta S = S_2 - S_1 = \frac{Q}{T}. \tag{11}$$

Unit: Energy divided by temperature: J/K.

Conceptual Analysis 4

Increasing entropy

An amount of heat Q is added to each of two quantities of an ideal gas. Gas A is at absolute temperature T, and gas B is at absolute temperature $2T$. Each gas is allowed to expand isothermally. Which gas undergoes the greater entropy change?

A. gas A.
B. gas B.
C. Both have the same entropy change.

SOLUTION For each gas, the change in entropy for the isothermal process is the amount of heat added, divided by the absolute temperature. The absolute temperature for gas B is twice as great as that for gas A, and the two amounts of heat are the same. So the entropy change of B is half that of A. The correct answer is A.

EXAMPLE 4 **Entropy change in melting ice**

Compute the change in entropy of 1.00 kilogram of ice at 0°C when it is melted and converted to water at 0°C.

SOLUTION

SET UP The temperature T is constant at 273 K, and the heat of fusion Q needed to melt the ice is $Q = mL_f = (1.00 \text{ kg})(334 \times 10^3 \text{ J/kg}) = 334 \times 10^3 \text{ J}$.

SOLVE From Equation 11, the increase in entropy of the system is

$$\Delta S = \frac{Q}{T} = \frac{3.34 \times 10^5 \text{ J}}{273 \text{ K}} = 1220 \text{ J/K}.$$

REFLECT The entropy of the system increases as heat is added to it. The disorder increases because the water molecules in the liq-

uid state have more freedom to move than when they were locked in a crystal structure. In any *isothermal* reversible process, the change of entropy equals the heat transferred divided by the absolute temperature. When we refreeze the water, its entropy change is $\Delta S = -1220 \text{ J/K}$.

Practice Problem: When 50 g of liquid water at 0°C freezes into a 50 g ice cube at 0°C, what is the change in entropy of the material? *Answer:* $\Delta S = -61 \text{ J/K}$.

We can generalize the definition of entropy change to include *any* reversible process leading from one state to another, whether it is isothermal or not. We represent the process as a series of infinitesimal reversible steps. During a typical step, an infinitesimal quantity of heat ΔQ is added to the system at absolute temperature T. Then we sum the quotients $\Delta Q/T$ for the entire process. If T varies during the process, then carrying out this sum requires calculus.

Because entropy is a measure of the disorder of a system in any specific state, it must depend only on the current state of the system, not on its past history. We'll show later, by using the second law of thermodynamics, that this is indeed the case. When a system proceeds from an initial state with entropy S_1 to a final state with entropy S_2, the change in entropy $\Delta S = S_2 - S_1$, defined by Equation 11, does not depend on the path leading from the initial to the final state, but is the same for *all possible* processes leading from state 1 to state 2. Thus, if the entropy of one state of a system is assigned a certain value, the entropies of all other states of that system also have definite values, and those values depend only on the state of the system. We recall that *internal energy* also has this property, although entropy and internal energy are very different quantities.

As with internal energy, the preceding discussion does not define entropy itself, but only the *change* in entropy in any given process. To complete the definition, we may arbitrarily assign a value to the entropy of a system in one specified reference state and then calculate the entropy of any other state with reference to this assigned value.

EXAMPLE 5 An adiabatic expansion

A gas expands adiabatically and reversibly. What is its change in entropy?

SOLUTION

SET UP AND SOLVE In an adiabatic process, no heat enters or leaves the system; $Q = 0$, and there is *no* change in entropy: $\Delta S = 0$. Every *reversible* adiabatic process is a constant-entropy process.

REFLECT The increase in disorder resulting from the gas occupying a greater volume after the expansion is exactly balanced by the decrease in disorder associated with the lowered temperature of the gas and its decreased molecular speeds.

EXAMPLE 6 Entropy and the Carnot cycle

The Carnot engine in Example 2 (Section 6) takes 2000 J of heat from a reservoir at 500 K, does some work, and discards some heat to a reservoir at 350 K. Find the total entropy change in the engine during one cycle.

SOLUTION

SET UP AND SOLVE During the isothermal expansion at 500 K, the engine takes in 2000 J and its entropy change is

$$\Delta S = \frac{Q}{T} = \frac{2000 \text{ J}}{500 \text{ K}} = 4.0 \text{ J/K}.$$

During the isothermal compression at 350 K, the engine gives off 1400 J of heat and its entropy change is

$$\Delta S = \frac{-1400 \text{ J}}{350 \text{ K}} = -4.0 \text{ J/K}.$$

The entropy change of the engine during each of the two adiabatic processes is zero. Thus, the total entropy change in the engine during one cycle is $4.0 \text{ J/K} + 0 - 4.0 \text{ J/K} + 0 = 0$.

REFLECT The total entropy change of the two heat reservoirs is also zero, although each individual reservoir has a nonzero entropy change. This cycle contains no irreversible processes, and the total entropy change of the system and its surroundings is zero.

Entropy in Irreversible Processes

In an idealized reversible process involving only equilibrium states, the total entropy change of the system and its surroundings is zero. But all *irreversible* processes involve an increase in entropy. Unlike energy, entropy is *not* a conserved quantity. The entropy of an isolated system can change, but, as we shall see, it can never decrease. **An entropy increase occurs in every natural (irreversible) process if all systems taking part in the process are included.** Example 7 (below) illustrates an increase in entropy during an irreversible process in an isolated system.

The fact that entropy is a function only of the *state* of a system shows us how to compute entropy changes in *irreversible* (non-equilibrium) processes, to which Equation 11 is not applicable. We simply invent a path connecting the given initial and final states that *does* consist entirely of reversible equilibrium processes, and we compute the total entropy change for that alternative path. It is not the actual path, but the entropy change must be the same as that for the actual path.

EXAMPLE 7 A free expansion

A thermally insulated box is divided by a partition into two compartments, each having volume V. (Figure 13). Initially, one compartment contains n moles of an ideal gas at temperature T, and the other compartment is evacuated. We then break the partition, and the gas expands to fill both compartments. What is the entropy change in this free-expansion process?

Continued

SOLUTION

SET UP For the given process, $Q = 0$, $W = 0$, $\Delta U = 0$, and therefore (because the system is an ideal gas), $\Delta T = 0$. We might think that the entropy change is zero, because there is no heat exchange. But Equation 11 is valid only for *reversible* processes; the free expansion described here is *not* reversible, and there is an entropy change. To calculate ΔS, we use the fact that the entropy change depends only on the initial and final states. We can devise a *reversible* process having the same end points, use Equation 11 to calculate its entropy change, and thus determine the entropy change in the original process.

SOLVE The appropriate reversible process in this case is an isothermal expansion from V to $2V$ at temperature T, shown on the pV diagram of Figure 13c. The gas does work during this substitute expansion, so heat must be supplied to keep the internal energy constant. The total heat equals the total work, which is given by the equation:

$$W = Q = nRT \ln \frac{V_2}{V_1}.$$

Thus, the entropy change is

$$\Delta S = \frac{Q}{T} = \frac{nRT \ln \frac{2V}{V}}{T} = nR \ln 2,$$

and this is also the entropy change for the free expansion. For 1 mole,

$$\Delta S = (1 \text{ mol})[8.314 \text{ J}/(\text{mol} \cdot \text{K})](0.693)$$
$$= 5.76 \text{ J/K}.$$

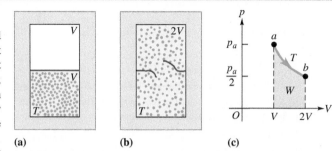

(a)   (b)   (c)

▲ **FIGURE 13** (a, b) Free expansion of an insulated ideal gas, an irreversible process. (c) An example of a reversible process that has the same initial and final states as the free expansion and thus has the same change in entropy.

REFLECT The entropy change ΔS is proportional to the amount of substance (n moles) and is independent of the temperature T (provided that it is constant). The increase in disorder is due to the increased randomness of position resulting from the increase in volume.

Practice Problem: In a free expansion, 2.00 mol of an ideal gas expands from an initial volume of 1.50 L to a final volume of 6.00 L. What is the increase in entropy? *Answer:* 23.1 J/K.

EXAMPLE 8 **Mixing hot and cold water**

Suppose 1.00 kg of water at 100°C is placed in thermal contact with 1.00 kg of water at 0°C. Find the approximate total change in entropy when the hot water cools to 99°C and the cold water warms to 1°C. Assume that the specific heat capacity of water is constant at 4190 J/(kg · K) over the given temperature range.

SOLUTION

SET UP AND SOLVE This process involves irreversible heat flow because of the temperature differences. The first 4190 J of heat transferred cools the hot water to 99°C (372 K) and warms the cold water from 0°C to 1°C (274 K). The net change of entropy of the hot water is approximately

$$\Delta S_{\text{hot}} = \frac{-4190 \text{ J}}{372 \text{ K}} = -11.3 \text{ J/K}.$$

(During this process, the temperature actually varies from 373 K to 372 K, but the resulting error in the calculation is very small.) The change of entropy of the cold water is approximately

$$\Delta S_{\text{cold}} = \frac{+4190 \text{ J}}{274 \text{ K}} = +15.3 \text{ J/K}.$$

The total change of entropy of the system during this process is

$$\Delta S_{\text{hot}} + \Delta S_{\text{cold}} = -11.3 \text{ J/K} + 15.3 \text{ J/K} = +4.0 \text{ J/K}.$$

Further increases in entropy occur as the system approaches thermal equilibrium at 50°C (323 K). Because the two temperatures vary continuously during this heat exchange, we would need methods of calculus to calculate the entropy changes precisely. It turns out that the total entropy change of the hot water is $\Delta S_{\text{hot}} = -603 \text{ J/K}$, the total entropy change of the cold water is $\Delta S_{\text{cold}} = 705 \text{ J/K}$, and the total entropy change of the system is $705 \text{ J/K} - 603 \text{ J/K} = 102 \text{ J/K}$.

REFLECT The total entropy of the final state is greater than that of the initial state, corresponding to increasing disorder as the distinction between the hotter and colder molecules gradually disappears. We could have reached the same end state by simply mixing the two quantities of water, also an irreversible process. The entropy depends only on the state of the system, and the total entropy change would be the same, 102 J/K.

Practice Problem: Repeat the approximate calculation for the total entropy change when the hot water cools from 76°C to 75°C and the cool water warms from 24°C to 25°C. *Answer:* 2.0 J/K.

Entropy and the Second Law

The mixing of substances at different temperatures and the flow of heat from a higher to a lower temperature are characteristic of *all* natural (that is, irreversible) processes. When all the entropy changes in the process are included, the increases in entropy are always found to be greater than the decreases. In the special case of a *reversible* process, the increases and decreases are equal. Thus, we can state the following general principle: **When all systems taking part in a process are included, the total entropy either remains constant or increases.** Put another way, **no process is possible in which the total entropy decreases when all systems taking part in the process are included.** This alternative statement of the second law of thermodynamics, in terms of entropy, is equivalent to the "engine" and "refrigerator" statements discussed earlier.

The increase of entropy in every natural (irreversible) process measures the increase in disorder, or randomness, in the universe associated with that process. Consider again the example of mixing hot and cold water. We *might* have used the hot and cold water as the high- and low-temperature reservoirs of a heat engine. While removing heat from the hot water and giving heat to the cold water, we could have obtained some mechanical work. But once the hot and cold water have been mixed and have come to a uniform temperature, this opportunity to convert heat to mechanical work is lost irretrievably. The lukewarm water will never *unmix* itself and separate into hotter and colder portions. No decrease in *energy* occurs when the hot and cold water are mixed. What has been lost is not *energy,* but *opportunity*—the opportunity to convert part of the heat from the hot water into mechanical work. When entropy increases, energy becomes less *available,* and the universe has become more random, or "run down."

NASA

▲ **Application** **Flower power.** Sometimes the second law of thermodynamics is invoked to make the process of evolution seem impossible. If the universe tends toward disorder (increasing entropy), how could complex life forms have evolved from simpler, primitive forms? Similarly, it would seem impossible that a complex plant or animal could develop from a single cell. The flaw in this reasoning is that neither the earth nor an organism is a closed system. The earth constantly receives energy from the sun (and radiates "waste" heat to space). Organisms also constantly consume energy and transform it to power their activities. You eat food; plants use sunlight; the embryo in a bird's egg uses chemical energy stored in the yolk and white. If you were sealed off from a suitable source of energy, you would quickly die—and then, indeed, entropy would take its course.

8 The Kelvin Temperature Scale

When we studied temperature scales, we expressed the need for a temperature scale that doesn't depend on the properties or behavior of any particular material. We can now use the Carnot cycle to define such a scale. We've learned that the efficiency of a Carnot engine operating between two heat reservoirs at absolute temperatures T_H and T_C is independent of the nature of the working substance and that it depends only on the temperatures. If several Carnot engines with different working substances operate between the same two heat reservoirs, their thermal efficiencies are all the same:

$$e = \frac{Q_H + Q_C}{Q_H} = 1 + \frac{Q_C}{Q_H}.$$

Therefore, the ratio Q_C/Q_H is the same for *all* Carnot engines operating between two given temperatures T_H and T_C.

Kelvin proposed that we *define* the ratio of the temperatures, T_C/T_H, to be equal to the magnitude of the ratio Q_C/Q_H of the quantities of heat absorbed and rejected:

$$\frac{T_C}{T_H} = \frac{|Q_C|}{|Q_H|} = -\frac{Q_C}{Q_H}. \tag{12}$$

Equation 12 looks identical to Equation 8, but there is a subtle and crucial difference. The temperatures in Equation 8 are based on an ideal-gas thermometer. But Equation 12 *defines* a temperature scale that is based on the Carnot cycle and the second law of thermodynamics and is independent of the behavior of any particular substance. Thus, the **Kelvin temperature scale** is truly *absolute.*

Samantha Brown/AFP/Getty Images

▲ Application **Zero power.** Using knowledge of the principles of physics and energy conservation, architects are designing homes of the future that will consume no net power. These homes, called "zero-power homes," are designed to generate as much power as they consume, allowing their owners to have an annual energy bill of $0. They can do this by using a combination of rooftop photovoltaic cells, solar water heaters, state-of-the-art insulation, energy-efficient appliances, and computer-controlled power distribution systems. Some can even generate excess power, which can be sold back to "the grid" to generate income. Of course, this net negative energy use does not violate the laws of thermodynamics: The house is not a closed system. The negative energy use by these homes results from the efficient collection and use of the vast amounts of solar energy reaching the homes each year.

To complete the definition of the Kelvin scale, we assign the arbitrary value of 273.16 K to the temperature of the triple point of water. As we discussed in Section 2, this is the unique temperature at which gas, liquid, and solid phases of water can coexist in phase equilibrium. When a substance is taken around a Carnot cycle, the ratio of the heat absorbed to the heat rejected, $|Q_H|/|Q_C|$, is equal to the ratio of the temperatures of the reservoirs, *as expressed on the gas scale,* defined in Section 2. Since, on both scales, the triple point of water is chosen to be 273.16 K, it follows that *the Kelvin and the ideal-gas scales are identical.*

The zero point on the Kelvin scale is called **absolute zero.** There are theoretical reasons for believing that absolute zero cannot be attained experimentally, although temperatures below 10^{-7} K have been achieved. The more closely we approach absolute zero, the more difficult it is to get yet closer. Absolute zero can also be interpreted on a molecular level, although this must be done with some care. Because of quantum effects, it would *not* be correct to say that at $T = 0$, all molecular motion ceases. At absolute zero, the system has its *minimum* possible total energy (kinetic plus potential). One statement of the *third law of thermodynamics* is that it is impossible to reach absolute zero in a finite number of thermodynamic steps.

9 Energy Resources: A Case Study in Thermodynamics

The laws of thermodynamics place very general limitations on the conversion of energy from one form to another. In these times of increasing energy demand and diminishing resources, such matters are of the utmost practical importance. We conclude this chapter with a brief discussion of a few energy-conversion systems, present and proposed.

About half of the electric power generated in the United States is obtained from coal-fired steam-turbine generating plants. Modern boilers can transfer about 80% to 90% of the heat of combustion of coal into steam. The theoretical maximum thermal efficiency of the turbine, given by Equation 9, is usually limited to about 0.55, and the actual efficiency is typically 90% of this value, or approximately 0.50. The efficiency of large generators in converting mechanical power to electrical power is very high, typically 99%. Thus, the overall thermal efficiency of such a plant is roughly (0.85)(0.50)(0.99), or at most about 40%.

The Tennessee Valley Authority's Kingston power plant has a generating capacity of about 1 gigawatt (1000 MW, or 10^9 W) of electrical power. The steam is heated to about 540°C (1000°F) at a pressure of more than 120 atm (1.24×10^7 Pa, or 1800 psi). The plant burns 14,000 tons of coal per day (13 million kg, the equivalent of 140 railroad cars), and the overall thermal efficiency is about 35%.

In a nuclear power plant, the heat that generates steam is supplied by a nuclear reaction rather than the chemical reaction of burning coal. The steam turbines in nuclear power plants have the same theoretical efficiency limit as those in coal-fired plants. At present, it is not practical to run nuclear reactors at temperatures and pressures as high as those in coal boilers, so the thermal efficiency of a nuclear plant is somewhat lower, typically 30%.

In the year 2005, about 20% of the world's electric power supply came from nuclear power plants. High construction costs, questions of public safety, and the problem of disposal of radioactive waste have slowed the development of additional nuclear power. However, there is also increasing concern about the environmental impact of coal-burning power plants. The health hazards of coal smoke are serious and well documented, and the burning of coal contributes to global warming through the greenhouse effect. It is important to manage our development of energy resources so as to minimize the risks to human life and health, and nuclear power continues to receive attention as a future energy resource. We noted at the end of Section 6 that thermal pollution from both coal-fired and nuclear plants poses serious environmental problems.

Solar energy is an inviting possibility. The power per unit surface area in the sun's radiation (before it passes through the earth's atmosphere) is approximately 1.4 kW/m^2. A maximum of about 1.0 kW/m^2 reaches the surface of the earth on a clear day, and the average over a 24-hour period is about 0.2 kW/m^2. This radiation can be collected and used to heat water for home use (Figure 14a).

A different solar-energy scheme is to use banks of photovoltaic (PV) cells (Figure 14b) for the direct conversion of solar energy to electricity. Such a system is not a heat engine in the usual sense and is not limited by the Carnot efficiency. There are other fundamental limitations on photocell efficiency, but 50% seems attainable in multilayer semiconductor photocells. Because of high capital costs, the price of PV-produced energy is about 25 cents per kilowatt-hour (compared with about 12 cents for conventional coal-fired steam-turbine plants). But such a system offers many advantages, such as lack of noise, lack of moving parts, minimal maintenance requirements, and freedom from pollution. Capital costs are likely to drop with improved technology, and PV systems continue to be studied and developed.

The energy of wind, fundamentally solar in origin, can be gathered and converted by "wind farms" of windmills (Figure 14c). The largest wind farms are located in California, where the state government encourages their use. However, the Great Plains states alone have enough wind energy to theoretically meet the electrical power needs of the entire United States. As with PV systems, the capital costs of such systems are higher than for coal-fired generating plants of equal capacity.

Biomass is yet another mechanism for using solar energy. Plants absorb solar energy and store it; the energy can be utilized by burning the plant matter or by using fermentation and distillation to make alcohols. Ethanol made from fermented corn is used in the United States as a gasoline additive, although its cost is not quite competitive at present crude-oil price levels. An important feature of biomass materials is that they take as much carbon dioxide out of the atmosphere when they grow as is released when they burn; thus, they don't contribute to the greenhouse effect.

An indirect scheme for the collection and conversion of solar energy would use the temperature gradient in the oceans. In the Caribbean, for example, the water temperature near the surface is about 25°C, and at a depth of a few hundred meters it is about 10°C. The second law of thermodynamics forbids cooling the ocean and converting the extracted heat completely into work, but there is nothing to forbid running a heat engine between those two temperatures. The thermodynamic efficiency would be very low (about 5%), but a vast supply of energy would be available.

The present level of activity in energy-conversion research in the United States is rather low in comparison to the period of the 1970s, when we experienced a serious energy shortage. The disadvantages of excessive reliance on non-renewable resources such as oil—especially imported oil—are not hard to see. Critics have accused the U.S government of not having a coherent and effective energy policy compared with other countries. As we humans use up our available fossil-fuel resources, and as developing countries require more of the world's supply, we will certainly have to become more active in developing alternative energy sources. The principles of thermodynamics will play a central role in this development.

Absorber plate covered by glass

Tubes carry heated fluid

Insulation

(a) Passive solar collecting panel for home water heating

(b) A telephone powered by photovoltaic cells

Amos Zezmer/Omni-Photo Communications, Inc.

Shutterstock

(c) Windmills generating electricity

▲ FIGURE 14 Three sources of energy other than the burning of fossil fuels.

CHAPTER SUMMARY

Directions of Thermodynamic Processes

(Section 1) Heat flows spontaneously from a hotter object to a cooler object, never the reverse. A **reversible process (equilibrium process)** is a process whose direction can be reversed by an infinitesimal change in the conditions of the process.

Heat Engines

(Section 2) A **heat engine** takes heat Q_H from a source, converts part of it to work W, and discards the remainder, $|Q_C|$, at a lower temperature. The **thermal efficiency** e of a heat engine is

$$e = \frac{W}{Q_H} = 1 + \frac{Q_C}{Q_H} = 1 - \frac{|Q_C|}{|Q_H|}. \quad (4)$$

Internal Combustion Engines and Refrigerators

(Sections 3–4) An idealized model of the thermodynamic processes that take place in a gasoline engine is called the **Otto cycle.** The theoretical efficiency of the Otto cycle is about 50%; those of real gasoline engines are typically around 20%.

A **refrigerator** takes heat Q_C from a cold place, has an input W of work, and discards heat $|Q_H|$ at a warmer place. The **performance coefficient** K of a refrigerator is defined as

$$K = \frac{Q_C}{|W|} = \frac{|Q_C|}{|Q_H| - |Q_C|}. \quad (7)$$

The Second Law of Thermodynamics

(Section 5) The **second law of thermodynamics** describes the directionality of natural thermodynamic processes. It can be stated in several equivalent forms. The "engine" statement is "No cyclic process can convert heat completely into work." The "refrigerator" statement is "No cyclic process can transfer heat from a cold place to a hotter place with no input of mechanical work."

The Carnot Engine: The Most Efficient Heat Engine

(Section 6) The **Carnot cycle** operates between two heat reservoirs at temperatures T_H and T_C and uses only reversible processes. Its thermal efficiency is

$$e_{\text{Carnot}} = 1 - \frac{T_C}{T_H} = \frac{T_H - T_C}{T_H}. \quad (9)$$

No engine operating between the same two temperatures can be more efficient than a Carnot engine. All Carnot engines operating between the same two temperatures have the same efficiency.

Entropy

(Section 7) **Entropy** is a quantitative measure of the disorder of a system. The entropy change in a reversible isothermal process is $\Delta S = Q/T$ (Equation 11), where T is absolute temperature. The second law can be stated in terms of entropy: The entropy of an isolated system may increase, but can never decrease. When a system interacts with its surroundings, the total entropy of system and surroundings can never decrease.

Continued

The Kelvin Temperature Scale

(Section 8) The Kelvin temperature scale is based on the efficiency of the Carnot cycle and is independent of the properties of any specific material. The zero point on the Kelvin scale is absolute zero.

Energy Resources: A Case Study in Thermodynamics

(Section 9) About half of the electric power generated in the United States is obtained from coal-fired steam-turbine generating plants. The theoretical maximum thermal efficiency of the turbine, given by Equation 9, is usually limited to about 0.55, and the actual overall efficiency is about 40%. In a nuclear power plant, the heat that generates steam is supplied by a nuclear reaction rather than the chemical reaction of burning coal; the thermal efficiency of a nuclear plant is typically 30%. Other sources of energy include the sun, wind, ethanol from fermented corn, and thermal gradients in the ocean.

The Second Law of Thermodynamics: Problem Set

For instructor-assigned homework, go to www.masteringphysics.com

Conceptual Questions

1. Household refrigerators have arrays or coils of tubing on the outside, usually at the back or bottom. When the refrigerator is running, the tubing becomes quite hot. Where does the heat come from?

2. A chef tries to cool his kitchen on a hot day by leaving the door of the walk-in refrigerator open. Will this strategy work? Would the result be different if the chef used an old-fashioned icebox (which is simply an insulated box with a compartment holding ice)?

3. Imagine a special air filter placed in a window of a house. The tiny holes in the filter allow only air molecules moving faster than a certain speed to exit the house, and allow only air molecules moving slower than that speed to enter the house from outside. Explain why such an air filter would cool the house, and why the second law of thermodynamics makes building such a filter an impossible task.

4. A growing plant creates a highly complex and organized structure out of simple materials, such as air, water, and minerals. Does this violate the second law of thermodynamics? What is the plant's ultimate source of energy?

5. Why must a room air conditioner be placed in a window rather than just set on the floor and plugged in? Why can a refrigerator be set on the floor and plugged in?

6. If you pour a cup of hot water into a cup of cold water, you wind up with two cups of lukewarm water. (a) Is this process reversible or irreversible? Why? (b) Does the entropy increase or decrease? How can this be, since no heat was added to (or removed from) the system?

7. How can the thermal conduction of heat from a hot object to a cold object increase entropy when the same amount of heat that flows out of the hot object flows into the cold one?

8. How can the free expansion of a gas into a vacuum increase entropy when no heat is added to (or subtracted from) this gas?

9. Does the second law of thermodynamics say that heat can *never* go from a cold object to a hot object? Explain.

10. When a wet cloth is hung up in a hot wind in the desert, it is cooled by evaporation to a temperature that may be 20°C or so below that of the air. Discuss this process in light of the second law of thermodynamics.

11. In what ways is a heat pump different from (or similar to) a refrigerator?

12. Does the second law of thermodynamics say that entropy (disorder) can never decrease? Explain and give a few examples to illustrate your answer.

13. *Why* does heat *not* flow from a cold to a hot object? How does heat "know" it should obey the second law of thermodynamics? Explain by thinking about collisions at the molecular level.

14. Some people have suggested that the idea that life originated from nonliving materials violates the second law of thermodynamics because the molecules would have to go from a less ordered to a more ordered state, decreasing entropy. What is wrong with this argument?

15. What would be the efficiency of a Carnot engine operating with $T_H = T_C$? What would be the efficiency if $T_C = 0$ K and T_H were any temperature above 0 K? Interpret your answers.

16. The first law of thermodynamics is sometimes paraphrased as "You can't get something for nothing." The second law has been paraphrased as "You can't even break even." Explain why these statements are good summaries of those two laws.

17. Would it be more economical to run a refrigerator with a high or a low coefficient of performance? Why?

Multiple-Choice Problems

1. An insulated box has a barrier that confines a gas to only one side of the box. The barrier springs a leak, allowing the gas to

flow and occupy both sides of the box. Which statement best describes the entropy of this system?

A. The entropy is greater in the first state, with all the gas on one side of the box.

B. The entropy is greater in the second state, with the gas on both sides of the box.

C. The entropy is the same in both states, since no heat was added to the gas and its temperature did not change.

2. Suppose you put a hot object in contact with a cold object and observe (with some wonder) that heat flows from the cold object to the hot object, making the cold one colder and the hot one hotter. This process would violate

A. only the first law of thermodynamics.

B. only the second law of thermodynamics.

C. both the first and the second laws of thermodynamics.

3. Carnot engine A operates between temperatures of 500°C and 300°C; Carnot engine B operates between temperatures of 900°C and 700°C. How do the efficiencies of the two engines compare?

A. Engine A has higher efficiency.

B. Engine B has higher efficiency.

C. The efficiencies of the two engines are the same.

4. The thermal efficiency formula $e = W/Q_H$ is valid for which of the following heat engines? (There may be more than one correct choice.)

A. Carnot engine.

B. Otto engine.

C. Diesel engine.

D. Any other type of heat engine.

5. The thermal efficiency formula $e = 1 - T_C/T_H$ is valid for which of the following heat engines? (There may be more than one correct choice.)

A. Carnot engine.   B. Otto engine.

C. Diesel engine.   D. Any other type of heat engine.

6. A refrigerator consumes a certain amount of electrical energy in order to operate. In terms of the thermodynamic cycle of this refrigerator, this electrical energy is equal to

A. the work done on the gas.

B. the heat extracted from the food in the refrigerator.

C. the heat expelled into the room.

D. the sum of all three quantities in choices A, B, and C.

7. Which of the following statements is a consequence of the *second* law of thermodynamics? (There may be more than one correct choice.)

A. The efficiency of a heat engine can never be greater than unity.

B. Heat can never flow from a cold object to a hot object unless work is done.

C. Energy is conserved in all thermodynamics processes.

D. Even a perfect heat engine cannot convert all of the heat put into it to work.

8. You want to increase the efficiency of a Carnot heat engine by changing the temperature of either its hot or its cold reservoir by the same number of degrees ΔT. Which of the following choices will produce the *greater* increase in its thermodynamic efficiency?

A. Increase the temperature of the hot reservoir by ΔT.

B. Decrease the temperature of the cold reservoir by ΔT.

C. It would not matter. Both choices would produce the same increase in efficiency, since ΔT is the same for both.

9. Two Carnot heat engines operate between the same hot and cold reservoirs, but one has a greater compression ratio than the other. Which statement is true about their thermal efficiencies?

A. The one with the greater compression ratio will have the greater efficiency.

B. The one with the greater compression ratio will have the lesser efficiency.

C. Both will have the same efficiency.

10. You put 250 g of water into the freezer and make ice cubes. Which of the following statements is true about this process? (There may be more than one correct choice.)

A. The entropy of the water increases.

B. The entropy of the room increases.

C. The amount of heat removed from the water is equal to the amount of heat ejected into the room.

D. More heat is ejected into the room than was removed from the water.

E. The work done by the refrigerator is equal to the heat removed from the water.

11. If you mix cold milk with hot coffee in an insulated Styrofoam™ cup, which of the following things happen? (There may be more than one correct choice.)

A. The entropy of the milk increases.

B. The entropy of the coffee decreases by the same amount that the entropy of the milk increased.

C. The net entropy of the coffee–milk mixture does not change, because no heat was added to this system.

D. The entropy of the coffee–milk mixture increases.

12. Suppose a Carnot refrigerator is used to cool the interior of a food storage locker from room temperature to 5°C. As the temperature of the locker drops, the performance coefficient of the refrigerator

A. increases.

B. decreases.

C. is constant.

13. A glass of water left outside on a cold night freezes into solid ice, and its entropy decreases. Which statement is true of this process:

A. The entropy of the surrounding air does not change.

B. The entropy of the water changes more than the entropy of the surrounding air.

C. The entropy of the surrounding air changes more than the entropy of the water.

D. The entropy of the water and the entropy of the surrounding air change by equal amounts.

14. If we run an ideal Carnot heat engine in *reverse,* which of the following statements about it must be true? (There may be more than one correct choice.)

A. Heat enters the gas at the cold reservoir and goes out of the gas at the hot reservoir.

B. The amount of heat transferred at the hot reservoir is equal to the amount of heat transferred at the cold reservoir.

C. It is able to perform a net amount of useful work, such as pumping water from a well, during each cycle.

D. It can transfer heat from a cold object to a hot object.

15. Which of the following processes would be a *violation* of the second law of thermodynamics? (There may be more than one correct choice.)

A. All the kinetic energy of an object is transformed into heat.

B. All the heat put into the operating gas of a heat engine during one cycle is transformed into work.

C. A refrigerator removes 100 cal of heat from milk while using only 75 cal of electrical energy to operate.

D. A heat engine does 25 J of work while expelling only 10 J of heat to the cold reservoir.

Problems

2 Heat Engines

1. • A coal-fired power plant that operates at an efficiency of 38% generates 750 MW of electric power. How much heat does the plant discharge to the environment in one day?

2. • Each cycle, a certain heat engine expels 250 J of heat when you put in 325 J of heat. Find the efficiency of this engine and the amount of work you get out of the 325 J heat input.

3. • A diesel engine performs 2200 J of mechanical work and discards 4300 J of heat each cycle. (a) How much heat must be supplied to the engine in each cycle? (b) What is the thermal efficiency of the engine?

4. • An aircraft engine takes in 9000 J of heat and discards 6400 J each cycle. (a) What is the mechanical work output of the engine during one cycle? (b) What is the thermal efficiency of the engine?

5. • **A gasoline engine.** A gasoline engine takes in 1.61×10^4 J of heat and delivers 3700 J of work per cycle. The heat is obtained by burning gasoline with a heat of combustion of 4.60×10^4 J/g. (a) What is the thermal efficiency of the engine? (b) How much heat is discarded in each cycle? (c) What mass of fuel is burned in each cycle? (d) If the engine goes through 60.0 cycles per second, what is its power output in kilowatts? In horsepower?

6. • A gasoline engine has a power output of 180 kW (about 241 hp). Its thermal efficiency is 28.0%. (a) How much heat must be supplied to the engine per second? (b) How much heat is discarded by the engine per second?

7. • A certain nuclear power plant has a mechanical power output (used to drive an electric generator) of 330 MW. Its rate of heat input from the nuclear reactor is 1300 MW. (a) What is the thermal efficiency of the system? (b) At what rate is heat discarded by the system?

8. •• Figure 15 shows a pV diagram for a heat engine that uses 1.40 moles of an ideal diatomic gas. (a) How much heat goes into this gas per cycle, and where in the cycle does it occur? (b) How much heat is ejected by the gas per cycle, and where does it occur? (c) How much work does this engine do each cycle? (d) What is the thermal efficiency of the engine?

9. •• The pV diagram in Figure 16 shows a cycle of a heat engine that uses 0.250 mole of an ideal gas having $\gamma = 1.40$. The curved part ab of the cycle is adiabatic. (a) Find the pressure of the gas at point a. (b) How much heat enters this gas per cycle, and where does it happen? (c) How much heat leaves this gas in a cycle, and where does it occur? (d) How much work does this engine do in a cycle? (e) What is the thermal efficiency of the engine?

3 Internal Combustion Engines

10. • An Otto engine uses a gas having $\gamma = 1.40$ and has a compression ratio of 8.50. (a) Out of every gallon of fuel this engine burns, what fraction is wasted (i.e., produces energy that is wasted)? (b) If you could change the compression ratio to 10.0 instead, what percentage of the fuel would be wasted?

11. • What compression ratio r must an Otto cycle have to achieve an ideal efficiency of 65.0% if the gas used in the chamber has $\gamma = 1.40$?

12. • For an Otto engine with a compression ratio of 7.50, you have your choice of using an ideal monatomic or ideal diatomic gas. Which one would give you greater efficiency? Calculate the efficiency in both cases to find out.

13. •• (a) Calculate the theoretical efficiency for an Otto cycle engine with $\gamma = 1.40$ and $r = 9.50$. (b) If this engine takes in 10,000 J of heat from burning its fuel, how much heat does it discard to the outside air?

4 Refrigerators

14. • In one cycle, a freezer uses 785 J of electrical energy in order to remove 1750 J of heat from its freezer compartment at 10°F. (a) What is the coefficient of performance of this freezer? (b) How much heat does it expel into the room during this cycle?

15. • A refrigerator has a coefficient of performance of 2.10. Each cycle, it absorbs 3.40×10^4 J of heat from the cold reservoir. (a) How much mechanical energy is required each cycle to operate the refrigerator? (b) During each cycle, how much heat is discarded to the high-temperature reservoir?

16. • A window air-conditioner unit absorbs 9.80×10^4 J of heat per minute from the room being cooled and in the same period deposits 1.44×10^5 J of heat into the outside air. What is the power consumption of the unit in watts?

17. •• A freezer has a coefficient of performance of 2.40. The freezer is to convert 1.80 kg of water at 25.0°C to 1.80 kg of ice at −5.0°C in 1 hour. (a) What amount of heat must be removed from the water at 25.0°C to convert it to ice at −5.0°C? (b) How much electrical energy is consumed by the freezer during this hour? c) How much wasted heat is rejected to the room in which the freezer sits?

18. •• A cooling unit for chilling the water of an aquarium gives specifications of 1/10 hp and 1270 Btu/h. Assuming the unit produces its 1/10 hp at 70.0% efficiency, calculate its performance coefficient.

6 The Carnot Engine: The Most Efficient Heat Engine

19. • A Carnot engine whose high-temperature reservoir is at 620 K takes in 550 J of heat at this temperature in each cycle and gives up 335 J to the low-temperature reservoir. (a) How

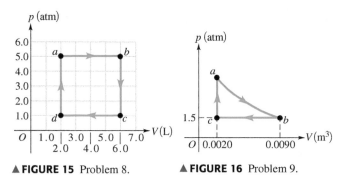

p (atm)

6.0
5.0 a ━━━━━━ b
4.0
3.0
2.0
1.0 d c
        ┕━━━━━━━━━━▶ V(L)
O 1.0 | 3.0 | 5.0 | 7.0
       2.0   4.0   6.0

▲ **FIGURE 15** Problem 8.

p (atm)

         a
1.5 ─ c b
        ┕━━━━━━━━━━▶ V(m³)
O 0.0020   0.0090

▲ **FIGURE 16** Problem 9.

much mechanical work does the engine perform during each cycle? (b) What is the temperature of the low-temperature reservoir? (c) What is the thermal efficiency of the cycle?

20. • A heat engine is to be built to extract energy from the temperature gradient in the ocean. If the surface and deepwater temperatures are 25°C and 8°C, respectively, what is the maximum efficiency such an engine can have?

21. • A Carnot engine is operated between two heat reservoirs at temperatures of 520 K and 300 K. (a) If the engine receives 6.45 kJ of heat energy from the reservoir at 520 K in each cycle, how many joules per cycle does it reject to the reservoir at 300 K? (b) How much mechanical work is performed by the engine during each cycle? (c) What is the thermal efficiency of the engine?

22. •• A Carnot engine has an efficiency of 59% and performs 2.5×10^4 J of work in each cycle. (a) How much heat does the engine extract from its heat source in each cycle? (b) Suppose the engine exhausts heat at room temperature $(20.0°C)$. What is the temperature of its heat source?

23. •• An ice-making machine operates in a Carnot cycle. It takes heat from water at 0.0°C and rejects heat to a room at 24.0°C. Suppose that 85.0 kg of water at 0.0°C are converted to ice at 0.0°C. (a) How much heat is rejected to the room? (b) How much energy must be supplied to the device?

24. •• A Carnot freezer that runs on electricity removes heat from the freezer compartment, which is at −10°C, and expels it into the room at 20°C. You put an ice-cube tray containing 375 g of water at 18°C into the freezer. (a) What is the coefficient of performance of this freezer? (b) How much energy is needed to freeze this water? (c) How much electrical energy must be supplied to the freezer to freeze the water? (d) How much heat does the freezer expel into the room while freezing the ice?

25. •• The pV diagram in Figure 17 shows a general Carnot cycle for an engine, with the hot and cold thermal reservoir segments identified. Segments ab and cd are isothermal, while the other two are adiabatic. (a) If this engine is used as a heat engine, what is the direction of the cycle, clockwise or counterclockwise? In which segments does heat enter the gas, and in which ones does it leave the gas? (b) If the engine is used as a refrigerator, what is the direction of the cycle? In which segments does heat enter the gas, and in which ones does it leave the gas? Also, which segments take place at the inside of the refrigerator, and which ones occur in the air of the room in which the refrigerator is operating? (c) If the engine is used as a heat pump–air conditioner, what is the direction of the cycle, and in which segments does heat enter the gas and in which ones does it leave the gas? Which segments take place inside of the house and which ones occur outside? (d) If the engine is used as a heat pump–house heater, what is the direction of the cycle? In which segments does heat enter the gas and in which ones does it leave the gas? Which segments take place inside of the house and which ones occur outside?

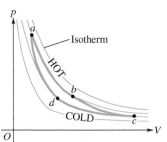

▲ FIGURE 17 Problem 27.

7 Entropy

26. • A sophomore with nothing better to do adds heat to 0.350 kg of ice at 0.00°C until it is all melted. (a) What is the change in entropy of the water? (b) The source of the heat is a very massive body at a temperature of 25.0°C. What is the change in entropy of this body? (c) What is the total change in entropy of the water and the heat source?

27. • A 4.50 kg block of ice at 0.00°C falls into the ocean and melts. The average temperature of the ocean is 3.50°C, including all the deep water. By how much does the melting of this ice change the entropy of the world? Does it make it larger or smaller? (*Hint:* Do you think that the ocean will change temperature appreciably as the ice melts?)

28. •• A large factory furnace maintained at 175°C at its outer surface is wrapped in an insulating blanket of thermal conductivity 0.055 $W/(m \cdot K)$ which is thick enough that the outer surface of the insulation is at 42°C while heat escapes from the furnace at a steady rate of 125 W for each square meter of surface area. By how much does each square meter of the furnace change the entropy of the factory every second?

29. •• You decide to take a nice hot bath but discover that your thoughtless roommate has used up most of the hot water. You fill the tub with 270 kg of 30.0°C water and attempt to warm it further by pouring in 5.00 kg of boiling water from the stove. (a) Is this a reversible or an irreversible process? Use physical reasoning to explain. (b) Calculate the final temperature of the bath water. (c) Calculate the net change in entropy of the system (bath water + boiling water), assuming no heat exchange with the air or the tub itself.

30. •• If 25.0 g of the metal gallium melts in your hand, what is the change in entropy of the gallium in this process? What about the change in entropy of your hand? Is it positive or negative? Is its magnitude greater or less than that of the change in entropy of the gallium? The melting temperature of gallium is 29.8°C, and its heat of fusion is 8.04×10^4 J/kg.

31. •• Three moles of an ideal gas undergo a reversible isothermal compression at 20.0°C. During this compression, 1850 J of work is done on the gas. What is the change in entropy of the gas?

32. •• **Entropy change due to driving.** Premium gasoline produces 1.23×10^8 J of heat per gallon when it is burned at a temperature of approximately 400°C (although the amount can vary with the fuel mixture). If the car's engine is 25% efficient, three-fourths of that heat is expelled into the air, typically at 20°C. If your car gets 35 miles per gallon of gas, by how much does the car's engine change the entropy of the world when you drive 1.0 mile? Does it decrease or increase it?

33. •• **Entropy of metabolism.** An average sleeping person
BIO metabolizes at a rate of about 80 W by digesting food or burning fat. Typically, 20% of this energy goes into bodily functions, such as cell repair, pumping blood, and other uses of mechanical energy, while the rest goes to heat. Most people get rid of all of this excess heat by transferring it (by conduction and the flow of blood) to the surface of the body, where it is radiated away. The normal internal temperature of the body (where the metabolism takes place) is 37°C, and the skin is typically 7 C° cooler. By how much does the person's entropy change per second due to this heat transfer?

34. •• **Entropy change from digesting fat.** Digesting fat pro-
BIO duces 9.3 food calories per gram of fat, and typically 80% of
this energy goes to heat when metabolized. The body then
moves all this heat to the surface by a combination of thermal
conductivity and motion of the blood. The internal temperature
of the body (where digestion occurs) is normally 37°C, and the
surface is usually about 30°C. By how much does the digestion
and metabolism of a 2.50 g pat of butter change your body's
entropy? Does it increase or decrease?

9 Energy Resources: A Case Study in Thermodynamics

35. • **Solar collectors.** A well-insulated house of moderate size in
a temperate climate requires an average heat input rate of
20.0 kW. If this heat is to be supplied by a solar collector with
an average (night and day) energy input of 300 W/m² and a
collection efficiency of 60.0%, what area of solar collector is
required?

36. • **Solar power.** A solar power plant is to be built with an average power output capacity of 2500 MW in a location where
the average power from the sun's radiation is 200 W/m² at
the earth's surface. What land area (in km² and mi²) must
the solar collectors occupy if they are (a) photocells with 42%
efficiency, (b) mirrors that generate steam for a turbine-
generator unit with an overall efficiency of 21%?

37. •• An experimental power plant at the Natural Energy Laboratory of Hawaii generates electricity from the temperature
gradient of the ocean. The surface and deep-water temperatures are 27°C and 6°C, respectively. (a) What is the maximum
theoretical efficiency of this power plant? (b) If the power
plant is to produce 210 kW of power, at what rate must heat be
extracted from the warm water? At what rate must heat be
absorbed by the cold water? Assume the maximum theoretical
efficiency. (c) The cold water that enters the plant leaves it at a
temperature of 10°C. What must be the flow rate of cold water
through the system? Give your answer in kg/h and L/h.

38. •• **Solar water heater.** A solar water heater for domestic hot-
water supply uses solar collecting panels with a collection efficiency of 50% in a location where the average solar-energy
input is 200 W/m². If the water comes into the house at 15.0°C
and is to be heated to 60.0°C, what volume of water can be
heated per hour if the area of the collector is 30.0 m²?

General Problems

39. •• You are designing a Carnot engine that has 2 mol of CO_2
as its working substance; the gas may be treated as ideal. The
gas is to have a maximum temperature of 527°C and a maximum pressure of 5.00 atm. With a heat input of 400 J per
cycle, you want 300 J of useful work. (a) Find the temperature
of the cold reservoir. (b) For how many cycles must this engine
run to melt completely a 10.0-kg block of ice originally at
0.0°C, using only the heat rejected by the engine?

40. •• A heat engine takes 0.350 mol of an ideal diatomic gas
around the cycle shown in the pV diagram of Figure 18.
Process 1 → 2 is at constant volume, process 2 → 3 is adiabatic, and process 3 → 1 is at a constant pressure of 1.00 atm.
The value of γ for this gas is 1.40. (a) Find the pressure and
volume at points 1, 2, and 3. (b) Calculate Q, W, and ΔU for
each of the three processes. (c) Find the net work done by the

gas in the cycle. (d) Find the
net heat flow into the engine
in one cycle. (e) What is the
thermal efficiency of the
engine? How does this efficiency compare with that
of a Carnot-cycle engine
operating between the same
minimum and maximum
temperatures T_1 and T_2?

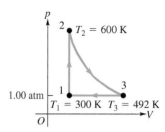
▲ **FIGURE 18** Problem 40.

41. •• As a budding mechanical engineer, you are called upon to
design a Carnot engine that has 2.00 moles of He gas (see Table A
at the end of this problem set) as its working substance and that
operates from a high-temperature reservoir at 500°C. The engine
is to lift a 15.0 kg weight 2.00 m per cycle, using 500 J of heat
input. The gas in the engine chamber can have a minimum volume of 5.00 L during the cycle. (a) Draw a pV diagram for this
cycle. In your diagram, show where heat enters and leaves the
gas. (b) What must be the temperature of the cold reservoir?
(c) What is the thermal efficiency of the engine? (d) How much
heat energy does this engine waste per cycle? (e) What is the
maximum pressure that the gas chamber will have to withstand?

42. •• The Kwik-Freez Appliance Co. wants you to design a food
freezer that will keep the freezing compartment at −5.0°C and
will operate in a room at 20.0°C. The freezer is to make 5.00 kg
of ice at 0.0°C, starting with water at 20.0°C. Find the least possible amount of electrical energy needed to make this ice and the
smallest possible amount of heat expelled into the room.

43. •• A Carnot engine operates between two heat reservoirs at
temperatures T_H and T_C. An inventor proposes to increase the
efficiency by running one engine between T_H and an intermediate temperature T' and a second engine between T' and T_C,
using as input the heat expelled by the first engine. Compute
the efficiency of this composite system, and compare it to that
of the original engine.

44. •• A cylinder contains oxygen gas (O_2) at a pressure of
2.00 atm. The volume is 4.00 L, and the temperature is 300 K.
Assume that the oxygen may be treated as an ideal gas. The
oxygen is carried through the following processes:
(i) Heated at constant pressure from the initial state (state 1)
to state 2, which has $T = 450$ K.
(ii) Cooled at constant volume to 250 K (state 3).
(iii) Compressed at constant temperature to a volume of
4.00 L (state 4).
(iv) Heated at constant volume to 300 K, which takes the system back to state 1.
(a) Show these four processes in a pV diagram, giving the
numerical values of p and V in each of the four states. (b) Calculate Q and W for each of the four processes. (c) Calculate the
net work done by the oxygen. (d) What is the efficiency of this
device as a heat engine? How does this efficiency compare
with that of a Carnot-cycle engine operating between the same
minimum and maximum temperatures of 250 K and 450 K?

45. •• **Human entropy.** A person having skin of surface area
BIO 1.85 m² and temperature 30.0°C is resting in an insulated room
where the ambient air temperature is 20.0°C. In this state, a
person gets rid of excess heat by radiation. By how much does
the person change the entropy of the air in this room each second? (Recall that the room radiates back into the person and
that the emissivity of the skin is 1.00.)

46. •• A typical coal-fired power plant generates 1000 MW of usable power at an overall thermal efficiency of 40%. (a) What is the rate of heat input to the plant? (b) The plant burns anthracite coal, which has a heat of combustion of 2.65×10^7 J/kg. How much coal does the plant use per day, if it operates continuously? (c) At what rate is heat ejected into the cool reservoir, which is the nearby river? (d) The river's temperature is 18.0°C before it reaches the power plant and 18.5°C after it has received the plant's waste heat. Calculate the river's flow rate, in cubic meters per second. (e) By how much does the river's entropy increase each second?

47. •• **A human engine.** You decide to use your body as a Carnot
BIO heat engine. The operating gas is in a tube with one end in your mouth (where the temperature is 37.0°C) and the other end at the surface of your skin, at 30.0°C. (a) What is the maximum efficiency of such a heat engine? Would it be a very useful engine? (b) Suppose you want to use this human engine to lift a 2.50 kg box from the floor to a tabletop 1.20 m above the floor. How much must you increase the gravitational potential energy and how much heat input is needed to accomplish this? (c) How many 350 calorie (those are *food* calories, remember) candy bars must you eat to lift the box in this way? Recall that 80% of the food energy goes into heat.

48. •• What is the thermal efficiency of an engine that operates by taking n moles of diatomic ideal gas through the cycle $1 \rightarrow 2 \rightarrow 3 \rightarrow 4 \rightarrow 1$ shown in Fig. 19?

49. •• One end of a copper rod is immersed in boiling water at 100°C and the other end in an ice–water mixture at 0°C. The sides of the rod are insulated. After steady-state conditions have been achieved in the rod, 0.160 kg of ice melts in a certain time interval. For this time interval, find (a) the entropy change of the boiling water, (b) the entropy change of the ice–water mixture, (c) the entropy change of the copper rod, (d) the total entropy change of the entire system.

50. •• The pV diagram in Figure 20 shows a heat engine operating on 0.850 mol of H_2. (See Table A at the end of this problem set.) Segment ca is isothermal. (a) Without doing any calculations, identify the segments during which heat enters the gas and those during which it leaves the gas. Explain your reasoning. (b) Find the thermal efficiency of this heat engine, treating the gas as ideal.

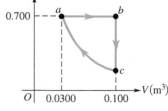
▲ **FIGURE 20** Problem 50.

51. •• Calculate the coefficient of performance of the engine in the previous problem if it is run in reverse, as a refrigerator.

▲ **FIGURE 19** Problem 48.

TABLE A   Molar heat capacities of gases at low pressure

Type of gas	Gas	$C_V(\text{J}/(\text{mol}\cdot\text{K}))$	$C_p(\text{J}/(\text{mol}\cdot\text{K}))$	$C_p - C_V(\text{J}/(\text{mol}\cdot\text{K}))$	γ
Monatomic	He	12.47	20.78	8.31	1.67
	Ar	12.47	20.78	8.31	1.67
Diatomic	H_2	20.42	28.74	8.32	1.41
	N_2	20.76	29.07	8.31	1.40
	O_2	20.85	29.17	8.31	1.40
	CO	20.85	29.16	8.31	1.40
Polyatomic	CO_2	28.46	36.94	8.48	1.30
	SO_2	31.39	40.37	8.98	1.29
	H_2S	25.95	34.60	8.65	1.33

The Second Law of Thermodynamics: Problem Set

ANSWERS TO SELECTED PROBLEMS

Conceptual Questions

1. For a refrigerator device, $|Q_H| = |Q_C| + |W|$. This says that the heat energy $|Q_H|$ deposited into the room is the same as the heat energy $|Q_C|$ removed from the food compartment plus the amount of mechanical energy required to operate the refrigerator (inputed to the device as electrical energy). The tubing is where heat flows from the device into the room.

5. For an air conditioner or refrigerator the amount of heat $|Q_H|$ that flows out of the device is greater than the heat $|Q_C|$ that flows into the device. In fact, $|Q_H| = |Q_C| + |W|$, where $|W|$ is the energy supplied to operate the device. If an air conditioner is set on the floor and plugged in, $|Q_C|$ is removed from the room but $|Q_H|$ is ejected into the room. Since $|Q_H|$ is larger than $|Q_C|$, the room is heated rather than cooled. A refrigerator also adds heat to the room in which it is placed. That heat must be removed, for example by a window air conditioner, or else the room will be heated.

7. The change in entropy depends not only on the heat flow but is also inversely proportional to the Kelvin temperature at which that heat flow occurs. The negative heat flow out of the hot object occurs at a higher temperature than the positive heat flow into the cold object, so the positive entropy change is greater than the negative entropy change and the net entropy change is positive.

9. No. The second law says this can never be the sole result of a process for an isolated system. But a device can cause this to happen if mechanical energy is inputed to the device. A refrigerator is an example of a device that moves heat from a cold object (the food) to a warm object (the room).

11. Both devices move heat energy from a cooler object to a warmer object. For a refrigerator the purpose of the device is to remove heat from the cooler object (the food compartment). The heat deposited into the warmer object (the room) is waste heat. For a heat pump operating in the winter, the purpose of the device is to deposit heat into the warmer object (the interior of the building).

13. In a hot object the random motions of the atoms (or molecules) are more energetic than in a cold object. When the two objects are in contact their atoms collide and in the collision kinetic energy is transferred from the atoms in the hot object to the atoms in the cold object. In the collisions energy is transferred in this direction and not in the reverse direction.

17. The coefficient of performance of a refrigerator is the ratio of the magnitude of the heat $|Q_C|$ removed at the low temperature reservoir to the magnitude of the work $|W|$ required to operate the device. Removal of $|Q_C|$ is the useful action of the device and $|W|$ is what you have to pay for, so it is most economical to operate a refrigerator with a large coefficient of performance.

Multiple-Choice Problems

1. B
3. A
5. A
7. B, D
9. C
11. A, D
13. C
15. B

Problems

1. 1.1×10^{14} J
3. (a) 6500 J (b) 34%

5. (a) 23% (b) 12,400 J (c) 0.350 g
   (d) 222 kW, 298 hp
7. (a) 25% (b) 970 MW
9. (a) 12.3 atm (b) 5470 J; process ca
   (c) 3723 J; process bc (d) 1747 J
   (e) 31.9%
11. 13.8
13. (a) 59.4% (b) 4060 J
15. (a) 1.62×10^4 J (b) 5.02×10^4 J
17. (a) 8.09×10^5 J (b) 3.37×10^5 J
    (c) 1.14×10^6 J
19. (a) 215 J (b) 378 K (c) 39.1%
21. (a) -3.72×10^3 J (b) 2.73×10^3 J
    (c) 42.3%
23. (a) -3.09×10^7 J (b) 2.5×10^6 J
25. (a) clockwise; heat enters in ab and leaves in cd (b) counterclockwise; heat enters in dc and leaves in ba; dc inside refrigerator and ba in room (c) counterclockwise; heat enters in dc and leaves in ba; dc inside house and ba outside (d) counterclockwise; heat enters in dc and leaves in ba; dc outside house and ba inside
27. 70 J/K; increases
29. (a) irreversible (b) 304.42 K (c) 470 J/K
31. -6.31 J/K
33. -4.8×10^{-3} J/K
35. 111 m^2
37. (a) 7.0% (b) 3.0 MW; 2.8 MW
    (c) 6×10^5 kg/h = 6×10^5 L/h
39. (a) $-73°$ C (b) 3.34×10^4 cycles
41. (b) $45°$ C (c) 58.9% (d) 206 J
    (e) 2.57×10^6 Pa
43. $1 - T_C/T_H$; same
45. 0.379 J/K
47. (a) 2.26%; no (b) 29.4 J; 1.30×10^3 J
    (c) 1.11×10^{-3} candy bars
49. (a) -143 J/K (b) 196 J/K (c) 0
    (d) 53 J/K
51. 6.17

589

Unit Conversion Factors

LENGTH

$1 \text{ m} = 100 \text{ cm} = 1000 \text{ mm} = 10^6 \text{ } \mu\text{m} = 10^9 \text{ nm}$

$1 \text{ km} = 1000 \text{ m} = 0.6214 \text{ mi}$

$1 \text{ m} = 3.281 \text{ ft} = 39.37 \text{ in.}$

$1 \text{ cm} = 0.3937 \text{ in.}$

$1 \text{ in.} = 2.540 \text{ cm}$

$1 \text{ ft} = 30.48 \text{ cm}$

$1 \text{ yd} = 91.44 \text{ cm}$

$1 \text{ mi} = 5280 \text{ ft} = 1.609 \text{ km}$

$1 \text{ Å} = 10^{-10} \text{ m} = 10^{-8} \text{ cm} = 10^{-1} \text{ nm}$

$1 \text{ nautical mile} = 6080 \text{ ft}$

$1 \text{ light year} = 9.461 \times 10^{15} \text{ m}$

AREA

$1 \text{ cm}^2 = 0.155 \text{ in.}^2$

$1 \text{ m}^2 = 10^4 \text{ cm}^2 = 10.76 \text{ ft}^2$

$1 \text{ in.}^2 = 6.452 \text{ cm}^2$

$1 \text{ ft}^2 = 144 \text{ in.}^2 = 0.0929 \text{ m}^2$

VOLUME

$1 \text{ liter} = 1000 \text{ cm}^3 = 10^{-3} \text{ m}^3$
$\quad = 0.03531 \text{ ft}^3 = 61.02 \text{ in.}^3$

$1 \text{ ft}^3 = 0.02832 \text{ m}^3 = 28.32 \text{ liters} = 7.477 \text{ gallons}$

$1 \text{ gallon} = 3.788 \text{ liters}$

TIME

$1 \text{ min} = 60 \text{ s}$

$1 \text{ h} = 3600 \text{ s}$

$1 \text{ d} = 86{,}400 \text{ s}$

$1 \text{ y} = 365.24 \text{ d} = 3.156 \times 10^7 \text{ s}$

ANGLE

$1 \text{ rad} = 57.30° = 180°/\pi$

$1° = 0.01745 \text{ rad} = \pi/180 \text{ rad}$

$1 \text{ revolution} = 360° = 2\pi \text{ rad}$

$1 \text{ rev/min (rpm)} = 0.1047 \text{ rad/s}$

SPEED

$1 \text{ m/s} = 3.281 \text{ ft/s}$

$1 \text{ ft/s} = 0.3048 \text{ m/s}$

$1 \text{ mi/min} = 60 \text{ mi/h} = 88 \text{ ft/s}$

$1 \text{ km/h} = 0.2778 \text{ m/s} = 0.6214 \text{ mi/h}$

$1 \text{ mi/h} = 1.466 \text{ ft/s} = 0.4470 \text{ m/s} = 1.609 \text{ km/h}$

$1 \text{ furlong/fortnight} = 1.662 \times 10^{-4} \text{ m/s}$

ACCELERATION

$1 \text{ m/s}^2 = 100 \text{ cm/s}^2 = 3.281 \text{ ft/s}^2$

$1 \text{ cm/s}^2 = 0.01 \text{ m/s}^2 = 0.03281 \text{ ft/s}^2$

$1 \text{ ft/s}^2 = 0.3048 \text{ m/s}^2 = 30.48 \text{ cm/s}^2$

$1 \text{ mi/h} \cdot \text{s} = 1.467 \text{ ft/s}^2$

MASS

$1 \text{ kg} = 10^3 \text{ g} = 0.0685 \text{ slug}$

$1 \text{ g} = 6.85 \times 10^{-5} \text{ slug}$

$1 \text{ slug} = 14.59 \text{ kg}$

$1 \text{ u} = 1.661 \times 10^{-27} \text{ kg}$

$1 \text{ kg has a weight of } 2.205 \text{ lb when } g = 9.80 \text{ m/s}^2$

FORCE

$1 \text{ N} = 10^5 \text{ dyn} = 0.2248 \text{ lb}$

$1 \text{ lb} = 4.448 \text{ N} = 4.448 \times 10^5 \text{ dyn}$

PRESSURE

$1 \text{ Pa} = 1 \text{ N/m}^2 = 1.450 \times 10^{-4} \text{ lb/in.}^2 = 0.209 \text{ lb/ft}^2$

$1 \text{ bar} = 10^5 \text{ Pa}$

$1 \text{ lb/in.}^2 = 6895 \text{ Pa}$

$1 \text{ lb/ft}^2 = 47.88 \text{ Pa}$

$1 \text{ atm} = 1.013 \times 10^5 \text{ Pa} = 1.013 \text{ bar}$
$\quad = 14.7 \text{ lb/in.}^2 = 2117 \text{ lb/ft}^2$

$1 \text{ mm Hg} = 1 \text{ torr} = 133.3 \text{ Pa}$

ENERGY

$1 \text{ J} = 10^7 \text{ ergs} = 0.239 \text{ cal}$

$1 \text{ cal} = 4.186 \text{ J (based on } 15° \text{ calorie)}$

$1 \text{ ft} \cdot \text{lb} = 1.356 \text{ J}$

$1 \text{ Btu} = 1055 \text{ J} = 252 \text{ cal} = 778 \text{ ft} \cdot \text{lb}$

$1 \text{ eV} = 1.602 \times 10^{-19} \text{ J}$

$1 \text{ kWh} = 3.60 \times 10^6 \text{ J}$

MASS–ENERGY EQUIVALENCE

$1 \text{ kg} \leftrightarrow 8.988 \times 10^{16} \text{ J}$

$1 \text{ u} \leftrightarrow 931.5 \text{ MeV}$

$1 \text{ eV} \leftrightarrow 1.074 - 10^{-9} \text{ u}$

POWER

$1 \text{ W} = 1 \text{ J/s}$

$1 \text{ hp} = 746 \text{ W} = 550 \text{ ft} \cdot \text{lb/s}$

$1 \text{ Btu/h} = 0.293 \text{ W}$

The International System of Units

The Système International d'Unités, abbreviated SI, is the system developed by the General Conference on Weights and Measures and adopted by nearly all the industrial nations of the world. The following material is adapted from B. N. Taylor, ed., National Institute of Standards and Technology Spec. Pub. 811 (U.S. Govt. Printing Office, Washington, DC, 1995). See also **http://physics.nist.gov/cuu**

Quantity	Name of unit	Symbol	Equivalent units
SI base units			
length	meter	m	
mass	kilogram	kg	
time	second	s	
electric current	ampere	A	
thermodynamic temperature	kelvin	K	
amount of substance	mole	mol	
luminous intensity	candela	cd	
SI derived units			**Equivalent units**
area	square meter	m^2	
volume	cubic meter	m^3	
frequency	hertz	Hz	s^{-1}
mass density (density)	kilogram per cubic meter	kg/m^3	
speed, velocity	meter per second	m/s	
angular velocity	radian per second	rad/s	
acceleration	meter per second squared	m/s^2	
angular acceleration	radian per second squared	rad/s^2	
force	newton	N	$kg \cdot m/s^2$
pressure (mechanical stress)	pascal	Pa	N/m^2
kinematic viscosity	square meter per second	m^2/s	
dynamic viscosity	newton-second per square meter	$N \cdot s/m^2$	
work, energy, quantity of heat	joule	J	$N \cdot m$
power	watt	W	J/s
quantity of electricity	coulomb	C	$A \cdot s$
potential difference, electromotive force	volt	V	$J/C, W/A$
electric field strength	volt per meter	V/m	N/C
electric resistance	ohm	Ω	V/A
capacitance	farad	F	$A \cdot s/V$
magnetic flux	weber	Wb	$V \cdot s$
inductance	henry	H	$V \cdot s/A$
magnetic flux density	tesla	T	Wb/m^2
magnetic field strength	ampere per meter	A/m	
magnetomotive force	ampere	A	
luminous flux	lumen	lm	$cd \cdot sr$
luminance	candela per square meter	cd/m^2	
illuminance	lux	lx	lm/m^2
wave number	1 per meter	m^{-1}	
entropy	joule per kelvin	J/K	
specific heat capacity	joule per kilogram-kelvin	$J/(kg \cdot K)$	
thermal conductivity	watt per meter-kelvin	$W/(m \cdot K)$	

Quantity	Name of unit	Symbol	Equivalent units
radiant intensity	watt per steradian	W/sr	
activity (of a radioactive source)	becquerel	Bq	s^{-1}
radiation dose	gray	Gy	J/kg
radiation dose equivalent	sievert	Sv	J/kg
SI supplementary units			
plane angle	radian	rad	
solid angle	steradian	sr	

Definitions of SI Units

meter (m)   The *meter* is the length equal to the distance traveled by light, in vacuum, in a time of 1/299,792,458 second.

kilogram (kg)   The *kilogram* is the unit of mass; it is equal to the mass of the international prototype of the kilogram. (The international prototype of the kilogram is a particular cylinder of platinum-iridium alloy that is preserved in a vault at Sèvres, France, by the International Bureau of Weights and Measures.)

second (s)   The *second* is the duration of 9,192,631,770 periods of the radiation corresponding to the transition between the two hyperfine levels of the ground state of the cesium-133 atom.

ampere (A)   The *ampere* is that constant current that, if maintained in two straight parallel conductors of infinite length, of negligible circular cross section, and placed 1 meter apart in vacuum, would produce between these conductors a force equal to 2×10^{-7} newton per meter of length.

kelvin (K)   The *kelvin,* unit of thermodynamic temperature, is the fraction 1/273.16 of the thermodynamic temperature of the triple point of water.

ohm (V)   The *ohm* is the electric resistance between two points of a conductor when a constant difference of potential of 1 volt, applied between these two points, produces in this conductor a current of 1 ampere, this conductor not being the source of any electromotive force.

coulomb (C)   The *coulomb* is the quantity of electricity transported in 1 second by a current of 1 ampere.

candela (cd)   The *candela* is the luminous intensity, in a given direction, of a source that emits monochromatic radiation of frequency 540×10^{12} hertz and that has a radiant intensity in that direction of 1/683 watt per steradian.

mole (mol)   The *mole* is the amount of substance of a system that contains as many elementary entities as there are carbon atoms in 0.012 kg of carbon 12. The elementary entities must be specified and may be atoms, molecules, ions, electrons, other particles, or specified groups of such particles.

newton (N)   The *newton* is that force that gives to a mass of 1 kilogram an acceleration of 1 meter per second per second.

joule (J)   The *joule* is the work done when the point of application of a constant force of 1 newton is displaced a distance of 1 meter in the direction of the force.

watt (W)   The *watt* is the power that gives rise to the production of energy at the rate of 1 joule per second.

volt (V)   The *volt* is the difference of electric potential between two points of a conducting wire carrying a constant current of 1 ampere, when the power dissipated between these points is equal to 1 watt.

weber (Wb)   The *weber* is the magnetic flux that, linking a circuit of one turn, produces in it an electromotive force of 1 volt as it is reduced to zero at a uniform rate in 1 second.

lumen (lm)   The *lumen* is the luminous flux emitted in a solid angle of 1 steradian by a uniform point source having an intensity of 1 candela.

farad (F)   The *farad* is the capacitance of a capacitor between the plates of which there appears a difference of potential of 1 volt when it is charged by a quantity of electricity equal to 1 coulomb.

henry (H)   The *henry* is the inductance of a closed circuit in which an electromotive force of 1 volt is produced when the electric current in the circuit varies uniformly at a rate of 1 ampere per second.

radian (rad)   The *radian* is the plane angle between two radii of a circle that cut off on the circumference an arc equal in length to the radius.

steradian (sr)   The *steradian* is the solid angle that, having its vertex in the center of a sphere, cuts off an area of the surface of the sphere equal to that of a square with sides of length equal to the radius of the sphere.

Numerical Constants

Fundamental Physical Constants*

Name	Symbol	Value
Speed of light in vacuum	c	$2.99792458 \times 10^8 \, \text{m/s}$
Magnitude of charge of electron	e	$1.60217653(14) \times 10^{-19} \, \text{C}$
Gravitational constant	G	$6.6742(10) \times 10^{-11} \, \text{N} \cdot \text{m}^2/\text{kg}^2$
Planck's constant	h	$6.6260693(11) \times 10^{-34} \, \text{J} \cdot \text{s}$
Boltzmann constant	k	$1.3806505(24) \times 10^{-23} \, \text{J/K}$
Avogadro's number	N_A	$6.0221415(10) \times 10^{23} \, \text{molecules/mol}$
Gas constant	R	$8.314472(15) \, \text{J/(mol} \cdot \text{K)}$
Mass of electron	m_e	$9.1093826(16) \times 10^{-31} \, \text{kg}$
Mass of proton	m_p	$1.67262171(29) \times 10^{-27} \, \text{kg}$
Mass of neutron	m_n	$1.67492728(29) \times 10^{-27} \, \text{kg}$
Permeability of vacuum	μ_0	$4\pi \times 10^{-7} \, \text{Wb/T} \cdot \text{m/A}$
Permittivity of vacuum	$\epsilon_0 = 1/\mu_0 c^2$	$8.854187817 \cdots \times 10^{-12} \, \text{C}^2/(\text{N} \cdot \text{m}^2)$
	$1/4\pi\epsilon_0$	$8.987551787 \cdots \times 10^9 \, \text{N} \cdot \text{m}^2/\text{C}^2$

Other Useful Constants*

Name	Symbol	Value
Mechanical equivalent of heat		$4.186 \, \text{J/cal} \, (15° \, \text{calorie})$
Standard atmospheric pressure	1 atm	$1.01325 \times 10^5 \, \text{Pa}$
Absolute zero	0 K	$-273.15°\text{C}$
Electron volt	1 eV	$1.60217653(14) \times 10^{-19} \, \text{J}$
Unified atomic mass unit	1 u	$1.66053886(28) \times 10^{-27} \, \text{kg}$
Electron rest energy	$m_e c^2$	$0.510998918(44) \, \text{MeV}$
Volume of ideal gas (0°C and 1 atm)		$22.413996(39) \, \text{liter/mol}$
Acceleration due to gravity (standard)	g	$9.80 \, \text{m/s}^2$

*Source: National Institute of Standards and Technology (**http://physics.nist.gov/cuu**). Numbers in parentheses show the uncertainty in the final digits of the main number; for example, the number 1.6454(21) means 1.6454 ± 0.0021. Values shown without uncertainties are exact.

Astronomical Data[†]

Body	Mass (kg)	Radius (m)	Orbit radius (m)	Orbit period
Sun	1.99×10^{30}	6.96×10^{8}	—	—
Moon	7.35×10^{22}	1.74×10^{6}	3.84×10^{8}	27.3 d
Mercury	3.30×10^{23}	2.44×10^{6}	5.79×10^{10}	88.0 d
Venus	4.87×10^{24}	6.05×10^{6}	1.08×10^{11}	224.7 d
Earth	5.97×10^{24}	6.38×10^{6}	1.50×10^{11}	365.3 d
Mars	6.42×10^{23}	3.40×10^{6}	2.28×10^{11}	687.0 d
Jupiter	1.90×10^{27}	6.91×10^{7}	7.78×10^{11}	11.86 y
Saturn	5.68×10^{26}	6.03×10^{7}	1.43×10^{12}	29.45 y
Uranus	8.68×10^{25}	2.56×10^{7}	2.87×10^{12}	84.02 y
Neptune	1.02×10^{26}	2.48×10^{7}	4.50×10^{12}	164.8 y
Pluto	1.31×10^{22}	1.15×10^{6}	5.91×10^{12}	247.9 y

[†]Source: NASA Jet Propulsion LaboratorySolar System Dynamics Group (**http://ssd.jpl.nasa.gov**), and P. Kenneth Seidelmann, ed., ***Explanatory Supplement to the Astronomical Almanac*** (University Science Books, Mill Valley, CA, 1992), pp. 704–706. For each body, "radius" is its radius at its equator and "orbit radius" is its average distance from the sun (for the planets) or from the earth (for the moon).

Prefixes for Powers of 10

Power of ten	Prefix	Abbreviation	Pronunciation
10^{-24}	yocto-	y	*yoc*-toe
10^{-21}	zepto-	z	*zep*-toe
10^{-18}	atto-	a	*at*-toe
10^{-15}	femto-	f	*fem*-toe
10^{-12}	pico-	p	*pee*-koe
10^{-9}	nano-	n	*nan*-oe
10^{-6}	micro-	μ	*my*-crow
10^{-3}	milli-	m	*mil*-i
10^{-2}	centi-	c	*cen*-ti
10^{3}	kilo-	k	*kil*-oe
10^{6}	mega-	M	*meg*-a
10^{9}	giga-	G	*jig*-a or *gig*-a
10^{12}	tera-	T	*ter*-a
10^{15}	peta-	P	*pet*-a
10^{18}	exa-	E	*ex*-a
10^{21}	zetta-	Z	*zet*-a
10^{24}	yotta-	Y	*yot*-a

Examples:

1 femtometer = 1 fm = 10^{-15} m

1 picosecond = 1 ps = 10^{-12} s

1 nanocoulomb = 1 nC = 10^{-9} C

1 microkelvin = 1 μK = 10^{-6} K

1 millivolt = 1 mV = 10^{-3} V

1 kilopascal = 1 kPa = 10^{3} Pa

1 megawatt = 1 MW = 10^{6} W

1 gigahertz = 1 GHz = 10^{9} Hz

APPENDIX

The Greek Alphabet

Name	Capital	Lowercase	Name	Capital	Lowercase
Alpha	A	α	Nu	N	ν
Beta	B	β	Xi	Ξ	ξ
Gamma	Γ	γ	Omicron	O	o
Delta	Δ	δ	Pi	Π	π
Epsilon	E	ϵ	Rho	P	ρ
Zeta	Z	ζ	Sigma	Σ	σ
Eta	H	η	Tau	T	τ
Theta	Θ	θ	Upsilon	Υ	υ
Iota	I	ι	Phi	Φ	ϕ
Kappa	K	κ	Chi	X	χ
Lambda	Λ	λ	Psi	Ψ	ψ
Mu	M	μ	Omega	Ω	ω

From Appendix B of *College Physics*, Ninth Edition, Hugh D. Young. Copyright © 2012 by Pearson Education, Inc. Published by Pearson Addison-Wesley. All rights reserved.

Periodic Table of the Elements

Group Period	1	2	3	4	5	6	7	8	9	10	11	12	13	14	15	16	17	18
1	1 **H** 1.008																	2 **He** 4.003
2	3 **Li** 6.941	4 **Be** 9.012											5 **B** 10.811	6 **C** 12.011	7 **N** 14.007	8 **O** 15.999	9 **F** 18.998	10 **Ne** 20.180
3	11 **Na** 22.990	12 **Mg** 24.305											13 **Al** 26.982	14 **Si** 28.086	15 **P** 30.974	16 **S** 32.065	17 **Cl** 35.453	18 **Ar** 39.948
4	19 **K** 39.098	20 **Ca** 40.078	21 **Sc** 44.956	22 **Ti** 47.867	23 **V** 50.942	24 **Cr** 51.996	25 **Mn** 54.938	26 **Fe** 55.845	27 **Co** 58.933	28 **Ni** 58.693	29 **Cu** 63.546	30 **Zn** 65.409	31 **Ga** 69.723	32 **Ge** 72.64	33 **As** 74.922	34 **Se** 78.96	35 **Br** 79.904	36 **Kr** 83.798
5	37 **Rb** 85.468	38 **Sr** 87.62	39 **Y** 88.906	40 **Zr** 91.224	41 **Nb** 92.906	42 **Mo** 95.94	43 **Tc** (98)	44 **Ru** 101.07	45 **Rh** 102.906	46 **Pd** 106.42	47 **Ag** 107.868	48 **Cd** 112.411	49 **In** 114.818	50 **Sn** 118.710	51 **Sb** 121.760	52 **Te** 127.60	53 **I** 126.904	54 **Xe** 131.293
6	55 **Cs** 132.905	56 **Ba** 137.327	71 **Lu** 174.967	72 **Hf** 178.49	73 **Ta** 180.948	74 **W** 183.84	75 **Re** 186.207	76 **Os** 190.23	77 **Ir** 192.217	78 **Pt** 195.078	79 **Au** 196.967	80 **Hg** 200.59	81 **Tl** 204.383	82 **Pb** 207.2	83 **Bi** 208.980	84 **Po** (209)	85 **At** (210)	86 **Rn** (222)
7	87 **Fr** (223)	88 **Ra** (226)	103 **Lr** (262)	104 **Rf** (261)	105 **Db** (262)	106 **Sg** (266)	107 **Bh** (264)	108 **Hs** (269)	109 **Mt** (268)	110 **Ds** (271)	111 **Rg** (272)	112 **Uub** (285)	113 **Uut** (284)	114 **Uuq** (289)	115 **Uup** (288)	116 **Uuh** (292)	117 **Uus** (294)	118 **Uuo**

Lanthanoids

57 **La** 138.905	58 **Ce** 140.116	59 **Pr** 140.908	60 **Nd** 144.24	61 **Pm** (145)	62 **Sm** 150.36	63 **Eu** 151.964	64 **Gd** 157.25	65 **Tb** 158.925	66 **Dy** 162.500	67 **Ho** 164.930	68 **Er** 167.259	69 **Tm** 168.934	70 **Yb** 173.04

Actinoids

89 **Ac** (227)	90 **TH** (232)	91 **Pa** (231)	92 **U** (238)	93 **Np** (237)	94 **Pu** (244)	95 **Am** (243)	96 **Cm** (247)	97 **Bk** (247)	98 **Cf** (251)	99 **Es** (252)	100 **Fm** (257)	101 **Md** (258)	102 **No** (259)

For each element the average atomic mass of the mixture of isotopes occurring in nature is shown. For elements having no stable isotope, the approximate atomic mass of the longest-lived isotope is shown in parentheses. For elements that have been predicted but not yet confirmed, no atomic mass is given. All atomic masses are expressed in atomic mass units $(1\ u = 1.660538728(83) \times 10^{-27}\ kg)$, equivalent to grams per mole (g/mol).

Index

Page references followed by "f" indicate illustrated figures or photographs; followed by "t" indicates a table.

A

Absolute pressure, 445-446, 468, 549-551
Absolute temperature, 479, 517-519, 547-548, 573-574
Absolute temperature scale, 479
absolute zero, 479, 513, 578, 595
acceleration
 and air resistance, 67, 79
 and mass, 105, 133, 184, 199, 205, 238, 273, 307, 323, 350, 468
Acceleration
 angular acceleration, 287, 307-310, 318, 347-351, 387, 593
 centripetal, 89-90, 98, 174-178, 195, 211, 294, 342, 358
 constant angular acceleration, 290-292, 307-310, 329, 349
 due to gravity, 53, 67-68, 79, 99, 116, 129, 145, 167, 185-186, 221, 241, 295, 336, 381-382, 388, 469-470, 595
acceleration
 in Newton's second law, 115
Acceleration
 in simple harmonic motion, 371-372, 390
 in uniform circular motion, 90, 97, 174-175, 195, 342, 374
 instantaneous angular acceleration, 289
 linear acceleration, 292-294, 323, 348
 Newton's second law of motion, 110
 nonuniform, 185
 of center of mass, 270-271, 335
 periodic motion, 174, 367-369, 387
 radial component of, 293-294, 328
 signs of, 40-41, 144
 simple harmonic motion, 368-369, 387-388
 straight-line motion, 31, 73, 288
 two-dimensional motion, 72
acceleration
 weight during, 388
Acceleration due to gravity, 53, 67-68, 79, 99, 116, 132, 145, 167, 185-186, 221, 241, 295, 336, 381-382, 388, 469-470, 595
Acceleration vector, 76-79, 193, 295
Acceleration vectors, 91
Accelerometer, 144-145, 169
Acid rain, 501
acoustics, 124, 406
actin, 150, 223
Action/reaction pair
 identifying, 159, 212
 propulsion, 272-273
Addition
 of vectors, 13, 26, 251
 significant figures, 22
adhesive forces, 454
adiabatic process, 539
Adiabatic processes, 547-548, 570
Air
 density, 24, 85, 154, 243, 282, 347, 368, 399, 439-441, 468-474, 488, 508, 549, 563
 speed of sound in, 24, 64, 399, 435
 thermal conductivity, 494-495, 509-510, 587
Air conditioners, 505, 533, 562
air drag, 66-68, 89, 147, 207, 237-239, 257, 303, 463
air masses, 129
Air motion
 forces, 1, 26, 43-44, 89, 105-110, 131, 138, 164-165, 173-177, 201, 204, 239-242, 251-258, 277, 287, 319, 347-349, 361-363, 388-389, 396, 441, 470, 505, 524-525
air pressure, 442, 467, 519, 553

Air resistance, 2-3, 31, 63, 72, 97-100, 108, 164, 188, 195, 206, 242, 272, 278, 471
Alcohols, 579
Aldrin, Buzz, 116
Alloy, 4, 112, 468, 481, 512, 594
Alpha Centauri, 68
Alpha decay, 372
Alpha particle, 281
alpha particles, 284
altitude, 7, 53, 72, 186-187, 199, 217, 241, 549
altitudes, 519, 550
Aluminum
 breaking stress, 368, 485
 bulk modulus, 365-366, 393
 coefficient of linear expansion, 480, 507
 coefficient of volume expansion, 482-483, 507
 Young's modulus, 363-364, 392-393, 484
alveoli, 28
Amino acid, 24
ammonia, 522-523, 549, 565
Ammonia
 critical-point data, 523
 triple-point data, 522-523
Ampere, 593-594
amplitude, 369, 387, 397-402, 433-434
Amplitude
 forced oscillation, 383-384
 of sound waves, 399
 of waves, 399, 432
Angular acceleration
 tangential component of acceleration, 293
 tangential component of instantaneous acceleration, 294
 torque and, 321-322, 349
Angular displacement, 288, 314, 326-327, 392
Angular momentum
 conservation of, 204-206, 249, 279, 299-300, 307, 318, 351, 371, 460, 518
 definition, 112, 251, 290, 327, 370
 initial angular momentum, 335, 351
 of particle, 251, 297, 321
angular momentum
 spin, 307, 350-351, 461, 518
Angular momentum
 vector angular momentum, 341
Angular position, 290-291, 319, 393
Angular velocity
 precession angular velocity, 342-343
 vector angular velocity, 341
Animals
 sweating or panting, 491
 temperature control, 508
 tendons, 163
Anti-damping force, 384
Antifreeze, 440
Antimatter, 113
Antimony
 heat of fusion, 489-490, 513
 heat of vaporization, 489-491, 513
Antineutrino, 285
Antinodes
 longitudinal standing waves, 410-411, 434
Antiparallel vectors, 13-14
apparent weight, 197, 470
Aqueous humor, 469
Arc length, 288
Archimedes's principle, 448, 470
Area, 23-24, 50-51, 66, 148, 163, 185, 200, 204-205, 243, 267-268, 282, 311, 362-367, 387-389, 416-417, 441-442, 469, 475, 506, 521, 551, 565, 586-587, 591, 593-594
arteries, 69, 382, 444, 469, 495
Arteriosclerosis, 460
arthritis, 426
asteroids, 246, 278
astronomy, 425
Atmosphere

composition of, 437
Atmospheric moisture
 temperature changes, 492, 514, 530, 548
Atmospheric pressure, 389, 411, 442-445, 467, 477-478, 511, 515, 549, 595
Atomic clock, 4
Atomic mass, 264, 595, 599
atomic mass unit, 595
Atomic mass units, 264, 599
Atomic physics
 hydrogen atom, 553
Atomic structure
 electric charge, 205
 isotopes, 599
 quantum mechanics, 205
atoms
 characteristics of, 524
 kinds of, 494, 515, 556
Atom(s)
 nucleus of, 158, 285
Atoms
 periodic table
  groups, 524
atoms
 size of, 5, 481
Atoms
 subatomic particles, 118
ATP (adenosine triphosphate)
 in photosynthesis, 572
ATP molecule, 150, 232
AU, 599
Average angular acceleration, 289-290
Average angular velocity, 288, 314
Average power, 232-234, 243-244, 328-329, 350, 416, 587
average speed, 4, 34-35, 61-64, 99, 293, 515, 550
Average velocity
 freely falling body, 24
Avogadro's number, 515-516, 595
axis tilt
 change of, 31, 76, 113, 156, 253, 288, 315, 330, 374, 526
Axon, 51

B

Ballistic pendulum, 260
bar, 26, 164, 196, 223, 282, 307-308, 349, 362-363, 389, 465, 496-497, 506, 591
barometer, 446-447, 472
barometric pressure, 447
bars, 13, 241, 314, 447, 496-497, 505, 588-589
Basalt, 186
Batteries
 ideal, 531
 real, 3
Beam
 width, 359
Beat frequency, 419-421, 436-438
Beats, 29, 68, 277, 313, 419-421, 436-438
benzene, 440, 474
Bernoulli's equation
 applications, 138-139, 232, 271, 425-426, 459, 471, 500, 523
 deriving, 216, 446
 problem-solving, 8, 44, 83, 124, 138-139, 176, 214-215, 254, 299, 323, 378, 409, 458, 481, 519, 562
Bernoulli's principle, 457
Beta decay, 158, 285
Beta particle, 285
big bang, 158, 432
binary star systems
 close, 147-148, 228, 250, 334, 357, 383, 427, 478, 559
Binary-star systems
 mass in, 205, 271, 380
 planets in, 182

biomass, 579
Black holes, 190-191
black holes
    evaporation of, 508
Blackbody, 500, 510
bladder, 470
blood, 6, 25, 43, 68-69, 166, 191, 197, 243, 382, 389,
    440, 469-473, 475, 507, 553, 586-587
Blood pressure, 447-448, 469-471, 491
blood vessels, 382, 460, 469
body temperature, 477, 507-509, 552
Boiling
    of water, 477-478, 505-510, 538, 549, 558, 585-587
Boiling point, 478, 513, 549
Boltzmann constant, 527, 595
Boltzmann's constant, 545
bone, 27, 164-165, 282, 353, 362, 389, 401
Boundary conditions, 404
Boyle, Robert, 517
Boyle's law, 517
Brahe, Tycho, 192
brain, 1, 64, 166, 223, 327, 416, 432, 469, 491, 508
Breakers, 481
Breaking stress, 368, 389, 485
brightness, 559
brightness, of stars
    apparent, 197
British system of units, 6
Brownian motion, 51
Btu, 486-487, 562, 585, 591
bubble chamber, 113
Bulk modulus, 365-366, 387, 523
Buoyancy, 154, 439, 470, 532
Buoyant force, 449-451, 467-468

C
Calculations
    consistency of units, 9, 481
    order-of-magnitude estimates, 11
    scientific notation, 10-11
    with scalar quantities, 12
calorie, 487, 591, 595
Calorimetry, 492, 509
Cameras, 83, 500
Cancellation, 414-415
Candela, 593-594
Capacitors
    components of, 24
capillaries, 69, 197, 473
Capillarity, 451, 471
Carbon
    forms of, 512
carbon atomic mass number of
    fusion of, 496
Carbon dioxide
    dry ice, 522
Carnot cycle, 569-572, 586
Carnot engine, 569-572, 584-587
Carnot engines, 572
Carnot refrigerator, 571-572, 584
carriers, 108
Cars
    power distribution systems, 578
Cartesian coordinates, 73
Catapults, 108
Cavendish balance, 183-184
Cavendish, Henry, 183
CDs, 309
cells
    animal, 492, 577
    plant, 77, 579
    types of, 366, 492
Celsius temperature scale, 477
Centaur, 274
Center of curvature, 200
Center of gravity, 321, 353-355, 449
center of gravity (CG), 336
Center of mass
    motion of, 2-3, 72, 97, 108, 129-130, 148, 166,
        181-182, 204-205, 242, 257, 282,
        287-288, 307, 321-322, 361, 387-388,
        398-400, 433, 454, 494, 530-531, 547
    rotation around, 351
    velocity, 7, 50, 65-67, 72-74, 97-103, 105, 130,
        138, 162, 173-174, 210, 239, 250-252,
        278-281, 287-289, 307-309, 319,
        350-351, 369, 390, 425, 454-455, 471,
        525, 593
Centrifugal force, 177-178, 195

Centripetal acceleration, 89-92, 98, 174, 197, 294
Centripetal force, 175, 195-196, 211, 296, 334
cephalopods, 285
cgs metric system, 117
chain reaction, 25
changes
    chemical, 150, 205, 483, 516, 547, 560
    physical, 2-4, 109, 144, 186, 205-206, 273, 318,
        376, 456, 488, 505, 517, 573
Chaotic behavior, 464
Charge distribution
    symmetric, 184, 269, 312
Charges
    like, 39
    moving, 37
    opposite, 118-120, 156
Charles, Jacques, 517
Charles's law, 517
chemical bonds
    polar, 549
Chemical classification, matter
    pure, 206, 477, 516, 549, 561
    solution, 9, 34, 75, 117, 151, 189, 221, 247,
        260-262, 298, 335, 442, 482, 516,
        571-572
    suspension, 335-337
Chemical elements
    periodic table, 516, 550, 599
chemical energy, 150, 205, 247, 532, 577
chemical reactions
    and energy transfer, 532
    in cells, 491
    rate of, 246, 491, 559
chloroplasts, 572
cholesterol, 472
Circle of reference, 371
Circuit diagram symbols
    bulb, 450
    capacitors, 24
    ground, 26, 54, 82, 115, 129, 168-169, 197-199,
        212, 353-355, 560, 594
Circular motion
    dynamics of, 180, 324-326
    in walking, 182
    period of, 44, 66, 97, 174, 308-309, 376, 387, 420,
        579
    satellite motion, 173, 198
    uniform circular motion, 89-91, 97, 173-175, 195,
        210, 342, 374
Circular orbits, 101, 182
Circulation patterns
    global, 498
circulatory system
    heart, 27, 68-69, 121, 167, 232, 243, 437, 470, 498
circumpolar stars
    paths of, 129
Classical physics
    limits of, 205
clouds
    weather, 507-508
coal, 113, 240, 472, 485, 532, 558, 585
cochlea, 416
Coefficient of kinetic friction, 148, 165-171, 199,
    238-240, 280, 314, 349-350
Coefficient of linear expansion, 480, 507
Coefficient of rolling friction, 150, 166
Coefficient of static friction, 150, 165-167, 178, 197,
    327, 359, 392
Coefficient of viscosity, 462
Coefficient of volume expansion, 482-483, 507
coefficients, 151, 161-162, 245, 481-483, 512, 567
Coefficient of kinetic friction, 166, 243
Coefficient of performance
    Carnot, 570-572, 584-587
cohesive forces, 542
Cold reservoir, 506, 561, 584-585
"Cold weld", 148
collisions
    elastic, 159, 205-206, 244, 263-264, 277-278, 525
Collisions
    elastic collisions, 262-263, 281
collisions
    inelastic, 257-259, 278
Collisions
    inelastic collisions, 257-258, 280
    pressure and, 547-548
combustion, 491, 532-533, 560, 585
comets, 200
communications satellites, 97, 199, 309

competition, 34, 87
Component vectors, 16, 107
Components of, 16-20, 24, 32-33, 73-81, 99-100, 107,
    131, 139-140, 174, 226, 250-252, 279,
    294-295, 320-321, 353, 375, 421, 448
Components, of vectors, 16, 26, 251
Compression, 155, 167, 218, 241, 259, 278, 362-365,
    389, 399, 521, 549, 560, 584-586
Compression ratio, 544, 563-565, 584-585
Compression stroke, 540, 549, 563-565
compressions, 399
Compressive strain, 363
Compressive stress, 362-363
Concentration, 440
condensation, 489, 521
Conduction, 493-503, 505, 517, 583
Conductor, 497, 506, 594
conductors, 493-494, 594
Conductors
    current, 494-495, 593-594
    isolated, 492
    parallel conductors, 594
Configuration, 217, 353
Conjunction, 568
conservation
    of angular momentum, 318, 351, 518
    of energy, 204-207, 241, 249, 299-300, 307, 331,
        439, 467, 491-492, 514, 518, 577-579
    of momentum, 249-260, 278-279, 461
Conservation laws
    universal conservation law, 331
Conservation of angular momentum, 318, 351, 518
Conservation of energy
    in a well, 300, 324, 537
    in thermodynamics, 536, 578, 587
    with conservative forces, 226
    with nonconservative forces, 229
Conservation of mass
    in fluid flow, 455
Conservation of mechanical energy, 224, 253, 371,
    460
Conservation of momentum, 249, 279
Conservative forces, 219
Conservative system, 219
Consistency of units, 9, 23, 378, 458, 481
Consonance, 421
Consonant interval, 427
Constant angular acceleration, 290-292, 307-310, 329,
    349
Constant-acceleration motion
    in a plane, 72, 99, 113, 264, 293
    in a straight line, 3, 32, 63, 78, 108-110, 130, 171,
        175, 196, 272, 280, 524
Constant-pressure process, 538
Constant(s)
    Newton's, 2, 107-117, 129, 138, 162, 173, 197,
        204, 237, 249-253, 287, 307, 321-322,
        381, 525-526
Constant-temperature process, 540
Constant-volume gas thermometer, 478
Constant-volume process, 534, 547
Constructive interference, 414-415, 435
Contact force, 106, 138, 326
Contact forces, 147
Continuity equation, 455-456
Convection, 491, 505
convection currents, 498
Coordinate, 18-19, 31-32, 72, 107, 139, 179, 210, 252,
    287-288, 319, 368, 402-403
Coordinate systems
    Cartesian, 19
    displacement and, 32-33, 208, 373, 396
Copernican revolution
    Newton's laws and, 187
copper, 363, 388, 440, 468, 481-482, 507, 588
Cornu spiral applications
    wire, 156-157, 161, 433, 476
cosmic microwave background (CMB)
    temperature of, 498-500
Coulomb, 593-594
Coulomb's law
    principle of superposition, 183
Crab Nebula, 198
crater, 240
crests, 396, 433
Critical mass, 25
Critical point, 522-523, 549
Critical pressure, 523
Critical temperature, 521

Crystal lattice, 494, 524
Crystals, 464, 480, 505
Current
    creating, 499
    displacement, 25, 72-74, 156, 368-370, 457
currents
    electric, 499
    surface, 495-496
Curveball, 461
cycles per second, 562-563, 585
Cyclic processes, 560

D

Damped oscillations, 383
Damping, 383-384, 387
dark matter
    cold, 476, 518, 547-548, 561, 583-585
    extraordinary, 495
Decay
    rate, 498-500
Deceleration, 40, 117
Decibels, 3, 417, 431
Deep space, 283
Deformation elastic forces
    Hooke's law, 155-156, 167-169, 217-219, 240,
        362-369, 389
degrees, 288, 308-309, 389, 477-480, 505, 519, 547,
    573, 584
Degrees of freedom, 531, 554-555
Delta, 32, 121, 597
Density
    critical, 25, 460, 521-523, 549
    of gases, 517, 555
density
    of Pluto, 199-200
Density
    of fluids, 439, 498
    uncompressed, 27
deposition, 456
Derivative, 36
Destructive interference, 414-415, 435
development
    human, 1, 27-28, 500-501
dew, 489
Dewar flask, 500
Diamond
    crystal structure of, 524
diaphragm, 410-411, 434
Diastolic pressure, 447, 469
Diatomic gas, 545, 550, 585
Diatomic molecules, 531
Diesel cycle, 564-565
Diesel engine, 237, 543-544, 554, 564, 584-585
Diesel, Rudolph, 564
Difference tone, 421
digestion, 587
Dinosaurs, 246
Dipole oscillator
    moment, 376
    resonant frequency, 376
direct proportion, 111
direction, 1, 23, 32-35, 61-63, 73-78, 97, 106-111,
    130-132, 140, 161, 173-175, 195, 208-211,
    239, 250, 279-281, 287, 307, 318, 349, 363,
    390, 396-397, 431, 441, 474, 494-495,
    524-525, 551, 559, 586, 594
Disorder
    entropy, 558, 583-584
Displaced fluid, 449
Displacement
    average velocity, 32-34, 61-64, 73-75
    from equilibrium, 159, 235, 368, 391, 402, 438
    of sinusoidal waves, 404
Displacement nodes, 410-412, 434
Displacement vectors, 12, 222, 269
Dissipative force, 207
Dissipative forces, 209, 383, 393
Dissonance, 421
Distillation, 579
Disturbance, 395-397
divides, 51, 177, 221, 343
DNA, 158, 192, 328
Dolphins, 425, 435
Doppler effect
    light, 4, 147, 183, 225, 348, 387-388, 416, 432, 498
    sound, 87, 122, 413-416, 431-432, 564
Dose equivalent, 594
double helix, 328
Double-slit interference

intensity of, 416, 433
drag, 66-68, 89, 117, 132, 147-148, 167, 176, 207,
    237-238, 257, 281, 303, 463, 471
Drag force, 154-155, 463, 471
Driven oscillation, 383
Driving force, 383-384
Driving frequency, 384
Dry ice, 507, 522
DVDs, 309
Dynamics, 31, 105, 131, 143, 173, 287, 323-326, 439,
    596

E

eardrum, 390, 416, 435, 469
Earth
    atmosphere of, 507, 549
    circumference of, 66, 92, 201, 392
    diameter of, 5, 25, 134, 197, 309-310, 350, 388,
        468, 507-508
    dimensions of, 509-510, 519
    escape speed from, 550
    gravitational attraction, 53, 106, 157-158, 191-193
    gravity map, 185
    interior of, 186, 390
    internal structure of, 158
    life on, 205, 559
    rotation of, 201, 351, 381
Earth, atmosphere
    composition, 186, 200, 437
    layers of, 440, 510
    scale height, 100
Earth, interior
    crust, 499
    inner core, 186, 426
    outer core, 186
Earthquake, 332, 361, 387, 396-397, 432
Earthquakes, 69, 395
Earths (extrasolar planets)
    super, 109
Earth's history
    Extinctions, 246
    model of, 101, 181, 580
Echo, 403, 433
Echolocation, 3
ecology, 484, 513
EER, 567
efficiency, 24, 207, 241, 262, 417, 491, 512, 558,
    583-588
Efficiency, 561
Einstein, Albert, 27
Elastic collision, 262-265, 278, 525
Elastic collisions, 262-263, 281
Elastic deformation, 206, 367
Elastic forces, 138, 167, 224-226
Elastic modulus, 362
Elastic potential energy, 206-208, 240, 258-259, 278,
    385, 390, 438
Elasticity, 217, 262, 367-368, 524
    tensile stress, 362-364, 388
    volume stress, 362
Electric charge
    electric field, 115, 190, 593
electric circuits
    parallel, 310, 328, 594
    series, 27, 353, 533-535, 574
Electric current, 157, 369, 487, 593-594
electric currents
    and magnetic fields, 205
Electric field
    calculating, 28, 536
    cells and, 327
    pulses, 431
    work, 204-206, 327-329, 350-352, 488, 531-536,
        559, 593-594
Electric fields
    transformations of, 206
    uniform, 308, 342, 349-355, 532, 559
Electric flux
    definition of, 329, 486, 573
Electric motors
    power of, 243, 328, 498-499
Electric potential
    batteries, 2, 531
Electric potential energy
    mechanical energy and, 226
Electric power, 312, 416, 560, 585
Electric resistance, 593-594
electrical potential energy, 2
Electrical power, 233, 237, 417, 578-579

electrical resistance, 24, 476
Electricity
    ampere, 593-594
    atoms and, 494
    conductor, 594
    coulomb, 593-594
    electric current, 593-594
    electric resistance, 593-594
    insulators, 494
Electromagnetic fields
    forces and, 159, 362
Electromagnetic induction
    experiments, 494
Electromagnetic interactions, 157-158
Electromagnetic radiation, 4, 494
Electromagnetic spectrum, 432
Electromagnetic wave, 425
Electromagnetic waves
    energy in, 158, 259-260, 371, 390, 498
    in vacuum, 2-4
    momentum of, 261
    sinusoidal waves, 398, 434
    speed of, 4, 68-69, 198-200, 246, 260, 390, 395,
        432-437
Electron microscope, 372
Electron volt, 595
Electrons
    acceleration of, 24, 112, 594
    mass of, 25, 112, 284-285, 493, 594
    velocity of, 111, 284-285
Electroweak interaction, 158
Elements, 204, 301, 340, 425, 488-489, 516, 599
elements
    heavy, 301
elements (chemical)
    atoms in, 516
    periodic table of, 516, 599
Ellipse, 188
elongation
    greatest, 387
Emission spectrum
    molecular, 502
Emissivity, 498-500, 510, 587
energy
    bond, 531
Energy
    conservation of energy, 204-206, 241, 249,
        299-300, 307, 331, 439, 467, 492, 514,
        532
    dark, 3, 499
energy
    internal, 158, 205, 237, 252-253, 277, 302, 307,
        327, 475, 507-509, 521, 548, 560,
        585-587
    kinetic, 149-151, 204-208, 237-243, 250, 277-281,
        287, 307-308, 325, 347, 368, 387, 435,
        476, 508, 524-528, 547-549, 559-560,
        584
Energy
    nuclear energy, 205
    of springs, 157
    relativistic, 249
energy
    solar, 190, 210, 237, 282, 381, 445, 500-501, 527,
        578-579, 587
Energy
    stored, 206-207, 238, 258, 280-281, 312, 328, 382,
        507, 554, 577
energy
    thermal, 238, 284, 357, 475-476, 506, 517-522,
        547, 559, 584-585, 593
Energy
    transfer and transformation, 205
    transformation of, 206, 560
energy
    transitions, 4, 514, 521, 549
Energy
    units of, 4-5, 82, 217, 237, 266, 366, 417, 494,
        518-519
    vacuum, 2-4, 445, 467, 498, 512, 535, 553, 558,
        583, 594, 595
energy
    work–energy theorem, 212-214, 300, 456
Energy diagrams
    equilibrium positions, 247
Energy efficiency rating (EER), 567
energy of atoms
    of electrons, 287
    rate of flow of, 468

temperature and, 205, 437, 475-476, 510, 517, 550, 559
unit of, 4, 117, 209, 288, 319, 361-362, 440, 479, 518, 594
Energy transformations, 475, 533, 561
energy transport
convective, 498-499
radiative, 500
Energy-conversion research, 579
Energy-flow diagram, 561
Engines
steam engines, 533, 564
English units, 8, 132
Entropy, 558, 583-584, 593
Environment, 43, 105-106, 129, 191, 252, 277, 358, 511, 532, 567, 585
Equal temperament, 427
Equation of continuity, 465
Equation of motion, 323-325
equation of state, 517, 556
Equations
for projectile motion, 81
of motion with constant acceleration, 44, 114, 215
Equations of motion
Equations of state
ideal-gas equation, 517-518, 547
equator, 4, 97, 199, 596
Equilibrium
conditions for, 141, 336
displacement from, 217, 371-372, 391
dynamic, 318
equilibrium
mechanical, 127, 147, 223-226, 241-242, 371-372, 390, 395-403, 437-438, 447, 481, 508, 531-533, 559-560
Equilibrium
one-dimensional, 140
phase, 367, 398, 488-492, 508, 518, 560
phase equilibrium, 489, 521, 565
equilibrium
rotational, 317-319, 347-348, 370, 531, 554-555
Equilibrium
stable, 341, 385, 449, 521
static, 148-151, 161, 178, 245, 326, 359, 392
thermal equilibrium, 475-477, 506, 532, 547, 559
two-dimensional, 141
unstable, 158, 454
Equilibrium processes, 532, 559
Equilibrium states, 517, 559
Equipartition theorem, 555
Eris (dwarf planet)
discovery of, 190
Erosion, 456
escape speed, 191, 527-528, 550
Escape speed
of Mercury, 469-470, 507
escape velocity, 68, 188, 284
ethane, 554
ethanol, 440, 474, 476, 507, 579
Ether, 565
ethyl alcohol, 490, 513
eukaryotic cells
first, 76, 415
European Southern Observatory, 139
eV, 591
Evaporation, 475, 508, 547, 583
Evaporative cooling, 491, 508
event horizon, 190-191
Events
time of, 266-267
excretion, 191
exercise, 25, 151-152, 241, 292, 309, 357, 392, 498, 507
exoplanet detection
transit, 426
exoskeleton, 224
Expansion, 399, 478, 507, 533-535, 547-548, 559-560, 583
Expansion of water, 483-484, 510
Experiment, 2, 63, 107, 150, 167, 185, 198, 259, 335-336, 415, 467, 477, 508-509, 536
Explosions, 25, 426
exponents, 11
External forces, 253-258, 277, 322
Extinction, 246
extinctions, 246
Extracorporeal shock-wave lithotripsy, 426
extrasolar planet(s)
detecting, 282

orbital periods of, 199

F

Fact, 11, 27, 36, 67, 75, 107, 149, 165, 175, 196, 207-208, 242-243, 256, 291, 312, 336-337, 381, 402, 431, 446, 467, 484-485, 513, 534, 558-559, 589
Falling objects
kinetic energy, 204-208, 237-243, 250, 277-281, 287, 307-308, 325, 347, 371-373, 390, 435, 494, 508, 556, 559-560, 589
fault, 332
Fermi, Enrico, 11
Fever, 487, 509
Field point
magnetic field, 101, 593
First law of thermodynamics, 531, 550
Floating, 450
flowers, 175
Fluid dynamics, 439
Fluid friction, 154
Fluid mechanics
buoyancy, 154, 439, 470
Pascal's law, 365, 442-444
pressure
in liquid, 450
pressure in a fluid, 365, 442-443, 474
surface tension, 439, 471
viscosity, 448, 471-472
Fluid flow
laminar, 455-456, 473
Poiseuille's law, 463
turbulence, 456, 471
Venturi meter, 460, 473
viscosity and, 462, 471
Fluids
capillarity, 465, 471
ideal fluid, 462
pressure in, 463, 470-471
real fluids, 466
Focal length
effective, 209, 244-245, 307, 318-319, 382, 462, 475, 505
fog, 69, 129, 471, 489
Food calorie, 486
Force
acceleration and, 53, 79, 103, 133, 145, 176, 309, 323
force
and motion, 31, 72, 138, 207, 293
Force
anti-damping force, 384
buoyant, 449-451, 467-468
buoyant force, 449-451, 467-468
centrifugal, 178, 195
centrifugal force, 177-178, 195
centripetal force, 175, 195-196, 211, 296, 342
combining, 12, 266, 280, 296, 309, 322
conservative, 219
conservative forces, 219
contact force, 106, 138, 326
dissipative force, 207
elastic forces, 138, 167, 226
external, 222, 254, 277, 322, 357, 443-444, 470, 549
external forces, 254, 277, 322
free-body diagram, 123, 129, 139-141, 163-164, 175-179, 195, 211, 320, 353-357, 450-451
friction force, 106, 132-133, 148-152, 161-162, 175, 199, 215, 239, 286, 326-327, 350, 368
from potential energy, 247, 372
force
gravitational, 53, 79-80, 106, 134, 173, 195-198, 206-208, 238, 272, 301, 321, 379, 442, 473, 524
Force
gravitational force, 60, 89, 134, 183-184, 197-198, 206, 336
in circular motion, 173, 196
in nature, 148, 182, 524
internal forces, 266, 286, 322
kinetic-friction force, 148
magnetic, 101, 205, 593-594
measuring, 9-10, 106, 129, 166, 391, 447, 473, 548
force
net, 79, 107, 129, 144, 167, 174-177, 201, 215, 239, 266, 279, 300, 321-322, 348, 469
Force

Newton's first law, 109-110, 135, 138, 174, 336
Newton's third law, 123-124, 129, 140-141, 162, 182, 237, 271, 286, 322, 359, 526
nonconservative, 226, 242, 300, 335, 382
nonconservative forces, 226, 242, 300, 335, 382
normal force, 106, 132-133, 139, 167, 175, 195, 211, 239, 286, 323, 349-350
restoring, 245, 369
resultant, 13-15, 25-27, 94, 107, 211, 266, 310, 449
SI units of, 7, 24, 163, 530
spring force, 222, 368
static-friction force, 148
superposition of, 107
superposition of forces, 107
force
support, 26, 101, 116, 163, 201, 241, 337, 353, 387, 401, 443, 467
Force
total force, 134, 183, 245, 275, 321, 442, 469, 484-485, 533
types, 27, 106, 206-207, 361-362, 446, 550
Force constant, 133, 156-157, 161-162, 217-219, 238, 280, 364, 388
Force per unit area, 363, 441, 525-526
force vector, 25, 107, 139, 193, 319
Forced convection, 497-498
Forced oscillation, 383-384
Forces, 1, 26, 43-44, 89, 105-110, 131-133, 138-145, 164-165, 173-177, 201, 204, 239-242, 249, 277, 287, 319, 347-349, 361-363, 388-389, 396, 441-442, 470, 480, 505, 515
Force(s)
fundamental, 7, 54, 79, 111, 138, 161, 182-183, 204, 272, 318, 530
force(s)
strong, 110, 129, 181, 195, 240, 350, 368, 474
weak, 149, 195
Forward direction, 26, 41, 129, 195, 239
fossil fuels, 501, 560
Foucault, Jean-Bernard-Léon, 381
Foucault pendulum, 381, 510
fracture, 68, 168, 282, 367-368, 392
Frame of reference, 57, 92, 110, 129, 138-139, 178, 216, 254, 287, 325, 381
frames of reference, 57-58, 92-93, 110, 216, 251, 425
Free convection, 497
Free expansion, 535, 559, 583
free fall, 53, 67, 79, 97, 116-118, 146, 185, 195, 220-221, 301, 311, 325-326, 452
Free fall
moon in, 158
Free-body diagrams, 122-127, 132-134, 140, 165-166, 180, 215, 286, 324, 369
free-fall, 190, 393
Freely falling objects, 2, 53, 68, 81, 391
Freezing, 440, 477, 505, 523, 586-587
Freezing point, 440, 483-484, 505, 523
Frequency
beat, 27, 419, 436-437
for standing waves on a string, 407
frequency
natural, 383-384, 387-388, 417
Frequency
of oscillation, 376, 387
periodic wave, 398
simple pendulum, 380-381, 387
frequency
wave, 397, 432-433, 593
frequency of waves, 425
fresh water, 449-450, 470, 554, 560
Fresnel equations
metal, 148, 331, 492
friction, 56, 86, 108, 129, 142-143, 162, 178-179, 195, 207-208, 238-239, 253, 280, 300, 309, 322, 347, 368-369, 387, 444, 558-560
Friction
coefficients of, 167
rolling, 116, 142, 166, 178, 243, 284, 301, 309, 325-326, 350
rolling friction, 150, 166, 246, 303
Friction force, 106, 132-133, 147-152, 161-162, 175, 199, 212, 239, 286, 326-327, 350, 368
Frictionless surface, 109, 132, 144, 242, 280, 390
Front, 8, 32, 64, 98, 129, 170, 176, 199, 220, 245, 294, 309, 355, 374, 422, 436-437, 442, 474, 567
frost, 489
fruit, 241
Fuel, 24, 32, 64, 130, 147, 262, 277, 532, 554, 560,

585-586
fundamental forces, 158
Fundamental frequency, 407-410, 431
fungi, 83
Fusion
    nuclear, 501, 549, 559-560, 585
    proton, 549

G

g, 6, 79, 182, 438, 446, 514, 516, 548, 562, 588
Galaxies
    masses of, 331
    receding, 425
    visible, 425
galaxy, 6, 302, 318, 516
Galilean transformation
    of position, 207
Galilei, Galileo, 2, 105
Galileo Galilei, 2, 105
Galileo (Galileo Galilei)
    and acceleration, 54, 105
Gamma, 597
Gamma rays
    applications of, 425
Gas
    greenhouse, 501
gas giants, 527
Gas thermometer, 478, 577
gas(es)
    and temperature, 502, 517, 552, 587
gases
    atmospheric pressure and, 520
Gases
    compression, 521, 549, 560
    diatomic, 527, 550, 587-588
    expansion, 478, 533-534, 547-548, 559-560
    free expansion, 541, 559
    frictional effects, 150
    molar heat capacities, 525, 555, 564, 588
    molecular properties, 524
    monatomic, 437, 516, 550-551, 588
    phase changes, 522
    standard temperature and pressure (STP), 519, 550
Gauge pressure, 445-446, 468-469, 520, 549
Gaussian beam
    characteristics, 377, 421
general theory of relativity, 190
generators, 578
geocentric model of universe
    early development of, 192
Geometric optics
    principles of, 2-3, 335
Geosynchronous orbits, 97
Geothermal power plant, 560
Giant stars, 25
Glaucoma, 444, 469
gliding, 285
global positioning system (GPS), 91
Global warming, 347, 468, 510, 578
gold, 11, 175, 284-285, 384, 389, 440, 468, 477, 513
GPS, 91
Grand Canyon, 469
Grand Unified Theory (GUT), 158
Granite, 142-143
granules, 77
Graph
    velocity versus time, 42-44, 70
graphite, 264, 358, 376, 523
gravitation
    law of, 2, 173
Gravitational constant, 182-183, 595
Gravitational fields, 190
Gravitational force
    torque due to, 321, 359
    weight and, 125, 133, 149, 178, 214, 323, 352, 450, 472
Gravitational forces, 109, 157-158, 182-184, 198, 231, 321, 524
Gravitational interactions, 118, 157-158, 173, 235
Gravitational mass, 118
Gravitational potential energy, 206-208, 238, 301-302, 313, 457, 588
Gravity
    and pressure, 465, 473, 549-550
gravity
    and speed, 132, 241, 282
    and weight, 115-116, 132, 392, 441
    center of, 3, 78, 100-101, 161, 181, 198, 227, 272,

278, 295, 320-321, 352-359, 449
Gravity
    center of gravity, 321, 353-355, 449
    Newton's law of, 182, 197
    Newton's law of gravitation, 182, 197
    on Mars, 67-68, 102, 186, 381-382, 391
    particles and, 182
    quantum, 192
    rotation and, 321
    sensing, 3, 67, 77
gravity
    specific, 2-3, 122, 210, 337, 401-403, 441, 469, 550
    strength of, 353, 388
    zero, 52, 67-68, 78-80, 98, 108-109, 129-130, 139-140, 162, 181, 195, 209-212, 237-238, 252-253, 277, 320, 355, 390, 448-449, 595
Greek alphabet, 597
greenhouse effect, 501, 578-579
Greenhouse gas, 501
Ground state, 594
GUT, 158
gyroscope, 318, 354

H

hair cells, 416
Halftone, 427
Harmonic series, 407
Harmonics, 407, 434-435
health, 200, 521, 578-579
health risks, 200
hearing, 3, 25, 390, 410, 433
Hearing
    human ear, 415-416
    temporary deafness, 418
Heat
    calorimetry, 492, 509
    heat capacities, 487, 508, 524-525, 550, 564, 588
    heat transfer, 475, 505, 536-537, 554, 559, 586
heat
    kilocalorie, 486
    latent, 489
Heat
    of fusion, 489, 513, 559, 586
    of vaporization, 489, 508-509, 523
    quantity, 205-206, 476, 507, 516, 560-563, 593-594
heat
    quantity of, 232, 476, 507, 516, 560-561, 593-594
Heat
    solar energy, 501, 579
    specific heat capacity, 486-487, 506, 530, 550, 576, 593
    thermal expansion, 481, 507
    work and, 204-206, 240, 531, 585
Heat capacities
    ideal gas, 515, 549-552, 563-564, 595
    molar heat capacity, 524, 555
Heat current, 494-495, 562
Heat engines
    heat pump, 567, 583
    ideal-gas, 520, 547, 577-578
    internal combustion engines, 560, 585
    perfect, 25, 584
    refrigerators, 475, 531, 559, 583
    thermal efficiency, 561-564, 584-588
    thermal efficiency of, 561
Heat of combustion, 491, 532, 562-564, 585
Heat of fusion, 489-490, 513, 574, 586
Heat of sublimation, 491
Heat of vaporization, 489-491, 508-509, 521
Heat flow, 485, 506, 532, 558-559, 587
Heat pump, 567, 583
heat transfer
    by conduction, 494-495, 510, 532
    by convection, 501
    by radiation, 491, 510, 587
Heat transfer
    conduction, 493-499, 505, 532, 583
    convection, 491, 505
    during volume changes, 533
    radiation, 491, 505, 579, 587, 594
helium, 25, 197, 281, 401, 434, 448-449, 467, 478, 512-513, 516, 548-549
Helium balloon, 449
Hertz, 370, 420, 593-594
Hertz, Heinrich, 370
Hertzsprung-Russell (H-R) diagram
    development of, 157

"High C", 399
High-energy particle collisions, 158
High-energy physics
    conservation laws, 205, 280
    nuclear fusion, 549, 559
    nuclear reactions, 158, 560
    nuclear fission, 264
High-mass star
    end of, 25, 39, 62, 73, 100, 106, 132, 140, 168-169, 177, 196-197, 220, 242, 273-274, 282, 299, 308-309, 320, 348-350, 364, 390-392, 398, 433, 446, 467, 484, 506-508, 544, 548-549, 563-564, 587
Hooke, Robert, 155, 362
Hooke's Law, 155-156, 161, 217-219, 240, 362-369, 389
horizon, 190-191
    event, 190-191
Hot reservoir, 506, 560-561, 584
hour, 6, 24, 33, 108, 209, 237, 308, 508-509, 550, 562-563, 585
Hourglass, 28
Hubble Space Telescope, 2
human body
    center of gravity of, 336, 358-359, 449
Human body
    evaporative cooling, 498, 508
    eye, 390, 469
    fever, 487, 509
    heat transfer within, 498
human body
    muscles, 27-28, 150, 163, 182, 241, 354-356, 388, 495
Human body
    oxygen absorption, 520
    radiation and, 499
human body
    senses, 157
    skeleton, 382
Human body
    temperature, 12, 27, 239, 414, 434, 475-480, 507-512, 519, 547-549, 559-561, 585-589
    weightlessness, 191, 199-200, 391
Human ear, 415-416
humans
    environmental impact of, 578
Humidity, 481, 505
Hurricanes, 94, 287, 425, 518
Huygens probe, 198
Hydraulic jack, 443
Hydraulic lift, 443-444, 470
Hydrogen atom
    mass, 24-25, 284-285, 400-401, 432-433, 489, 512, 515-517, 548-549
Hydrometer, 440
hydrothermal vents, 478
hypothesis, 68
Hz, 370, 391, 399, 431, 593, 596

I

ice, 89, 105, 131-132, 147, 173, 196, 240, 256, 279, 312, 329, 355, 470, 475-476, 505, 522-523, 549, 558, 585-586
Ice
    melting, 488-489, 510, 522, 574
Ideal blackbody, 500, 510
Ideal gas
    adiabatic processes, 547-548, 570
    cooling, 475, 564-566, 585
    isothermal expansion, 535, 548, 570
    kinetic molecular theory, 524
    partial pressure, 519-521
    properties, 364, 389, 395, 475-476, 515, 551, 577
ideal gas law, 539, 556
Ideal gases, 520, 547
Ideal insulator, 476
Ideal fluid, 454
Ideal-gas constant, 518
Ideal-gas equation, 517-521, 547
Ideal-gas processes
    constant-pressure process, 538
    constant-temperature process, 540
    constant-volume process, 534, 547
    pV diagram, 521, 548, 563-564, 585
    work in, 532, 548, 586
Idealized models, 1, 147, 361, 439
Illuminance, 593
Image, 158, 294, 426, 435, 491, 524
Imaging, 297, 370, 426

Impulse, 266-269, 277
Inclined plane, 170, 302-303
Incompressible fluids, 455, 473
Inelastic collision, 258-261, 278, 333, 568
Inelastic collisions, 257-258, 280
Inertia, 109, 297-302, 307-308, 321-322, 350-352
Inertial frame of reference, 110, 129, 138, 178, 216, 254, 287, 325, 381
Inertial mass, 112
Infrared light, 500
Infrared radiation, 500, 510
infrared waves, 498
Initial angular momentum, 335, 351
Initial conditions, 292
Inner core, 186, 426
insects, 368, 425, 452, 550
Instantaneous acceleration
    angular motion, 292
Instantaneous angular acceleration, 289
Instantaneous angular velocity, 288
Instantaneous power, 232-233, 329
instantaneous speed, 39, 74
Insulators, 3, 494
Intensity, 416-420, 431-433, 593-594
Intensity level, 418-419, 431-432
Interacting systems
    analyzing, 120, 331
Interaction, 105-106, 147-148, 182, 206, 253-254, 278, 333, 485, 542
Interactions, 118-119, 138, 173, 205, 266, 331, 476-477, 524
interference
    constructive, 415, 435
Interference
    constructive interference, 414-415, 435
interference
    destructive, 415, 435
Interference
    destructive interference, 414-415, 435
    mechanical waves, 413-416, 434-436
Internal combustion engines, 560, 585
internal energy, 205, 237, 261, 521, 548, 560
Internal energy
    entropy and, 573-575
Internal forces, 252-253, 286, 322
International System of Units, 593-594
Inverse relation, 51
inverse square law
    for light, 499
Inverse-square relation, 51
Ions, 365, 524, 594
iridium, 4, 594
iron, 157, 259, 309, 339, 354, 363, 387, 440, 467, 481, 506-507
Irreversible processes, 559-560
Isobaric process, 539-540
Isolated system, 204-206, 253, 286, 331-333, 492, 537, 575, 589
Isotherm, 543
Isothermal (constant-temperature) process, 543
Isothermal process, 539-541, 573-574
Isotherms, 521
Isotope, 549, 599
Isotopes, 599

J

joints, 388, 480
joule, 209, 485-486, 567, 593-594
Joule (J), 209, 594
Joule, James, 485
Jovian planet
    moons of, 190
jumping, 134, 164, 224
Junction, 496-497
Jupiter, 100, 130, 187, 200, 241, 282, 472, 527, 596
    gravity of, 187, 199, 471
    rotation rate of, 199-200

K

Kelvin, Lord, 479
Kelvin scale, 478-479, 578
Kelvin temperature scale, 479, 577
Kepler, Johannes, 192
kidney, 426
Kilogram, 4-6, 23, 106, 241-242, 296, 440, 486, 506, 516, 574, 593-594
kilogram (kg), 594
kilowatt, 5, 232, 237, 579

kilowatt-hour, 233-234, 237, 579
Kinematics, 31, 69, 105, 173, 290
    circular motion, 173-174
kinetic energy
    and momentum, 254, 331
Kinetic energy
    equation for, 9, 81, 153, 224, 254, 296, 324-326, 366, 406, 456, 493
    falling object, 219
    gas molecules, 518, 548
    momentum and, 250, 278-279, 331, 351, 525
    random kinetic energy, 526
    rotational kinetic energy, 298, 307, 347, 531
    total kinetic energy, 205, 258, 277, 297, 308, 334-335, 548
    translational kinetic energy, 302, 312, 526-528, 549
Kinetic friction, 148-151, 161, 178, 199, 208, 238-240, 280, 314, 327, 349-350
Kinetic-friction force, 148
Kundt's tube, 410-411

L

Laminar flow, 463
Laminar flow, 455-456
lander, 53, 67, 143, 186-187, 469
larynx, 434
Laser
    operation, 330
Laser beam, 183, 309
Laser light, 309
latent heat, 489
Latent heat of fusion, 489
lattice, 494, 524
Launch angle, 81, 103
Lava, 499
law, 2, 108-110, 129, 138, 167-168, 173, 197, 204-206, 237, 250-253, 280, 307, 321-322, 359, 362-369, 389, 442-444, 476-477, 517, 547, 558-562, 584
law of gravitation, 2, 173, 197
Law of inertia, 110
Law of thermodynamics, 476-477, 531-532, 550, 558-560, 583-584
Leaning Tower of Pisa, 2, 53-54, 98
Lens
    design, 426
Lever, 319, 348
Lever arm, 319
life
    origin of, 68, 148, 452
life sciences, 475
Lifetime, 25
Lift, 26, 67, 115-116, 129, 152, 176, 205, 237, 340-342, 351, 389, 443-444, 470-472, 515, 554, 587-588
light
    and gravitation, 176-178, 199-201
    frequencies of, 387, 432
Light
    interference, 415
    laser light, 309
    propagation of, 403, 433
light
    sources of, 416
Light
    visible light, 24, 190, 247, 390, 432, 498, 510
light
    white, 25, 163, 244
Light waves
    Doppler effect for, 425
Light year, 68, 591
lightning, 64, 399, 431
light-years, 200
limestone, 528
Limit, 8, 24, 31, 74, 101, 107, 170, 182, 232-233, 245, 288-289, 368, 389, 421, 479, 578
Line of action, 319-320, 449
Linear acceleration, 292-294, 323, 348
Linear momentum, 251, 318, 352
Linear thermal expansion, 480
Linear velocity, 293
liquid nitrogen, 549
Liquid-in-tube thermometer, 477
Liquids
    boiling, 488, 513, 522-523
    evaporation, 475, 511, 547
    negative pressure, 454
    structure of, 387, 416, 475, 524
Lithotripsy, 426

Load, 168, 212, 388-389, 401, 554
Longitudinal standing waves, 410-411, 434
Longitudinal wave, 396
longitudinal waves, 396-397
Longitudinal waves
    sound waves as, 399
Loop, 244-245, 284, 452, 534, 550-551
Loudness, 399, 431
Loudspeakers, 384, 415
low-mass stars
    convection in, 498
Lumen, 593-594
lungs, 28, 450, 470, 508, 521, 549
Lux, 593

M

Machine, 66, 143, 168, 173, 204, 241, 268, 277, 307, 355-356, 383, 469, 559-560, 586
macroscopic world, 223
Magnetic fields, 205
magnetic fields
    Earth's, 100-101
Magnetic force
    direction of, 15, 26-27, 32, 78-79, 100, 106-107, 132, 144-145, 161, 173-175, 196-198, 208-211, 239, 254, 280-281, 293-295, 310, 318, 354-355, 375, 396, 524, 594
    effects of, 55, 72, 191, 243, 391, 454, 471
    magnitude of, 13-15, 24, 53, 73, 100-102, 106, 133-135, 139-141, 164-166, 174, 200-201, 214-216, 239, 266, 277-279, 293-296, 310, 319-321, 351-352, 369, 388-390, 450-451, 471, 525-526
    right-hand rule for, 341
Magnetic flux density, 593
magnitude, 1, 23-26, 43, 61-62, 73-79, 99-102, 105-106, 131-135, 139-142, 161, 173-177, 198, 208-209, 246, 250, 277, 293-296, 307, 318-325, 351-352, 362-364, 388, 416, 441-444, 471, 489, 525-526, 554, 561, 586, 595
    absolute, 91, 445, 471, 490, 526-527, 553, 561, 595
Main sequence
    leaving, 561
mammals, 3, 170
Manometer, 446-447, 473
Marianas Trench, 389, 445
Mars, 7, 67-68, 102, 115, 169, 186-187, 199-200, 284, 391, 469, 518, 549, 596
    surface of, 103, 114, 169, 185-187, 198-200, 283, 391, 468-470, 549-550
    water on, 101, 122, 470
Mars Exploration Rover, 169
mass
    and density, 399, 488
    and volume, 28, 364, 518, 548
Mass
    inertial, 110, 129, 138, 178, 216, 251, 325, 381, 400
    molar, 516, 548, 564
    Newton's second law, 110, 131, 144, 164-165, 176-177, 199, 213, 250-253, 307, 321-322
    of astronomical objects, 190, 272
    weight compared, 199
    zero-gravity environment, 129, 252, 277
Mass density, 433, 593
mass extinction, 246
mass extinctions, 246
Mass flow rate, 456
mass(es)
    of black holes, 191
    of electron, 595
Mass(es)
    of planets, 157, 173, 527
mass(es)
    of proton, 595
Mass(es)
    of the Moon, 116, 184, 198, 221, 284, 309, 382, 507
matter
    kinetic theory of, 524, 549
Matter
    molar mass, 516, 548-549
matter
    phases of, 515, 549, 578
Mean free path, 547
Meandering, 456

Measurement
  units, 3, 223, 440-441
Mechanical energy
  dissipation, 207
  elastic potential energy, 206-208, 240, 258-259,
    278, 385, 390, 438
  gravitational potential energy, 206-208, 238,
    301-302, 313, 588
  total mechanical energy, 207, 237, 371-372, 390
mechanical equilibrium, 532-533, 569
Mechanical interaction, 127
Mechanical thermostats, 481
Mechanical waves
  beats, 68, 277, 419-421, 436-438
  intensity, 416-420, 431-433, 593-594
  mathematical description, 401-402, 433
  wave speed, 397-398, 433
Mechanics, 7, 31, 105, 138, 192, 204-205, 249, 347,
  372, 398, 439, 515
Medical applications
  lithotripsy, 426
  of radiation, 499-500
  thermography, 500
  ultrasonic imaging, 426
Medium, 51, 106, 367, 395-401, 434, 493
  for electromagnetic waves, 425
Melting
  of ice, 488-491, 509-511, 522-523, 574, 585-587
Melting point, 490, 513
mercury barometer, 446
metals
  transition, 514
Meteor, 68, 99, 240, 258
meteorology, 441
metric system, 4-5, 117
microscopic level, 148, 207, 547
Microwaves, 4, 432
Middle C, 399, 434
migration, 101
Milky Way Galaxy
  disk, 269, 297-298, 308, 318
  plane of, 298, 310, 319
  size and shape of, 3
millimeters of mercury, 469-470
Miniature machines, 223
mining, 501
minute, 5-6, 27, 68-69, 113, 199, 232, 244, 254-255,
  289, 308-310, 331, 354, 390, 397, 432, 480,
  511, 550, 585
Modeling, 168, 351, 364, 440
Models, 1, 79, 147, 361, 439
Molar heat capacity, 524, 555
Molar mass, 516, 548-549
Molar specific heat, 530
Molar specific heats
  at constant pressure, 541-543, 550-552, 564, 587
  at constant volume, 527, 550-551, 564, 587
mole, 515, 555, 593, 599
Molecular bonds, 531
Molecular speed, 528, 547
Molecular speeds, 528-529, 573
Molecular structure
  diatomic molecules, 531
Molecular vibration, 554
Moment, 99, 134, 167, 191, 297-302, 307-308,
  319-326, 349-350, 376
Moment arm, 319-324, 358-359
Moment of inertia, 297-302, 307-308, 321-322,
  350-352
momentum
  and collisions, 258
  and impulse, 268
  and kinetic energy, 204, 250, 278-279, 331, 351
Momentum
  angular, 205, 251, 318-319, 347-348, 462, 518
  angular momentum, 205, 251, 318, 347, 518
  center of mass, 269-272, 278, 335-337, 347-348
  components, 113-114, 250-252, 279, 330, 348, 526
  conservation of angular momentum, 318, 351, 518
momentum
  decreasing, 352, 462
Momentum
  elastic collision, 262-265, 278, 525
  impulse, 267-269, 277
  impulse and, 267, 281
momentum
  increasing, 462, 524
Momentum
  kinetic energy and, 205, 262

linear momentum, 251, 318, 352
  rocket propulsion, 272, 283
  total momentum, 251-258, 277
Monatomic gases, 531
Moon (Earth)
  orbital speed of, 189, 198
Moon (Earth's)
  and gravity, 115
  orbit of, 186, 199, 286
Moon(s)
  of Jupiter, 100, 200, 241, 282
  of Mars, 199, 549
  of Saturn, 470, 507
moons (planetary)
  Neptune, 190
motion
  Brownian, 51
Motion
  constant-acceleration motion, 59, 80
motion
  describing, 3, 31, 72, 105, 287, 331, 385, 390, 433
Motion
  kilogram, 4, 106, 241-242, 296, 440, 516, 574
  net force
    vector, 12, 31-32, 72-73, 102, 106-110, 148,
     171, 174-176, 196, 209, 268-269,
     294-296, 320, 354, 374
motion
  Newton's laws of, 2, 72, 105, 129
  Newton's first law of, 108
  Newton's second law of, 110
  projectile, 72, 97, 108, 187-188, 222, 257, 325, 464
Motion
  projectile motion, 72, 99-100, 187, 227, 325
  proper, 4, 309, 388, 416, 567
  speed
    in units, 82, 264
motion
  translational, 302-304, 307, 323, 352, 526-527, 554
Motion
  translational motion, 302, 323, 526, 554
motion
  vibrational, 371, 526, 554
Motion diagrams
  acceleration vectors, 91
  complete, 14, 66, 92, 102, 120, 132, 149, 169, 173,
    199, 204, 254, 288, 307, 352, 369-370,
    393, 398, 461, 574
  displacement vectors, 12, 222, 269
  examples of, 1, 50, 79, 122-123, 138, 224-225,
    258, 301, 325, 361, 395-396, 524
  velocity vectors, 14, 93, 425
Motors, 65, 150, 243, 308, 328, 426
Mount Everest, 445, 520
Musical tones
  difference tone, 421
  harmonics, 410, 434
  "high C", 399
  organ pipe, 411-414, 431-432
  overtones, 412, 434
  piano, 399, 431
  pitch, 377, 413-414, 431
  string instruments, 427
  timbre, 414
  wind instruments, 410, 431
mutations, genetic
  point, 327-328
myosin, 150, 232

N

Nanomachines, 150
NASA, 6-7, 116, 158, 185-186, 200, 208, 274, 302,
  318, 392, 516, 577, 596
Natural convection, 497-498
Natural frequency, 383-384
natural philosophy, 105
natural sciences, 395
Negative pressure, 454
Negative work, 210, 238, 393, 534, 572
Neptune
  rings of, 190
nervous system
  central, 110, 197, 322, 456, 531, 579
neurons
  motor, 51
Neutron, 25, 198, 285, 357, 440, 474, 549, 595
neutron star, 25, 198, 357, 440, 474
neutrons, 25, 112, 258, 357
Newton, Isaac

laws of motion, 105-106, 192
Newton (N), 594
Newtonian mechanics, 205
Newtonian synthesis, 192
Newton's laws, 2, 72, 105, 129, 187, 204, 249, 287,
  439, 525
Newton's laws of motion
  contact forces and friction, 147
  equilibrium problems, 138, 336
  force, 12, 31, 72, 102, 105, 129-131, 139-142,
    161-171, 173-185, 195-201, 204,
    238-243, 260, 277-278, 293, 310,
    318-324, 349-350, 362-365, 387-392,
    396, 448-449, 525-526, 593-594
  first law, 108-110, 135, 138, 174, 336, 381, 532,
    558-560, 583-584
  second law, 110, 131, 143-146, 164-166, 174, 199,
    213, 250-252, 307, 321-322, 526,
    558-560, 583-584
  third law, 118-121, 129, 140-141, 162, 182, 223,
    247, 252, 322, 359, 526, 578
Newton's first law of motion, 108
Newton's second law of motion
  for rotational motion, 318
  in terms of momentum, 251
Newton's third law of motion
  conservation of momentum and, 259
  reasoning with, 478
Night sky, 99
nitrogen
  liquid, 489-491, 511, 515, 549-550, 565
Nodal points
  table, 21, 40, 61, 99, 130, 148, 161, 258, 292, 308,
    341-342, 352, 397, 440-441, 470-472,
    522-524, 552, 587-588
node, 410, 431
Noise, 150, 417-418, 431-432, 579
Noise control, 426
Nonconservative forces, 226, 242, 300, 335, 382, 393
Non-equilibrium processes, 532, 559
Non-equilibrium states, 517
normal, 106, 132-133, 139, 162, 175, 195, 211-212,
  239, 253, 284, 323-324, 349-350, 368, 389,
  404-405, 433, 441, 469-471, 477-479,
  508-509, 520-521, 567, 586
Normal force
  kinetic-friction force and, 148
North Pole, 4, 359, 468
Nuclear energy, 205
Nuclear force, 158
Nuclear fusion, 549, 559
nuclear fusion
  in stars, 158
  mass and, 10, 196, 205, 246, 259, 282, 514
Nuclear power, 501, 578-579, 585
Nuclear reactions, 158, 560
Nuclear reactors
  hazards of, 578
Nuclear fission, 264
nucleus
  atomic, 6, 23-24, 158, 264
Nucleus
  beta decay, 158, 285
nucleus
  cell, 25, 51
  comet, 200
Nucleus
  properties of, 548-550
  radius of, 25, 197, 282
Nucleus/nuclei
  of comet, 200
Numerical constants, 10, 595-596
nylon, 141, 163, 388, 401, 467

O

observable universe
  limit of, 182
ocean floor, 433, 478
ocean water, 285, 501, 508
Ocean, waves, 395
ocean waves, 395
oceanography, 398
Oceans
  seawater, 445, 469
octane, 564
Octave, 413, 432
ohms, 24
One-dimensional equilibrium, 140
Oort equation

second, 7-9, 23-24, 32-33, 63, 80, 113-118, 144-145, 174, 209, 251-253, 297, 321, 377, 390, 404, 433, 452, 471-472, 488, 517, 560-566
Open-tube manometer, 446
Operational definition, 3
optic nerve, 444
Optical instruments
  microscope, 524
  telescopes, 139, 432
Optical parametric oscillator (OPO)
  tuning, 369, 390, 427, 436
Orbital period, 195
orbital resonance
  rings, 190
orbiter, 7
Orbits
  circular, 90-91, 97, 181-183, 197-199, 210, 245, 309
orbits
  elliptical, 187
  geosynchronous, 97, 199
Order-of-magnitude estimates, 11
Ordinary matter, 158
organ, 410-414, 431-432
Organ pipe, 411-414, 431-432
organelles, 572
Oscillation
  damped and forced oscillations, 382, 391
Oscillations
  angular frequency, 379-380, 390-391
  damped, 382-383, 391
  driven, 383
  frequency of, 381-384, 390-392
  vertical, 391-392
Otto cycle, 563-565, 585
Outer core, 186
outer planets, 195
Overtones, 407-408, 434
oxygen gas, 550, 587
oxygen molecule, 516, 549

P

panspermia, 68
Parabola, 82, 98, 372
Parabolic trajectory, 82, 187, 272, 277
Parallel plates
  potential, 207-208, 238, 300-301, 524, 593-594
Parallel-plate capacitor
  capacitance of, 594
Particles
  system of, 251, 277-278, 593-594
particle(s)
  waves and, 3, 395-396
pascal (Pa), 441
Path, 3, 25, 35-36, 72-76, 97, 113, 173-181, 207, 257, 281, 294-295, 315, 321, 375, 392-393, 414-415, 454, 494, 534-536, 547-548, 574-575
pc, 522-523
Pendulum, 2, 28, 197, 244, 260, 368, 387-388, 396, 510
  ballistic, 260
Percent elongation, 367
Perfect fifth, 427
Performance coefficient, 565-567, 584-585
Period
  orbital, 189, 195
Periodic mechanical waves, 397, 432
Periodic motion
  pendulum, 2, 197, 260, 368, 387-388, 396
Periodic table, 516, 550, 599
permeability, 595
Permeability of vacuum, 595
Permittivity, 595
Phase, 69, 186, 367, 398, 488-492, 508, 518, 549, 560
Phase changes
  critical point, 522-523, 549
  triple point, 523, 578
Phase diagram, 521-522
Phase equilibrium, 489, 521, 565
phases of matter
  changes of, 536, 548
Phosphor, 368
photosynthesis, 247, 572
Photovoltaic cells, 578-579
Physical constants, 595
Physical laws, 1, 327, 376, 464, 573

physical properties, 376, 523
Physical quantity, 3-4, 109, 205, 297, 318
physical state, 488
Physical theories, 1, 492
physics, 1-3, 23-24, 31-32, 61, 71, 97, 105, 129-130, 137, 161, 173, 195, 203-206, 237, 249, 277, 287, 307, 317, 347, 361, 387, 395, 431, 439, 467, 475, 505, 515, 547, 557, 583, 591, 593, 595, 597, 599
Physics
  historical perspective, 192
Piano, 164, 351, 368, 399, 431
Pitch, 66, 109, 377, 390, 408, 431
placenta, 355
Planck constant
  reduced, 68, 166, 200, 237, 267, 280, 332-334, 377, 399, 484, 510, 527, 594
Planck's constant, 595
Plane
  acceleration in, 66-67, 75, 176, 309
  relative velocity in, 92, 101
Planet X, 99, 132, 309, 472
Planetary motion
  and Newton's laws, 133-134
  laws of, 2-3, 41, 72, 105, 129, 138, 192, 204, 572
Planetary system
  discovery, 190
Planet(s)
  giant, 25, 245
  minor, 102
Planets
  orbital motion, 192
planet(s)
  radii of, 308
plasma
  compressing, 548
Plastic deformation, 368
Plasticity, 367
plate tectonics, 64
plates, 64, 337, 454, 501, 594
Point charge
  potential energy of, 247, 259, 300-301, 371, 438
  potential of, 594
Polar, 510, 549
population
  growth of, 464
Position
  as function of time, 291
  simple harmonic oscillator, 377
Position vector, 73-74, 99, 320, 374
Position-versus-time graphs
  average velocity and, 61, 99
Positive sense of rotation, 319
Positive work, 210, 532-533, 548, 561
Positron, 113
potential difference, 593
potential energy
  electrical, 2, 150, 223, 237, 327, 383, 417, 476, 508, 524, 558, 584-585
Potential energy
  force from, 190, 239, 333
Potential-energy curve, 372
pounds, 7, 24, 116-117, 132, 245, 296, 441, 468-469
Power
  average power, 233-234, 243-244, 328-329, 350, 416, 587
  instantaneous power, 233, 329
Power lines, 312
Power stroke, 150, 232, 540, 563-564
powers of 10, 22, 596
Powers-of-ten notation, 5
Precession, 341-343
Precision, of numbers, 11
Pressure
  absolute pressure, 446, 468, 549-551
pressure
  atmospheric, 389, 411, 442-444, 469, 477-478, 511, 515, 549, 595
Pressure
  atmospheric pressure, 389, 411, 442-444, 467, 477-478, 511, 515, 549, 595
pressure
  barometric, 447, 519
Pressure
  blood pressure, 447-448, 469-471, 491
  gauge pressure, 446, 468-469, 520, 549
  in a fluid, 365, 410, 442-444, 474
  in liquids, 524
Pressure amplitude, 415

Pressure gauge, 446-447, 476, 517
Pressure gauges, 446
pressure gradient, 462, 472
Pressure nodes, 410
Principle of superposition, 183, 404-405
probe, 121, 131, 198, 390
products, 22, 191, 297, 501, 563
projectile motion
  and air drag, 257, 303
  and satellites, 157, 173
Projectile motion
  equations for, 44, 79-81, 142, 262-264, 290, 323, 374
  launch angle, 81, 103
  symmetry in, 86
Projectiles
  exploding, 266
Projection, 100, 375
propane, 472, 553
Proportional reasoning, 50-51, 66, 92
Proportionality, 53, 150, 163, 321, 362-363, 480-481, 518
Proportionality constant, 154, 163, 363, 480, 518
proportions
  inverse, 51
Propulsion, 7, 272-274, 283-284, 596
Protein, 150, 217, 508
Proton, 277-278, 549, 595
protons, 25, 112, 157, 197
pulleys, 296, 307

Q

Quadratic relation, 51
Quality, 12, 414
Quantity of heat, 485-486, 507, 532, 561, 593
Quantum chromodynamics (QCD), 158
Quantum mechanics
  history of, 158, 192
  models, 6-8, 439
  tunneling, 372
Quantum physics
  lasers, 2
  x rays, 190, 426, 432
quartz, 28, 183, 361, 481-482, 512

R

Rad, 26, 178, 288-290, 307-309, 321, 352, 370, 390, 438, 591, 593
radar, 99, 425, 431
Radial component of acceleration, 293-294
Radian, 288, 377, 593
Radians, 23, 288, 307-308, 327-329, 366
Radiant, 594
radiant energy
  absorption of, 500
  emission of, 488
radiation
  background, 499
  beta, 158
Radiation
  blackbody, 500, 510
radiation
  electromagnetic, 4, 157-159, 425, 494
  environmental, 426, 501, 578-579
Radiation
  health hazards of, 578
radiation
  particle, 3, 157
radiation
  ultraviolet, 498
Radiation dose, 594
radiative energy, 500
radiative transfer
  equation of, 521
radio waves, 199, 425
radioactive decay, 285
Radius of curvature, 101
radon, 550
Random kinetic energy, 526
Randomness, 558-559
ranges, 83, 408, 521, 550
rarefaction, 399
Rate of fusion, 559
Raynaud's syndrome, 382
Recoil, 255, 278-279
Recumbent bicycles, 209
red blood cells, 6, 469
red light, 4

Red shift, 425
Reddening, 197
Reduction, 334, 499
Reflective sail, 262
Reference frames
    accelerating, 110, 130, 145
Reference point, 319, 375-376, 447
Refrigerators, 475, 531, 559, 583
    coefficient of performance, 585-586
Relative humidity, 489
Relativity
    events, 190
    general, 57, 190, 206
    measurements, 192, 426
relativity
    of motion, 189, 204
Relativity
    of time, 59
    relative velocity, 58, 425
    special, 58, 206, 425
    speed of light, 58, 190-191, 425
    theory of, 58, 190, 205, 425
    work and energy, 204-206
Remote sensing, 67
replication, 328
research
    applied, 159, 465
reservoirs, 561, 584
Resistance
    equivalent, 4, 107, 134, 284, 593-594
resolution, 232
resonance, 382-384, 437-438
Resonance
    standing-wave, 437
Resonance peak, 384
Rest energy, 595
Restoring force, 245, 369-370, 393
Resultant, 13-16, 26, 94, 107, 131, 211-212, 266, 310, 405, 449
Resultant vector, 13-14
retina, 390, 444
Reversible processes, 576
Rigid body
    equilibrium of, 138-140, 163, 318, 352
    potential energy, 2, 211, 240-242, 278, 300-303, 313, 382, 388, 438, 524, 560, 588
Rigid-body equilibrium, 337
R–L circuit
    current in, 157, 369, 594
Rocket propulsion, 272, 283
rocks
    volcanic, 67
rods, 175, 298, 310, 355, 388, 480, 506
Rolling friction, 150, 166, 246, 303
Root-mean-square speed, 529, 547
Rotation
    about a moving axis, 305, 311, 325
    kinetic energy of, 292, 307-308, 325, 531
    positive sense of rotation, 319
    with constant angular acceleration, 291-292, 307-309
Rotational dynamics
    right-hand rule, 341-343
    torque, 319-320, 347
    vector nature of angular quantities, 341, 354
Rotational energy, 299, 310
rotational equilibrium, 336, 347
Rotational kinematics, 290
Rotational kinetic energy, 298, 307, 347, 531
rotational motion, 251, 287-288, 307, 318-319, 350, 370, 531
Rotational motion
    angular velocity, 288-295, 307-309, 318, 350-351, 374-376, 387, 462
    dynamics, 31, 105, 131, 173, 287, 323-326, 439
    moment of inertia, 297-302, 307-308, 321-322, 350-352
first law of thermodynamics, 485, 532, 558, 583-584
rubber, 148, 206-207, 240, 310, 339, 361, 387, 452, 471
Rutherford, Ernest, 284

S

salts, 365
Satellite motion, 173, 198
satellites, 91, 97, 157, 173, 195, 309
Satellites
    circular orbits, 188
satellites

communications, 97, 199, 309
Scalar quantities, 12-13
scalar quantity, 12-13, 34, 95, 209, 365, 492
Schrödinger's equation
    boundary conditions, 404
    solving, 44-45, 83, 124-125, 138-139, 176, 214-215, 254-255, 299, 320, 367, 409, 458, 481, 519, 562
Schwarzschild, Karl, 190
Schwarzschild radius, 190-191
science
    and technology, 595
Scientific notation, 5, 28
Scuba diving, 469, 520
Seawater, 25, 285, 389, 433, 440, 469
Second condition for equilibrium, 336
Second law of thermodynamics, 558-559, 583-584
seeds, 68
Seeing, 399
Seismic waves
    earthquake, 361, 396-397, 432
Seismograph, 397
Self-excited oscillation, 384
semicircular canals, 327
Semitone, 437
SETI, 432
shear forces, 367, 389, 454
Shear modulus, 366-367, 389, 401
Shear strain, 366-367, 389
shear stress, 362
shell, 25, 103, 277, 301, 311, 326, 350, 472
Shock absorbers, 383, 392
Shock wave, 426
SI system of units, 28
SI units, 7, 23-24, 118, 132, 163, 183, 209, 279, 458, 486, 512, 518-519, 562, 594
Significant figures, 22
Silicon, 391, 487, 524
silver, 440, 474, 487, 509, 523
Simple harmonic motion (SHM)
    and circular motion, 181
    circle of reference, 371
    equations of, 47, 114, 215, 325-326, 374, 390, 517, 548
    kinematics of, 173
    problem-solving strategy, 48, 83, 124, 144, 176, 214-215, 299, 323, 378, 409, 458, 495, 519
Simple pendulum, 380-381, 387
Simultaneous equations, 152, 262-264, 323
Sinusoidal longitudinal wave, 399-400
Sinusoidal sound wave, 415
Sinusoidal standing wave, 405
Sinusoidal transverse wave, 397-398
Sinusoidal wave, 395
Slip-and-stick phenomenon, 150
Slipping
    rolling without, 309, 350
Smog, 516
snow, 105, 145, 167, 240, 425, 445, 505
sodium chloride, 524
Soft iron, 367-368
soil, 77, 454
Solar day
    mean, 3, 191, 237, 331, 445, 516
Solar energy, 237, 500-501, 578-579
Solar heating system, 501
solar neutrino
    problem, 168-170, 186, 197-198, 209, 237-238, 281-283, 382, 446, 499, 528, 578, 586-588
solar power, 501, 587
Solar radiation, 501
Solar system
    black holes, 190-191
    gravity on Mars, 186
    inner, 186, 199-200, 223, 309, 327, 350, 389, 416, 496, 506-507
    masses of astronomical objects, 190
    Milky Way, 516
solar system
    Moon, 68, 115-116, 129-130, 158, 161, 184, 199, 221, 241, 272, 282, 309, 348, 382, 470, 507, 596
    overview of, 235
    scale of, 117, 134, 349
    studying, 205, 318, 361, 398, 517, 551
    sun, 6, 28, 158, 188, 197-198, 237, 282, 309, 351, 496, 507, 518, 553, 572, 596

Solar wind, 169
solids
    crystalline, 523-524
Solids
    molecules, 371, 481, 515-516, 547-548
solutions
    aqueous, 483
Sonar, 421, 433
Sound
    decibels, 417, 431
    intensity level, 418-419, 431-432
    musical sounds
        fundamental frequency, 410, 431
        quality, 414
    shock wave, 426
    sonar, 421, 433
Sound intensity, 416-419, 431-432
Sound level, 417-418, 431
Sound waves
    echo, 403, 433
    loudspeakers, 415
    speed of sound, 24, 64, 168, 295, 399, 432
Sources of energy, 579
space
    at, 33, 67, 132, 157, 184, 199, 238, 272, 311, 357, 414, 444
Space
    conservation of momentum, 249, 279
    curvature of, 199-200
Space program
    inertia, 116-117, 301-302, 311-313, 347
Space Shuttle, 40, 133, 249, 495
Space Station, 25, 199-201, 274, 358
Space/time structure
    ordinary matter, 158
special theory of relativity, 58, 425
    motion and, 2, 154, 173-174, 195-196, 526
specific gravity, 465, 469
Specific heat capacity, 486-488, 506, 530, 550, 576, 593
speed
    average, 4, 23, 33, 61-65, 73-78, 99, 163-164, 181, 198, 210, 241, 267-271, 278, 288-291, 310, 350, 377, 388, 405, 435, 461, 469, 507-511, 525-526, 547-548, 596
    instantaneous, 36-39, 61, 74-77, 173-174, 232-233, 250, 288-289, 315, 375
    terminal, 167, 244, 331, 463, 471-472
Speed
    work and energy to calculate, 214
Speed of efflux, 459-460
Speed of light
    in a vacuum, 53
    relativity, 58, 190, 425
Speed of sound, 24, 64, 168, 295, 399, 432
speedometer, 35, 61, 312
sperm, 469
Sphygmomanometer, 447
Spirit rover, 518
Spring balance, 106, 155-156, 165, 185, 373, 472
Spring constant, 156, 217, 238, 259, 364
Spring force, 156, 222-224, 368
Spring scale, 130, 162, 191, 218
Springs
    force and, 127, 157, 222, 240, 393
    restoring force and, 393
SS, 357
Stability, 311
Stable equilibrium, 368
Stadium, 279
standard atmospheric pressure, 467, 595
Standard SI, 5
Standard temperature and pressure (STP), 519, 550
standing wave, 405-406, 431
Standing waves
    electromagnetic waves, 247, 361, 425, 432, 498
    longitudinal, 200, 358, 396-401, 434
    musical instruments, 411
    nodes, 406
    nodes and antinodes, 409-410
    normal modes, 404-405, 433
    on string, 432
    sinusoidal, 395, 434
    sound waves, 2, 390, 396, 432
Star formation
    modeling, 440
stars
    binary, 272
    neutron, 25, 198, 440

supernova, 158
white dwarfs, 25
State coordinates, 517
State variables, 517
Static friction, 149-150, 165-167, 178, 197, 326-327, 350, 392
Static-friction force, 148
Steady flow, 454-456
Steam, 188, 245, 421, 476, 506, 517, 560-561, 587
Steam engines, 533, 564
Stefan–Boltzmann constant, 498
Stopped pipe, 412-414, 435
storms, 431, 518
Straight-line motion
    acceleration, 21, 24, 31, 62-63, 72, 97-103, 105, 129-131, 143-147, 164-167, 173-179, 197-201, 204, 237-238, 250, 278, 287, 307-310, 318-319, 347-351, 368, 387, 456, 470, 517, 593-594
    deceleration, 40, 117
    freely falling objects, 2, 53, 68, 81, 391
    proportional reasoning, 50-51, 66, 92
Strain, 355, 361-366, 388-389, 442, 484
Stream flow geometry
    discharge, 472
    gradient, 462, 472
streams, 208, 463, 471, 484, 513
Stress, 33, 361-366, 389, 441-442, 484-485, 507, 593
stresses, 362, 426, 454, 485
String instruments, 408
strings, 158, 161, 175-176, 200, 260, 355, 361-362, 392, 404, 432
Strong interaction, 158, 257
Subatomic particles, 113, 258, 281
sublimation, 489, 522
sulfur, 490, 513, 549
Sun
    radiation of, 499
    weight of, 28, 156-157, 182, 197, 237, 301, 357, 509
Supercomputers, 464
supermassive black hole
    weighing, 353-354
Supernova, 158
Supernovae, 25, 158
superposition, 107, 183, 403-405, 431
Superposition
    of forces, 106-108, 182
    principle of, 183, 404-405
Superposition principle, 405
surf, 398
Surf pool, 398
surface temperature, 507, 549
Surface tension, 439, 471, 524
Surface water
    turbulent, 455-456, 473
Suspension, 138, 335-337, 361
swim bladder, 470
Symmetry, in projectile motion, 86
system, 4-7, 28, 31-32, 69, 72-73, 111, 130, 141-142, 162-165, 179, 198-200, 204, 241, 251-263, 277-280, 287, 308, 319, 348, 362, 390-391, 395-397, 435, 445, 471, 476, 505-506, 517-521, 551, 558-563, 584-585, 593-594, 596
Systems
    disordered, 559
    total momentum of, 251, 277
Systolic pressure, 447, 469

T
Talbot, 73
Tangential acceleration, 294, 307
Tangential component of acceleration, 293
Tangential component of instantaneous acceleration, 294
tangential velocity, 295
technology, 3-4, 501, 524, 579, 595
Telescopes, 139, 432
temperature
    body, 12, 434-435, 475, 508-509, 520, 547, 560, 586
    energy and, 205-207, 500, 532, 560, 588
Temperature gradient, 494, 569, 587
Temperature scales
    Celsius scale, 477, 556
    Fahrenheit scale, 477
Tendons, 27, 163, 207, 240, 388
Tensile strain, 362-363

Tensile strength, 368, 388, 426
Tensile stress, 362-364, 388, 484-485
tension, 106, 130-131, 139-140, 161, 174, 196, 239-240, 283, 324-326, 348, 362-364, 387-388, 397, 431, 439, 470-471, 484, 524
Tension force, 106, 139, 176-177, 340, 362, 452-453
Teflon, 148
Terminal speed, 471-472
terminal velocity, 154-155, 167, 244
theory, 1-3, 58, 68, 158, 190-192, 205, 425, 464, 524, 549
Theory of everything (TOE), 158
Theory of relativity, 58, 190, 205, 425
Thermal conductivity, 494-495, 506, 587, 593
Thermal conductors, 494
Thermal efficiency
    heat engines, 560, 584
Thermal efficiency
    maximum possible, 569
thermal energy, 238, 284, 357, 508
Thermal energy
    dissipative forces, 209, 383, 393
    microscopic, 207, 416, 515, 547
    quantity of heat, 485-486, 507, 532, 561, 593
Thermal equilibrium, 475-477, 506, 532, 547, 559
thermal expansion
    and water, 500, 509, 549
Thermal expansion
    linear, 356, 480-483, 507
    volume, 475-476, 507-508, 515, 547-554, 563-564, 587, 593
    water, 237, 283-285, 398, 476-480, 505-507, 516, 549-551, 558, 583-584, 594
Thermal interactions, 477
Thermal properties of matter
    phase change, 488, 514, 518, 560
Thermal stress, 484-485
Thermodynamic equilibrium, 532, 559
Thermodynamic processes
    equilibrium processes, 532, 559
    irreversible processes, 559-560
    isobaric process, 539-540
    isothermal process, 539-541, 573-574
    non-equilibrium processes, 532, 559
    reversible processes, 576
Thermodynamic systems
    heat transfer during volume changes, 534
    work done during volume changes, 533
Thermodynamics
    energy resources, 578-579, 587
    first law of, 531, 550
    first law of, 485, 532, 558, 583-584
    second law of, 558-559, 583-584
thermodynamics
    third law of, 578
Thermodynamics
    zeroth law of, 476-477
Thermometers, 476-478, 507, 523
thermometers
    Celsius, 477-480, 507, 523
Thermometers
    constant-volume gas thermometer, 478
thermometers
    Fahrenheit, 477-480, 507, 523
    Kelvin, 478, 507
thermostat, 481, 505
Thin lens
    combinations, 427
Thin lenses
    equation, 7, 140, 224, 297-298, 325, 390, 413, 433, 471, 498-500, 505, 534
Third law of thermodynamics, 578
Threshold of hearing, 416
thrust, 7, 26, 122, 134-135, 168, 176, 233, 273-274, 358
Thunderstorms, 425
Timbre, 414
Time
    beginning of, 48, 118, 205, 514
time
    railroad, 92-93, 113, 233
Time delay, 64, 399
tissue, 217, 245, 382, 388, 426, 435, 532
Tonometer, 444
Tornadoes, 425, 518
Torque
    angular momentum and, 351
    due to gravitational force, 336
    line of action, 319, 449

    moment arm, 319, 358-359
    sign, 319
Torricelli, Evangelista, 446
Torricelli's theorem, 459
Torsion balance, 183
Total angular momentum, 330-333, 351
Total energy, 204, 260, 303, 310, 372-373, 390, 501, 578
Total force, 113, 134, 157, 183, 245, 275, 321, 442, 469, 484-485, 533
Total kinetic energy, 205, 258, 277, 297, 308, 334-335, 548
Total mass, 25, 146, 167, 186, 196, 205, 261, 284, 298, 325, 352, 400, 436, 455, 509, 516-517
Total mechanical energy, 207, 237, 371-372, 390
Total momentum, 251-258, 277
Total random kinetic energy, 526
Trajectory, 7, 79-83, 99-100, 118, 187-188, 207, 257, 277, 461-462
    in projectile motion, 80, 100, 227
    parabolic, 82, 103-104, 187, 257, 277
transit
    lower, 425-427, 484
    upper, 427
Transitions
    allowed, 548
translation, 326
Translational kinetic energy, 302, 312, 526-528, 549
Translational motion, 302, 323, 526, 554-555
Transmission, 142, 333, 361, 395
transportation, 294
transverse waves, 397, 433-434
Traveling waves, 404
Trigonometric functions, 16-17
trigonometry, 15, 26, 211
Triple point, 523, 578, 594
troughs, 396
true weight, 165, 191
tsunami, 332
Turbulence
    gas, 565
Turbulent flow, 463
Turbulent flow, 455
Two-dimensional equilibrium, 141
Two-dimensional motion
    acceleration in a plane, 75, 99
    velocity in a plane, 72, 99
Two-liquid barometer, 447
Tycho Brahe, 192

U
Ultrasonic imaging, 426
ultrasonic waves, 426
ultrasound, 370, 390, 426, 435-436
ultraviolet light, 432
ultraviolet radiation, 498
Uncertainty, 9-10, 595
Unified atomic mass unit, 595
Uniform circular motion, 89-91, 97, 173-175, 195, 210, 342, 374
Uniform motion, 110
Unit volume, 186, 365, 439-440, 518
units
    astronomical, 182
Units
    British system, 6-7, 117, 209, 362
units
    British thermal, 486
Units
    consistency of, 9, 23, 378, 458, 481
units
    of speed, 9
Units
    SI system, 28
Universal conservation law, 331
Universe
    age of, 9
    closed, 577-578
    expansion of, 576
universe
    galaxies, 425
    stars, 109, 158, 425
U-tube, 445

V
Vacuum bottle, 500
vacuum permittivity, 595
vapor, 446, 519, 549, 563

Vapor pressure, 573
variation, 3, 96, 118, 133, 154, 164, 187, 199, 241, 268, 410, 436, 443, 469, 478, 533, 567
Vector, 12, 23-25, 31-34, 72-77, 99, 106-110, 139, 171, 174-176, 196, 209, 250, 290, 320, 354, 365, 404-405, 442
Vector addition, 12-13, 25, 92, 107, 252, 404
Vector algebra
    subtraction, 15
Vector angular momentum, 341
Vector angular velocity, 341
Vector quantities, 12-14, 33, 72, 106, 180, 209, 255, 341
Vector quantity, 12-13, 31-34, 73-75, 106, 250-252, 341, 365, 421
Vector subtraction, 15
Vector sum, 13-16, 29, 76, 107-110, 139, 171, 174-176, 211-212, 251-253, 294-296, 322, 404-405, 442
Vectors
    area, 23-24, 268
    component, 16, 23, 32-34, 90, 106, 140, 222, 255, 320, 355
    position, 3, 27, 32-33, 72-74, 108, 130, 221, 260, 319-320, 354, 426
    unit, 4, 91, 106, 223, 260, 319
veins, 69, 444, 469, 495
velocity
    escape, 68, 188, 284, 527
Velocity
    linear velocity, 293
velocity
    radial, 90, 100-101, 174, 290, 307, 319-321, 358, 378-379, 387
Velocity
    relative, 56-58, 64, 72, 98, 110, 135, 148-149, 178, 220, 254, 277-278, 287, 315, 324, 374, 392, 421-425, 454
velocity
    tangential, 293-296, 307, 320-321, 375
Velocity vectors, 14, 93, 425
Venus, 197, 528, 549-550, 596
vertebrates, 223
vibrational motion, 526
Vibrations, 28, 207-208, 361, 390, 410, 432, 531, 555
vibrations
    forced, 382-384, 391
Virus, 376, 391
Visible light, 24, 190, 247, 390, 432, 498, 510
Visible spectrum, 425
vocal cords, 389-390
Volcanic rock, 560
Volcanoes, 199, 241
Volcanoes/volcanism
    on Io, 199, 241
Volume
    flow rate, 28, 462
    unit volume, 186, 365, 439-440, 518
Volume changes
    heat transfer during, 534
Volume expansion, 482-483, 507
Volume expansion coefficient, 483
Volume flow rate, 50-51, 455-456, 471
Volume strain, 364-365
Volume stress, 362

W

walking, 12, 34, 63, 92, 165, 181, 197, 282, 314, 321, 421, 437, 452
Waste heat, 560, 588-589
water
    drinking, 24, 505
Water
    forms, 51, 243-246, 286, 393, 399, 453, 475, 505, 568
water
    fresh, 445, 472, 554, 560
    heat of vaporization of, 508-509
Water
    life and, 397, 477, 579
water
    on Earth, 25, 67-68, 99, 116-117, 130, 185, 195-196, 388, 440, 470, 483, 510, 518, 549, 559
Water
    on Europa, 472
water
    thermal expansion of, 483, 510
Water

thin film of, 452
water
    waves of, 361, 396, 436
Watt, 494, 593-594
Watt, James, 245
watt (W), 232, 494, 594
watts, 5, 245, 562, 585
Wave frequency, 400
Wave function
    drawing, 290
Wave number, 433, 593
Waveform, 398
wavelength, 4, 24, 398-403, 431-437
Wavelength
    of standing waves, 414
wavelength
    rest, 423-424, 437
wave(s)
    amplitude of, 416
Waves
    frequency, 361, 389-391, 398-402, 431-438
    hertz, 370, 420
waves
    infrasonic, 415
    plane, 259
    radio, 199, 361, 395, 432
    seismic, 69
Waves
    shear, 69, 362, 389, 401
    speed, 68-69, 198-200, 246, 260-261, 369-370, 390, 395, 431-437
wave(s)
    standing, 406-407, 431
waves
    transverse, 396-404, 433-434
    ultrasonic, 370, 415, 432
Weather
    hurricanes
        thunderstorms, 425
        tornadoes, 425
weather
    wind, 426, 431, 498
Weight
    in an elevator, 126, 130, 169, 387
weight
    true, 10, 27-28, 105, 130, 161-162, 178, 195, 222, 241, 294, 325, 410, 450, 467-470, 547-549
Weightlessness, 191, 199-200, 391
White dwarfs, 25
Wind instruments, 410, 431
wood, 242, 258, 278, 310, 339, 368, 467-468, 476, 505
Work
    and potential energy, 231
    heat and, 485, 509, 530, 551, 562, 585
    sign of, 180, 290, 319
Work-energy theorem
    Bernoulli equation, 457
Working substance, 560-562, 587
Workless refrigerator, 567-568

X
X rays
    Sun in, 190
xylem, 454

Y
Year
    leap, 242

Z
Zero
    of potential energy, 206, 237-238
zero gravity, 200
Zero-gravity environment, 129, 252, 277
Zeroth law of thermodynamics, 476-477